AVIATION MUSEUMS AND COLLECTIONS OF MAINLAND EUROPE

Bob Ogden

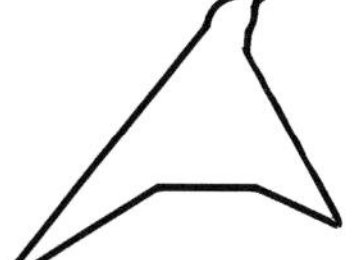

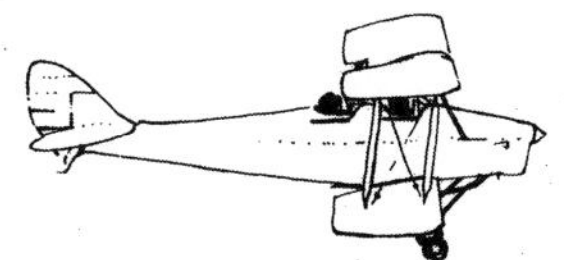

Published by:
Air-Britain (Historians) Ltd

Membership details:
1 Rose Cottages, 179 Penn Road,
Hazlemere, Bucks HP15 7NE
Website:
www.air-britain.co.uk

Sales department:
41 Penhurst Road, Leigh,
Tonbridge, Kent TN11 8HL
eMail:
sales@air-britain.co.uk

Correspondence regarding this publication to:
Bob Ogden, 13 Western Avenue,
Woodley, Berkshire RG5 3BJ

ISBN: 0 85130 375 7

Printed by The Cromwell Press Ltd,
Trowbridge, Wiltshire BA14 0XB

COVER PHOTOGRAPHS:

Front: *This airworthy Catalina operated by Stitching Neptune is pictured at the Aviodrome at Lelystad. The aircraft has been painted in the colours of one operated by the Dutch Navy in the 1940s and 1950s.(Willem Honders)*

Rear: *On show in the Yakovlev Design Bureau Museum in Moscow is this UT-1 dating from the late 1930's. Over twelve hundred were built and the type was used for primary training for more than a decade.*

This East German MiG-15UTI was one of the first aircraft to arrive at the Museo dell'Aviazione near San Marino. The aircraft was delivered in 1960 and was in use until 1974.

CONTENTS

MAP OF EUROPE

INTRODUCTION

It is several years since I compiled a book covering some areas of mainland Europe. This period has seen many changes in both the political and geographical map of the area. This book covers the countries which were in Volumes 3, 4 and 9 of 'Aircraft Museums and Collections of the World'. Since they were published the number of museums and collections has increased by fifty percent and there are a third more aircraft mentioned. There are several reasons for this and I am sure that in many countries there are still more discoveries to be made. Visits to military bases in some areas have increased and more information is now available on the Internet. Photographs published of some collections show more as yet unidentified aircraft in the background. Also in a number of countries there has been a reduction in the size of their military forces which has resulted in types being sold or donated to museums. An interest in preserving one's local heritage also seems to be growing. Unfortunately a few museums have closed in recent years. The inclusion of clubs which are connected to the ever popular vintage glider movement is maintained and also of those which have significant numbers of vintage and classic aircraft. I am sure that there are more to be found in this area. Once again military bases with three or more preserved aircraft are included even if they do not have a specific museum. Several museums which do not have any complete aircraft but are devoted to aviation are also listed. All aircraft are included whether civil or military as I find it particularly frustrating to find only partial listings. I know I am not alone in thinking this.

There have been significant developments in a number of countries. The museums in Austria have continued with their progress and Red Bull has constructed a superb hall at Salzburg. In Belgium the main aircraft museum is working towards opening its reserve store at Kapellen and the excellent Stampe Museum has built new exhibition hangars. A number of new collections in Bulgaria have opened in recent years. New museums have appeared in Denmark. The Technical Museum at Helsingor has concentrated all its exhibitions on one larger site. The aviation section has combined with the Danmarks Flyvemuseum which lost its halls at Billund. The Dansk Veteranflysamling is currently constructing a third hangar to house its growing collection of military aircraft. Near Tartu in Estonia a new museum is being developed. A number of aircraft have arrived from around Europe and new buildings should be ready soon. The preservation movement in Finland remains healthy with more airframes being restored and new museums being opened. The Musée de l'Air at Le Bourget still has halls closed because of structural problems but some smaller new hangars have been built. The naval aviation museum at Rochefort has moved buildings but is still not open on a regular basis. The impressive Musée Régional de l'Air at Angers has continued to unearth types which have been in store for many years. Other collections in the country are also making significant progress. The Deutsches Tecnikmuseum in Berlin now has its new aviation hall open and the Segelflugmuseum at the Wasserkuppe has enlarged its exhibition space. New museums are appearing in the country and several interesting types, including an Antovov An-22 and a Tupolev Tu-144 have appeared at others. The closing of Dittelandia in Italy has resulted the disappearance of a number of airframes. In Iceland the museum at Akureyri is making significant progress. The Aviodome in the Netherlands shut its doors and has moved to Lelystad to become the Aviodrome. At Gardermoen north of Oslo an excellent new exhibition is now open and the group at Kjeller is steadily restoring aircraft and constructing replicas. In Poland the museum at Krakow has put more types on show and has plans to construct more halls. In this country preserved aircraft are appearing at many locations. The Museu do Ar in Portugal hopes to construct a new complex at Sintra and also establish an exhibition in the north of the country. The main Romanian museum north of Bucharest is expanding with the erection of new buildings. In Russia more collections have been found and I sure that the picture here is far from complete. In Slovakia two major museums have opened in the last few years and others are being developed. The Museo del Aire at Cuatro Vientos near Madrid has plans to construct more hangars. Also in the country new museums and preservation groups are being set up. In Sweden as bases close groups of volunteers are setting up museums and active military sites are also developing their collections. In Switzerland new halls have been built at Dubendorf. Military bases in Turkey have expanded their collections and new museums have opened. The situation in the Ukraine is excellent with a major new exhibition at Kiev and development of several others at particularly Lugansk and Poltava.

In general the situation in the area covered is healthy and I hope that progress is maintained.

ACKNOWLEDGEMENTS

Thanks are due to the following who have sent me reports of their travels, helped with aircraft details, loaned magazines and photographs. Many museums have also replied to my requests and I am grateful for their assistance.

Jozef Andal, MDeniz Ayvaz, Daniel Brackx, Ian Burnett, Keith Dexter, Graham Dinsdale, Tony Eastwood, Christian Emrich, Rui Ferreira, Peter Foster, Peter-Michael Gerhardt, Willem Honders, Paul Jackson, Tommy Johansson, Reinhard Keimel, Dimitriy Komissarov, Stewart Lanham, Coert Monk, Tomas Meze, Tony Morris, Bjorn Olsen, Bo Bang Petersen, Nigel Ponsford, Bob Rongé, Douglas Rough, Bob Ruffle, Lars Søe-Jensen, Sven Scheiderbauer, Klaas-Reinder Sluijs, Mort Stanley, Trevor Stone, Alex Trandafir, Evi Vaik.

I would also like particularly to thank the members of Air-Britain who have encouraged me to compile this book.

NOTES

For most museums and collections the following information is stated.

COUNTRIES
For each country a two or three letter code is allocated. Each museum has been given a number so that the index can be used to trace a particular type of aircraft. The number is also shown on the appropriate map which is normally found after the country heading. Maps are not provided for some countries and all are drawn to different scales.

ADDRESS
The full postal address is given wherever possible. For some voluntary/private organisations the address stated may be that of the owner or an official of the organisation.

TELEPHONE/FAX/E-MAIL
Wherever possible these are given. For some voluntary/private organisations those stated may be that of the owner or an official of the organisation. These details often change so check before making contact.

ADMISSION
The times stated are the latest available and cannot be guaranteed. Intending visitors should check before travelling. The twenty four hour clock has been used and local times stated. For those not familiar with this system – an a.m. time is as follows 8 a.m. is 0800 – noon is 1200: for a p.m. time add 12 hours i.e. 4 p.m. is 1600. Where 'By Prior Permission Only' is shown the aircraft are on private property or are in restricted areas and normally cannot be seen by the casual caller. Most of the flying collections are based on active airfields and can be seen only with the permission of the airfield operator in addition to that of the owners.

LOCATION
A rough guide to the location of the museum/collection is shown on the map and in the heading. If a museum has aircraft at more than one site a list of these will be given and the number of the location will follow the status symbol.

AIRCRAFT TYPE
Many aircraft have a manufacturers and service number as well as a name. Where known the full manufacturer's designation is given with the service number in brackets. For a licence built type which has been given a new designation, the original in the country of design is shown in square brackets. If the type has been constructed by a number of companies the designing firm is stated.

For homebuilt aircraft and some gliders the designer is named. Shown in brackets after the type name is either its former type if the aircraft has undergone major modifications or the service designations in the order allocated. The symbol (R) denotes a replica which may be an accurate copy built to flying standards. (FSM) denotes a full size model with the correct dimensions.

REGISTRATION/MILITARY SERIAL
The markings normally carried by the aircraft are stated. Many machines are painted in their former markings for display purposes and the serial given may not be a current allocation. False markings are shown in inverted commas i.e. 'A4567'. Some aircraft carry no markings and the current allocation is normally stated.

CONSTRUCTOR'S/ MANUFACTURER'S NUMBERS
This is normally the only true way to identify an aircraft and wherever possible this is stated. Some manufacturers do not allocate c/ns – particularly for military aircraft on the assumption that they will keep the same serial for life. In some cases line numbers or fuselage numbers are given. Although not true c/ns they do provide a means of identification. Some registers quote military serials, part numbers etc. as the c/n.

PREVIOUS IDENTITIES/NOTES
These are given in chronological order starting with the initial allocation. Where the country is unclear this is stated in brackets. Reservations which were not taken up are also shown in brackets. Standard abbreviations have been used for many military serials and the civil country identification markings will be found in registers. Additional information may be given here.

STATUS
The system developed by the Smithsonian Institution is used.

- **A** Active – capable of flight and in most cases with a current permit.
- **C** Under restoration or rebuild.
- **D** Derelict or severely damaged – may be restored eventually.
- **PV** On public view – normally in the museum premises.
- **RA** Research accessible – may be seen by serious researchers with prior permission.
- **S** Stored – may be crated or in a restricted area.
- **X** Carries false markings.

Combinations of these may be used. If a number is stated after the codes refer to the location codes for the museum.

ALBANIA

ALBANIAN AIR FORCE HEADQUARTERS DISPLAY (ALB1)

Address:	Tirana.
Admission:	By prior permission only.
Location:	In the city.

In 1914 when Albania was a principality in the Austro-Hungarian Empire an order was placed for three Lohner aircraft. These were never delivered and it was not until 1947 that an Air Force was formed. The country had become independent the previous year and was under Soviet influence. Russian types were supplied but after a falling out most of its aircraft came from China. In the early 1990s a few western built helicopters were purchased for VIP operations and police work. The current economic conditions mean that only a few aircraft are regularly flown. A small display of photographs and memorabilia is located in the building.

TYPE	REG/SER	CON. NO.	PI/NOTES	STATUS
☐ Shenyang F-6 [Mikoyan-Gurevich MiG-19S]	001	1307 (?)		RA

BERAT-KUÇOVË AIR BASE COLLECTION (ALB2)

Address:	Krahu Ajror, Repart I Ushtarak 4020, Berat.
Admission:	By prior permission only.
Location:	About 10 km. north of Berat.

This base, which opened in May 1955, housed fighter units up to 2000. A few examples of the Shenyang F-5 and FT-5 still remain active. Four examples of types previously flown have been preserved. Albania has been supplied with a number of Chinese built aircraft in recent times. For the past few years flying training has been carried out using Nanchang CJ-6As. The students come from the Air Force Academy at Vlorë. The airfield is now being rebuilt to NATO standards and in addition the air force overhaul plant is located here.

TYPE	REG/SER	CON. NO.	PI/NOTES	STATUS
☐ Mikoyan-Gurevich MiG-15bis	5-48	3022		RA
☐ Mikoyan-Gurevich MiG-15UTI	5-09	2709		RA
☐ Shenyang F-5 [Mikoyan-Gurevich MiG-17F]	4-13	1703		RA
☐ Shenyang F-6 [Mikoyan-Gurevich MiG-19S]	4-22	4226		RA

NATIONAL ARMOURY MUSEUM (ALB3)

Address:	The Citadel, Gjirokastra.
Admission:	Daily 1000-sunset.
Location:	In the town which is in the south of the country.

The T-33 is displayed at the castle, which also has an excellent collection of armaments dating from the middle ages. Uniforms, photographs documents and vehicles can be seen. From the 1920s and during the German occupation the site was used as a prison. The collection was looted in a disturbance in 1997 but there is still a great deal to be seen and the view from the battlements is spectacular. The former U.S.A.F. aircraft is said to have been forced down while flying over the country on a spying mission.

TYPE	REG/SER	CON. NO.	PI/NOTES	STATUS
☐ Lockheed 580 (T-33A)	51-4413	580-5708		PV

RINAS AIR FORCE BASE COLLECTION (ALB4)

Address:	Krahu Ajror, Repart Ushtarak 4020, Rinas.
Tel :	04-363 369 (Airport)
Admission:	By prior permission only.
Location:	About 20 km north west of Tirana.

The military base at the field, which also serves as the main international airport for the country, houses a number of units. Two Shenyang F-6s from a batch of seventy delivered in the late 1960s are preserved near the main gate. The Chinese built Ilyushin Il-28 is located in a hangar and is destined to go to a museum.

TYPE	REG/SER	CON. NO.	PI/NOTES	STATUS
☐ Harbin H-5 [Ilyushin Il-28]	3-608	400609		RA
☐ Shenyang F-6 [Mikoyan-Gurevich MiG-19S]	40/20	1215	3-15	RA
☐ Shenyang F-6 [Mikoyan-Gurevich MiG-19S]]	40/20	3238		RA

ARMENIA

MOTHER OF ARMENIA MONUMENT AND MUSEUM (ARM1)

Address:	Hakhtanak Park, 2 Azatutian, Yerevan.
Tel:	25 14 00
Admission:	Aircraft on permanent view.
Location:	In the northern part of the city

The 75 foot high statue houses a military museum in its base. This was set up to celebrate the victory over the German forces in World War II. The country was part of the Soviet Union for many years and its airfields housed a number of fighter aircraft. In addition to the MiG there are also a number of tanks to be seen.

TYPE	REG/SER	CON. NO.	PI/NOTES	STATUS
☐ Mikoyan-Gurevich MiG-19S	'111'			PVX

AUSTRIA

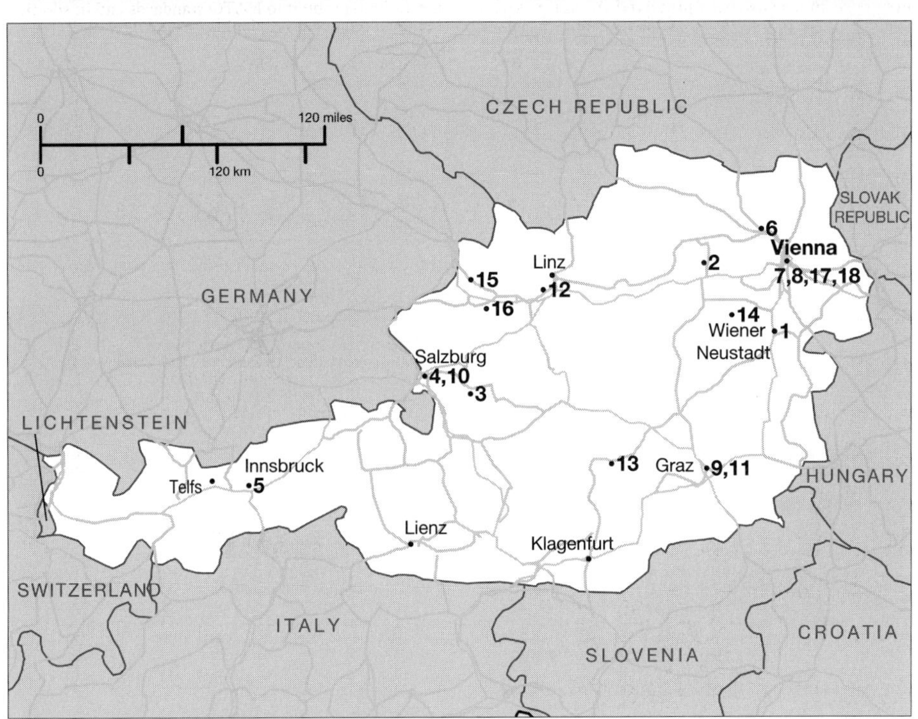

AVIATICUM (AUT1)

Address:	Ferdinand Graf von Zeppelin Strasse, A-2700 Wiener Neustadt.
Tel:	02622-88630
Fax:	02622-88670
Email:	aviaticum@utanet.at
Admission:	Tuesday-Thursday 1000-1700; Friday-Sunday 1000-1900.
Location:	On the B17 about 5 km north of Wiener Neustadt.

The Osterreiches Segelflyg Museum was formed in 1983 with the aim of setting up an exhibition at the gliding field at Hundsheim. A small display was staged in a building and components, documents, photographs and models could be seen. Plans to construct a hangar came to nothing and other sites were investigated. These came to fruition in June 1999 when the exhibition opened at Wiener Neustadt. The history of soaring flight in the country is portrayed in detail. The first gliders in the country were built in the early years of the twentieth century. This excellent exhibition now has over twenty sailplanes on show dating from 1940 up to the early 1980s. The oldest is one of the few surviving examples of the graceful Gövier which first appeared in 1938. Other classic German designs include the Jacobs designed Meise, a Dittmar Condor, a pair of diminutive Hutter 17s and two SG-38 primaries. A range of post-war Scheibe designs can also be seen. Three of Erwin Musger's sailplanes are on show. The two seater Mg 19 first flew in late 1951. The Mg 19a was ready in 1955 and the following year took part in the World Gliding Championships at St. Yan in France. The single seat Mg 23 appeared in 1955 and entered production at the Oberlerchner factory in 1962. About one hundred were built. At the current time there are no examples of modern composite sailplanes on view but this will no doubt be rectified in the future. The replica of the 1912 Taube F was built by Heinz Linner in the mid-1980s and first flew from Wiener Neustadt in 1991. Original 1912 plans from the Lohner company were used but the airframe was fitted with an 80 hp Walter Minor engine. Herr Linner had ambitious plans to produce a series of replicas of early Austrian designs but these have been put on hold for the time being. The Alpla company has built several motor gliders. The AVo 60 powered by a Limbach engine first flew in 1964 and was active for a decade. A development the Avo 68 was put into production and about thirty were completed. The two seat AFW 8 is one of several designs by the technical university in Vienna. The sole example built made its maiden flight in November 1962 and was in use for just over a year. Hang gliding is a popular sport in the mountainous terrain and there are several manufacturers in the country. One of the most prolific is Airwave set up at Innsbruck by Markus Villinger. His first design, the Duplex, appeared in 2000 and since then more than a dozen models have been produced. Other hang gliders and microlights are on view. The first balloon flight in Austria took place in the early 1800s. This sport is represented by one gas and one hot air model.

TYPE	REG/SER	CON. NO.	PI/NOTES	STATUS
☐ Airwave Magic 155 Hang Glider				PV
☐ Akademische Fliegerschaft Wien AFW 8	OE-0523	2		PV
☐ Alpla AVo 60	OE-9094	001		PV
☐ Bell 47G-4	N8478L	3339		PV
☐ Bensen B-8M Gyrocopter	OE-AXW	01		PV
☐ Bölkow BO 208C Junior	OE-ASA	698	(D-EABL)	PV
☐ Bücker T-131PA Jungmann	OE-VCD	02	SP-FPY, (SP-YPY)	PV
☐ Cameron N-77 Hot Air Balloon	OE-DZO	559		PV
☐ Da Vinci Flying Machine (FSM)				PV
☐ Dallach Sunwheel R	OE-7022	011		PV
☐ Dittmar Condor IV/3	OE-0981	3		PV
☐ Göppingen Gö 4 Gövier II (D.F.S. 108-61)	OE-0104			PV
☐ Guerchais-Roche SA.104 Emouchet	OE-0215			PV
☐ Hütter H 17	OE-0050	1		PV
☐ Hütter H 17B	OE-0350	03		PV
☐ Jacobs Meise (D.F.S. 108-70)	OE-0124	635		PV
☐ Jacobs Weihe (D.F.S. 108-68)	OE-0277	490		RA
☐ Lilienthal Sturmflügelmodell (R)				PV
☐ Lohner Etrich Taube F (R)	OE-CET	01		PV
☐ Meteor FL.54	OE-ABA	1114	I-FELC	PV
☐ Mitchell Cohen Wing Hang Glider				PV
☐ Musger Mg 19 Steinadler	OE-0197	005		PV
☐ Musger Mg 19a Steinadler	OE-0389	024		RA
☐ Musger Mg 23	OE-0425	05		PV
☐ Musger Mg 23SL	OE-0690	17		PV
☐ Raab Doppelraab IV	OE-0333	37		PV
☐ Riedinger K-945/2-Ri Gas Balloon	OE-DZG	8.525		PV
☐ Santos-Dumont XX Demoiselle (R)	OE-XUD8	01		PV
☐ Scheibe 138 Specht	OE-0290	108/54		PV
☐ Scheibe Mü 13E Bergfalke I	OE-0278	04		RA
☐ Scheibe Bergfalke II	OE-0307	03		PV
☐ Scheibe Bergfalke II/55	OE-0436	3		RA
☐ Scheibe L-Spatz W	OE-0699	259		PV
☐ Scheibe Spatz B	OE-0387	1		PV
☐ Schleicher Ka-4 Rhönlerche II	OE-0884	659		PV
☐ Schleicher Ka-6CR Rhönsegler	OE-0636	6205		PV
☐ Schneider Grunau SG-38 (D.F.S. 108-14)	OE-0107	1		PV
☐ Schneider Grunau SG-38 (D.F.S. 108-14)	OE-0177	1		RA
☐ Schneider Grunau Baby III (D.F.S. 108-66)	OE-0236	1		PV
☐ Spider 6D/ Hazard 15M	OE-8113	196		PV
☐ Steinbach Sport Hang Glider				PV
☐ Szybowcowy Zaklad Doswiadczalny S.Z.D.9bis Bocian 1D	OE-0562	P-392		RA
☐ Szybowcowy Zaklad Doswiadczalny S.Z.D.22C Mucha Standard	SP-2262	F-646		PV
☐ Westermeyer WE.04 (WE.03)	OE-AXB	02		PV

EISENBAHNER SPORTVEREIN ST. POLTEN (AUT2)

Address:	Sektion Segelflug, Werkstattenstrasse 17, A-3100 St. Polten.
Tel:	02742-814192
Admission:	By prior permission only.
Location:	About 5 km south west of the town off Road 39.

The organisation runs all sporting activities in the region. The gliding section is based at the local airfield. Until recently the group owned the motor powered prototype version of the Kaiser Ka-2 sailplane. Very few such conversions of the successful Rhönschwalbe were carried out. This aircraft has recently been sold back to Germany. The unusual shaped Doppelraab is now something of a rarity. The prototype flew in 1951 at Dachau near Munich. The fuselage seated the pilot and the instructor was perched behind him under the wing. The idea was to produce a cheap two seat primary trainer. Kits were supplied to clubs and individuals before Wolf Hirth put the type into production. Two early composite designs are in regular use. The Cirrus dates from the early 1970s and the Jantar is a decade younger.

TYPE	REG/SER	CON. NO.	PI/NOTES	STATUS
☐ Raab Doppelraab IV	OE-0252	007		RAA
☐ Scheibe Bergfalke II/55	OE-0427	047		RAA
☐ Scheibe Bergfalke II/55	OE-0249	4		RAA
☐ Scheibe L-Spatz 55	OE-0602	R53/H/240		RAA
☐ Scheibe SF-25C Falke	OE-9171	44233	D-KDCC	RA
☐ Schempp-Hirth Standard Cirrus	OE-5056	594		RAA
☐ Schleicher K.8B	OE-0753	8434/ZW		RAA
☐ Szybowcowy Zaklad Doswiadczalny S.Z.D.48-1 Jantar Standard 2	OE-5254	B-1037		RAA

This Chinese built Ilyushin Il-28 is hangared at Rinas Air Force Base. The bomber is due to move to a museum. (Bob Ruffle)

The only aircraft currently displayed near the Mother of Armenia monument is this MiG-19S. (Paul Haigh)

Resting on a balcony at the Technical Museum in Vienna is a 1918 Berg D1 built in the city. Hanging in front is the Gumpert G 2 constructed in 1934. (Rudolf Höfling)

This superbly restored Albatros B I is in the Heeresgeschichtliches Museum in Vienna.

The unique Felbmayer, built in 1965, is on view in the Fahrzeug-Technik-Luftfahrt Museum at Bad Ischl.

This Lisunov Li-2 in Soviet World War II colours is parked outside the impressive Museum of the Great Patriotic War in Minsk. (Juha Ritaranta)

FAHRZEUG-TECHNIK-LUFTFAHRT MUSEUM (AUT3)

Address:	Bad Ischl-Salzkammergut, Sulzbach 178, A-4820 Lauffen.
Tel:	06132-26658
Fax:	06132-23934
Email:	Fahrzeugmuseum@aon.at
Admission:	April-October Daily 0900-1800.
Location:	About 3 km south of the town on the Road 145.

This privately owned museum opened in 1990 and has on show a wide range of cars and motor cycles. Agricultural vehicles, fire engines, railway locomotives and military vehicles can also be seen, along with models, photographs posters and trophies. One large building is currently in use and in the near future a new exhibition hall, which will house most of the military aircraft, will be constructed, The Kain helicopter was built in Austria in 1964 and is powered by a 75 hp Boxer motor. It is believed to have made a few short flights. There are very few Enstrom helicopters in museums and the example on show came from Germany. Two experimental homebuilts can also be seen. The Löhr, with delta wings, was built in 1990 and based on the principles of Alexander Lippisch. The Felbermayer is another flying wing design. A number of types recently retired from Austrian military service have been acquired. Some of them are in poor condition and composite airframes will be constructed from the components. The SAAB 29 flew over eight hundred hours with 2 Squadron at Graz between 1961 and 1972. Austria ordered forty SAAB 105s and the first were delivered in July 1970. The rear fuselages and tails of two destroyed in crashes are in store. A number of former East German Air Force machines arrived in the late 1980s along with several from Czechoslovakia and one from Hungary. Some aircraft are stored off site until the new exhibition has been completed. Gliding has always been popular in Austria and this aspect of aviation is represented in the exhibition. This museum made great progress in its first few years and the ambitious development plans should turn it into one of the major transport collections in the country.

TYPE	REG/SER	CON. NO.	PI/NOTES	STATUS
☐ Aero L-29RS Delfin	2610	792610	In Czech markings.	RA
☐ Aero L-39ZO Albatros	28+14	731017	154 (DDR)	RA
☐ Agusta-Bell 204B	4D-BF	3072		PV
☐ Agusta-Bell 204B	4D-BK	3144	Boom only.	RAD
☐ Agusta-Bell 204B	4D+BM	3155	Boom and other parts only.	RA
☐ Agusta-Bell 204B	4D-BY	3204		PV
☐ Antonov An-2	OK-NYA	113947302		PV
☐ Cessna 305C Bird Dog (L-19E) (O-1E)	3A-BK	23937	57-6023	RAD
☐ Cessna 305C Bird Dog (L-19E) (O-1E)	3A-BL	23938	57-6024	RAD
☐ Enstrom F-28A-D	D-HOLD	185		PV
☐ Felbermayr Nurfluger				PV
☐ Kain Helicopter	OE-HWK			PV
☐ Löhr Deltaflug				PV
☐ Mikoyan-Gurevich MiG-15bis	350	31532350	In Hungarian markings.	PV
☐ Mikoyan-Gurevich MiG-19S	0201	050201	In Czech markings.	PV
☐ Mikoyan-Gurevich MiG-21F-13	0310	560310	In Czech markings.	PV
☐ Mikoyan-Gurevich MiG-21F-13	'1002'	760603	0603 – In Czech markings.	PVD
☐ Mikoyan-Gurevich MiG-21PFM	4405	94A4405	In Czech markings.	PV
☐ Mikoyan-Gurevich MiG-21SPS (MiG-21PFM)	22+32	94A4506	833 (DDR)	RA
☐ Mikoyan-Gurevich MiG-21U-400	23+86	661119	237 (DDR)	PV
☐ Mikoyan-Gurevich MiG-21UM	23+78	02695163	204 (DDR)	PV
☐ Mikoyan-Gurevich MiG-23ML	20+14	0390324627	336 (DDR)	PV
☐ Mil Mi-4	4143	04143	In Czech. Markings.	PV
☐ Mil Mi-8PS	93+38	10550	962 (DDR)	RA
☐ Mil Mi-8T	93+08	10538	922 (DDR)	RA
☐ Scheibe L-Spatz 55	D-9074	567	(D-KOHN)	PV
☐ Schneider ESG 31 Grunau Baby IIB (D.F.S. 108-62)	OE-0244	02		PV
☐ Sukhoi Su-7BKL			In false North Korean markings.	RA
☐ Sukhoi Su-22M4	25+23	26510	723 (DDR)	PV
☐ Sukhoi Su-22UM3K	25+47	17532369809	113 (DDR)	RA
☐ Svenska Aeroplan Aktiebolaget (SAAB) 29F (29B) (J 29B) (J 29F)	2-I	29466	Fv29466	PV
☐ Svenska Aeroplan Aktiebolaget (SAAB) 105ÖE		105401	Parts only.	RAD
☐ Svenska Aeroplan Aktiebolaget (SAAB) 105ÖE		105406	Parts only.	RAD
☐ Yakovlev Yak-11				RA
☐ Yakovlev Yak-18				RA

FIRST AUSTRIAN DC-3 DAKOTA CLUB (AUT4)

Address:	P.O. Box 51, A-5035 Salzburg-Flughafen.
Tel:	0664-411-0852
Fax:	06415-6669
Email:	DC-3Club@aon.at
Admission:	By prior permission only.
Location:	In the south western suburbs of the city.

This enthusiastic group has restored its DC-3 in the markings of the first one flown by Austrian Airlines. The company used three examples of the type between 1963 and 1966. The aircraft, based at Salzburg, served with the United States Air Force from April 1944 until November 1945. After two weeks registered to T.W.A. it then spent more than half a century in corporate and local airline use in the U.S.A.

TYPE	REG/SER	CON. NO.	PI/NOTES	STATUS
☐ Douglas DC-3A-456 Skytrain (C-47A)	'OE-LBC'	13073	42-93189, NC88823, N35F, N86B, N86U	RA

FLIEGERCLUB SCHWAZ (AUT5)

Address:	Sonnseite 10, A-6130 Schwaz.
Tel :	05242-71813
Email:	Mtschu@chello.at
Admission:	By prior permission only.
Location:	At Innsbruck airport which is about 3 km west of the city off Road 171.

An example of the graceful Musger Mg 19 is in service with this club. The remainder of the sailplanes are classic German designs. More modern types are also operated along with a fleet of tugs.

TYPE	REG/SER	CON. NO.	PI/NOTES	STATUS
☐ Bölkow Phoebus B-1	OE-0928	730		RAA
☐ Grob G.102 Astir CS	OE-5622	1240	D7321	RAA
☐ Musger Mg 19a Steinadler	OE-0415	036		RAA
☐ Schleicher Ka-6E Rhönsegler	OE-0727	4016		RAA
☐ Schleicher K.8B	OE-0901	8083A		RAA
☐ Schleicher K.8B	OE-0641	8179		RAA

FLIEGERGRUPPE ROT-WEISS-ROT (AUT6)

Address:	Fliegerregiment 1, Fliegerhorst Brumowski, A-3425 Langenlebarn.
Tel:	02272-623080
Fax:	00727-3943
Admission:	By prior permission only.
Location:	About 5 km south east of Tulln off the road to Königstetten.

The Historic Flight was set up in the mid-1990s to keep examples of withdrawn types in airworthy condition. Austria was the only country, apart from Sweden, to operate the Saab J-29. Thirty were delivered in 1961 and they remained in service until 1972. Twenty four Safirs were acquired in 1964/5 and were used for basic training and communications for almost thirty years. The Bell 47 was the first type of helicopter flown by the new Austrian Air Force and three were purchased soon after its formation in 1955. The Bird Dog entered service in 1958 and eventually thirty were flown with the last being withdrawn in late 1997.

TYPE	REG/SER	CON. NO.	PI/NOTES	STATUS
☐ Bell 47G-2 Sioux (H-13H) (OH-13H)	3B-HD	2482	58-6987	RAA
☐ Cessna 305A Bird Dog (L-19A) (O-1A)	3A-CG	22589	51-12275, OE-CCG, N44431	RAA
☐ Svenska Aeroplan Aktiebolaget (SAAB) 29F (29B) (J 29B) (J 29F)	2-F	29449	29449 – identity doubtful.	RAA
☐ Svenska Aeroplan Aktiebolaget (SAAB) 91D Safir	3F-SP	91451		RAA
☐ Svenska Aeroplan Aktiebolaget (SAAB) 91D Safir	3F-SJ	91468	Preserved on airfield.	RA

FLUGZEUG-OLDIES (AUT7)

Address:	Flughafen Schwechat, Postfach 1, A-1300 Wien.
Tel:	01-7007-0 (Airport)
Fax:	01-7007-0
Admission:	Currently closed,
Location:	About 15 km south east of the city off the A.4.

Air Classic set up a display at the airport in the 1980s but the aircraft were taken over by the airport authority some years ago. A photographic display traces the history of the airports which have served Vienna and the Austrian airlines which have flown from them. The Viking is one of three which were in use as a restaurant in Holland in the 1970s. The Austrian Air Force operated thirty SAAB 29s and apart from Sweden was the only country to fly the distinctive jet fighter. The Former Czech Delfin is a fairly recent arrival and was exchanged for the Nord Pingouin and the Texan which spent many years on show. The spectators' gallery is now closed for building development. The Viking has been put on show near the local McDonalds restaurant.

TYPE	REG/SER	CON. NO.	PI/NOTES	STATUS
☐ Aero L-29R Delfin	2614	792614	In Czech markings.	S
☐ Bristol 171 Sycamore HR.52	78+09	13461	DA+391, CB+???, AS+320, CC+070, LC+113	S
☐ Percival P.66 Pembroke C.54	54+27	P.66/1019	GB+361, BF+561, XA+110, 54+27, 'G-AOJG' – front fuselage only.	S
☐ Svenska Aeroplan Aktiebolaget (SAAB) 29F (29B) (J 29B) (J 29F)	2-I	29392	Fv29392	S
☐ Vickers 639 Viking 1 (498 Viking 1A)		115	G-AGRW	PV
☐ Zlin Z-37 Cmelak	D-ESVZ	20-29	DM-SVZ, DDR-SVZ	S

HEERESGESCHICHTLICHES MUSEUM (AUT8)

Address: Arsenal,
Objekt 1,
A-1030 Wien.
Tel: 079-561-0
Fax: 052-00-177-07
Email: bmlv.hgm@magnet.at
Admission: Saturday-Thursday 1000-1600.
Location: In the eastern suburbs of the city.

This display is housed in the oldest museum building in the city. The complex was built between 1850 and 1856 and originally two rooms housed the Court Arms Collection. These were later transferred to the Museum of Fine Arts. The Imperial Military Museum opened in 1891 but the exhibition was severely damaged towards the end of World War II. In 1955 the Museum of Military History was set up in the restored building. A superb display of armaments, medals, uniforms and weapons was put on show. The museum owns one of the most significant collections of old cannons with over five hundred on display. The complex military and political history of the country is portrayed in detail. The small aeronautical section traces the history and development of the Imperial Austro-Hungarian Air Force in World War I and of the current service, which was set up in 1955. The Albatros B I is a prototype built under licence in the country. This biplane has been superbly restored to original condition. The first types used by the new Air Force were four Yakovlev Yak-11s and four Yak-18s donated by the Soviet Union. One example of each type has been preserved.

TYPE	REG/SER	CON. NO.	PI/NOTES	STATUS
☐ Albatros B I	20.01	1		PV
☐ Fieseler Fi 156C-3/trop Storch (S 14)	D-ENPE	110253	Fv3818, OE-ADO, D-ELYN – on loan from TM.	PV
☐ Mikoyan-Gurevich MiG-21R	26112		In Yugoslavian markings.	PV
☐ North American NA-168 Texan (T-6G) (LT-6G)	4C-TE	168-295	49-3191 – also reported as c/n 168-253 49-3149, 4C-TC.	S
☐ Schneider ESG 31 Grunau Baby IIB	OE-0340	030.24		RA
☐ Svenska Aeroplan Aktiebolaget (SAAB) 29F (29B) (J 29B) (J 29F)	1-0	29566	Fv29566	S
☐ Svenska Aeroplan Aktiebolaget (SAAB) 91D Safir	3F-SW	91462	Possibly c/n 91450 3F-SO.	S
☐ Yakovlev Yak-11	4C-AF	171227		PV
☐ Yakovlev Yak-18	3A-AA	10113		S

ÖSTERREICHISCHES LUFTFAHRTMUSEUM (AUT9)

Address: Flughafen Thalerhof,
Postfach 15,
A-8073 Feldkirchen.
Tel: 0316-291541 (Airport)
Email: Luftfahrtmuseu@gmx.at
Admission: May-October Sunday 1000-2000.
Location: At Graz Airport which is about 10 km south of the city off Road 67.

A group of enthusiasts was formed in 1979 with the aim of setting up a museum. Four years later two sailplanes designed by a local man, Erwin Musger, were put on show in the terminal building at Thalerhof Airport. Erwin Musger was born in 1909 and died in 1985. His first glider was built in 1932 and several designs were flown before the outbreak of World War II. The Mg 19 appeared in 1952 and this and the Mg 23 of 1955 were put into production by the Oberlerchner company. He also built a low wing monoplane powered by a 22 h.p. Mercedes engine in 1937. A great step forward occurred in 1984 with the arrival of a Venom from Switzerland and three aircraft from Poland. More types were acquired along with engines, components and historic material. The museum opened in a compound near the terminal on May 28th 1987 and buildings were put up on the site. In 1989, to celebrate the seventy fifth anniversary of the airport, construction of the Erwin Musger Hall commenced on a site a short distance away from the main airport buildings. The aim of the exhibition is to trace the history of both civil and military aviation in the country. Under restoration is one of few surviving Klemm L 20s. This low wing two seater monoplane was built in 1928 and the major airframe components survived after many years in store. The collection includes several gliders and light aircraft. The Culk is a motor glider which made its first flight in 1985. The design featured a pusher Göbler-Hirth motor. The Meteor FL-55 is a 1950s development of the pre-war Avia FL-3 designed by Francis Lombardi. Military types have arrived from Hungary, Sweden and Switzerland in recent years. The crash remains of the Messerschmitt Bf 110 were recovered from a lake in the mid-1980s. The aircraft was shot down by a USAAF P-38 Lightning on April 23rd 1944. Until recently the Austrian Air Force has been the only country to operate SAAB military types. An example of the 29 has been joined by three former Swedish Air Force machines which have been loaned by the museum at Malmslatt. These complement the ex-Swiss Air Force Hunter and Mirage so that a range of classic jets can be seen.

TYPE	REG/SER	CON. NO.	PI/NOTES	STATUS
☐ Agusta-Bell 204B	4D-BP	3160		RA
☐ Agusta-Bell 204B	4D-BT	3192		PV
☐ Antonov An-2TP	2919	1G 29-19		PV
☐ Bell 47G-2 Sioux (H-13H) (OH-13H)	3B-HA	2479	58-6984	PV
☐ Cessna 305C Bird Dog (L-19E) (O-1E)	3A-BF	23933	57-6019	PV
☐ Cessna F150L	OE-ATP	F1501093		PV
☐ Culk RC-1 Easy	OE-9244	1		RA
☐ Dassault Mirage IIIS	J-2309	999	In Swiss markings.	PV
☐ Dassault Mirage IIIS	J-2319	1009	Front fuselage only – In Swiss markings.	PV
☐ De Havilland D.H.112 Venom FB.4	J-1733	903	In Swiss markings	PV
☐ De Havilland D.H.115 Vampire T.55 (T.11)	'5C-YC'	15450	XD598, 5C-YA	PVX
☐ Hawker P.1099 Hunter F.58	J-4094	41H/697461	In Swiss markings.	PV
☐ Jacobs Weihe (D.F.S. 108-68)	OE-0241	408		RA
☐ Klemm L 20 B 1	OE-DFG			RAC
☐ Luscombe 8F Silvaire	OE-APD	6012	HB-DUO	PV
☐ Messerschmitt Bf 110G-2			Small components.	PVD
☐ Meteor FL.55BM	OE-DBS	1132	I-FELU	RA
☐ Mikoyan-Gurevich MiG-21MF	4406	964406	In Hungarian markings.	PV
☐ Musger Mg 19a Steinadler	OE-0604	044		PV
☐ Musger Mg 19c Steinadler	OE-0344	021		PV
☐ Musger Mg 23	OE-0338	02		RA
☐ Noorduyn Harvard IIB [North American NA-77 (AT-16)]	PH-KMA	14A-1216	43-12917, FT-176, B-56 (Netherlands), 043 (Netherlands), PH-SAZ	RA
☐ Panstwowe Zaklady Lotnicze (PZL) TS-11 Iskra 100	0221	1H 02-21	0221, 221 – in Polish markings	PV
☐ Raab Doppelraab IV	OE-0327	2-34		RA
☐ Scheibe Bergfalke II	OE-0284	110/54		RA
☐ Scheibe L-Spatz 55	OE-0798	740		RA
☐ Schneider ESG 31 Grunau Baby IIB (D.F.S. 108-49)	OE-0041	003374		RA
☐ Schneider Grunau SG-38 (D.F.S. 108-14)	OE-0168			RA
☐ Svenska Aeroplan Aktiebolaget (SAAB) 29F (29B) (J 29B) (J 29F)	2-H	29541	Fv29541	PV
☐ Svenska Aeroplan Aktiebolaget (SAAB) 32E Lansen (32B) (J 32B) (J 32E)	Fv32510	32510	On loan from FVM, SWE,	PV
☐ Svenska Aeroplan Aktiebolaget (SAAB) 35C Draken (35A) (J 35A) (Sk 35C)	Fv35804	35016	Fv35016 – on loan from FVM, SWE.	PV
☐ Svenska Aeroplan Aktiebolaget (SAAB) 37 Viggen (JA 37) (JA 37D) (JA 37DI)	Fv37431	37431	On loan from FVM, SWE.	PV
☐ Swearingen SA.226TC Metro II	OE-LSA	TC-315	N1014X	PVD
☐ Szybowcowy Zaklad Doswiadczalny S.Z.D.30 Pirat	OE-0968	W-315		PV
☐ Wytwornia Sprzetu Komunikacyjnego (WSK) Lim-2 [MiG-15bis]	1326	1B 013-26	In Polish markings	PV
☐ Yakovlev Yak-11	4C-AH	171229	4A-AH	PV

RED BULL AVIATION FLUGMUSEUM (AUT10)

Address:	Wilhelm Spazier Strasse 7 Flughafen Salzburg, A-5020 Salzburg.
Tel:	05262-68976
Email:	info@flyingbulls.at
Admission:	Daily 0900-2200.
Location:	In the south western suburbs of the city.

The company began acquiring warbirds in the 1980s and initially housed them at Innsbruck. A modern new museum complex has now been completed at Salzburg. The privately owned Corsair resides in the group hangar. This aircraft served in the United States Navy before being sold on the civilian market. The aircraft served with the Honduran Air Force from 1960 to 1978, then returned to the U.S.A., and eventually arrived in Austria in the early 1990s. One loss which occurred when the aircraft landed on water was that of the S.C.A.N.30. This was one of forty one Grumman Widgeons built under licence in the 1950s in France. The former Luftwaffe Alpha Jets appear at shows as an aerobatic team. The DC-6B, the penultimate built, was delivered to JAT in Yugoslavia in 1958 and was then transferred to the Air Force. After arriving from Africa it was recently restored and has since visited a number of shows. The Lightning is being rebuilt in the U.S.A. The aircraft was sold on the civil market in 1946 and enjoyed a long career as a racer. For a time it was part of the Confederate Air Force fleet. In recent years it was flown by 'Lefty' Gardner and named 'White Lightning'. The Mitchell served as a tanker in the 1960s and 1970s. The aircraft was derelict at Mesa in Arizona for more than a decade before being restored. The B-25 was then the flagship of the Kansas City Warbirds fleet from 1977 until 1995. The Huey Cobra arrived at Salzburg in December 2005. This fearsome looking helicopter will appear at several airshows in the near future. The display is complemented by several modern types which are flown on company business.

TYPE	REG/SER	CON. NO.	PI/NOTES	STATUS
☐ Baumgartner-Kunz XC-K2				PV
☐ Bell 47G-3 B-2 Soloy	D-HEBA	3575		PVA
☐ Bell 209 Huey Cobra (TAH-1F)	N11FX	003		PVA
☐ Boeing-Stearman E75 Kaydet (PT-13D)	OE-AMM	75-5032	42-16869, N5379N	PVA
☐ Cessna 208 Caravan	OE-ODM	20800257		PVA
☐ Cessna 550 Citation II	OE-GDM	5500707		PVA
☐ Dassault Falcon 900EX	OE-IDM	31	F-WWIV, F-GVDP	PVA
☐ Dornier-Breguet Alpha Jet A	40+31	0031	(D-IADM)	PV
☐ Dornier-Breguet Alpha Jet A	D-ICDM	0035	40+35	PVA
☐ Dornier-Breguet Alpha Jet A	40+50	0050	(D-IBDM)	PV
☐ Dornier-Breguet Alpha Jet A	D-IDDM	0076	40+76	PVA
☐ Dornier-Breguet Alpha Jet A	D-IADM	0111	41+11	PVA
☐ Dornier-Breguet Alpha Jet A	D-IBDM	0130	41+30	PVA
☐ Douglas DC-6B	N996DM	45563	YU-AFA, 7451 (Yugoslavia), 73101 (Yugoslavia), 110 (Zambia), V5-NCF	PVA
☐ Eurocopter AS.355N Twin Ecureuil	OE-XDM	5708	F-WWPR	PVA
☐ Lockheed 422-87-23 Lightning (P-38L) (F-5G)	N25Y	422-8509	44-53254, NX25Y	RAC
☐ North American NA-108 Mitchell (B-25J)	N6123C	108-47647	44-86893	PVA
☐ North American NA-200 Trojan (T-28B)	OE-ESA	200-250	Bu138179, N3905H	PVA
☐ Pilatus PC-6/B2-H4 Turbo Porter	OE-EMD	928		PVA
☐ Piper PA-18-105 Super Cub	OE-AFK	18-2415	N301T	PVA
☐ Piper PA-18-150 Super Cub	OE-CDM	18-09019	N189PC	PVA
☐ Pitts S-2B Special	OE-AMW	9158		PVA
☐ Vought F4U-4 Corsair	OE-EAS	9149	Bu96995, N5221V, N4908M	PVA

SAMMLUNG FLIEGERHORST GRAZ – THALERHOF (AUT11)

Address:	Fliegerhorst Nittner, Waldweg 6, A-8401 Kalsdorf.
Tel:	0316-29409-0
Fax:	059133-6130-309
Admission:	By prior permission only.
Location:	About 10 km south of the city off Road 67.

The airfield opened in 1913 and in the inter-war period was used by gliders under the terms of the peace treaty. The Germans occupied the site during World War II. As powered flying was again banned from 1945 sailplanes were once more operated from the airfield. When Austria was again allowed to have its own Air Force in 1955 a fighter base opened and a civil area was constructed on the other side of the field. Currently operational is a squadron flying the Northrop F-5E and the SAAB 105. The F-5Es recently replaced the Draken.

TYPE	REG/SER	CON. NO.	PI/NOTES	STATUS
☐ De Havilland D.H.115 Vampire T.55	5C-YC	15798	G-5-14	RA
☐ Svenska Aeroplan Aktiebolaget (SAAB) 29F (29B) (J 29B) (J 29F)	2-D	29588	Fv29588	RA
☐ Svenska Aeroplan Aktiebolaget (SAAB) 35ÖE Draken (35D) (J 35D)	01	351401 (35313)	Fv35313	RA

SAMMLUNG FLIEGERHORST LINZ – HORSCHING (AUT12)

Address:	Fliegerhorst Vogler, A-4063 Horsching.
Tel:	07221-700-0
Fax:	07221-700-17210
Admission:	By prior permission only.
Location:	About 10 km south west of the city north of Road 1.

The airfield, which also serves as the civil airport for the city, is now home to transport and helicopter units as well as a squadron flying the SAAB 105. There is also a maintenance facility on the military side. Fighter units have served at the base and the two SAAB designs preserved are a reminder of this.

TYPE	REG/SER	CON. NO.	PI/NOTES	STATUS
☐ Agusta-Bell 204B	4D-BX	3203		RA
☐ Svenska Aeroplan Aktiebolaget (SAAB) 29F (29B) (J 29B) (J 29F)	1-M	29443	Fv29443	RA
☐ Svenska Aeroplan Aktiebolaget (SAAB) 35J Draken (35F-1) (J 35F-1) (J 35J)	'07'	35607	Fv35607	RAX

SAMMLUNG FLIEGERHORST ZELTWEG (AUT13)

Address:	Fliegerhorst Hinterstoisser, A-8740 Zeltweg.
Tel:	03577-225360
Admission:	By prior permission only.
Location:	About 6 km east of Judenburg off Road 78.

Zeltweg opened as a military field in the late 1950s. The base is currently home to a squadron of SAAB Drakens which are scheduled to be withdrawn in the near future. There is also a flying school on the field using Pilatus PC-7s. Eight aircraft are currently preserved. The Fiat G.46 is one of five obtained from Italy in the late 1950s and flown for a few years. The Fouga Magister has recently returned from the Republic of Ireland.

TYPE	REG/SER	CON. NO.	PI/NOTES	STATUS
☐ Cessna 305A Bird Dog (L-19A) (O-1A)	3A-CO	22216	51-7477	RA
☐ Cessna 305C Bird Dog (L-19E) (O-1E)	3A-BM	23939	57-6025	RA
☐ Fiat G.46-4B	3A-BB	157	MM53397	PV
☐ Fouga CM.170R Magister	4D-YL	359	4D-YL, 217 (Eire)	RA
☐ Sud-Est SE.3130 Alouette II	'3D-XJ'			RA
☐ Svenska Aeroplan Aktiebolaget (SAAB) 35D Draken (J 35D)	'25'	35339	Fv35339	RAX
☐ Svenska Aeroplan Aktiebolaget (SAAB) 35J Draken (35F-2) (J 35F-2) (J 35J)	Fv35531	35531		RA
☐ Svenska Aeroplan Aktiebolaget (SAAB) 91D Safir	3F-SR	91455		RA

SAMMLUNG HOFER (AUT14)

Address:	Webgasse 1/8, A-1060 Wien.
Admission:	By prior permission only.
Location:	At Wiener-Neustadt West airfield which ia about 3 km north west of the town.

This interesting private collection includes an SG-38 which was one of a batch built in the 1950s. The prototype of this primary type first flew in the late 1930s and large numbers were built. The remainder of the fleet consists of classic German types along with a Piper Super Cub often used as a tug.

TYPE	REG/SER	CON. NO.	PI/NOTES	STATUS
☐ Piper PA-18-150 Super Cub	OE-ADF	18-7510		RAA
☐ Scheibe L-Spatz 55	OE-0460	R219/H234		RAA
☐ Scheibe SF-25D Falke	OE-9189	4679D	D-KBAE	RAA
☐ Schleicher K.8B	OE-0585	8153		RAA
☐ Schleicher ASW-15B	OE-5331	15347	OE-5001	RAA
☐ Schleicher ASW-19	OE-5174	19168		RAA
☐ Schneider Grunau SG-38 (D.F.S. 108-14)	OE-0097	7		RAA

SCHÄRDINGER FLIEGER UNION (AUT15)

Address:	Linzer Strasse 506, A-4780 Schärding.
Tel:	07711-2239
Email:	segelflug@lols.at
Admission:	By prior permission only.
Location:	At Schärding-Suben airfield which is about 7 km south of the town off Road 148.

Several classic gliders are operated by the club along with more modern designs. The oldest is the Austrian built Grunau SG-38 which is occasionally flown using bungee launches. The Phoebus prototype made its maiden flight in 1964 and the type was produced in substantial numbers in three versions. Three examples of Schleicher designs are also in the fleet. The Piper Super Cub is used for towing the gliders.

TYPE	REG/SER	CON. NO.	PI/NOTES	STATUS
☐ Bölkow Phoebus C	OE-5548	852	D-0089	RAA
☐ Grob G.103 Twin III Aero	OE-5572	3E447C77170		RAA
☐ Piper PA-18-150 Super Cub	OE-AGB	18-7445		RAA
☐ Rolladen-Schneider LS-4	OE-5479	4477		RAA
☐ Schleicher K.7	OE-5003	7248		RAA
☐ Schleicher K.8B	OE-0814	8686		RAA
☐ Schleicher ASW-19	OE-5117	19104		RAA
☐ Schneider Grunau SG-38 (D.F.S. 108-14)	OE-5410	01		RAA
☐ Szybowcowy Zaklad Doswiadczalny S.Z.D. 51-1 Junior	OE-5677	511199244		RAA

SEGELFLUG UND MODELLBAU CLUB KIRCHDORF (AUT16)

Address:	Hauptplatz 7 A-4560 Kirchdorf a.d. Krems.
Tel:	07582-61590
Fax:	07582-61590-1
Email:	Smbc@utanet.at
Admission:	By prior permission only.
Location:	About 3 km south of the town off Road 120.

Three examples of the Grunau Baby are flown by this active group. The Polish designed Bocian first flew in May 1953 and the design was steadily developed. A large number were built over the next decade and the type achieved success in many competitions and also set several class records. The club has a thriving modelling section and a number of classic designs have been built to show the development of sailplanes over the years.

TYPE	REG/SER	CON. NO.	PI/NOTES	STATUS
☐ Grob G.103 Twin II	OE-5258	3522		RAA
☐ Piper PA-18-150 Super Cub	OE-CDP	18-5664	N7196D, (D-ECEQ), OE-ADH, D-EADP	RAA
☐ Rolladen-Schneider LS-4	OE-5138	4298		RAA
☐ Schleicher K.8B	OE-0678	8363		RAA
☐ Schleicher K.8B	OE-0678	8363		RAA
☐ Schneider ESG 31 Grunau Baby IIB	OE-0126	01		RAA
☐ Schneider ESG 31 Grunau Baby IIB	OE-0277	1		RAA
☐ Schneider ESG 31 Grunau Baby IIB	OE-0038	004290		RAA
☐ Szybowcowy Zaklad Doswiadczalny S.Z.D.9bis Bocian 1D	OE-0562	P-392		RAA

TECHNISCHES MUSEUM FUR INDUSTRIE UND GEWERBE (AUT17)

Address:	Mariahilfer Strasse 212, A-1140 Wien.
Tel:	01-89998-6000
Fax:	01-89998-4444
Email:	mbox@tmw.ac.at
Admission:	Monday-Saturday 0900-1800; Sunday 1000-1800.
Location:	In the city centre near the Schönbrunn Palace.

Many European capital cities set up technical museums in the early part of the twentieth century. The exhibition in Vienna opened in 1918 and the displays traced the development of industry and technology in more than thirty sections. The museum closed in the early 1990s for major refurbishment and re-opened in June 1999. An aeronautical section was added in 1927 and includes several early models. The oldest aircraft is an original Lilienthal glider built in 1894. The second Taube, with its distinctive wing shape, constructed by Igo Etrich in 1910, is a prized exhibit. The ungainly Pischof Autoplan dates from the same year but this unique machine is currently in store after spending many years hanging from the roof of the building. The Aviatik D was built under licence in the city by Thone and Fiala in 1918. Gliding has always been important in Austria and a range of types has been acquired. The Kermer Wien dates from 1923 and this is now in store along with some classic German types and indigenous designs. Bruno Gumpert constructed the G1 primary in 1931 and three years later the developed G2 appeared. He went on to build two advanced models, the Schwalbe I and II which flew in the late 1930s. Leopold Harbich from Vienna designed the 12/49 primary which first flew in 1951. Three examples were built and on one a nacelle for the pilot was fitted. Oskar Westmeyer built a Bensen B-8 gyrocopter in 1966 and steadily developed the concept over the next twelve years. The WE 04 was his last model and was fitted with a 100 h.p. engine which he designed and built. Light aircraft, balloons and man-powered machines are in this interesting collection and it is hoped that more can be placed on show in the not too distant future.

TYPE	REG/SER	CON. NO.	PI/NOTES	STATUS
☐ Aérospatiale AS.355F Ecureuil	OE-FXA	5056		PV
☐ Bell 47G-2 Sioux (H-13H) (OH-13H)	3B-HO	2493	58-6998	RA
☐ Berg D I [Aviatik]	101.37			PV
☐ Blaha Krupka-Berg Glider				RA
☐ Bussard Gas Balloon				PV
☐ De Havilland D.H.104 Dove 5	OE-BVM	04488		RA
☐ Donauwerft Kermer Wien				RA
☐ Drache k.u.k Type N Kite				RA
☐ Drache Le Cornu Kite				PV
☐ Egkher Muskelkraft				RA
☐ Etrich II Taube				PV
☐ Fieseler Fi 156C-3/trop Storch (S 14)	D-ENPE	110253	Fv3818, OE-ADO, D-ELYN – on loan to Heer LM.	–
☐ Gardan GY-80 Horizon 160	OE-DGG	27		RA
☐ Gumpert G2	OE-0017		OE-Anger	PV

TYPE	REG/SER	CON. NO.	PI/NOTES	STATUS
☐ Harbich Ha 12/49	OE-0210	03		RA
☐ Hütter H 17B	OE-0341	02		PV
☐ Lilienthal Sturmflügelmodell				PV
☐ Lilienthal Sturmflügelmodell (R)				RA
☐ Musger Mg 19a Steinadler	OE-0399	033		RA
☐ Musger Mg 23SL	OE-0766	23		RA
☐ Oberlerchner JOB 15-150/2	OE-BLF	068		RA
☐ Osterreich Aero Club Standard Austria	OE-0410	01		RA
☐ Pischof Autoplan				RA
☐ Rheintaler Sport				RA
☐ Schneider ESG 31 Grunau Baby IIB	OE-0064	030688		RA
☐ Sonntag Muskelkraft				RA
☐ Thunder Ax.6-56 Hot Air Balloon				PV
☐ Vega Gas Balloon				RA
☐ Westermayer WE.04	OE-XAW	03		PV
☐ Wickenhauser Sportflugzeug				RA

WIEN – SCHWECHAT SAMMLUNG (AUT18)

Address:	Brauhausstrass 10, Object 105, A-2320 Schwechat.
Admission:	By prior permission only.
Location:	Close to the airport which is about 15 km south east of the city off the A4.

The group which owns these aircraft is hoping to restore the majority to flying condition. Some are in a rather neglected state and it will take a great deal of work to realise the ambitious plan. The Pingouin and Texan were once part of the now defunct Air Classic collection in Germany and were exhibited at airport terminals. The Sky Walker is a German designed two seater microlight normally powered by a 50 h.p. Rotax engine. The Polish designed Gawron was developed from the Yakovlev Yak-12M for crop spraying duties. A slightly swept wing with endplates and larger elevators on the tail were fitted. The prototype flew in April 1958 and over three hundred were built. The type has also been built under licence in Indonesia by the Nurtanio company.

TYPE	REG/SER	CON. NO.	PI/NOTES	STATUS
☐ Bensen B-8 Gyroglider				RA
☐ Nord N.1002 Pingouin II [Messerschmitt Bf 108B]	'08-12'	163	163, HB-OAR, (D-EHUX), D-EOAR	RA
☐ North American NA-182 Texan (T-6G)	F-BMJO	182-383	51-14696, 114696 (France)	RA
☐ Osterreich Aero Club Standard Austria	OE-0662	13		RA
☐ Panstwowe Zaklady Lotnicze (PZL) 101A Gawron	OE-AFP	63090		RA
☐ Panstwowe Zaklady Lotnicze (PZL) 101A Gawron	OE-AFB	119325		RA
☐ Leichtflugzeug Sky Walker II-300E	OE-7009	191		RA
☐ Zlin Z-226 Trener 6	OE-BUS	290		RA

BELARUS

BELARUSIAN STATE MUSEUM OF THE GREAT PATRIOTIC WAR (BEL1)

Address:	Prospekt Francisk Skorina 25A, Minsk.
Tel:	017-227-11-16
Admission:	Tuesday-Sunday 1100-1800.
Location:	In the centre of the city.

In June 1942 the Committee of the Communist Party of Belarus started acquiring items relating to the struggle of local people in the war against Germany. The area was the scene of bitter fighting and there was an active underground movement. This extensive collection included homemade weapons, documents, uniforms, magazines, paintings and personal items. These were exhibited in Moscow in November 1942 under the name of 'Belarus Fighting'. The collection returned to Minsk and for several years this was the only display in the former Soviet Union honouring the conflict. In 1966 a purpose built museum was constructed and the exhibition has continued to grow. The displays cover many aspects of the war which is portrayed in great detail. There are a number of lifelike dioramas. Exhibitions now include the later military history of the region which is now an independent country. Large numbers of Li-2s were used in the war and one is exhibited outside along with a number of military vehicles, tanks and weapons.

TYPE	REG/SER	CON. NO.	PI/NOTES	STATUS
☐ Lisunov Li-2 [Douglas DC-3 modified]	22			PV--

BELGIUM

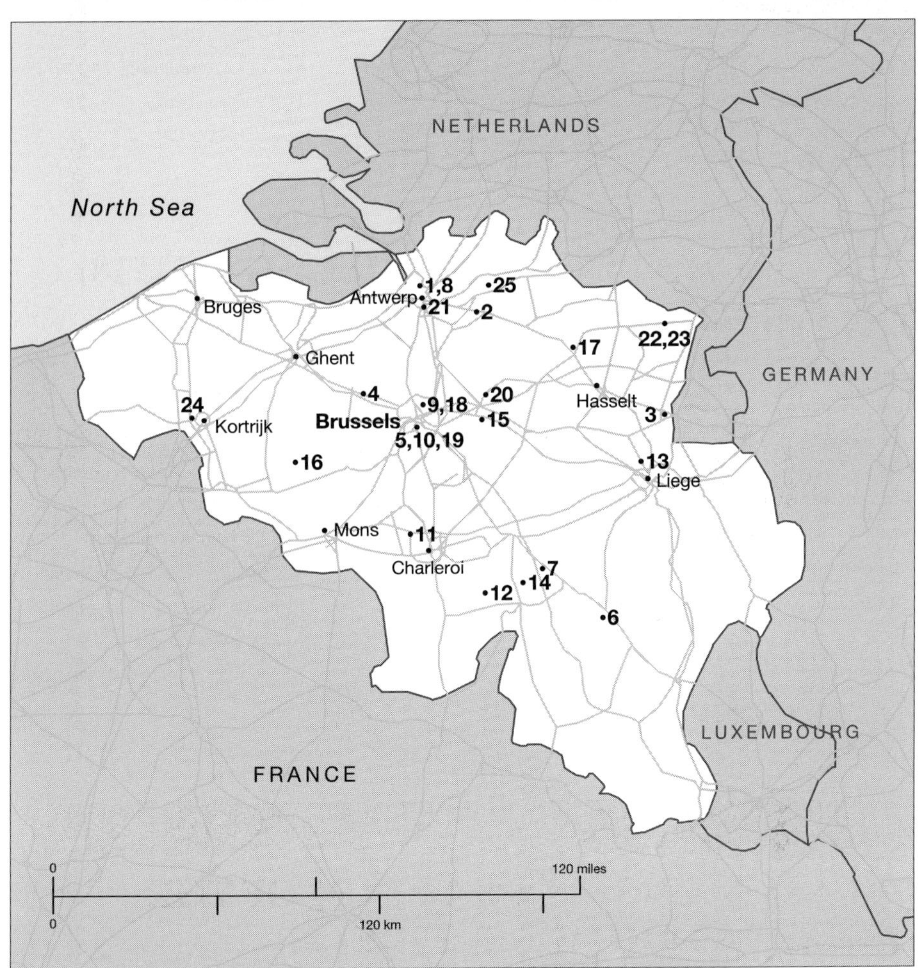

AERO CLUB BRASSCHAAT (BLG1)

Address:	Het Leeg 54, B-2930 Brasschaat.
Tel:	03 663 11 55
Fax:	03 630 27 69
Email:	stijn.mennes@pandora.be
Admission:	By prior permission only.
Location:	The airfield is about 15 km north of Antwerpen off Road N.117

Members of the club fly four former military Super Cubs based on part of the Army airfield. Two of these are in military colours. The quartet often appear at shows in the region. The Belgian Army was supplied with one hundred and fifty seven Super Cubs under the Military Defense Aid Program. Two came from this source and the others from the armies in France and Holland. In Belgium the type replaced the Auster AOP.6. The aircraft used by the club are all ninety five horsepower versions. There are a number of more modern aircraft flown by members. Several classic gliders are also in use and the Pawnee serves as a tug for the fleet. In the clubhouse are several photographs of aircraft previously flown by the club and items of memorabilia. The Army is moving out of the site but the club should stay. For years pilot training in fixed wing aircraft and helicopters had taken place. Some operational units were once in residence but these left some time ago.

TYPE	REG/SER	CON. NO.	PI/NOTES	STATUS
☐ Grob G.102 Astir CS-77	OO-ZWZ	1776		RAA
☐ Let L-13 Blanik	OO-ZIF	026857		RAA
☐ Let L-13 Blanik	OO-ZJQ	026928	OE-5236, D-0935	RAA
☐ Let L-23 Super Blanik	OO-ZNQ	907624	(BGA.3666), OK-0238	RAA
☐ Piper PA-18-95 Super Cub (L-18C)	OO-SPG	18-1650	51-15650, 15650 (France), OO-HMU, OO-LGB, (OO-VIC)	RAA
☐ Piper PA-18-95 Super Cub (L-18C)	OO-LGB	18-2060	52-2460, R-53 (Netherlands), OO-SPG	RAA
☐ Piper PA-18-95 Super Cub (L-18C)	OO-AAP	18-3214	53-4814, L-140, OL-L40, (OO-ACF)	RAA
☐ Piper PA-18-95 Super Cub (L-18C)	OO-ATY	18-3221	53-4821, L-147, OL-L47	RAA
☐ Piper PA-25-235 Pawnee C	OO-TUG	25-4088	N4447Y	RAA
☐ Schleicher K.8B	OO-ZAV	8707		RAA
☐ Schleicher K.8B	OO-ZZV	8820	PH-417	RAA
☐ Schleicher K.8B	OO-ZDT	8909	PH-452	RAA
☐ Schleicher ASK-21	OO-YWT	21086	D-6129	RAA
☐ Szybowcowy Zaklad Doswiadczalny S.Z.D.48-3 Jantar Standard 3	OO-ZWM	B-1419		RAA

BALLOONS REST IN PEACE (BLG2)

Address:	Voortkapelseweg 18, B-2250 Olen.
Tel:	014 26 30 50
Email:	bart@specialshapes.nu
Admission:	By prior permission only.
Location:	About 30 km east of Antwerpen off the N.152.

This collection was started in 1998 by Bart Geeraets with the aim of preserving retired balloons. They are regularly inflated and displayed at shows in Belgium and Holland. The majority of the collection is of British origin but others are being sought. The Schaut is a local design and the only one constructed was withdrawn from flying in 1986. The Durondeau company produced a small series of a number of versions in Belgium. A replica of the Montgolfiere Balloon has been acquired along with a Cameron version of the historic design.

TYPE	REG/SER	CON. NO.	PI/NOTES	STATUS
☐ Cameron Helix Oilcan 61SS Hot Air Balloon	G-HLIX	1192	On loan from Balloon Preservation Group, England.	RA
☐ Cameron N Ele 90SS Hot Air Balloon	G-WBMG	3086	G-BUYV	RA
☐ Cameron N-56 Hot Air Balloon	OO-BAX	385	G-BSUN	RA
☐ Cameron N-65 Hot Air Balloon	OO-BAY	1032		RA
☐ Cameron N-77 Hot Air Balloon	OO-BJL	1128		RA
☐ Cameron N-77 Hot Air Balloon	OO-BLA	1267		RA
☐ Cameron N-77 Hot Air Balloon	OO-BIG	798		RA
☐ Cameron N-90 Hot Air Balloon	G-COMP	1564	On loan from Balloon Preservation Group, England.	RA
☐ Cameron N-90 Hot Air Balloon	OO-BGH	3249	G-BVKI	RA
☐ Cameron N-105 Hot Air Balloon	OO-BCV	1852		RA
☐ Cameron N-120 Hot Air Balloon	OO-BEJ	4605		RA
☐ Cameron O-77 Hot Air Balloon	OO-BTB	1001		RA
☐ Cameron O-77 Hot Air Balloon	OO-GDF	155		RA
☐ Cameron O-77 Hot Air Balloon	OO-BJB	2224		RA
☐ Cameron O-77 Hot Air Balloon	OO-RUP	437		RA
☐ Cameron O-84 Hot Air Balloon	OO-EOL	27		RA
☐ Cameron O-90 Hot Air Balloon	OO-BVW	1938		RA
☐ Cameron O-120 Hot Air Balloon	PH-PVB	3314		RA
☐ Cameron S-65 Hot Air Balloon	OO-GDB	14		RA
☐ Cameron Special Shape Montgolfiere Hot Air Balloon	OO-BGA	806		RA
☐ Cameron Special Shape Salami Hot Air Balloon	OO-BIM	1048		RA
☐ Colt 90A Hot Air Balloon	OO-BVL	1698		RA
☐ Colt 105A Hot Air Balloon	PH-LPB	1192		RA
☐ Colt 105A Hot Air Balloon	PH-LOL	846		RA
☐ Colt Jumbo SS Hot Air Balloon	G-UMBO	747	On loan from Balloon Preservation Group, England.	RA
☐ Colt Orangina Bottle Hot Air Balloon	OO-BUE	1247	G-PULP	RA
☐ Colt Special Shape Football Hot Air Balloon	PH-LEV	2174	G-OALS, (PH-BHL)	RA
☐ Durondeau L.220 Hot Air Balloon	OO-BIC	014		RA
☐ Lindstrand LBL-150A Hot Air Balloon	PH-TUT	040		RA
☐ Montgolfier Hot Air Balloon (R)				RA
☐ Raven Europe FS-57A Hot Air Balloon	D-Selzen	E-212		RA
☐ Raven Europe RX-7 Rally Hot Air Balloon	D-Harxheim	E-056		RA
☐ Raven Europe S-60A Hot Air Balloon	D-OHKL	E-222	D-Mathes	RA
☐ Schaut 1500 Hot Air Balloon	OO-SWF	1		RA
☐ Thunder Ax.7-77 Series 1 Hot Air Balloon	OO-BRM	1111	On loan to Balloon Preservation Group, England.	–
☐ Thunder Ax.7-77Z Hot Air Balloon	PH-DVL	682		RA
☐ Ultra Magic M-77 Hot Air Balloon	OO-BOK	77/21		RA

BELGISCH MILITAR RADIO EN COMMUNICATIE MUSEUM (BLG3)

Address:	B-3260 Lanaken.
Admission:	Not yet open.
Location:	About 5 km north west of Maastricht, Netherlands off Road 78.

The owner of this collection of radios and communications equipment is setting up a museum in the town. Several military vehicles and four aircraft will be on view when the site opens. The two seat Starfighter and MiG-23UB came on long term loan from the Piet Smedts collection in the Netherlands several years ago. The two Hungarian MiG-21MFs were both withdrawn at Kecskemet in the late 1990s.

TYPE	REG/SER	CON. NO.	PI/NOTES	STATUS
☐ Lockheed 583-10-20 Starfighter (TF-104G)	28+22	583F-5952	KE+210, DC+364 – on loan from Auto. Piet Smedts, NET.	RA
☐ Mikoyan-Gurevich MiG-21MF	9312	969312	In Hungarian markings.	RA
☐ Mikoyan-Gurevich MiG-21MF	9513	969513	In Hungarian markings.	RA
☐ Mikoyan-Gurevich MiG-23UB	20+59	A1038221	107 (DDR) – on loan from Auto. Piet Smedts, NET.	RA

BROKEN WINGS MUSEUM (BLG4)

Address:	Leuvestraat 4B, B-9320 Erembodgem.
Email:	cynrik@telenet.be
Admission:	Sunday 1400-1800.
Location:	About 3 km south east ofAalst on Route 9.

This interesting collection was set up by the Belgian Aviation History Association and has recently moved into larger premises close to where the society was formed. On show are items recovered from crash sites, photographs, models, documents etc. tracing the history of aviation in the country. The group possesses a large archive of photographs and documents and its members research all aspects of aviation in the country. In the hall is a Norécrin which is under restoration. This French design developed by the Nord company from the Messerchmitt Bf 108 first flew in 1945. The type won a contest for touring aircraft and well over three hundred and fifty were completed. The centre fuselage section of a Waco Hadrian glider was recovered after many years exposure to the elements. Many transport gliders were abandoned after landing and several were used by locals as storage buildings. This is being rebuilt and fitted out. A recent arrival is the Focke-Wulf Fw 190 which was dug up in 2004. The fuselage is almost complete and this is being restored. Small portions of the remainder of the airframe were also recovered from the crash site. The D-9 version appeared in 1944 and the type was produced at both Cottbus and Kassel and supplied to several squadrons. The full size Liberator replica was built for film work and as it is too large to fit in the building it is used as a travelling exhibit to publicise the activities of the association. The Rhönlerche glider is currently in store at another location. A turret from a Fortress was found in 2004 and the excavation of the remains of a P-38 Lightning and a Messerchmitt Bf 109 also took place.

TYPE	REG/SER	CON. NO.	PI/NOTES	STATUS
☐ Consolidated 24 Liberator (B-24D) (FSM)	'124226'			RAX
☐ Focke-Wulf Fw 190D-9		210102		PVC
☐ Nord N.1203 Norécrin	F-BEBU	56		PV
☐ Schleicher Ka-4 Rhönlerche II				RA
☐ Waco NZR Hadrian (CG-4A)			Centre fuselage section.	PVC

CENTRUM VOOR GESCHIEDEMS VAN RIJKSWACHT (BLG5)

Address:	Luchtmachtlaan 33, B-1040 Brussels.
Tel:	02 642 69 29
Fax:	02 642 63 69
Admission:	Tuesday-Friday 0900-1200 1300-1630.
Location:	In the city just north of the Gare du Midi.

The Belgian Police have used a number of helicopters and fixed wing aircraft in recent years. One of the retired Alouette IIs joined the museum in 2001. The type entered service in 1968. The displays trace the history of police work in the country. On show are photographs, documents, uniforms, and items of memorabilia along with vehicles. The main flying base for the service is on the military side at Melsbroek. Currently in use are small numbers of Cessna 182s, Sud SA.330L Pumas and McDonnell-Douglas MD-520Ns and MD-900s.

TYPE	REG/SER	CON. NO.	PI/NOTES	STATUS
☐ Sud-Est SE.3130 Alouette II	G-93	2004	A-93	PV

COLLECTION DE WOUTERS (BLG6)

Address:	Rue Tillette 15, B-5537 Anhee.
Email:	bruno.dewouters@skynet.be
Admission:	By prior permission only.
Location:	At St. Hubert airfield which is just north east of the town off Route 89.

Bruno de Wouters has acquired an interesting collection of classic sailplanes from several countries. The active gliders are normally based at St. Hubert with the others in a workshop near his home. The oldest is the diminutive Hütter H 17B. Many of the fleet were acquired from France. The Carmam types were produced from Italian designs from the Turin Polytechnic. The Slingsby T.45 first flew in October 1957 but was soon lost when it crashed into some telephone wires at Sutton Bank. Fred Slingsby said it looked like a Swallow and the name stuck. One hundred and six had been built before the factory fire of 1968 destroyed several on the line.

TYPE	REG/SER	CON. NO.	PI/NOTES	STATUS
☐ Bölkow Phoebus B-1	OO-YWB	855	OE-0872, BGA.4901	RA
☐ Carmam M.100S Mésange	OO-ZRP	13	F-CCSB	RAA
☐ Carmam M.200 Foehn	OO-ZLY	28	F-CCDY	RAA
☐ Carmam M.200 Foehn	OO-ZLF	45	F-CDHV	RAA
☐ Caudron C.800 Épervier	F-CAVC	9937/277		RA
☐ Hütter H 17B				RA
☐ LCA-Scheibe 11 Topaze	F-CEEL	12		RA
☐ Schleicher Ka-2B Rhönschwalbe	OO-SZD	196/56		RA
☐ Schleicher ASK-14	F-CALP			RA
☐ Slingsby T.45 Swallow	OO-YWL	1566	BGA.1339	RAA

COLLECTION HENRARD (BLG7)

Address:	Rue de Porcheresse 11, B-5361 Hamois-Mohiville.
Tel:	083-612194
Fax:	083-612194
Email:	henrard.f@belgacom.net
Admission:	By prior permission only.
Location:	The village of Mohiville is about 20 km north east of Dinant off road N.4.

Firmin Henrard is an active member of the vintage gliding movement in the country and sailplanes from this collection are often seen at rallies throughout Europe. The superb Rhönbussard was built in Germany in the 1930s and is one of few left in airworthy condition. Over two hundred were built after the prototype made its maiden flight in 1933. The Caudron 800 series and the Nord 2000 (a license built Meise) were ordered in large numbers to start up gliding clubs in France after World War II. The Sohaj was designed in Czechoslovakia as a replacement for the Olympia Meise. The prototype flew in 1947 and three marks were produced. One hundred and twenty six examples of the second version were constructed and gave excellent service for many years.

TYPE	REG/SER	CON. NO.	PI/NOTES	STATUS
☐ Avialsa-Scheibe A.60 Fauconnet [L-Spatz-55]	OO-ZWF	8	F-CCLD	RAA
☐ Fauvel AV.36	OO-ZIG	219	D-5510	RA
☐ Jacobs Rhönbussard (D.F.S. 108-50)	OO-ZVO		D-????, F-????, OO-ZVA	RAA
☐ Nord N.2000 [Jacobs Meise]	OO-ZHQ	10393/63	F-CAYP	RAA
☐ Schleicher ASK-14	F-CASD	14026	D-KOIA	RAA
☐ Schleicher Ka-4 Rhönlerche II	OO-ZUL	596		RAC
☐ Schneider ESG 31 Grunau Baby IIB	OO-ZFH			RAA
☐ Slingsby T.31B Cadet TX.3	OO-ZXN	1179	XN240 – part owner.	RAA
☐ Slingsby T.38 Grasshopper TX.1	BGA.3439	1263	XP464	RA
☐ Zlin LG-125 Sohaj 2	OO-ZPM	178		RA

COLLECTION VORMEZEELE (BLG8)

Address:	Diksmuidelei 7, B-2930 Brasschaat.
Tel:	03-663-2604
Email:	fred.vor@belgacom.net
Admission:	Not available for viewing as the aircraft are on an active military base.
Location:	Brasschaat airfield is about 15 km north of Antwerpen off road N.117.

Retired army officer Eric Vormezeele has assembled this interesting collection of aircraft over the last few years. The majority are housed in hangars in the military area of the Belgian Army Aviation School at Brasschaat and can normally be seen when they appear at airshows in the region. The Spanish built Messerschmitt 109 was used at Tablada in Spain in taxiing scenes in the 'Battle of Britain' film in the late 1960s and after a spell in the U.S.A. was bought in 1985. A lengthy restoration followed. The fighter took to the air again on August 8th 1994 and has since flown on a few more occasions. The early Tiger Moth was flown in England by the Midland Aero Club at Castle Bromwich for a short time before being impressed during World War II. Sold in 1953 it was allocated another British registration but after conversion was immediately sold to Belgium.

TYPE	REG/SER	CON. NO.	PI/NOTES	STATUS
☐ Boeing-Stearman A75N1 Kaydet (PT-17)	G-IIIG	75-4354	42-16191, N61827, G-BSDR	RAA
☐ De Havilland D.H.82A Tiger Moth	OO-BYL	3882	G-AFNR, W7952, G-ANBU	RAC
☐ Fiat G.46-4A	I-AEHO	143	MM53093	RA
☐ Fiat G.46-4A	OO-VOR	199	MM53293, I-AEKI	RAA
☐ Hispano HA-1112M1L [Messerschmitt Bf 109G]	OO-MAF	201	C.4K-131	RAA
☐ Noorduyn Harvard IIB [North American NA-77 (AT-16)]	'H-50'	14A-1494	43-13195, FT454, B-84 (Netherlands), 098 (Netherlands), OO-DAF	RAAX
☐ Nord N.1101 Noralpha (Ramier I) [Messerschmitt Me 208]	OO-VAF	119	119 (France), F-ZJDG, F-BHER	RA
☐ Nord N.1101 Ramier I [Messerschmitt Me 208]	34	34	In French markings.	RA
☐ North American NA-88 Texan (AT-6C) (Harvard IIA)	H-39	88-9728	41-33265, EX292, 7182 (South Africa), EX292	RA
☐ North American NA-171 Trojan (T-28A) (AT-28D)	FG-244	171-50	50-0244 – In Zairean markings Possibly OO-KLY reserved.	RA
☐ Sud-Est SE.3130 Alouette II	A-37	1803		RA

DOCUMENTATIECENTRUM VAN DE 15 WING (BLG9)

Address:	Haachste Steenweg 138, B-1820 Melsbroek.
Tel:	02-752-4650
Admission:	On Mondays by prior permission only.
Location:	At the military base on the northern side of Zaventem Airport which is about 12 km north east of Brussels

The centre was formed in 1992 to preserve the traditions of the wing and show the history of the field built by the Germans in 1940. An exhibition of photographs, documents, models, uniforms and components has been set up in a building on the base. The unit was set up at Evère in February 1948 from the former 169 Wing. 20 Smaldeel flew Ansons and Dakotas and 21 Smaldeel Dakotas, Dominies and Oxfords. The move to Melsbroek occurred in 1950. The C-119 is being restored by members of the group. Forty six Flying Boxcars served in Belgium with the first arriving in 1952. They flew with the transport wing until the early 1970s when most were scrapped. Belgium was the first overseas customer for Pembroke and twelve were ordered in the mid-1950s. and these were also withdrawn in the mid-1970s. The Anson is being rebuilt to represent one of examples used by the Air Force on communications duties between 1946 and 1954. In total twelve Anson 1s and two Mark 12s were flown. The Alouette is stored in the nearby Police hangar. For many years an Oxford was preserved outside a restaurant close to the military site but unfortunately this rotted away.

TYPE	REG/SER	CON. NO.	PI/NOTES	STATUS
☐ Avro 652A Anson C.19	TX192			RAC
☐ Fairchild 110 Flying Boxcar (C-119F) (C-119G)	CP-10	10690	51-2701 – On loan from KLM.	RA
☐ Percival P.66 Pembroke C.51	RM-7	P.66/27		RA
☐ Sud-Est SE.3130 Alouette II	G-94	2102	A-94	RA

KONINKLIJK LEGERMUSEUM / MUSÉE ROYAL DE L'ARMÉE (BLG10)

Address:	Jubelpark 3 / Parc du Cinquantenaire 3, B-1040 Brussel / Bruxelles.
Tel:	02-734-2157
Email:	nfocom@klm-mra.be
Admission:	Tuesday-Sunday 0900-1200 1300-1645.
Location:	About 2.5 km east of the city centre on the N.3 to Louvain, close to the outer ring road.

Constructed in 1881 to commemorate the fiftieth anniversary of Belgium's independence, the vast Palais du Cinquantenaire is ideal for museum use. Part of the complex has housed the Army Museum for many years. The Belgian Air Force started as a branch of the Army Balloon Company. A separate aviation unit was formed at Brasschaat in 1912 and by the following year had four squadrons. During World War I a variety of types were operated from airfields around the country. The building was neither bombed nor looted during World War II and the exhibition was unaltered for years. Up to the late 1960s about fifteen aircraft, mainly from the World War I period, were suspended from the ceilings of the museum halls. Many had spent almost half a century untouched. After World War II a similar number of more modern types were acquired and stored in the adjacent former great jousting hall. In the 1960s Colonel Mike Terlinden and Warrant Officer Jean Booten were recovering from crashes in the same military hospital when they came up with a plan for a separate aeronautical museum. The military authorities were supportive and Jean Booten was put in charge. Tarmac was laid over the sand floor of the jousting hall and the surrounding galleries and adjoining rooms cleaned up. The aircraft in the Army Museum were gradually taken down and restored and the balcony above the main hall now presents one of the most comprehensive displays of World War I aeroplanes in the world. Aircraft from both sides in the conflict can be seen. Two famous Sopwith types are on view. Three Belgian squadrons used the 1½ Strutter and the one in the upper gallery joined the museum in 1920. Nearby is a Camel. This aircraft was restored at Bierset and now wears the colours of the 11th Escadrille. Very few Schrek flying boats have survived. The Franco British Aviation Company constructed a number of similar models which were used by allied forces. Over the last three decades the collection has grown and many machines are now in store at Vissanaken. There are plans to open up this site on a regular basis and put on a display. However, there is still a great deal of work to be done before this project is ready. The staff and a large number of volunteers have worked with enthusiasm to restore many rare aircraft to exhibition standard. Civil and military types have been gathered from all parts of the country and a number of exchange deals have taken place in order to enhance the exhibition. In one a Harvard and a Meteor moved to Prague and a Delfin and a MiG-15 arrived in Brussels. One of the earliest aircraft on show is the recently restored Bataille Triplane. Constructed in 1912 the aircraft flew for a short time before being put in store at the family factory. The remains were donated to the museum in 1972 and in the 1980s the rebuild commenced. A Percival Gull was found in the 1970s after more than forty years in store in a barn near Waterloo. The aircraft had crashed on a flight from England and was dismantled locally. This rare machine is now resplendent in its original colours. A number of fairly modern types recently withdrawn from service can now be seen. Gliders and homebuilt aircraft feature prominently in the display. The collection has grown into one of the largest in Europe with several unique types on show especially Belgian designs such as the Kreit and Lambrickx KL-2 and the SABCA Poncelet Vivette. The shoulder wing KL-2 was registered in September 1934 and was based at Diest-Schaffen. The aircraft was stored during the war and fortunately survived. In the early 1920s many ultralight aircraft were developed and the Poncelet Vivette is a typical example. Two were constructed and the example in the collection was withdrawn in 1931. The museum now has responsibility for many military aircraft displayed around the country.

TYPE	REG/SER	CON. NO.	PI/NOTES	STATUS
☐ Aero L-29R Delfin	2808	892808		PV
☐ Aeronca 7AC Champion	OO-SND	7AC-4047		RA
☐ Agusta A.109BA	H-08	3008		PV
☐ Airspeed AS.10 Oxford I	O-16	PAC.936	Now thought to be ex MP455 and not HN130.	PVC
☐ Auster J/1 Autocrat	OO-ABN	2047		SD
☐ Auster K AOP.6	OO-FDD	2817	VT978, A-9	SD
☐ Auster K AOP.6	VT979	2818	VT979, A-3, OO-FDA	PV
☐ Auster K AOP.6	OO-FDB	2820	VT981, A-7	SD
☐ Auster K AOP.6	OO-FDC	2827	VT988, A-8	SD
☐ Auster K AOP.6	A-11	2829	VT990, A-11, OO-FDE	PV
☐ Auster K AOP.6	OO-FDJ	2832	VT993, A-17	S
☐ Auster K AOP.6	OO-FDH	2834	VT995, A-15 – parts used in former 'A-16' monument at Brasschaat.	SD
☐ Auster K AOP.6	'A-16'	2836	VT997, A-22, OO-FDL	S
☐ Aviatik C I	C.227/16	832		PVC
☐ Avro Canada C.100 Canuck 5 (CF-100)	18534	434	18534, A-690	PV
☐ Bataille Triplane				PV
☐ Blériot XI			Wings and engine only.	PVC
☐ Boeing 707-329	OO-SJA	17623	Front fuselage section	PV
☐ Breguet 905S Fauvette	OO-ZJN	45	F-CCJO	S
☐ Bristol 14 F.2B Fighter	'66'		BAPC.19 – composite incorporates parts of J8264.	PVX
☐ Bristol 149 Bolingbroke IVT	10038		9895/10038 (Canada) – composite of at least two aircraft.	PVX
☐ Britten-Norman BN-2A-21 Islander	B-05	501	At Bierset.	RA
☐ Britten-Norman BN-2A-21 Islander	B-06	510	G-BDPU	PV
☐ Bücker Bü 181B Bestmann	TP+CP	021969	TP+CP, (OO-SNE), OO-RVD	PV
☐ Bücker Bü 181B-1 Bestmann	OO-BLJ	0216168/FR-1	F-BBLJ, OO-RVA	RA
☐ Caudron C.800 Épervier		9816/156	F-CBTZ	PV
☐ Caudron G.3	'C.2531'		F-AFDC (?) – in French Markings.	PVX
☐ Cessna 310B	OO-SEL	35524	N5324A, OO-CUC, 9O-CUC, 9Q-CUC, OO-CUC	RA
☐ Cessna 310B	OO-SEH	35630	N5430A, OO-CES, 9Q-CES	RA
☐ Chandellon Helicopter				S
☐ Croses EC-3 Pouplume	OO-33		OO-33, 'OO-BAM'	PV
☐ Dassault MD-450 Ouragan	320	320	In French Markings	PV
☐ Dassault Mystère IVA	191	191	At Weelde.	RA
☐ Dassault Super Mystère B2	145	145	At Weelde.	RA
☐ Dassault Mirage 5BA	BA-03	03	At Namur.	PV
☐ Dassault Mirage 5BA	BA-15	15		PV
☐ Dassault Mirage 5BA	BA-16	16	On loan to Museé Lallement.	–
☐ Dassault Mirage 5BA	BA-22	22	On loan to Museé Lallement.	–
☐ Dassault Mirage 5BA	BA-26	26	On loan to Evere HQ.	–
☐ Dassault Mirage 5BA	BA-30	30	At Spa.	PV
☐ Dassault Mirage 5BR	BR-04	304	On loan to Museé Lallement.	–
☐ Dassault Mirage 5BR	BR-10	310	On loan to Museé du 1 Wing.	–
☐ De Havilland D.H.82A Tiger Moth	OO-EVS	3272	K4276, G-AOJX	RA
☐ De Havilland D.H.82A Tiger Moth	OO-GDR	3775	N6445, A-39 (Netherlands), PH-UEZ	PVD
☐ De Havilland D.H.82A Tiger Moth	OO-SOF	82592	G-AFWF, W6420, G-AMTL – on loan to Sabena Old Timers.	–
☐ De Havilland D.H.82A Tiger Moth	'T-24'	83728	T7238, G-AMJD, OO-SOI	PVX
☐ De Havilland D.H.82A Tiger Moth	OO-SOX	83830	T7303	S
☐ De Havilland D.H.82A Tiger Moth	OO-SOW	84567	T6100, G-APPT – incorporates parts of c/n 82166 N6922, G-APBY, OO-SOK.	S
☐ De Havilland D.H.82A Tiger Moth	T6534	84875	T6534, G-AMTP, OO-EVT	PV
☐ De Havilland D.H.82A Tiger Moth	OO-EVH	85832	DE972, T-27	S
☐ De Havilland D.H.82A Tiger Moth	OO-EVG	86338	NL981, T-15	S

De Havilland D.H.82A Tiger Moth	OO-EVD	86517	NM209, T-22 – at Diest-Schaffen.	RA
De Havilland D.H.89A Dragon Rapide (D.H.89B Dominie I)	OO-CNP	6458	RS922, G-AKNV, EI-AGK, G-AKNV, OO-AFG	PVC
De Havilland D.H.98 Mosquito NF.30	MB-24	984597	RK952	PV
De Havilland D.H.115 Vampire T.11	XH292	15610	XH292, 'MT-11'	PV
De Havilland D.H.C.1 Chipmunk T.20	P-130	C1/0109	12-130 (Denmark) – In Danish markings.	RAC
De Havilland D.H.C.3 Otter (UC-1) (U-1B)	OO-SUD	297	Bu144669 – incorporates parts of c/n 148 OO-HAD.	PV
Dornier Do 27J-1	OL-D04	2101	D-4, OL-D04, DO-4	PV
Dornier Do 28D-1 Skyservant	OO-GEO	4023	OY-DLS, D-IDWM, PH-NVB – on loan to a technical school in Ostend	–
Douglas A-26B Invader	N67160	28044	(44-34765), N67160, D-CAFY	PVC
Douglas DC-3A-467 Skytrain (C-47B)	K-16	20823	43-16357	PV
Fairchild 110 Flying Boxcar (C-119F) (C-119G)	CP-10	10690	51-2701 – On loan to 15 Wing, Melsbroek.	–
Fairchild 110 Flying Boxcar (C-119G)	CP-46	254	53-8151	PVC
Fairchild 24R9 Forwarder (UC-61K) (Argus III)	43-14987	R9-951	43-14987, HB713, ZS-BWM, ZS-BYN, F-OADB, F-BAMB, OO-LUT	PV
Fairchild 24R9 Forwarder (UC-61K) (Argus III)	OO-LMV	R9-1069	44-83108, KK451, F-OAAY, F-BDAL, N9759F	RA
Fairey Battle I	'T-30'		R3950, 1899 (Canada)	PVX
Farman F.11A-2				PV
Farman-Voisin				PVC
Fiat G.91R/3	30+85	91-348	KD+338, ED+252, BD+243	PV
Fieseler Fi 103A-1				PV
Fieseler Fi 156C-3 Storch (S 14)	KR+QX	5503	KR+QX, Fv3822, OE-ADT	PVC
Focke-Wulf Weihe 50	PL-50	7/50	c/n also reported as 62-07 – with Air Cadets at Goetsenhoven.	RA
Fokker Dr I (R)	'425/17'		Replica containing many original parts.	PVX
Fouga CM.170R Magister	MT-49	222	On loan to Beauvechain A.F.B.	–
Fouga CM.170R Magister	MT-3	260	Due to be mounted on a rounabout near Brustem.	–
Fouga CM.170R Magister	MT-23	280		PV
Fouga CM.170R Magister	MT-24	281		PV
Fulmar Trident	OO-521			PV
General Dynamics 401 Fighting Falcon (F-16A)	FA-01	6H-1	78-0116	PV
General Dynamics 401 Fighting Falcon (F-16A)	FA-04	6H-4	78-0119 – On to Museé Lallement.	–
General Dynamics 401 Fighting Falcon (F-16A)	FA-10	6H-10	On loan to Beauvechain AFB.	–
General Dynamics 401 Fighting Falcon (F-16A)	FA-113	6H-113	88-0038 – Fin from c/n 6H-59 – on loan to Museé du 1 Wing.	–
Gloster Meteor F.8	EG-18	6339	On loan to to Museé International Chièvres.	–
Gloster Meteor F.8	EG-79	6521	On loan to Beauvechain A.F.B.	–
Gloster Meteor F.8	EG-224			PV
Gloster Meteor NF.11	NF.11-3		WM298	RA
Göppingen Gö 4 Gövier III	OO-ZPJ	413		S
Grasshopper Model Mono 01	OO-501	GH/01/81/00		PV
Halberstadt C V	3471/18	1541	Was marked '3441/18' but is believed to be 3471/18.	PV
Hanriot HD-1	HD-78	VIII/5153		PV
Hawker Hurricane IIC	'LF345'		LF658	PVX
Hawker P.1067 Hunter F.4		41H/691136	Cockpit section only.	PV
Hawker P.1067 Hunter F.4	'IF-83'	AF/HCF/9	ID-16 – At Beauvechain AFB.	–
Hawker P.1067 Hunter F.4	ID-26	AF/HCF/19	At Beauvechain AFB.	–
Hawker P.1067 Hunter F.4	'IF-70'	AF/HCF/59	ID-46 – marked as an F.6	PVX
Hawker P.1067 Hunter F.4	ID-123	8679	On loan to Koksidje AFB.	–
Hawker P.1099 Hunter F.6	IF-65	8815		RA
Hawker P.1099 Hunter F.58	J-4077	41H/697444	In Swiss markings.	PV
Huntair Pathfinder II	OO-570	124		PV
Jodel D.9 Bébé	OO-15			PVC
Jodel D.9 Bébé	OO-40			S
Junkers Ju 52/3mg7e	OO-AGU	501196	7U+IK, 6309 (Portugal), – fin from c/n 501219 501219 (Norway), 6310 (Portugal)	PV
Kassel 12				PV
Kreit & Lambrickx KL-2	OO-ANP			PV
Let C-11 [Yakovlev Yak-11]	'1706'	171317	1317 (Czechoslovakia)	PVX
Livingstone BO-2 Hang Glider				PV
Lockheed 580 (T-33A)	FT-24	580-7788	52-9892 – on loan to Musée du 1 Wing.	–
Lockheed 580 (T-33A)	FT-34	580-9584	55-3043	PV
Lockheed 683-10-19 Starfighter (F-104G)	FX-02	683-9017	On loan to V Kleine Brogel.	–
Lockheed 683-10-19 Starfighter (F-104G)	FX-04	683-9019	On loan to Musée du 1 Wing.	–
Lockheed 683-10-19 Starfighter (F-104G)	FX-12	683-9029		PV
Lockheed 683-10-19 Starfighter (F-104G)	FX-15	683-9034	At Tongeren.	–
Lockheed 683-10-19 Starfighter (F-104G)	'FX-23'	683-9046	FX-21 – on loan to S. du S.	–
Lockheed 683-10-19 Starfighter (F-104G)	'FX-69'	683-9090	FX-47 – with tail of c/n 683-9115 FX-69 – on loan to Musée du 1 Wing.	–

Type	Reg/Ser	Con. No.	PI/Notes	Status
☐ Lockheed 683-10-19 Starfighter (F-104G)	FX-53	683-9096	At Saffraanberg.	–
☐ Lockheed 683-10-19 Starfighter (F-104G)	FX-86	683-9147	At Kleine Brogel AFB.	–
☐ Lockheed 683-10-19 Starfighter (F-104G)	FX-94	683-9164	On roundabout near Kleine Brogel AFB.	–
☐ Luft-Verkehrs-Gesellschaft (L.V.G.) C VI	5141/18	4981		PV
☐ McDonnell M.36BA Voodoo (F-101B)	'59-322'	694	58-0322	RA
☐ McDonnell M.98DF Phantom II (RF-4C)	68-0590	3579		PV
☐ Mignet HM-290 Pou-du-Ciel				S
☐ Mignet HM-293 Pou-du-Ciel	OO-11			PV
☐ Mignet HM-293 Pou-du-Ciel	OO-33		OO-33, 'OO-BAM'	PV
☐ Mikoyan-Gurevich MiG-15bis	3911	623911	In Czech markings	PV
☐ Mikoyan-Gurevich MiG-21bis	24+29	75033205	874 (DDR) – on loan to Musée du 1 Wing.	–
☐ Mikoyan-Gurevich MiG-21F-13	'77'	742107	F2157 (Indonesia) – in false Soviet markings.	PVX
☐ Mikoyan-Gurevich MiG-23BN	'23'	0393204421	4421 (Egypt) – in false Soviet markings.	PVX
☐ Mikoyan-Gurevich MiG-23ML	20+21	0390324640		RAC
☐ Mil Mi-24D	96+33	340273	528 (DDR)	PV
☐ Mil Mi-24D	530	340274	530 (DDR), 96+35 – on loan to Musée Bierset.	–
☐ Miles M.14A Hawk Trainer 3 (Magister)	'T-9800'	1992(?)	T9800, TMR-50, G-1, OO-NIC – c/n 1992 is T9705.	PVX
☐ Miles M.38 Messenger 2A	G-AKIS	6725		S
☐ Mooney M.20A	OO-KBL	1293	N1066B, OE-DKR, F-BKBL	RA
☐ Morane-Saulnier MS.230	'1066'	1066	F-BEJO – in Belgian markings.	PVX
☐ Morane-Saulnier MS.315	F-BCNT	350		PV
☐ Morane-Saulnier MS.500 Criquet [Fieseler Fi 156 Storch]	F-BFCD	374	374	SD
☐ Morane-Saulnier MS.880B Rallye Club	F-BSAM	1555		S
☐ Morane-Saulnier MS.892A Commodore 150	OO-TAO	10457		PV
☐ Nieuport 23C.1	N5024			PVC
☐ Nord N.1002 Pingouin II [Messerschmitt Bf 108B]	'W No 184'	184	184, F-BERF – in false Luftwaffe markings.	PVX
☐ North American NA-108 Mitchell (B-25J) (TB-25N)	'151632'	108-34200	44-30925, NL9494Z, G-BWGR	RAX
☐ North American NA-191 Sabre (F-86F)	5316	191-938	52-5242 – in Portuguese markings.	PV
☐ North American NA-88 Texan (AT-6D) (Harvard III)	H-21	88-15950	42-84169, EZ256, 7630 (South Africa)	PV
☐ Panstwowe Zaklady Lotnicze (PZL) TS-11 Iskra 100bisB	1014	1H 10-14		RA
☐ Percival D.2 Gull Four II	G-ACGR	D.29		PV
☐ Percival P.31C Proctor IV	P-4	H.578	NP171	PV
☐ Percival P.40 Prentice T.1	OO-OPO	PAC/215	VS613, G-AOPO	S
☐ Percival P.44 Proctor 5	OO-ARM	Ae.84	G-AHZY	S
☐ Percival P.66 Pembroke C.51	RM-4	P.66/21		PV
☐ Percival P.66 Pembroke C.51	RM-7	P.66/27	On loan to 15 Wing Melsbroek.	–
☐ Piper J-3C-65 Cub (L-4H)	OO-GEG	11694	43-30403	SD
☐ Piper J-3C-65 Cub (L-4J)	OO-AVX	13128	44-80832	S
☐ Piper PA-18-95 Super Cub (L-18C)	OO-LGA	18-1597	51-15597, F-BLLM	SD
☐ Piper PA-18-95 Super Cub (L-18C)	OL-L87	18-3149	53-4749, L-87	PV
☐ Piper PA-18-135 Super Cub (L-21B)	LB-03	18-3842	54-2642	RA
☐ Pissoort JP.II	OO-118	01	OO-LJP	PV
☐ Republic F-84E Thunderjet	'FS-2'		51-9599, FS-17 – on loan to Kleine Brogel AFB.	RAX
☐ Republic F-84E Thunderjet	'FS-7'		51-9583, K-6 (Netherlands) – on loan to Museé Lallement.	–
☐ Republic F-84F Thunderstreak	FU-30		52-7169	PV
☐ Republic F-84F Thunderstreak	FU-33		52-7192 – on loan to Mus Int. Chièvres.	–
☐ Republic F-84F Thunderstreak	FU-36		52-7157	RA
☐ Republic F-84F Thunderstreak	FU-50		52-7011 – stored at Florennes AFB.	–
☐ Republic F-84F Thunderstreak	FU-51		52-7215 – at Namur-Temploux airfield.	PV
☐ Republic F-84F Thunderstreak	FU-66		53-6677 – on loan to Kleine Brogel AFB.	–
☐ Republic F-84F Thunderstreak	FU-67		53-6681 – on loan to Kleine Brogel AFB.	–
☐ Republic F-84F Thunderstreak	FU-82		53-6587 – on loan to S.du S.	–
☐ Republic F-84F Thunderstreak	'FU-6'		53-6597, FU-103, 'FU-66' – on loan to Florennes AFB.	–
☐ Republic F-84F Thunderstreak	FU-108		53-6610 – on loan to Museé Lallement	–
☐ Republic F-84F Thunderstreak	'FU-52'		53-6783, FU-144 – on loan to Museé Lallement.	–
☐ Republic F-84F Thunderstreak	FU-145		53-6613 – at Kleine Brogel AFB.	–
☐ Republic F-84F Thunderstreak	FU-154		53-5806 – near Florennes AFB.	–
☐ Republic F-84F Thunderstreak	FU-179		53-6941 – on loan to Florennes AFB.	–
☐ Republic F-84F Thunderstreak	FU-188		52-6369, FU-188, 'FU-131' – at Kleine Brogel AFB.	–
☐ Republic F-84F Thunderstreak	FU-194		52-6378	RA

Type	Reg./Serial	c/n	Notes	Status
☐ Republic F-84G Thunderjet	'FZ-153'		51-10667, FZ-107 – tail from 51-10195, FZ-71.	PVX
☐ Republic RF-84F Thunderflash	FR-32		53-7646, BD+103, EA+103, EA+303 – on loan to Museé du 1 Wing.	-
☐ Republic RF-84F Thunderflash	FR-27		51-1922 – at Spa.	PV
☐ Republic RF-84F Thunderflash	FR-28		51-1945	PV
☐ Republic RF-84F Thunderflash	FR-29		51-11279 – on loan to VTZ. Evere.	-
☐ Republic RF-84F Thunderflash	FR-30		51-17015 – at Namur-Temploux.	PV
☐ Republic RF-84F Thunderflash	FR-33		53-7658, BD+105 (?), EA+105, EA+305 – at Florennes AFB.	RA
☐ Royal Aircraft Factory R.E.8	8	326	Possibly ex-A4719.	PV
☐ Schleicher Ka-2 Rhönschwalbe	PL-13	77/55	c/n also reported as 70/54.	RA
☐ Schleicher Ka-6CR Rhönsegler	OO-SZP	196		PV
☐ Schneider Grunau SG-38 (D.F.S. 108-14)	PL-21			S
☐ Schneider ESG 31 Grunau Baby II (D.F.S. 108-49)	OO-ZBA			S
☐ Schneider ESG 31 Grunau Baby II (D.F.S. 108-49)	PL-33	09/52		S
☐ Schneider ESG 31 Grunau Baby II (D.F.S. 108-49)	PL-36	77/55		S
☐ Schneider Grunau Baby III (D.F.S. 108-66)	PL-37	82/55		PV
☐ Schreck FBA Type H	5.160	55		PV
☐ SIAI-Marchetti SF.260MB	ST-11	10-11	On loan to Beauvechain AFB.	-
☐ SIAI-Marchetti SF.260MB	ST-14	10-14	On loan to Beauvechain AFB.	-
☐ Sikorsky S-58	B-4	SA-145	On loan to Koksijde AFB.	-
☐ Sikorsky S-58	B-6	SA-181		PV
☐ Sikorsky S-58	B-8	SA-185	On loan to Koksijde AFB.	-
☐ Skandinavisk Aero Industri (SAI) KZ III U-2	OO-MAA	72		PV
☐ Société Anonyme Belge de Constructions Aeronautiques (SABCA) Junior		2		S
☐ Société Anonyme Belge de Constructions Aeronautiques (SABCA) Junior		3		S
☐ Société Anonyme Belge de Constructions Aeronautiques (SABCA) Junior		10		S
☐ Société Anonyme Belge de Constructions Aeronautiques (SABCA) Junior		11		PV
☐ Société Anonyme Belge de Constructions Aeronautiques (SABCA) Poncelet Vivette	O-BAFH	2	O-BAFH, OO-AFH	PV
☐ Société Pour l'Aviation et ses Dérivés (SPAD) XIIIC.1	SP-49			PV
☐ Sopwith 1 1/2 Strutter	88	66(?)		PV
☐ Sopwith F.1 Camel	B5747		B5747, SC-11	PV
☐ Stamer-Lippisch Z-12 Zögling				RA
☐ Stamer-Lippisch Z-12 Zögling				RA
☐ Stampe & Renard S.R.7B	OO-SRZ	1003		PV
☐ Stampe & Vertongen S.V.4B	V-28	1170		PV
☐ Stampe & Vertongen S.V.4B	V-33	1175	In terminal at Brussels – Zaventem Airport.	PV
☐ Stampe & Vertongen S.V.4B	V-56	1198		PV
☐ Stampe & Vertongen S.V.4B	'OO-ATD'	1199	V-57, 'MX457'	PVX
☐ Stampe & Vertongen S.V.4B	V-64	1206		PV
☐ Stampe & Vertongen S.V.4C	'102'	28	28 (French), OO-CLH, F-BFZC – in false French markings.	PVX
☐ Stampe & Vertongen S.V.4C		180 (?)		RA
☐ Stampe & Vertongen S.V.4D (S.V.4B)	OO-SRS	1208		PV
☐ Stinson SR-10C Reliant	EL-AES	5714		RA
☐ Sud SA.318C Alouette II	A-41	1958		RA
☐ Sud SA.318C Alouette II	A-46	1964	On loan to Beauvechain AFB.	-
☐ Sud-Est SE.210 Caravelle VI-N	OO-SRA	64	F-WJAK	PV
☐ Sud-Est SE.3130 Alouette II	A-8	1467		RA
☐ Sud-Est SE.3130 Alouette II	A-11	1535		PV
☐ Sud-Est SE.3130 Alouette II	A-34	1791	At Bierset.	-
☐ Supermarine 361 Spitfire LF.IXc	'MJ360'	CBAF-IX-1301	MJ783, SM-15	PVX
☐ Supermarine 361 Spitfire LF.IXc (FSM)	'BS435'			PVX
☐ Supermarine 379 Spitfire F.XIVc	SG-57	6S.432331	RM921 – on loan to Museé Lallement.	-
☐ Supermarine 379 Spitfire F.XIVc	SG-55	6S.649170	MV246 – with parts of RM860, SG-37 and RM623, SG-46	PV
☐ Svenska Aeroplan Aktiebolaget (SAAB) 35A Draken (J 35A)	Fv35067	35067		PV
☐ Szybowcowy Zaklad Doswiadczalny S.Z.D.8bis Jaskolka	OO-ZSA	247		PV
☐ Tipsy S.2	'OO-TIP'	29	OO-ASB, G-AFVH	PVX
☐ Tipsy Trainer 1	G-AFRV	10		RAD
☐ Tipsy Belfair (Trainer 1)	G-AFJR	2		RA
☐ Tipsy T.66 Nipper II	'OO-NIP'	49 (?)	Composite	PVX
☐ Voisin LA5 b2			Fuselage and engine only	PV
☐ Westland Lysander IIIA	2219			RAC
☐ Westland Lysander IIIA	OO-SOT	Y1530	Composite of at least three ex-RCAF aircraft 2341, 2360 and 2442 – on loan to Sabena Old Timers.	-
☐ Wytwornia Sprzetu Komunikacyjnego (WSK) Lim-5 [MiG-17F]	418	1C 04-18		RA
☐ Zeppelin L 30			Nacelles only	PV

MUSÉE ARMERIE DU CENTRE (BLG11)

Address:	90 Rue du Couvert, B-7161 Haine St. Pierre.
Tel:	064-22-9073
Admission:	By prior permission only.
Location:	In the eastern part of the town which is on road N.27 about 20 km west of Charleroi.

This private collection of mainly military vehicles was started over forty years ago. Also on show are weapons, uniforms and memorabilia along with posters and photographs. The Noralpha, now painted in false German colours, was once owned by Eric Vormezeele at Braaschaat and moved to the site in the mid-1990s.

TYPE	REG/SER	CON. NO.	PI/NOTES	STATUS
☐ Butterfly	OO-519	03		RA
☐ Nord N.1101 Noralpha (Ramier I) [Messerschmitt Me 208]		103	103, F-BLEZ, OO-RLR – in false Luftwaffe markings.	PVX
☐ Raab Doppelraab IV			D-5328	PVX

MUSÉE COLONEL AVIATEUR R. LALLEMENT (BLG12)

Address:	Base Jean Offenberg, B-5620 Florennes.
Tel:	071-68-80-24
Admission:	Friday-Saturday 1330-1430; Last Sunday in month 1330-1730.
Location:	The airfield is about 20 km west of Dinant north of road N.97.

Built by the Germans in 1942 the airfield at Florennes was liberated by the Americans in 1944 and handed over to the Belgian Air Force in 1947. The first squadron to move in operated Spitfires. In 1955 a Spitfire, once the personal aircraft of the base commander Colonel Roger Lallement was mounted outside the wing headquarters. A building to house the aircraft was constructed and this opened on September 12th 1992. On May 31st 1997 a second hall was ready and here examples of types flown from the field can be seen.

TYPE	REG/SER	CON. NO.	PI/NOTES	STATUS
☐ Dassault Mirage 5BA	BA-07	7	Front fuselage only.	PV
☐ Dassault Mirage 5BA	BA-16	16	On loan from KLM.	PV
☐ Dassault Mirage 5BA	BA-22	22	On loan from KLM.	PV
☐ Dassault Mirage 5BR	BR-04	304	On loan from KLM.	PV
☐ General Dynamics 401 Fighting Falcon (F-16A)	FA-04	6H-4	78-0119- on loan from KLM.	PV
☐ Republic F-84E Thunderjet	'FS-7'		51-9583, K-6 (Netherlands)	PVX
☐ Republic F-84F Thunderstreak	FU-154		53-6806	RA
☐ Republic F-84F Thunderstreak	'FU-52'		53-6783, FU-144 – on loan from KLM.	PVX
☐ Republic F-84F Thunderstreak	'FU-6'		53-6597, FU-103, 'FU-66'	RAX
☐ Republic F-84F Thunderstreak	FU-108		53-6610	RA
☐ Republic F-84F Thunderstreak	FU-179		53-6941 – On loan from KLM.	RA
☐ Supermarine 379 Spitfire FR.XIVe	SG-57	6S.432331	RM921 – On loan from KLM.	PV

MUSÉE DE LA BASE DE BIERSET (BLG13)

Address:	Caserne de Cubber, Chee de Liege, B-4460 Grace Hollogne.
Tel:	04-250-7132
Admission:	Thursday 1000-1200 1400-1600; First Sunday in month 1000-1200.
Location:	About 9 km west of Liege off road N.637.

This interesting museum is housed in one of the 1920s buildings constructed at the original airfield site. The history of the base, its units and aircraft are traced with a comprehensive display of photographs, memorabilia, models, components and uniforms. A new airfield, a short distance away, was built after World War II and for many years was an Air Force Base as well as serving as the civil airport for the city.

TYPE	REG/SER	CON. NO.	PI/NOTES	STATUS
☐ Agusta A.109BA	H-09		3009	PV
☐ Auster K AOP.6	'A-16'		Composite of c/n 2815 VT976, A-5 and c/n 2836 VT997, A-22, OO-FDL	PVX
☐ Britten-Norman BN-2A-21 Islander	B-11	549	G-BEED	RA
☐ Dornier Do 27J-1	OL-D02	2058	D-9505, D-2, OL-DO-2, D-02	RA
☐ Mil Mi-24D	96+35	340274	530 (DDR) – on loan from KLM.	RA
☐ Sud-Est SE.3130 Alouette II	A-34	1791		PV

The oldest glider in Firmin Henrard's collection is this Jacobs Rhönbussard. (Firmin Henrard)

The first French built S.V.4A is shown flying over Antwerp Airport. This biplane is part of the Stampe Museum collection. (Bob Rongé)

Visitors to the Citadel at Dinant will see this Gloster Meteor when they emerge from the lift which takes them to the top of the hill.

MUSÉE DE LA CITADELLE (BLG14)

Address:	Place Reine Astrid 3-5, B-5500 Dinant.
Tel:	082-22-36-70
Fax:	082-22-65-04
Admission:	Daily 1000-1800.
Location:	In the centre of the town.

This historic hilltop fortress attracts many visitors and there are regular guided tours of the buildings. Positioned outside the old part of the fort is the Meteor which was flown by the Belgian Air Force until 1958. The aircraft then spent a short period on target towing duties before moving to the site in early 1960s.

TYPE	REG/SER	CON. NO.	PI/NOTES	STATUS
☐ Gloster Meteor F.8	EG-162	6496	EG-162, (OO-ARU)	PV

MUSÉE DU 1 WING (BLG15)

Address:	Base Charles Roman, B-1320 Beauvechain.
Tel:	010-23-22-2
Admission:	Monday-Friday 0800-1700 by appointment. First and third Sunday in month 1000-1600.
Location:	About 6 km south of the town which is about 10 km south of Leuven.

This airfield was constructed for Luftwaffe use in the early 1940s. In late 1946 two Spitfire squadrons of the Belgian Air Force arrived from Fassberg in Germany. The wing was established on February 1st 1948. Since then it has flown Meteors, Mosquitos, Hunters, CF-100s, Starfighters and now the F-16. The displays in the museum trace the history of the wing. Some of the aircraft are parked around the airfield.

TYPE	REG/SER	CON. NO.	PI/NOTES	STATUS
☐ Dassault Mirage 5BR	BR-10	310	On loan from KLM.	RA
☐ Dornier-Breguet Alpha Jet A	AT-16	B16/1056		RAD
☐ Fouga CM.170R Magister	MT-49	222	On loan from KLM.	RA
☐ General Dynamics 401 Fighting Falcon (F-16A)	FA-10	6H-10	78-0125	PV
☐ General Dynamics 401 Fighting Falcon (F-16A)	FA-113	6H-113	88-0038 – fin from c/n 6H-59 80-3550, FA-59. – On loan from KLM.	PV
☐ Gloster Meteor F.8	'EG-80'	6521	EG-79 – on loan from KLM.	PVX
☐ Hawker P.1067 Hunter F.4	'IF-83'	AF/HCF/9	ID-16	RADX
☐ Hawker P.1067 Hunter F.4	ID-26	AF/HCF/19		RAD
☐ Lockheed 580 (T-33A)	FT-24	580-7788	52-9892 – on loan from KLM.	PV
☐ Lockheed 683-10-19 Starfighter (F-104G)	FX-04	683-9019		PV
☐ Lockheed 683-10-19 Starfighter (F-104G)	'FX-69'	683-9090	FX-47 with tail of c/n 683-9115 FX-69 – on loan from KLM.	PVX
☐ Mikoyan-Gurevich MiG-21bis	24+29	75033205	874 (DDR) – On loan from KLM.	PV
☐ Republic RF-84F Thunderflash	FR-32		53-7646, BD+103 (?), EA+103, EA+303 – on loan from K.LM.	PV
☐ SIAI-Marchetti SF.260MB	ST-11	10-11		PV
☐ SIAI-Marchetti SF.260MB	ST-14	10-14	On loan from KLM.	RA
☐ Sud SA.318C Alouette II	A-46	1964	On loan from KLM.	RA

MUSÉE INTERNATIONAL DE LA BASE AÉRIENNE DE CHIÈVRES (BLG16)

Address:	c/o 49 Rue Watterman, B-7860 Lessines.
Tel:	068-33-65-28
Fax:	068-33-74-53
Admission:	By prior permission only.
Location:	About 8 km south east of Ath.

In 1917 it was proposed that the site should be used as an airfield. In the late 1930s the Belgian Government started construction and the work was completed during the German occupation. A wing of Messerschmitt Bf 109s was in residence. Since then the field has been used by American and Belgian units. The airfield is now home to SHAPE and the Americans have a small number of aircraft in residence. The display has been set up in a former German building on the site and the complex history of the base is portrayed.

TYPE	REG/SER	CON. NO.	PI/NOTES	STATUS
☐ Gloster Meteor F.8	EG-18	6339	On loan from KLM.	RA
☐ Republic F-84F Thunderstreak	FU-33		52-7192 – on loan from KLM.	RA

MUSEUM VAN HET KAMP VAN BEVERLOO (BLG17)

Address:	Hechtese Steenweg 9, B-3970 Leopoldsburg.
Tel:	011 34 48 04
Email:	museumkvb@belgacom.net
Admission:	Monday-Friday 1300-1700.
Location:	In the town which is on road N.73 about 20 km north of Hasselt. The airfield is about 3 km east of the town on Route 73.

The town has been an important military base for many years and is still home to army units. The museum opened in 1972 in a former military hospital and traces the history of the camp and the regiments that have served in the area. On show are photographs, documents, weapons, uniforms and badges. There is a collection of military vehicles showing the development of these over the years. The Thunderstreak which was outside the building for a long period has now moved to the local airfield.

TYPE	REG/SER	CON. NO.	PI/NOTES	STATUS
☐ Republic F-84F Thunderstreak	FU-177		53-6888 – at nearby airfield.	PV

SABENA OLD TIMER FOUNDATION (BLG18)

Address:	Nationale Luchthaven, B-1930 Zaventem. (Will change in near future)
Tel:	02-723-59-67 ext 1386
Fax:	02-723-47-99
Email:	Yves.Cartilier@ping.be
Admission:	By prior permission only.
Location:	The airport is about 12 km north east of the city centre off the outer ring.

The airline SABENA was formed in May 1923 and in the early 1980s a group of former engineers set up a workshop at the company headquarters at Zaventem Airport. The first project undertaken was the Lysander which the Brussels museum obtained from Canada in 1971. The restoration commenced in 1982 and the aircraft was completed and flew again in August 1988 painted in a World War II night operations scheme. This aircraft has been involved in a few minor incidents and is normally to be found at Grimbergen. The airline used a small fleet of Cessna 310s at Grimbergen on training and communications duties. Large numbers of Tiger Moths flew in Belgium on both military and civil duties. The example in the workshop was delivered to the Cardiff Aeroplane Club in 1939 before being impressed in January 1940. The Lodestar will be restored in the colours of an example operated by civilian crews in World War II. Despite the demise of the airline the work continues on all the projects. The new owners of the site need the space so alternative premises are being sought.

TYPE	REG/SER	CON. NO.	PI/NOTES	STATUS
☐ Cessna 310B	OO-SEI	35636	(N5436A)	RAC
☐ De Havilland D.H.82A Tiger Moth	OO-SOF	82592	G-AFWF, W6420, G-AMTL – on loan from KLM.	RAC
☐ Lockheed 18-56-23 Lodestar (C-60A)	N7001	18-2427	42-55966, NC7000, N7000	RAC
☐ Nord NC.856A Norvigie	54	54	In French markings.	RA
☐ Westland Lysander IIIA	OO-SOT	Y1530	Composite of ex RCAF aircraft 2341, 2360 and mainly 2442 – on loan from KLM.	RAA

SALLE DE SOUVENIR DU QUARTIER ROI ALBERT I (BLG19)

Address:	Quartier Roi Albert I, Rue de la Fusee 70, B-1130 Bruxelles.
Tel:	02-701-5314
Fax:	02-701-6625
Admission:	Thursday 1200-1600 by appointment.
Location:	In the north eastern suburbs of the city.

The historic airfield at Evère opened in the 1920s and was the original location for the SABCA factory. The field was an important Air Force base up to 1940 as well as serving as the airport for the city and as a site for international flying meetings. The airfield was in use again in the years just after the end of World War II before it became too close to the expanding city. At the present time the buildings are used for administrative purposes for the Belgian Air Force and for NATO. The display, set up in 1995, is housed in a 1929 building once used by SABENA. One room is devoted to the history of the airfield, the airlines which used it in the early days, aviation pioneers, the occupation and NATO. A second hall covers the history and development of the Belgian Air Force. On show is an interesting collection of models, documents, uniforms and photographs. The four aircraft on loan from the military museum in the city are parked around the complex.

TYPE	REG/SER	CON. NO.	PI/NOTES	STATUS
☐ Dassault Mirage 5BA	BA-26	26	On loan from KLM.	RA
☐ Lockheed 683-10-19 Starfighter (F-104G)	'FX-23'	683-9046	FX-21 – on loan from KLM.	RAX
☐ Republic F-84F Thunderstreak	FU-82		53-6587 – on loan from KLM.	RA
☐ Republic RF-84F Thunderflash	FR-29		51-11279 – on loan from KLM.	RA

SPORTIMONIUM (BLG20)

Address:	Tervuursevest 62, B-3001 Leuven.
Tel:	016 22 54 38
Fax:	016 20 1595
Admission:	Monday-Friday 0830-1200 1300-1700.
Location:	In the centre of the town.

Run by Sports Flanders, the museum is devoted to all aspects of recreation and competition. Many sports are featured and the visitor can find out details of clubs and societies in the area. In residence are a number of coaches and local residents can take part in many activities. There is a fully equipped gymnasium in the complex. The section on ballooning includes a Cameron basket plus a number of photographs.

TYPE	REG/SER	CON. NO.	PI/NOTES	STATUS
☐ Cameron N-77 Hot Air Balloon	OO-BMA	841	(OO-BVR) – Basket only.	PV

STAMPE & VERTONGEN MUSEUM (BLG21)

Address:	Bus 3, Luchthaven Antwerpen, B-2100 Antwerpen.
Tel:	0475-695-334
Email:	stampe@skynet.be
Admission:	Saturday-Sunday 1400-1700.
Location:	In the south western suburbs of the city.

Jean Stampe was born at Molenbeek in 1889. He flew in World War I, was wounded seven times, and shot down in March 1918. He flew King Albert over the Front Line on several occasions. At the end of the conflict he became one of two pilots allocated to the King flying a SPAD XI and a Bristol Fighter. He left the army in 1922 and decided to open a flying school at Antwerp in partnership with Réné Vertongen. Among the types used was a Fokker D VII. The firm ferried about thirty Bristol Fighters from Croydon to Brussels for military use. In 1923 they asked Alfred Renard to design a suitable trainer for the school. The R.S.V. 32 was built in a dance hall at Evère and first flew in late 1923. Over fifty examples of the biplane powered by a variety of engines were completed in the factory constructed at Antwerp but sadly none have survived. Over the next decade several other designs were produced. The firm was also a de Havilland agent and imported a number of types. Yuri Ivanov joined the company as a designer. Sadly he was killed along with Jean's son Leon in the crash of the twin engined S.V.10 in November 1935 but not before he had created a number of models. In 1933 the S.V.4 appeared. Five were built and four years later a modified version the S.V.4B was ready and went into production. Just over seven hundred S.V.4As and S.V.4Cs were built in France along with another one hundred and fifty in Algeria between 1945 and 1950. Post-war another sixty six were built in Antwerp. The Antwerp Stampe Centre set up a museum honouring their local manufacturer. A room tracing the life of Jean Stampe and his aircraft is the centrepiece of the display. The complex was enlarged in 2001. A range of Stampes is on show including one S.V.4E which has been re-engined with a modern flat four motor. A number of similar conversions have been carried out both in Europe and America. There are more privately owned S.V.4s based at Deurne and at neighbouring airfields and these are sometimes to be seen at the museum. There is a collection of World War I replicas. These represent types which Stampe would have flown in or encountered during the conflict. The Fokker D VII has been painted in the colours of the first aircraft operated by the school in 1923. A gallery has been constructed above the hangar containing the flying aircraft so that these can be viewed. Pleasure flights are normally available in Stampe aircraft but it is recommended that these are booked in advance.

TYPE	REG/SER	CON. NO.	PI/NOTES	STATUS
☐ Albatros D Va (R)	N986RS	7160/17		PVA
☐ Fieseler Fi 103A-1		'256978'		PVX
☐ Fokker D VII (R)	'O-BOBE'	02	F-BNDF, EI-APT, N903AC	PVAX
☐ Fokker D VIII (R)	N111EV	A-2		PVA
☐ Fokker Dr I (R)	PH-EBF	102/NVAV-91	N5505V – on loan from SVV, NET	PVX
☐ Nieuport 17 (R)	N2262G	CS007		PVA
☐ Nieuport 28C.1 (R)	N128CX	1192		PVA
☐ North American NA-168 Texan (T-6G)	N4109C	SA-078	7727 (South Africa), ZU-AGC	RAA
☐ Sopwith F.1 Camel (R)	N2257J	CS006		PVA
☐ Stampe & Vertongen S.V.4A	OO-GWC	1	1, F-BFVA, N9480A	RAA
☐ Stampe & Vertongen S.V.4B	OO-EIR	1144	V-4	RA
☐ Stampe & Vertongen S.V.4B	OO-GWD	1160	V-18, SLN-03, G-BRMC	RAA
☐ Stampe & Vertongen S.V.4B	OO-GWB	1171	V-29, (OO-GWR)	RAA
☐ Stampe & Vertongen S.V.4B	OO-BPL	1194	V-52	PV
☐ Stampe & Vertongen S.V.4C	OO-GWA	478	F-BDBO, N1042N	RAA
☐ Stampe & Vertongen S.V.4E (S.V.4C)	OO-KAT	416	416, F-BCQZ	PVA

TIGER AIR FORCES MUSEUM (BLG22)

Address:	Maarlosedijk, B-3990 Peer.
Tel:	011-637059
Admission:	Not yet open.
Location:	Near the main gate to Kleine Brogel A.F.B. which is off the N.73 between Leopoldsburg and Bree

The museum aims to trace the links between the village of Peer and the base of Kleine Brogel which has hosted several 'Tiger Meet' contests. In 1960s one Royal Air Force and one U.S.A.F unit who both used a Tiger's head in their badges got together. This led to other squadrons in NATO making contact and in 1962 eight squadrons were represented. Regular gatherings have been held ever since and aircraft are often painted in yellow and black 'Tiger' markings for the event. The Starfighter moved to the site in 1989 and has been joined by the Thunderstreak. Archive material on the meetings at the base has been collected along with many photographs. Problems with the local authority have delayed the opening of what promises to be an interesting display.

TYPE	REG/SER	CON. NO.	PI/NOTES	STATUS
☐ General Dynamics 401 Fighting Falcon (F-16A)	FA-79	6H-79	80-3570 – tail only.	RA
☐ Lockheed 683-10-19 Starfighter (F-104G)	FX-61	683-9104	At Kleine Brogel AFB.	RA
☐ Republic F-84F Thunderstreak	FU-185		52-6569	RA

VLIEGTUIGVERZAMELING KLEINE BROGEL (BLG23)

Address:	Belgische Luchtmacht, Vliegbasis Kleine Brogel, B-3990 Peer.
Tel:	011-63-2581
Admission:	By prior permission only.
Location:	The base is about 4 km north of Peer off the road to Grote Brogel.

In December 1951 three squadrons, 23, 27 and 31 moved from Beauvechain to Chièvres to form Number 10 Wing equipped with Spitfire XIVs. The Republic F-84G Thunderjet was soon introduced. The unit moved to Bruggen in Germany in 1953 and the following year transferred to the newly completed Kleine Brogel. The three squadrons were re-equipped with Thunderstreaks in 1956. In June 1962 No 27 was disbanded and in the spring of 1964 Starfighters arrived for the remaining two squadrons. The F-16 arrived in the mid-1980s and the two squadrons in the wing are No.31 'Tiger' and No.349. The latter was formed as a Royal Air Force unit at Lagos in 1942 with Belgian personnel. The OCU for the F-16 is also in residence. The preserved aircraft represent types flown by the wing and several are parked outside the squadron headquarters around the field.

TYPE	REG/SER	CON. NO.	PI/NOTES	STATUS
☐ Lockheed 683-10-19 Starfighter (F-104G)	FX-02	683-9017	On loan from KLM.	RA
☐ Lockheed 683-10-19 Starfighter (F-104G)	FX-86	683-9147		RA
☐ Republic F-84E Thunderjet	'FS-2'		51-9599, FS-17 – on loan from KLM.	RAX
☐ Republic F-84F Thunderstreak	FU-66		53-6677 – on loan from KLM	RA
☐ Republic F-84F Thunderstreak	FU-67		53-6681 – on loan from KLM	PV
☐ Republic F-84F Thunderstreak	FU-145		53-6613	RA
☐ Republic F-84F Thunderstreak	FU-188		52-6369, FU-188, 'FU-131'	RA

VLIEGTUIGVERZAMELING ROBERT LANDUYT (FLYING LEGENDS) (BLG24)

Address:	Avenue de Rooverstrasse 15, B-8000 Bruges.
Tel:	050-354860
Email:	Flyinglegends_collection@yahoo.co.uk
Admission:	By prior permission only.
Location:	At Wevelghem airfield which is about 5 km west of Kortrijk on road N.8.

Housed in a hangar at Wevelghem this collection of classic aircraft has been assembled over the last few years. In 1997 the founder Robert Landuyt died. His family decided to carry on maintaining and operating the fleet. The Hawker Fury replica was built at Lands End in England by Vivian Bellamy and his son Rod for the late Patrick Lindsay. This classic biplane is powered by a Rolls-Royce Kestrel engine and is painted in the colours of a 43 Squadron aircraft. This squadron operated the type from Tangmere between May 1931 and February 1939. The replica Fury made its maiden flight on December 11th 1985. The Finnish designed Viima is one of just a few to be exported. Twenty three were flown by the Air Force from the late 1930s until 1962. Over three hundred Morane-Saulnier 315 parasol trainers were built in the 1930s and a small number after World War II. They gave excellent service with many French aero clubs for several years. One of the Stampe S.V4s has been fitted with a Lycoming flat four engine which replaces the original Renault.

TYPE	REG/SER	CON. NO.	PI/NOTES	STATUS
☐ Boeing-Stearman A75N1 Kaydet (PT-17)	OO-USN	75-4695	42-16532, N54280, YS-272P, N37744, N17PT	RAA
☐ De Havilland D.H.82A Tiger Moth	OO-TGM	3318	G-ADCG, BB731, A728, A2126, G-ADCG	RAA
☐ Hawker Fury (R)	G-BKBB	WA/6	G-BKBB, OO-XFU, OO-HFU	RAA
☐ Morane-Saulnier MS.317 (MS.315)	OO-MOR	6533/279	279 (France), F-BGIL, N315MS	RAA
☐ Stampe & Vertongen S.V.4C	OO-LYR	109	109 (France), F-BMME	RAA
☐ Stampe & Vertongen S.V.4E (S.V.4C)	OO-SVT	9	9 (France), F-BGGO, N17810, N15JJ, N9SV	RAA
☐ Valtion Lentokonetehdas Viima II	OO-EBL	VI-3	VI-3, OH-VIG, G-BAAY	RAA

WINGS OF WAR – MEERHOUT AERONAUTICAL TRUST (BLG25)

Address:	Acaciaweg 3, B-2450 Meerhout.
Tel:	014 30 20 56
Admission:	By prior permission only.
Location:	In the town which is about 5 km south east of Geel.

In 1976 Didier Hindryckx was given a collection of military insignia by his father. The following year he made a decision to concentrate on aeronautical items. In 1981 a move to Meerhout occurred and a group was formed with local enthusiasts. The only complete aircraft currently in the collection is the Magister which was flown by the leader of the 'Red Devils' aerobatic team. The Battle fuselage section and wing were obtained from the museum in Brussels after they had completed their rebuild. The collection includes components and engines, many recovered from crash sites, as well as uniforms and books. Mounted as a memorial is a tailplane from a 466 Squadron Royal Australian Air Force Wellington which crashed at Meerhout. The group hopes to erect a larger structure for a permanent exhibition hall so that all the collection can be displayed.

TYPE	REG/SER	CON. NO.	PI/NOTES	STATUS
☐ Fairey Battle IT			Fuselage and other parts	RA
☐ Fouga CM.170R Magister	MT-31	288		PV

BOSNIA AND HERZEGOVINA

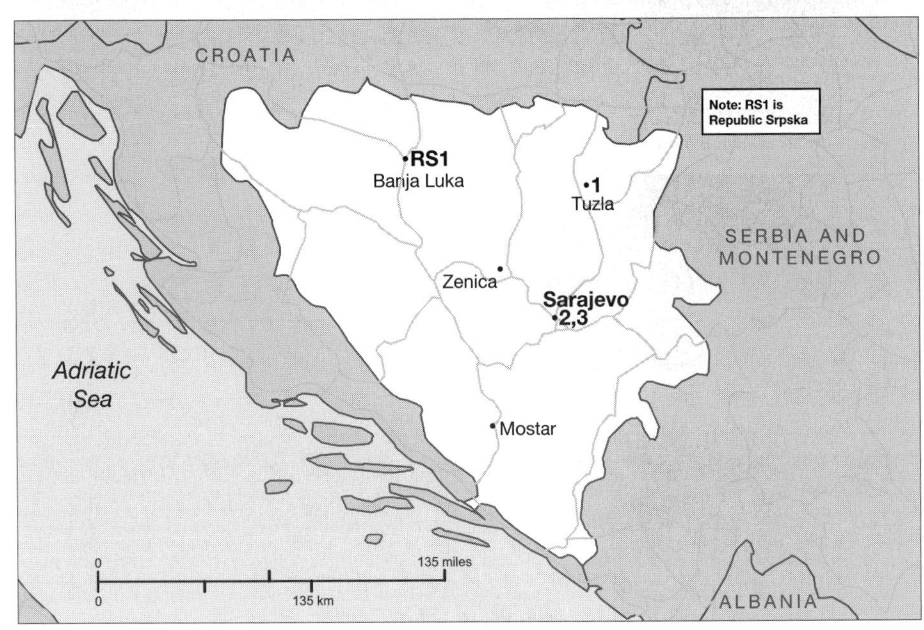

About three hundred and forty Antonov An-14s were built and on is on show at Plovdiv. (Bob Ruffle)

The Naval Museum at Varna is home to this Mil Mi-4.

Amongst the aircraft parked outside the Voenen (Army) Museum in Sofia is this camouflaged MiG-21bis. (Bob Ruffle)

AEROKLUB TUZLA (BOS1)

Address:	Klosterska 1, Tuzla.
Tel:	061-649066
Email:	Ak-tuzla@hotmail.com
Admission:	By prior permission only.
Location:	Just south east of the town.

The aeroclub has been in existence for over fifty years and has a number of interesting aircraft in its fleet. The initial equipment included several primary gliders. Awaiting restoration is the Kraguj. Over one hundred and fifty examples of this low wing monoplane powered by a 340 hp Lycoming engine were delivered to the Yugoslav Air Force in the late 1960s. The type was primarily used on close support duties. One was left at the field after the recent conflicts and it has been taken over by the club. The Wilga is being rebuilt to serve as a glider tug.

TYPE	REG/SER	CON. NO.	PI/NOTES	STATUS
☐ Let L-13 Blanik	T9-5581	026254 (?)	YU-5361 (?)	RAA
☐ Panstwowe Zaklady Lotnicze (PZL) 104 Wilga 80	YU-DHW			RAA
☐ Piper PA-18-150 Super Cub	T9-DBZ	18-7809158	N82084, YU-DBZ	RAA
☐ Soko J-20 Kraguj	30113	13		RA
☐ Utva Fabrica Aviona 75				RAA
☐ Utva Fabrica Aviona 75				RAA
☐ Utva Fabrica Aviona 75	T9-DGI		53173 (Yugoslavia), YU-DGI	RAA
☐ Vazduhoplovno Tehnicki Centar – Vrsac VTC-76 Jastreb Vuk-T				RAA
☐ Vazduhoplovno Tehnicki Centar – Vrsac VTC-76 Jastreb Vuk-T				RAA
☐ Zlin Z-526F Trener Master	T9-CDG	1296	YU-CDG	RAA

HISTORIJSKI MUZEJ BOSNE I HERCEGOVINE (BOS2)

Address:	Zmaja od Bosne 5, Sarajevo.
Tel:	033-21-04-10
Fax:	033-65-66-29
Admission:	Tuesday-Sunday 1000-1700.
Location:	In the centre of the city.

The collections trace the history of the city and its surroundings from early times up to the present day. The displays show urban life from early times and now include the recent conflict which resulted in the splitting up of Yugoslavia. The D.F.S. 230 glider frame is a recent arrival and was found in the area. Many examples of the type were used by the German forces in World War II and then abandoned.

TYPE	REG/SER	CON. NO.	PI/NOTES	STATUS
☐ Jacobs D.F.S. 230C-1			Fuselage frame only.	PVD

SARAJEVO INTERNATIONAL AIRPORT COLLECTION (BOS3)

Address:	Kurta Schorka 36, 71210 Sarajevo.
Tel:	033 289 100
Fax:	033 460 123
Email:	info@sarajevo-airport.ba
Admission:	By prior permission only.
Location:	In the south western suburbs of the city.

Reports have been received of a collection of former Yugoslav Air Force aircraft preserved at the airport. About forty MiG-21F-13s were supplied to Yugoslavia in 1960 and the majority were withdrawn from service by the late 1970s. The locally designed Galeb served in the fighter and attack roles and one Super Galeb has been flown by the Bosnian forces. Further details would be most welcome.

TYPE	REG/SER	CON. NO.	PI/NOTES	STATUS
☐ Mikoyan-Gurevich MiG-21F-13	22518			RA
☐ Soko J-20 Kraguj	30110	10		RA
☐ Soko N-60 Galeb G-2	23003			RA
☐ Zlin Z-526F Trener Master	T9-CDG	1296	YU-CDG	RAA

BULGARIA

BALTCHIK AIRPORT COLLECTION (BUL1)

Address:	Baltchik Airport, Baltchik.
Admission:	By prior permission only
Location:	Just north east of the town.

The airfield housed fighter units during World War II. When the conflict ended it became home to the 15th Fighter Air Regiment which was in residence until 1994. For the next four years the site housed a MiG-15bis unit. Later a number of MiG-21 variants were in use along with Aero L-29 Delfin trainers. The military moved out in 1998 and the field is now used by charter airlines and serves as an air-sea rescue centre. There are plans to modernise the airport. The preserved aircraft are believed to have been left behind.

TYPE	REG/SER	CON. NO.	PI/NOTES	STATUS
☐ Mikoyan-Gurevich MiG-17F	64			RA
☐ Mikoyan-Gurevich MiG-17F	101			RA
☐ Mikoyan-Gurevich MiG-21PFM	65	9400S18		RA

BEZMER AIR FORCE BASE COLLECTION (BUL2)

Address:	22 Shturmova Aviaconna Baza, Bezmer, Jambol.
Admission:	By prior permission only.
Location:	About 10 km west of Jambol.

During World War I the site was an Imperial German Air Service airship station and a large hangar was constructed. The Bulgarian dirigible 'Komanda' was in residence from 1916 to the end of the conflict. Balloon units used the field in the inter-war period. A reconnaissance unit was based at Bezmer during World War II. MiG-17s were operated for many years until replaced by the Sukhoi Su-25 in the mid-1980s. The base is due to close in 2007. Two aircraft are preserved by the main gate with the others inside the camp.

TYPE	REG/SER	CON. NO.	PI/NOTES	STATUS
☐ Aero L-29 Delfin	79	094148		RA
☐ Mikoyan-Gurevich MiG-15UTI	121	1117151		RA
☐ Mikoyan-Gurevich MiG-15UTI	216			RA
☐ Mikoyan-Gurevich MiG-17F	030			PV
☐ Mikoyan-Gurevich MiG-17F	82			RA
☐ Wytwornia Sprzetu Komunikacyjnego (WSK) Lim-5 [MiG-17F]	144	1C 018 (?)		RA
☐ Yakovlev Yak-23	119			PV

BOURGAS AIRPORT AVIATIONEXPO (BUL3)

Address:	8007 Bourgas.
Tel:	056-28151/7 ext 509
Fax:	056-39045
Email:	museum@bourgas-airport.com
Admission:	Daily 0900-1700
Location:	About 10 km north east of the town.

The display opened on October 16th 1998 in a hangar at the airport. The aim of the collection is to trace the history of flying in the country with emphasis on the airliners which have used the field. The Antonov An-2 has been used in a variety of roles in Bulgaria by both the Air Force and civilian operators. The large An-12 four engined transport flew with Bulair and Balkan before being withdrawn. The An-24 has served the airlines in Bulgaria for many yearsand many examples of the type were built. Another type which gave sterling service was the Ilyushin Il-14. Produced in substantial numbers the twin engined airline flew with most Soviet bloc countries. The only indigenous design on show is the Laz-7. The type powered by a Walter Minor engine was used by aero clubs. The developed Laz-7M fitted with an M-11FR radial resembled the Yak-18 and was for a long period the basic Air Force trainer. The two Polish PZL powered aircraft were used in agricultural work and glider towing around the country. The only glider to be seen is the Foka. This type has been built in considerable numbers and exported to several countries. A number of military types have been acquired to enhance the display and show the contribution of the Air Force to aviation in the region. Associated exhibitions of photographs, memorabilia, uniforms and documents have been set up in the building.

TYPE	REG/SER	CON. NO.	PI/NOTES	STATUS
☐ Aero L-29 Delfin	64	892942		PV
☐ Antonov An-2R	LZ-1089	1G 82-46	CCCP-56489, RA-56489	PV
☐ Antonov An-12B	LZ-BAB	8346002		PV
☐ Antonov An-14A	LZ-7001	601613	LZ-TEA	PV
☐ Antonov An-14A	100	903102		PV
☐ Antonov An-24B	LZ-ANL	67302206	DM-SBA	PV
☐ Antonov An-24B	LZ-ANF	77303407	Nose section only.	PV
☐ Ilyushin Il-14P	LZ-ILE	14803040		PV
☐ Lazarov Laz-7M	LZ-M34		On loan from MA.	PV
☐ Mikoyan-Gurevich MiG-17F	62	1690		PV
☐ Mikoyan-Gurevich MiG-21PFM	39	94MO-08		PV
☐ Mil Mi-2	'01'	543005063	202	PVX
☐ Panstwowe Zaklady Lotnicze (PZL) 101A Gawron	LZ-102	63115	SP-CHA	PV
☐ Panstwowe Zaklady Lotnicze (PZL) M-18 Dromader	LZ-8001	1Z 008-11		PV
☐ Szybowcowy Zaklad Doswiadczalny S.Z.D.32A Foka 5	LZ-304	W-421		PV
☐ Tupolev Tu-134	LZ-TUA	8350405	Fin and tailplane only.	PV
☐ Tupolev Tu-154B-2	LZ-BTU	81A-484	CCCP-85484	PV

BULGARSKI VOENNOVAZDUSHNI HEADQUARTERS (BUL4)

Address:	Tsarigradsko Shose, Sofia.
Admission:	By prior permission only.
Location:	Near the civil airport which is in the south eastern suburbs of the city.

An Army Aviation Corps was formed in 1912 but this lasted about a year. A service was set up with German assistance in 1915 but this was disbanded when the country surrendered in 1918. The imposed restrictions were renounced in the mid-1930s and an Air Force came into being. The equipment used during World War II was of mainly German origin. After the Warsaw Pact was established the aircraft came from the Soviet bloc. Three types, including an indigenous Laz-7 trainer, are displayed at the Headquarters building where there is also a display of photographs and memorabilia tracing the history and traditions of the service.

TYPE	REG/SER	CON. NO.	PI/NOTES	STATUS
☐ Lazarov Laz-7				RA
☐ Mikoyan-Gurevich MiG-19S	01		001	RA
☐ Mikoyan-Gurevich MiG-21PF	223	760813		RA

CHESHNEGIROVO AIR FORCE BASE COLLECTION (BUL5)

Address:	Sadovo.
Admission:	By prior permission only.
Location:	About 20 km. east of Plovdiv in the south eastern suburbs of Sadovo off Route 8.

The airfield was constructed in the 1950s and was home to the 25th Fighter Bomber Air Regiment flying the MiG-17. These were replaced by the MiG-23BN in 1976 and these stayed until the base closed in 2000. Also in use during this period were MiG-23UBs and Aero L-39 Albatros trainers. Reports suggest that the airfield may be reactivated in the near future. The preserved aircraft are believed to still be here.

TYPE	REG/SER	CON. NO.	PI/NOTES	STATUS
☐ Aero L-29 Delfin	40	792451		RA
☐ Mikoyan-Gurevich MiG-17F	41			RA
☐ Mikoyan-Gurevich MiG-21PFM	41	940M010		RA
☐ Mikoyan-Gurevich MiG-23BN	51	0393208751		RA
☐ Mikoyan-Gurevich MiG-23BN	66	0393209366	In town.	PV

DOBROSLAVTZI AIR FORCE BASE COLLECTION (BUL6)

Address:	Aerodrom, Dobroslavtzi.
Admission:	By prior permission only.
Location:	North east of Sofia close to the ring road and just west of Novi Iskra off Route 16.

Constructed in the 1930s the base was home to fighter units of the Air Force. A number of MiG types, formerly operated from the field, have been saved. The first MiG-15s arrived in the country in 1954 and the last few MiG-15UTI trainers were withdrawn from service in the late 1990s. The MiG-23 was operated up to 2002. The site recently closed but the preserved aircraft are believed to still be there.

TYPE	REG/SER	CON. NO.	PI/NOTES	STATUS
☐ Ilyushin Il-14G	95			RA
☐ Mikoyan-Gurevich MiG-15UTI	'03'		221	RAX
☐ Mikoyan-Gurevich MiG-17	'28'	7207	72, '2'	RAX
☐ Mikoyan-Gurevich MiG-17F	136			RA
☐ Mikoyan-Gurevich MiG-19PM	'19'	65210932	932	RAX

GRAF IGNATIEVO AIR FORCE BASE MUSEUM (BUL7)

Address:	3 Iztrebitelna Aviocionna Basa, Graf Ignatievo, Plovdiv.
Admission:	By prior permission only.
Location:	About 20 km north of Plovdiv off Route 64 and just south of the town.

The field is home to front line fighter units flying MiG-21s and MiG-29s. Previously MiG-15s, MiG-17s and MiG-19s were used. A collection of types formerly flown by the based squadrons has been assembled. The Aero L-29 has been used for basic training for many years and most bases had a small number attached. The first jet fighter to serve with the Air Force was the Yak-23 and around forty were delivered in 1953. These were supplemented the following year with the arrival of the MiG-15. The airfield opened in the late 1940s and a museum has been set up in one of the buildings. The history of the base is portrayed with many photos, uniforms and documents along with aircraft components, instruments and items of memorabilia. The story of the squadrons which have flown from Graf Ignatievo is also told. There is a military overhaul facility on the field and large numbers of stored aircraft are also present awaiting their fate.

TYPE	REG/SER	CON. NO.	PI/NOTES	STATUS
☐ Aero L-29 Delfin	85	194235		RA
☐ Mikoyan-Gurevich MiG-15UTI	199			RA
☐ Mikoyan-Gurevich MiG-17F	56			RA
☐ Mikoyan-Gurevich MiG-19S	'681'		04, '1300'	RAX
☐ Mikoyan-Gurevich MiG-19S	96			RA
☐ Mikoyan-Gurevich MiG-21PFM	66	9400S03		RA
☐ Mikoyan-Gurevich MiG-23BN	63	0393215763		RA
☐ Yakovlev Yak-23	51			RA

KAMENETZ AIR FORCE BASE COLLECTION (BUL8)

Address:	12 Utchebna Aviocionna Basa, Kamenetz, Letnica
Admission:	By prior permission only.
Location:	About 30 km east of Pleven and just north west of Letnica.

The airfield was built in the 1930s and for the last half century has been used for training. After World War II Polikarpov Po-2s, Yakovlev Yak-18s and the Laz-7 were used before the arrival of more advanced types. The first jet to see service at the field was the MiG-15UTI which was followed by the Aero L 29 Delfin and MiG-21Us. The Air Force School moved in during 2003 and they now operate Aero L-39s and the recently delivered Pilatus PC-9s. A history room has been set up to show the traditions of the service. On show are uniforms, documents, trophies, models, photographs and unit badges. The collection of preserved aircraft is intended to show the students examples of types previously operated.

TYPE	REG/SER	CON. NO.	PI/NOTES	STATUS
☐ Aero L-29 Delfin	74	094035		RA
☐ Mikoyan-Gurevich MiG-15UTI	'121'	3808		RAX
☐ Mikoyan-Gurevich MiG-17F	02			RA
☐ Mikoyan-Gurevich MiG-17F	82			RA
☐ Mikoyan-Gurevich MiG-17F	'122'	51310004		RAX
☐ Mikoyan-Gurevich MiG-21F-13	07	6994635		RA
☐ Mikoyan-Gurevich MiG-21PF	'123'	760815	125	RAX
☐ Mikoyan-Gurevich MiG-21UM	07	516913016		RA

KRUMOVO AIR FORCE BASE COLLECTION (BUL9)

Address:	24 Vertoletna Aviocionna Basa, Krumovo, Plovdiv 9.
Admission:	By prior permission only.
Location:	About 8 km south east of Plovdiv off Route 86.

Located next to the Bulgarian Air Force Museum the airfield is the main helicopter base in the country. Four Mil types which have been flown from the field are preserved. The Mi-2 was used for training at Krumovo until the late 1990s and the Navy operated a small number of Mi-4s from Varna. Ten Mil-8s were delivered with the first arriving in 1968. They remained operational until 2000 and some were sold on the civilian market. The Polish built derivative of the Mil Mi-1 was only used in small numbers at the base.

TYPE	REG/SER	CON. NO.	PI/NOTES	STATUS
☐ Mil Mi-2	203	543006063		RA
☐ Mil Mi-4A	44			RA
☐ Mil Mi-8T	301	10301		RA
☐ Wytwornia Sprzetu Komunikacyjnego (WSK) SM-1/300 [Mil Mi-1]	01			RA

MORSKI MUZEUM (BUL10)

Address:	2 Chervenormeiski Boulevard, Varna.
Tel:	052-22406/23935
Admission:	Tuesday-Saturday 0900-1700; Sunday 1300-1900.
Location:	On the waterfront near the port.

Displays at the museum highlight military operations in the Black Sea and on the Danube. The development of the military and merchant fleets is portrayed in the exhibition of photographs and models. The Bulgarian military fleet was established in the 1890s with help from Russia. The collection includes a torpedo boat moored nearby and other ships. The Arado Ar 196, now at Plovdiv, was on show here for many years. The Mi-4 entered service at the nearby naval airfield in 1957 and flown until 1979 when replaced by the Mi-14. The sole Ka-25 used by the navy was delivered in 1984 and flew for seven years.

TYPE	REG/SER	CON. NO.	PI/NOTES	STATUS
☐ Arado Ar 196A-5 (A-3)	3	0219	On loan to Muzel na Aviatsiyata Voennovazdushni Sili.	–
☐ Kamov Ka-25PL (Ka-25BSh)	821	10702		PV
☐ Mil Mi-4A	45			PV

MUZEL NA AVIATSIYATA VOENNOVAZDUSHNI SILI (BUL11)

Address:	24 Vertoletna Aviocionna Basa, Krumovo, Plovdiv 9.
Tel:	032-273-171
Admission:	Daily 0800-1600.
Location:	About 15 km south east of the town off Route 86.

Military flying started in the 1912-3 Balkan War. The small force flew about a dozen Blériot and Bristol monoplanes against Turkish forces. The corps was resurrected in 1915 when the country entered World War I on the side of the Central Powers by declaring war on Serbia. Aircraft were supplied by Austria and Germany as well as pilots seconded from these two countries. After surrendering in September 1918 military flying was banned. The government decided to break the terms of the treaty in the late 1930s and aircraft were ordered from abroad. A state aircraft factory was established near Sofia and indigenous designs appeared. Czech and Polish types were ordered but not all these had been delivered when Germany invaded Poland. Bulgaria sided with Germany in 1941, aircraft were supplied to the Air Force, and large numbers of Luftwaffe machines were based in the country. After the end of the conflict Bulgaria joined the Soviet bloc and a number of types were delivered over the years. Set up a few years ago the museum traces the history of military aviation in the country. The indoor exhibition hall houses models, memorabilia, uniforms, engines and components. One display highlights significant events in Bulgarian aviation starting with the first balloon ascent in 1892. A rare aircraft on show is the Arado Ar 196 mounted on floats. Twelve were flown by the Bulgarian Navy from Varna during World War II. The Ar 196 was, for many years, on how at the Naval Museum in Varna until a high ranking officer ordered it to be destroyed as it was of Nazi origin. Fortunately it was hidden away and has now been restored in period colours. One early aircraft is the reportedly unflown monoplane built by Georgi Bosinov in 1912. The Ilyushin Il-2, the Tupolev Tu-2, the Yakovlev Yak-9 and one of the Yakovlev Yak-23s were formerly on show outside the Central Army Museum in Sofia. Nikolai Popovski built his helicopter using some parts from Mil Mi-1s. The majority of the collection consists of types used in recent years. A range of MiG jets is on show and these are arranged in groups so that variants of the same model can he compared. The Lisunov Li-2 was obtained from Russia in a deal which is believed to have returned the Yak-3, once on display in Sofia, to its country of origin. A range of light aircraft and gliders can also be seen. More types are scheduled to join the display as they are withdrawn from use. The museum has made significant progress in a short time.

TYPE	REG/SER	CON. NO.	PI/NOTES	STATUS
☐ Aero L-29 Delfin	11	491028		PV
☐ Aero L-60 Brigadyr	LZ-606	150901	LZ-LEF (?)	PVD
☐ Antonov An-2M	025	801822		PV
☐ Antonov A-11	01			RA
☐ Antonov An-14A	110	003308		PV
☐ Antonov An-24B	LZ-ANE	77303406		PV
☐ Arado Ar 196A-5 (A-3)	3	0219	On loan from Morski Muzeum.	PV
☐ Biser				RA
☐ Canadair CL-90 Starfighter (CF-104) [Lockheed 683-04-12]	63-899	683A-1199	12899, 104899 – in Turkish markings.	PV
☐ Fenix VII				RA
☐ Georgi Bosinov 7				PV
☐ Ilyushin Il-2m3	425			PV
☐ Ilyushin Il-14T	97			PV
☐ Ilyushin Il-18D	46			PV
☐ Ilyushin Il-28R	43	2504		PV
☐ Kamov Ka-26	LZ-6018	7203008		PV
☐ Karlov ZAK-1	31			PV
☐ Karlov ZAK-1	LZ-M04			PV
☐ Lazarov Laz-7	31			RA
☐ Lazarov Laz-7M	LZ-M34		On loan to Bourgas.	–
☐ Let L-200D Morava	20	171202	OK-RHD	PV
☐ Let L-200D Morava	10	171310	OK-SHE	PV
☐ Lisunov Li-2T [Douglas DC-3 modified]			CCCP-13381	PVX
☐ Mikoyan-Gurevich MiG-15bis				RA
☐ Mikoyan-Gurevich MiG-15bis		130060		RA
☐ Mikoyan-Gurevich MiG-15UTI	202			PV
☐ Mikoyan-Gurevich MiG-17F	30			PV
☐ Mikoyan-Gurevich MiG-17F	150	7138		PV
☐ Mikoyan-Gurevich MiG-17F	71	71652		PV
☐ Mikoyan-Gurevich MiG-17PF	21	7137		PV
☐ Mikoyan-Gurevich MiG-17PF	22			PV
☐ Mikoyan-Gurevich MiG-19PM	936	65210936		PV
☐ Mikoyan-Gurevich MiG-19PT	506			PV
☐ Mikoyan-Gurevich MiG-19S	030			PV
☐ Mikoyan-Gurevich MiG-19SF	882			PV
☐ Mikoyan-Gurevich MiG-21F-13	501	741101		PV
☐ Mikoyan-Gurevich MiG-21MA	613	960613		PV
☐ Mikoyan-Gurevich MiG-21MF	52	969402		PV
☐ Mikoyan-Gurevich MiG-21PF	20	760804		PV
☐ Mikoyan-Gurevich MiG-21PFM	62	940ME10		PV
☐ Mikoyan-Gurevich MiG-21UM	34	516977066		PV
☐ Mikoyan-Gurevich MiG-21US	05	07685143		PV
☐ Mikoyan-Gurevich MiG-23BN	79	0393208379		PV

☐ Mikoyan-Gurevich MiG-23BN	50	0393215750		PV
☐ Mikoyan-Gurevich MiG-23MF	670	0390213670		PV
☐ Mikoyan-Gurevich MiG-23MLD	390	0390325390		PV
☐ Mikoyan-Gurevich MiG-23UB	021	A1037621		PV
☐ Mil Mi-2	30			PV
☐ Mil Mi-2	209	544205065		PV
☐ Mil Mi-4A	51			PV
☐ Mil Mi-4A	52			PV
☐ Mil Mi-4A	53			PV
☐ Mil Mi-4MA	54	02112		PV
☐ Mil Mi-8T	302	10302		PV
☐ Mil Mi-14BT	812	U-5008		PV
☐ Mil Mi-24D	101	U-5065		PV
☐ Panstwowe Zaklady Lotnicze (PZL) 101A Gawron	LZ-009			PV
☐ Panstwowe Zaklady Lotnicze (PZL) 101A Gawron	LZ-130	119271		PV
☐ Panstwowe Zaklady Lotnicze (PZL) 101A Gawron	LZ-128	119279		PV
☐ Polikarpov Po-2	LZ-K19			PV
☐ Popovski H11B.1				PV
☐ Soro	LZ-001			PV
☐ Sukhoi Su-22M4	818	27818		PV
☐ Sukhoi Su-22UM3K	206	17532372206		PV
☐ Szybowcowy Zaklad Doswiadczalny S.Z.D.30C Pirat	LZ-834	P-834		PV
☐ Szybowcowy Zaklad Doswiadczalny S.Z.D.32A Foka 5	LZ-307	W-467		RA
☐ Tupolev Tu-2S	27		251	PV
☐ Wytwornia Sprzetu Komunikacyjnego (WSK) Lim-5R (Lim-5) [MiG-17PF]	30	1C 15-23		PV
☐ Wytwornia Sprzetu Komunikacyjnego (WSK) SM-1/300 [Mil Mi-1]	LZ-5017			PV
☐ Wytwornia Sprzetu Komunikacyjnego (WSK) SM-1W [Mil Mi-1M]	12			PV
☐ Yakovlev Yak-9U	7		326	PV
☐ Yakovlev Yak-11	55			PV
☐ Yakovlev Yak-18	31			PV
☐ Yakovlev Yak-23	42		42, 142	PV
☐ Yakovlev Yak-23	45			PV
☐ Yakovlev Yak-23	23	421		PV
☐ Yakovlev Yak-50	LZ-501	791509	DM-WQY (?)	PV
☐ Yakovlev Yak-52	02	800502	In Soviet markings.	PV
☐ Zlin Z-37 Cmelak	LZ-3002			PV
☐ Zlin Z-37 Cmelak	LZ-3027			PV
☐ Zlin Z-37 Cmelak	LZ-3037			PV
☐ Zlin Z-526 Trener Master	LZ-711	1043 (?)	LZ-011	PV

NACIONALEN MUZEJ ZA ISTORIJA (BUL12)

Address:	16 Viloshko Iale str, Sofia 1618.
Tel:	02-955-4280
Fax:	02 955-7602
Email:	info@historymuseum.org
Admission:	November-April daily 0900-1645; May-October daily 0930-1730.
Location:	About 8 km south of the city.

Founded in 1973 the museum aims to trace all aspects of Bulgarian culture and history from the pre-historic times up to the present. The collection of artefacts is one of the largest in the Balkans. The four aircraft are recent additions to the impressive exhibition and represent types flown over the last few years.

TYPE	REG/SER	CON. NO.	PI/NOTES	STATUS
☐ Mikoyan-Gurevich MiG-21bis-Lasur (MiG-21bis)	525	75003025		PV
☐ Mikoyan-Gurevich MiG-23MLA	070	2960324870		PV
☐ Mikoyan-Gurevich MiG-23UB	29	A1038318		PV
☐ Mil Mi-24D	113	04394		PV

VOENEN MUZEI (BUL13)

Address:	92 Cherkovna Boulevard, Sofia
Admission:	Wednesday-Sunday 0900-1700.
Location:	In the south western part of the city centre.

The museum was established in 1917 and traces the military history of the country since the early Balkan wars. The collection was formerly located in Skobelev Boulevard and lost most of its aircraft when the Plovdiv museum opened. A new site next to the military academy opened recently and several withdrawn aircraft have been put on show. A large collection of uniforms, guns and military vehicles can also be seen.

TYPE	REG/SER	CON. NO.	PI/NOTES	STATUS
☐ Aero L-29 Delfin	63	892941		PV
☐ Mikoyan-Gurevich MiG-15UTI	03			PV
☐ Mikoyan-Gurevich MiG-17F	28			PV
☐ Mikoyan-Gurevich MiG-19PM	939	65210939		PV
☐ Mikoyan-Gurevich MiG-21bis	501	75019901		PV
☐ Mikoyan-Gurevich MiG-21PFM	67	940MK20		PV
☐ Mikoyan-Gurevich MiG-23MLA	867	2960324867		PV
☐ Mikoyan-Gurevich MiG-23UB	26	A1037856		PV
☐ Mil Mi-2	205	563109093		PV
☐ Mil Mi-8T	303	10303		PV
☐ Mil Mi-24D	108	U-5089		PV
☐ Sukhoi Su-22M4	511	36511		PV

VOZDUSHNI VOISKI AKADEMIE MUZEUM (BUL14)

Address:	Dolna Metropolija Air Force Base, 5856 Pleven.
Tel:	064-82-2079
Fax:	064-82 -2602
Email:	info@af-acad.bg
Admission:	By prior permission only.
Location:	About 10 km north west of Pleven and south of the town.

Founded in 1945 the Academy trains all Air Force ground and aircrew. The museum traces the history of the base and the traditions of the force are highlighted. A collection of photographs and memorabilia can be seen. The aircraft are on show outside the building. The L-29 Delfin is currently used to train pilots.

TYPE	REG/SER	CON. NO.	PI/NOTES	STATUS
☐ Aero L-29 Delfin	67	094028		RA
☐ Aero L-29 Delfin	29	691940		RA
☐ Mikoyan-Gurevich MiG-15UTI	113			RA
☐ Mikoyan-Gurevich MiG-17F	100			RA
☐ Mikoyan-Gurevich MiG-17F	147			RA
☐ Mikoyan-Gurevich MiG-21PFM	36	94M005		RA
☐ Mikoyan-Gurevich MiG-21PFM	'26'	94M009	40	RAX
☐ Mikoyan-Gurevich MiG-21U	01	662216		RA
☐ Mil Mi-2	208	563146103		RA
☐ Mil Mi-24D	111	04392		RA
☐ Sukhoi Su-22M4	716	27716		RA

CROATIA

DUBROVNIK AIRPORT COLLECTION (CRO1)

Address:	20117 Dubrovnik.
Email:	info@airport-dubrovnik.hr
Admission:	On permanent view.
Location:	About 12 km south east of the city off Route 2.

The Vrabac glider has recently been put on show in the terminal building along with a display of photographs and models tracing the history of the airport. There are plans to enlarge the collection.

TYPE	REG/SER	CON. NO.	PI/NOTES	STATUS
☐ Sostaric Vrabac				PV

TEHNIČKI MUZEJ (CRO2)

Address:	Savska Cesta 18, 41000 Zagreb.
Tel:	01 43 54 46
Fax:	01 42 84 31
Email:	tehnicki.muzej@zg.tel.hr
Admission:	Tuesday, Thursday-Friday 0800-1400; Wednesday 0800-1200 1400-1700; Saturday-Sunday 0800-1200.
Location:	In the city centre near the main station.

Established in 1954 the museum opened to the public nine years later. The displays highlight energy transfer, transport, mining, astronomy, agriculture and space technology. There is a section devoted to the work and inventions of Nikola Tesla. Space restrictions mean that only about half of the aircraft in the collection are on show at any one time. More than two hundred Fizir biplanes were constructed and the type was used by aero clubs in the late 1940s. The D.A.R. 9 is a modified Focke-Wulf Stieglitz. In 1946 the Yugoslav Air Force held a competition for a trainer suitable for both military and civil use. The winner was the Trojka designed by Boris Cijan and the prototype flew in 1947. Over one hundred and fifty P-47 Thunderbolts were supplied to Yugoslavia in 1951. The museum obtained the Republic aircraft in a deal which saw an Ikarus S-49C move to Belgrade. The Aero 3/1 primary trainer entered production in the late 1950s and the prototype is on show. Ivan Sostaric built his first glider, the Vrabac, in 1939 and after World War II more than ten further designs appeared. The Bell 47 was removed in the recent conflict but returned when peace was declared.

TYPE	REG/SER	CON. NO.	PI/NOTES	STATUS
☐ Agusta-Bell 47J-2A	YU-HAL	2091		PV
☐ Bücker Bü 131B Jungmann	YU-CLY	865	0865	RA
☐ Cijan C-3 Trojka	YU-CGT		0777	PV
☐ Dârzjhavna Aeroplanna Rabotiilnitsa D.A.R.9 [Focke Wulf Fw 44 Stieglitz]	9784		YU-CGD – possibly 9406/YU-CGJ	PV
☐ Glider				RA
☐ Modly				RA
☐ Republic P-47D Thunderbolt	13109		(USAAF)	PV
☐ Sostaric Cavka	YU-2068			RA
☐ Sostaric Jastreb	YU-3015			PV
☐ Sostaric Roda	YU-5153			PV
☐ Utva Fabrica Aviona Aero 3-1	40001			PV
☐ Vajic V-55	YU-CXE			RA
☐ Yakovlev UT-2	YU-CGL		0333	RA
☐ Zmaj Fizir FN	YU-CGO		9002	PV

ZADAR AIR BASE COLLECTION (CRO3)

Address:	93 Zrakoplovna Baza Zemunik, Zadar.
Admission:	By prior permission only.
Location:	About 8 km east of the town off Route 2.

Croatia established its own forces in 1992 and obtained some former Yugoslav Air Force machines which were based in the new country. Combat types were also acquired from the Ukraine. A collection of preserved aircraft has been set up at the field and this may be the start of plans for a military aviation museum.

TYPE	REG/SER	CON. NO.	PI/NOTES	STATUS
☐ Douglas DC-3A-456 Skytrain (C-47A)	71203			RAD
☐ Mikoyan-Gurevich MiG-21UM	195		22903 (Yugoslavia)	RA
☐ North American NA-173 Sabre (F-86D)	10684			RA
☐ Soko J-20 Kraguj	701			RA
☐ Soko J-21 Jastreb	601			RA
☐ Soko J-22 Orao	25???			RA
☐ Soko N-60 Galeb G-2A	661			RA
☐ Utva Fabrica Aviona 60H	YU-DBO		50503	RA

CYPRUS

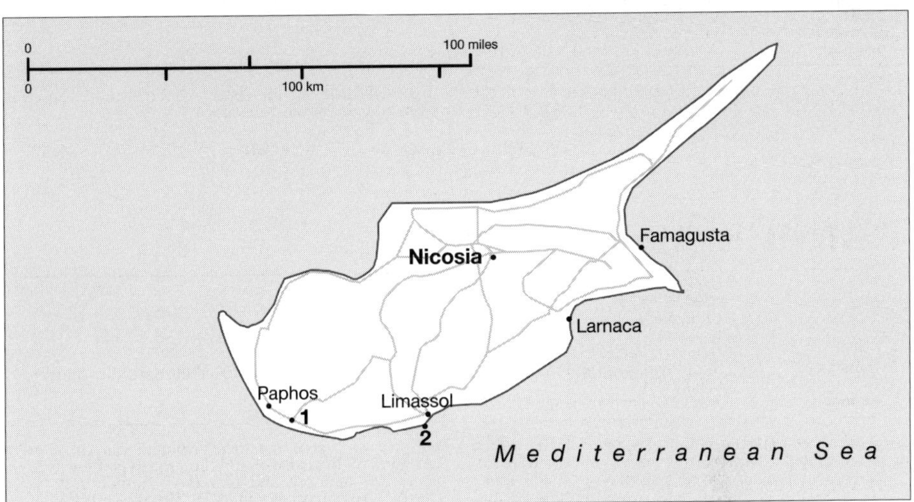

CONSTANTINIDES COLLECTION (CY1)

Address:	25 Achaeans Street, Nicosia.
Tel:	02-465580
Admission:	By prior permission only.
Location:	At Paphos Airfield about 10 km south east of the town coast.

Savvas Constaninides purchased two of the former 8 Squadron Shackletons in July 1991 and later in the month the pair were flown to Paphos. The Flamant was flown regularly by a group in France.

TYPE	REG/SER	CON. NO.	PI/NOTES	STATUS
☐ Avro 696 Shackleton AEW.2 (MR.2)	WL747			RA
☐ Avro 696 Shackleton AEW.2 (MR.2)	WL757			RA
☐ Dassault MD-312 Flamant	F-AZEN	250	250, (N250DF)	RA

ROYAL AIR FORCE AKROTIRI COLLECTION (CY2)

Address:	Sovereign Base, BFPO 53, RAF Akrotiri.
Tel:	–
Email	Sbaafas@cytanet.com.cy
Admission:	By prior permission only.
Location:	Just south east of the town.

The airfield opened in 1956 and has been an important staging post for the R.A.F. Meteors and Venoms were the first regular occupants. During the Suez Crisis French Air Force squadrons operated from the field. Since then many R.A.F. units have been based at the site. Types flown have included Javelins, Canberras, Pembrokes, Lightnings, Phantoms, Hastings and Argosies. A helicopter unit flying Griffins is currently stationed at the field. Four aircraft have been preserved with three near the main gate.

TYPE	REG/SER	CON. NO.	PI/NOTES	STATUS
☐ English Electric P.26 Lightning F.6	XS929	95262		RA
☐ McDonnell M.98 Phantom FGR.2	XV470	3288		RA
☐ Westland-Sikorsky WS-55 Whirlwind HAR.10 (HAR.2)	XD184	WA.27		RA
☐ Westland-Sikorsky WS-58 Wessex HC.2	XR504	WA.129		RA

CZECH REPUBLIC

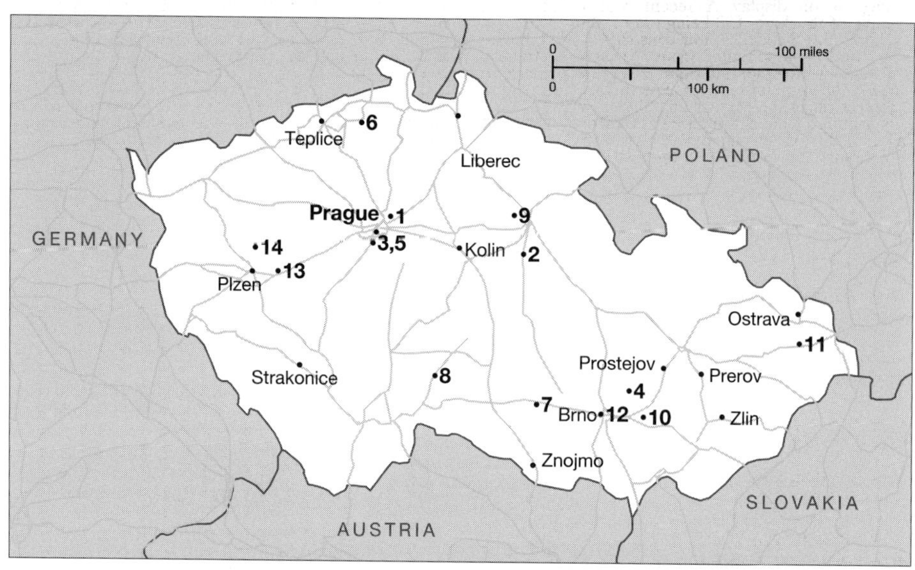

HISTORICKÝ ÚSTAV ARMADÝ ČESKÉ REPUBLICKY – LETECKÉ MÚZEUM KBELY (CZ1)

Address:	Mladoboleslavska, Kbely, 197 00 Praha.
Tel:	0973 207 511
Fax:	0973 541 308
Email:	museum@army.cz
Admission:	May-October Tuesday – Sunday 1000-1800.
Location:	About 8 km north east of the city centre on Route 10 (E.14).

Kbely was the first Czechoslovak military airfield and in the inter-war period staged some of the best air shows in Europe. The first scheduled flight by Czechoslovak Airlines left the field for Bratislava in October 1923. At the current time test units of the Czech Republic Air Force are based at the site. In the mid-1960s the Military Museum in Prague set up a task force to recover and preserve historic aircraft from around the country. The airframes were transported to Kbely for storage. In 1968 to mark the fiftieth anniversary of Czechoslovak aviation a major flying display was held at Kbely. The stored aircraft were put on show and later the exhibition became the Air and Space section of the Military Museum. Initially one hangar was used and around fifty aircraft were on show. The numbers grew rapidly and now three further hangars and a large outside display area house the collection. In 1988 one of two surviving Wagner type hangars, dating from the opening of the field, was restored. This building now contains many early aircraft including the fuselage of the first Czech aircraft, the Bohemia B-5. A nearby Picha hangar constructed in the inter-war period was also rebuilt and this is home to a number of World War II types. In the inter-war period the country had a flourishing aviation industry with many successful designs emerging from the factories. Products from most of these companies can be seen and gaps in the range have been filled by building accurate replicas. Letov constructed a series of outstanding biplanes starting with the S-1 in 1920. The collection has a 1921 S-2 on show along with two versions of the 1925 S-20 and several other machines. The first Aero aircraft, the A-1, was a licence built Brandenburg 76 but this was soon followed by original designs. The A-10 airliner on show was constructed from the remains of an original aircraft complete with cabin furnished to the lavish standards of the period. Replicas of the A-11 and A-12 are on view along with a 1924 A-18C and a 1930 Ap-32. The company name lived on after World War II with the successful 45 and 145 series. The Avia company exhibited its BH-1 low wing monoplane at the 1920 Prague exhibition and the design was developed over the next four years for both military and civil use. The BH-11c on show won the 1926 Coppa d'Italia and survived in a dilapidated condition in the West Bohemia Museum at Plzen until 1965 when it was moved to Kbely. Products from the Praga and Zlin factories are also on display. A few aircraft from the World War II period have survived and the later Soviet influence is evident with many Ilyushin, MiG, Mil, Sukhoi and Tupolev types on view. Examples of almost all post war Czech models have been collected. As types are withdrawn they will join the collection. Among the foreign designs in the collection is the last surviving Saro Cloud. This aircraft undertook a sales tour of Europe in 1935 and at the end was purchased by the national airline who re-engined it with Walter Pollux radials. The airframe was put in store during the conflict and the wings were lost. The shortened body was used as a motor launch but now the magnificently restored fuselage is on display. A recent rebuild led to an example of the Aero C-3 being put on show. The type, a licence built Siebel 204, was constructed using Czech parts and components from French airframes. Exchanges with other museums have taken place to broaden the range of types exhibited. This has resulted in the arrival of the Meteor and Texan from Belgium. Also acquired from abroad are the ex-Royal Air Force Phantom, the former Vietnamese Northrop F-5, the T-33 from France, the Vampire from Switzerland and the Draken and Viggen from Sweden. A change of name to The Historical Institute of the Army of the Czech Republic – Aviation Museum Kbely occurred a few years ago. This superb museum has in its collection over sixty types which cannot be seen anywhere else in the world. Many associated displays have been set up which trace the history and development of aviation in the country with some emphasis on the local industry. There is a large collection of engines to be seen. When the country divided a few aircraft were transferred to the Slovak Republic for its museums. Several of the aircraft on show were restored in what is now Slovakia.

TYPE	REG/SER	CON. NO.	PI/NOTES	STATUS
☐ Aero 45	OK-EPC	50151		RA
☐ Aero 45	OK-DMO	4911		PV
☐ Aero 45	OK-EGN	5079		RA
☐ Aero Super 45S	OK-KGF	170419	At Ruzyne Airport.	PV
☐ Aero 145	OK-06	02-002	OK-KDA	RA
☐ Aero Ae-10 [Brandenburg 76]	Ae.10-21	21		PV
☐ Aero A-10	L-BALB	3	Partial replica	PV
☐ Aero Ab-11 (R)	'L-BUCD'	'17'		PVX
☐ Aero A-12 (R)	'A.12-4'			PVX
☐ Aero A-18 (R)	'2-36'	5		PVX
☐ Aero A-18c	'A.18-5'		Partial replica using original wings and other components.	PVX
☐ Aero Ap-32	'Ap.32-25'		Partial Replica	RACX
☐ Aero C-2B-1 [Arado Ar 96B]			Centre section only	S
☐ Aero C-3A [Siebel Si 204D-1]			Fuselage, tail and part of wing only	S
☐ Aero C-3A [Siebel Si 204D-1]	OK-ADR	224	Fuselage only.	RA
☐ Aero C-3AF [Siebel Si 204D-1]	OK-?LQ	622	FX-05(?), D-20(?) - part of fuselage.	S
☐ Aero C-104 [Bücker Bü 131D Jungmann]	OK-AXM	167	On loan to Technicke Muzeum Tatra.	–
☐ Aero C-104 [Bücker Bü 131D Jungmann]	A-27	227	A-27, OK-AQO	PV
☐ Aero C-104S [Bücker Bü 131D Jungmann]	OK-RXE	001		RAA
☐ Aero XL-29 Delfin	OK-70	0003/2	OK-14	PV
☐ Aero L-29 Delfin	0003	190003		RA
☐ Aero L-29 Delfin	0010	190010		PV
☐ Aero L-29 Delfin	0108	290108		S
☐ Aero L-29 Delfin	0321	590321		RA
☐ Aero L-29 Delfin	2206	692206		RA
☐ Aero L-29 Delfin	3241	993241		PV
☐ Aero L-29 Delfin	3247	993247		PV
☐ Aero L-29 Delfin	OK-70	X-2		PV
☐ Aero L-29A Akrobat	3027	893027		RA
☐ Aero L-29R Delfin	2827	892827		PV
☐ Aero L-29RS Delfin	2606	792606		RA
☐ Aero XL-39 Albatros	OK-182	002		PV
☐ Aero L-39 Albatros	'3905'	X-05	OK-25, OK-184	PVX
☐ Aero L-39C Albatros	0002	130002	OK-182	RA
☐ Aero L-39C Albatros	0115	330115	Original fuselage.	RA
☐ Aero L-39C Albatros	33	330207	In Soviet markings.	PV
☐ Aero L-39C Albatros	0441	530441	Original fuselage.	RA
☐ Aero L-39C Albatros	0448	530448	Original fuselage.	RA
☐ Aero L-39M Albatros (FSM)	'79'			PVX
☐ Aero L-39V Albatros	0725	630725		RA
☐ Aero L-39V Albatros	0740	630740		RA
☐ Aero L-39V Albatros		890002		RA
☐ Aero L-39V Albatros	3908	X-08		RA
☐ Aero L-60 Brigadyr	OK-KOS	001/1	OK-01	PV
☐ Aero XL-160 Brigadyr	0414	150414		PV
☐ Antonov An-2	7006	117047306		RA
☐ Antonov An-2R	OK-KIS	1G 190-13		RA
☐ Antonov An-24B	7109	17307109		RA
☐ Antonov An-24B	2904	77302904		RA
☐ Antonov An-30	1107	1107		RA
☐ Auster K AOP.6	A-16	2835	VT996, A-16, OO-FDI	PV
☐ Avia 14/32 [Ilyushin Il-14M]	OK-MCI	805119		RA
☐ Avia 14M [Ilyushin Il-14M]	6104	806104	OK-MCK - possible identity	RA
☐ Avia 14MFG (14M) [Ilyushin Il-14P]	6102	806102	6102, OK-MCB	RA
☐ Avia 14T [Ilyushin Il-14T]	3108	813108		RA
☐ Avia 14T [Ilyushin Il-14T]	3141	913141		RA
☐ Avia B-10	'C 155'	20	Partial replica	PVX
☐ Avia BH-11A	OK-LIQ	1001		PV
☐ Avia BH-11C	L-BONK	18	L-BONK, OK-IZZ	PV
☐ Avia BH-11K		17		PV
☐ Avia Bk-11 (R)	'2'	3		PVX
☐ Avia BH-18 (R)				PV
☐ Avia Ba-122 (R)	'OK-AVE'	'2'		PVX
☐ Avia S-199 [Messerschmitt Bf 109G-12]	UF-25	S199-178	Fuselage and wings only	PV
☐ Avia CS-199 [Messerschmitt Bf 109G-12]	UC-26	CS199-565		PV

Avia S-92 [Messerschmitt Me 262A]	V-34	S92-4		PV
Avia CS-92 [Messerschmitt Me 262B-1a]	V-35	51104		RA
Avia B-33 [Ilyushin Il-10]	5502	B33-5502		PV
Avia CB-33 [Ilyushin Il-10U]	5271	CB33-5271		PV
Avia B-228 [Ilyushin Il-28B]	2107	52107		S
Avia B-228 [Ilyushin Il-28RTR]	6926	56926	BA-11	RA
Avia B-534	H-6	226	Partial replica	PV
Benes-Mraz Be 50 (R)				RAC
Bensen B-8 Gyroglider				PV
Bohemia B-5			Incomplete.	PVD
Centralne Studium Samolotow (CSS) 13 [Polikarpov Po-2]	SP-BHA	42089		PV
Ceskoslovenska Vedecko Technicka Spolecnost Autogyro			On loan	S
Ceskoslovenska Vedecko Technicka Spolecnost Gyroglider			On loan	S
Chvala Ultralight				RA
Commonwealth CA-27 Sabre 30 [North American F-86]	'A94-923'	CA27-22	A94-922	PVX
Dassault Super Mystère B2				RA
De Havilland D.H.82A Tiger Moth	'R5148'	86536	PG627, PH-UAM, D-EBIG	PVX
De Havilland D.H.100 Vampire FB.6	J-1161	670	In Swiss markings.	RA
Dobias Gyroglider				S
Douglas DC-3-229	N143J	1995	NC18119, N403D, N143JR	RA
Dvoracek BDv-2				S
Elsnic EL-2M Sedy Vik		5		PV
Fieseler Fi 156C-7 Storch	HO-20	475448	HO-20, OK-AIP	PV
Focke-Wulf Fw 190A-5		1214(?)	Wings only	S
Fouga CM.170R Magister	38	38	38 (France), N71FM	RA
Gloster Meteor F.8	EG-247	7021	In Belgian markings.	RA
Henschel Hs 293A-1		242886		PV
Hütter H 17A (D.F.S. 108-67)				S
Ilyushin Il-2m3				RAD
Ilyushin Il-2m3	38	12438		PV
Ilyushin Il-10	OK-20	003	OK-167	RA
Ilyushin Il-14FG (Il-14P)	0603	4340603		RA
Ilyushin Il-18V (Il-18B)	OK-NAA	189001604	CCCP-75703 (?)	PV
Ilyushin Il-28B	2107	52107		RA
Ilyushin Il-28RT	2303	52303		RA
Ilyushin Il-28RT	3303	53303		RA
Ilyushin Il-28RTR	6926	56926	DE-51, BA-11	PV
Ilyushin Il-28U	0501	650100-501	CD-10	RA
Janowski J-2B	OK-ZUU			PV
Jirasek Ornithopthera				S
Junkers Ju 52/3m			Centre section and other small parts only	S
Kabele Homebuilt			Parts only	S
Kratochvil Gyroglider				PV
Kratochvil KLZ-VII				S
Kratochvil KLZ-VII				S
Kubat Glider				PV
Lavochkin La-7	77		On loan from NTM	PV
Let C-11 [Yakovlev Yak-11]	OK-JZE	171511	OK-JIL, OK-242	PVA
Let C-11 [Yakovlev Yak-11]	1706	171706	OK-JIM	RA
Let C-11 [Yakovlev Yak-11]	1727	171727		PV
Let C-11 [Yakovlev Yak-11]			Major parts.	S
Let C-11 [Yakovlev Yak-11]				RA
Let XL-13 Blanik				RA
Let XL-13 Blanik	OK-6202	03		PV
Let L-13 Blanik	OK-4835	173110		PV
Let L-200A Morava	0705	170705		RA
Let L-200D Morava	1125	171125		PV
Let XL-410 Turbolet	OK-20	170003	OK-63, OK-YKF	S
Let L-410UVP Turbolet	OK-IYA	X 0101	OK-160, OK-IYA, OK-026	PV
Letov LF-107 Lunak	OK-0804	7		S
Letov LF-107 Lunak	OK-0826	38		S
Letov LF-107 Lunak	OK-0835	51		PV
Letov LF-107 Lunak	OK-0838	54		S
Letov LF-107 Lunak	OK-0841	57		S
Letov LF-109 Pionyr	OK-2209	17		PV
Letov LF-109 Pionyr	OK-2251	59		S
Letov LF-109 Pionyr	OK-4070	0506		S
Letov MK-1 Kocour				S
Letov S-2		44		PV
Letov S-20	E-10	50	Partial replica	PV
Letov S-20J			Wing only	PV
Letov S-218 Smolik	C-49	18	C-48, OK-ZOB	PV
Letov SK-38 Komar [Schneider Grunau SG-38 modified]	OK-5069	128		PV
Lisunov Li-2D [Douglas DC-3 modified]	OK-WDI	23442710	D-37(?), OK-PYP, 2710	RA
Lisunov Li-2P [Douglas DC-3 modified]	3002	23443002	OK-GAH, D-38, 3002	RA
Lockheed 580 (T-33A)	'8550'	580-8550	53-5211, 35211 (France)	PVX
Matejcek M-15	OK-0401	5		S

☐ Matejcek M-18	OK-1400	7		RA
☐ Matejcek M-25	OK-2402	10		RA
☐ McDonnell M.98 Phantom FGR.2	XT899	2507		PV
☐ Mignet HM-14 Pou-du-Ciel				PV
☐ Mikoyan-Gurevich MiG-15	1720	231720		PV
☐ Mikoyan-Gurevich MiG-15bis	3512			RA
☐ Mikoyan-Gurevich MiG-15bis	25		In North Korean markings.	PV
☐ Mikoyan-Gurevich MiG-15bis	3841	623841		PV
☐ Mikoyan-Gurevich MiG-15bis	3925	623925		RA
☐ Mikoyan-Gurevich MiG-15bis	3949	713949		RA
☐ Mikoyan-Gurevich MiG-15bisR	0738	530738		RA
☐ Mikoyan-Gurevich MiG-15bisR	3671	613671		PV
☐ Mikoyan-Gurevich MiG-15bisSB (MiG-15bis)	3058	143058		RA
☐ Mikoyan-Gurevich MiG-15bisSB (MiG-15bis)	3255	613255		PV
☐ Mikoyan-Gurevich MiG-15bisT	3131	713131		PV
☐ Mikoyan-Gurevich MiG-15SB (MiG-15)	1186	141186		RA
☐ Mikoyan-Gurevich MiG-15SB (MiG-15)	1585	141585		RA
☐ Mikoyan-Gurevich MiG-15SB (MiG-15)	1713	231713		RA
☐ Mikoyan-Gurevich MiG-15UTI	2611	142611		RA
☐ Mikoyan-Gurevich MiG-15UTI	OK-10	612744	2744	RA
☐ Mikoyan-Gurevich MiG-15UTI	OK-010	822210	2210	RAD
☐ Mikoyan-Gurevich MiG-15UTI	2512	922512		RA
☐ Mikoyan-Gurevich MiG-15UTI-P	2626	722626	OK-10	PV
☐ Mikoyan-Gurevich MiG-17PF	0101	000101		RA
☐ Mikoyan-Gurevich MiG-17PF	0201	000201		PV
☐ Mikoyan-Gurevich MiG-17PF	0872	000872		PV
☐ Mikoyan-Gurevich MiG-17PF	1015	001015		PV
☐ Mikoyan-Gurevich MiG-19P	0742	62210742		RA
☐ Mikoyan-Gurevich MiG-19P	0813	62210813		PV
☐ Mikoyan-Gurevich MiG-19PM	1043	65211043		PV
☐ Mikoyan-Gurevich MiG-19S	0414	150414		PV
☐ Mikoyan-Gurevich MiG-19S	1006	61211006		RA
☐ Mikoyan-Gurevich MiG-21F-13	1013	161013		RA
☐ Mikoyan-Gurevich MiG-21F-13	0210	460210		RA
☐ Mikoyan-Gurevich MiG-21F-13	0212	460212		RA
☐ Mikoyan-Gurevich MiG-21F-13	0304	560304		RA
☐ Mikoyan-Gurevich MiG-21F-13	0305	560305		RA
☐ Mikoyan-Gurevich MiG-21F-13	0313	560313		PV
☐ Mikoyan-Gurevich MiG-21F-13	0613	760613		PV
☐ Mikoyan-Gurevich MiG-21MF	7705	967705		RA
☐ Mikoyan-Gurevich MiG-21MF-75	2410	96002410		RA
☐ Mikoyan-Gurevich MiG-21MFN (MiG-21MF) (MiG-21MF-75)	4405	96004405		PV
☐ Mikoyan-Gurevich MiG-21PF	0302	760302		RA
☐ Mikoyan-Gurevich MiG-21PF	0308	760308		PV
☐ Mikoyan-Gurevich MiG-21PF	1305	761305		RA
☐ Mikoyan-Gurevich MiG-21PF	1309	761309		RA
☐ Mikoyan-Gurevich MiG-21PFM	4411	94A4411		PV
☐ Mikoyan-Gurevich MiG-21PFM	4609	94A4609		RA
☐ Mikoyan-Gurevich MiG-21R	1501	94R01501		PV
☐ Mikoyan-Gurevich MiG-21U-600	2820	662820		RA
☐ Mikoyan-Gurevich MiG-21U-600	4916	664916		RA
☐ Mikoyan-Gurevich MiG-21UM	3166	516931066		RA
☐ Mikoyan-Gurevich MiG-21UM	3181	516931081		PV
☐ Mikoyan-Gurevich MiG-21UM	9332	516999332		PV
☐ Mikoyan-Gurevich MiG-21US	0948	09685148		RA
☐ Mikoyan-Gurevich MiG-23BN	5735	0393215735		RA
☐ Mikoyan-Gurevich MiG-23BN	9825	0393219825		PV
☐ Mikoyan-Gurevich MiG-23BN	9831	0393219831		PV
☐ Mikoyan-Gurevich MiG-23BN	9863	0393219863	Front fuselage only.	PV
☐ Mikoyan-Gurevich MiG-23MF	3641	039021364	Front fuselage only.	PV
☐ Mikoyan-Gurevich MiG-23MF	3646	0390213646		PV
☐ Mikoyan-Gurevich MiG-23MF	3922	0390213922		PV
☐ Mikoyan-Gurevich MiG-23ML	2406	0390322406		PV
☐ Mikoyan-Gurevich MiG-23UB	7905	A1037905		PV
☐ Mil Mi-2	B-2047	5311147060		RA
☐ Mil Mi-2	2509	532509072		RA
☐ Mil Mi-2	B-2530	539430105		PV
☐ Mil Mi-4	0751	0751		RAD
☐ Mil Mi-4	0138	20138		PV
☐ Mil Mi-4	0538	20138		PV
☐ Mil Mi-4A	2143	02143		RA
☐ Mil Mi-8PS	0830	10830	B-8130	RA
☐ Mil Mi-8T	0133	0133		RA
☐ Mil Mi-8T	0313	0313		PV
☐ Mil Mi-8T	0910	0910		RA
☐ Mil Mi-8T	0819	10819		RA
☐ Mil Mi-8T	0820	10820		RA
☐ Mil Mi-8T	1232	1232		RA
☐ Mil Mi-8T	1532	1532		RA
☐ Mil Mi-24D	0220	340220		PV
☐ Mil Mi-24V				RA
☐ Morane-Saulnier MS.230	1077	1077		PV

☐ Motor Balloon			Gondola only	PV
☐ Mraz M-1C Sokol	OK-BHM	127		PV
☐ Mraz M-1D Sokol	OK-DID	289	Wings only	S
☐ Nieuport 11 (Scale R)	OK-ZUD	00943		RAA
☐ Noorduyn Harvard IIB [North American NA-77 (AT-16)]	FT422	14A-1462	43-13163, FT422, B-67 (Netherlands)	PV
☐ Nord N.1002 Pingouin II [Messerschmitt Bf 108B]				RA
☐ Nord NC.702 Martinet [Siebel Si 204A-1]	315	315	Fuselage only.	RA
☐ Nord NC.702 Martinet [Siebel Si 204A-1]	'LB-05'	350	350 – composite – painted as Aero C-3A.	PVX
☐ North American NA-191 Sabre (F-86F)				RA
☐ Northrop N-156E Tiger II (F-5E)	00878	R.1059	73-0878 – in Vietnamese markings.	PV
☐ Olansky Ultralight				RA
☐ Orlican L-40 Meta-Sokol	OK-KHN	150002/002		PV
☐ Orlican VT-15				RA
☐ Orlican VT-16 Orlik 1	OK-1408	150104		RA
☐ Orlican VT-16 Orlik 1	OK-2408	150120		PV
☐ Orlican VT-116 Orlik II	OK-3433	150102		S
☐ Orlican VT-116 Orlik II ZK	OK-6437			S
☐ Panstwowe Zaklady Lotnicze (PZL) 104 Wilga 35A	SP-CRU	59049		RA
☐ Piper J-3C-65 Cub (L-4J)	'10'	12406	44-80110, SP-AHB	PVX
☐ Praga E-114M Air Baby	OK-BGL	125	On loan from NTM	PV
☐ Praga XE-1				PV
☐ Rapac Glider				PV
☐ Republic P-47D Thunderbolt			(USAAF) – front fuselage only.	RA
☐ Rogallo Standard Hang Glider				S
☐ Saunders-Roe A.19 Cloud	OK-BAK	A.19/5	G-ACGO	PV
☐ Schneider ESG 31 Grunau Baby IIA	OK-3001	1514	Wings only	S
☐ Schneider ESG 31 Grunau Baby IIB	OK-8055			PV
☐ Schneider ESG 31 Grunau Baby IIB	OK-8387			S
☐ Société Pour l'Aviation et ses Dérivés (SPAD) VIIC1	11583	S11583	L-BIZL	PV
☐ Soko 522	23500	123		RA
☐ Stakr Homebuilt			Wings only	S
☐ Stinson 108-2 Voyager	C-FBAM	108-3210	CF-BAM	S
☐ Sukhoi Su-7BKL	5919	5919		RA
☐ Sukhoi Su-7BKL	6428	6428		RA
☐ Sukhoi Su-7BKL	6513	6513		PV
☐ Sukhoi Su-7BM	5616	5616		PV
☐ Sukhoi Su-7UM	1017	1017		PV
☐ Sukhoi Su-22M4K	4006	40306		PV
☐ Sukhoi Su-25K	9098	25508109098		PV
☐ Supermarine 361 Spitfire LF.IXe	TE565		On loan from NTM.	PV
☐ Svenska Aeroplan Aktiebolaget (SAAB) 35J Draken (35F-2) (J 35F-2) (J 35J)	Fv35518	35518		PV
☐ Svenska Aeroplan Aktiebolaget (SAAB) 37 Viggen (SF 37) (AJSF 37)	Fv37957	37957	On loan from FVM.	PV
☐ Taylor E-2 Cub	OK-ATW	147	OK-AT?	PV
☐ Trejbal-Prasil Glider				PV
☐ Tupolev Tu-104A	OK-LDA	76600503		RA
☐ Tupolev Tu-134A	OK-EFJ	23128	Front fuselage only.	RA
☐ Tupolev Tu-154B-2	0601	0601		RA
☐ Vaculik-Sidi Motor-Glider				S
☐ VOSLM BAK-01				PV
☐ Vykumny a Zkusebni Letecky Ustav (VZLU) HC-2 Heli-Baby	OK-09	A	OK-IVA	PV
☐ Vykumny a Zkusebni Letecky Ustav (VZLU) HC-3	OK-04	02	OK-16, OK-VZA	S
☐ Vykumny a Zkusebni Letecky Ustav (VZLU) L-8 (TOM-8))	OK-08	04		PV
☐ Vykumny a Zkusebni Letecky Ustav (VZLU)-Orlican HC-4-4			Fuselage only	PV
☐ Vyvojova Skupina Brno VSB-66 Orlice	OK-1900		On loan	PV
☐ Vyvojova Skupina Morava VSM-40 Demant	OK-6203	04	On loan to Aeroklub Zbraslavice.	–
☐ Vyvojova Skupina Morava VSM-40 Demant	OK-9801	7		PV
☐ Vyvojove Plachtarske Dilny Medlanky L-21 Spartak	OK-6702	02		PV
☐ Vyvojove Plachtarske Dilny Medlanky L-21 Spartak	OK-6703	03		S
☐ Wytwornia Sprzetu Komunikacyjnego (WSK) SM-1/300 [Mil Mi-1]	1005	S111005		S
☐ Wytwornia Sprzetu Komunikacyjnego (WSK) SM-1Wb [Mil Mi-1M]	4003	404003		PV
☐ Wytwornia Sprzetu Komunikacyjnego (WSK) SM-1Wb [Mil Mi-1M]	6014	506014		S
☐ Wytwornia Sprzetu Komunikacyjnego (WSK) SM-2	OK-RUV	S203009	OK-BYK.	S
☐ Yakovlev Yak-12R	OK-JEN	14425		S
☐ Yakovlev Yak-17	30	IS-1001		PV
☐ Yakovlev Yak-23	HX-51	10101		PV
☐ Yakovlev Yak-40	0723	9230723	OK-BYG, OK-020 (?)	RA
☐ Zlin HC-102 Heli Baby	OK-RVE	0108		S
☐ Zlin HC-102 Heli Baby	OK-RVX	0426		S
☐ Zlin HC-102 Heli Baby	OK-RXA	0436		PV
☐ Zlin XII	OK-TBX	170	Partial replica	PV
☐ Zlin Z-22 Junak	OO-FRE	82	LX-MAI, OO-GUY	PV

TYPE	REG/SER	CON. NO.	PI/NOTES	STATUS
☐ Zlin Z-23 Honza	OK-5629	128		PV
☐ Zlin Z-24 Krajanek	OK-8233	225		PV
☐ Zlin Z-24 Krajanek	OK-8565	260		RAC
☐ Zlin Z-24 Krajanek	OK-8548	49		RA
☐ Zlin Z-25 Sohaj	OK-8853	62		PV
☐ Zlin Z-26 Trener	OK-FRI	601		PV
☐ Zlin Z-26/126 Trener	UC-36	536	UC-36, OK-EXF – Z-26 fuselage with Z-126 wings.	PV
☐ Zlin XZ-37 Cmelak	OK-SJB	001		S
☐ Zlin Z-37 Cmelak	OK-12	00-06	OK-UJE	S
☐ Zlin Z-42	OK-XSB	0003		S
☐ Zlin Z-43S	OK-078	0001	OK-YKN	S
☐ Zlin Z-50LS	OK-IRG	0017		PV
☐ Zlin LG-123 Honza	OK-5149			S
☐ Zlin LG-124 Galanka	OK-1724	35		PV
☐ Zlin LG-125 Sohaj 2	OK-1794			S
☐ Zlin LG-125 Sohaj 2	OK-0706	506		S
☐ Zlin LG-125 Sohaj 2	OK-1968	605		RAA
☐ Zlin Z-126 Trener	OK-HLJ	721		RAA
☐ Zlin LG-130 Kmotr	OK-1240	11		PV
☐ Zlin LG-130 Kmotr	OK-1267	39		S
☐ Zlin Z-135 Heli Trainer (Z-35)	OK-045	1		PV
☐ Zlin Z-226 Trener 6	OK-MPN	259		RA
☐ Zlin Z-226A Akrobat	OK-KMA	0108		PV
☐ Zlin Z-226AS Akrobat	OK-KMB	0208		RA
☐ Zlin Z-226B Bohatyr	OK-MPM	258		RA
☐ Zlin Z-326A Akrobat	DM-WKB	596		PV
☐ Zlin Z-381 [Bücker Bü 181D Bestmann]	'UA-264'	370	OK-DJR	PVX
☐ ZlinVT-425 Sohaj 3	OK-5425			RA
☐ ZlinVT-425 Sohaj 3	OK-5312	0208		S
☐ ZlinVT-425 Sohaj 3	OK-5339	0310		S
☐ ZlinVT-425 Sohaj 3	OK-5368	0415		S
☐ ZlinVT-425 Sohaj 3	OK-5378	0425		S
☐ ZlinVT-425 Sohaj 3	OK-0711	0511		PV

MÚZEUM KASPAR (CZ2)

Address:	c/o Vychodocske Divadlo, Divadelni 50, 530 01 Pardubice.
Tel:	040-516631.
Admission:	Not yet open.
Location:	Planned to be in the town.

In 1911 Jan Kaspar flew a monoplane from his home town of Pardubice to Prague, a distance of about 100 km. The aircraft is now on show at the National Technical Museum in Prague. The machine was similar to the Blériot XI. Kaspar had seen drawings of the French aircraft but did not know the actual dimensions so his aircraft had a different fuselage length and wingspan. Plans are underway to establish a museum in Pardubice and a replica of one of Kaspar's later monoplanes is being built. The Delfin has been transferred from the collection at Kbely. Some of Kaspar's personal belongings are on show in the town museum.

TYPE	REG/SER	CON. NO.	PI/NOTES	STATUS
☐ Aero L-29R Delfin				RA
☐ Kaspar Monoplane (R)				RAC

MÚZEUM POLICIE (CZ3)

Address:	Ke Karlovu 453/1, 120 00 Praha 2.
Tel:	02224-922183
Fax:	0974-84091
Email	Muzeum@mvcr.cz
Admission:	Tuesday-Sunday 1000-1700.
Location:	In the city centre east of the river.

Housed in part of a former monastery the museum initially opened in the mid-1960s. The first displays highlighted the work of the Border Police and in 1973 the museum became the National Security Police Museum. In 1990 the exhibition was reorganised to cover all aspects of police work in the state and the new halls opened on April 12th 1991. Cars from the inter-war period up to modern day vehicles are on view along with weapons. In the 1920s the state police had an aviation section and models of the types used can be seen. The autogyro, on show in the grounds, was built for an attempt to escape from the country.

TYPE	REG/SER	CON. NO.	PI/NOTES	STATUS
☐ Homebuilt Autogyro				PV
☐ Mil Mi-2P	B-2911	536011029		PV

NADACE LETECKÉ HISTORICKÉ SPOLEČNOSTI VYŠKOV (CZ4)

Address:	Sidlisti Vita Nejedleho 1, 682 03 Vyškov.
Tel:	0604-789651
Email:	muzeum@LHS-Vyskov.cz
Admission:	Saturday, Sunday 0900-1200 1400-1800.
Location:	About 2 km north of the town on the old road to Prostejov.

Established on February 27th 1993 the Air Historical Company Foundation opened its exhibition the following April. The organisation has close ties with the military authorities and recently withdrawn types are being added to the display. Several World War II crash sites have been investigated and many items recovered. This work has been carried out over the last thirty years by local enthusiasts. On show are components from a Heinkel He 111, an Ilyushin Il-2 and a Vickers Wellington along with engines and memorabilia. Several parts from German aircraft, including a Focke Wulf Fw 190 and a Messerschmitt Bf 109, can also be seen. Accurate records are being assembled of all crashes in the area. This section is enhanced with photographs of the digs. The aircraft display consists mainly of military types although a few civil designs have arrived. Many MiG jet fighters are on view and later models are expected. Three versions of the Sukhoi Su-7 can be seen along with the Su-25. A Su-22 is expected at any time. Seven Mil helicopters, two of which are Polish built are displayed. Ten Ilyushin Il-10 front fuselages have been found. At least one will be put on permanent show and the others will probably be exchanged. The Avia 14 was in service from 1957 until 1992 and a pair has been preserved. The exhibits are maintained in excellent condition and a number, which have spent years outside at military bases are being restored by the team of volunteers. A wide range of military vehicles is also on show and these include, tanks, guns, trucks, ambulances, radar stations and track laying lorries.

TYPE	REG/SER	CON. NO.	PI/NOTES	STATUS
☐ Aero L-39V Albatros	0720	630720		PV
☐ Aero L-39V Albatros	0735	630735		PV
☐ Avia 14T [Ilyushin Il-14T]	3133	913133		PV
☐ Avia 14T [Ilyushin Il-14T]	3144	913144		PV
☐ Ilyushin Il-10			Front fuselage only.	PVD
☐ Ilyushin Il-10			Front fuselage only.	PVD
☐ Ilyushin Il-10			Front fuselage only.	PVD
☐ Ilyushin Il-10			Front fuselage only.	PVD
☐ Ilyushin Il-10			Front fuselage only.	PVD
☐ Ilyushin Il-10			Front fuselage only.	PVD
☐ Ilyushin Il-10			Front fuselage only.	PVD
☐ Ilyushin Il-10			Front fuselage only.	PVD
☐ Ilyushin Il-10			Front fuselage only.	PVD
☐ Ilyushin Il-10			Front fuselage only.	PVD
☐ Ilyushin Il-28RT	2404	52404		PV
☐ Let L-200A Morava	OK-PLU	170812		RA
☐ Mikoyan-Gurevich MiG-15bisSB (MiG-15bis)	3912	623912		PV
☐ Mikoyan-Gurevich MiG-19PM	1102	65211102		PV
☐ Mikoyan-Gurevich MiG-19S	0412	150412		PV
☐ Mikoyan-Gurevich MiG-19S	0423	150423		PV
☐ Mikoyan-Gurevich MiG-21F-13	1003	061003		PV
☐ Mikoyan-Gurevich MiG-21F-13	1106	161106		PV
☐ Mikoyan-Gurevich MiG-21F-13	1111	261111		PV
☐ Mikoyan-Gurevich MiG-21MA	2703	962703		PV
☐ Mikoyan-Gurevich MiG-21PF	1212	761212		PV
☐ Mikoyan-Gurevich MiG-21PF	1311	761311		PV
☐ Mikoyan-Gurevich MiG-21PF	1313	761313		PV
☐ Mikoyan-Gurevich MiG-21PFM	8001	94N8001		PV
☐ Mikoyan-Gurevich MiG-21R	2101	94R02101		PV
☐ Mikoyan-Gurevich MiG-21U-400	0817	660817		PV
☐ Mikoyan-Gurevich MiG-23BN	5734	0393215734		PV
☐ Mikoyan-Gurevich MiG-23BN	9820	0393219820		PV
☐ Mikoyan-Gurevich MiG-23MF	3645	0390213645	Front fuselage only.	PV
☐ Mikoyan-Gurevich MiG-23MF	7183	0390217183		PV
☐ Mikoyan-Gurevich MiG-23ML	3304	03903323304		PV
☐ Mil Mi-2	B-2745	5310345097		PV
☐ Mil Mi-4	4139	04139		PV
☐ Mil Mi-4	0599	0599		PV
☐ Mil Mi-8T	OK-FXE	10546	931 (DDR), 93+17	PV
☐ Mil Mi-8T	0818	10818		PV
☐ Sukhoi Su-7BKL	6427	6427		PV
☐ Sukhoi Su-7BKL	6511	6511		PV
☐ Sukhoi Su-7BM	5521	5521		PV
☐ Sukhoi Su-7UM	1015	1015		PV
☐ Sukhoi Su-7UM	1016	1016		PV
☐ Sukhoi Su-22M4	3405	34205	Due soon.	-
☐ Sukhoi Su-25K	9013	25508109013		PV
☐ Wytwornia Sprzetu Komunikacyjnego (WSK) SM-1Wb [Mil Mi-1M]	4005	404005		PV
☐ Wytwornia Sprzetu Komunikacyjnego (WSK) SM-1Wb [Mil Mi-1M]	6017	506017		PV
☐ Zlin Z-37 Cmelak	OK-WJT	03-14		PV

This colourful L-39V Albatros is on show at Vyskov.

This Aero built Jungmann has been painted to represent the first Tatra T-131. It can be seen in the Tatra Museum at Koprivnice.

This Kazan built Mil Mi-8T served with the Czechoslovakian Air Force before becoming a civil aircraft. The helicopter is now at the Zruc Air Park. (Douglas Rough)

NÁRODNI TECHNICKÉ MÚZEUM (CZ5)

Address:	Kostelni 42, 17078 Praha 7.
Tel:	0220-399111
Fax:	0220-399200
Email:	info@ntm.cz
Admission:	Tuesday-Sunday 0900-1700
Location:	In the city centre just north of the river.

The origins of the collection go back to 1799 and the present museum was established as the Technical Museum of the Kingdom of Bohemia in 1908. The first location was at the Schwarzenburg Palace in Prague Castle and even then there was a fairly large aeronautical section. When the Czechoslovak Republic was founded in 1918 the museum was overcrowded and plans were put forward for a new building. These premises were ready in 1941 but the museum did not move in until 1945. The collection was nationalised in 1951 and became the central technical museum of the country. The transport department, which includes aviation, occupies the large main hall. When the air and space section of the Military Museum was set up at Kbely there was an exchange of exhibits. The earliest machines on view are balloons. Two of Igo Etrich's designs are on show – these are a 1905 attempt to produce a powered glider and his 1927 Limusina. A prized exhibit is the 1911 monoplane in which the first Czech pilot, Jan Kaspar, flew from Pardubice to Prague. World War I is represented by three biplanes which are all believed to be the only survivors of their type. These are a Russian Anatra carrying post-World War I Czech markings, an Austrian Knoller C II in Austro-Hungarian colours and an American Morse LWF. Also on show is an excellent range of engines with many from the Walter company. The technical aspects of many aspects of aviation are highlighted in many of the informative displays.

TYPE	REG/SER	CON. NO.	PI/NOTES	STATUS
☐ Aero C-104 [Bücker Bü 131D Jungmann]	OK-AXY	254		PV
☐ Aero L-39C Albatros	0107	230107		PV
☐ Anatra DS Anasalja	'11120'	3979	010.091	PVX
☐ Avia BH-10	OK-AVO	14	B10.14	PV
☐ Avia BH-9	OK-IPF	9	B9.9	PV
☐ Bensen B-8W Gyroglider				RA
☐ Brandenburg D I	28.68		Fuselage only	RA
☐ Etrich Taube Limusina				PV
☐ Etrich Zanonia				PV
☐ Jacobs Weihe (D.F.S. 108-68)	OK-8303			RA
☐ Janacek Delta C Hang Glider				PV
☐ Kantor-Kuklik Racek III Mrkev	OK-8340			RA
☐ Kaspar Monoplane		76		PV
☐ Knoller C II	119.15	15		PV
☐ Lavochkin La-7	77		On loan to Kbely.	–
☐ Letov LF-107 Lunak	OK-0821	35		RA
☐ Mignet HM-14 Pou-du-Ciel				PV
☐ Mikoyan-Gurevich MiG-21F-13	0202	460202	At Kbely.	RA
☐ Morse LWF Scout	4			PV
☐ Mraz K-65 Cap [Fieseler Fi 156C-3 Storch]	OK-DFJ	165		RA
☐ Mraz M-1C Sokol	OK-AHN	118		PV
☐ Phönix D VI (?)			Fuselage only	RA
☐ Piper J-3C-65 Cub (L-4H)	OK-UXE	12254	44-79958, OK-YIE – at Moravska Trebova airport.	RAA
☐ Praha PB.3	OK-8465			PV
☐ Ressel Balloon (1893)			Parts only	RA
☐ Silimon IS 3D	OK-9811	013	YR-903	RA
☐ Simunek VBS-1 Kunkaldo	L-BILG			PV
☐ Supermarine 361 Spitfire LF.IXe	TE565		On loan to Kbely	–
☐ Vykumny a Zkusebni Letecky Ustav (VZLU) HC-2 Heli-Baby	RA-05	B	OK-10, 0002	PV
☐ Zlin XIII	OK-TBZ	1		PV
☐ Zlin Z-24 Krajanek	OK-8560	46		RA
☐ Zlin Z-25 Sohaj	OK-8672	5		RA
☐ Zlin Z-50LA (Z-50L)	OK-IRF	016		PV
☐ Zlin LG-125 Sohaj 2	OK-8755	116		RA
☐ Zlin LG-125 Sohaj 2	OK-8767	128		RA
☐ Zlin LG-130 Kmotr	OK-1242	13	On loan to Aeroklub Brno.	–
☐ Zlin Z-225 Medak	OK-1781	1		RA
☐ Zlin Z-381 [Bücker Bü 181D Bestmann]	OK-DRK	318	OK-DRH	RA
☐ Zodiac Balloon 'Praha'			Parts only	PV

SBIRKA CÁSLAV (CZ6)

Address:	21 Zakladna Taktickeho Letectva, Caslav.
Admission:	By prior permission only.
Location:	About 15 km east of Usti.

Caslav is one of the few military airfields in the country which remained open after the country split. At the present time it houses squadrons flying MiG-21s and L-159s. There is also a maintenance base at the site. The two Sukhoi Su-7s are by the buildings on the north side of the base and the MiG-15 is near the control tower.

TYPE	REG/SER	CON. NO.	PI/NOTES	STATUS
☐ Aero L-29 Delfin	1720	691720		RA
☐ Aero L-39C Albatros	0108	230108		RA
☐ Mikoyan-Gurevich MiG-15	5206	225206		RA
☐ Mikoyan-Gurevich MiG-21MF	4003	964003		RA
☐ Mikoyan-Gurevich MiG-21MF	5212	965212		RA
☐ Mikoyan-Gurevich MiG-23BN	5733	0393215733		RA
☐ Mikoyan-Gurevich MiG-23ML	4850	0390324850		RA
☐ Sukhoi Su-7BM	5516	5516		RA
☐ Sukhoi Su-7BM	5526	5526		RA

SBIRKA NÁMĚŠT'NAD OSLAVOU (CZ7)

Address: 32 Takticiho Stihachio Letectva,
675 71 Namest Nad Oslavou.
Admission: By prior permission only.
Location: About 8 km south west of the town just north of Sedlec.

The airfield was used by fighter and attack units for many years. The two Sukhoi Su-7s are mounted as a memorial inside the base. The type arrived at Namest in 1965 and was withdrawn in 1990.

TYPE	REG/SER	CON. NO.	PI/NOTES	STATUS
☐ Aero L-29RS Delfin	2807	892807		RA
☐ Mikoyan-Gurevich MiG-15bis	'1986'		Also carries '1981'	RAX
☐ Sukhoi Su-7BM	'1990'	5317	5317, '1964'	RAX
☐ Sukhoi Su-7BM	'1965'	5320	5320, '` 1956'	RAX
☐ Sukhoi Su-25K	5007	25508105007		RA

SBIRKA POKORNY (CZ8)

Address: Ceska Olesna 105,
378 55 Popelin.
Admission: By prior permission only.
Location: About 15 km north east of Jindrichuv Hradec.

This private collection of MiG fighters resides at the owner's home. Work is taking place to reassemble and restore the airframes to display standard. All the aircraft served with the Air Force for many years.

TYPE	REG/SER	CON. NO.	PI/NOTES	STATUS
☐ Mikoyan-Gurevich MiG-15UTI	2462	722462	Front fuselage only.	RA
☐ Mikoyan-Gurevich MiG-15UTI	2514	922514		RA
☐ Mikoyan-Gurevich MiG-19PM	1041	65211041		RA
☐ Mikoyan-Gurevich MiG-19S	0876	61210876		RA
☐ Mikoyan-Gurevich MiG-21F-13				RA

SBIRKA ROUDNICE (CZ9)

Address : 503 27 Roudnice.
Admission: By prior permission only.
Location: About 10 km west of Hradec Kralove on Route 11.

The owner of this surplus yard has put a several ex Air Force MiG fighters on display in the premises. These have been acquired from military bases and other collections in the country.

TYPE	REG/SER	CON. NO.	PI/NOTES	STATUS
☐ Mikoyan-Gurevich MiG-15bis	3839	623839		RA
☐ Mikoyan-Gurevich MiG-15bisSB	3904	623904		RA
☐ Mikoyan-Gurevich MiG-19S	0503	150503		RA
☐ Mikoyan-Gurevich MiG-21F-13	1005	061005		RA
☐ Sukhoi Su-22M4K	3706	37406	Fuselage only.	RA

SLOVAČKE LETECKÉ MÚZEUM (CZ10)

Address: P.O. Box 34,
686 04 Kunovice.
Tel: 0632-5680
Admission: Saturday-Sunday 1000-1700.
Location: Just south of the town off Route 55.

Set up in 1951 the Let National Corporation opened its factory at Kunovice in 1954. The first type to be produced was the C-11, a licence built Yakovlev Yak-11, and seven hundred and seven were constructed. The last Aero 45s were assembled at the site and these were followed by all Super Aero 45s, Aero 145s, L-200 Moravas and the L-13 Blanik glider. Work was also undertaken in the factory on the L-29 Delfin and L-39 Albatros trainers and the Z-37 Cmelak. The prototype of the L-410 Turbolet flew in 1969 and well over a thousand had been produced before the plant closed. The museum was established in the mid-1980s by members of the local aero club and factory personnel. The display was initially located in the centre of the airfield but in 1989 moved to a site near the club premises. Almost all models produced at the factory can he seen along with several military types. A restoration programme is being carried out and a number of the smaller types are now in excellent condition. Six examples of versions of the Turbolet can be seen. A replica of the Tatra 101 low wing monoplane built in 1938 is being constructed. Only the prototype of this design was completed.

TYPE	REG/SER	CON. NO.	PI/NOTES	STATUS
☐ Aero 45	OK-FHA	51163		PV
☐ Aero 145	OK-PHI	171812		RA
☐ Aero L-29 Delfin	0113	290113		PV
☐ Aero L-29A Akrobat	0517	390517	OK-SZA	PV
☐ Aero L-29R Delfin	2613	792613		PV
☐ Avia 14FG (14) [Ilyushin Il-14P]	1103	601103		PV
☐ Avia 14T [Ilyushin Il-14T]	3157	013157		PV
☐ Let C-11 [Yakovlev Yak-11]	PK-35	171721		PV
☐ Let L-200A Morava	OK-PLF	170719		PV
☐ Let L-200D Morava	OK-RFS	171116		PV
☐ Let L-210 Morava (L-200D)	OK-PHB	170814		PV
☐ Let XL-410 Turbolet	OK-YKE	690001	OK-60	PV
☐ Let XL-410 Turbolet	OK-ZKA	700004		PV
☐ Let L-410A Turbolet	OK-ADO	710005		PV
☐ Let L-410A Turbolet	OK-ADP	710101		PV
☐ Let L-410M Turbolet	OK-022	750401		PV
☐ Let L-410UVP Turbolet	OK-030	X-01 (760604)	OK-166	PV
☐ Mikoyan-Gurevich MiG-15bisSB (MiG-15bis)	3005	713005		PV
☐ Mikoyan-Gurevich MiG-19PM	1040	65211040		PV
☐ Mikoyan-Gurevich MiG-21F-13	0514	660514		PV
☐ Mil Mi-4A	1874	1874		PV
☐ Sukhoi Su-7BM	5530	5530		PV
☐ Sukhoi Su-7UB	0510	0510		PV
☐ Tatra 101 (R)				RAC
☐ Zlin Z-37A Cmelak	DDR-SNK	06-15	DM-SNK	PV
☐ Zlin Z-226B Bohatyr	OK-MPW	269		PV
☐ Zlin Z-326 Trener Master	OK-IFD	739		PV

TECHNICKÉ MÚZEUM TATRA (CZ11)

Address:	Zahumenni 369, 742 21 Koprivnice.
Tel:	0555-871106
Fax:	0555-821415
Email:	technicka@tatramuzuem.cz
Admission:	Daily 0800-1600.
Location:	About 30 km south of Ostrava , about 5 km south of Road No.48 (E.7).

The company can trace its origins back to 1771 and the present group came into being in 1923 when the Ringhoffer Wagon Factory in Prague merged with the Koprivnice Wagon Factory. The famous range of Tatra cars has been made since 1897 and the first product of the factory, 'The President' is the pride of the automobile collection of the National Technical Museum in Prague. In 1935 an affiliated plant, the Studenka Wagon Factory, became the site for Tatra Aircraft. Licences were acquired for the Avro 626 and the Bücker Jungmann. Only one example of the British design was constructed and the thirty seventh production Jungmann was delivered from Germany to serve as a pattern for the thirty five Tatra T-13ls built. An Aero built Jungmann, loaned from the museum at Kbely, has been painted in the colours of the first T-131. The museum contains an excellent collection of cars and vehicles produced by the company and its associates

TYPE	REG/SER	CON. NO.	PI/NOTES	STATUS
☐ Aero C-104 [Bücker Bü 131D Jungmann]	'OK-TAB'	167	OK-AXM – painted to represent Tatra T-131 No 1 – on loan from Kbely	PVX

TECHNICKÉ MÚZEUM V BRNĚ (CZ12)

Address:	Purkynova 105, 612 00 Brno-Kralovo.
Tel:	0541-421411
Fax:	0541-214418
Email:	info@technicalmuseum.cz
Admission:	Tuesday-Sunday 0900-1700.
Location:	In the north western part of the city close to the ring road.

Established as a separate institution in 1961 the museum was housed in a former Ursuline convent in the Moravian capital. The building has now been reclaimed by the religious order and the last displays moved out in 1996. The Zlin Trener has been restored to flying condition and is kept at Slatina airfield. This will eventually he joined by the Bohatyr which is under at rebuild at Kunovice. The new exhibition opened in 2001 and presents a superb display of all aspects of technology. There is an excellent collection of mechanical musical instruments. The aeronautical section includes several engines and components and a large collection of model sailplanes. An outstation at Lisin in the suburbs of the city houses two aircraft and several buses and railway engines along with commercial vehicles.

TYPE	REG/SER	CON. NO.	PI/NOTES	STATUS
☐ Aero L-29 Delfin	2404	792404		PV
☐ Aero L-29R Delfin	'8291'	892821	2821 – At Lisin.	PVX
☐ Kunovsky-Drdla KD-67 Gyroglider				S
☐ Letov LF-107 Lunak	OK-0830	46		S
☐ Mikoyan-Gurevich MiG-19S	0511	150511		PV
☐ Mikoyan-Gurevich MiG-21F-13	0520	660520	At Lisin.	PV
☐ Mikoyan-Gurevich MiG-21MFN (MiG-21MF) (MiG-21MF-75)	5612	965612		PV
☐ Sukhoi Su-22M4K	3402	34102		PV
☐ Sukhoi Su-25K	1003	25508110003		PV
☐ Technicka Academie A-70				S
☐ Technicka Academie XA-66 Aeron	OK-80			S
☐ Vykumny a Zkusebni Letecky Ustav (VZLU) L-208 (TOM-208)			Fuselage only.	P
☐ Vykumny a Zkusebni Letecky Ustav (VZLU) L-8 (TOM-8)			Fuselage only.	PV
☐ Zlin HC-102 Heli Baby	0215		OK-RVL	PV
☐ Zlin Z-126 Trener	OK-HLK	722	At Slatina Airfield.	RAA
☐ Zlin Z-226B Bohatyr	OK-MPR	263		RAC
☐ Zlin VT-425 Sohaj 3	OK-5377			S

VOJENSKÉ MÚZEUM (CZ13)

Address: Demarkacni Lini,
33701 Rokycany.
Tel: 0371-728344
Email: hoblik.m@seznam.cz
Admission: Mid-May – September daily 0900-1700
Location : In the town which is about 12 km east of Plzen on Route 4.

This local military history museum which has a number of vehicles on show has recently acquired its first helicopter. The Mil-24 has been painted in Soviet colours. The collection which includes documents, photographs, uniforms and weapons is run by the local military history club.

TYPE	REG/SER	CON. NO.	PI/NOTES	STATUS
☐ Mil Mi-24D	'33'	340102	0102 – In false Soviet markings.	PVX

ZRUČ AIR PARK (CZ14)

Address: C.15
330 07 Druztova.
Tel: 0377-824560
Admission: Saturday-Sunday 1000-1700.
Location: About 8 km north of Plzen just west of Zruc.

Owned by Karel Taranlik this privately run museum has assembled a large number of aircraft in a short time. An outside park houses most of the collection along with several military vehicles. A nearby store is home to types awaiting restoration. The park is dominated by several versions of the Avia 14, a licence built Ilyushin Il-14. Several duplicate types have been acquired and these are available for exchange. The Aero built Siebel Si 204 is a rarity but unfortunately only the fuselage has been acquired. The owner would like to put on display aircraft not used in the country and several exchanges have recently taken place. Some of the machines were in poor condition when they arrived and the rebuilding of some is underway. The rear fuselage of the KC-97 came from an aircraft which was scrapped in France. In a small building is a display of models, instruments and components. There are long term plans to construct a display hangar so that some of the gliders can be exhibited.

TYPE	REG/SER	CON. NO.	PI/NOTES	STATUS
☐ Aero C-3A [Siebel Si 204D-1]	OK-AYA	313	Fuselage only.	PVD
☐ Aero L-29 Delfin	0101	290101		PV
☐ Aero L-29R Delfin	2810	892810		PV
☐ Aero L-29RS Delfin	2611	792611		PV
☐ Aero L-39ZA Albatros	OK-190	X11	OK-190, OK-HXA	PV
☐ Aero Super 45S	OK-FHH	51170		PVD
☐ Aero Super 45S	OK-KGC	04-017		RA
☐ Antonov An-2R	OK-KIF	1G 186-37		PV

☐ Avia 14FG (14) [Ilyushin Il-14P]				RA
☐ Avia 14FG (14) [Ilyushin Il-14P]	6103	806103		PV
☐ Avia 14MF [Ilyushin Il-14M]	3146	913146		PV
☐ Avia 14P [Ilyushin Il-14P]	3111	703111	3111, OK-LCC	PVD
☐ Avia 14T [Ilyushin Il-14T]	3114	913114		PVD
☐ Avia 14T [Ilyushin Il-14T]	'OK-LCC'	913145	3145 – wings only.	PVX
☐ Avia 14T [Ilyushin Il-14T]	3159	913159		PVD
☐ Bensen B-8 Gyroglider				RA
☐ Boeing 367-76-66 Stratofreighter (KC-97G) (KC-97L)	N49549	17062	53-0280 – rear fuselage only.	PV
☐ Cessna F150F	D-EBIV	F1500047		PV
☐ Dassault Mirage IIIR	304	304		PV
☐ Dassault Super Mystère B2	46	46	May be 83.	PV
☐ Fiat G.91R/3	32+70	91-540	KD+530, EC+112, MD+112	RA
☐ Ilyushin Il-10			Centre section.	PV
☐ Ilyushin Il-12			Front fuselage only.	PV
☐ Ilyushin Il-14S	0507	4340507		PV
☐ Ilyushin Il-18V	OK-PAE	181002902		PV
☐ Ilyushin Il-28			Nose only.	RA
☐ Ilyushin Il-28				RAD
☐ Ilyushin Il-28			Nose only.	RA
☐ Let C-11 [Yakovlev Yak-11]	OK-IIF	170206	Wings only.	PV
☐ Let L-13 Blanik	OK-3700		Front fuselage only.	RA
☐ Let L-200D Morava	SP-NXN	171312	CCCP-02120	PV
☐ Let L-200D Morava	SP-NXB	171410		PVD
☐ Let L-200D Morava	OK-UHB	171419	Front fuselage only.	PV
☐ Let L-410A Turbolet	OK-EKB	740309	OK-EKB, OK-EDB	PV
☐ Let L-410A Turbolet		770003	Fuselage only.	PV
☐ Let L-410MA Turbolet	0502	750502		PV
☐ Let L-410UVP Turbolet	OK-028	810625		PV
☐ Let L-410UVP Turbolet	OK-IYB	X 0102	OK-162	PV
☐ Letov LF-109 Pionyr	OK-4166	0817 (?)		RA
☐ Lockheed 583-04-15 Starfighter (CF-104D)	104648	583A-5318	Tail from c/n 583A-5304 12634, 104634	PV
☐ Lockheed 683-10-19 Starfighter (F-104G)	FX-93	683-9160	In Belgian markings.	PV
☐ Mikoyan-Gurevich MiG-15bis	0551	220551		PV
☐ Mikoyan-Gurevich MiG-15bis	5237	225237		PV
☐ Mikoyan-Gurevich MiG-15bis	3943	713943		PV
☐ Mikoyan-Gurevich MiG-15bis	3945	713945		PV
☐ Mikoyan-Gurevich MiG-15bisSB (MiG-15bis)	3133	713133		PV
☐ Mikoyan-Gurevich MiG-15SB (MiG-15)	'4117'	141142	1142	PVX
☐ Mikoyan-Gurevich MiG-15UTI	2501	722501		PV
☐ Mikoyan-Gurevich MiG-19PM	0918	65210918		PV
☐ Mikoyan-Gurevich MiG-21F-13	1009	161009		PV
☐ Mikoyan-Gurevich MiG-21F-13	0309	560309		PV
☐ Mikoyan-Gurevich MiG-21F-13	0312	560312		PV
☐ Mikoyan-Gurevich MiG-21F-13	0602	760602		PV
☐ Mikoyan-Gurevich MiG-21F-13	0711	760711		PV
☐ Mikoyan-Gurevich MiG-21MA	1207	961207	Composite with parts from MiG-21MF c/n 964307 4307	PV
☐ Mikoyan-Gurevich MiG-21MF	4307	964307	Rear fuselage and wings.	RA
☐ Mikoyan-Gurevich MiG-21MF	5303	965303		PV
☐ Mikoyan-Gurevich MiG-21MF	9409	969409	Front fuselage only.	RA
☐ Mikoyan-Gurevich MiG-21US	0133	01685133		PV
☐ Mikoyan-Gurevich MiG-23BN	9814	0393219814		PV
☐ Mikoyan-Gurevich MiG-23UB	8327	A1038327		PVD
☐ Mil Mi-2	0715	5110715088		PV
☐ Mil Mi-2	B-2743	5310343097	Tailboom and other parts.	PV
☐ Mil Mi-4	2543	12143		PV
☐ Mil Mi-8PS	0815	10815		PV
☐ Mil Mi-8T	OK-YXB	041032	1032 – With boom from c/n 051632 1632, OK-YXC.	PV
☐ Mil Mi-24D	0216	M340216		PV
☐ Panstwowe Zaklady Lotnicze (PZL) M-18A Dromader	OK-SGQ	1Z 017-18		RA
☐ Panstwowe Zaklady Lotnicze (PZL) M-18A Dromader	OK-TGA	1Z 018-10		RA
☐ Sukhoi Su-7BKL	6502	6502		PV
☐ Sukhoi Su-7BKL	6509	6509		PV
☐ Sukhoi Su-7UM	1014	1014		RA
☐ Sukhoi Su-22M4K	3313	33813	Rear fuselage only.	RA
☐ Sukhoi Su-22M4K	3407	34307	Front fuselage only.	PV
☐ Supermarine 300 Spitfire F.I (FSM)	'R6811'			PVX
☐ Supermarine 300 Spitfire F.I (FSM)	'R6813'			PVX
☐ Tupolev Tu-134A	OK-AFA	1351406	Front fuselage only.	PV
☐ Wytwornia Sprzetu Komunikacyjnego (WSK) SM-1W [Mil Mi-1M]	'4943'	W04043	4043	PVX
☐ Wytwornia Sprzetu Komunikacyjnego (WSK) SM-1Wb [Mil Mi-1M]	4033	404033	4033, OK-UVE	PV
☐ Zlin HC-102 Heli Baby	0107	0107		PVD
☐ Zlin Z-37 Cmelak			Fuselage frame only.	PV
☐ Zlin Z-37 Cmelak	OK-VJM	01-05	Parts from c/n 08-23 OK-YKG	PV
☐ Zlin Z-37 Cmelak	OK-WJI	02-10		PV

☐ Zlin Z-37 Cmelak	OK-YKG	08-23	Wings from c/n 01-05 OK-VJM	PV
☐ Zlin Z-37A Cmelak	OK-AJC	13-12		RA
☐ Zlin Z-37A Cmelak	OK-AJE	13-19	HA-MCJ, OK-AJE, HA-MFJ	PV
☐ Zlin Z-37A Cmelak	OK-AKF	13-26		PV
☐ Zlin Z-37A Cmelak	OK-NJA	25-01	Wings only.	RA
☐ Zlin VT-425 Sohaj 3	OK-5439			RA

DENMARK

AALBORG MARINEMUSEUM (DEN1)

Address:	Vestre Fjordvej 8, DK-9000 Aalborg.
Tel:	98 11 78 03
Fax:	98 13 61 86
Admission:	February- April September-December daily 1000-1600; May-August daily 1000-1800.
Location:	In the centre of the city.

Denmark has a long tradition as a maritime nation and displays at this museum trace, the history of the Navy. Models of ships, uniforms, memorabilia, photographs and documents are on view.

TYPE	REG/SER	CON. NO.	PI/NOTES	STATUS
☐ Sud-Est SE.3160 Alouette III	M-070	1070	At Kastrup Airport.	RA

AALHOLM AUTOMOBIL MUSEUM (DEN2)

Address:	Aalholm Parkvej 17, DK-4880 Nysted.
Tel:	54 87 19 11
Fax:	54 87 11 58
Email:	gods@aalholm.dk
Admission:	May September mid-October Saturday-Sunday 1000-1600; June-August daily 1000-1700.
Location:	West of Nysted which is about 15 km south west of Nykobing off Route 283.

Situated in a building in the grounds of the historic castle, the museum has on view over one hundred and fifty vehicles from many countries. The collection was set up by Baron Otto Raben-Levetzau and has its origins in three cars stored by his father in a barn on the estate. There are now many classic types on show together with components, posters and trophies. The Wright biplane is believed to be a replica, containing some original parts, constructed by Jean Salis in France. The museum closed for a time but is now open again.

TYPE	REG/SER	CON. NO.	PI/NOTES	STATUS
☐ Svenska Aeroplan Aktiebolaget (SAAB) 35XD Draken (F-35)	A-007	351007	On loan from FHS.	PV
☐ Wright Flyer (R)				PV

AERONAUTISK AKTIVITETSCENTER (DEN3)

Address:	Køge Landvej, DK-2660 Brøndby Strand.
Tel:	04484-3464
Email:	gren@mail.tele.dk
Admission:	By prior permission only.
Location:	About 20 km south west of Copenhagen.

Avedøre airfield opened in 1917 and has seen both military and civilian use. Many of the early hangars still survive and restoration projects are among the activities taking place. There are regular open days and fly-ins.

TYPE	REG/SER	CON. NO.	PI/NOTES	STATUS
☐ American Aviation AA-1 Yankee	OY-BYK			RAC
☐ Ellehammer 1909 (R)				RAC
☐ Noorduyn Harvard IIB [North American NA-77 (AT-16)]				RAC
☐ Piper PA-18-135 Super Cub (L-21B)	OY-AZZ	18-3165	53-4765, OL-L91 (Belgium), 66-654 (Denmark), Y-654 (Denmark)	RAC
☐ Skandinavisk Aero Industri (SAI) KZ III U-2	OY-DVA	74		RA

BAKS TRAKTOR OG LANDSBRUGMASKINMUSEUM (DEN4)

Address:	Rebslagerveg 1, Solbjerg, DK-7950 Erslev.
Tel:	97 74 10 28
Admission:	Monday-Friday 0800-1800; Saturday-Sunday 0900-1700.
Location:	About 12 km south of Thisted on Route 26.

This museum houses, in one large hall, more than three hundred and fifty tractors, steam traction engines, carriages and stationary motors dating from the end of the nineteenth century. The only aircraft on view is one of two Transavia Airtruks imported into Denmark by Korn og Foderstofkompagniet in 1972/3. In addition to agricultural duties the pair were used to disperse oil slicks around the coast.

TYPE	REG/SER	CON. NO.	PI/NOTES	STATUS
☐ Transavia PL-12 Airtruk	OY-DRL	1135		PV

DANMARKS TEKNISKE MUSEUM – DANMARKS FLYVEMUSEUM (DEN5)

Address:	Fabriksvej 25, DK-3000 Helsingør.
Tel:	49 22 26 11
Fax:	49 22 66 11
Email:	bbp@flymuseet.DK
Admission:	Tuesday-Sunday 1000-1700.
Location:	In the town which is about 40 km north of Copenhagen.

The museum had two sites in the historic town but the last few years have seen many changes. At the main site displays of engineering, manufacturing and scientific equipment were on show. The traffic section housing vehicles and associated equipment was located on the other side of the town. A former foundry building was acquired and this opened in 2000 as the Ellehammer Aviation Museum. Now the whole collection has moved here and five large halls are in use. An important section is devoted to the pioneer aviator J.C.H. Ellehammer. He made a tethered flight on September 12th 1906 on the island of Lindholm. Several of his aircraft are on view including the historic machine. A monoplane from 1909 can be seen along with a one-third scale test model of his 1912 helicopter. Ellehammer's engines were ahead of their time but his lack of knowledge of aerodynamics hindered progress. The Glenten, built in 1910/11 by Robert Svendson, was the first aircraft operated by the Danish Navy. Also on show is a replica hull of the 'Maagen 3' fitted with the original wings of the 'Maagen 2'. The museum plans to rebuild the 'Maagen 2' and complete the replica of the '3'. The Blohm und Voss Bv 138 flying boat was located on the seabed just off the coast. The airframe is in reasonable condition considering that it has spent over fifty years under water. The museum raised the wreck and it is the only example of the type that can be seen. The Seremet collection consists of gyrogliders, autogyros, powered parachutes and a number of other man lifting devices. The Danmarks Flyvemuseum acquired a large collection over the years and from 1989 to 1997 many of the aircraft were exhibited in a purpose built complex at Billund. When this was lost they decided to join with the Technical Museum.

TYPE	REG/SER	CON. NO.	PI/NOTES	STATUS
☐ Aero Commander 560E	OY-ADS	612-40		RA
☐ Blohm und Voss Bv 138C-1	NJ+HE	310050	Raised from sea.	PVD
☐ BUF-1	9-35			PV
☐ Canadair CL-90 Starfighter (CF-104) [Lockheed 683-04-12]	R-896	683A-1196	12896 (Canada), 104896 (Canada) – on loan from FHS.	PV
☐ Cessna T.337D Super Skymaster	OY-CBB	1000		PVC
☐ Consolidated 28-6A Catalina (PBY-6A)	L-861	2105	Bu64035, 82-861 – on loan from FHS.	PV
☐ De Havilland D.H.82A Tiger Moth	'S-16'	82869	R4961, G-APJP, SE-GXO	PVX
☐ De Havilland D.H.89A Dragon Rapide (D.H.89B Dominie I)	OY-AAO	6775	NR676, G-AIWY	PV
☐ De Havilland D.H.104 Dove 6	OY-DHZ	04476	G-AOUF, D-IBYW – on loan to DVS.	–
☐ Donnet-Lévêque 'Maagen 2'				PV
☐ Donnet-Lévêque 'Maagen 3'			With parts from 'Maagen 2'	RAC
☐ Douglas DC-3A-456 Skytrain (C-47A)	'OY-DDA'	9664	42-23802, LN-IAP, 68-681, K-681 – on loan from FHS.	PV
☐ Douglas DC-7C	OY-KNB	44929	Front fuselage only.	PV
☐ Douglas DC-7C	OY-KND	45221	Front fuselage only.	RA
☐ Douglas DC-8			Front fuselage only.	PV
☐ Douglas DC-9			Front fuselage only.	RA
☐ Ellehammer 1906				PVC
☐ Ellehammer 1906 (FSM)				PV
☐ Ellehammer Standard Monoplane 1909				PV
☐ Ellehammer Helikopter 1911			Scale experimental model	PV
☐ Ellehammer Helikopter 1912				RAC
☐ Fairchild 24R9 Forwarder (UC-61K) (Argus III)	OY-EAZ	R9-962	43-14998, HB724, SE-BCG, OH-FCC, SE-CPA	RA
☐ Fairchild M-62A-4 Cornell (PT-26) (Cornell I)	'179'	T43-4640	44-19528, EW581, 253, L-DI (Norway), LN-BIF – in Norwegian markings.	PVX
☐ Fibera KK-1e Utu	OY-XCJ	15	OH-LKC, OH-349	RA
☐ Focke-Achgelis Fa 330A-1 Bachstelze	100032	100032	On loan to Egeskov VM.	–
☐ Fokker D.XXI	J-49.		Fuselage frame only – on loan from Tojhusmuseet.	RAD
☐ Friedrichshafen FF.49C (FSM)	'T-DABA'			PVCX
☐ General Aircraft Monospar ST-25	OY-DAZ	95	G-AEYF – on loan to Egeskov VM.	–

☐ Gloster Meteor F.4	43-461	G5/294		PV
☐ Grob G.102 Astir CS			Cockpit section only.	RA
☐ Hawker P.1067 Hunter F.51	E-401	41H/680260	47-401 – on loan from FHS.	PV
☐ Hogslund/Traugott-Olsen 2G	OY-100		OY-ATX	PV
☐ Hütter H 17A (D.F.S. 108-67)	OY-61	186	D-10-824, OY-61, OY-AXM – on loan to Egeskov VM.	–
☐ Larsen Glider				PV
☐ Lockheed 580 (T-33A)	DT-491	580-5786	51-4491 – on loan from FHS.	PV
☐ Lockheed 580 (T-33A)	DT-923	580-6707	51-8923 – On loan from FHS.	PV
☐ Mølhede-Petersen XMP-2				RA
☐ Miles M.65 Gemini 1A	G-AKDK	6469		RA
☐ Nielsen & Winther Aa (R)			On loan from DVS.	PV
☐ Percival P.34A Proctor III	OY-ACP	H.274	HM364, 62-605	PV
☐ Percival P.66 President	OY-AVA	P.66/79	G-AOJG, 69-697, M-697	RA
☐ Polliwagen	OY-CYS	8607-1794N		PV
☐ Polyteknisk Polyt II	OY-55	PFG2	OY-55, OY-AFX	PV
☐ Republic F-84G Thunderjet	'A-777'		51-10777, K-126 (Netherlands) – on loan from FHS.	PVX
☐ Ridinger Balloon			Basket only.	PV
☐ Riley 65 (Cessna 310)	OY-DRH	35407	N5207A, G-ASSZ	RA
☐ Rotec Rally 2B				RA
☐ Schneider ESG 31 Grunau Baby IIB (D.F.S. 108-49)	OY-ABX		OY-87	PV
☐ Schneider Grunau SG-38 (D.F.S. 108-14)	OY-86		On show at Danish Transport Centre Service Area, Vejle.	PV
☐ Seremet WS-1 Helicopter				PV
☐ Seremet WS-2 Gyroglider				PV
☐ Seremet WS-3 Hang Glider				PV
☐ Seremet WS-5 Powered Parachute				PV
☐ Seremet WS-9 Autogyro				PV
☐ Seremet WS-14 Liftbaelte				PV
☐ Seremet WS-15 Mini Helicopter				PV
☐ Seremet WS-19X Autogyro				PV
☐ Seremet WS-21 Powered Parachute				PV
☐ Seremet WS-24 Autogyro				PV
☐ Seremet WS-25 Powered Parachute				PV
☐ Seremet WS-29 Jet Strap-on Wing				PV
☐ Sikorsky S-55C	S-883	551031	88-883 – on loan from FHS.	PV
☐ Skandinavisk Aero Industri (SAI) KZ II Sport	OY-DOU	13	OY-DOU, SE-ANM – on loan to DVS.	–
☐ Skandinavisk Aero Industri (SAI) KZ II Træner	11-113	121	Fuselage frame only.	PV
☐ Skandinavisk Aero Industri (SAI) KZ III	SE-ANY	45		PV
☐ Skandinavisk Aero Industri (SAI) KZ III U	61-661	50	50, 62-611, OY-ACT	RA
☐ Skandinavisk Aero Industri (SAI) KZ IV	OY-DZU	70	OY-DZU, (SE-EGX)	PV
☐ Sud-Est SE.210 Caravelle III			Front fuselage only.	RA
☐ Sud-Est SE.210 Caravelle III	OY-KRD	47		PV
☐ Svendsen Glenten			Copy of Henri Farman	RA
☐ Svenska Aeroplan Aktiebolaget (SAAB) L-17A (B 17A)	Fv17320	17320	Fv17320, SE-BWC	PV
☐ Svenska Aeroplan Aktiebolaget (SAAB) 29F (29B) (J 29B) (J 29F)	Fv29487	29487		RA
☐ Svenska Aeroplan Aktiebolaget (SAAB) 35XD Draken (F-35)	A-001	351001	On loan from FHS.	PV
☐ Szybowcowy Zaklad Doswiadczalny S.Z.D.25A Lis	OY-FOX	765		RA

DANSK SVÆVEFLYHISTORISK KLUB (DEN6)

Address:	Seglen 69, DK-8800 Viborg.
Tel:	86 67 60 68
Admission:	By prior permission only.
Location:	At a number of airfields and at a workshop at Billund Airport which is about 30 km west of Vejle on Route 28.

This thriving club has an active membership devoted to returning historic gliders to airworthy condition. A workshop was set up at Billund Airport in 2000 after the group was forced to vacate the large storage hangar once used by the Danmarks Flyvemuseum. Funds are being raised to construct a hangar so that the fleet can be displayed fully rigged. The sailplanes are regularly flown and attend meetings throughout Europe. Members of the group own several more types and many of these are active.

TYPE	REG/SER	CON. NO.	PI/NOTES	STATUS
☐ Akaflieg München Mü 13d	OY-MUX	108		RA
☐ Elliott AP.5 EoN Olympia 2	OY-XEF	EoN/059	Z-962, OY-BKX, Z-962	RAA
☐ Hogslund/Traugott-Olsen 2G	OY-AVX	DA-7	OY-121	RAA
☐ Hütter H 17A (D.F.S. 108-67)	OY-CJX	CJ-1		RAA
☐ Jacobs Kranich IIB (D.F.S. 108-30) (SE 103)	OY-KRX	077	Fv8216, SE-SPK	RA
☐ Scheibe 138 Specht	OY-VEX	401		RAA
☐ Scheibe Bergfalke II	OY-BXN	102	D-9338, D-5394	RA
☐ Scheibe Bergfalke II	OY-MLX	185	D-3209, D-3655	RA

☐ Scheibe L-Spatz 55	OY-AXV	525		RA
☐ Scheibe L-Spatz 55	OY-AXR	526		RA
☐ Scheibe L-Spatz 55	OY-XED	794	D-1530	RAA
☐ Scheibe SF-26A Standard	OY-BJX	5022		RA
☐ Schleicher Ka-4 Rhönlerche II				RA
☐ Schleicher Ka-4 Rhönlerche II	OY-DNX	139	D-4340	RA
☐ Schleicher Ka-6CR Rhönsegler	OY-DJX	6177		RA
☐ Schleicher K.7	OY-XFC	476	Z-982	RA
☐ Schleicher K.8B	OY-AYX	1104		RAA
☐ Schleicher K.8B	OY-BXV	8		RA
☐ Schneider ESG 31 Grunau Baby IIB	OY-AXO	3	OY-93	RAA
☐ Schneider ESG 31 Grunau Baby IIB	Z-943	PFG-07		RAC
☐ Schneider Grunau SG-38 (D.F.S. 108-14)	OY-BFX			RA
☐ Stamer-Lippisch Z-12 Zögling	OY-XSE	01-92		RAA
☐ Szybowcowy Zaklad Doswiadczalny S.Z.D.8 Jaskolka	OY-XCN	248		RA
☐ Szybowcowy Zaklad Doswiadczalny S.Z.D.9bis Bocian 1D	OY-DSX	F-861		RA
☐ Szybowcowy Zaklad Doswiadczalny S.Z.D.22B Mucha Standard	OY-XAI	F-512		RAA
☐ Szybowcowy Zaklad Doswiadczalny S.Z.D.25A Lis	OY-DXX	F-757		RA
☐ Szybowcowy Zaklad Doswiadczalny S.Z.D.30 Pirat	OY-DXL	W-323		RA

DANSK VETERANFLYSAMLING (DEN7)

Address:	Stauning Lufthavn, DK-6900 Skjern.
Tel:	97 36 93 33
Admission:	May-October daily 1100-1700.
Location:	Stauning Airport is on Route 181 between Ringkoping and Skjern about 60 km north of Esbjerg.

In April 1975 members of the K.Z. Veteranflyklubben decided to set up a museum. The aim was to establish a collection of airworthy aircraft along with workshops for restorers and homebuilders. A site on the approach road to the terminal building at Stauning Airport was acquired and construction of a hangar soon started. The museum opened in 1977 and a second hall devoted to the designs of Kramme and Zeuthen was dedicated on April 20th 1990. This unique display contains examples of all the eleven types built by Skandinavisk Aero Industri between 1937 and 1958. A replica of their first design the K.Z. I was started in Odense in the 1970s and completed at Stauning. The original K.Z. I made its first flight in February 1937. Powered by a 38 hp. A.B.C. Scorpion engine the aircraft disappeared during World War II. The three versions of the KZ II can be seen including the sole surviving Sport model, which is on loan from the Danmarks Flyvemuseum. Two examples of the Kupe remain in Denmark and another is stored in Switzerland. One G I primary glider was constructed in 1943 and the type did not enter production. One K.Z. III is exhibited in ambulance configuration and one of the two K.Z. IVs built is in similar colours. The one on show was the first built and flew in May 1944. The second, now at Helsingor, was not ready until 1949. The twin engined IV crashed at Stauning in 1979 and the rebuild took more than a decade. Only two K.Z. VIII aerobatic monoplanes were built. The first flew in 1949 and the second was assembled in 1961 in Germany. Twelve KZ Xs were ordered by the Danish Army in the early 1950s. The prototype flew in September 1951 but a series of crashes caused the type to be grounded. The example on show was fitted with enlarged wings and tail surfaces and is the sole survivor of the type. The Ellehammer replica first flew in February 1950. Powered by a Cirrus Hermes m engine this aircraft was used by a 'Flying Circus'. An exhibition tracing the history of the company has been set up with many photographs and models on view. In addition a range of modern military types is being added to the exhibition. Work has started on a new hangar which will house the military aircraft and thus enable the majority of the collection to be placed under cover.

TYPE	REG/SER	CON. NO.	PI/NOTES	STATUS
☐ Auster J/1 Autocrat	OY-???	124	G-AFWN, D-EKOM	PVC
☐ Avro 504N	110	50	On loan from Tojhusmuseet.	PV
☐ Berg and Storm BS.III			On loan from Tojhusmuseet.	PV
☐ Bücker Bü 181B-1 Bestmann (Sk 25)	OY-AVZ	25073	Fv25073, D-ELET	PVA
☐ Canadair CL-90 Starfighter (CF-104) [Lockheed 683-04-12]	R-888	683A-1188	12888 (Canada), 104888 (Canada) – on loan from FHS.	RA
☐ De Havilland D.H.82A Tiger Moth	OY-ECH	85234	DE164, G-ANCY, OO-DLA	PVA
☐ De Havilland D.H.82A Tiger Moth	OY-DVP	85506	DE526, D-EDIS, N38013	PVC
☐ De Havilland D.H.87B Hornet Moth	OY-DEZ	8040	VR-RAI, OY-DEZ, SE-ALD, G-AMZO	PVA
☐ De Havilland D.H.104 Dove 6	OY-DHZ	04476	G-AOUF, D-IBYW – on loan from DF.	PVC
☐ De Havilland D.H.C.1 Chipmunk 21	OY-DHJ	C1/0470	G-AMMA	RAC
☐ De Havilland D.H.C.1 Chipmunk 22 (T.20)	OY-FLV	C1/0878	12-143, P-143 (Denmark)	PVA
☐ De Havilland D.H.C.1 Chipmunk 22 (T.20)	OY-ALD	C1/0902	12-147 (Denmark), P-147 (Denmark)	PVA
☐ Douglas DC-3A-456 Skytrain (C-47A)	K-687	19200	42-100737, 100737 (Norway), 68-687 – on loan from FHS.	PVC
☐ Druine D.31 Turbulent	OY-AMG	278		PVA
☐ Ellehammer 1906 (FSM)				PVC
☐ Fairchild 24W41A Forwarder (C-61A) (UC-61A) (Argus II)	D-EDAV	W41A-464	43-14500, FS583, HB-EAS	RA
☐ Fairchild 24W41A Forwarder (C-61A) (UC-61A) (Argus II)	OY-ANO	W41A-834	43-14870, HB597, HB-EAK, D-EHIB	RAC
☐ Fairey Firefly TT.1 (F.1)	SE-CAW	F6121	PP392	RAC

Type	Reg.	c/n	Other info	Status
☐ Fokker D.XXI	J-49		Fuselage frame only – on loan from Tojhusmuseet.	RAD
☐ Gloster Meteor F.4	B-499		43-499	PV
☐ Hawker Dankok	158	OV54	On loan from Tojhusmuseet.	PV
☐ Hogslund/Traugott-Olsen 2G	OY-ARX		OY-119	RA
☐ Hogslund/Traugott-Olsen 2G	OY-BLX	5		PV
☐ Hollænder H.T.1 (Hollschmidt 222)	OY-FAI	1		PV
☐ Hughes 500M	H-245	24-0245M		RA
☐ Lockheed 580 (T-33A)	DT-884	580-6668	51-8884 – on loan from FHS.	RA
☐ Luton L.A.4 Minor		1124	Possibly c/n PAL-1124 G-ASCY, EI-ATP	RAC
☐ Mignet HM-14 Pou-du-Ciel				PV
☐ Nielsen & Winther Aa (R)			On loan to DTM.	–
☐ Noorduyn Harvard IIB [North American NA-77 (AT-16)]	Fv16126	14-426	42-889, FE692	RAC
☐ Noorduyn Harvard IIB [North American NA-77 (AT-16)]	OY-IIB	14A-966	43-12667,FS826,31-309	PVA
☐ Piper J-3C-65 Cub (L-4J)	OY-ALF	12591	44-80295, HB-OBR, D-EGAR	PVA
☐ Piper J-3F-50 Cub	OY-ABT	2475		PVA
☐ Piper J-4A Cub Coupe	OY-AVH	4-449	NC22765, N22765, D-EBYP	RAC
☐ Piper PA-16 Clipper	OY-AKM	16-101	HB-OOE, N9979F, D-EKUW	PVA
☐ Piper PA-25-150 Pawnee				RAC
☐ Raab Doppelraab IV	OY-XIT	03	D-6351	PV
☐ Rearwin 9000L Sportster	OY-AVJ	567D	SE-AGB	PVC
☐ Republic F-84G Thunderjet	A-047		52-3047 – front fuselage only.	RA
☐ Republic F-84G Thunderjet	A-057		52-3057 – on loan from FHS.	PV
☐ Republic F-84G Thunderjet	A-515		51-10515 – front fuselage only – on loan from FHS.	PV
☐ Scheibe Mü 13E Bergfalke I	OY-REX	102	D-0002, D-0040	PV
☐ Scheibe Bergfalke II	OY-AXS	01		PV
☐ Scheibe Spatz B	OY-AXU	524		PV
☐ Schneider ESG 31 Grunau Baby IIB	OY-AUX	PFG 8		PV
☐ Schneider Grunau SG-38 (D.F.S. 108-14)	OY-AKX		OY-94	PV
☐ Sikorsky S-55C	S-884	551032	88-884 (Denmark) – on loan from FHS.	PVC
☐ Sikorsky S-61A-1	U-240	61240		PVC
☐ Skandinavisk Aero Industri (SAI) KZ Ellehammer (R)	OY-ACE	204		PV
☐ Skandinavisk Aero Industri (SAI) KZ GI	OY-ASX	44	OY-54	PV
☐ Skandinavisk Aero Industri (SAI) KZ I (R)	OY-KZI		(OY-CMZ)	PVC
☐ Skandinavisk Aero Industri (SAI) KZ II Kupe	OY-AEA	27	(OY-DUY), SE-ANR, OH-SPJ, OH-KZT	PVA
☐ Skandinavisk Aero Industri (SAI) KZ II Sport	OY-DOU	13	OY-DOU, SE-ANM – on loan from D.F.	PV
☐ Skandinavisk Aero Industri (SAI) KZ II Træner	OY-FAK	115	115, 11-107	PVA
☐ Skandinavisk Aero Industri (SAI) KZ II Træner	OY-FAE	119	119, 11-111 – fuselage from c/n 113 113, 11-105.	RA
☐ Skandinavisk Aero Industri (SAI) KZ III U-3	OY-DZA	66		PVA
☐ Skandinavisk Aero Industri (SAI) KZ IV	OY-DIZ	43		PVA
☐ Skandinavisk Aero Industri (SAI) KZ VII U-4	OY-AAU	158		PVA
☐ Skandinavisk Aero Industri (SAI) KZ VII U-4	O-622	184	63-622 – on loan from FHS.	PV
☐ Skandinavisk Aero Industri (SAI) KZ VIII	OY-DRR	203	D-EBIZ	PVA
☐ Skandinavisk Aero Industri (SAI) KZ X	OY-AOL	205	OY-ACL	PVA
☐ Stampe & Vertongen S.V.4B	OY-DBC	1204	V-62	PVA
☐ Supermarine 361 Spitfire HF.IXc	'41-401'		MA298, 6462M – on loan from Tojhusmuseet.	PVX
☐ Svenska Aeroplan Aktiebolaget (SAAB) 35XD Draken (F-35)	A-009	351009	On loan from FHS.	PV
☐ Svenska Aeroplan Aktiebolaget (SAAB) 35XD Draken (RF-35)	AR-118	351118		PV
☐ Taylorcraft Plus D (Auster 1)	LB381	228	LB381, G-AHKO, D-ECOD, OY-DSH	PVC
☐ Transavia PL-12 Airtruk	OY-DVZ	1238	VH-ETZ	PVA
☐ Wendell Aircraft Production WAP.201	9-230	2		RA

EGESKOV VETERANMUSEUM (DEN8)

Address:	DK-5772 Kværndrup.
Tel:	09 27 10 16
Admission:	May-mid June Daily 1000-1700; mid-June-September Daily 0900-1800; October-April Saturday-Sunday 1000-1730.
Location:	About 2 km west of the town off Route 44 to Faborg.

The sixteenth century castle at Egeskov has been a tourist attraction for many years and the site is steadily being developed. The rooms of the castle contain many interesting period exhibits and the grounds are attractively laid out. The Veteranmuseum opened in 1967 in a large outbuilding and now the farm machinery, carriages and motor cycles have been moved to an adjoining structure whilst the main hall concentrates on aviation and motoring. The Danmarks Flyvemuseum has loaned aircraft to Egeskov over the years and their superbly restored Monospar was moved from Billund in the late 1990s. Only two examples of the type remain in existence. The one on show was built in 1937 and arrived in Denmark in 1939. Zone-Redningskorpset operated it in the ambulance role until the mid-1960s. The work of J.C.H. Ellehammer is highlighted.

TYPE	REG/SER	CON.NO	PI/NOTES	STATUS
☐ Brodersen Monoplane				RA
☐ Canadair CL-90 Starfighter (CF-104) [Lockheed 683-04-12]			Front fuselage only.	PV
☐ Canadair CL-90 Starfighter (CF-104) [Lockheed 683-04-12]	R-814	683A-1114	12814 (Canada), 104814 (Canada) – on loan from FHS.	PV
☐ De Havilland D.H.82A Tiger Moth	NL913	86356	NL913, G-AOFR, SE-COX, OY-BAK, 'S-11'	PV
☐ De Havilland D.H.C.1 Chipmunk T.20	P-127	C1/0106	12-127 – on loan from FHS.	PV
☐ Focke-Achgelis Fa 330A-1 Bachstelze	100032	100032	On loan from DTM.	PV
☐ General Aircraft Monospar ST-25	OY-DAZ	95	G-AEYF – on loan from DTM.	PV
☐ Hawker P.1067 Hunter F.51	E-426	41H/680285	47-426 – front fuselage – only – on loan from FHS.	PV
☐ Hütter H 17A (D.F.S. 108-67)	OY-61	186	D-10-824, OY-61, OY-AXH – on loan from DTM.	PV
☐ Mignet HM-14 Pou-du-Ciel (R)				PV
☐ Noorduyn Harvard IIB [North American NA-77	31-324	14A-1420 (AT-16)]	43-13121, FT380	PV
☐ Republic F-84G Thunderjet	A-792		51-9792 – with tail from 51-10094 – on loan from FHS.	RA
☐ Robertson B1-RD	9-27			RA
☐ Sud-Est SE.3160 Alouette III	M-388	1388	On loan from FHS.	PV
☐ Svenska Aeroplan Aktiebolaget (SAAB) 35XD Draken (F-35)	A-012	351012	On loan from FHS.	PV

EGNSMUSEET I VANDEL (DEN9)

Address:	Grindstedvej 30, DK-7184 Vandel.
Tel:	75 88 54 89
Admission:	May-October Monday-Friday 1300-1500 Saturday 1400-1600 ; November-April Monday-Friday 1300-1500.
Location:	About 8 km east of Billund on Route 28.

Established in 1981 this small local history museum displays a range of country crafts. There are many interesting items to be found in the well thought out displays. Vandel airfield was built during the German occupation of Denmark and after the end of World War II was used by the Danish Air Force.

TYPE	REG/SER	CON. NO.	PI/NOTES	STATUS
☐ Republic F-84G Thunderjet	A-708		51-10708, FZ-120 (Belgium) – on loan from FHS.	PV

FLYVESTATION KARUP'S HISTORISKE FORENING MUSEET (DEN10)

Address:	Gedhusvagten, Herningvej, DK-7470 Karup J.
Tel:	97 10 15 50 ext 2560
Admission:	First Thursday in month 1530-1800 – and every Wednesday 1300-1630 or by prior permission.
Location:	By the secondary gate to the base which is about 16 km south west of Viborg on Route 12.

Karup was constructed for use by the Luftwaffe during the German occupation of Denmark. After a short period in Royal Air Force control it was given to the Danish military authorities in 1947. Until recently it was home to fighter units but now the main flying training school has its home at the field. A small museum tracing the history of the airfield and the squadrons which have served there has been set up in a former guardhouse at the secondary base gate. The display opened in December 1981 with photographs, documents, uniforms, components and items of memorabilia on show. There are also pieces recovered from crash sites and some engines. At the rear of the building is a park where examples of types which have served at Karup can be seen.

TYPE	REG/SER	CON. NO.	PI/NOTES	STATUS
☐ Lockheed 580 (T-33A)	DT-905	580-6689	51-8905 – on loan from FHS.	PV
☐ North American NA-243 Super Sabre (F-100F) (TF-100F)	GT-949	243-225	56-3949 – on loan from FHS.	PV
☐ Republic RF-84F Thunderflash	C-274		51-11274 – on loan from FHS.	PV
☐ Republic F-84G Thunderjet	A-665		51-16665 – tail from 51-10477, A-477 – on loan from FHS.	PV
☐ Skandinavisk Aero Industri (SAI) KZ VII U-4	O-620	182	63-620, O-620, OY-ATK – on loan from FHS.	PV
☐ Svenska Aeroplan Aktiebolaget (SAAB) 35XD Draken (F-35)	A-014	351014	On loan from FHS.	PV
☐ Svenska Aeroplan Aktiebolaget (SAAB) 35XD Draken (RF-35)	AR-112	351112	On base gate.	PV

The superb car museum at Aalholm houses this Wright Flyer.

A view of the main hall of the Military Museum at Aalborg. (GM)

Only two General Aircraft Monospars survive and this example is displayed in the Veteranmuseum at Egeskov.

FLYVEVABNETS HISTORISKE SAMLING (DEN11)

Address:	Flyvertaktisk Kommando, Gedhus, DK-7470 Karup.
Tel:	97 10 15 50 ext 6004.
Email:	flyhis@mail.dk
Admission:	By prior permission only.
Location:	Aalborg airfield is about 7 km north west of the town on Route 1. Karup is about 16 km south west of Viborg on Route 12. Skrydstrup airfield is about 15 km west of Haderslev.

Military flying started in Denmark in 1911 and over the next three decades a variety of types were flown. Unfortunately very few aircraft from this period survived as almost all were lost when the Germans took over the country. In recent years the Danish Air Force has collected many airframes and several have been restored at bases throughout the country. Included in the inventory are gate guardians, instructional airframes and aircraft held by flying units. A range of British and American combat types has been saved. Aircraft have been loaned to museums in Denmark and abroad as well as to private companies and many are stored for future transactions. The Danish Air Force ordered twenty Meteor F.4s in the late 1940s and these served at Karup and Aalborg until 1957. Nine T.7s arrived in the early 1950s and twenty F.8s were delivered at the same time. Also arriving from the Armstrong Whitworth factory at Coventry were twenty NF.11s. and six of these were converted into TT.20s. One example of each version has been saved. Six PBY-5A Catalinas were delivered in the late 1940s and early 1950s. These were supplemented in the late 1950s by eight PBY-6As. Normally based at Værlose a number were always on detachment at Narssarssuak in Greenland. Also based at Værlose was a unit flying the Sikorsky S-55C. Five of the seven were sold in England and two retained for preservation. Twenty seven Chipmunks were used for primary training and communications duties. The type was in use from 1950 until 1976. Most bases had gliding clubs and a locally designed Polyt III has been saved. As types are withdrawn from use several will be allocated to the collection and displayed around the country.

TYPE	REG/SER	CON. NO.	PI/NOTES	STATUS
☐ Canadair CL-90 Starfighter (CF-104) [Lockheed 683-04-12]	R-704	683A-1004	12704 (Canada), 104704 (Canada)	RA
☐ Canadair CL-90 Starfighter (CF-104) [Lockheed 683-04-12]	R-757	683A-1057	12757 (Canada), 104757 (Canada)	RA
☐ Canadair CL-90 Starfighter (CF-104) [Lockheed 683-04-12]	R-771	683A-1071	12771 (Canada), 104771 (Canada) – at Aalborg.	RA
☐ Canadair CL-90 Starfighter (CF-104) [Lockheed 683-04-12]	R-812	683A-1112	12812 (Canada), 104812 (Canada)	RA
☐ Canadair CL-90 Starfighter (CF-104) [Lockheed 683-04-12]	R-814	683A-1114	12814 (Canada), 104814 (Canada) – on loan to Egeskov VM.	–
☐ Canadair CL-90 Starfighter (CF-104) [Lockheed 683-04-12]	R-825	683A-1125	12825 (Canada), 104825 (Canada) – at Aalborg.	RA
☐ Canadair CL-90 Starfighter (CF-104) [Lockheed 683-04-12]	R-832	683A-1132	12832 (Canada), 104832 (Canada) – at Aalborg.	RA
☐ Canadair CL-90 Starfighter (CF-104) [Lockheed 683-04-12]	R-846	683A-1146	12846 (Canada) 104846 (Canada)	RA
☐ Canadair CL-90 Starfighter (CF-104) [Lockheed 683-04-12]	R-851	683A-1151	12851 (Canada), 104851 (Canada) – on loan to Garnisons Museum.	–
☐ Canadair CL-90 Starfighter (CF-104) [Lockheed 683-04-12]	R-855	683A-1155	12855 (Canada), 104855 (Canada) – at Aalborg.	RA
☐ Canadair CL-90 Starfighter (CF-104) [Lockheed 683-04-12]	R-888	683A-1188	12888 (Canada), 104888 (Canada) – on loan to DVS.	–
☐ Canadair CL-90 Starfighter (CF-104) [Lockheed 683-04-12]	R-896	683A-1196	12896 (Canada), 104896 (Canada) – on loan to DTM.	–
☐ Consolidated 28-6A Catalina (PBY-6A)	L-861	2105	Bu64035, 82-861 – on loan to DTM.	–
☐ De Havilland D.H.C.1 Chipmunk T.20	P-127	C1/0106	12-127 – on loan to Egeskov VM.	–
☐ Douglas DC-3A-456 Skytrain (C-47A)	K-687	19200	42-100737, 100737 (Norway,) 68-687 – on loan to DVS.	–
☐ Douglas DC-3A-456 Skytrain (C-47A)	'OY-DDA'	9664	42-23802, LN-IAP, 68-681, K-681 – on loan to DTM	–
☐ Gloster Meteor F.4	43-469	G5/302	At Aalborg.	–
☐ Gloster Meteor T.7	BT-265	G5/354	22-265 – at Aalborg.	RA
☐ Gloster Meteor F.8	44-491	G5/365	On loan to Karup HM.	–
☐ Gloster Meteor NF.11 (NF.11) (TT.20)	51-504	5545	(WM387) – on loan to Garnisons Museum	–
☐ Hawker P.1067 Hunter F.51	E-401	41H/680260	47-401 – on loan to DTM.	–
☐ Hawker P.1067 Hunter F.51	E-426	41H/680285	47-426 – front fuselage only – on loan to Egeskov VM.	–
☐ Lockheed 580 (T-33A)	DT-491	580-5786	51-4491 – on loan to DTM.	–
☐ Lockheed 580 (T-33A)	DT-497	580-5829	51-6497	RA
☐ Lockheed 580 (T-33A)	DT-847	580-6179	51-6847	RA
☐ Lockheed 580 (T-33A)	DT-884	580-6668	51-8884 – on loan to DVS.	–
☐ Lockheed 580 (T-33A)	DT-905	580-6689	51-8905 – on loan to Karup HM.	–
☐ Lockheed 580 (T-33A)	DT-923	580-6707	51-8923 – on loan to DTM.	–
☐ Lockheed 580 (T-33A)	DT-102	580-6886	51-9102	RA
☐ Lockheed 580 (T-33A)	DT-289	580-7073	51-9289 – on loan to Garnisons Museum.	–

☐ Lockheed 583-04-15 Starfighter (CF-104D)	RT-655	583A-5325	12655 (Canada), 104655 (Canada)	RA
☐ Lockheed 583-04-15 Starfighter (CF-104D)	RT-657	583A-5327	12657 (Canada), 104657 (Canada) – at Aalborg.	RA
☐ Lockheed 583-04-15 Starfighter (CF-104D)	RT-664	583A-5334	12664 (Canada), 104664 (Canada) – at Aalborg.	RA
☐ Lockheed 583-04-15 Starfighter (CF-104D)	RT-667	583A-5337	12667 (Canada), 104667 (Canada)	RA
☐ Noorduyn Harvard IIB [North American NA-77 (AT-16)]	31-306	14-748	42-12501, FH114	–
☐ North American NA-173 Sabre (F-86D)	F-028	173-172	51-6028 – at Aalborg.	RA
☐ North American NA-173 Sabre (F-86D)	F-421	173-554	51-8421 – on loan to Garnisons Museum.	–
☐ North American NA-243 Super Sabre (F-100F) (TF-100F)	GT-870	243-146	56-3870 – at Skrydstrup.	RA
☐ North American NA-243 Super Sabre (F-100F) (TF-100F)	GT-908	243-184	56-3908 – on loan to DAVS.	RA
☐ North American NA-243 Super Sabre (F-100F) (TF-100F)	GT-927	243-203	56-3927	–
☐ North American NA-243 Super Sabre (F-100F) (TF-100F)	GT-949	243-225	56-3949 – on loan to Karup HM.	–
☐ North American NA-243 Super Sabre (F-100F) (TF-100F)	GT-961	243-237	56-3961	RA
☐ Polyteknisk Polyt III	OY-XFA	1	Z-931, 92-931 – on loan to Garnisons Museum.	–
☐ Republic RF-84F Thunderflash	C-264		52-7264 – at Karup.	RA
☐ Republic RF-84F Thunderflash	C-274		51-11274 – on loan to Karup HM.	–
☐ Republic RF-84F Thunderflash	C-054		51-17054 – at Karup.	RA
☐ Republic RF-84F Thunderflash	C-581		53-7581	RA
☐ Republic F-84G Thunderjet	A-996		51-9996 – on loan to Garnisons Museum	RA
☐ Republic F-84G Thunderjet	51-9978		51-9978, K-50 (Netherlands) – front fuselage at Tojhusmuseet.	RA
☐ Republic F-84G Thunderjet	A-803		51-9803 – at Torp airfield in Norway.	RA
☐ Republic F-84G Thunderjet	A-515		51-10515 – front fuselage only – on loan to DVS.	–
☐ Republic F-84G Thunderjet	110603		51-10603, A-603 – at Skrydstrup	RA
☐ Republic F-84G Thunderjet	A-708		51-10708, FZ-120 (Belgium) – on loan to Egnsmuseet.	–
☐ Republic F-84G Thunderjet	'A-777'		51-10777, K-126 (Netherlands) – on loan to DTM.	–
☐ Republic F-84G Thunderjet	A-665		51-16665 – tail from 51-10477, A-477 – on loan to Karup HM.	–
☐ Republic F-84G Thunderjet	A-057		52-3057 – on loan to DVS.	–
☐ Sikorsky S-55C	S-883	551031	88-883 – on loan to DTM.	–
☐ Sikorsky S-55C	S-884	551032	88-884 (Denmark) – on loan to DVS.	–
☐ Skandinavisk Aero Industri (SAI) KZ VII U-4	O-620	182	63-620, O-620, OY-ATK – on loan to Karup HM.	–
☐ Sud-Est SE.3160 Alouette III	M-388	1388	On loan to Egeskov VM.	–
☐ Svenska Aeroplan Aktiebolaget (SAAB) 35XD Draken (F-35)	A-001	351001	On loan to DTM.	–
☐ Svenska Aeroplan Aktiebolaget (SAAB) 35XD Draken (F-35)	A-002	351002	At Jonstruplejren.	RA
☐ Svenska Aeroplan Aktiebolaget (SAAB) 35XD Draken (F-35)	A-004	351004	At Skrydstrup.	RA
☐ Svenska Aeroplan Aktiebolaget (SAAB) 35XD Draken (F-35)	A-005	351005	On loan to K old. Langs.	–
☐ Svenska Aeroplan Aktiebolaget (SAAB) 35XD Draken (F-35)	A-006	351006		RA
☐ Svenska Aeroplan Aktiebolaget (SAAB) 35XD Draken (F-35)	A-007	351007	On loan to Aalholm AM.	–
☐ Svenska Aeroplan Aktiebolaget (SAAB) 35XD Draken (F-35)	A-008	351008	At Randers.	RA
☐ Svenska Aeroplan Aktiebolaget (SAAB) 35XD Draken (F-35)	A-009	351009	On loan to DAVS.	–
☐ Svenska Aeroplan Aktiebolaget (SAAB) 35XD Draken (F-35)	A-010	351010	On loan to Garnisons museum.	–
☐ Svenska Aeroplan Aktiebolaget (SAAB) 35XD Draken (F-35)	A-011	351011	On loan to Grimsby-Cleethorpes APS, England.	–
☐ Svenska Aeroplan Aktiebolaget (SAAB) 35XD Draken (F-35)	A-012	351012	On loan to Egeskov VM.	–
☐ Svenska Aeroplan Aktiebolaget (SAAB) 35XD Draken (F-35)	A-014	351014	On loan to Karup HM.	–
☐ Svenska Aeroplan Aktiebolaget (SAAB) 35XD Draken (F-35)	A-017	351017	At Skive.	RA
☐ Svenska Aeroplan Aktiebolaget (SAAB) 35XD Draken (F-35)	A-018	351018	At Kastrup.	RA
☐ Svenska Aeroplan Aktiebolaget (SAAB) 35XD Draken (F-35)	A-019	351019	At Grena.	RA
☐ Svenska Aeroplan Aktiebolaget (SAAB) 35XD Draken (RF-35)	AR-102	351102	At Tonder.	RA
☐ Svenska Aeroplan Aktiebolaget (SAAB) 35XD Draken (RF-35)	AR-104	351104		RA

TYPE	REG/SER	CON. NO.	PI/NOTES	STATUS
☐ Svenska Aeroplan Aktiebolaget (SAAB) 35XD Draken (RF-35)	AR-105	351105	At Roskilde.	RA
☐ Svenska Aeroplan Aktiebolaget (SAAB) 35XD Draken (RF-35)	AR-107	351107	On loan to Newark AM, England.	–
☐ Svenska Aeroplan Aktiebolaget (SAAB) 35XD Draken (RF-35)	AR-108	351108		RA
☐ Svenska Aeroplan Aktiebolaget (SAAB) 35XD Draken (RF-35)	AR-113	351113		RAA
☐ Svenska Aeroplan Aktiebolaget (SAAB) 35XD Draken (RF-35)	AR-114	351114	On loan to FHS, Norway.	–
☐ Svenska Aeroplan Aktiebolaget (SAAB) 35XD Draken (RF-35)	AR-115	351115		RA
☐ Svenska Aeroplan Aktiebolaget (SAAB) 35XD Draken (RF-35)	AR-118	351118	On loan to DAVS.	–
☐ Svenska Aeroplan Aktiebolaget (SAAB) 35XD Draken (RF-35)	AR-120	351120	On loan to NLS, Norway.	–
☐ Svenska Aeroplan Aktiebolaget (SAAB) 35XD Draken (TF-35)	AT-158	351158		RA
☐ Svenska Aeroplan Aktiebolaget (SAAB) 35XD Draken (TF-35)	AT-160	351160	On loan to FVM, Sweden.	–

FORENINGEN FOR FLYVENDE MUSEUMFLY (DEN12)

Address: DC-3 Vennerne,
P.O. Box 16,
DK-3500 Værlose.
Email: dakotatk@post6.tele.dk
Admission: By prior permission only.
Location: Normally at Værlose Air Force base which is about 15 km north west of Copenhagen.

The group was formed in the early 1990s to operate the C-47 which was once part of the Air Force Historical Collection, This aircraft was delivered to the U.S.A.A.F. in April 1944 and a year later joined the Royal Norwegian Air Force. Sold to the Norwegian airline D.N.L. in 1946 it became part of the SAS fleet following the merger of the Danish, Norwegian and Swedish national carriers. In 1953 the C-47 was sold to the Danish Air Force who operated it for thirty years The Bohnstedt-Petersen Company then leased the aircraft for a period. The C-47 is a regular visitor to air shows around Europe.

TYPE	REG/SER	CON. NO.	PI/NOTES	STATUS
☐ Douglas DC-3A-456 Skytrain (C-47A)	OY-BPB	20019	43-15553, LN-IAT, 68-682, K-682	RAA

FORSVARS OG GARNISONS MUSEUM (DEN13)

Address: Skydenbanevej 22,
DK-9000 Aalborg.
Tel: 98 12 88 21
Fax: 98 12 88 24
Email: info@forvarsmuseum.dk
Admission: April-May September- mid October daily 1100-1600; June-August daily 1000-1700.
Location: In the northern part of the town.

Aalborg has housed military units from 1779 and since World War II has been the largest garrison in the country. During the conflict the Germans set up three airfields and an extensive defence system. The museum, in a former German seaplane maintenance hangar, traces this period in a series of displays incorporating models, dioramas, photographs, and documents. There are several tanks, armoured personnel carriers and a range of weapons on view. The aviation section includes combat types which flew from bases in the area. The Air Force still uses one field and in residence are F-16 fighters. The transport unit moved in March 2004 from Værlose and they operate C-130 Hercules and Canadair CL-604 Challengers. The sole Polyt III glider flown by the Air Force is displayed in the colours it wore after it was sold for civilian use.

TYPE	REG/SER	CON. NO.	PI/NOTES	STATUS
☐ Canadair CL-90 Starfighter (CF-104) [Lockheed 683-04-12]	R-851	683A-1151	12851 (Canada), 104851 (Canada) – on loan from FHS.	PV
☐ Gloster Meteor NF.11 (NF.11) (TT.20)	51-504	5545	(WM387), 51-504, H-504 – on loan from FHS.	PV
☐ Lockheed 580 (T-33A)	DT-289	580-7073	51-9289 – on loan from FHS.	PV
☐ North American NA-173 Sabre (F-86D)	F-421	173-554	51-8421 – on loan from FHS.	PV
☐ Polyteknisk Polyt III	OY-XFA	1	Z-931, 92-931 – on loan from FHS.	PV
☐ Republic F-84G Thunderjet	A-996		51-9996 – on loan from FHS.	PV
☐ Svenska Aeroplan Aktiebolaget (SAAB) 35XD Draken (F-35)	A-010	351010	On loan from FHS.	PV

KASTRUP AIRPORT TERMINAL DISPLAY (DEN14)

Address:	P.O. Box 74, Lufthavnsboulevarden 6, DK-2770 Kastrup.
Tel:	32 31 32 31
Email:	cphweb@cph.dk
Admission:	By prior permission only.
Location:	In the south eastern suburbs of Copenhagen.

Several years ago the 1930s terminal at Kastrup was moved across the airport when the site was developed. The listed building has been superbly restored to original condition. The Convair was the mainstay of the S.A.S. fleet and its passengers used the terminal for many years before the move. A CV-440 was found in Bolivia and made airworthy for the journey. The aircraft was initially used by Eastern Airlines in the U.S.A.

TYPE	REG/SER	CON. NO.	PI/NOTES	STATUS
☐ Convair 440-86	CP-1040	422	N9308	RA

KOLDKRIGSMUSEET LANGELANDSFORTET (DEN15)

Address:	Vognsbjergvej 4b, Sonderbro, DK-5935 Bagenkop.
Tel:	56 50 62 01
Fax:	56 50 59 35
Email:	langelandsmuseum@rudham.dk
Admission:	Mid May-October Monday-Friday 1000-1700 Saturday-Sunday 1300-1700.
Location:	About 20 km south of Rudk-bing.

During the cold war Langelands Fort, with its extensive underground tunnel system, was responsible for the surveillance of the Baltic area. The site closed in 1993 and is now part of the Langelands Museum. There are many weapons, grenades, electronic equipment etc. on show. The history of the period is portrayed in the detailed exhibition which covers many aspects of the topic with particular reference to the local region.

TYPE	REG/SER	CON. NO.	PI/NOTES	STATUS
☐ Mikoyan-Gurevich MiG-23MF	010	0390221010	In Polish markings.	PV
☐ Svenska Aeroplan Aktiebolaget (SAAB) 35XD Draken (F-35)	A-005	351005	On loan from FHS.	PV

MORTENSEN MUSEUM (DEN16)

Address:	Hillerodvejer 180, Dragstrup, DK-3250 Gilleleje.
Tel:	49 71 97 91
Admission:	By prior permission only.
Location:	About 20 km north west of Helsingor.

Henrik Mortensen started collecting World War II items many years ago. In the late 1980s he acquired an instrument panel from one of the forty five Bf 110s left in Denmark and subsequently blown up. The first idea was to include it in a replica cockpit but an original port wing was obtained and the project grew into a full size reproduction. Vehicles including a towing tractor, a 1939 Opel staff car and a motor cycle with sidecar can be seen.

TYPE	REG/SER	CON. NO.	PI/NOTES	STATUS
☐ Messerschmitt Bf 110 (R)			Incorporates some original parts.	RAX

SPANGKUK (DEN17)

Address:	DK-7184 Vandel.
Admission:	By prior permission only.
Location:	About 8 km east of Billund south of Route 28.

This private collection is being assembled with the aim of creating a museum at the airfield at Vandel which closed on July 1st 2003. Thunderstreaks and T-33s once served with the resident units. Long term plans envisage the construction of an exhibition hall where the history of the base and its units will be portrayed.

TYPE	REG/SER	CON. NO.	PI/NOTES	STATUS
☐ Lockheed 580 (T-33A)	DT-404	580-5699	51-4404	RA
☐ Lockheed 580 (T-33A)	DT-450	580-5745	51-4450 – Front fuselage only.	RA
☐ Republic RF-84F Thunderflash	C-865		51-1865	RA
☐ Republic RF-84F Thunderflash	C-253		53-7253	RA
☐ Republic RF-84F Thunderflash	C-324		52-7234	RA
☐ Republic RF-84F Thunderflash	C-651		53-7651	RA
☐ Svenska Aeroplan Aktiebolaget (SAAB) 35E Draken (S 35E)	Fv35931	35931		RA

TOJHUSMUSEET (DEN18)

Address:	Tojhusgade 3, D-1214 Kobenhavn K.
Tel:	33 11 60 37 (Mus)
Fax:	33 93 71 52
Email:	Thm@thm.dk
Admission:	Tuesday-Sunday 1000-1600.
Location:	In the city centre near Christiansborg Castle.

This military museum is housed in the Royal Arsenal building erected by King Christian IV between 1598 and 1604. The Cannon Hall on the ground floor is the longest arched hall in Europe. The Arsenal started its collection of arms in the seventeenth century and formed a museum in 1838. The Tojhusmuseet was established in 1928 and obtained the use of the whole Arsenal building a decade later. For many years three aircraft were displayed in the Cannon Hall but they moved to Billund and were joined by the Spitfire which had been on show at Egeskov. Now they are at Stauning. Still on view are sixteen aero engines and a superb display of arms.

TYPE	REG/SER	CON. NO.	PI/NOTES	STATUS
☐ Avro 504N	110	50	On loan to DVS.	–
☐ Berg and Storm BS.III			On loan to DVS.	–
☐ Fieseler Fi 103A-1				RA
☐ Fokker D.XXI	J-49		Fuselage frame only – on loan to DVS.	–
☐ Hawker Dankok	158	OV54	On loan to DVS.	–
☐ Republic F-84G Thunderjet	K-50		51-9978 – front fuselage only – in Dutch markings – on loan from FHS.	PV
☐ Supermarine 361 Spitfire HF.IXc	'41-401'		MA298, 6462M – on loan to DVS.	–
☐ Svenska Aeroplan Aktiebolaget (SAAB) 35XD Draken (RF-35)	AR-109	351109		RA

ZEPPELIN MUSEUM TONDER (D19)

Address:	Gasvaerksvej 1, DK-6270 Tonder.
Tel:	74 72 72 54
Fax:	74 72 72 55
Email:	zeppelin@zeppelin-museum.dk
Admission:	May-October Saturday-Sunday 1200-1700
Location:	In the northern part of the town.

From 1864 until 1920 the area around Tonder was part of Germany. Two airship hangars were completed in March 1915 and on the 23rd of the month the Parseval PL-25 arrived. A larger 'Toska' hangar was later built. The first Zeppelin, the L-7, took up station on April 25th 1915 and was in residence until it was shot down on a North Sea patrol in May 1916. The museum, which opened in May 1999, also covers general army themes and there are vehicles and weapons on show. In the nearby forest the remains of the airship base can be seen. The site was also used by Albatros fighters and one of the original hangars still stands.

ZONE MUSEET (D20)

Address:	Skyttensvej 2, DK-4300 Holbæk.
Tel:	53 43 01 94
Admission:	May-October daily 1100-1500; November- April Tuesday-Friday 0900-1500.
Location:	In the southern part of the town.

This small museum houses an impressive range of rescue vehicles and fire engines. The collection is located in the former Zone Redningskorpset station which was in use from 1930 until 1963. Under restoration to flying condition is an ambulance version of the KZ III which was used by the service.

TYPE	REG/SER	CON. NO.	PI/NOTES	STATUS
☐ Skandinavisk Aero Industri (SAI) KZ III U-1	OY-DHY	55		RAC

The Danish Air Force operated a number of Drakens. This one is on show at the base museum at Karup.

The small local museum in Vandel exhibits this Republic Thunderjet.

A former Swedish Air Force Viggen is a new exhibit at the Lennundusmuuseum. (LM)

ESTONIA

LENNUNDUSMUUSEUM (EST1)

Address:	Veskiorg 1, Haaslava vald, 62101 Tartu.
Tel:	0513-5490
Fax:	0409-681
Email:	mati.meos@tartuenergia.ee
Admission:	May-August daily 1000-1700.
Location:	About 10 km south of Tartu

Opened on June 14th 2002 this museum is steadily acquiring aircraft from around Europe. The first to arrive were the two Mil Helicopters and these were followed by the jets. These have come from four countries and the collection is due to increase over the next few months. An exhibition has been set up in a building on the site. On show are models and photographs and the history of Estonian aviation is portrayed. A new main hall is under construction and this will more than treble the display area.

TYPE	REG/SER	CON. NO.	PI/NOTES	STATUS
☐ Aero L-29 Delfin			Due soon.	–
☐ Dassault Mirage IIIRS	R-2112	1035	In Swiss markings.	PV
☐ Mikoyan-Gurevich MiG-21MF	9011	969011	In Polish markings.	PV
☐ Mikoyan-Gurevich MiG-23MLD	32	03900315497	In Ukranian markings.	PV
☐ Mil Mi-2		511611090		PV
☐ Mil Mi-2RL	0615	510615018	In Polish markings.	PV
☐ Mil Mi-8S	ES-PMA	10532	93+42, 976 (DDR)	PV
☐ Panstwowe Zaklady Lotnicze (PZL) 104 Wilga 35A	ES-TAB	15800578	(DOSAAF)	PV
☐ Panstwowe Zaklady Lotnicze (PZL) TS-11 Iskra	1234	3H 12-34	In Polish markings.	PV
☐ Sukhoi Su-22M4	3212	23212	In Polish markings.	PV
☐ Sukhoi Su-24	39	1515304	In Ukranian markings.	PV
☐ Svenska Aeroplan Aktiebolaget (SAAB) 37 Viggen (JA 37) (JA 37D) (JA 37DI)	Fv37429	37429	On loan from FVM, SWE.	PV

MODEL CLUB MUSEUM (EST2)

Address:	76608 Keila.
Admission:	By prior permission only.
Location:	In the town which is about 25 km south east of Talinn.

The club has set up its headquarters in the fuselage of the transport and plans to set up an exhibition covering many aspects of model building. The aircraft was built at Irkutsk in the early 1960s for use by Soviet Air Force.

TYPE	REG/SER	CON. NO.	PI/NOTES	STATUS
☐ Antonov An-12BP	82	2901901		PV

The only aircraft on show at the Anti-Aircraft Museum north of Helsinki is this Fouga Magister.

The Air Force in Finland operated several versions of the MiG-21. This two seat MiG-21U is parked outside the Keski-Suomen Ilmailumuseo. (Douglas Rough)

Several airframes awaiting restoration are in the museum hangar at Vesivehmaa. Shown here is the Blackburn Ripon.

FINLAND

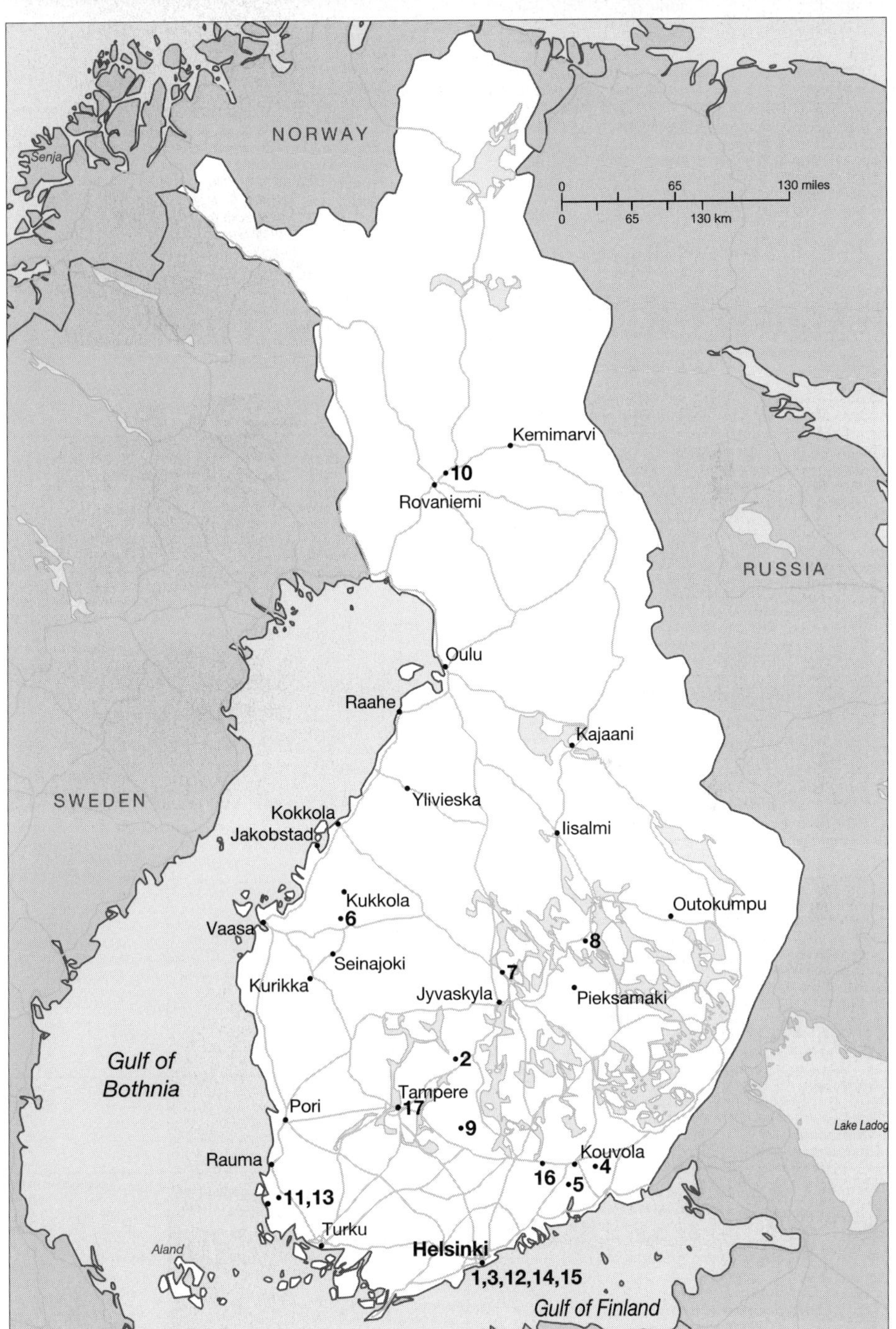
NORWAY
Senja
0
65
130 miles
0
65
130 km
Kemimarvi
10
Rovaniemi
RUSSIA
Oulu
Raahe
Kajaani
SWEDEN
Ylivieska
Kokkola
Jakobstad
Iisalmi
Kukkola
6
Outokumpu
Vaasa
8
Seinajoki
7
Kurikka
Jyvaskyla
Pieksamaki
2
Gulf of Bothnia
Tampere
Pori
17
9
Lake Ladoga
Rauma
Kouvola
4
16
5
11,13
Turku
Aland
Helsinki
1,3,12,14,15
Gulf of Finland

AIRVETERAN (FIN1)

Address:	Huone 55, Helsinki Malmi Airport FIN-0700 Helsinki.
Tel:	09-379060
Admission:	By prior permission only.
Location:	At Vantaa Airport which is about 20 km north of the city.

The company was formed in 1985 as a non-profit group dedicated to keeping historic aircraft in Finland. Two former Finnish Air Force DC-3s were acquired in 1986. One, in airworthy condition, is based at Vantaa Airport. The other aircraft is currently in store. Both served with Finnair and the Air Force for many years.

TYPE	REG/SER	CON. NO.	PI/NOTES	STATUS
☐ Douglas DC-3A-453 Skytrooper (C-53C)	OH-LCH	6346	(NC34953), 43-2033, OH-LCH, DO-11	RAA
☐ Douglas DC-3A-456 Skytrain (C-47A)	OH-LCD	19309	42-100846, OH-LCD, DO-8	RA

HALLINPORTTI ILMAILUMUSEO (FIN2)

Address:	FIN-35600 Halli.
Tel:	03-1816-6120
Admission:	June-mid August Monday-Friday 1300-1700 Saturday-Sunday 1200-1800.
Location:	About 70 km north east of Tampere, 20 km west of Jamsa.

The airfield is home to the test centre for the Finnish Air Force and the Valmet aircraft factory. The museum was set up by members of the Lentotekniikan Kilta (Aviation Technical Guild), a group of past and present air force personnel. The current site opened on August 3rd 1980 and consists of a hangar, an exhibition hall and an office and library building. A large collection of photographs, components, documents, engines and memorabilia can be seen. A former fitter who had worked on the type during its service days restored the Bulldog to static condition. There are several other rare types on view including the Rumpler 6B. This biplane is mounted on floats and joined the museum in the rnid-1980s after a period at Kauhava Air Force Base. The Czechoslovakian Aero A-11 has been rebuilt following its move from Vesivehmaa. There are long term plans to construct a new exhibition hall.

TYPE	REG/SER	CON. NO.	PI/NOTES	STATUS
☐ Aero A-11	AE-47			PV
☐ Bristol 105A Bulldog IV	BU-59	7810		PV
☐ Caudron G.3	1E 18			PV
☐ Focke-Wulf Fw 44J Stieglitz	SZ-5			PVC
☐ Folland Fo.141 Gnat F.1	GN-103	FL-16	G-39-10	RA
☐ Ilmailuvoimien D.27 Haukka II	HA-41	2		PV
☐ Karhumaki Karhu 48	OH-VKK	5	Fuselage frame only	PV
☐ Mikoyan-Gurevich MiG-15UTI	MU-1	922221		PV
☐ Mikoyan-Gurevich MiG-21bis	MG-131	75084511		RA
☐ Mikoyan-Gurevich MiG-21bis/T	MG-124	75084151		RA
☐ Mikoyan-Gurevich MiG-21bis/T	MG-133	75084545		RA
☐ Rumpler 6B	5A 1			PV
☐ Svenska Aeroplan Aktiebolaget (SAAB) 35B Draken (J 35B)	Fv35252	35252		RA
☐ Svenska Aeroplan Aktiebolaget (SAAB) 35BS Draken (35B) (J 35B)	DK-208	35214	Fv35214	RA
☐ Svenska Aeroplan Aktiebolaget (SAAB) 35FS Draken (35F-1) (J 35F-1)	DK-247	35441		RA
☐ Svenska Aeroplan Aktiebolaget (SAAB) 35XS Draken (J 35XS)	DK-201	351301	On plinth in town.	PV
☐ Valtion Lentokonetehdas Saaski II	LK-1	2	(OH-MVA)	PV

ILMATORJUNTA MUSEO (FIN3)

Address:	Varuskunta Alue, FIN-04300 Hyrylä.
Tel:	09-181-62371
Admission:	May-mid September Tuesday-Saturday 1100-1700.
Location:	In the town close to the junction of Roads 145 and 148.

This anti-aircraft museum was established on the military camp at Santahamina in the late 1950s. The anti-aircraft school moved to Hyrylä in 1963 and a proposal to open the museum in the 1721 Captains' Living Quarters was put forward. The display opened in 1969 and a new exhibition hall was added in 1996. Over five thousand items are in the collection and those on view include fire control equipment, sound detection machines, radar, searchlights, artillery, and ground-to-air missiles plus a reconstruction of a World War II control room.

TYPE	REG/SER	CON. NO.	PI/NOTES	STATUS
☐ Fouga CM.170-2 Magister (CM.170A)	FM-50	50		PV

KAAKKOIS-SUOMEN ILMAILUMUSEOYHDISTYS (FIN4)

Address:	Lappeenranta Airport, FIN-53600 Lappeenranta.
Tel:	044-266-0250
Email:	k.marttinen@mail.wwnet.fi
Admission:	Mid-May- mid September daily 1100-1700.
Location:	In the western suburbs of the town.

Set up by the Aviation Museum Society of South East Finland this museum has its home in a hangar at Lappeenranta. There is a display of items recovered from crash sites including engines and components from Bristol Blenheim BL-133, a Junkers Ju 88A-4, a Messerschmitt Bf 109 and a Tupolev Tu-2. The aircraft collection is expanding and a number of former Air Force machines have arrived with more due. The sole Hurricane remaining in Finland was on show here for a time but has now moved back into store. Twelve Mark I examples of the famous fighter were delivered in 1940 and these were joined by a IIB acquired as war booty. They were withdrawn from service in 1944 and one was saved for preservation. Local aviation history is portrayed in a display of photographs, memorabilia, models, uniforms and documents.

TYPE	REG/SER	CON. NO.	PI/NOTES	STATUS
☐ Mikoyan-Gurevich MiG-21bis/T	MG-127	75084215		PV
☐ Mil Mi-4	HR-2	08114		PV
☐ Mil Mi-8T	HS-11	13307		PV
☐ Svenska Aeroplan Aktiebolaget (SAAB) 35XS Draken (J 35XS)	DK-213	351307		PV
☐ Svenska Aeroplan Aktiebolaget (SAAB) 91D Safir	SF-31	91440	SF-31, OH-SFB	PV

KARHULAN ILMAILUKERHON LENTOMUSEO (FIN5)

Address:	c/o Pentti Lehtinen, Harjanteenkatu 18, FIN-48600 Karhula.
Tel:	05-261-044
Fax:	05-261-044
Email:	mikko.vanttine@kymp.net
Admission:	Daily 1000-1800.
Location:	At Kymi airfield which is about 12 km north of Karhula off Road 357.

Kymi airfield was built in 1943 for military use. Messerschmitt Bf 109Gs were based at the field along with liaison and training types. The Air Force left in the late 1950s. A flying and gliding club was formed in 1945 and since then has used a wide range of designs. In August 1992 the Air Force donated a Fouga Magister to the club and the idea of a museum was born. A new purpose built hangar was completed in the autumn of 1995 and three aircraft were initially on view. The first primary glider operated by the club was an Harakka I. In use from 1947 until 1958 the airframe was then put in store. Restoration of the glider started in 1989. It flew again in early 1995 and is the only airworthy example of the type. Also on show is an Harakka II obtained from the Inkeroinen Flying Club and this can be seen along with the only Harakka III built. Dating from 1948 the aircraft arrived at Kymi in 1957 and was operated for three years. The Gauntlet was found in a derelict condition by a farmer in the late 1970s. Painstakingly rebuilt by Kalevi Eskonmaa an instructor at the air force technical school at Halli, the biplane flew again on May 10th 1982. The airframe was modified to take an Alvis Leonides engine in place of the original Bristol Mercury resulting in a longer nose. Finland obtained twenty four examples of the biplane fighter from England in 1940. They were donated by South Africa. A number of military jets can also be seen. Two versions of the MiG-21, a Draken, a Gnat and a Magister are in the collection.

TYPE	REG/SER	CON. NO.	PI/NOTES	STATUS
☐ Fibera KK-1e Utu	'OH-LKF'	16	OH-347	PVX
☐ Focke-Wulf Fw 44J Stieglitz	SZ-18	2778	SZ-18, D-EXWO	PV
☐ Folland Fo.141 Gnat F.1	GN-107	FL-31		PV
☐ Fouga CM.170-2 Magister (CM.170A)	'FM-49'	43	fm-43	PVX
☐ Gloster Gauntlet	'GT-400'	G5/35957	K5271 – OH-XGT allocated.	PVAX
☐ Harakka I	H-12	11		PVA
☐ Harakka II	H-57	25		PVC
☐ Harakka IIN	H-50	19		PV
☐ Mikoyan-Gurevich MiG-21bis	MG-116	75083895		PV
☐ Mikoyan-Gurevich MiG-21F-13	MG-34	740404	Front fuselage only.	PV
☐ Mikoyan-Gurevich MiG-21F-13	MG-78	741205		PV
☐ Polyteknikkojen Ilmailukerho PIK-5c Cumulus	OH-151	15		PV
☐ Polyteknikkojen Ilmailukerho PIK-7 Harakka III	OH-031	1	H-34	PV
☐ Polyteknikkojen Ilmailukerho PIK-16c Vasama	OH-VAN	29	OH-307 – Rear fuselage only.	PV
☐ Schleicher K.8B	OH-348	14	OH-RTU	PVA
☐ Svenska Aeroplan Aktiebolaget (SAAB) 35FS Draken (35F-1) (J 35F-1)	DK-259	35499	Fv35499	PV
☐ Vans RV-6	OH-XOT	20261		PV

KAUHAVA AIR FORCE BASE MUSEUM (FIN6)

Address:	P.O. Box 5, FIN-62201 Kauhava.
Tel:	06-181-3111
Email:	Lentosotakoulu@mil.fi
Admission:	By prior permission only.
Location:	Just north of the town which is about 15 km north of Lapua.

The Air Academy is based at this field along with the associated flying traing squadron. Two Fouga Magisters are preserved by the main gate and the cockpit of another is located in a building. The preserved Safir is also used for instructional purposes. The Vinka and Safir parts are in the base costume museum.

TYPE	REG/SER	CON. NO.	PI/NOTES	STATUS
☐ Fouga CM.170-2 Magister (CM.170)	FM-21	225		RA
☐ Fouga CM.170-2 Magister (CM.170A)	FM-67	67	Front fuselage only.	RA
☐ Fouga CM.170-2 Magister (CM.170A)	FM-82	82		RA
☐ Mikoyan-Gurevich MiG-21bis	MG-130	75084403	Stored at Menkijärvi.	RA
☐ Svenska Aeroplan Aktiebolaget (SAAB) 35FS Draken (35F-1) (J 35F-1)	DK-249	35455	Fv35455 – Stored at Menkijärvi.	RA
☐ Svenska Aeroplan Aktiebolaget (SAAB) 91D Safir	SF-7	91353		RA
☐ Svenska Aeroplan Aktiebolaget (SAAB) 91D Safir	SF-31	91440	Parts only.	RA
☐ Valmet L-70 Vinka	VN-13	14	Parts only.	RA

KESKI-SUOMEN ILMAILUMUSEO (FIN7)

Address:	Kulkantie 1, FIN-41160 Tikkakoski.
Tel:	014-3725125
Fax:	014-3753620
Email:	keski-soumenilmailumuseo@kolumbus.fi
Admission:	June-August 15 daily 1000-2000; August 16-May daily 1100-1700.
Location:	About 20 km north of Jyvaskyla – off the E.4 on the road to the military base.

The idea of an Air Force Museum was first suggested in 1922 and as a result several historic aircraft were stored at bases around the country. In 1968 members of the non-commissioned officers club at Luonetjarvi Air Base at Tikkakoski asked for funds to restore antique aircraft. The remains of the Gordou-Leseurre fighter arrived at the field and this was soon joined in the workshops by other airframes. Restoration work spread to several more bases and the idea of a museum was resurrected. The Aviation Museum of Central Finland opened on June 1st 1979 in a refurbished hangar on the base. Space was limited and the collection grew steadily. A decision was taken in 1983 to convert a former factory building near the main gate to the airfield. The original display closed in 1988 and the new exhibition opened on June 18th 1989. The emphasis is on military aircraft and the displays trace the history of the Finnish Air Force and its units. One of the first aircraft presented to the country was a Swedish built Thulin D. The donor was Count Eric von Rosen whose personal emblem, a blue Swastika, became the symbol of the fledgling force. A partial replica of the Thulin has been constructed using the fuselage of the second donated to the force. Many British built aircraft can be seen including the sole surviving Martinsyde Buzzard, the last type to be made by the firm before it went into liquidation. Fifteen Buzzards were sold to Finland by the Aircraft Disposal Company. The Avro 504K was restored to pristine condition at Rissala in the late 1960s. The rebuild of a Finnish built Bristol Blenheim, which spent a long period on the base gate, was started over twenty years ago but the aircraft has not yet been put on display. Two unique French machines are the Gordou-Leseurre and the Morane-Saulnier MS.50C. According to most published sources Finland ordered nineteen GL-21s from the French factory in 1923/4 and assembled one more from spares. The museum now believes its aircraft to be a GL-22 with a slightly altered wing profile and other small differences. There are several indigenous designs on view The Pyorremyrsky fighter is of mainly wooden construction and is powered by a Daimler Benz DB 605 engine Two were ordered in 1942, one was completed and the other cancelled.

TYPE	REG/SER	CON. NO.	PI/NOTES	STATUS
☐ Arado Ar 66c			Fuselage frame only.	RAD
☐ Avro 504K	AV-57		E448, G-EBNU, 1H49	PV
☐ Bell 26E Airacobra (P-39Q)	26		44-2664 – in Soviet markings – wings from 44-3255.	PV
☐ Breguet 14A2	3C 30			PVC
☐ Bristol 142 Blenheim I			Front fuselage only.	PV
☐ Bristol 142 Blenheim I			Front fuselage only.	RA
☐ Bristol 149 Blenheim IV	BL-200	VI/3(?)	Assembled from Yugoslav parts.	RAC
☐ Caudron G.3			Nacelle and small parts only.	RA
☐ Cessna F172H	OH-CNH	F1720519		RA
☐ De Havilland D.H.60X Moth	OH-EJA	10/29	MO-105, (K-SILC), OH-ILC, OH-MAH	PV
☐ De Havilland D.H.60X Moth	OH-ILA	477	(K-SALF), K-SILA	PV
☐ De Havilland D.H.82A Tiger Moth (Lycoming)	OH-XLA	85167	T6958, G-AMJR, OH-ELA	PV
☐ De Havilland D.H.100 Vampire FB.52	VA-6	V0696		RA
☐ De Havilland D.H.115 Vampire T.55	VT-8	15719		PV
☐ De Havilland D.H.C.2 Beaver	OH-MVM	790		RA
☐ Douglas DC-2-115E	DO-1	1354	PH-AKH, SE-AKE, DC-1	RA
☐ Douglas DC-3A-456 Skytrain (C-47A)	DO-4	14070/25515	43-48254, OH-LCF	PV
☐ Focke-Wulf Fw 44J Stieglitz	SZ-4	2895	D-EXWK, SZ-4, OH-SZO	PV

☐ Focke-Wulf Fw 44J Stieglitz	SZ-25	2928	D-EXWQ	RA
☐ Fokker C.X	FK-113		Fuselage frame only	RAD
☐ Fokker C.X	FK-115		Fuselage frame only	RAD
☐ Fokker C.X	FK-133		Fuselage frame only.	RAD
☐ Fokker D.10	FO-42		8E 3 -fuselage frame only	RA
☐ Fokker D.XXI	FR-110	III/11		PV
☐ Folland Fo.141 Gnat F.1	GN-101	FL-8	G-39-6	PV
☐ Folland Fo.141 Gnat F.1	GN-104	FL-19		PV
☐ Fouga CM.170-2 Magister (CM.170A)	FM-45	45		PV
☐ Fouga CM.170-2 Magister (CM.170R)	FM-14	246		RA
☐ Gourdou-Leseurre GL.22B3	8F12	60	8F12, GL-12	PV
☐ Harakka I	H-17			RA
☐ Harakka II	H-54			RA
☐ Hawker Hurricane I	HC-452	41H/11096	N2394, HU-452	RA
☐ Ilyushin Il-2m3			Centre fuselage only.	RAD
☐ Ilyushin Il-28R	NH-4	1106		PV
☐ Jacobs Meise (D.F.S. 108-70)	OH-OAB	2		RA
☐ Jacobs Weihe (D.F.S. 108-68)	OH-WAB	201	OH-JAMI 3, OH-WAB, OH-133	RA
☐ Malmo Flygindustri MFI-9 Junior	OH-MFB	12	SE-EBY	PV
☐ Martinsyde F.4 Buzzard	MA-24		D4326	PV
☐ Messerschmitt Bf 109E-7	'12'	3285		RAD
☐ Messerschmitt Bf 109G-6/Y	MT-507	167271		PV
☐ Mignet HM-14 Pou-du-Ciel	OH-KAA	1		RA
☐ Mignet HM-14 Pou-du-Ciel	OH-KAB			PV
☐ Mikoyan-Gurevich MiG-3			Wing and other parts.	PV
☐ Mikoyan-Gurevich MiG-3			Rear fuselage and engine.	RA
☐ Mikoyan-Gurevich MiG-15UTI	MU-4	722375		PV
☐ Mikoyan-Gurevich MiG-21bis	MG-138	75084608		PV
☐ Mikoyan-Gurevich MiG-21bis	MG-136	75098129	Front fuselage only.	PV
☐ Mikoyan-Gurevich MiG-21F-13	MG-92	741721		PV
☐ Mikoyan-Gurevich MiG-21U	MK-103	661416		PV
☐ Mikoyan-Gurevich MiG-21UM	MK-126	516999410		PV
☐ Mil Mi-1M	OH-HRC	1181		PV
☐ Mil Mi-4	HR-1	07114		PV
☐ Morane-Saulnier MS.50C	MS-52		2G 7	PV
☐ Noorduyn Norseman VI (C-64A) (UC-64A)	OH-NOA	646	44-70381, HB-UIK – less wings.	RA
☐ Paatalo Tiira				PV
☐ Percival P.66 Pembroke C.53	PR-2	P.66/70		RA
☐ Polikarpov U-2	1	11429	At Tampere.	RA
☐ Polyteknikkojen Ilmailukerho PIK-3b	OH-YKE	5	OH-YKE, OH-199	RA
☐ Polyteknikkojen Ilmailukerho PIK-5b Cumulus	OH-PAX	21	OH-PAX, OH-157	RA
☐ Polyteknikkojen Ilmailukerho PIK-5c Cumulus	OH-PBA	23		RA
☐ Rantala Gyroglider				RA
☐ Schneider ESG 31 Grunau Baby II (D.F.S. 108-49)	OH-KUOPIO2	15/36	OH-KUOPIO2, OH-BAD	RA
☐ Svenska Aeroplan Aktiebolaget (SAAB) 35BS Draken (35B) (J 35B)	DK-202	35265	Fv35265 – At Air Force Academy.	RA
☐ Svenska Aeroplan Aktiebolaget (SAAB) 35CS Draken (35A) (35C) (J 35A) (Sk 35C)	DK-270	35812 (35020)	Fv35020, Fv35812	PV
☐ Svenska Aeroplan Aktiebolaget (SAAB) 35FS Draken (35F-1) (J 35F-1)	DK-233	35443	Fv35443 – Front fuselage only.	PV
☐ Svenska Aeroplan Aktiebolaget (SAAB) 35FS Draken (35F-1) (J 35F-1)	DK-241	35448	Fv35448	PV
☐ Svenska Aeroplan Aktiebolaget (SAAB) 35XS Draken (J 35XS)				
☐ Svenska Aeroplan Aktiebolaget (SAAB) 91D Safir	SF-2	91348		PV
☐ Svenska Aeroplan Aktiebolaget (SAAB) 91D Safir	SF-8	91354	Cockpit section only	PV
☐ Svenska Aeroplan Aktiebolaget (SAAB) 91D Safir	OH-SFD	91443	SF-34	RA
☐ Svenska Aeroplan Aktiebolaget (SAAB) 91D Safir	OH-SFE	91444	SF-35	RA
☐ Szybowcowy Zaklad Doswiadczalny S.Z.D.10bis Czapla	OH-KCD	W-33	OH-KCD, OH-209	RA
☐ Szybowcowy Zaklad Doswiadczalny S.Z.D.22C Mucha Standard	OH-258	F-674	OH-MSE	RA
☐ Thulin D [Morane-Saulnier L]	F 4	1	15 (Sweden) – fuselage only.	RAD
☐ Thulin D [Morane-Saulnier L] (R)	'F 1'			PVX
☐ Tupolev ANT-40 (SB-2)	'12/117'		Crash remains.	RAD
☐ Valmet L-90 TP Redigo	OH-VTP	001	Rear fuselage and tail only.	RA
☐ Valmet LEKO 70				RA
☐ Valmet Vihuri II	VH-18			PV
☐ Valtion Lentokonetehdas Humu	HM-671	632567		PV
☐ Valtion Lentokonetehdas Myrsky II	MY-10		Fuselage frame only	RAD
☐ Valtion Lentokonetehdas Myrsky II	MY-5		Fuselage frame only	RAD
☐ Valtion Lentokonetehdas Myrsky II	MY-9		Fuselage frame only	RAD
☐ Valtion Lentokonetehdas Myrsky II	MY-14	II/10	Fuselage frame only.	RAD
☐ Valtion Lentokonetehdas Pyorremyrsky	PM-1	1		PV
☐ Valtion Lentokonetehdas Pyry II	PY-35	34		RA
☐ Valtion Lentokonetehdas Pyry II (I)	PY-1	1		RA
☐ Valtion Lentokonetehdas Saaski I	SA-95	1	K-SASA – fuselage frame only.	RA
☐ Valtion Lentokonetehdas Tuisku				RAD
☐ Valtion Lentokonetehdas Viima II			Parts only.	RA
☐ Wytwornia Sprzetu Komunikacyjnego (WSK) Lim-5 [MiG-17F]	1709	1C 17-09	In Polish markings.	RA
☐ Wytwornia Sprzetu Komunikacyjnego (WSK) SM-1/600Sz [Mil Mi-1A]	HK-2	S1A07030		RA

The Finnish Automobile Club Museum at Uusikaupunki displays this PIK-3b glider.

Vaino Bremer made several long distance flights in this Junkers Junior. The aircraft is owned by the Soumen Ilmailumuseo and can be seen in the main terminal at Helsinki-Vantaa Airport.

An exhibition building was constructed at Utti to house this Messerschmitt Bf 109G which was exposed to the elements for many years. (Douglas Rough)

KUOPIO-RISSALA BASE COLLECTION (FIN8)

Address:	PL 5, FIN-70901 Toivala.
Tel:	014-181-0111
Email:	karjalanlennosto@mil.fi
Admission:	By prior permission only.
Location:	About 15 km north of Kuopio and 5 km north of Toivola.

MiG-21s were based at the field for many years. The F-13 model is located by the civil terminal and the two bis variants are preserved inside the military base. All three were operated by the resident unit and the final flights were made in October 1998. The field is now home to Hawks and Hornets along with a communications and training squadron flying the Piper Chieftain and the indigenous Redigo and Vinka.

TYPE	REG/SER	CON. NO.	PI/NOTES	STATUS
☐ Mikoyan-Gurevich MiG-21bis	MG-119	75098121		RA
☐ Mikoyan-Gurevich MiG-21bis	MG-134	75098143	Front fuselage only.	RA
☐ Mikoyan-Gurevich MiG-21F-13	MG-61	741117		RA

MUSEOKONEIDEN VARASOHANGAARI LAHTI-VESIVEHMAA (FIN9)

Address:	Lahden Ilmasilta, P.O. Box 166, FIN-15101 Lahti.
Tel:	0804-871635
Admission:	May-October Saturday-Sunday 1100-1800 or by prior permission.
Location:	About 24 km north east of Lahti on Road 313.

The Vesivehmaa Storage Hangar is located on a former World War II fighter base north of Lahti. Since 1948 the building has been used to house a number of dismantled aircraft. The military authorities are to be congratulated for their foresight in preserving many unique types tracing the history of the Finnish Air Force. A few civil aircraft were also in residence. With the growing interest in preservation in the 1960s aircraft were taken to a number of bases and technical schools for rebuild. The skills of these volunteer teams can be seen in other museums around the country. In the late 1970s the management of the hangar was taken over by a branch of the Finnish Aviation Museum Society who organised the remaining aircraft so they could be viewed more easily. A few years ago an Aero A-11 was moved to Halli and a Caudron C.60 to the Suomen Ilmailumuseo. The sole surviving Blackburn Ripon dominates the hangar. One example was delivered from the Yorkshire company in 1928 and another twenty five were built in the State Aviation Factory at Tampere between 1931 and 1934. They were operated on both normal undercarriages and floats. The type remained in service until 1945 and the aircraft is the only surviving large Blackburn biplane in the world. The French government sent a mission to Finland soon after the country gained its independence. Orders resulting from this included the Breguet 14 (the survivor is now at Tikkakoski) and the Caudron C.59. The Breguet 14 was built in large numbers and served in many countries. Finland purchased thirty eight which were delivered between 1919 and 1922. Only three Caudron C.59s were ordered they were operated from 1923 until 1931. Six Caudron C.714s were donated by France in 1940 and they were soon in service. The Czech A.32 is a rarity and sixteen were ordered in the late 1920s. The biplane was in use until 1944. Rare Finnish aircraft include the sole Haukka I fighter flown for a short period in 1927. The only Kurki dating from 1927 has also survived as well as one of five Kotkas built in 1931. Finland acquired one British built Gamecock in 1927 and another the following year. Fifteen were then built under licence. A fuselage frame can be seen along with other small components. The Gnat and MiG-15 moved in several years ago to add variety and these were later joined by the MiG-21, Mil Mi-8 and Draken. The first MiG-21F-13 arrived in Finland in 1963 and later versions of the classic type were delivered in the 1970s. The Seabee joined the collection in the late 1990s. The aircraft overturned on landing on water in 1959. The pilot had inadvertently left the undercarriage down after take off from land. Despite the many lakes in Finland only two examples of the amphibian served in the country. Components from downed aircraft have also been collected with a number of Soviet wrecks recovered. Research has been carried out on other crash sites so more interesting pieces can be expected when time and funds permit.

TYPE	REG/SER	CON. NO.	PI/NOTES	STATUS
☐ Aero A-32	AEj-59	59		PV
☐ Blackburn Ripon IIF	RI-140	12		PV
☐ Caudron C.59	CA-50		2E 5	PV
☐ Caudron C.714	CA-556	8583/6		PV
☐ De Havilland D.H.115 Vampire T.55			Fuselage pod only.	PVD
☐ De Havilland D.H.115 Vampire T.55	VT-6	15756	Fuselage pod only.	RA
☐ Focke-Wulf Fw 44J Stieglitz	SZ-35		Fuselage frame only	PVD
☐ Fokker C.VE	FO-75		Rear fuselage only.	PVD
☐ Folland Fo.141 Gnat F.1	GN-112	FL-47		PV
☐ Fouga CM.170-2 Magister (CM.170A)	FM-71	71		PV
☐ Gloster Gamecock II			Fuselage frame only	PVD
☐ Ilmailuvoimien D.26 Haukka I	HA-39			PV
☐ Ilmailuvoimien K.1 Kurki				PV
☐ Kassel 12A	13	1	Stored for Suomen Ilmailumuseo, Helsinki.	PV
☐ Lavochkin LaGG-3			Rear fuselage only.	

TYPE	REG/SER	CON. NO.	PI/NOTES	STATUS
☐ Mikoyan-Gurevich MiG-3		2171	Wing and other parts only.	PV
☐ Mikoyan-Gurevich MiG-15UTI	MU-2	822028		PV
☐ Mikoyan-Gurevich MiG-21bis	MG-140	75084645		RA
☐ Mil Mi-8PS	HS-5	13305		PV
☐ Petlyakov Pe-2FT			Crash remains	PVD
☐ Polyteknikkojen Ilmailukerho PIK-3c Kajava	OH-233	11	OH-YKO	PV
☐ Republic RC-3 Seabee	OH-EGA	679		PV
☐ Schleicher Ka-4 Rhönlerche II	OH-207	591		PV
☐ Svenska Aeroplan Aktiebolaget (SAAB) 35XS Draken (J 35XS)	DK-207	351304		PV
☐ Szybowcowy Zaklad Doswiadczalny S.Z.D.22B Mucha Standard	OH-MSA	F-513	Fuselage parts and wings only.	PV
☐ Szybowcowy Zaklad Doswiadczalny S.Z.D.22C Mucha Standard	OH-248	F-673		PV
☐ Tupolev ANT-40 (SB-2)	'16/250'		Rear fuselage only.	PVD
☐ Tupolev ANT-40 (SB-2)			Fuselage and tail parts only.	PVD
☐ Valtion Lentokonetehdas E.30 Kotka II	KA-147	4		PV
☐ Valtion Lentokonetehdas Pyry II	PY-26	25	Fuselage frame.	PVD

ROVANIEMI BASE COLLECTION (FIN10)

Address: P.O. Box 22,
FIN-96101 Rovaniemi.
Tel: 016-181-0111
Email: Lapinlennosto@mil.fi
Admission: By prior permission only.
Location: About 10 km north east of the town off Route 4.

Located within the Arctic Circle this base provides the defence of the northern borders of the country. The field also serves as the civil airport for the region and many flights arrive in the pre-Christmas period. The resident 11 Squadron was the last to operate the Draken and these have been replaced by the Hornet. One squadron of Hawks will move from here to Kauhava during 2006. Twelve Gnats were delivered in 1959 and after being withdrawn in 1972 the survivors were allocated for preservation at museums.

TYPE	REG/SER	CON. NO.	PI/NOTES	STATUS
☐ Folland Fo.141 Gnat F.1	GN-110	FL-44		RA
☐ Svenska Aeroplan Aktiebolaget (SAAB) 35A Draken (J 35A)	DK-200	35026	Fv35026	RA
☐ Svenska Aeroplan Aktiebolaget (SAAB) 35FS Draken (35F-1) (J 35F-1)	DK-255	35483	Fv35483	RA
☐ Svenska Aeroplan Aktiebolaget (SAAB) 35XS Draken (J 35XS)	DK-211	351306		RA

SAAB-VALMETIN AUTOMUSEO (FIN11)

Address: Tehtaankatu,
FIN-23500 Uusikaupunki.
Tel: 02-845-22712
Admission: April-September daily 1100-1700.
Location: The town is about 75 km north west of Turku on Road 198.

For many years SAAB cars were produced at the Valmet factory in the town. The museum was set up to display the range of types which came off the assembly lines. On show are examples of the 95, 96 and 99 all of which were built here. The Finnish Air Force bought thirty five Safirs which were delivered between 1958 and 1963. The type served until the early 1980s when it was replaced by the Vinka. A second hall is being set up as a car repair museum which traces the developments in garage equipment and maintenance techniques. The visitor can see the rapid advances made over the years. The museum is attached to Finnish Vintage Car Club display.

TYPE	REG/SER	CON. NO.	PI/NOTES	STATUS
☐ Svenska Aeroplan Aktiebolaget (SAAB) 91D Safir	SF-5	91351		PV

SOTAMUSEO (FIN12)

Address: Suomenlinna Iso Mustasaari,
Rakennus C77,
FIN-00170 Helsinki.
Tel: 09-1812-6381.
Fax: 09-1812-6390
Email: Sotamuseo@mil.fi
Admission: February-mid May October-November Saturday-Sunday 1100-1500; mid-May-August daily 1100-1700; September daily 1100-1500.
Location: On the island off Helsinki.

The historic fortress of Suomenlinna was built on six islands off the southern tip of Helsinki. Construction started in 1748 when the site was part of the Swedish Empire. The Russians gained control of the fort in 1808 and occupied it until Finland won its independence in 1917. The Air Force Factory was built on one of the islands in 1922. This facility became the State Factory in 1930 and moved to Tampere in 1936. The base was used by the military until 1973 and is now a major tourist attraction. There is a regular ferry service from the city harbour to the island. Several buildings were converted into museums. The 1881 Artillery Hall houses a collection of heavy World War II weapons and displays trace the story of the Finnish conflicts of this period. The first Finnish fighter aircraft, the C.24, was built at Suomenlinna. The sole example had a brief military career before being put into store. After a long period at Vesivehmaa it was moved to Halli for restoration and took up its present position in 1989 when the museum opened.

TYPE	REG/SER	CON. NO.	PI/NOTES	STATUS
☐ Ilmailuvoimien C.24	8F 4	1		PV

SUOMEN AUTOMOBIILIHISTORIALLINEN KLUBI AUTOMUSEO (FIN13)

Address:	Tehtaankatu, FIN-23500 Uusikaupunki.4
Tel:	02-845-22712
Admission:	April-September daily 1100-1700.
Location:	The town is about 75 km north west of Turku on Road 198.

The museum contains several vintage cars owned by members of the club. A number of classics from the early days can be seen along with modern designs and racers. There are many trophies, photographs, documents and components on view. The sole aircraft on show is an indigenous glider, a Pik-3b. The sailplane was built in 1957 and flew for ten years at Lappeenranta. After eleven years in store it was totally rebuilt and became active again with a local owner until 1984 when it was presented to the museum.

TYPE	REG/SER	CON. NO.	PI/NOTES	STATUS
☐ Polyteknikkojen Ilmailukerho PIK-3b	OH-175	4	OH-YKD	PV

SUOMEN ILMAILUMUSEO (FIN14)

Address:	P.L.42, Tietotie 3, FIN-01531 Helsinki-Vantaa 53.
Tel:	09-8700-870
Fax:	09-8700-8720
Email:	info@suomenilmailumuseo.fi
Admission:	Daily 1100-1800.
Location:	Just off the approach road to the airport which is about 20 km. north of Helsinki.

The Ilmailumuseo RY (Finnish Aviation Museum Society) was formed in 1969 and its members have contributed to the excellent state of the preservation movement in the country. In 1972 the society opened an exhibition in the basement of the terminal building at Vantaa Airport. The area was long and narrow so no assembled aircraft could be shown but an informative display of models, photographs, documents, engines and components could be seen. In 1979 work started on a large display building on one of the approach roads to the terminal and this was ready two years later. Over twenty aircraft were exhibited inside with others parked outside. The collection continued to grow and a second hall was ready for the 1990 season. An area for special exhibitions links the two buildings and the complex also includes a large library and archive section. Two storage hangars are located on the site. There is also a workshop where restoration is carried out. One hall is primarily devoted to military aviation and the other to civil, but in both areas several gliders and light aircraft are suspended from the ceiling. The history of aviation in the country is portrayed in detail with many interesting and informative displays. Finnair was formed in 1923 as Aero OY and operated Junkers F 13 floatplanes from a site near Helsinki. The history of the company is highlighted and a Convair 440 flown for many years is on view. The development of model aviation is also portrayed with many flying examples on show. One of the first light aircraft built in the country was the Adaridi evaluated by the Air Force in 1923. The society obtained this high wing monoplane from the Vesivehmaa storage hangar and rebuilt the machine in the early 1970s. The last surviving IVL A 22 floatplane is a prized exhibit. The aircraft is a modified licence built Hansa-Brandenburg 33 and was the first type built at the Air Force Factory at Suomenlinna. One hundred and twenty two were produced and were in service from 1922-1936. Thirty Caudron C.60s were bought from France in 1923/4 and four years later another thirty four were built under licence. On show in the terminal building is the Junkers A 50 Junior in which Vaino Bremer made many long distance solo flights. In May 1932 he took off from Helsinki and flew to Cape Town. He returned to Dessau where the Junior was built. He flew thirty thousand kilometres in two hundred and thirty two hours. The display contains a number of indigenous light aircraft. The Heinonen HK-1 flew from Madrid to Turku in 1957 setting a record for aircraft of less than 500 kg. The small Eklund TE-1 flew as an amphibian in February 1949 and was converted to a flying boat in 1954. The TE-1 was withdrawn in 1969. Only two Karhu 48 high wing cabin monoplanes were built in the late 1940s and one is on show. Several powered aircraft and gliders designed by members of the Polytechnic Institute form important part of the display. The fuselage of one of the few surviving DC-2s was recovered from a long period of storage in the area. Modern types are being added as they are withdrawn from use. The excellent displays present a comprehensive picture flying in the country which has had an interesting and varied history.

TYPE	REG/SER	CON. NO.	PI/NOTES	STATUS
☐ Bede BD-5B	OH-XMP	MP003/2412		RAD
☐ Beech 95-A55 Baron	OH-BBA	TC-261	SE-EUT, OH-APU, OH-BBA, OY-DPK	PV
☐ Bell 47D-1	OH-HIA	646		PV
☐ Blomqvist & Nyberg Monoplane		1		PV
☐ Brewster B.239 Buffalo	BW-239		Small parts only.	PV
☐ Bristol 142 Blenheim I	BL-180	V/20	Rear fuselage only.	PVD
☐ Bryan/Schreder HP-16	OH-450X	01	OH-450 – fuselage only.	PV
☐ Caudron C.60	CA-84	24		PV
☐ Cessna F150J	OH-CBQ	F1500526		PV
☐ Convair 440 (340-40)	OH-LRB	73		PV
☐ De Havilland D.H.100 Vampire FB.52	VA-2	V0692		PV
☐ De Havilland D.H.115 Vampire T.55	VT-9	15720		PV
☐ De Havilland D.H.C.2 Beaver	OH-MVL	141		PV
☐ Douglas DC-2-115	DO-3	1562	OK-AIC, D-AAIO, OH-DLB, OH-LDB – fuselage only.	PV
☐ Douglas DC-3A-214	OH-VKB	1975	SE-BAC	PV
☐ Eklund TE-1b (TE-1)	OH-TEA	1		PV
☐ Fairchild 24W41 Forwarder (C-61) (UC-61) (Argus I)	OH-FCK	W41-287	41-38843, EV779, G-AKIZ	RA
☐ Fairchild 24W41 Forwarder (C-61) (UC-61) (Argus I)	OH-FCJ	W41-324	42-32119, FK315, G-AJPC	RA
☐ Fibera KK-1e Utu	OH-355	13	OH-LKE	PV
☐ Fibera KK-1e Utu	OH-368	21/68	OH-LKI	PV
☐ Fieseler Fi 156K-1 Storch	OH-FSA	4230	ST-112, OH-VSF	PV
☐ Focke-Wulf Fw 44J Stieglitz				RAC
☐ Folland Fo.141 Gnat F.1	GN-105	FL-23		PV
☐ Folland Fo.141 Gnat F.1	GN-106	FL-28		PV
☐ Fouga CM.170-2 Magister (CM.170A)	FM-42	42		PV
☐ Gloster Gamecock	GA-58	15	Rear fuselage only.	PVD
☐ Harakka I	H-5	5/46		PV
☐ Harakka II	H-56	24/52		PV
☐ Heinonen HK-1 Keltiainen	OH-HKA	1		PV
☐ Ilmailuvoimien A.22 Hansa [Hansa Brandenburg W 33]	IL-2	2	4D2	PV
☐ Jacobs Meise (D.F.S. 108-70)	OH-OAA	1/45	OH-OAA, OH-134	PV
☐ Jacobs Weihe (D.F.S. 108-68)	OH-WAA	200	OH-JAMI 2	RA
☐ Junkers A 50 ce Junior	OH-ABB	3530	D-1915 – in main terminal.	PV
☐ Karhumaki Karhu 48B (48)	OH-VKL	6	OH-VKL, OH-KUA	PV
☐ Kassel 12A	'13'	1		PV
☐ KIP-VK3-1 Hot Air Balloon	OH-XMH	1		PV
☐ Klemm L 25 d	OH-KLA	137	K-SABA, OH-ABA	PV
☐ Kokkola Ko-04 Super Upstart	OH-XYY	01		PV
☐ Kyrölä Monoplane				RA
☐ Let L-13N Blanik	'OH-VLK'	172620	(DOSAAF), OH-282	PVX
☐ Letov S-218 Smolik	'SM-153'	26/VL	SM-162, OH-SME	PVX
☐ Lippisch Hols Der Teufel	OH-KOPI		Rear fuselage only.	PV
☐ Lockheed 18-07-01 Lodestar	OH-VKU	18-2006	F-ARTF, (N9965F), N9955F	PV
☐ Mahe Scout	OH-U017	012		PV
☐ Martenko U 165 Atol 450	U165	U1658801	On loan to Tied.H.	–
☐ Messerschmitt Bf 109G-2	MT-208	14743	RJ+SM	PVD
☐ Mignet HM-14 Pou-du-Ciel (R)	'OH-BFA'	1		PV
☐ Mikoyan-Gurevich MiG-21bis	MG-111	75064540		PV
☐ Mikoyan-Gurevich MiG-21bis	MG-135	75084554		RA
☐ Mikoyan-Gurevich MiG-21F-13	'MG-127'	741204	MG-77	PVX
☐ Mikoyan-Gurevich MiG-21UM	MK-105	516917001		PV
☐ Mil Mi-4	HR-3	09114		PV
☐ Mil Mi-8T	HS-1	13301		PV
☐ Piper PA-28R-180 Cherokee Arrow	OH-PJN	28R-30885	(SE-FDY)	PV
☐ Polikarpov I-16 tip 15 (UTI-4)	UT-1		VH-22	PV
☐ Polyteknikkojen Ilmailukerho PIK-3a Kanttikolmonen	OH-YKA	1	OH-PCA	PV
☐ Polyteknikkojen Ilmailukerho PIK-3c Kajava	OH-201	3	OH-YKY	PV
☐ Polyteknikkojen Ilmailukerho PIK-5b Cumulus	OH-PAR	16/50	OH-PAR, OH-152	PV
☐ Polyteknikkojen Ilmailukerho PIK-10 Mootoribaby	OH-PXA	1	Converted from Grunau Baby II OH-BAB	PV
☐ Polyteknikkojen Ilmailukerho PIK-11 Tumppu	OH-YMA	1		PV
☐ Polyteknikkojen Ilmailukerho PIK-12 Gabriel	OH-KYC	3	OH-KYC, OH-318	PV
☐ Polyteknikkojen Ilmailukerho PIK-16c Vasama	OH-571	38		PV
☐ Polyteknikkojen Ilmailukerho PIK-20	OH-425X	001		PV
☐ Quickie Aircraft Quickie 1 (Rutan 54)	OH-XQA	1049		RA
☐ Schneider ESG 29 Grunau 9 (D.F.S. 108-10)	G-36	22/39		PV
☐ Schneider ESG 31 Grunau Baby II (D.F.S. 108-49)	OH-BAR		At Rayskala	S
☐ Schneider ESG 31 Grunau Baby IIB	OH-BAA	12/43	OH-JAMI 5	PV
☐ Schneider Grunau SG-38 (D.F.S. 108-14)	SG-1	79		PV
☐ Sisilisko	OH-SAB	1	OH-PSB – at Tampere.	RAC
☐ Svenska Aeroplan Aktiebolaget (SAAB) 35BS Draken (35B) (J 35B)	DK-206	35245	Fv35245	PV
☐ Svenska Aeroplan Aktiebolaget (SAAB) 35CS Draken (35A) (35C) (J 35A) (Sk 35C)	DK-262	35823 (35037)	Fv35037, Fv35823	PV
☐ Svenska Aeroplan Aktiebolaget (SAAB) 91D Safir	SF-9	91355		PV
☐ Svenska Aeroplan Aktiebolaget (SAAB) 91D Safir	SF-10	91356	Fuselage only.	PV

TYPE	REG/SER	CON. NO.	PI/NOTES	STATUS
☐ Szybowcowy Zaklad Doswiadczalny S.Z.D.9bis Bocian 1A	OH-177	P-284	OH-KBZ	PV
☐ Szybowcowy Zaklad Doswiadczalny S.Z.D.10bis Czapla	OH-KCC	W-51	OH-KCC, OH-204	PV
☐ Thunder and Colt GA-42 Gas Airship	OH-ITA	1152	G-BRXM – gondola only.	PV
☐ Valmet Tuuli TL-III	OH-XTL	1	TL-1	RA
☐ Valmet Vihuri II			Front fuselage only.	RA
☐ Valmet Vihuri II	VH-25		Front fuselage only.	RA
☐ Valtion Lentokonetehdas Pyry II	PY-16	15	Fuselage frame only.	RAD
☐ Valtion Lentokonetehdas Pyry II	PY-27	26		PV
☐ Valtion Lentokonetehdas Pyry II	PY-30	29	Fuselage frame only.	RAD
☐ Valtion Lentokonetehdas Pyry II	PY-5	4	Fuselage frame.	RAD
☐ Valtion Lentokonetehdas Saaski II	SA-122	II/5	SA-122, 'SA-131'	PV
☐ Valtion Lentokonetehdas Tuisku	TU-169	20	Fuselage frame and parts.	RA
☐ Valtion Lentokonetehdas Tuisku	TU-178	29		PV
☐ Valtion Lentokonetehdas Viima II	OH-VII	VI-21	VI-21	PVA
☐ Viri				RAC
☐ Wassmer WA.54 Atlantic	OH-WAC	138	At Malmi Airport.	RAA
☐ Wojskowe Warsztaty Szybowcowe W.W.S.1 Salamandra	OH-SAA	147	OH-PIK 6	PV
☐ Wytwornia Sprzetu Komunikacyjnego (WSK) SM-1/600Sz [Mil Mi-1A]	HK-1	S1A07029	Also quoted as A07029.	PV
☐ Zlin Z-37 Cmelak	OH-CMB	04-09		RAC

TIEDEKESKUS HEUREKA (FIN15)

Address: Tiedepuisto 1,
Tikkurila,
FIN-01300 Vantaa.
Tel: 09-85799
Fax: 09-873-4142
Email: info@heureka.fi
Admission: Daily 1000-1800 (Closes at 2000 on Thursday)
Location: Just north of Ring 3 and 7 km south east of Vantaa Airport.

This 'hands-on' centre has many innovative displays showing recent developments in science. The history of the subjects is also featured. The only aircraft on view is the prototype of an indigenous amphibious ultralight.

TYPE	REG/SER	CON. NO.	PI/NOTES	STATUS
☐ Martenko U 165 Atol 450	U165	U1658801	On loan from Suomen Ilmus.	PV

UTTI MEMORIAL (FIN16)

Address: P.O. Box 5,
FIN-45411 Utti.
Tel: 05-1812-5111
Admission: On permanent view.
Location: About 15 km east of Kouvola on Route 6.

The base is now used by the Army for helicopter and parachute training. For many years it was an Air Force fighter base and then housed transport units. The Messerchmitt was on show in the open for a long time but it has now been placed in a glass pagoda to protect it from the harsh winter weather.

TYPE	REG/SER	CON. NO.	PI/NOTES	STATUS
☐ Messerschmitt Bf 109G-6	MT-452	165277		PV

VALMET DISPLAY (FIN17)

Address: Lentokenetehtaantie 10,
FIN-33500 Tampere.
Tel: 931-658111
Admission: On permanent view.
Location: In the western suburbs of the city.

The State Aircraft Factory (Valtion Lentokonetehdas) later Valmet, moved to Tampere in 1936 and produced many original designs. Located outside the plant on the site of the old airport is a glass building containing the sole Viima I built in 1935. In 1938/9 twenty examples of the improved Viima II were delivered to the Air Force.

TYPE	REG/SER	CON. NO.	PI/NOTES	STATUS
☐ Valtion Lentokonetehdas Viima I	VI-1	1		PV

The impressive Resistance Museum at Tergnier is home to this Beech 18.

Hanging in the foyer of the Mémorial de Caen is this replica Hawker Typhoon.

Michel Pont obtained the first Dassault Mirage IV to go on show in a privately run museum. The delta is parked in the grounds of the Château at Savigny-les-Beaune.

FRANCE

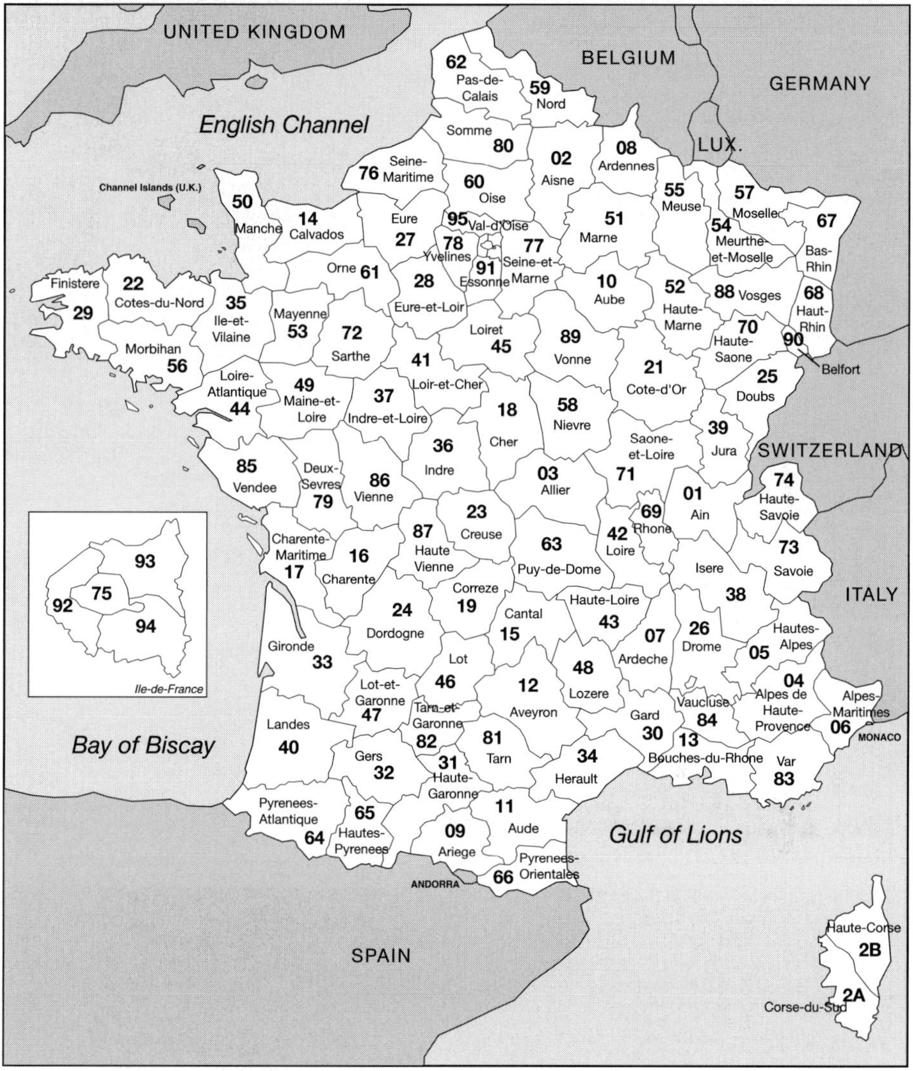

Key

01 Ain
02 Aisne
03 Allier
04 Alpes-de-Haute Provence
05 Hautes-Alpes
06 Alpes-Maritimes
07 Ardèche
08 Ardennes
09 Ariège
10 Aube
11 Aude
12 Aveyron
13 Bouches-du-Rhône
14 Calvados
15 Cantal
16 Charente
17 Charente-Maritime
18 Cher
19 Corrèze
21 Côte-d'Or
22 Côtes-d'Armor
23 Creuse
24 Dordogne
25 Doubs
26 Drôme
27 Eure
28 Eure-et-Loir
29 Finistère
30 Gard
31 Haute-Garonne
32 Gers
33 Gironde
34 Hérault
35 Ile-et-Vilaine
36 Indre
37 Indre-et-Loire
38 Isère
39 Jura
40 Landes
41 Loir-et-Cher
42 Loire
43 Haute-Loire
44 Loire-Atlantique
45 Loiret
46 Lot
47 Lot-et-Garonne
48 Lozère
49 Maine-et-Loire
50 Manche
51 Marne
52 Haute-Marne
53 Mayenne
54 Moselle
55 Meuse
56 Morbihan
57 Meurthe-et-Moselle
58 Nièvre
59 Nord
60 Oise
61 Orne
62 Pas-de-Calais
63 Puy-de-Dôme
64 Pyrénées-Atlantiques
65 Hautes-Pyrénées
66 Pyrénées-Orientales
67 Bas-Rhin
67 Haut-Rhin
69 Rhône
70 Haute-Saône
71 Saône-et-Loire
72 Sarthe
73 Savoie
74 Haute-Savoie
75 Paris
76 Seine-Maritime
77 Seine-et-Marne
78 Yvelines
79 Deux-Sèvres
80 Somme
81 Tarn
82 Tarn-et-Garonne
83 Var
84 Vaucluse
85 Vendée
86 Vienne
87 Haute-Vienne
88 Vosges
89 Vonne
90 Territoire de Belfort
91 Essonne
92 Hauts-de-Seine
93 Seine-Saint-Denis
94 Val-de-Marne
95 Val-d'Oise
2A Corse-du-Sud
2B Haute-Course

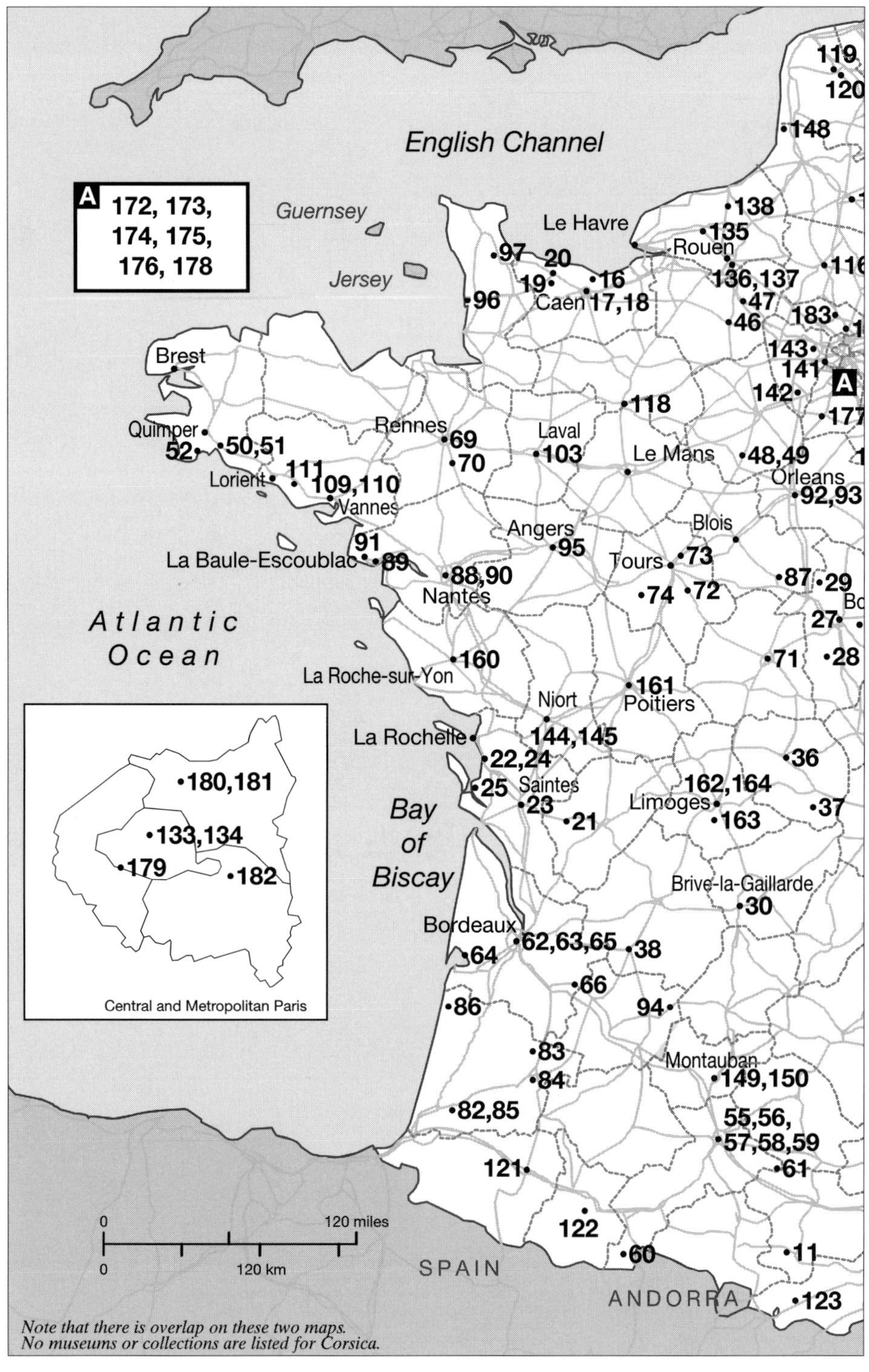

Note that there is overlap on these two maps.
No museums or collections are listed for Corsica.

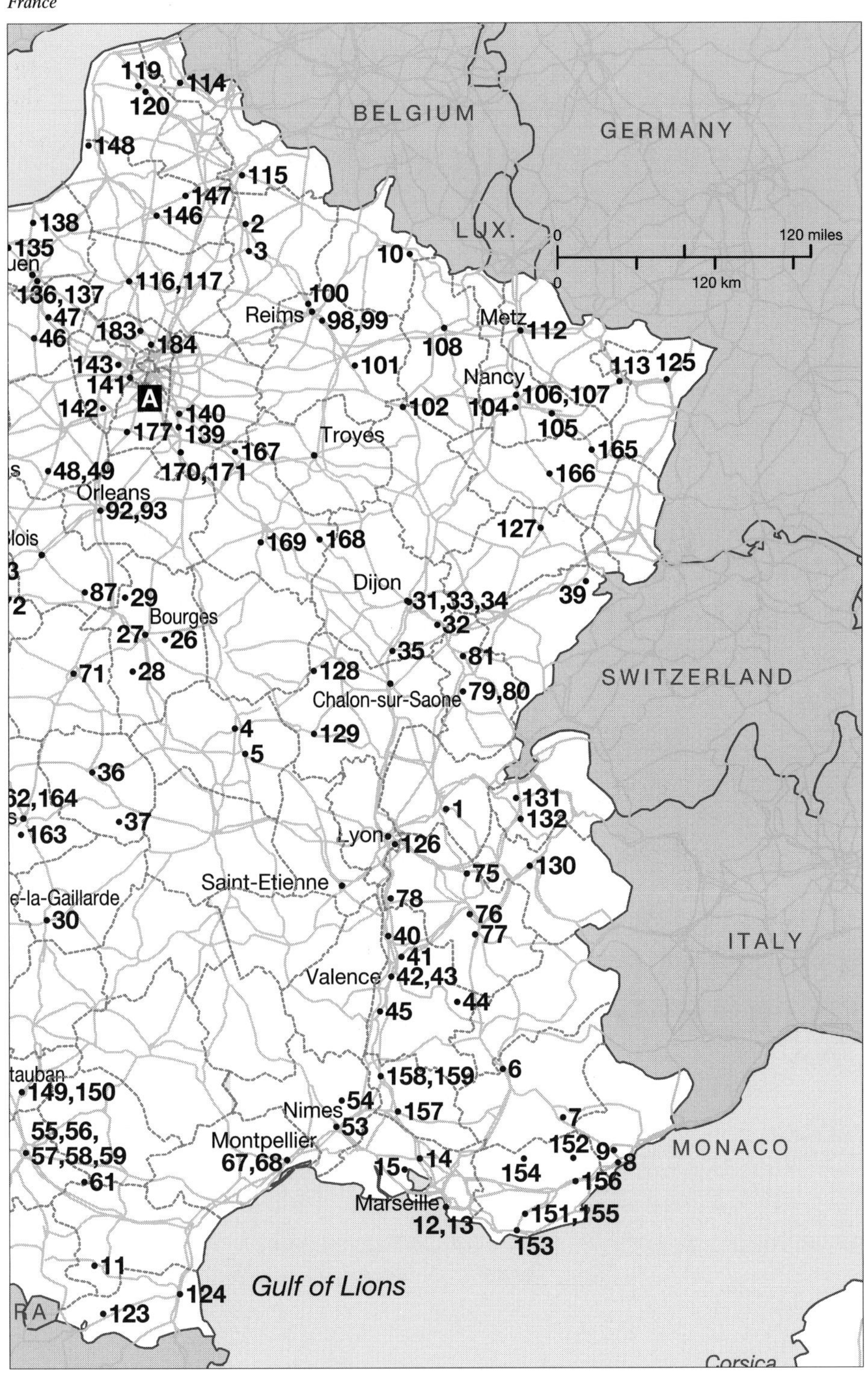
BELGIUM
GERMANY
LUX.
SWITZERLAND
ITALY
MONACO
Gulf of Lions
Corsica
0
120 miles
0
120 km
Reims
Metz
Nancy
Troyes
Orleans
Blois
Bourges
Dijon
Chalon-sur-Saone
Lyon
Saint-Etienne
Valence
Nimes
Montpellier
Marseille
A
119
120
114
148
115
147
146
138
135
2
3
10
116,117
136,137
100
98,99
47
46
183
184
143
141
142
140
177
139
170,171
167
48,49
92,93
108
112
101
102
104
106,107
113
125
105
165
166
127
169
168
87
29
27
26
31,33,34
32
39
35
81
71
28
128
79,80
4
129
5
36
163
37
1
131
132
126
130
75
30
78
76
77
40
41
42,43
44
45
6
158,159
149,150
54
157
55,56,
57,58,59
53
67,68
7
152
9
8
14
15
154
156
61
12,13
151,155
153
11
124
123

01 AIN

COLLECTION DE LA BASE AÉRIENNE D'AMBÉRIEU-EN-BUGEY (FRA1)

Address:	Base Aérienne 278. 01500 Ambérieu-en-Bugey.
Tel:	04 74 38 21 52
Fax:	04 74 38 21 52
Admission:	By prior permission only.
Location:	Just north west of the town off the N84.

The Texan has been preserved inside the main gate for twenty years and has now been joined by the Super Mystère. The falsely painted Mirage IIIRD is located in the centre of a roundabout outside the base.

TYPE	REG/SER	CON. NO.	PI/NOTES	STATUS
☐ Dassault Super Mystère B2	136	136		RA
☐ Dassault Mirage IIIRD	'356'	368	368	PVX
☐ North American NA-182 Texan (T-6G)	51-14688	182-375		RA

02 AISNE

ASSOCIATION AÉRONAUTIQUE RÉTRO CLUB DE L'AISNE (FRA2)

Address:	6 Rue Rossini, 02100 St. Quentin.
Tel:	03 23 68 79 08
Fax:	03 23 68 79 34
Admission:	By prior permission only.
Location:	At Roupy airfield which is about 7 km south west of the St. Quentin on the D 930.

The only glider currently with this group, formed in the 1990s, is one of the hundred and fifty five L-Spatzs built under licence by Avialsa at Haguenau. Other sailplanes should soon join the collection.

TYPE	REG/SER	CON. NO.	PI/NOTES	STATUS
☐ Avialsa-Scheibe A.60 Fauconnet [L-Spatz 55]	F-CAMF	4		RAA

MUSÉE DÉPARTEMENTAL DE LA RÉSISTANCE ET DE LA DEPORTATION EN PICARDIE (FRA3)

Address:	Place Carnégie, Fargniers, 02700 Tergnier.
Tel:	03 23 57 93 71
Email:	musee.resist.deport.picardie@wanadoo.fr
Admission:	Wednesday-Saturday 1400-1800; Sunday 1430-1830.
Location:	In the centre of Fargniers which is about 25 km north west of Laon.

This informative museum traces the period in which Picardie was occupied by the Germans in World War II. The history of the conflict is also portrayed. There are many poignant displays showing the deportation of civilians to the concentration camps. The Citroen used by the Gestapo in the region is a prized exhibit. The acts of sabotage, the illicit radio work and the weapons used by the patriots are vividly highlighted.

TYPE	REG/SER	CON. NO.	PI/NOTES	STATUS
☐ Beech D18S Expeditor (C-45G)				PV

03 ALLIER

COLLECTION BESSON (FRA4)

Address: 03301 Besson.
Admission: By prior permission only.
Location: About 12 km south west of Moulins off the N145.

Reports have been published of this collection displayed on private property. Further news would be most welcome. The Mirage came from Châteaudun and was dismantled on site with the majority being scrapped. The three helicopters were all civilian operated and have so far not been identified. A T-6G Texan was once stored in a nearby village but the aircraft here is said to be a former U.S. Navy SNJ-6.

TYPE	REG/SER	CON. NO.	PI/NOTES	STATUS
☐ Dassault Mirage 5F	37	37	Front fuselage only.	RA
☐ North American NA-121 Texan (SNJ-6)				RA
☐ Sud SA.341F Gazelle				RA
☐ Sud SA.341F Gazelle				RA
☐ Sud-Est SE.3130 Alouette II				RA

COLLECTION DE LA BASE AÉRIENNE DE VARENNES-SUR-ALLIER (FRA5)

Address: Base Aérienne 277,
03159 Varennes-sur-Allier.
Tel: 04 70 47 69 99
Fax: 04 70 47 69 30
Admission: By prior permission only.
Location: At two locations in the town.

The three preserved aircraft are located at two sites at this large depot. The airfield is no longer operational and the Magister is at the Captain Rousseau site with the Mirage the gate guard at the south camp. A vast quantity of stores is held in the many warehouses and the field is sometimes used as a reserve base.

TYPE	REG/SER	CON. NO.	PI/NOTES	STATUS
☐ Dassault Mystère IVA	63	63		RA
☐ Dassault Mirage IIIB	'277'	247	247	RAX
☐ Fouga CM.170R Magister	152	152		RA

04 ALPES-DE-HAUTE PROVENCE

COLLECTION RAGOT (FRA6)

Address: Montée des Esclapes,
04600 Montfort.
Tel: 04 92 64 06 42
Fax: 04 92 64 06 42
Email: avia40p@aol.com
Admission: By prior permission only.
Location: At a private workshop in the area and at St. Aubin airfield.

This private collection of vintage gliders includes an Avia 40P which returned to France in the mid-1990s after several years in store at Perranporth in England. Dating from 1942 this sailplane has recently been restored to flying condition. About forty were built with the prototype first taking to the air in 1935. In 1944 and 1946 the Avia 40 set world distance and duration records for female pilots. The prototype S-18 made its maiden flight in 1936 and the design was developed over the next fifteen years. The example in the collection was built in Switzerland by the Ister company at Wilder in 1951 and also saw use in Belgium.

TYPE	REG/SER	CON. NO.	PI/NOTES	STATUS
☐ Avia 40P	BGA.680	117		RAA
☐ Schleicher ASH-25	F-CGKU	25028		RAA
☐ Spalinger S-18-III	F-AZBI	416	HB-201, OO-ZPG	RA

MUSÉE DÉPARTEMENTAL DE LA RÉSISTANCE (FRA7)

Address:	Plan de la Palud, 04120 Castellane.
Tel:	04 92 83 78 25
Admission:	Daily 0900-1930.
Location:	About 2 km north west of the town on the N85.

The story of the local resistance fighters is portrayed in this museum. There are many harrowing tales shown in the displays. There was a great deal of opposition to the German occupiers in this mountainous region. A number of realistic dioramas with period vehicles and weapons have been constructed. On show are uniforms, radio transmitters, documents, models, maps and photographs. Parked outside, as an attraction to passing motorists, is a Fouga Magister which used to be preserved at a miniature train museum in Nice.

TYPE	REG/SER	CON. NO.	PI/NOTES	STATUS
☐ Fouga CM.170R Magister	135	135		PV

06 ALPES-MARITIMES

AILES ANCIENNES AZURÉENES (FRA8)

Address:	109A Rue de Roubine, 06150 Cannes Bocca.
Tel:	04 93 38 06 04
Fax:	04 93 38 06 04
Email:	ugsy@add.org
Admission:	By prior permission only.
Location:	Near Cannes-Mandelieu airfield which is about 5 km west of the town.

Etienne Romano set up a company with his brother at Cannes just after World War I. The three seater R 1 flying boat first flew on January 22nd 1922 and three were completed. The type was successful and Romano built a large factory at Bocca near to Mandelieu Airport which opened in 1931. A number of designs were produced over the next few years before the firm was nationalised in 1936. Aircraft were produced at the plant until just after World War II when missile research and production took over. The local A.A. group has completed a replica of the Romano R 1 which is now on show at in the excellent seaplane museum at Biscarosse. Work has started on a second example which will be completed to flying standards.

TYPE	REG/SER	CON. NO.	PI/NOTES	STATUS
☐ Romano R 1 (R)			On loan to Musée Historique de l'Hydraviation.	–
☐ Romano R 1 (R)				RAC

MUSÉE DE L'AUTOMOBILISTE (FRA9)

Address:	Aires de Breguieres, 06250 Mougins.
Tel:	04 93 69 27 80
Fax:	04 93 46 01 36
Email:	musauto@club-internet.fr
Admission:	April-September daily 1000-1900; October-May daily 1000-1800.
Location:	About 5 km north of Cannes – entrance in the motorway service area on the A 8.

Over one hundred vintage and classic hundred cars dating from 1900 are on show in this museum along with models, photographs, documents and trophies. Three collectors joined together in the early 1980s to construct the building and to pool their resources. The display opened in 1984 and contains an excellent selection of racing cars from the 1920s to modern times. There is a large collection of Ferraris ranging from road types through to Formula 1 machines of recent years. Among the cars is a 1926 Delage D1 fitted with a torpedo body. This vehicle was once owned by Louis Blériot. The Blériot XI was constructed in England by E.M.K. Aviation in Hertfordshire using some original parts. After a minor crash the airframe was rebuilt at La Ferté Alais by Salis Aviation and is the only aircraft displayed. Cycles, motor cycles, motor scooters, commercial and military vehicles are also on show in this superb exhibition. Replicas of car workshops of different periods have been constructed to show the rapid advances in automobile technology.

TYPE	REG/SER	CON. NO.	PI/NOTES	STATUS
☐ Blériot XI (R)		EMK.010 and PFA/88-10864	BAPC.132, (G-BLXI)	PV

08 ARDENNES

MUSÉE DES DÉBUTS DE L'AVIATION (FRA10)

Address:	Aérodrome de Sedan-Douzy, 08140 Douzy.
Tel:	03 24 26 38 70
Admission:	April and October Saturday-Sunday 1400- 1800; May and September Tuesday-Sunday 1400-1800; June-August Tuesday-Sunday 1000-1200 1400-1800.
Location:	On the D 964 about 1 km south of Douzy which is 8 km south east of Sedan.

Roger Sommer was born in 1877 and died in 1965. In the early years he designed and constructed a number of bipalnes and monoplanes. In 1908 he opened a flying school at Douzy. The following year he set a world duration record of almost two and a half hours at Châlons-sur Marne. To honour his work an informative museum has been built at Douzy. The centrepiece is a faithful replica of his 1910 biplane. Models of his other designs, photographs, documents and memorabilia trace the work of Sommer and other local aviators.

TYPE	REG/SER	CON. NO.	PI/NOTES	STATUS
☐ Sommer Biplane (R)				PV

11 AUDE

LES PLANEURS DE PUIVERT EN QUERCORB (FRA11)

Address:	Aérodrome, 11500 Puivert.
Tel:	04 68 20 80 14
Admission:	By prior permission only.
Location:	Just south east of the town off the D 117.

Amongst the classic fleet of this club is an example of the Carmam Foehn which was originally designed in Italy. The type was produced in France in the mid-1970s and sixty were built. The Aiglon was designed as a private venture by Robert Jacquet and Jean Pottier. The prototype flew in June 1974 and over forty were completed.

TYPE	REG/SER	CON. NO.	PI/NOTES	STATUS
☐ Avialsa-Scheibe A.60 Fauconnet [L-Spatz 55]	F-CCQT	42K		RAA
☐ Carmam JP.15/36A Aiglon	F-CETG	9		RAA
☐ Carmam M.200 Foehn	F-CCXY	9		RAA
☐ Schleicher Ka-6E Rhönsegler	F-CDTM	4350		RAA
☐ Schleicher ASW-15B	F-CEGG	15271		RAA
☐ Wassmer WA.22 Super Javelot	F-CCOL	84		RAA
☐ Wassmer WA.30 Bijave	F-CCNF	56		RA
☐ Wassmer WA.30 Bijave	F-CCNH	58		RAA
☐ Wassmer WA.30 Bijave	F-CDUX	278		RAA

13 BOUCHES DU RHONE

ASSOCIATION NORATLAS DE PROVENCE (FRA12)

Address:	Aéroport de Marseille-Provence, 13725 Marignane Cedex.
Tel:	04 90 09 90 35
Fax:	04 90 09 91 64
Email:	noratlas.de.provence@wanadoo.fr
Admission:	By prior permission only.
Location:	The airport is about 20 km north west of the city off the N 113.

This organisation was formed in the late 1990s to keep in flying condition a Noratlas once owned by the now defunct Escadrille Pégase branch of Ailes Anciennes. The French Air Force operated over two hundred examples of the twin boom transport for about thirty years from the early 1950s.

TYPE	REG/SER	CON. NO.	PI/NOTES	STATUS
☐ Nord N.2501 Noratlas	F-AZVM	105	105	RAA

ASSOCIATION UN CANADAIR POUR SAINT-VICTORET (FRA13)

Address:	Mairie, 13730 St. Victoret.
Tel:	04 42 15 32 00
Fax:	04 42 89 21 47
Admission:	On permanent view.
Location:	About 1 km east of the town of Marignane.

A fleet of Canadair CL-215s was flown on water bombing tasks from Marignane for many years. When the type was withdrawn in 2003/4 the local community formed an association to preserve one in the town which is located at the end of the main runway at Marignane. The aircraft was dismantled, moved the short distance, mounted on plinths and dedicated in June 2005. The front fuselage of another has also been saved.

TYPE	REG/SER	CON. NO.	PI/NOTES	STATUS
☐ Canadair CL-215-I	F-ZBBD/29	1029	Front fuselage only.	RA
☐ Canadair CL-215-II	F-ZBBV/46	1046	C-GAOS	PV

COLLECTION DE LA BASE AÉRIENNE DE SALON DE PROVENCE (FRA14)

Address:	Base Aérienne 701, 13661 Salon-de-Provence Air.
Tel:	04 90 53 90 90
Fax:	04 90 45 14 74
Admission:	By prior permission only.
Location:	About 2 km south east of the town off the D 68.

The site is home to the Air Force College which trains officers in all aspects of the service. The unit was originally formed at Versailles in 1925 as the École Militaire de l'Air and a move to Salon occurred in November 1937. A hard runway was installed in 1954. The first Fouga Magisters arrived in May 1956 and the type was in use for forty years. An aerobatic team 'Patrouille de l'École de l'Air' was formed in 1957 and this became the 'Patrouille de France' seven years later. The collection is dispersed around the site.

TYPE	REG/SER	CON. NO.	PI/NOTES	STATUS
☐ Breguet / British Aircraft Corporation Jaguar A	A123	A123		RA
☐ Dassault Mystère IVA	182	182		RA
☐ Dassault Mystère IVA	289	289		RA
☐ Dassault Mirage IIIC	3	3		RA
☐ Fouga CM.170R Magister	499	499		RA
☐ Fouga CM.170R Magister	531	531	At a roundabout near the base.	PV
☐ Fouga CM.170R Magister	572	572		RA

CONSERVATOIRE DU PATRIMOINE AÉRONAUTIQUE ISTRÉEN (FRA15)

Address:	B.P. 33, 13128 Istres-Air.
Tel:	04 42 56 14 80
Admission:	Not yet open.
Location:	Just west of the town off the N.1569.

A flying school was set up at Istres during World War I and the site has been in use ever since. The field is home to a section of the Centre d'Essais en Vol which uses a wide variety of types on trials work and the École du Personnel Navigant d'Essais et de Reception which is the French military test pilots school. This collection was set up in 1999 by Ailes Anciennes-Crau / Etang de Berre and has premises on the field. The aim is to set up a museum to which the public has access. A large number of books and magazines have been acquired for the setting up of an archive tracing the history of the base and aviation in general.

TYPE	REG/SER	CON.NO	PI/NOTES	STATUS
☐ Breguet / British Aircraft Corporation Jaguar A	A133	A133		PV
☐ Dassault MD-452C Mystère IIC	147	147	On base.	RA
☐ Dassault Mirage IIIB	203	203		RA
☐ Dassault Mirage IIIB	234	234		RA
☐ Dassault Mirage IIIC				RA
☐ Dassault Falcon 20G	F-WDFJ	362	(F-WZAS), F-WATF, F-WDFJ, F-GDFJ	RA
☐ Fouga CM.170R Magister				RAX
☐ Sud SA.360 Dauphin		1004		RA
☐ Vought F-8P Crusader (F-8E(FN))			Due soon.	–

14 CALVADOS

AIRBORNE MUSEUM PEGASUS BRIDGE (FRA16)

Address:	Avenue du Major Howard, 14860 Ranville.
Tel:	02 32 78 19 44
Fax:	02 31 78 19 42
Email:	infopegasus@normandy1944.com
Admission:	April-September daily 0930-1830; February-March October-November daily 1000-1300 1400-1700.
Location:	About 10 km north east of Caen on the D.224.

This museum opened in June 2000 and portrays the exploits of the 6th (Airborne) Division when they landed on D-Day. The exhibition replaced the former display alongside the Pegasus Cafe. The story of the famous battle is told in vivid detail. On show are artefacts, uniforms, models and documents. There are several weapons and vehicles which took part in the operation. Visitors can walk across the original Pegasus Bridge which has been moved to the museum grounds. A section of a Horsa fuselage is preserved in a second hall. Photographs show the glider landings which were an essential part of the operation.

TYPE	REG/SER	CON. NO.	PI/NOTES	STATUS
☐ Airspeed AS.58 Horsa I (FSM)	'PF800'			PVX
☐ Airspeed AS.58 Horsa II			Fuselage section.	PV

ASSOCIATION AVIANTIC (FRA17)

Address:	Rue de la Delle du Renard, 14280 Buron St. Conquest.
Tel:	02 31 95 06 30
Admission:	By prior permission only.
Location:	At Carpiquet Airport which is about 6 km west of Caen on the D.9

This private collection, housed in its own hangar and workshop, has seen several changes to its fleet over the last few years. A classic Potez 600 was sold and this is now being rebuilt to flying condition at Orbigny. Three former Royal Air Force Bulldogs arrived in 2001. The Vampire was acquired from Switzerland several years ago by a member of the group and is a regular performer at shows in the region.

TYPE	REG/SER	CON. NO.	PI/NOTES	STATUS
☐ De Havilland D.H.100 Vampire FB.6	F-AZHH	708	J-1199 (Switzerland)	RAA
☐ North American NA-88 Texan (AT-6D)	F-AZSC	88-15943	41-34672, NC10592, C.6-154	RAA
☐ Scottish Aviation Bulldog 120/121 (T.1)	F-AZLZ	BH120/217	XX531	RAA
☐ Scottish Aviation Bulldog 120/121 (T.1)	F-AZOZ	BH120/221	XX535	RAA
☐ Scottish Aviation Bulldog 120/121 (T.1)	F-AZLK	BH120/321	XX663	RAA
☐ Yakovlev Yak-50	F-AZYO	3201		RAA

MÉMORIAL DE CAEN (FRA18)

Address:	Esplanade Dwight D.Eisenhower, 14066 Caen.
Tel:	02 31 06 06 44
Fax:	02 31 06 01 68
Email:	contact@memorial-caen.fr
Admission:	May-September daily 0900-1900; October-April daily 1000-1830. Closed January 1st-15th.
Location:	In the north western outskirts of the city.

This impressive museum, which opened in 1988, uses modern audio and visual effects to present the story of the battles which took place over Normandy after the Allied landings in 1944. Also covered is the uneasy peace between the two world wars, the occupation of France, World War II and D-Day. The replica Hawker Typhoon hangs over the entrance hall. This fighter designed by Sydney Camm carried out many rocket attacks on the retreating Nazi forces. The former Czech MiG-21 is painted in false Soviet colours.

TYPE	REG/SER	CON. NO.	PI/NOTES	STATUS
☐ Hawker Typhoon IB (FSM)	'JP656'			PVX
☐ Mikoyan-Gurevich MiG-21R	'45'	94R01903	1903 (Czechoslovakia) – in false Soviet markings.	PVX

MUSÉE DES BALLONS (FRA19)

Address:	Château de Balleroy, 14490 Balleroy
Tel:	02 31 21 60 61
Fax:	02 31 21 51 77
Email:	forbes.inc@wanadoo.fr
Admission:	Mid-March-mid October Wednesday-Monday 0900-1200 1400-1800. July-August daily 1000-1800.
Location:	On the D 13 about 20 km south of Bayeux.

The Château was built between 1626 and 1631 and houses many treasures. These can be seen during the same hours as the balloon museum. The estate was purchased in 1970 by the late American publisher Malcolm Forbes. The museum opened on May 31st 1975 in one of the outbuildings and at the time was the only one devoted to this form of flight. A wide range of objects is displayed on the two floors. The story of the sport from the first flight by Pilatre de Rosier in the Montgolfier brothers balloon on November 21st 1783 to modern hot air and gas types is portrayed. On show are pictures, models, documents and components.

TYPE	REG/SER	CON. NO.	PI/NOTES	STATUS
☐ Balloon Works Firefly 7 Hot Air Balloon	F-BXUM	725	N2008F	RA
☐ Balloon Works Firefly 7 Hot Air Balloon	N3696J	F7-197		RA
☐ Balloon Works Firefly 7 Hot Air Balloon	N71052	F7-38		RAA
☐ Balloon Works Firefly 8-24 Hot Air Balloon	N37225	F8-022		RAA
☐ Balloon Works Firefly 8-24 Hot Air Balloon	F-GEAO	F8-023	N37228	PV
☐ Balloon Works Firefly 8-24 Hot Air Balloon	N71270	F8-134		RAA
☐ Balloon Works Firefly 8-24 Hot Air Balloon	F-GKMF	F8-362		RAA
☐ Cameron Bust 80SS Hot Air Balloon	G-BNJU	1324		RAA
☐ Cameron Château 84SS Hot Air Balloon	G-BTCZ	2246		RAA
☐ Cameron Château 84SS Hot Air Balloon	G-BKBR	743		RA
☐ Cameron Egg 89SS Hot Air Balloon	G-BNFK	1436		RAA
☐ Cameron Elephant 77SS Hot Air Balloon	G-BLRW	1074		RAA
☐ Cameron Harley 78SS Hot Air Balloon	G-BMUN	1188		RAA
☐ Cameron Macaw 90SS Hot Air Balloon	G-BRWZ	2206		RAA
☐ Cameron Magazine 90SS Hot Air Balloon	G-BPOV	1890		RAA
☐ Cameron Minaret SS Hot Air Balloon	G-BKNM	900		RA
☐ Cameron Ship 90SS Hot Air Balloon	G-BPSP	1848		RAA
☐ Cameron Sphinx 72SS Hot Air Balloon	G-BLFE	1011		RA
☐ Cameron Sultan 80SS Hot Air Balloon	G-TURK	1711		RAA
☐ Cameron Temple 80SS Hot Air Balloon	G-BMWN	1211		RAA
☐ Forbes Windborne Hot Air Balloon	N20AP	001		PV
☐ Raven CA50 Hot Air Balloon	N11979	107		PV
☐ Yost Q58 Hot Air Balloon	N1626B	2		PV
☐ Yost Silver Fox Hot Air Balloon	N92897			PV

MUSÉE MEMORIAL DE LA BATAILLE DE NORMANDIE 1944 (FRA20)

Address:	Boulevard du 6 Juin, 14400 Bayeux.
Email:	museedelabataille@free.fr
Admission:	Currently closed
Location:	In the south western part of the town on the ring road.

The curator was told by the local authorities to reduce the size of the exhibition and he refused. The majority of the collection is in store and it is hoped that a new location can be found. This impressive museum once traced the story of the seventy seven days of the battle. Large numbers of detailed maps traced the development of the invasion and the subsequent liberation of the area. The substantial remains of a Spitfire, recovered in 1989, and reported missing in July 1944 could be seen. The fighter crash landed near Faugeron-le-Buison and the pilot Flying Officer Harold Kramer was hidden for three weeks before he was captured by German forces.

TYPE	REG/SER	CON. NO.	PI/NOTES	STATUS
☐ Supermarine 361 Spitfire LF.IXb	NH341		Marked as ML295	SD

16 CHARENTE

COLLECTION DE LA BASE AÉRIENNE DE COGNAC (FRA21)

Address:	Base Aérienne 709, 16190 Cognac Air.
Tel:	05 45 32 73 00
Fax:	05 45 32 73 03
Email:	Cognac@ba709.air.defense.gouv.fr
Admission:	By prior permission only.
Location:	About 3 km south of the town on the D 731.

Basic flying training on a large fleet of TB-10 Epsilons takes place at this base. Students normally spend about six months under instruction. The resident unit is a combination of two schools. A number of Harvards from Marrakech in Morocco moved into Cognac in 1961 and these were replaced by Magisters in the summer of 1964. The Magister element of another unit, which had also been in Morocco, transferred from Orange in July 1965 and the type was in use for thirty years. The Mirage IIIE is currently used for ground instruction but has been displayed at open days. The first primary flying school in the French Air Force was formed at Istres in 1917 and the Cognac unit carries on this tradition. There is also a thriving aero club, founded in 1935, on the other side of the airfield. Prior to World War II a different airfield was in use. The club moved to its present site in 1948 and was the first in the country to set up a gliding section specifically for military personnel. Powered aircraft and sailplanes are in their fleet. Members are restoring several classic aircraft.

TYPE	REG/SER	CON. NO.	PI/NOTES	STATUS
☐ Aérospatiale TB.30 Epsilon	24	24		RAA
☐ Dassault Mirage IIIE	516	516		RA
☐ Fouga CM.170R Magister	198	198		RA
☐ Fouga CM.170R Magister	324	324		RA
☐ Fouga CM.170R Magister	376	376		RA

17 CHARENTE MARITIME

COLLECTION DE LA BASE AÉRIENNE DE ROCHEFORT-ST. AGNANT (FRA22)

Address:	Base Aérienne 721, 17133 Rochefort Air.
Tel:	05 46 83 08 40
Fax:	05 46 82 07 42
Admission:	By prior permission only.
Location:	About 6 km south of the town off the D 733.

Completed in 1978 this new base houses a major technical school. Prior to this the Armée de l'Air and the Aéronavale had used a joint facility at nearby Soubise, which is is now used by the Gendarmerie. The students are taught all aspects of airframe, engine and electronics technology. The unique Mirage IIIT is mounted just inside the main gate. The airframe was constructed as a test bed for the American engines being built under licence by S.N.E.C.M.A. This prototype first flew on June 4th 1964 and was retired five years later. The rear fuselage has a greater diameter than the standard Mirage III to accommodate the larger engines. The aircraft was also used for other test roles and a great deal of valuable data was acquired which helped the development of the Mirage family. The Jaguar and the Mirage F.1C have recently joined the collection and more types are expected for the display. In the school are many instructional airframes which are used for a variety of tasks. On the site there is a mock-up airfield with a hangar and other installations to train students in how to move and service aircraft under operational conditions. Types currently present include Mirage IIIBs, Mirage IIIEs, Mirage IIIRs, Mirage IIIRDs, Mirage F.1Cs, Fouga Magisters, and Jaguar Es.

TYPE	REG/SER	CON. NO.	PI/NOTES	STATUS
☐ Breguet / British Aircraft Corporation Jaguar E	E18	E18		RA
☐ Dassault MD-312 Flamant	196	196		RA
☐ Dassault Mirage IIIE	401	401	On roundabout near base.	PV
☐ Dassault Mirage IIIE	563	563		RA
☐ Dassault Mirage IIIT	01	01		RA
☐ Dassault Mirage IVA	4	4		RA
☐ Dassault Mirage F.1C	16	16		RA
☐ Nord N.2501 Noratlas	122	122		RA

COLLECTION DE LA BASE AÉRIENNE DE SAINTES (FRA23)

Address:	Base Aérienne 722, Les Gondes, 17136 Saintes Air.
Tel:	05 46 93 05 11
Fax:	05 46 93 39 51
Admission:	By prior permission only.
Location:	About 4 km south of Saintes on the N 137.

This base, on the side of the local club airfield, houses a technical training school. For many years aircraft have been preserved close to the gate and on the main parade ground. Some airframes seem to double up as instructional aids. The Mystère IVA has recently been repainted and can be seen near the main gate. The black painted Super Mystère is parked among the buildings. The Mirage IIIE is now believed to be the genuine 401.

TYPE	REG/SER	CON. NO.	PI/NOTES	STATUS
☐ Carmam JP.15/36 Aiglon	P53			RA
☐ Dassault Mystère IVA	'186'	11	11	RAX
☐ Dassault Super Mystère B2	156	156		RA
☐ Dassault Mirage IIIC	1	1		RA
☐ Dassault Mirage IIIE	401	401	On roundabout near base.	PVX

MUSÉE DES TRADITIONS DE L'AÉRONAUTIQUE NAVALE (FRA24)

Address:	Base Aéronavale de Rochefort-Soubise, 17300 Rochefort.
Tel:	05 46 87 11 22 ext 22500
Admission:	Currently closed.
Location:	In the south western suburbs of the town.

The service was formed on March 12th 1912 with four aircraft and by the outbreak of World War I fourteen were on strength. During the conflict several seaplane bases and airfields were set up around the French and North African coasts. The first aircraft carrier, the Béarn, was commissioned in 1927 and when World War II broke out around three hundred and fifty, mainly obsolescent, aircraft were in use. In the post war period modern types were acquired and at the current time six airfields and two carriers are in service. The base at Rochefort was set up during World War I and its buildings included two airship hangars. In recent years the field has not been used by operational units. Until 1978 a joint Armée de l'Air and Aéronavale technical training school was in residence. The Air Force then moved to their new facility at St. Agnant. The plans for a museum were put forward several years ago and a former airship hangar which had been reduced in height in the 1930s for aircraft use was allocated. The collection was officially opened on September 30th 1988 but as yet visitors are not admitted on a regular basis. The rooms along the side housed fascinating displays tracing the history of the service from its formation. On show were models, photographs, uniforms, components, instruments, engines etc. Several ground instructional airframes were moved from the nearby workshops and these were joined by recently retired types. A range of aircraft operated since World War II is now present. Under restoration is a Dewoitine D.520DC loaned by the Musée de l'Air. The first prototype of this low wing fighter flew in October 1938. The type soon entered production and over four hundred had been completed when France was occupied. The Germans allowed almost another five hundred to be made. The D.520DC is a two seat conversion and about thirteen were completed. The sole Jaguar M, intended for naval use, was tested at the C.E.V. but no orders were placed for this version. The site is now used by the Gendarmerie and most of the aircraft are now in the former C.E.A.N. hangar where the displays are being set up again. The former building is now used for restoration. A team of volunteers has worked for years to get this project off the ground and hopefully their dreams will be realised one day. A vast amount of unique material has been donated and needs to be exhibited.

TYPE	REG/SER	CON. NO.	PI/NOTES	STATUS
☐ Agusta-Bell 47G	056	056	056, CAN-7	RA
☐ Beech C18S Expeditor (C-45F) (UC-45F) (JRB-4)	66425	8643	44-87384, Bu66425	RA
☐ Beech D18S Expeditor (SNB-5) (TC-45J) (UC-45J)	709		Bu134709, 134709	RA
☐ Breguet / British Aircraft Corporation Jaguar M	05	M05	F-ZWRJ	RA
☐ Breguet 1050 Alizé	1	1		RA
☐ Breguet 1050 Alizé	8	8	Preserved outside base.	RA
☐ Breguet 1050 Alizé	15	15		RA
☐ Caudron C.800 Épervier	F-CAFB	9865/205	On loan from M.A.	RA
☐ Consolidated 28-5A Canso A	F-ZBAR	CV 449	11100 (Canada), CF-NJP – front fuselage only.	RA
☐ Dassault MD-312 Flamant	294	294		RA
☐ Dassault Etendard IVM	01	01	Preserved by base gate.	RA
☐ Dassault Etendard IVM	05	05		RA
☐ Dassault Etendard IVM	7	7		RA
☐ Dassault Super Etendard	02	02		RA
☐ Dewoitine D.520DC	'408'	650	650 – on loan from M.A.	RACX
☐ Douglas DC-3A-467 Skytrain (C-47B) (Dakota IV)	77116	16700/33448	44-77116, KP229, K-36 (Belgium)	RA

☐ Fouga CM.175 Zéphyr	1	1		RA
☐ Fouga CM.175 Zéphyr	20	20		RA
☐ Fouga CM.175 Zéphyr	24	24		RA
☐ Lockheed 726-45-14 Neptune (P2V-7)	144688	726-7139	Bu144688	RA
☐ Max Holste MH.1521M Broussard	CAN16	258	258	RA
☐ Morane-Saulnier MS.760A Paris I	31	31		RA
☐ Morane-Saulnier MS.760A Paris I	33	33		RA
☐ North American NA-81 Harvard II	3820	81-4087	3820 (Canada)	RA
☐ Piper PA-31-350 Navajo B	925	31-7300925		RA
☐ Sikorsky S-58	150	SA-150		RA
☐ Stampe & Vertongen S.V.4C	'7'	38	On loan from M.A.	RAX
☐ Sud-Est Aquilon 203 [De Havilland D.H.112]	53	53	On loan from M.A.	RA
☐ Sud-Est SE.3130 Alouette II	41	1041	Also reported as 138.	RA
☐ Vertol V.43 (H-21C)	'H20'	FR-63	FR63	RAX
☐ Vought F-8P Crusader (F-8E(FN))	11	1228	(Bu151743)	RA
☐ Westland WG.13 Lynx HAS.2	04	4/20	XX911, F-ZKCV	RA
☐ Zodiac ZD			Nacelle only – on loan from MA.	RA

MUSÉE MIGNET/ COLLECTION MONNEREAU (FRA25)

Address:	Aérodrome de Bois Fleurie, 17320 Marennes.
Tel:	05 46 85 06 51
Admission:	By prior permission only.
Location:	Just north east of the town

Albert Baron built a number of Mignet designs in the area and his HM-293 is now suspended from the roof of one of the buildings. Components of some of his other aircraft can be seen along with photographs and documents. Jean-Michel Monnereau has acquired three Mignet types along with two other unique homebuilts.

TYPE	REG/SER	CON. NO.	PI/NOTES	STATUS
☐ Chatelain AC.5 Bijou	F-PHQO	01		RA
☐ Langray GL-1	F-PXDV	01	(F-WXDV)	RAA
☐ Mignet HM-8				RA
☐ Mignet HM-8				RA
☐ Mignet HM-293 Pou-du-Ciel	F-PFRH	AB 05 (04)	F-WFRH	RA
☐ Mignet HM-360 Pou-du-Ciel	F-PFKC	1		RAA

18 CHER

COLLECTION DE LA BASE AÉRIENNE D'AVORD (FRA26)

Address:	Base Aérienne 702, Avenue Bourges, 18502 Avord.
Tel:	02 48 69 13 05
Fax:	02 48 69 16 38
Admission:	By prior permission only.
Location:	About 2 km north of the town which is about 18 km south east of Bourges.

A Camp d'Aviation was set up at Avord in September 1910 to train military pilots. The Luftwaffe used the base during World War II and in 1944 it was almost completely destroyed by Allied bombing. A twin engine conversion school was established in 1945 and for many years it was equipped with the Flamant and two examples of the type have been preserved. The Brazilian Embraer Xingu is now flown and these first arrived at the field in 1982. A Mirage IVA joined the collection in the mid-1990s.

TYPE	REG/SER	CON. NO.	PI/NOTES	STATUS
☐ Dassault MD-312 Flamant	146	146		RA
☐ Dassault MD-312 Flamant	229	229		RA
☐ Dassault Mystère IVA				RA
☐ Dassault Super Mystère B2	99	99	At local barracks at Savigny-en-Septaine.	RA
☐ Dassault Mirage IIIB	214	214	On show in village.	PV
☐ Dassault Mirage IIIE	489	489		RA
☐ Dassault Mirage IVA	29	29		RA

COLLECTION ÉCOLE SUPERIÉURE ET D'APPLICATION DU MATÉRIEL (FRA27)

Address:	L.P. 709, Quartier Auger Carnot, 18015 Bourges Cedex.
Tel:	02 48 68 74 99
Admission:	By prior permission only.
Location:	In the south east of the town between the D976 and N76.

The site is a main training base for A.L.A.T. officers and has been in the town for almost sixty years. The school was originally established at Mèknes in Morocco in 1943. A move to Bourges took place in 1945 and in the early 1960s the officer's school transferred from Fontainebleu. A new complex was built at this time. Three types which have flown with the service have been preserved to show students some of the traditions of the force. Several instructional airframes are located in the workshop area of the school.

TYPE	REG/SER	CON. NO.	PI/NOTES	STATUS
☐ Cessna 305C Bird Dog (L-19E) (O-1E)	24523	24523		RA
☐ Sud-Est SE.3130 Alouette II	1228	1228		RA
☐ Sud-Est SE.3160 Alouette III	1363	1363		RA

MUSÉE AÉRONAUTIQUE DU BERRY (FRA28)

Address:	Les Cocardiers du Ciel, 31 Avenue Jean-Louis Boneur, 18160 Touchay.
Tel:	02 48 60 16 49
Email:	museeaeronautiqueduberry@wanadoo.fr
Admission:	By prior permission only.
Location:	About 6 km south east of Lignières.

Members of Les Cocardiers du Ciel are in the process of establishing a museum. A hangar and workshop have been constructed at Michel Balland's home. Restoration of the Mystère IVA is nearly complete. This aircraft was once at the museum at Savingy. A rare Mystère IIC which came from a park in Henin-Beaumont has been exchanged with the Musée de l'Air for a Super Mystère B2. The IIC will go to the Conservatoire at Bordeaux close to the Dassault factory where it was built. Work on one of the ex-Cognac Fouga Magisters is progressing. Expected from Rochefort is a Mirage IIIRD which had been in use as an instructional airframe A collection of engines, uniforms, photographs, components, documents etc. has been acquired. The early Norécrin is in store in a nearby building. Associated material is being acquired so that a display can be set up.

TYPE	REG/SER	CON. NO.	PI/NOTES	STATUS
☐ Dassault Mystère IVA	293	293		PV
☐ Dassault Super Mystère B2	59	59	On loan from M.A.	PV
☐ Dassault Mirage IIIC	44	44		PV
☐ Dassault Mirage IIIRD			Due soon	–
☐ Dassault Etendard IVM	41	41		PV
☐ Fouga CM.170R Magister	394	394		PV
☐ Fouga CM.170R Magister	484	484		PV
☐ Fouga CM.170R Magister	568	568		PV
☐ Nord N.1201 Norécrin	F-BDSF	11		RA
☐ Sikorsky S-58	1376			PV

MUSEÉ HISTORIMAGE (FRA29)

Address:	National Federation André Maginot, 18330 Neuvy-sur-Barangeon.
Tel:	02 48 52 64 00
Fax:	02 48 52 64 02
Email:	historimage@grande-garenne.com
Admission:	Tuesday-Sunday 0930-1200 1400-1800.
Location:	In the town which is on the D926 about 18 km north east of Vierzon.

The story of war over the centuries is told in a series of innovative audio-visual displays. The conflicts from the early times up to modern days are all featured. The World War II Normandy landings and the work of André Maginot in constructing the complex defence structures are among the events highlighted. On show are weapons, documents, photographs and uniforms to enhance the exhibition. The former Italian Harvard is mounted outside the building and has been painted in French period colours.

TYPE	REG/SER	CON. NO.	PI/NOTES	STATUS
☐ Noorduyn Harvard IIB [North American NA-77]		07/??	(USAAF), MM54144 – In false French markings.	PVX

19 CORRÈZE

ASSOCIATION POUR LA SAUVEGARDE DU PATRIMOINE AÉRIEN DE L'ARMÉE DE L'AIR (FRA30)

Address:	Aérodrome de Brive Laroche, 19100 Brive-Lagaillarde.
Tel:	05 55 86 88 37 (Airport)
Admission:	By prior permission only.
Location:	About 5 km west of the town off the N 89.

Formed in the early-1990s with the aim of preserving mainly ex-Air Force types, this group has assembled an interesting collection. One former Naval aircraft has arrived. The Etendard IVM entered service with the French Navy in 1962 and sixty nine examples were delivered.

TYPE	REG/SER	CON. NO.	PI/NOTES	STATUS
☐ Dassault MD-311 Flamant	288	288		RA
☐ Dassault Mirage IIIRD	359	359		RA
☐ Dassault Etendard IVM	16	16		RA
☐ Fouga CM.170R Magister	44	44		RA
☐ Nord N.1203 Norécrin				RAC
☐ Nord N.1203 Norécrin				RAC

21 CÔTE D'OR

AILES ANCIENNES DIJON-BOURGOGNE (FRA31)

Address:	7 Boulevard Mansard, 21000 Dijon.
Tel:	03 80 65 26 61
Admission:	By prior permission only.
Location:	At a workshop in the city.

The group is planning to acquire a Pou-du-Ciel in the near future and restore it for static exhibition. The HM-18 first appeared in 1936 and the prototype was sold to England. A number of others were started in France.

TYPE	REG/SER	CON. NO.	PI/NOTES	STATUS
☐ Mignet HM-18 Pou-du-Ciel			Due soon.	–

ASSOCIATION DE SAUVEGARD DU PATRIMOINE POTEZ 25 (FRA32)

Address:	28 Rue Bizot, 21130 Les Maillys.
Email:	courier@potez25.assso.fr
Admission:	By prior permission only.
Location:	About 12 km north west of Dole on the D.20.

The Potez 25 first flew in 1925 and about four thousand were built mainly for military use. Two replicas are being built by this group using original drawings. Work started several years ago and the first is well under way. This will be painted in the colours of one flown crashed in the Andes by Aéropostale pilot Henri Guillaumet. One example is destined for the Musée de l'Air at Le Bourget and the other will be airworthy.

TYPE	REG/SER	CON. NO.	PI/NOTES	STATUS
☐ Potez 25 (R)				RAC
☐ Potez 25 (R)				RAC

ASSOCIATION POUR LA SAUVEGARDE DE L'AVIATION DE CHASSE (FRA33)

Address:	B.P. 25, Aeroport de Dijon-Longvic, 21601 Longvic Cedex.
Admission:	By prior permission only.
Location:	About 4 km south east of the town off the D 966.

This group, made up of current and former fighter pilots, recently flew a Fouga Magister as well as the Alcyon. However the jet has been sold and their only aircraft is currently airworthy at Dijon.

TYPE	REG/SER	CON. NO.	PI/NOTES	STATUS
☐ Morane-Saulnier MS.733 Alcyon	F-AZZO	108	108, F-BMMU	RAA

MUSÉE DE LA BASE AÉRIENNE DE DIJON-LONGVIC (FRA34)

Address:	Base Aérienne 102, 21032 Dijon Cedex.
Tel:	03 80 65 49 12
Fax:	03 80 65 86 88
Admission:	By prior permission only.
Location:	About 4 km south east of the town off the D 966.

The 2nd Fighter Wing was set up in Germany in November 1945 when two squadrons of Spitfires were transferred from the Royal Air Force. After a short period in Indochina the unit was disbanded only to be reformed in Germany with P-47 Thunderbolts. Since then it has flown Vampires, Mistrals, Ouragans, Mystère IVAs, Mirage IIICs, Mirage IIIEs and now the Mirage 2000. In 1961, at Dijon, it became the first unit to operate the Mirage IIIC. The preserved aircraft are located inside the main gate and by the ramp. The Mirage IIIC front fuselage is displayed inside the base museum which traces the military history of the airfield and its units.

TYPE	REG/SER	CON. NO.	PI/NOTES	STATUS
☐ Dassault Mystère IVA	290	290		RA
☐ Dassault Mirage IIIC			Front fuselage only.	RA
☐ Dassault Mirage IIIC	30	30		RA
☐ Dassault Mirage IIIE	'425'	–		RAX
☐ Dassault Mirage 5F	14	14		RA
☐ Dassault Mirage 2000C (FSM)	'22'			RAX
☐ Max Holste MH.1521M Broussard	226	226		RA
☐ Sikorsky S-58	479	SKY-479		RA

MUSÉE DU CHÂTEAU DE SAVIGNY (FRA35)

Address:	Château de Savigny, 21420 Savigny-lès-Beaune.
Tel:	03 80 21 55 03
Fax:	03 80 21 54 84
Email:	contact@chateau-savigny.com
Admission:	March-October daily 0900-1200 1400-1830; November-February daily 0900-1200 1400-1730.
Location:	About 6 km north west of Beaune on the D 2.

The first château at Savigny was built in 1340 but was demolished in 1478 as a punitive measure against the owner. The majority of the present building dates from the start of the seventeenth century. Now owned by Michel Pont the estate has much to offer for the visitor. Wine production was restarted a quarter of a century ago and its products are on sale in the reception area. Rooms in the main building house a superb collection of over five hundred motor cycles, including many racing machines, dating from 1903 to 1960. Also in this area are exhibitions tracing the history of aviation with components, more than six hundred and fifty models, photographs and memorabilia on show. The 1930s Pou-du-Ciel, acquired in 1987, and the hang glider are displayed here. The Mignet design spent many years in store in the locality. Another section exhibits a range of prototype Abarth cars. Michel Pont served in the Air Force and he had the idea of establishing a museum of post World War II combat aircraft. The first to arrive was Mirage IIIR No. 323 which was placed in the grounds on July 12th 1986. Eleven airframes were acquired in 1987 and another fifteen arrived the following year. Now almost seventy aircraft are on show with another thirty in store and available for exchange. The site is being improved and the aircraft are arranged in lines in fenced enclosures. Deals with Belgium resulted in a number of Thunderstreaks arriving, along with a pair of Starfighters. Exchanges have also taken place with museums in Germany, Poland and Portugal to enhance the exhibition. The first Mirage IV in private ownership arrived in 1987 from Bordeaux. Almost the whole range of Dassault jets which have served operationally from the early 1950s up to the Mirage F.1 can be seen. American, British, Italian, Polish and Russian designs are on view in this excellent collection. The search for new types continues and more exhibits are due to arrive in the near future.

TYPE	REG/SER	CON. NO.	PI/NOTES	STATUS
☐ Aero L-29 Delfin	2608	792608		PV
☐ Breguet / British Aircraft Corporation Jaguar A	A8	A8		PV
☐ Breguet / British Aircraft Corporation Jaguar A	A21	A21		PV
☐ Breguet / British Aircraft Corporation Jaguar A	A36	A36		RA
☐ Breguet / British Aircraft Corporation Jaguar A	A72	A72		RA
☐ Breguet 1050 Alizé	04	04		PV
☐ Canadair CL-13B Sabre 6 [North American F-86E]	JA+339	1651	BB+2??, JD+234, JD+334, JA+334, JA+239, JD+339	PV
☐ Canadair CL-30 Silver Star 3 (CT-133) [Lockheed 580 (T-33AN)]	21029	T33-029		PV
☐ Canadair CL-30 Silver Star 3 (CT-133) [Lockheed 580 (T-33AN)]	21127	T33-127		RA
☐ Canadair CL-90 Starfighter (CF-104) [Lockheed 683-04-12]	104799	683A-1099	12799 – tail from c/n 683A-1050 12750 (Canada), 104750 (Canada)	PV
☐ Dassault MD-450 Ouragan	'251'	215	215	PVX
☐ Dassault MD-450 Ouragan	230	230		PV
☐ Dassault MD-452C Mystère IIC	013	013		PV
☐ Dassault Mystère IVA	24	24	Nose on show.	PV/RA
☐ Dassault Mystère IVA	37	37	With tail from c/n 47.	PV
☐ Dassault Mystère IVA	39	39		RA
☐ Dassault Mystère IVA	100	100		RA
☐ Dassault Mystère IVA	116	116		RA
☐ Dassault Super Mystère B2	02	02		PV
☐ Dassault Super Mystère B2	50	50		RA
☐ Dassault Super Mystère B2	60	60	Front fuselage only.	PV
☐ Dassault Super Mystère B2	69	69		PV
☐ Dassault Super Mystère B2	91	91		RA
☐ Dassault Super Mystère B2	118	118		PV
☐ Dassault Mirage IIIA	06	06		PV
☐ Dassault Mirage IIIB	216	216	Tail from c/n 218.	PV
☐ Dassault Mirage IIIC	35	35		RA
☐ Dassault Mirage IIIC	37	37		RA
☐ Dassault Mirage IIIC	50	50		PV
☐ Dassault Mirage IIIE			Front fuselage only.	PV
☐ Dassault Mirage IIIE	402	402		RA
☐ Dassault Mirage IIIE	438	438	Possible identity.	PV
☐ Dassault Mirage IIIE	499	499		RA
☐ Dassault Mirage IIIE	501	501	Fuselage only.	RA
☐ Dassault Mirage IIIO	001	001		PV
☐ Dassault Mirage IIIR	323	323		PV
☐ Dassault Mirage IIIR	324	324		RA
☐ Dassault Mirage IIIR	327	327		RA
☐ Dassault Mirage IIIRD	354	354		PV
☐ Dassault Mirage IIIV				RA
☐ Dassault Mirage IVA	18	18		PV
☐ Dassault Mirage IVA	6	6		PV
☐ Dassault Mirage 5F	9	9	Composite.	PV
☐ Dassault Mirage F.1C			Fuselage only.	RA
☐ Dassault Mirage F.1C	9	9		PV
☐ Dassault Etendard IVM			Front fuselage only.	PV
☐ Dassault Etendard IVP	166	166		PV
☐ Dassault Super Etendard	60	66		PV
☐ De Havilland D.H.100 Vampire FB.6	J-1178	687	In Swiss markings.	PV
☐ De Havilland D.H.112 Venom FB.1	J-1545	755	In Swiss markings.	PV
☐ De Havilland D.H.115 Vampire T.55	185	15775	In Irish markings – on loan from M.A.	PV
☐ English Electric P.1B Lightning F.1A	XM178	95065	XM178, 8418M	PV
☐ Fiat G.91R/3	32+43	91-512	KD+502, EC+305, MO+305, MB+129	PV
☐ Fiat G.91T/3 (T/1)	1801	91-2-0003	BD+103, 34+03 – in Portuguese markings.	PV
☐ Fouga CM.170R Magister	'493'	14	14, F-WGPU	PVX
☐ Fouga CM.170R Magister	48	48		PV
☐ Fouga CM.170R Magister	MT-33	290	In Belgian markings.	PV
☐ Fouga CM.175 Zéphyr	2	2		PV
☐ Gloster Meteor T.7	F6		WA607, F-BEAR	PV
☐ Gloster Meteor NF.11	NF.11-24		WM382 – on loan from M.A.	PV
☐ Gloster Meteor TT.20 (NF.11)	SE-DCH	5549	(WM391), 51-508 (Denmark), H-508 (Denmark), (D-CAKU)	RA
☐ Gloster Meteor TT.20 (NF.11)	SE-DCF	5562	(WM395), 51-512 (Denmark), H-512 (Denmark), (D-CAKY)	PV
☐ Hawker P.1067 Hunter F.4	ID-44	8138	In Belgian markings – on loan from M.A.	PV
☐ Hiway Super Scorpion Hang Glider				PV
☐ Lockheed 583-10-20 Starfighter (TF-104G)	FC-08	583G-5105	In Belgian markings	PV
☐ Lockheed 683-10-19 Starfighter (F-104G)	FX-90	683-9154	In Belgian markings.	PV
☐ Mignet HM-14 Pou-du-Ciel				PV
☐ Mikoyan-Gurevich MiG-19S	0219	050219	In Czech. markings.	PV
☐ Mikoyan-Gurevich MiG-21M	1904	961904	In Polish markings.	PV
☐ Mikoyan-Gurevich MiG-21MF	23+43	96001091	774 (DDR)	PV
☐ Mikoyan-Gurevich MiG-21U-600	2718	662718	In Polish markings.	PV
☐ Mikoyan-Gurevich MiG-23MF	3887	0390213877	In Czech markings.	PV

☐ Mil Mi-2M	0625	510625038	625 – In Polish markings.	PV
☐ Morane-Saulnier MS.733 Alcyon			Due soon.	–
☐ Morane-Saulnier MS.760A Paris I	46	46		PV
☐ Nord N.2501 Noratlas	92	92	Fuselage only.	RA
☐ Nord N.2501 Noratlas	149	149	Fuselage only.	RA
☐ Nord N.2501 Noratlas	151	151		PV
☐ North American NA-88 Texan (AT-6C)	1527	88-10673	41-33553, EX580, 7248 (South Africa) – in Portuguese markings – also reported as 1734.	PV
☐ North American NA-223 Super Sabre (F-100D)	42130	223-10	54-2130 – fitted with tail from c/n 223-115 54-2235, 42235	PV
☐ North American NA-224 Super Sabre (F-100D)	52739	224-6	55-2739 – fitted with tail from c/n 223-10 54-2130, 42130.	RA
☐ North American NA-243 Super Sabre (F-100F)	63937	243-213	56-3937 – fitted with tail from c/n 223-173 54-2293.	PV
☐ North American NA-243 Super Sabre (F-100F)	64017	243-293	56-4017	RA
☐ Republic F-84E Thunderjet	51-9592			RA
☐ Republic F-84F Thunderstreak	FU-21		52-7170 – in Belgian markings	RA
☐ Republic F-84F Thunderstreak	FU-31		52-7178 – in Belgian markings.	RA
☐ Republic F-84F Thunderstreak	FU-45		52-7210 – in Belgian markings.	PV
☐ Republic F-84F Thunderstreak	FU-97		53-6539 – in Belgian markings.	RA
☐ Republic F-84F Thunderstreak	FU-29		52-7175 – in Belgian markings.	PV
☐ Republic F-84F Thunderstreak	FU-106		53-6722 – in Belgian markings.	RA
☐ Republic F-84F Thunderstreak	FU-116		53-6738 – in Belgian markings.	RA
☐ Republic F-84F Thunderstreak	52-9003		Tail from 52-7170, FU-21	PV
☐ Republic RF-84F Thunderflash	FR-26		51-1886 – in Belgian markings.	PV
☐ Republic F-84G Thunderjet	'110885'		51-10838, 5216 (Portugal)	PVX
☐ Republic F-105F Thunderchief	63-8357	F-134		PV
☐ Sikorsky S-58	114	SA-114		PV
☐ Sud-Est SE.3130 Alouette II	1247	1247		PV
☐ Sud-Ouest SO-4050 Vautour IIA	2	2		PV
☐ Sud-Ouest SO-4050 Vautour IIN	304	11	On loan from M.A.	PV
☐ Sukhoi Su-7BKL	813	7813	In Polish markings.	PV
☐ Sukhoi Su-20R	6259	74209	In Polish markings.	PV
☐ Vought F-8J Crusader (F8U-2NE) (F-8E)			Front fuselage only.	PV
☐ Vought F-8J Crusader (F8U-2NE) (F-8E)			Front fuselage only.	PV
☐ Vought F-8J Crusader (F8U-2NE) (F-8E)			Front fuselage only.	PV
☐ Vought F-8J Crusader (F8U-2NE) (F-8E)			Front fuselage only.	PV
☐ Vought F-8P Crusader (F-8E(FN))	'Bu150879'			PVX
☐ Vought F-8P Crusader (F-8E(FN))	35	1252	(Bu151766)	PVX
☐ Westland-Sikorsky WS-55 Whirlwind HAR.2	130	WA.130		PV
☐ Wytwornia Sprzetu Komunikacyjnego (WSK) Lim-2 [MiG-15bis]	1811	1B 018-11		PV
☐ Wytwornia Sprzetu Komunikacyjnego (WSK) SBLim-2 (Lim-1) [MiG-15] [MiG-15UTI]	720	1A 07-020		PV
☐ Wytwornia Sprzetu Komunikacyjnego (WSK) Lim-6bis (Lim-5M) [MiG-17F]	306	1F 03-06		PV

23 CREUSE

ASSOCIATION AÉRONAUTIQUE CREUSOISE (FRA36)

Address:	Centre de Vol à Voile, Aérodrome de Guéret, 23170 Lepaud.
Tel:	05 55 65 74 21
Email:	polanezencreuse@yahoo.fr
Admission:	By prior permission only.
Location:	About 6 km east of Guéret off the D 4.

This organisation is a member of Dédale and operates a fleet of classic gliders from both France and Germany. Two Siren Edelweiss prototypes flew in 1962 and the following year the pair took part in the world gliding championships in Argentina. One, piloted by Jacki Lacheny finished second. The design was modified after the contest and a production model won the standard class at the 1965 championships held at South Cerney in England. Over fifty examples of the sleek design were produced in the mid-1960s. The Wassmer company constructed its first glider in the mid-1950s and initially concentrated on training sailplanes.

TYPE	REG/SER	CON. NO.	PI/NOTES	STATUS
☐ Bölkow Phoebus CWB	F-CDOL	925		RAA
☐ Carmam M.100S Mésange				RAA
☐ Schempp-Hirth HS-7 Mini-Nimbus	F-CFAB	130		RAA
☐ Schempp-Hirth Janus B	F-CEPP	95		RAA

TYPE	REG/SER	CON. NO.	PI/NOTES	STATUS
☐ Siren C.30S Edelweiss	F-CDAK	30		RAA
☐ Wassmer WA.22A Super Javelot	F-CCRB	94		RAA
☐ Wassmer WA.28 Espadon	F-CEOF	111		RAA
☐ Wassmer WA.30 Bijave	F-CDJG	213		RAA

MÉMORIAL DE LA PAIX (FRA37)

Address:	23100 Féniers.
Admission:	On permanent view.
Location:	In the centre of the village which is about 15 km south of Felletin off the D.19.

The village has housed a military camp for many years. During World War II many battles were fought in the area. There was also an active Resistance group operating in the region. A small memorial has been erected to honour those who lost their lives. A Fouga Magister has been preserved.

TYPE	REG/SER	CON. NO.	PI/NOTES	STATUS
☐ Fouga CM.170R Magister	477	477		PV

24 DORDOGNE

ASSOCIATION DES CAGES A POULES D'AQUITAINE (FRA38)

Address:	La Tissanderie, Liorac-sur-Louyre, 24520 Mouleydier.
Admission:	By prior permission only.
Location:	At a private airfield north of Liorac which is about 15 km north east of Bergerac.

Based at a picturesque private airfield set in the hills above the Louvre valley this collection owns one of the two Max Holste 52s known to survive. The prototype of this low wing all metal two seater made its maiden flight in 1947 and only thirteen were built. The aircraft in the group was withdrawn in 1989 and a slow rebuild started several years ago. The Nord N.3400 is in store and the two Cubs are regularly flown.

TYPE	REG/SER	CON. NO.	PI/NOTES	STATUS
☐ Max Holste MH.52R	F-BFEP	11	F-BDXX	RA
☐ Nord N.3400				RA
☐ Piper J-3C-65 Cub (L-4H)	F-BFYD	8979	42-38410	RAA
☐ Piper J-3C-65 Cub (L-4H)	F-GLMS	12192	44-79896, NC78919, N78919, G-ANXP, D-EGUL, PH-CMS, (OO-LSD), OO-GMS	RAA

25 DOUBS

ASSOCIATION MONTBELIARD DASSAULT 312 (FRA39)

Address:	Route de l'Aérodrome, 25420 Courcelles les Montbeliard
Tel:	03 80 95 17 87
Admission:	By prior permission only.
Location:	The airfield is in the south western suburbs of the town.

This group acquired its Flamant from the now defunct Association Til-Retro in 2004. During its military service it was operated at Châteaudun from 1953 to 1957 and then by the twin engine conversion school at Avord until its retirement in 1984. Restored by the group at Til it is now resplendent in the colours it wore at Avord.

TYPE	REG/SER	CON. NO.	PI/NOTES	STATUS
☐ Dassault MD-312 Flamant	F-AZES	226	226	RAA

26 DRÔME

AÉRO RÉTRO (FRA40)

Address:	Aérodrome de St. Rambert d'Albon, 26140 Albon.
Tel:	04 75 03 03 58
Email:	aeroretro@aol.com
Admission:	No definite hours – someone may be present when the airfield is open.
Location:	About 4 km. south of the town on the N 7 and about 60 km. south of Lyon.

Christian Martin founded this organisation in 1977 and close links are maintained with Amicale Jean-Baptiste Salis. The hangar complex was started in the 1980s and has been extended over the years. The first aircraft to be restored were a 1935 Caudron Luciole and a Morane-Saulnier MS.315. These are regular performers at meetings in the area. The Texan and Pilatus P.2 soon joined the fleet along with the French built Fieseler Storch. The pair of Czecholovakian Yaks were part of a batch of over thirty purchased in Egypt by Jean Salis. Restoration of a Ranger engined Fairchild 24 was completed in the late 1990s. Work on a 1940 Caudron Aiglon is progressing along with that on a Tiger Moth being built up from spares. A Dewoitine D.27 and a Nord N.1002 are also in the workshops. A derelict Caudon C.60 dating from 1921 was acquired in the mid-1990s and hopefully the rebuild of this biplane will soon start. A fairly recent arrival is the fuselage of a pre-World War I Morane-Borel. Three static types are the HM-14 Pou-du-Ciel, a 1977 replica of the Santos-Dumont Demoiselle and the Mirage IIIE. Classic types from a number of countries can be seen.

TYPE	REG/SER	CON. NO.	PI/NOTES	STATUS
☐ Beech D17S (GB-2)	F-AZLA	4829	Bu33030, NC221, N1255N	RAA
☐ Boeing-Stearman A75N1 Kaydet (PT-17)	F-AZST	75-2184	41-8625, N61860 – also reported as c/n 75-2814	RAA
☐ Caudron C.272/5 Luciole	F-AZAL	7153/16	F-AOBS, F-PJKE	RAA
☐ Caudron C.60 (C.59)	F-AIEX	5966/684		RAD
☐ Caudron C.601 Aiglon	F-PGOI	01-AR		RAC
☐ Cessna 305C Bird Dog (L-19E) (O-1E)	24581	24581		RAD
☐ Construcciones Aeronáuticas (CASA) 1.131E [Bücker Bü 131 Jungmann]	F-AZVS	1035	E.3B-???	RAA
☐ Dassault Mirage IIIE	586	586		RA
☐ De Havilland D.H.82A Tiger Moth			Major components.	RAD
☐ De Havilland D.H.82A Tiger Moth			Being built from spares	RAC
☐ De Havilland D.H.C.1 Chipmunk 22 (T.10)	F-AZVA	C1/0188	WB739	RAA
☐ De Havilland D.H.C.1 Chipmunk 22 (T.10)	F-AZSM	C1/0789	WP914	RAA
☐ Dewoitine D.27	F-AZ??			RAC
☐ Douglas AD-4NA Skyraider (AD-4N)	F-AZDQ	7756	Bu126956, 45 (France), TR-KMP, F-WZDQ	RAA
☐ Fairchild 24R	F-PBCM	01-1996	Possibly converted from 24W41A Forwarder (C-61A) (UC-61A) (Argus II) c/n W41A- 495 43-14531, FS614	RAA
☐ Fouga CM.170R Magister	F-WMDM	206	206, F-WDUD	RA
☐ Jodel DR.1050 Ambassadeur	F-BJYV	258		RAA
☐ Let C-11 [Yakovlev Yak-11]	F-AZJB	25111/03	539 (Egypt), F-YAKA	RAA
☐ Let C-18M [Yakovlev Yak-18U]	F-AZFG	1609	640 (Egypt)	RAA
☐ Mignet HM-14 Pou-du-Ciel				RA
☐ Morane Borel			Fuselage only.	RAD
☐ Morane-Saulnier MS.315 (MS.315) (MS.317)	F-AZAH	6508/254	254, F-BBZO	RAA
☐ Morane-Saulnier MS.500 Criquet (MS.500) (MS.505) [Fieseler Fi 156 Storch]	F-AZDA	226/22	F-BBUG	RAA
☐ Nord N.1002 Pingouin II [Messerschmitt Bf 108B]	F-AZKV	142	142, F-BFRQ	RAC
☐ Nord N.1002 Pingouin II [Messerschmitt Bf 108B]		173	173, F-BAUF	RA
☐ Nord N.1101 Noralpha (Ramier I) [Messerschmitt Me 208]	F-WZCZ	77	77, F-WZCZ, F-AZCZ	RAC
☐ Nord N.1300 [Schneider Grunau Baby IIB]				RA
☐ Nord NC.858S (NC.853S)	F-BFSY	77		RAA
☐ North American NA-88 Texan (AT-6D) (SNJ-5)	F-AZBL	88-17667	42-85886, Bu90699, N9801C, F-AZBL, F-WZBM	RAA
☐ Pilatus P.2-05	F-AZCC	37	A-117 (Switzerland), U-117 (Switzerland) – in false Luftwaffe colours representing an Arado Ar 96.	RAAX
☐ Piper J-3C-90 Cub (J-3C-65) (L-4H)				RA
☐ Piper J-3C-90 Cub (J-3C-65) (L-4J)	F-BBTD	13148	45-4408, HB-OVU	RAC
☐ Piper J-3C-90 Cub (J-3C-65) (O-59A) (L-4A)	F-BEGU	10384	42-29093, F-BEGU, F-OTAN-2	RAD
☐ Sabatier				RA
☐ Santos-Dumont XX Demoiselle (R)				RA
☐ Scottish Aviation Bulldog 120/121 (T.1)	F-AZKJ	BH120/248	XX555	RAA
☐ Scottish Aviation Bulldog 120/121 (T.1)	F-AZKI	BH120/273	XX615	RAA
☐ Société Industrielle Pour l'Aéronautique (SIPA) S.903 (S.901)	F-PCHR	01	Possibly a rebuild of c/n 22 F-BEYZ	RA
☐ Société Industrielle Pour l'Aéronautique (SIPA) S.903 (S.901)	F-AZEK	99	F-BGHY, F-BEJZ	RAA

AMICALE ROMANAISE D'AVIATION ANCIENNE (FRA41)

Address:	Terrain des Chasses, 26100 Romans-sur-Isere.
Tel:	04 75 70 06 76
Admission:	By prior permission only.
Location:	At Romans-St. Paul airfield which is about 3 km north east of the town on the N.92.

This active group has its own hangar at the picturesque airfield in the Isère valley. Two Nord Norécrins are owned with one currently in flying condition. The type won a 1945 contest organised by the French Ministry of Transport. Almost four hundred were built between 1948 and 1956. The major components of a Nord N.1002 are stored and hopefully this aircraft will be rebuilt in the not too distant future. The Sicile was one of several developments of the D.112 series by Centre Est Aéronautique at Dijon.

TYPE	REG/SER	CON. NO.	PI/NOTES	STATUS
☐ Jodel DR.1051 Sicile	F-BLAD	404		RAA
☐ Max Holste MH.1521M Broussard	F-BNDD	240	240	RAA
☐ Morane-Saulnier MS.885 Super Rallye	F-GIIG	42	HB-EDP	RAA
☐ Nord N.1002 Pingouin II [Messerschmitt Bf 108B]	F-BFYY	242	Major components only	RAD
☐ Nord N.1203-III Norécrin (N.1203-II)	F-BHFK	230	F-BEUU	RAA
☐ Nord N.1203-VI Norécrin (N.1203) (N.1203-II)	F-BEOF	108		RA
☐ Piper PA-18-95 Super Cub (L-18C)	F-BOMB	18-1640	51-15640	RAA

COLLECTION DE LA BASE DE L'AVIATION LÉGÈRE DE L'ARMÉE DE TERRE DE VALENCE (FRA42)

Address:	GMAT, 26001 Valence-Chabeuil.
Admission:	By prior permission only.
Location:	The airfield is about 5 km east of Valence on the D.68.

This unit at Valence, which undertakes operational trials of all ALAT equipment, was formed at Satory in 1954 and moved to its current home on January 1st 1966. The Broussard is on a pole at the aeroclub and the others are inside the camp. The Sikorsy H-19 was moved from the now closed base at Lyon-Corbas.

TYPE	REG/SER	CON. NO.	PI/NOTES	STATUS
☐ Max Holste MH.1521M Broussard	24	24	On civil side of airfield.	PV
☐ Sikorsky S-55D Chickasaw (H-19D) (UH-19D)	52-7615	55623		RA
☐ Sud SA.341F Gazelle	1642	1642		RA
☐ Sud-Est SE.3130 Alouette II	1344	1344		RA
☐ Sud-Est SE.3130 Alouette II	1949	1949		RA
☐ Sud-Est SE.3160 Alouette III	1354	1354		RA

COLLECTION MAGRANER (FRA43)

Address:	69 Rue Henri Foucques Duparc, 26000 Valence.
Tel:	04 75 55 31 58
Admission:	By prior permission only.
Location:	In store in the town.

The aircraft are owned by Andres Magraner who left Aéro Rétro in late 1999 and moved them to his private property. The Morane-Saulnier MS.181 parasol wing monoplane, powered by a 60 h.p. Salmson radial, was designed in the early 1930s for use by the Compagnie Française d'Aviation flying schools. The Auster was exchanged for a Hornet Moth which was stored in the area from the late 1930s. This biplane is now being rebuilt in New Zealand. The identity of the Auster is in some doubt because G-AGVJ was withdrawn from use in the 1960s and donated some components to the rebuild of another. The Turbulent was built in Valence in 1956 and flew until 1968. After a period in store it moved to St. Rambert before returning to Valence.

TYPE	REG/SER	CON. NO.	PI/NOTES	STATUS
☐ Auster J/1N Alpha (J/1 Autocrat)	F-AZJN	1861 (?)	G-AGVJ (?)	RA
☐ Druine D.31 Turbulent	F-PHLD	A27		RAC
☐ Morane-Saulnier MS.181	F-AJQL	4		RA
☐ Nord NC.858S (NC.853S)	F-BEZH	101		RA

MUSÉE DE LA RÉSISTANCE EN VERCORS (FRA44)

Address:	Rue Foura, 26420 Vassieux-en-Vercors,
Tel:	04 75 48 28 46
Fax:	04 75 48 29 57
Admission:	April-October Daily 1000-1200 1400-1800.
Location:	In the village of Vassieux which is about 8 km south of La Chapelle on the D 76 about 40 km east of Valence.

Joseph la Picarella was a member of the French Resistance and at the end of the conflict he spent years researching and gathering material. In July 1944 the village of Vassieux was completely destroyed when three thousand resistance fighters opposed over ten times as many German troops. All who survived the onslaught were tortured before being killed. The Germans used glider borne soldiers to press home the attack and many skeletons of these airframes can still be seen in the area. When he retired in 1973 Joseph la Picarella bought an old farm which he converted into this excellent museum. In addition to the frame of the D.F.S. 230 there are parts from a Halifax which crashed in the area on February 8th 1942 and components of a Bloch 152. The village also constructed a memorial to those who lost their lives in the battle.

TYPE	REG/SER	CON. NO.	PI/NOTES	STATUS
☐ Jacobs D.F.S. 230C-1				PVD

MUSÉE EUROPÉEN DE L'AVIATION DE CHASSE (FRA45)

Address:	Aérodrome d'Ancône, 26200 Montélimar.
Tel:	04 75 53 79 49
Fax:	04 75 01 51 89
Email:	avions26@aol.com
Admission:	Monday-Friday 1400-1700; Saturday-Sunday 1430-1800.
Location:	In the north western suburbs of the town off the D 165.

The Amicale des Avions Anciens de la Drôme was formed in the mid-1980s and acquired a Flamant. This aircraft sadly crashed on September 5th 1999 at Issoire killing the crew of two. The group later decided to set up a museum featuring fighter aircraft although other types are in the collection. An exhibition hall displays engines, components models, weapons, ejector seats and photographs. There are plans to extend the indoor area and to improve the display. A small hangar and workshop houses some of the light aircraft. The aircraft collection features types from several countries. The sole Mirage IIIEX is an upgraded version of the standard IIIE and was converted by Dassault in the late 1980s. Other variants of this classic delta are also on show, including three from Switzerland, along with other jets from the company. Also once used by the Swiss Air Force are the pair of Vampires and the Hunter. A former Cosford Vampire Trainer was flown to France inside a Transall in June 1989. One of the ex-Luftwaffe Broncos is maintained in flying condition and is a popular performer at shows. The Starfighter came from the Belgian Air Force, the Fiat G.91 from Italy and the two MiGs from Germany. One of the few remaining Mauboussin M.123s still in flying condition is owned by one of the museum members. Several aircraft have been loaned by the Musée de l'Air. The Neptune is due to arrive from Brienne-le-Château and the Mirage IVA and the Sikorsky S-58 will be moved from the closed Air Force Base at Apt. A fairly recent arrival is the derelict airframe of a Potez 36. Large numbers of high wing two seater were built. The prototype first flew in 1929 The 36/14 appeared in October 1931 and was powered by a 95 h.p. Renault engine. The early example of the DC-3 is yet another highlight of the collection. The Swiss registered Paris is currently away for restoration but is due to return in the not too distant future. This museum has made rapid progress in a comparatively short time and has many interesting items on show.

TYPE	REG/SER	CON. NO.	PI/NOTES	STATUS
☐ Canadair CL-30 Silver Star 3 (CT-133) [Lockheed 580 (T-33AN)]	21113	T33-113		PV
☐ Canadair CL-30 Silver Star 3 (CT-133) [Lockheed 580 (T-33AN)]	'14045'	T33-121	21121, (N12424)	RAX
☐ Dassault MD-312 Flamant	172	172	172, F-AZAI – aero club aircraft.	PV
☐ Dassault MD-312 Flamant	F-AZEO	210	210	PV
☐ Dassault MD-450 Ouragan	214	214		PV
☐ Dassault Mystère IVA	186	186	On loan from M.A.	PV
☐ Dassault Mystère IVA	48	48		PV
☐ Dassault Super Mystère B2	21	21		PV
☐ Dassault Mirage IIIA	09	09		PV
☐ Dassault Mirage IIIBS	J-2001		In Swiss markings.	PV
☐ Dassault Mirage IIIC	11	11		PV
☐ Dassault Mirage IIIC	55	55		PV
☐ Dassault Mirage IIIEX (IIIE)	01	467	467	PV
☐ Dassault Mirage IIIRS	R-2103	1028	In Swiss markings.	PV
☐ Dassault Mirage IIIS	J-2304	994	In Swiss markings.	PV
☐ Dassault Mirage IVA	37	37		RA
☐ Dassault Mirage F.1B	505	505	Due soon.	-
☐ Dassault Mirage F.1C	37	37	Due soon.	PV

☐ Dassault Mirage G.8 (FSM)	02	02		PV
☐ Dassault Etendard IVM	30	30		PV
☐ Dassault Etendard IVM	59	59	Wings and tail only.	PV
☐ De Havilland D.H.100 Vampire FB.6	J-1142	651		PV
☐ De Havilland D.H.100 Vampire FB.6	J-1055	966		PV
☐ De Havilland D.H.115 Vampire T.11	XD613	15438	XD613, 8122M	PV
☐ Douglas DC-3A-453 Skytrooper (C-53C)	N56NA	4979	NC30026, 43-2023, NC19934, N93C, N81R, N400RS	PV
☐ Fiat G.91T/3 (T/1)	98+58	91-2-0021	EC+373, MD+373, 34+19	PV
☐ Fouga CM.170R Magister				PV
☐ Fouga CM.170R Magister	57	57		PV
☐ Fouga CM.170R Magister	101	101		PV
☐ Fouga CM.170R Magister	150	150		PVD
☐ Gloster Meteor NF.11	NF.11-1		(RAF) – on loan from M.A.	RA
☐ Hawker P.1099 Hunter F.58	J-4067	41H/697434	In Swiss markings.	PV
☐ Lockheed 426-45-17 Neptune (P2V-7)	147563	726-7177	Bu147563- on loan from M.A.	RA
☐ Lockheed 580 (T-33A)	94+54	580-9117	53-5778, DA+395, YA+702	PV
☐ Lockheed 683-10-19 Starfighter (F-104G)	FX-69	683-9115	In Belgian markings.	PV
☐ Mauboussin M.123 Corsaire (M.123C)	F-PCIP	183	F-BCIP	RAA
☐ Max Holste MH.1521M Broussard	F-GGKS	23	23, F-WGKS	PVA
☐ Max Holste MH.1521M Broussard	67	67	67, F-BNEU	RA
☐ Max Holste MH.1521M Broussard	F-GRES	124	124	PV
☐ Max Holste MH.1521M Broussard	211	211	211, F-WGKK	PV
☐ Mikoyan-Gurevich MiG-21U	23+94	663820	281 (DDR)	PV
☐ Mikoyan-Gurevich MiG-23MF	20+03	0390213097	582 (DDR)	PV
☐ Morane-Saulnier MS.733 Alcyon	F-BLXM	79	79	PVC
☐ Morane-Saulnier MS.760A Paris I	HB-PAA	69	HB-PAA, 'J-4117'	RAC
☐ Morane-Saulnier MS.760A Paris I	116	116		PV
☐ Morane-Saulnier MS.892A Commodore 150	F-BRMK	11406		PV
☐ Nord N.1002 Pingouin II [Messerschmitt Bf 108B]				RA
☐ Nord N.1002 Pingouin II [Messerschmitt Bf 108B]	F-BEAZ	90	90	RA
☐ Nord N.1002 Pingouin II [Messerschmitt Bf 108B]	F-BCAS	175	175	RA
☐ Nord N.2501 Noratlas	196	196		PV
☐ Nord N.2504 Noratlas	01	01	01, F-AZNA	RA
☐ North American NA-338 Bronco (OV-10B)	F-AZKM	338-9	Bu158300, D-9553, 99+24	PVA
☐ North American NA-338 Bronco (OV-10B)	99+27	338-12	Bu158303, D-9556	PV
☐ Piper PA-22-150 Tri-Pacer	F-GHXI	22-4476	N5801D, D-EANA, PH-RCH	PVA
☐ Potez 36/13	F-ALQT	2620	Probable identity.	RAC
☐ Republic F-84F Thunderstreak	FU-29		52-7175 – in Belgian markings.	PV
☐ Republic F-84G Thunderjet				PV
☐ Sikorsky S-58	84	SA-84		RA
☐ Stampe & Vertongen S.V.4C	F-BMRU	643	643 – on loan from M.A.	PVA
☐ Sud-Est SE.210 Caravelle III	116/F-ZACE	116	OH-LED – on loan from M.A.	PV
☐ Sud-Est SE.3130 Alouette II	152	1258		PV
☐ Svenska Aeroplan Aktiebolaget (SAAB) 37 Viggen (JA 37)	Fv37321	37321		PV
☐ Svenska Aeroplan Aktiebolaget (SAAB) 37 Viggen (Sk 37) (Sk 37E)	Fv37811	37811		PV
☐ Vought F-8P Crusader (F-8E(FN))	4	1216	Bu151735	PV

27 EURE

COLLECTION DE LA BASE AÉRIENNE D'EVREUX (FRA46)

Address:	Base Aérienne 105, 27037 Evreux Cedex.
Tel:	02 32 39 53 81
Fax:	02 32 39 63 50
Admission:	By prior permission only.
Location:	About 5 km east of the town off the N13.

The 64th Transport Wing was formed at Le Bourget in 1956 and moved to Evreux in 1970. A variety of types including the DC-6, Noratlas and Sahara were operated. This base now houses two squadrons flying the Transall. In addition a unit operates four versions used as air command posts. The Sahara was parked outside the aero club for many years but this has recently moved into the military area for restoration. Four examples of the giant transport, developed from the Breguet 763 airliner used by Air France, were operated by the unit.

TYPE	REG/SER	CON. NO.	PI/NOTES	STATUS
☐ Breguet 765 Sahara	501	501		RA
☐ Max Holste MH.1521M Broussard	253	253		RA
☐ Nord N.2501 Noratlas	156	156		RA
☐ Sikorsky S-58	167	SA-167		RA

MUSÉE DE L'ESCADRILLE 'NORMANDIE-NIEMEN' (FRA47)

Address:	Square de Lattre de Tassigny, Rue Raymond Phelip, 27700 Les Andelys.
Tel:	02 32 54 49 76
Fax:	02 32 54 49 76
Admission:	June-mid-September daily 1000-1200 1400-1800; Mid-September-May daily 1400-1800.
Location:	In the centre of the town which is about 30 km south east of Rouen.

This museum was set up in 1992 on the fiftieth anniversary of the formation of the famous fighter unit. General de Gaulle was instrumental in establishing the squadron 'Normandie' and ninety six French pilots were sent to the Eastern Front to serve with their Russian allies. Forty six of these volunteers lost their lives in the next three years. The initial equipment was the Yak-1 and Yak-3s and Yak-9s were later used. Stalin awarded the name 'Niemen' to the wing as it distinguished itself in the battle which led to troops crossing the river of that name. The museum was enlarged in early 2000 so that the majority of the large collection of artefacts can be shown. The history of the unit, its aircraft and personnel is portrayed in displays of models, uniforms, maps, photographs and memorabilia. The Mirage, painted in a special colour scheme, is mounted outside. This aircraft once served with the squadron that still bears the famous name. The unit is now at Colmar.

TYPE	REG/SER	CON. NO.	PI/NOTES	STATUS
☐ Dassault Mirage F.1C	101	101		PV

28 EURE ET LOIR

BUREAU CENTRAL DES RELATIONS EXTERIEURES (FRA48)

Address:	Base Aérienne 279, Route d'Orleans, 28200 Châteaudun Air.
Tel:	02 37 44 81 00
Admission:	By prior permission only.
Location:	About 3 km south east of the town off the D 955.

The airframes and front fuselages held by this organisation are used for recruiting displays and other publicity efforts. They travel throughout France from their Châteaudun base carrying out this work.

TYPE	REG/SER	CON. NO.	PI/NOTES	STATUS
☐ Breguet / British Aircraft Corporation Jaguar A	A41	A41		RA
☐ Breguet / British Aircraft Corporation Jaguar E	'E1'	E02	E02	RAX
☐ Dassault Mirage IIIA	08	08	Front fuselage only.	RA
☐ Dassault Mirage IIIB			Front fuselage only.	RA
☐ Dassault Mirage IIIC	83	83	Front fuselage only.	RA
☐ Dassault Mirage 2000C	03	03		RA
☐ Dassault Mirage F.1C	79		Front fuselage only.	RA
☐ Dassault Mirage F.1C-200	240		Front fuselage only.	RA
☐ Fouga CM.170R Magister	111	111		RA
☐ Fouga CM.170R Magister	401	401		RA
☐ Fouga CM.170R Magister	454	454		RA
☐ Mudry CAP.10B	101	101		RA
☐ Sud-Est SE.3130 Alouette II	171	1306		RA

COLLECTION DE LA BASE AÉRIENNE DE CHÂTEAUDUN (FRA49)

Address:	Base Aérienne 279, Route D'Orléans, 28200 Châteaudun Air.
Tel:	02 37 44 81 00
Fax:	02 37 44 82 73
Admission:	By prior permission only.
Location:	About 3 km south east of the town off the D 955.

This large base has been home to a major maintenance and storage unit since before World War II. German bomber and fighter squadrons were in residence during the conflict. They constructed hard runways and also built several hangars. Since peace was declared thousands of aircraft have been repaired, stored, scrapped and sold. Usually there are large numbers parked on the airfield and in the hangars. The preserved aircraft are at several locations around the site. They represent the many which have flown into the base and more types should soon join the collection. A small number of SOCATA TBM-700s are used for communications and ferry duties. In addition there are pilots based at the unit to carry out test flights on aircraft which have undergone major overhauls. A number of several instructional airframes are in use. Nearby is the central store for technical equipment.

TYPE	REG/SER	CON. NO.	PI/NOTES	STATUS
☐ Breguet / British Aircraft Corporation Jaguar A	A43	A43		RA
☐ Dassault MD-450 Ouragan	231	231		RA
☐ Dassault Mystère IVA	278	278		RA
☐ Dassault Super Mystère B2	79	79		RA
☐ Dassault Mirage IIIB	250	250		RA
☐ Dassault Mirage IIIRD	360	360		RA
☐ Dassault Mirage IIIRD	367	367		PV
☐ Dassault Mirage IVA	1	1		RA
☐ Dassault Mirage F.1C	10	10		RA
☐ Fouga CM.170R Magister	538	538		RA
☐ Nord N.2501 Noratlas	171	171		RA
☐ Republic F-84F Thunderstreak	'29117'		52-9061, 29061	RAX
☐ Sud-Ouest SO-4050 Vautour IIB	615	78		RA

29 FINISTÈRE

ASSOCIATION ARMOR AÉRO PASSION (FRA50)

Address:	Kerangall, 29800 Tremouvezan.
Email:	armor.aero.passion@wanadoo.fr
Admission:	By prior permission only.
Location:	At Quimper Airport which is about 5 km west of the town on the D.56. At Morlaix Airport which is about 3 km north east of the town off the D.46

Formed in June 1997, with the main aim of arousing interest in aviation in the region and of lowering the cost of participating, the group operates from both Morlaix and Quimper airfields. The first aircraft acquired was the Paris F-AZLT which is painted in an Aéronavale scheme. The French Navy operated small numbers of the jet. The example in the collection was bought in 2001 and after a four year rebuild took to the air again in 2005. A second MS.760 has recently been purchased. The Rallye is under restoration in the workshop at Morlaix and the Norécrin is being rebuilt at a local college. Both should be airworthy in the near future. Visits are arranged to airfields, factories and military bases and several educational courses are organised.

TYPE	REG/SER	CON. NO.	PI/NOTES	STATUS
☐ Morane-Saulnier MS.760A Paris I	F-AZLT	32	32	RAA
☐ Morane-Saulnier MS.760A Paris I	F-AZTL	85	85	RA
☐ Morane-Saulnier MS.880B Rallye Club	F-BNYP	893		RAC
☐ Nord N.1203 Norécrin				RAC

CONSERVATOIRE AÉRONAUTIQUE DE CORNOUAILLE (FRA51)

Address:	52 Rue Louis Pasteur, 29100 Douarnenez
Tel:	02 98 23 18 00
Admission:	By prior permission only
Location:	At Quimper airfield which is about 5 km south west of the town off the D.56.

Over forty Crusaders were used by the Aéronavale between 1964 and 1999. They were based at Landivisiau. This airfield was constructed in the mid-1960s and the first operational units moved in during the summer of 1967. The site is now the main shore base for carrier based aircraft. The group, which aims to set up a museum tracing the history of Landivisiau, is restoring the aircraft in a hangar at nearby Quimper.

TYPE	REG/SER	CON. NO.	PI/NOTES	STATUS
☐ Vought F-8P Crusader (F-8E(FN))	5	1218	Bu151736	RAC

MUSÉE AÉRONAUTIQUE DE CORNOUAILLES (FRA52)

Address:	Zone Artisan de Quélarn, 29740 Plobannelec.
Tel:	02 98 87 89 48
Admission:	By prior permission only.
Location:	About 2 km west of the town off the D 53.

Aircraft are being gathered at this microlight field for a museum which will trace the aeronautical history of the region. A collection of components, memorabilia, photographs and documents is in store. The Aéronavale have had several bases in the area over the years and the Etendard has been a regular sight in the local skies. The Sikorsky S-58s are all in a poor condition and two or three will be restored with the others being used for spares. French military S-58s came from three sources. Some were entirely constructed in the U.S.A., others were assembled by Sud Aviation from Sikorsky supplied kits and the remainder were completely French built. The museum has put forward plans for a purpose built exhibition hall along with offices and workshops.

TYPE	REG/SER	CON. NO.	PI/NOTES	STATUS
☐ Dassault Etendard IVM	14	14		PV
☐ Fouga CM.170R Magister			Due soon.	–
☐ McDonnell M.98DJ Phantom II (F-4C)	64-0922	1401		PV
☐ Sikorsky S-58	135	SA-135		PV
☐ Sikorsky S-58	148	SA-148		PV
☐ Sikorsky S-58	512	SKY-512		PVD
☐ Sikorsky S-58	640	SKY-640		PV
☐ Sikorsky S-58	688	SKY-688		PV
☐ Sikorsky S-58	705	SKY-705/SA-29		PV
☐ Sud-Est SE.3130 Alouette II		1680		PV
☐ Sud-Est SE.3130 Alouette II	809	1809		PV

30 GARD

COLLECTION DE LA BASE AÉRONAVALE DE NIMES-GARONS (FRA53)

Address:	Base Aéronavale, 30128 Nimes Armées.
Tel:	04 66 70 76 00
Fax:	04 66 70 08 63
Admission:	On permanent view.
Location:	About 8 km south of the town on the D 42.

The base was constructed in 1956 and is on the opposite side of the airfield from the civil airport. The last Alizés in Aéronavale service were based at the field. The type was withdrawn from use in 2000. The Atlantic was developed for N.A.T.O. use and four prototypes and eighty seven production examples were built for operation by France, Germany, Holland and Italy. Embraer Xingus and Nord N.262Es are based here along with the Atlantics. The C-47 was resident at the field for many years with the last being withdrawn in the late 1980s. Many stored and dumped airframes are located near the display area.

TYPE	REG/SER	CON. NO.	PI/NOTES	STATUS
☐ Breguet 1050 Alizé	5	5		PV
☐ Breguet 1150 Atlantic	31	31		PV
☐ Douglas DC-3A-360 Skytrain (C-47)	87	4579	41-18487, EI-ACG, EI-ALR – possible identity.	PV

MUSÉE DE L'AGRICULTURE ET DE LA LOCOMOTION (FRA54)

Address:	Moulin de Chalier, Arpaillargues, 30700 Uzès.
Tel:	04 66 22 68 54
Admission:	Tuesday-Sunday 0900-1200 1400-1800.
Location:	On the D.982 about 3 km south west of Uzès.

The historic mill in this small village houses an interesting collection of vehicles and agricultural machinery. The surrounding countryside produces many crops and the implements used to gather and harvest them over the ages can be seen. Also on show are bicycles, early cars and motor cycles. There is an impressive collection of steam powered vehicles. The Caudron 800 glider was used by the local aero club.

TYPE	REG/SER	CON. NO.	PI/NOTES	STATUS
☐ Caudron C.800 Épervier	F-CADM	393		PV

31 HAUTE GARONNE

ACADEMIE NATIONALE DE L'AIR ET DE L'ESPACE (FRA55)

Address: 1 Avenue Camille Flammarion,
31500 Toulouse.
Tel: 05 34 25 03 80
Fax: 05 61 26 37 56
Email: a.n.a.e@wanadoo.fr
Admission: By prior permission only.
Location: In the Aérospatiale Complex at Colomiers which is about 10 km west of the city of the N 124.

The two aircraft owned by the academy are parked by one of the gates to the Aérospatiale factory. The first French production Concorde made its maiden flight on December 6th 1973 and was used for training and presidential flights before its retirement. The Caravelle was one of the successes of the French aviation industry and two prototypes and two hundred and eighty production models were built at Toulouse.

TYPE	REG/SER	CON. NO.	PI/NOTES	STATUS
☐ Aérospatiale / British Aircraft Corporation Concorde	F-WTSB	01		RA
☐ Sud-Est SE.210 Caravelle 12	F-BTOE	280	F-WTOE	RA

AILES ANCIENNES TOULOUSE (FRA56)

Address: c/o M. Bruna-Rossi,
31 Rue du Rempart-Matabiau,
31000 Toulouse.
Tel: 05 61 21 70 01 / 05 61 18 61 77
Fax: 05 61 86 86 26
Email: aatlse@worldnet.fr
Admission: Saturday 0900-1200.
Location: In Avenue Clement Ader, near the plant at Blagnac airfield which is about 10 km west of the city.

This branch of Ailes Anciennes was set up in early 1980 with the aim of creating an aviation museum in a region which has been to the forefront in aircraft manufacture for many years. Premises consisting of a workshop, hangar, storage yards and outside parking have been obtained in the Aérospatiale factory area. A wide range of aircraft can be seen and a large collection of memorabilia, photographs, documents etc. is in store. The majority of the fleet consists of types used by the French military over the last half century but airframes have been acquired from Great Britain, Germany and Belgium. Four Breguet 765 Saharas were ordered and used along with former civil Br 761s and 763s on transport duties. This giant transport was moved from its last base at Evreux to Toulouse by road. An arrival a few years ago was one of the four modified Boeing Stratocruisers used by Aérospatiale to transport Airbus wings. These flew regularly between factories in England, France and Germany. A unique exhibit is the Deltavieux which was acquired in 1984 after three years of tracing a lead. This experimental jet delta dates from the 1950s. The Toulouse based ONERA carries out research in many fields of aeronautics and this is their only original design. The prototype Espadon first flew in 1948 and three SO-6020s and one SO-6021 were built. The third SO-6020 was modified before completion into the SO-6025 which was fitted with a rocket motor in the rear fuselage in addition to its jet engine. The type was one several designs investigating the use of light jet fighters which could operate from unprepared airstrips. The Dakota is familiar to many British enthusiasts as it was flown by Fairey Surveys from White Waltham for many years. The Caravelle was built at Toulouse and the example in the collection was used by Emperor Bokassa of the Central African Republic for a period in the late 1970s. There are a number of pre-war light aircraft in store including a Mignet HM-8 and the more familiar HM-14. One of the few remaining Caudron Phalène high wing monoplanes surviving is on loan from the Musée de l'Air. The prototype of this three seat high wing monoplane powered by a 120 h.p. Salmson radial made its maiden flight in 1932. The type was built in substantial numbers and later versions were fitted with in-line Renault and de Havilland Gipsy Major engines. Some of the restored aircraft are currently stored in one of the factory halls. Réne Barbero built a number of his own designs from the late 1940s up to the early 1970s. He was a Toulouse resident for many years and in 1972 produced the BG-10 with Maurice Gagnant. The aircraft was a modified Druine Turbulent fitted with a Volkswagen motor. After it was withdrawn in 1986 it spent a period in store before being acquired by the museum. The former Air France Concorde is owned by Airbus and can usually be seen from the museum site. Hopefully plans for a purpose built complex will soon come to fruition.

TYPE	REG/SER	CON. NO.	PI/NOTES	STATUS
☐ Aero Spacelines 377SGT-201 Super Guppy	F-BPPA	002	N212AS	PV
☐ Aérospatiale / British Aircraft Corporation Concorde 101	F-BVFC	100-009	F-BVFC, N94FC – at Airbus factory.	RA
☐ Aérospatiale AS.355 Ecureuil	F-WZJL	5001		PV
☐ Barbero-Gagnant BG.10	F-PTEP	01		RA
☐ Boeing 367-76-66 Stratofreighter (KC-97G) (KC-97L)	53-0278	17060	Front fuselage only.	RA
☐ Breguet 765 Sahara	504	504		PVC
☐ Brochet MB.50 Pipistrelle				RA
☐ Castel C.310P			Composite	RA
☐ Castel-Mauboussin CM.10		01(?)	Nose only	PV
☐ Caudron C.282/8 Phalène	F-AMKT	6770/26	On loan from M.A.	RAC
☐ Caudron C.800 Épervier	F-CAJN	9944/284		RA
☐ Dassault MD-312 Flamant	227	227		PV
☐ Dassault Mystère IVA	1	1	On loan from M.A.	PV
☐ Dassault Mystère IVA	44	44		PV
☐ Dassault Super Mystère B2	48	48		PV
☐ Dassault Mirage IIIC	'27'	86	86	PVX
☐ Dassault Mirage IIIC	90	90	On loan from M.A.	PV
☐ Dassault Mirage IIIE	491	491		PV
☐ Dassault Falcon 10	02	02	F-ZACB	PV
☐ De Havilland D.H.115 Vampire T.11	XE950	15463		PV
☐ Douglas A-26B Invader	39223	6936	41-39223, N74Y – on loan from M.A.	PVC
☐ Douglas DC-3A-456 Skytrain (C-47A) (Dakota III)	G-ALWC	13590	42-93654, KG723, G-ALWC, (F-GBOL)	PV
☐ Fouga CM.170R Magister	168	168		PV
☐ Fouga CM.170R Magister	178	178		PV
☐ Fournier RF.3	F-BLXJ	23		RA
☐ Gardan GY-80 Horizon 160	F-BLPO	39		PV
☐ Gloster Meteor NF.11	NF.11-8		WM303 - on loan from M.A.	PV
☐ Hawker P.1099 Hunter F.58	J-4065	41H/697432	In Swiss markings.	PV
☐ Jodel D.92 Bébé	F-PCJJ	90		PV
☐ Jodel D.112 Club				RA
☐ Lockheed 580 (T-33A)	'58-0468'	580-5524	51-4230, 14230	PVX
☐ Lockheed 683-10-19 Starfighter (F-104G)	21+91	683-7060	KE+360, DC+244	PV
☐ Max Holste MH.1521M Broussard	'F-BJLR'	139	139	PVX
☐ McDonnell M.36BA Voodoo (F-101B)	58-0282	654		PV
☐ Merville S.M.30	F-CCHN	01		RA
☐ Mignet HM-8B				RA
☐ Mignet HM-14 Pou-du-Ciel				RA
☐ Mikoyan-Gurevich MiG-15bisSB (MiG-15bis)		713001	3001 (Czechoslovakia	PV
☐ Mikoyan-Gurevich MiG-21M	22+86	960513	588 (DDR)	PV
☐ Mikoyan-Gurevich MiG-21SPS (MiG-21PFM)	770	94A4509	In DDR markings.	PV
☐ Morane-Saulnier MS.733 Alcyon	F-BMMT	106	106	PV
☐ Morane-Saulnier MS.760A Paris I	24	24		PV
☐ Morane-Saulnier MS.893A Commodore 180	F-BPMF	10761		PV
☐ Nord N.1101 Ramier I [Messerschmitt Me 208]	88	88	88, F-BBBZ	RA
☐ Nord N.1300 [Schneider Grunau Baby IIB]	F-CRQH	200	F-CAKT	PV
☐ Nord N.1300 [Schneider Grunau Baby IIB]	F-CROE	9	F-CBXS	PV
☐ Nord N.2501 Noratlas			Front fuselage only.	RA
☐ Nord N.2501 Noratlas	191	191		PV
☐ Nord N.2501 Noratlas	201	201		PV
☐ Nord N.3400	130	130		RA
☐ North American NA-182 Texan (T-6G)	'929975'			PVX
☐ North American NA-223 Super Sabre (F-100D)	54-2239	223-119		PV
☐ Office National d'Etudes at de Recherches Aéronautiques (ONERA) Deltaviex	F-WBHA	01 (2)		RA
☐ Piper J-3C-65 Cub (L-4J)	'13167'	12763	44-80467, F-BETX, D-EBOR, F-BETX	PVX
☐ Republic F-84E Thunderjet	51-9572	1339		PV
☐ Republic F-84F Thunderstreak	52-6789		52-6789, 26789 (Greece)	PV
☐ Republic F-84F Thunderstreak	FU-125		53-6760 - with tail from 53-6722, FU-106 - in Belgian markings.	PV
☐ Sikorsky S-55D Chickasaw (H-19D) (UH-19D)	52-7603	55543		PVD
☐ Sikorsky S-58	116	SA-116		RA
☐ Société de Constructions D'Avions de Tourisme et D'Affaires (SOCATA) ST.10 Diplomate	001	001		PV
☐ Sud SA.316B Alouette III	1665	1665		PV
☐ Sud SA.340 Gazelle	002	002	F-ZWRA	PV
☐ Sud SA.341 Gazelle		WA.33		RA
☐ Sud-Est SE.210 Caravelle 10B3/54T (10B3/52T)	F-GHMU	249	F-WJAK, OY-STE, F-WJAK, TL-ABB, F-GCJT	PV
☐ Sud-Est SE.3130 Alouette II	8	8		RA
☐ Sud-Est SE.3130 Alouette II			Fuselage only.	RA
☐ Sud-Ouest SO-1221 Djinn	51	51FR101	On loan from M.A.	RA
☐ Sud-Ouest SO-4050 Vautour IIB	640	119	On loan from MA.	PV
☐ Sud-Ouest SO-6025 Espadon (SO-6020)	01	01	03, F-WFRG - original c/n 03 when SO-6020.	RAC
☐ Vertol V.43 (H-21C)	'FR-26'	FR-106	FR-106 - on loan from ALAT Museum.	PVX
☐ Vought F-8P Crusader (F-8E(FN))	19	1236	(Bu151750)	PV

ASSOCIATION BREGUET XIV (FRA57)

Address:	Aérodrome de Lasbordes, 31400 Toulouse.
Tel:	05 62 16 29 92 (Aero Club)
Admission:	By prior permission only.
Location:	In the eastern suburbs of the city.

This organisation has constructed an accurate replica of the Breguet 14 of which about eight thousand were built. The type first flew in 1917 and served in a number of roles in many countries. Several different versions were produced. The aircraft is painted in the colours of the Latécoère Airlines which flew the type on its services. The maiden flight took place in November 2003 and it has appeared at several shows.

TYPE	REG/SER	CON. NO.	PI/NOTES	STATUS
☐ Breguet 14A2 (R)	F-POST	150-AB	F-WOST	RAA

COLLECTION DE LA BASE AÉRIENNE DE TOULOUSE-FRANCAZAL (FRA58)

Address:	Base Aérienne 101, Route Seysses, 31998 Toulouse Armées.
Tel:	05 61 07 62 35
Fax:	05 61 06 83 92
Admission:	By prior permission only.
Location:	About 7 km south west of the city on the D 15.

Home to the heavy transport operational conversion unit flying Transalls and CN.235s loaned by other wings, this field once housed fighter squadrons. One Noratlas and the Sikorsky S-58 are parked by the main gate.

TYPE	REG/SER	CON. NO.	PI/NOTES	STATUS
☐ Nord N.2501 Noratlas	115	115		RA
☐ Nord N.2501 Noratlas	208	208		RA
☐ Sikorsky S-58	154	SA-154		RA

ESCADRILLE CROIX DU SUD (FRA59)

Address:	8 Rue des Grives, 31830 Plaisance du Touch.
Tel:	05 61 86 51 06
Fax:	05 61 86 51 06
Admission:	By prior permission only.
Location:	At a number of locations in the Toulouse area.

This organisation was formed several years ago to rebuild and fly light aircraft. From 1997 until the end of 1999 workshops at the historic Toulouse-Montaudran airfield were in use but Air France has taken back the premises and the airframes have been dispersed around the area. The eventual plan is to set up a museum with an adjoining airfield. There are a number of interesting types in the collection. The Allard D-40, built in 1947, incorporated parts from the 1936 Mignet HM-210. After many years at Bordeaux-Yvrac airfield the airframe moved to Toulouse in the early 1990s. This machine will be rebuilt for static display and a Mignet HM-293 is under construction to fly. The Fiat G.46 arrived from Italy several years ago. The Rapide, which spent a period in France during its flying career, was damaged by a hurricane in the Antilles and subsequently vandalised.

TYPE	REG/SER	CON. NO.	PI/NOTES	STATUS
☐ Adam RA.14 Loisirs				RA
☐ Allard D-40 [Mignet HM-210 Pou-du-Ciel]	F-WFKA	03		RA
☐ Blériot XI (R)				RA
☐ Boeing 299-O Fortress (B-17G)	42-102463	7965	Parts of a wing and fin	RAD
☐ Caudron C.800 Épervier	F-CCAM	9923/263		RAC
☐ De Havilland D.H.82A Tiger Moth	138		Possibly c/n 85887 DF138, G-ANJH, F-BGZX	RA
☐ De Havilland D.H.89A Dragon Rapide (D.H.89B Dominie I)	N8053	6907	NR843, YI-ABG, G-ALGE, EI-AMN, F-BLXX – metal pieces only.	RAD
☐ Fiat G.46-4B	I-AEHJ	164	MM53404	RA
☐ Latécoère 28-2 (R)				RAC
☐ Mignet HM-293 Pou-du-Ciel				RAC
☐ Nord N.1002 Pingouin II [Messerschmitt Bf 108B]		93		RA
☐ Nord NC.856A Norvigie	13	13		RA
☐ Stampe & Vertongen S.V.4C	F-BDCE	534		RAC

MUSÉE DE L'AÉRONAUTIQUE "LEON ELISSALDE" (FRA60)

Address:	Rue Albert Camus, 31110 Bagnères de Luchon.
Tel:	05 61 79 29 87
Admission:	Tuesday,Thursday,Saturday 1400-1800
Location:	Next to the airfield which in the north eastern part of the town.

The fascinating story of aviation from 1934 to the arrival of Concorde is shown in this privately run museum. There are many relics recovered from crash sites. These include engines from a Halifax and a Dornier 217. Several modern motors are displayed along with models, parachutes and uniforms.

MUSÉE DE L'AVIATION LÉGÈRE (FRA61)

Address:	Aérodrome de la Montagne Noir, 31250 Revel.
Tel:	05 61 27 65 04
Fax:	05 61 27 56 70
Admission:	By prior permission only.
Location:	About 4 km south of the town on the D334.

This museum has been set up by two groups. Founded in 1981, the Association d'Animation Sportive Culturelle et Touristique operates a fleet of classic gliders and is restoring a Morane Criquet for use as a tug. The Breguet 901 first flew in 1954 and achieved success in the 1956 World Championships held at St. Yan. The two seat 904 made its maiden flight in 1956 and fifteen were built. The Caudron C.800s is one of the few of the type still airworthy. Several modern sailplanes are in use by the club. The Association pour le Patrimoine Aéronautique et Restoration D'Avions Typiques was formed in the early 1980s by a group of enthusiasts in the Graulhet area. They acquired a number of rare types. The Morane-Saulnier MS.563 is one of several prototypes built by the company in the late 1940s/early 1950s. This single seat aerobatic low wing monoplane was powered by a 105 h.p. Walter Minor engine. The Lacroix-Trussant Microplan was built in 1935 but not registered until 1948. The type was first flown in June 1939 and was then hidden during World War II. In 1949 it took to the air again at Cahors and was withdrawn in 1953. Alfred Huc was an amateur builder in the 1930s. In collaboration with André Raymond and Charles Guiraud they designed and flew the Coutouli. Restored in 1949 it flew at Mazemet in 1949 and was put into storage in 1953. Huc constructed the Riatou in Castres in the late 1940s. The high wing single seater was only active for a short time and has now spent over half a century in store. The survival of these three unique designs shows the ideas of the early home builders in France.

TYPE	REG/SER	CON. NO.	PI/NOTES	STATUS
☐ Adam RA.14 Loisirs	F-PGKA	15		RA
☐ Avia 11A				RA
☐ Avia 15A				RA
☐ Breguet 901S Mouette	F-CCCX	20		RAA
☐ Breguet 904S Nymphale	F-CCFZ	15		RAA
☐ Castel C.25S				RA
☐ Caudron C.800 Épervier	F-CAGT	9971/311		RAA
☐ Caudron C.800 Épervier				RAC
☐ Fouga CM.8/13	F-CROI	1	F-WFDI	RAA
☐ Huc HRG Coutouli	F-WAAJ	02		RA
☐ Huc Lou Riatou	F-WFKR	01		RA
☐ Lacroix-Trussaut LT-51 Microplan 01	F-WFKQ	01	F-WFKQ, F-PFKQ	RA
☐ Mauboussin M.127 Corsaire	F-PCIO	181	F-BCIO	RAA
☐ Morane-Saulnier MS.505 Criquet (MS.502) [Fieseler Fi 156 Storch]	F-BDQI	211/9		RAA
☐ Morane-Saulnier MS.563	F-BBGC	01	F-WBGC	RA
☐ Morane-Saulnier MS.893A Commodore 180	F-BSDB	11467		RAA
☐ Nord N.1203 Norécrin				RA
☐ Nord N.1203 Norécrin				RA
☐ Nord N.2000 [Jacobs Meise]	F-CAOP	60		RAC
☐ Nord NC.859	F-BDYO	4		RAC
☐ Potez 600	F-PNUX	3873	F-ANUX	RA
☐ Rolladen-Schneider LS-1D	F-CEHC	216		RAA
☐ Rolladen-Schneider LS-1F	F-CEKM	397		RAA
☐ Salmson D.7-T2 Cri Cri Major	F-PLUE	7	F-BFNE	RA
☐ Salmson D.7-T2 Cri Cri Major	F-BFNH	10		RAC
☐ Scheibe Mü 13E Bergfalke I	OO-ZPN			RAA
☐ Scheibe Bergfalke IV	F-CFTE	5844		RAA
☐ Scheibe SF-28A Tandem Falke	F-CFJD	57121	D-KNIH	RAA
☐ Schempp-Hirth Standard Cirrus	F-CBHR	250	D-1122	RAA
☐ Schleicher Ka-6E Rhönsegler	F-CDTG	4332		RAA
☐ Stampe & Vertongen S.V.4C	F-BDJG	624	F-BDFT	RAA
☐ Wassmer WA.20 Javelot I	F-CBQO	1		RAA
☐ Wassmer WA.20 Javelot I	F-CBQR	8		RAA
☐ Wassmer WA.21 Javelot II	F-CCHG	19		RAA
☐ Wassmer WA.30 Bijave	F-CCNC	53		RAA
☐ Wassmer WA.30 Bijave	F-CGIB	222	F-CDJS	RAA

33 GIRONDE

ASSOCIATION DASSAULT PASSION (FRA62)

Address:	B.P. 24, Avenue Marcel Dassault, 33701 Mérignac Cedex.
Tel:	05 56 13 90 00
Fax:	05 56 34 23 06
Email:	passion@dassault-aviation.fr
Admission:	By prior permission only.
Location:	About 10 km west of the city centre off the D 106.

Marcel Bloch was born in 1892 and trained as an aeronautical engineer. His first significant product was a propeller which appeared in 1916. He then set up a company with Henri Potez but he withdrew from aviation soon after the 1918 armistice. In 1928 he returned with his own firm and up to the German invasion many excellent military designs appeared. He was captured by the Germans and sent to Buchenwald. After World War II he changed his name to Dassault which was his resistance identity. His new company was established and in the last sixty years has produced jet fighters such as the Ouragan, Mystère and Super Mystère. The famous Mirage series was exported around the world. The Etendard and Rafale naval jets have also been successful. Small transports including the Flamant and Falcon series have been made in large numbers. The association was set up to trace the history of the company. Aircraft have been acquired and are currently in store at the Mérignac site.

TYPE	REG/SER	CON. NO.	PI/NOTES	STATUS
☐ Dassault MD-312 Flamant	F-AZDD	216	216, F-WZDD	RAA
☐ Dassault MD-312 Flamant	F-AZDE	251	251, F-WZDE	RAA
☐ Dassault Mirage IIIS	J-2325	1015	In Swiss markings	RA
☐ Dornier-Breguet Alpha Jet A				RA
☐ Fouga CM.175 Zéphyr	F-AZMO	14	14, F-WQCG	RAA

COLLECTION DE LA BASE AÉRIENNE DE BORDEAUX-MÉRIGNAC (FRA63)

Address:	Base Aérienne 106, B.P. 110 Mérignac-Air, 33998 Bordeaux Armées.
Tel:	05 56 34 84 24
Fax:	05 56 34 27 67
Admission:	By prior permission only.
Location:	About 10 km west of the city centre off the D 106.

The base has been used by the Air Force for many years but there are now no front line units in residence. The Mirage IVA conversion unit disbanded in 1992 and the Jaguar squadron left at the same time. Presently a training unit operates the TBM-700 and the AS.555 helicopter. Five preserved aircraft are located around the camp.

TYPE	REG/SER	CON. NO.	PI/NOTES	STATUS
☐ Dassault Mystère IVA	306	306		RA
☐ Dassault Mirage IIIE	454	454		RA
☐ Dassault Mirage IIIR	346	346		RA
☐ Dassault Mirage IVP (IVA)	11	11		RA
☐ Max Holste MH.1521M Broussard	285	285		RA

COLLECTION DE LA BASE AÉRIENNE DE CAZAUX (FRA64)

Address:	Base Aérienne 120, 33164 Cazaux Air.
Tel:	05 56 22 99 15
Fax:	05 56 22 25 50
Admission:	By prior permission only.
Location:	Just east of the town which is about 10 km south of Arcachon.

This important base is home to two squadrons operating the Alpha Jet and a number of test units. Aircraft from the test centre at Brétigny are due to move here in the near future. The location will provide less crowded skies for the experimental work. The preserved aircraft are located around the vast site.

TYPE	REG/SER	CON. NO.	PI/NOTES	STATUS
☐ Dassault Mystère IVA	120	120		RA
☐ Dassault Mirage IIIB	249	249		RA
☐ Dassault Mirage IIIC	85	85		RA
☐ Dassault Mirage IVP (IVA)	23	23		RA
☐ Dassault Mirage F.1C	04	04		RA
☐ General Dynamics 401 Fighting Falcon (F-16A)			In Belgian markings.	RA
☐ Morane-Saulnier MS.760B Paris IIR	100	100		RA

CONSERVATOIRE DE L'AIR ET DE L'ÉSPACE D'AQUITAINE (FRA65)

Address: Courier Général Base Aérienne 106,
B.P. 110 Mérignac-Air,
33998 Bordeaux Armées.
Tel: 05 56 47 73 05
Fax: 05 56 13 09 70
Email: caea@decollage.org
Admission: By prior permission only.
Location: At Bordeaux-Mérignac airport which is about 10 km west of the city off the D 106.

Formed in 1985 with the aim of establishing a museum this group has now assembled an interesting collection. The first balloon flight took place in the locality in 1784 and since then Aquitaine has seen a great deal of aviation activity. There are and have been military bases, airports and civil fields in the region. Also well over seven thousand aircraft have been constructed in the area. Members have acquired many documents, photographs, books and other artefacts tracing all aspects of local aviation. The Dassault company has its main factory at Mérignac and their products feature prominently. At the present time around ten restored aircraft are stored in a hangar on the military base. Restoration was carried out in a large structure which was built when the airport was developed in the mid-1930s. This building sited in the area of the old terminal was dismantled in 2001. Plans for a large purpose built museum have been put forward. For many years CIFAS 328 which undertook conversion and continuation training for the strategic bomber force was based at the field. They flew Mirage IIIBs, Mirage IVAs, and T-33s. Examples of these three types have been acquired. The first production Falcon is a prized exhibit. The prototype of this executive jet first flew in 1963 and the aircraft in the collection made its maiden flight from Mérignac on January 1st 1965. After its manufacturers trials were over it was used by Air France for pilot training. In 1963 it joined the C.E.V. at Istres and then at Melun in fly-by-wire trials. The range of post-war Dassault fighters is well represented. The Ouragan was the first French designed jet fighter to go into series production and over three hundred and fifty left the factory. The now rare Mystère IIC, a swept wing development of the Ouragan arrived from Touchay. The structurally different Mystère IVA gave excellent service for almost thirty years. The sole prototype of the IVN, dating from 1954, is also in the hangar. Two Super Mystères and a range of Mirage variants complete this part of the collection. The IIING was modified from the Mirage 50 by the fitting of 'canard wings' close to the air intakes, 'fly-by-wire' controls and upgraded electronics. The sole conversion first flew at Istres on December 21st 1982. Light aircraft include a 1930s Pou-du-Ciel and the recently arrived Mauboussin M.121 from the same period. The French built Siebel 204 and the Dewoitine D.520 are two now rare types loaned by the Musée de l'Air. The NC.702 was restored by Air Force personnel at the nearby base of Francazal. The Lutin 80 powered glider was constructed locally. Built of fibreglass and epoxy resin the first prototype of this pusher design made its maiden flight in May 1983. Fitted with a 35 h.p. JPX/PAL two cylinder engine the project was abandoned. The completed prototype and the second unfinished airframe were presented to the collection. There is the potential for an excellent museum in this aeronautically important region and hopefully it will not be long before the ambitious plans are realised.

TYPE	REG/SER	CON. NO.	PI/NOTES	STATUS
☐ Aérostructure Lutin 80	F-WAQM	01		RA
☐ Aérostructure Lutin 80		02		RA
☐ Breguet / British Aircraft Corporation Jaguar E	E02	E02	F-ZWRC	RA
☐ Canadair CL-215-II	F-ZBWW/47	1047		RA
☐ Canadair CL-30 Silver Star 3 (CT-133) [Lockheed 580 (T-33AN)]	21049	T33-049		RA
☐ Carmam JP.15/36A Aiglon	F-CETR	20		RA
☐ Dassault MD-312 Flamant	202	202		RA
☐ Dassault MD-450 Ouragan	232	232		RAC
☐ Dassault MD-452C Mystère IIC	104	104	On loan from M.A.	RA
☐ Dassault Mystère IVA	299	299		RA
☐ Dassault Mystère IVN	01	01	On loan from M.A.	RA
☐ Dassault Super Mystère B2	158	158		RA
☐ Dassault Mirage IIIB	204	204		RA
☐ Dassault Mirage IIIC	2	2		RA
☐ Dassault Mirage IIING (Mirage 50)	01	01		RA
☐ Dassault Mirage IIIRD	370	370		RA
☐ Dassault Mirage IVA	03	03	Front fuselage only.	RA
☐ Dassault Mirage IVP (IVA)	56	56		RA
☐ Dassault Mirage 5F	29	29		RA
☐ Dassault Mirage 2000B	01	B-01		RA
☐ Dassault Etendard IVM	40	40		RA
☐ Dassault Falcon 20C	145	145		RA
☐ Dassault Falcon 20C (20)	F-WMSH	1	F-WMSH, F-BMSH, 401	RA
☐ Dassault Falcon 20G (HU-25A)		01	Front fuselage only.	RA
☐ Dassault Falcon 20G	F-WDFJ	362	(F-WZAS), F-WATF	RA
☐ Dassault Falcon 30	F-WAMD	1	Fuselage only.	RAC

☐ Dassault Falcon 50	F-WNDB	1	Fuselage only.	RAC
☐ Dassault Mercure 100	F-BTTF	6		RA
☐ Dewoitine D.520	603	603	On loan from MA.	RAC
☐ Dornier-Breguet Alpha Jet A			Front fuselage only.	RA
☐ Douglas A-26B Invader	35859	29138	44-35859	RA
☐ Fauvel AV.36	F-CBRO	115		RA
☐ Fouga CM.170R Magister	'320'	370	370, 1370 (Cameroun)	RAX
☐ Fouga CM.170R Magister	1370	454	454	RA
☐ Mauboussin M.121P Corsaire	F-AMPA	110		RA
☐ Max Holste MH.1521M Broussard	228	228		RA
☐ Mignet HM-14 Pou-du-Ciel		130		RA
☐ Nieuport 17			Wing and other parts.	RA
☐ Nord N.1203-VI Norécrin	F-BIFU	368	F-BGFM, LX-GFM	RA
☐ Nord N.2501 Noratlas	111	111	111,F-WFYF	RA
☐ Nord N.2501 Noratlas	188	188		RA
☐ Nord N.3400	99	99		RA
☐ Nord NC.702 Martinet [Siebel Si 204A-1]	282	282	On loan from M.A.	RAC
☐ Nord NC.856A Norvigie	24	24	Fuselage frame only.	RAX
☐ Nord NC.856A Norvigie	F-BNRX	55	55	RA
☐ Nord NC.856A Norvigie	F-BNRZ	105	105	RA
☐ Sikorsky S-58	149	SA-149		RA
☐ Stampe & Vertongen S.V.4C	F-BBON	322		RAA
☐ Sud SA.341F Gazelle	1579	1579		RA
☐ Sud SA.365C Dauphin				RA
☐ Sud-Est SE.210 Caravelle 10B1R	F-BLKS	176	F-WLKS, F-BLKS, EC-BDC, EC-CAE, D-ACVK	RA
☐ Sud-Est SE.210 Caravelle VI-R	234	234	F-WJAL, LX-LGE, HB-ICP, F-BRGX	RA
☐ Sud-Est SE.3130 Alouette II	F-GIJK	1087		RA
☐ Sud-Est SE.3130 Alouette II	182	1112		RA
☐ Sud-Est SE.3130 Alouette II	A-18	1624	In Belgian markings.	RA
☐ Sud-Ouest SO-4050 Vautour IIB	636	112		RA
☐ Supaéro Petit Canard	F-WZVA	01		RA
☐ Vought F-8P Crusader (F-8E(FN))	32	1249	Bu151763	RAC
☐ Wassmer WA.22 Super Javelot	F-CCOI	81		RA
☐ Wassmer WA.30 Bijave	F-CCNB	52	Wings only.	RA
☐ Wassmer WA.30 Bijave	F-CCYQ	114	Wings only.	RA
☐ Wassmer WA.30 Bijave	F-CDET	180		RA

MUSÉES DE LA RÉOLE (FRA66)

Address: 19 Avenue Gabriel Chaigne, 33190 La Réole.
Tel: 05 56 61 29 25
Fax: 05 56 61 29 77
Email: info@les-musees.com
Admission: Mid June-mid September daily 1000-1800; mid-September-November April-mid June Wednesday-Saturday 1400-1800, Sunday 1000-1800; December-March Wednesday, Saturday 1400-1800 Sunday 1300-1800.
Location: Just east of the town centre.

Four museums are housed in a former tobacco factory in the centre of this historic town. Over one hundred cars can be seen in the Automobile Museum. A wide range of tractors and farm machinery is in the Agricultural Museum and the Railway Museum includes a train ride and an excellent model layout. The Military Museum traces the history of World War II with many dioramas and armoured vehicles. The two aircraft came from Savigny. The Thunderstreak is ex-Belgian Air Force and the Mystère, at the rear of the building, is a composite.

TYPE	REG/SER	CON. NO.	PI/NOTES	STATUS
☐ Dassault Mystère IVA	237	237	Composite.	PV
☐ Republic F-84F Thunderstreak			(USAF), (Belgium)	PV

34 HÉRAULT

ASSOCIATION ANTILOPE (FRA67)

Address: 192 Rue des Amandiers, 34980 St. Clement de Rivière.
Tel: 04 67 84 02 98
Fax: 04 67 84 02 98
Email: antilope@fr.fm
Admission: By prior permission only.
Location: At Montpellier-Méditérranée airport which is about 8 km south east of the town off the D 62.

A number of interesting types are maintained in airworthy condition by this association which takes its name from the first aircraft they acquired, the SIPA S.251. The sole prototype of the type, which was the first light aircraft to be designed with a single turboprop engine, flew in November 1962. The aircraft set a number of international closed circuit records in its class in the last quarter of 1964. In 1959 two Nord N.1101 airframes were fitted with an Astazou turboprop for test work. In 1960 SFERMA modified a Beech Travel Air to take two Astazous and after trials the airframe was fitted with larger tail surfaces. The type entered production in 1962 but only eighteen were completed due to a lack of orders. In 1961 the Nord company took over a part of Max Holste Aviation and continued the development of the MH-260. This was re-designated the Nord N.260 and ten were built. Work continued on the pressurised fuselage Nord N.262 which was also a Holste design although they had not started the construction of a airframe. Nord flew the prototype in December 1962 and one hundred and eleven were completed for civil and military use. The Fouga 90 is one of several developments of the basic Magister design and dates from 1978. The Epsilon has been the basic trainer for the French Air Force since the late 1970s and is still in use at Cognac. One has recently been acquired.

TYPE	REG/SER	CON. NO.	PI/NOTES	STATUS
☐ Aérospatiale TB.30 Epsilon				RAA
☐ Beech-SFERMA Marquis 60A	F-AZLP	10	F-BLLP	RAA
☐ Fouga 90	F-WZJB	01		RAC
☐ Fouga CM.170R Magister	F-WZLQ	126	126	RAC
☐ Nord N.1110 (Nord N.1101 Noralpha)	F-AZNR	1	150, F-WJDQ (Original c/n 150)	RAA
☐ Nord N.260	F-AZRH	03	F-BKRH	RAA
☐ Société Industrielle Pour l'Aéronautique (SIPA) S.251 Antilope	F-WJSS	1		RAC
☐ Sud-Ouest SO-1221 Djinn	F-GHIG	147FR97	1147	RAC

MUSÉE DE LA GENDARMERIE (FRA68)

Address:	Aéroport de Fréjorgues, 34134 Maugio.
Tel:	04 67 65 15 00
Admission:	By prior permission only.
Location:	About 8 km south east of the town off the D.62.

The force is setting up a museum at one of its sites in the area. An air detachment has been in residence at the airport for many years and the Cessna is stored in the hangar. The force has flown both helicopters and fixed wing aircraft from Montpellier. Further details of the project would be appreciated.

TYPE	REG/SER	CON. NO.	PI/NOTES	STATUS
☐ Cessna U206F	2147	02147	F-MJAB	RA

35 ILE-ET-VILAINE

ASSOCIATION AÉROSPECIALE (FRA69)

Address:	50 Rue Jules Valles, 35136 Saint Jacques de Landes.
Tel:	02 99 30 34 79
Fax:	02 99 35 38 49
Admission:	By prior permission only.
Location:	At airfield about 5 km south west of Rennes off the D 177.

A number of former Swiss Air Force aircraft were acquired by this group in the auction held at Dubendorf in late 1991. Two single seat and a pair of two seat Vampires are presently in the fleet. Two C-3605s used for target towing in the latter part of their military career later joined the collection along with a Pilatus P.3 trainer. A major setback occurred on April 26th 1998 when two Fouga Magisters collided in mid-air killing one of the founders of association, Yves Duval. The majority of the aircraft are housed in a military hangar at the airport but a smaller one by the aero club is also used. The Chipmunk is a fairly recent addition and is still in its Royal Air Force colours. The replica Pou-du-Ciel, built from original plans, is transported to many local events. The Nardi FN.333 three seat amphibian first flew in December 1952 and a four seat version took to the air two years later. Only a small number were built over the next few years with several assembled in Texas. The Mirage IIIRD and the Caravelle are parked on the airfield. The Mirage IIIE is in a special white colour scheme.

TYPE	REG/SER	CON. NO.	PI/NOTES	STATUS
☐ Dassault Mirage IIIE	514	514		RA
☐ Dassault Mirage IIIRD	351	351		RA
☐ De Havilland D.H.100 Vampire FB.6	F-AZHY	610	J-1101 (Switzerland)	RAA
☐ De Havilland D.H.100 Vampire FB.6	F-AZHI	652	J-1143 (Switzerland)	RAA
☐ De Havilland D.H.115 Vampire T.55	F-AZHU	870	U-1210 (Switzerland)	RAA
☐ De Havilland D.H.115 Vampire T.55	F-AZHV	983	U-1223 (Switzerland)	RAA
☐ De Havilland D.H.C.1 Chipmunk T.10	F-AZPD	C1/0027	WB575	RAA

☐ Eidgenössiches Flugzeugwerke Emmen C-3605 (C-3603-1)	F-AZGC	273	C-493, F-WZII	RAA
☐ Eidgenössiches Flugzeugwerke Emmen C-3605 (C-3603-1)	F-AZGD	330	C-550, F-WZIG	RAA
☐ Fouga CM.170R Magister	F-GKYD	172	172, F-WKYD	RAD
☐ Fouga CM.170R Magister	F-GKYE	201	201, F-WKYE	RAD
☐ Fouga CM.170R Magister	F-GOYD	203	203	RA
☐ Fouga CM.170R Magister	F-GKYF	315	315, F-WKYF	RAA
☐ Fouga CM.170R Magister	F-GRYD	393	393	RA
☐ Fouga CM.170R Magister	F-GJMN	424	424, F-WQCE	RAA
☐ Fouga CM.170R Magister	F-GPHD	445	445	RA
☐ Fouga CM.170R Magister	F-GSYD	455	455	RA
☐ Fouga CM.170R Magister	F-GUYD	465	465	RA
☐ Fouga CM.170R Magister	F-GSHD	529	529	RA
☐ Fouga CM.170R Magister	F-GTHD	530	530	RA
☐ Fouga CM.170R Magister	F-GUHD	533	533	RA
☐ Max Holste MH.1521M Broussard	F-GDPX	170	170, F-WDPX	RAA
☐ Max Holste MH.1521M Broussard	254	254	On military base.	RA
☐ Mignet HM-14 Pou-du-Ciel (R)				RA
☐ Morane-Saulnier MS.733 Alcyon	F-BMQC	200	200	RAA
☐ Nardi FN.333 Riviera	F-BTAM	0102	I-ELYO, (OO-DEB), OO-HAR, F-BTAM, N5HL	RA
☐ Nord NC.858S (NC.853S)	F-BEZG	100		RAC
☐ Pilatus P.3-03	F-AZHT	324	A-807, F-AZGU	RAA
☐ Sud-Est SE.210 Caravelle 12/58T	F-GCVJ	275	F-WJAL, OY-SAF	RA
☐ Sud-Est SE.3160 Alouette III	1076	1076	Identity doubtful.	RA

MANOIR DE L'AUTOMOBILE (FRA70)

Address:	Route de Lieuron, 35550 Lohéac.
Tel:	02 99 34 02 32
Fax:	02 99 34 05 01
Email:	manoirautomobile@sfep.fr
Admission:	Tuesday-Sunday 1000-1300 1400-1900.
Location:	About 2 km south west of the town on the D 50.

This large museum has been constructed on the foundations of a seventeenth century manor house. Over four hundred superbly restored cars, fifty horsedrawn vehicles and three thousand models are on show. A highlight is a formula one grid with eighteen racers in position. The famous twenty four hour race at Le Mans is featured prominently with several cars which have participated on show. There is an excellent collection of commercial vehicles to be seen with several specialised models on view. The development of the bus can be followed with types from early charabancs up to fairly modern coaches. A number of replica workshops have been built to show the advances in car servicing and repair over the last few decades. The only aircraft in the collection is Fouga Magister which was flown from Cognac until withdrawn from use.

TYPE	REG/SER	CON. NO.	PI/NOTES	STATUS
☐ Fouga CM.170R Magister	169	169		PV

36 INDRE

ASSOCIATION FOUG'AIR (FRA71)

Address:	55, Rue de la Republique, 36000 Châteauroux.
Tel:	02 54 08 08 46
Email:	bruno.chauvet@9online.fr
Admission:	By prior permission only.
Location:	At Villers airfield which is about 5 km north west of the town north of the N.143. Some aircraft are at other fields in the area

The organisation was formed in 1992 by a group of pilots who wished to fly and maintain vintage aircraft. Their first two aircraft were a former Portuguese Chipmunk which has been sold and a loaned Broussard. They soon acquired their own Broussard which was restored and made its first public appearance at a show at Villers in the summer of 1994. The collection has expanded and now contains several interesting types. The Waco UPF-7 first flew in 1939. One was evaluated by the Army Air Corps at Wright Field in the summer of 1939 and as a result thirteen were ordered for further trials. These proved that the biplane was ideal for the Civilian Pilot Training Program and six hundred were delivered. Very few have been used in Europe and the example in the collection is one of a pair imported into France in the late 1990s. The Beagle Terrier is a recent addition to the organisation and is resplendent in the silver scheme with yellow training bands which it wore when serving as an Auster T.7. The aircraft are regular participants at shows and meetings in the region. The two Spanish built Jungmanns are used for aerobatic work and the Fouga Magister is normally kept elsewhere. The pair of Pipers often appear as a duo. Both are resplendent in French military colours. The L-4 is brown and the L-18 is in a striking all yellow scheme.

TYPE	REG/SER	CON. NO.	PI/NOTES	STATUS
☐ Beagle A.61 Terrier 2 (Auster Q T.7)	F-AZTJ	B.604	WE591, G-ASAK	RAA
☐ Construcciones Aeronáuticas (CASA) 1.131E [Bücker Bü 131 Jungmann]	F-AZYY	2018	E.3B-414	RAA
☐ Construcciones Aeronáuticas (CASA) 1.131E [Bücker Bü 131 Jungmann]	F-AZBZ	2150 (?)	E.3B-549	RAA
☐ Fouga CM.170R Magister				RAA
☐ Max Holste MH.1521M Broussard	F-GIBN	261	261	RAA
☐ Piper J-3C-65 Cub (L-4H)	F-BCPN	11801	43-30510, OO-REA	RAA
☐ Piper PA-18-95 Super Cub (L-18C)	F-BOMM	18-1397	51-15397, 15397 (France)	RAA
☐ Stampe & Vertongen S.V.4A	F-BDNF	661		RAA
☐ Waco UPF-7	F-AZLC	5711	NC32079, N32079, (F-AZJC)	RAA

37 INDRE ET LOIRE

AILES ANCIENNES TOURAINE – AERO VINTAGE (FRA72)

Address:	8 Square du Village, 95110 Sannois.
Tel:	01 30 25 43 75
Fax:	01 30 25 43 75
Email:	c.a.s@tele.2.fr
Admission:	By prior permission only.
Location:	At Orbigny airfield which is close to the village which is about 45 km south east of Tours.

This branch was formed in the mid-1990s and the majority of its aircraft are in store in the Orbigny area although the Alcyon normally flies from Amboise. Many of the fleet are privately owned by members of the group. Plans envisage a museum in the area tracing local aviation history. The Mignet HM-8 dates from the late 1920s and was one of the first types for which plans were made available for the amateur constructor. The first so built flew at Angouleme in May 1929 and over the next few years over two hundred were started and many were successfully flown. The one in the collection is in a poor state after almost seventy years in store. The last of ten Caudron C.801s built in the early 1950s is one of several stored gliders. The design was developed from the successful C.800 which was built during the German occupation. The NC.850 series of light aircraft was designed by the Aerocentre company and production was taken over by Nord. The NC.856 tourer evolved into the NC.856A Norvigie two seat liaison and observation aircraft. Over one hundred were flown by ALAT from bases around the country. Only a few have been sold to civilian owners. There is company which rebuilds vintage aircraft located on the field. Many interesting projects are often in their workshops. The Potez 60 which has now been restored to flying condition was once in the Aviantic collection at Caen.

TYPE	REG/SER	CON. NO.	PI/NOTES	STATUS
☐ Arsenal Air 100	F-CADC	12		RAA
☐ Avialsa-Scheibe A.60 Fauconnet [L-Spatz 55]	F-CDBJ	82K		RA
☐ Avialsa-Scheibe A.60 Fauconnet [L-Spatz 55]	F-CDNF	153		RAA
☐ Breguet 900	F-CADF	5		RAD
☐ Breguet 904S Nymphale	F-CCFV	12		RA
☐ Carmam JP.15/36A Aiglon	F-CETB	4		RA
☐ Carmam M.100S Mésange	F-CCSS	30		RA
☐ Castel C.301S	F-CAQF	3		RA
☐ Castel C.301S	F-CRLU	1061	F-CAKC	RA
☐ Castel C.311P	F-CAIT	310/39		RA
☐ Caudron C.800 Épervier	F-CBII	9788/128		RA
☐ Caudron C.800 Épervier	F-CAJI	9877/217		RA
☐ Caudron C.800 Épervier	F-CBAK	9932/272		RA
☐ Caudron C.801	F-CBTK	9986/326/10		RA
☐ Cessna 305C Bird Dog (L-19E) (O-1E)	F-GFVC	24535	24535	RAD
☐ Fauvel AV.36	F-CRBL	131	F-CBSF	RA
☐ Fauvel AV.36	F-CBSJ	135		RA
☐ Guerchais-Roche SA.103 Emouchet	F-CRGB	146	F-CBVI	RA
☐ Mignet HM-8				RAD
☐ Morane-Saulnier MS.733 Alcyon	F-BGTR	9	At Amboise airfield.	RAA
☐ Nord N.1203 Norécrin	F-BEBI	39		RA
☐ Nord N.1300 [Schneider Grunau Baby IIB]	F-CRNV	70	F-CBEZ	RA
☐ Nord N.2000 [Jacobs Meise]	F-CBVR	10380/50		RA
☐ Nord NC.856A Norvigie	F-BNRU	10	10	RA
☐ Potez 60	F-AZSK	4190	F-AOSK	RAA
☐ Scheibe Bergfalke II/55	F-CCDK	207		RAA
☐ Wassmer WA.21 Javelot II	F-CCHI	22		RAD
☐ Wassmer WA.22A Super Javelot	F-CCTI	100		RA
☐ Wassmer WA.26P Squale	F-CDZC	68		RAA
☐ Wassmer WA.30 Bijave				RA
☐ Wassmer WA.30 Bijave	F-CCYK	108		RA
☐ Wassmer WA.30 Bijave	F-CDSH	263		RAC

COLLECTION DE LA BASE AÉRIENNE DE TOURS (FRA73)

Address:	Base Aérienne 705, Route Paris, 37067 Tours Cedex 2.
Tel:	02 47 54 02 81
Admission:	By prior permission only.
Location:	About 5 km north east of the city on the N 10.

The first French all weather jet fighter wing was formed at the base in January 1953 and initially used Meteor NF.11s which were replaced by Vautour IINs in 1957. The unit moved to Reims in 1961 and its place was taken by the École de Chasse which arrived from Méknes in Morocco with fifty five T-33s and forty Mystère IVAs. The Alpha Jet entered service in 1979 and is still in use with the resident squadrons. There is a traditions room on the base which traces the history of the airfield and the school.

TYPE	REG/SER	CON. NO.	PI/NOTES	STATUS
☐ Breguet / British Aircraft Corporation Jaguar A	A131	A131		RA
☐ Canadair CL-30 Silver Star 3 (CT-133) [Lockheed 580 (T-33AN)]	21330	T33-330	21330	RA
☐ Dassault MD-450 Ouragan	187	187		RA
☐ Dassault MD-450 Ouragan	'205'	227	227	RAX
☐ Dassault Mystère IVA	22	22		RA
☐ Dassault Mirage IIIB	219	219		RA
☐ Lockheed 580 (T-33A)	14420	580-5715	51-4420	RA

MUSÉE MAURICE DUFRESNE (FRA74)

Address:	Marnay, 37190 Azay le Rideau.
Tel:	02 47 45 36 18
Fax:	02 47 45 28 62
Email:	info@musee-dufresne.com
Admission:	Mid February- mid December daily 0915-1800 (closes at 1900 May-October).
Location:	In the village which is about 6 km. west of Azay le Rideau on the D 120.

Local entrepreneur Maurice Dufresne was born in the area in 1930. Over the years he collected a vast range of guns, agricultural equipment, cars, motor cycles, industrial machinery and items of interest including a 1792 guillotine used in the French Revolution. The large buildings now house over three thousand pieces of vintage machinery restored to original condition. Two aircraft are currently on show with a third under restoration nearby. The 1909 Blériot is displayed in a period setting with cars and motor cycles around it. The remains were found and the airframe and engine have been restored to original condition. The Caudron C.800 glider featured in the film 'La Grande Vadrouville'. The French Army acquired one hundred and eight of the distinctive 'banana' shaped Vertol H-21 helicopters. One example should soon join the exhibition.

TYPE	REG/SER	CON. NO.	PI/NOTES	STATUS
☐ Blériot XI		140		PV
☐ Caudron C.800 Épervier				PV
☐ Vertol V.43 (H-21C)	60	FR-60		RAC

38 ISÈRE

AÉROCLUB LES AILES DAUPHINOISES (FRA75)

Address:	Aérodrome de Cessieu, 49 Rue de la Gore, 38110 La Tour du Pin.
Tel:	04 74 88 32 67
Admission:	By prior permission only.
Location:	About 2 km south of Cessieu off the D 51A.

This club is part of the Dédale organisation which co-ordinates vintage glider flying in France. Four members of their fleet fall into this category. The Air 102 was developed from the 100 and ten were built in 1950. The Breguet company built a number of gliders in the late 1940s and 1950s and these were successful in many contests. The two seat Br.904S made its maiden flight in May 1956 and fifteen production examples were constructed for club use. Three more modern classic types are also operated.

TYPE	REG/SER	CON. NO.	PI/NOTES	STATUS
☐ Arsenal Air 102	F-CASB	36		RAA
☐ Breguet 904S Nymphale	F-CCFQ	7		RAA
☐ Caproni-Vizzola A.21S Calif	F-CHHF	218	HB-1180	RAA
☐ Caproni-Vizzola A.21S Calif	F-CEUF	241		RAA
☐ Glasflügel H205 Libelle	F-CEQI	152		RAA
☐ Wassmer WA.26P Squale	F-CDQH	12		RAA
☐ Wassmer WA.30 Bijave	F-CCME	8		RAA

ASSOCIATION LA TÊTE EN L'AIR (FRA76)

Address:	304 Chemins des Longs Prés, 38660 Lumbin.
Admission:	By prior permission only.
Location:	Near the village just off the N 90 about 15 km north east of Grenoble.

Members of this group have built a full scale wooden model of the Alpha Jet. The aircraft is painted in 'Patrouille de France' colours and is often exhibited at local events. The group has a display of photographs and memorabilia tracing the history of the type developed jointly with Germany.

TYPE	REG/SER	CON. NO.	PI/NOTES	STATUS
☐ Dornier-Breguet Alpha Jet A (FSM)				RAX

CENTRE D'ÉTUDE ET DE LOISIRS AÉROSPATIAUX DE GRENOBLE (FRA77)

Address:	Aérodrome de Versoud, 38420 Le Versoud.
Tel:	04 76 77 27 57
Email:	celag@mail.dotcom.fr
Admission:	Saturday 1400-1800 or by prior permission.
Location:	About 10 km north of the town near the D 523.

Formed in 1976 by the late Alexandre Gomis, this group originally occupied premises in the centre of the city. A move was made to the airport some years ago and the majority of the helicopters are housed in former military buildings. The three aims of the organisation are amateur aircraft construction, scale modelling and the restoration of helicopters. A large collection of scale models tracing the history of flight can be seen. There are long term plans to raise funds for a museum. A building will be constructed at the airport if the project succeeds. Several versions of the Alouette II and III can be seen. This very successful II first flew in 1955 and about seventeen hundred examples of it and its derivatives were built. Also almost fourteen hundred of the larger and more powerful III were constructed. There are many components, engines photographs and models in this collection. The technical development of rotary wing flight is portrayed in the exhibition The experimental Déchaux Hélicop-Jet is under restoration. This helicopter was built in the 1970s and tested at Issy. After a series of trials it was decided that the project should be abandoned and the airframe was stored in one of the hangars. The remains to the single seat prototype of the Djinn are in the storage building. This helicopter first flew in January 1953. The two seat development the SO.1221 was put into production. Many were used by the French Army and others in agricultural work. The two Sikorsky types were also used by the Army in France. Young members of the group are also rebuilding a Jodel D.112 so that they can gain flight experience in a light aircraft. This project is nearing completion. The Mirage IIIE is with a technical school on another part of the airfield and students from this organisation often are detailed to help with the helicopter work.

TYPE	REG/SER	CON. NO.	PI/NOTES	STATUS
☐ Dassault Mirage IIIE				RA
☐ Dechaux Helicop-Jet				RAC
☐ Sikorsky S-55B		55957	55-5957 quoted.	PVD
☐ Sikorsky S-58	177	SA-177		PVX
☐ Sud SA.316 Alouette III		01		RA
☐ Sud SA.319B Alouette III	2084	2084		PVC
☐ Sud SA.319B Alouette III	2112	2112		PVX
☐ Sud SA.330J Puma	F-GBLS	1407	Front fuselage only – possible identity.	PV
☐ Sud SA.341 Gazelle			Cabin only – constructor's mock-up.	PV
☐ Sud-Est SE.3130 Alouette II	57	1071		PV
☐ Sud-Est SE.3130 Alouette II	129	1219		PVD
☐ Sud-Est SE.3130 Alouette II	236	1440 (?)	Incorporates parts of c/n 1741	PV
☐ Sud-Est SE.3130 Alouette II	'252'	1488	488	PVCX
☐ Sud-Est SE.3130 Alouette II	1730	1730	Incorporatesparts of c/n 1219.	PVC
☐ Sud-Est SE.3160 Alouette III				PV
☐ Sud-Ouest SO-1220 Djinn	F-WCZX	1220.01	Parts only.	PV
☐ Sud-Ouest SO-1221PS Djinn	F-WGVU	FC-1	Fuselage only.	PV
☐ Vertol V.43 (H-21C)	41	FR-41		PVD
☐ Wytwornia Sprzetu Komunikacyjnego (WSK) SM-1Wb [Mil Mi-1M]	3009	403009	In Czech markings – on loan from M.A.	PV

MUSÉE AUTOMOBILE (FRA78)

Address: 38670 Chasse-sur-Rhone.
Admission: ?
Location: About 2km south of the town on the D.7.

Mention of a Fouga Magister mounted outside this museum hav appeared in French magazines. Reports by tourists to the area suggest that there are several cars on show along with lorries, motor cycles, bicycles and military vehicles. Attempts to find the correct name and details of the collection have been unsuccessful.

TYPE	REG/SER	CON. NO.	PI/NOTES	STATUS
☐ Fouga CM.170R Magister	F-GNYN	532	532	PV

39 JURA

AÉROCLUB DE LONS-LE-SAUNIER – SECTION RÉTRO (FRA79)

Address: L.P. 62,
39002 Lons-le-Saunier.
Tel: 03 84 24 71 81
Admission: By prior permission only.
Location: At Courlans airfield which is about 4 km west of the town on the N 78.

The aeroclub and some of its members maintain a fleet of classic types. The two Texans were operated by a group at Belleville before they moved to Lons in the late 1980s. The Stampe S,V.4 was the backbone of the club fleet in the 1950s and four are still at the field. The Super Cub has recently been restored. Two former Royal Air Force Bulldogs are fairly recent arrivals. The Czechoslovakian built Yak-11 is from the batch imported by Jean Salis from Egypt. Not many Nord N.1002s remain airworthy in France at the present time. A number of Zlin Treners were used for aerobatic training by the Government Flying School at St. Yan in the 1970s/80s.

TYPE	REG/SER	CON. NO.	PI/NOTES	STATUS
☐ Let C-11 [Yakovlev Yak-11]	F-AZIO	Y-5434		RAA
☐ Max Holste MH.1521C-1 Broussard (1521M)	F-GGCN	6	6	RAA
☐ Morane-Saulnier MS.733 Alcyon	F-BNEK	158	158	RAA
☐ Nord N.1002 Pingouin II [Messerschmitt Bf 108B]	F-AZMR	216	216, F-BFKR	RAA
☐ North American NA-168 Texan (T-6G)	F-AZCQ	168-141	49-3037, E.16-193 (Spain)	RAA
☐ North American NA-182 Texan (T-6G)	F-AZCV	182-143	51-14456, E.16-191 (Spain)	RAA
☐ Piper PA-18-150 Super Cub	F-GJOV	1809056		RAA
☐ Scottish Aviation Bulldog 120/121 (T.1)	F-AZOD	BH120/255	XX559	RAA
☐ Scottish Aviation Bulldog 120/121 (T.1)	F-AZOA	BH120/334	XX688	RAA
☐ Stampe & Vertongen S.V.4A	F-BCKT	286		RAA
☐ Stampe & Vertongen S.V.4C	F-GGVI	429	F-BCVI	RAA
☐ Stampe & Vertongen S.V.4C	F-BDDD	558		RAC
☐ Stampe & Vertongen S.V.4C	F-BDHC	1125		RAA
☐ Zlin Z-526 Trener Master	F-BRNA	1063		RAA

ASSOCIATION AIR MEMORIAL (FRA80)

Address: 162 Rue de Langefin,
39570 Maconay.
Tel: 03 84 25 36 31 or 03 84 47 05 45
Admission: By prior permission only.
Location: At the Lons-le-Saunier airfield which is about 4 km west of the town on the N 78.

This group was formed in 1982 by three enthusiasts to operate a Texan which later crashed killing the pilot. A hangar has now been constructed and the active aircraft are regular performers at shows around the country. The Alcyon is in the blue scheme used by the Aéronavale on some of its training aircraft. The Noratlas is owned by Support Air and is painted in blue and yellow 'European Community' colours. A Flamant has recently left the collection and the Stampe is under rebuild in the workshops.

TYPE	REG/SER	CON. NO.	PI/NOTES	STATUS
☐ Fouga CM.170R Magister	F-WDXH	2	2	RA
☐ Max Holste MH.1521M Broussard	F-GBEN	224	224	RAA
☐ Morane-Saulnier MS.733 Alcyon	F-GIQK	149	149, F-BMQK	RAA
☐ Nord N.2501 Noratlas	F-EURO	148	148 – owned by Support Air.	RAA
☐ Stampe & Vertongen S.V.4C				RAC

RÉTRO AIR FRANCHE-COMTÉ (FRA81)

Address:	105 Rue Trois Moulins, 39006 Lons-le-Saunier
Tel:	03 84 44 22 45
Admission:	By prior permission only.
Location:	At private properties in the Gray and Lons-le-Saunier areas.

This preservation group has been in existence for several years but little is known of its activities. A workshop in the Gray area is believed to be the location of most of the airframes. The majority of the collection has been obtained from local aero clubs. The Potez 36 high wing monoplane first appeared in 1929 and over two hundred were built over the next few years. The prototype Fauvel AV.22 tailless glider first flew near Cannes in 1956.

TYPE	REG/SER	CON. NO.	PI/NOTES	STATUS
☐ Auster J AOP.5	F-BFXF	977	MT343, G-AJYI	RA
☐ Castel C.301S	F-CAGV (?)	1224		RAC
☐ De Havilland D.H.82A Tiger Moth	F-BGDX	86610	PG713	RAC
☐ Fauvel AV.22	F-CCDC	01	F-WCDC	RA
☐ Guerchais-Roche SA.104 Emouchet	F-CROK	223	F-CAGZ, (F-CREZ)	RAC
☐ Nord N.1002 Pingouin II [Messerschmitt Bf 108B]	F-BBRC	203		RAD
☐ Potez 36/13				RAD
☐ Société Industrielle Pour l'Aéronautique (SIPA) S.903 (S.901)				RA
☐ Stampe & Vertongen S.V.4C	F-BDFF	610		RA

40 LANDES

AMICALE DES ANCIENS DE L'AVIATION LÉGÈRE DE L'ARMÉE DE TERRE (FRA82)

Address:	12 Rue Georges Chaulet, 40100 Dax.
Tel:	05 58 74 89 69
Admission:	By prior permission only.
Location:	At the north east corner of the airfield which is about 2 km south of the town on the D 106.

Formed by ex-A.L.A.T. pilots in the early 1990s the group currently has three aircraft which are used for pleasure flights to raise funds for the A.L.A.T. museum. Other types have been used in the past.

TYPE	REG/SER	CON. NO.	PI/NOTES	STATUS
☐ Bell 47G-1	F-BVKQ	722	722	RAA
☐ Cessna 305C Bird Dog (L-19E) (O-1E)	F-BIFB	24582	24582	RAA
☐ Cessna 305C Bird Dog (L-19E) (O-1E)	F-GEJK	24588	24588	RAA

ASSOCIATION NORD AÉRO (FRA83)

Address:	Hangar Sud, Aérodrome, 40370 Rion-des-Landes.
Tel:	05 58 57 19 87
Admission:	By prior permission only.
Location:	About 3 km south west of the town on the D 27.

This group offers flights in vintage aircraft in addition to restoration and construction work. A Morane-Saulnier H was built for the Museo del Aire in Spain and delivered in 2000. The so far unidentified Forwarder was obtained from the Paris area and work has just started to bring it back to flying condition.

TYPE	REG/SER	CON. NO.	PI/NOTES	STATUS
☐ Construcciones Aeronáuticas (CASA) 1.131E [Bücker Bü 131 Jungmann]	F-AZIQ		E.3B-625	RAA
☐ Construcciones Aeronáuticas (CASA) 1.131E [Bücker Bü 131 Jungmann]	F-AZLF	2036	E.3B-???	RAA
☐ Construcciones Aeronáuticas (CASA) 1.131E [Bücker Bü 131 Jungmann]	F-AZNB	2149	E.3B-???	RAA
☐ Fairchild 24W41A Forwarder (C-61A) (UC-61A) (Argus II)				RAC
☐ Piper PA-18-95 Super Cub (L-18C)	F-BOUE	18-1470	51-15470	RAA

COLLECTION DE LA BASE AÉRIENNE DE MONT-DE-MARSAN (FRA84)

Address:	Base Aérienne 118, 40490 Mont-de-Marsan Air.
Tel:	05 58 46 76 00
Fax:	05 58 46 79 44
Admission:	By prior permission only.
Location:	In the northern suburbs of the town.

This important base houses the Centre d'Expérimentations Aérienne Militaires which undertakes operational trials of military aircraft and ground equipment. The first squadron equipped with a new type carries out an initial working up period at the field. A strategic reconnaissance squadron using Mirage IVPs has recently been disbanded. A fighter unit operating Mirage 2000s is in residence along with a UAV group. A variety of transport types are normally based on the field. A number of. research duties are also carried out. The preserved aircraft represent types which have flown from the site.

TYPE	REG/SER	CON. NO.	PI/NOTES	STATUS
☐ Dassault Mystère IVA	'87'	234	234	RAX
☐ Dassault Super Mystère B2	153	153		RA
☐ Dassault Mirage IIIE	577	577		RA
☐ Dassault Mirage IVA	43	43		RA
☐ Dassault Mirage F.1CR	601	601		RA
☐ Fouga CM.170R Magister	542	542		RA
☐ Sud-Ouest SO-4050 Vautour IIN	364	134		RA
☐ Sukhoi Su-22M4	98+09	30916	590 (DDR), 25+27	RA

MUSÉE DE L'AVIATION LÉGÈRE DE L'ARMÉE DE TERRE ET DE L'HÉLICOPTÈRE (FRA85)

Address:	58 Avenue de l'Aérodrome, 40107 Dax.
Tel:	05 58 74 66 19
Fax:	05 58 74 66 19
Admission:	Monday-Saturday 1430-1730.
Location:	At the airfield which is about 3 km south west of the town on the D.6.

In 1946 observation squadrons of the Armée de l'Air were flying Piper Cubs and Morane-Saulnier Criquets in France, the French zone of Germany and the overseas colonies. In 1952 the Aviation Légère d'Observation d'Artillery was established and the first French Army pilots and mechanics were trained. The following year helicopters were introduced and the first squadron with Bell 47s, Hiller UH-12s and Sikorsky S-55s was formed in 1954. A.L.A.T. was established in 1954 and took over all aspects of Army flying. The Vertol H-21 with its distinctive 'banana' shaped fuselage was put into service in 1955. One hundred and eight were delivered and they served in troop-carrying and transport role for many years. French designed helicopters such as the Djinn and Alouette were were soon on strength along with fixed wing designs such as the Nord NC.856, N.3202, N3400 and the Max Holste Broussard. At the current time A.L.A.T. is almost completely equipped with helicopters. Just a few fixed wing types are used for communications, and light transport duties. Dax is home to the pilot training school of the service. The idea of a museum was put forward in the 1980s and aircraft, helicopters and associated material were collected at the site. In the mid-1990s a move was made to a large hangar on the northern side of the field. Here an excellent display tracing the history of Army flying in France from 1942 to the present day has been set up. On show are uniforms, missiles, guns, models and flags, including some seized in Vietnam. The operations in World War II, Algeria, Vietnam and Desert Storm are highlighted. The oldest machines are the Morane-Saulnier Criquet and the Stampe S.V.4. In the latter stages of World War II the Germans transferred production of the Storch to the Morane-Saulnier company. Many early Army pilots carried out their basic training on the Stampe so it is appropriate that one is on show. After the end of hostilities the firm carried on making the type for both military and civilian use. Displays of smaller items can be found in rooms behind the main hall. Nearby are workshops and storage hangars. A unique machine which did not see military use is the prototype of the Bruel-Duhamel-Molinari. This small helicopter was tested in the early 1950s and was then acquired by the Musée de l'Air. After spending decades in store it was moved to Dax for eventual rebuild.

TYPE	REG/SER	CON. NO.	PI/NOTES	STATUS
☐ Aérospatiale AS.332 Super Puma	02	02	F-WZCY	RA
☐ Agusta-Bell 47G-2	160	160		PV
☐ Bell 47G-1	1314	1314		PV
☐ Bell 47G-1	710	710	On loan from MA.	PV
☐ Bruel-Duhamel-Molinari Hélicoptère	F-WEPH	01	On loan from M.A.	RA
☐ Cessna 305C Bird Dog (L-19E) (O-1E)	24521	24521		RA
☐ Cessna 305C Bird Dog (L-19E) (O-1E)	24530	24530		PV
☐ Cessna 305C Bird Dog (L-19E) (O-1E)	24572	24572		RA
☐ Cessna 305C Bird Dog (L-19E) (O-1E)	24585	24585		RA
☐ Cessna 305C Bird Dog (L-19E) (O-1E)	24725	24725		PV
☐ Hiller UH12A	133	133	N8133H, F-OAHB	PV

☐ Max Holste MH.1521M Broussard	33	33M		RA
☐ Max Holste MH.1521M Broussard	266	266		RA
☐ Max Holste MH.1521M Broussard	269	269		PV
☐ Mil Mi-8TB	94+08	10568	814 (DDR)	RA
☐ Morane-Saulnier MS.505 Criquet (MS.502) [Fieseler Fi 156 Storch]	656	656	656, F-BDQQ	PV
☐ Nord N.3202B	66	66		PV
☐ Nord N.3202B1B	99	99	99, F-BNRO	PV
☐ Nord N.3400	75	75		PV
☐ Nord NC.853S			Fuselage frame only	RAD
☐ Nord NC.856A Norvigie				RA
☐ Nord NC.856A Norvigie	97	97	Composite.	PV
☐ Piper PA-18-95 Super Cub (L-18C)			Composite with parts of c/n 18-1363 and two others.	PV
☐ Piper PA-22-150 Tri-Pacer (PA-22-125)	25621	22-25	N621A, F-BFYP	PV
☐ Sikorsky S-55B		55864	On loan from M.A.	PV
☐ Sikorsky S-55B		551086	Incorporates parts of c/n 55603.	PV
☐ Sikorsky S-58	143	SA-143		PV
☐ Sikorsky S-58	53	SA-53	On loan from M.A.	RA
☐ Stampe & Vertongen S.V.4C	496	496	496, F-BDIZ	PV
☐ Sud SA.316B Alouette III	02	02		RA
☐ Sud SA.330B Puma	03	03	F-ZWWQ	RA
☐ Sud SA.330B Puma	05	05	F-ZWWR	RA
☐ Sud SA.330B Puma	1032	1032		RA
☐ Sud SA.330B Puma	1103	1103		RA
☐ Sud SA.341F Gazelle	1147	1147	At main gate to base.	PV
☐ Sud SA.349-2 (SA.341 Gazelle)	1201	1201		PV
☐ Sud SA.361H Dauphin	1003	1003		PV
☐ Sud-Est SE.3130 Alouette II				RA
☐ Sud-Est SE.3130 Alouette II	1094	1094	At main gate to base.	PV
☐ Sud-Est SE.3130 Alouette II	162	1162		PV
☐ Sud-Est SE.3130 Alouette II	1634	1634		PV
☐ Sud-Est SE.3160 Alouette III	002	002		PV
☐ Sud-Est SE.3160 Alouette III	01	01		PV
☐ Sud-Est SE.3160 Alouette III	1185	1185		RA
☐ Sud-Est SE.3160 Alouette III	A-414	1414	In Dutch markings.	RA
☐ Sud-Est SE.3160 Alouette III (SE.3160) (SA.319A)	'1001'	001		PVX
☐ Sud-Est SE.3180 Alouette Astazou	'1076'	1572	Composite.	PVX
☐ Sud-Est SE.3180 Alouette Astazou	1784	1784		RA
☐ Sud-Est SE.3180 Alouette Astazou	1797	1797		RA
☐ Sud-Est SE.3180 Alouette Astazou	2017	2017		RA
☐ Sud-Est SE.3180 Alouette Astazou	2117	2117		RA
☐ Sud-Ouest SO-1221 Djinn	12	12FR14		PV
☐ Sud-Ouest SO-1221 Djinn		66FR116		RA
☐ Sud-Ouest SO-1221 Djinn	F-BIUG	99FR149		PV
☐ Vertol V.43 (H-21C)	69	FR-69	On loan from M.A.	RA
☐ Vertol V.43 (H-21C)	94	FR-94		PV
☐ Vertol V.43 (H-21C)	106	FR-106	On loan to A.A. Toulouse	–

MUSÉE HISTORIQUE DE L'HYDRAVIATION (FRA86)

Address:	332 Avenue Louis Breguet, 40600 Biscarrosse.
Tel:	05 58 78 00 65
Fax:	05 58 78 81 97
Email:	musee.hydraviation@ville-biscarosse.fr
Admission:	July-August daily 1000-1900; April-June and September daily 1500-1900 ; October- March daily 1400-1800.
Location:	In the town close to the beach.

The first flight by a seaplane was made by Henri Fabre from the Etang du Berre near Marseille on March 28th 1910. During the 1930s and 1940s the lake at Biscarrosse housed an important seaplane base. Military aircraft of the Aéronavale were based at the site and at Hourtiquets two large hangars from this era still stand. During World War II the facilities were occupied by the Luftwaffe. In 1980 and 1981 two Dornier Do 24T-3s were raised by a private group but the fuselages were allowed to deteriorate and had to be scrapped. There are a number of other wrecks on the lake bed. The Latécoère company had its seaplane base at Biscarrosse and many designs were tested from the site. In 1947 Air France started a service to the West Indies using giant Latécoère 631 six engined flying boats and after a number of problems five were stored. In 1956 a hangar collapsed due to the weight of snow on the roof, most were badly damaged, and all were eventually scrapped. The town decided to set up a museum to trace the story of marine aviation and a superb exhibition has been set up. Photographs, models, memorabilia, components, documents, engines and uniforms can be seen. The development of the seaplane is told in detail and many interesting facts are shown in the displays. The history from the early days can be traced. In the 1980s an exhibition hall was built and the complete aircraft are on show in this area. The Thurston Teal was the first to arrive and this has been restored. Work on one of the Grumman Widgeons is being carried out. The replica Donnet Leveque, dating from World War I, was constructed by a team of volunteers. Two ultralight seaplanes are in the collection. The Serleg Amphibian was built near Quimper by Paul Legrand and made its maiden flight in the early 1990s.

TYPE	REG/SER	CON. NO.	PI/NOTES	STATUS
☐ Aerodyne Vector 610	50AF			PV
☐ Canadair CL-215-I	F-ZBBE/05	1005	Front fuselage only.	PV
☐ Donnet-Lévêque A (R)				PV
☐ Grumman G-44 Widgeon (OA-14)	G-DUCK	1218	NC28679, 42-38217, N58337, N3103Q	PVC
☐ Grumman G-44A Widgeon (J4F-2)	'NC28679'	1341	Bu37711, N750, N750M	PVX
☐ Partenavia Sea Sky				PV
☐ Romano R 1 (R)			On loan from A.A. Azurénnes.	PV
☐ Serleg 225EX	F-PZLM	001		PV
☐ Thurston TSC-1A1 Teal I	TU-TWA	16		PV

41 LOIR-ET-CHER

COLLECTION DE LA BASE AÉRIENNE DE ROMORANTIN (FRA87)

Address:	Base Aérienne 273, 41280 Romorantin.
Tel:	02 54 98 57 50
Admission:	By prior permission only.
Location:	About 5 km south west of the town on the D.724.

The main glider school of the Air Force was formed at the base in 1973. A fleet of sailplanes with a number of tugs is in use. Gliders are also in use at several other military airfields. The two jets are preserved outside and the gliders, representing types flown, are in one of the hangars with several mounted vertically on the walls. The two Wassmer types were used for many years and have only recently been withdrawn from use. A small number of Aiglons were flown and this design is no longer operated. The historic Caproni company began sailplane production at Vizzola in 1964 and later sold the business to Agusta. The last glider left the factory in 1983. Just over fifty A.21s were built and two were evaluated at Romorantin. The site also houses a large storage unit which among other duties holds technical documents on airframes, engines, and airfield equipment.

TYPE	REG/SER	CON. NO.	PI/NOTES	STATUS
☐ Caproni-Vizzola A.21S Calif	221	221	F-UMFM	RA
☐ Carmam JP.15/36A Aiglon	1	1		RA
☐ Dassault MD-450 Ouragan	297	297		RA
☐ Dassault Mirage IIIR	331	331		RA
☐ Schempp-Hirth Janus C	142	142/81		RA
☐ Schleicher ASW-20F	10	20109	Right half of glider only.	RA
☐ Wassmer WA.22 Super Javelot	138	138		RA
☐ Wassmer WA.30 Bijave	159	159		RA

44 LOIRE-ATLANTIQUE

AÉROSCOPE (FRA88)

Address:	Aéroport Nantes-Atlantique, 44346 Bougenais.
Tel:	02 40 84 81 43
Admission:	By prior permission only.
Location:	About 6 km south west of the town.

This group, formed in the 1990s, aims to set up a museum at the airport in conjunction with other local organisations. The Super Constellation was delivered to Air France in 1953 and flew with the company until 1963. A sale to Spain fell through as did one to Panama and the aircraft remained at Orly. Service with Air Fret and Catair on the Biafran airlift followed before the airliner was withdrawn at Nimes in 1973. The following year the 'Connie' was moved to Nantes to serve as a tourist attraction. Painted in the colours of the prototype it was parked on the approach road for many years. The aircraft is now being restored behind the hangars. The Noratlas, painted in a special colour scheme, and the Mirage are parked on the aeroclub ramp.

TYPE	REG/SER	CON. NO.	PI/NOTES	STATUS
☐ Dassault Mirage IIIB	224	224		RA
☐ Lockheed 1049G-02-82 Super Constellation (1049C-55-81) (1049E-01-55)	F-BRAD	1049C-4519	F-BGNJ, (EC-BEN)	RAC
☐ Nord N.2501 Noratlas	18	18		RA

ASSOCIATION JE ME SOUVIENS (FRA89)

Address:	Boulevard des Apprentis 404, 44602 Saint Nazaire.
Tel:	02 28 54 80 00
Fax:	02 28 54 81 31
Admission:	By prior permission only.
Location:	On the north side of the airport which is about 5 km north east of the town.

In the 1980s there were plans for a museum at the Aérospatiale factory. Three aircraft were acquired and restoration work commenced. The Fouga 90 has now gone to Association Antilope at Montpellier. The Vautour has been restored to pristine condition by members of this group. The twin engined jet is now parked close to the main gate of the works. Restoration of the sole surviving Bretagne is being carried out in a workshop. Forty five examples of the twin engined airliner were built and most were transferred for military use in France. The type was developed from the earlier Bellatrix prototypes. A single SO-30N and two SO-30Rs were tested.

TYPE	REG/SER	CON. NO.	PI/NOTES	STATUS
☐ Sud-Ouest SO-30P Bretagne.	37	37	F-WEHO, 37, 'F-BANZ'	PV
☐ Sud-Ouest SO-4050 Vautour IIB	632	106		PV

ASSOCIATION LES AÉROPLANES (FRA90)

Address:	1 Avenue Emile Bossier, 44000 Nantes.
Tel:	02 40 59 40 36
Email:	daniel.chateau@hotmail.com
Admission:	By prior permission only.
Location:	At the airport which is about 6 km south west of the town. At a number of locations in the suburbs of Nantes.

This long established group has assembled an interesting collection of gliders and light aircraft. The majority are currently stored in a military hangar at the airport. A workshop in a retail park to the west of the town is also in use. René Leduc built four light aircraft at Nantes between 1947 and 1975 as well as working on several projects. The RL-21 dates from 1960 and was powered by a Regnier engine. Another locally built rarity is the Krueger EK-51 which was built in the early 1950s and fitted with a 27 h.p. Ava motor. A number of Mignet designs have been acquired. Two pre-war HM-14s are in the workshops. A single seat HM-290 built at Royan in 1956 and owned for a time by Pierre Mignet, Henri's son, is in store. The prototype two seat HM-350 was built by Henri in Casablanca in 1956 and flown at Bordeaux and Castres until 1972. Also in the collection are a HM-380 and a prototype of the HM-1000 microlight dating from the mid-1980s. Emilien Croses of Macon developed the tandem wing concept. His first design the EC-1 Pouplume flew in 1957. The larger two seat all wood EC-6 made its maiden flight in 1965. Plans were made available and several have been completed. The post-war built Mauboussin is undergoing a major rebuild in the workshop. The M.129 was powered by a 70 hp. Minié engine. Members of the organisation own a number of active aircraft which are based at the airport and other airfields nearby. The Stinson Reliant is resplendent in World War II Royal Navy markings. The long term aim of the group is to set up a museum in the area probably in conjunction with the Aéroscope organisation.

TYPE	REG/SER	CON. NO.	PI/NOTES	STATUS
☐ Arsenal Air 100	F-CABP	9		RAC
☐ Arsenal Air 100	F-CAMA	37		RA
☐ Butterfly				RA
☐ Castel C.25S	F-CRDZ	96	F-CAND	RAD
☐ Castel C.301S	F-CRDA	106/56	F-CAHY	RA
☐ Castel C.301S	F-CRCR	1175	F-CBPF	RA
☐ Castel C.301S	F-CREJ	1192	F-CAKJ	RA
☐ Castel C.311P	F-CARO	276/5		RA
☐ Castel C.311P	F-CBYE	289/18		RA
☐ Caudron C.800 Épervier	F-CAHF	9898/238		RA
☐ Caudron C.800 Épervier	F-CCCE	9902/242		RA
☐ Croses LC-6 Criquet	F-PJRP	100		RAA
☐ De Havilland D.H.C.1 Chipmunk 22 (T.10)	F-AZUR	C1/0580	WK562	RAA
☐ Fauvel AV.22S	F-CCGN	4		RA
☐ Fournier RF-6B				RAC
☐ Jodel D.9 Bébé				RAA
☐ Jodel D.112 Club	F-BIEX	568	F-BIKX	RAA
☐ Kreuger EK.51 Welcome	F-WFOG	01		RA
☐ Leduc RL-21	F-WJDT	01		RA
☐ Let C-11 [Yakovlev Yak-11]				RAA
☐ Mauboussin M.129 Corsaire	F-BBSK	191		RAC
☐ Mignet HM-14 Pou-du-Ciel				RA
☐ Mignet HM-14 Pou-du-Ciel		25		RAC
☐ Mignet HM-290 Pou-du-Ciel	F-PERF	06		RA
☐ Mignet HM-350 Pou-du-Ciel	F-PHQT	01		RA
☐ Mignet HM-380 Pou-du-Ciel				RA
☐ Mignet HM-1000 Balerit	17-G			RA
☐ Nord N.1203-VI Norécrin				RAA
☐ Nord N.1300 [Schneider Grunau Baby IIB]	F-CRAM	144	F-CANY	RA
☐ Nord N.1300 [Schneider Grunau Baby IIB]	F-CRHA	194	F-CBFJ	RA

TYPE	REG/SER	CON. NO.	PI/NOTES	STATUS
☐ Nord N.1300 [Schneider Grunau Baby IIB]	F-CRAQ	216	F-CANP	RA
☐ Nord N.2000 [Jacobs Meise]	F-CBFP	10364/34		RA
☐ Nord N.2000 [Jacobs Meise]	F-CARZ	10400/70		RA
☐ Nord N.2000 [Jacobs Meise]	F-CAIX	10421/91		RA
☐ Piel CP.301C Emeraude				RA
☐ Piper PA-18-135 Super Cub (L-21B)	F-BSEC	18-5371	18-5371	RAA
☐ Schneider Grunau SG-38 (D.F.S. 108-14)	F-CBHK	124		RA
☐ Starck AS.70	F-PBGD	7		RA
☐ Stinson V-77 Reliant (AT-19)	F-AZGK	77-177	42-46816, FK990, NC770B, N770B	RAA
☐ Victor Minié V.M.A. 200 Milan [Jacobs Weihe]	F-CABX	25		RA
☐ Wassmer WA.30 Bijave				RA

MUSÉE AÉRONAUTIQUE PRESQ'ÎLE CÔTE D'AMOUR (FRA91)

Address:	Aérodrome La Baule-Escoublac, 44500 La Baule.
Tel:	02 51 75 10 43
Fax:	02 51 75 10 42
Admission:	Daily 1430-1830.
Location:	About 3 km east of the town off the N 771

Ailes Anciennes La Baule was formed in the early 1980s and it acquired its first aircraft soon after. This was a Caudron Luciole biplane which first flew in 1934. The aircraft was stored during World War II and was active again from 1947 to 1955. The aircraft was severely damaged at Ancenis when a pilot forgot to open the fuel cock. The airframe then spent over twenty years in a barn and suffered further when the roof blew off. The group acquired the remains for one franc and restored it to original condition. A Broussard, since sold, and Noralpha were then restored and the Morane-Saulnier MS.317 took to the air in 1999 after a major rebuild. This crashed in 2003 and is now being rebuilt with spares. The hangar is now open on a regular basis and a number of homebuilt types are also on view along with privately owned machines. A fairly recent arrival is the Blériot XI owned by the grandson of the pioneer. A Piper Cub which had been operated for several years crashed. The group has acquired an unfinished Wag Aero Sport Trainer and this is being completed

TYPE	REG/SER	CON. NO.	PI/NOTES	STATUS
☐ Blériot XI	F-AZIN	225	G-AVXV, BAPC.104	PV
☐ Caudron C.275 Luciole	F-AZCT	7474/692	F-APLM, F-BBCF	PVA
☐ Gardan GY-80 Horizon 160	F-BLPJ	44		PV
☐ Mignet HM-290 Pou-du-Ciel				PV
☐ Morane-Saulnier MS.317 (MS.315)	F-BHHF	6566/312	F-BCBR, – on loan from M.A.	PVC
☐ Nord N.1101 Noralpha (Ramier I) [Messerschmitt Me 208]	F-GJBQ	177	177 – M.A. aircraft	PVA
☐ Scottish Aviation Bulldog 120/121 (T.1)	F-AZTF	BH120/309	XX639	PVA
☐ Starck SN-01	F-PYBQ	1		PV
☐ Wag Aero Sport Trainer				RAC

45 LOIRET

COLLECTION DE LA BASE AÉRIENNE D'ORLÉANS-BRICY (FRA92)

Address:	B.P.01 Base Aérienne 123, 45998 Orléans.
Tel:	02 38 42 66 00
Fax:	02 38 42 68 66
Admission:	By prior permission only.
Location:	About 12 km north west of the city off the D.955.

This large base has housed transport units for many years. The wing was the first to operate the Noratlas and changed to Transalls in 1969/1971. Lockheed Hercules are also now in residence. Previously squadrons had flown Junkers 52s and Dakotas in Indo China. The Super Mystère is close to the airfield.

TYPE	REG/SER	CON. NO.	PI/NOTES	STATUS
☐ Dassault Super Mystère B2	9	9	At local barracks.	RA
☐ Nord N.2501 Noratlas	29	29		RA
☐ Transall C-160R	R155	155	Front fuselage only.	RA

COLLECTION GOUEFFON (FRA93)

Address:	58 Route de Gidy, 45140 Ormes.
Tel:	02 38 74 95 46
Admission:	By prior permission only.
Location:	In private premises in the Orléans area.

Airworthy sailplanes from this private collection may sometimes be seen at the local St. Denis-de-l'Hôtel airfield. The prototype Breguet Mouette is under restoration in the workshops. Five French built German designs are in store. These were built after World War II for club use. The Stralpes Crystal dates from the mid-1980s and only twelve were produced. Only a few Air 100s remain in use.

TYPE	REG/SER	CON. NO.	PI/NOTES	STATUS
☐ Arsenal Air 100	F-CAET	10		RAA
☐ Breguet 901S Mouette	F-CCCF	1		RAC
☐ Nord N.1300 [Schneider Grunau Baby IIB]				RA
☐ Nord N.1300 [Schneider Grunau Baby IIB]				RA
☐ Nord N.1300 [Schneider Grunau Baby IIB]	F-CRQM	88	F-CAQZ	RA
☐ Stralpes ST-15 Crystal	F-CBCK	10		RAA
☐ Victor Minié V.M.A. 200 Milan [Jacobs Weihe]				RA
☐ Victor Minié V.M.A. 200 Milan [Jacobs Weihe]	F-CBGS	21		RAC

47 LOT-ET-GARONNE

ASSOCIATION ORION (ASSOCIATION POUR LA SAUVEGARDE DES AVIONS ANCIENS) (FRA94)

Address:	Aérodrome de Carpete, 47200 Marmande.
Admission:	By prior permission only.
Location:	At Villeneuve-sur-Lot airfield which is about 5 km east of the town on the D.661 and at Marmande airfield which is 3 km east of the town.

This group has hangarage at both Marmande and Villenueve-sur-Lot airfields. The aircraft are mainly French types from the post World War II period and the majority are in flying condition. The wooden Microjet 200 was developed as the prototype for a low cost military trainer. Powered by two 243lb. thrust Microturbo engines it first flew in June 1980. In 1983 the pre-production all metal 200B emerged and three flying examples along with a static test airframe were built. Only a few Boisavia Mercurey four seat high wing monoplanes, from the forty four built, survive and hopefully the one in the collection will soon be restored to flying condition. Maurice Brochet designed and flew the MB.30, MB.40, MB.50 and MB.60 prototypes in the late 1940s and made plans available for amateur constructors. The two seat MB.70 first flew in 1950 and a small number were produced along with ten MB.80s. The MB.83 is an MB.80 with the original Minié engine replaced by a 90 h.p. Continental. Some of the aircraft are privately owned but are hangared by the group. A number of private airstrips in the region are also in use and some members of the fleet are based at these.

TYPE	REG/SER	CON. NO.	PI/NOTES	STATUS
☐ Boisavia B.601L Mercurey	F-BHVI	24		RA
☐ Brochet MB.83 (MB.80)	F-PGLH	88	F-BGLH	RAC
☐ Dassault Falcon 50 (FSM)				RA
☐ Dassault MD-311 Flamant	F-AZEH	274	274	RAA
☐ De Havilland D.H.C.1 Chipmunk 22 (T.10)	F-AZJQ	C1/0829	WP967	RAA
☐ Fouga CM.170R Magister	51	51		RA
☐ Fouga CM.170R Magister	F-AZKH	219	219, F-GJIR	RAA
☐ Fouga CM.170R Magister	411	411		RAC
☐ Fouga CM.170R Magister	F-GKEI	479	479, F-GLEZ, (F-GLSA)	RAA
☐ Fouga CM.170R Magister	F-GJIJ	482	482	RAA
☐ Fouga CM.170R Magister	546	546		RA
☐ Microturbo Microjet 200	F-WZJF	01		RA
☐ Morane-Saulnier MS.317 (MS.315)	F-BCNN	6592/338		RAA
☐ Morane-Saulnier MS.733 Alcyon	F-BLKG	85	85	RAC
☐ Morane-Saulnier MS.733 Alcyon	F-BLXS	114	114 – on loan from M.A.	RAA
☐ Morane-Saulnier MS.893E Rallye 180GT	F-BXDO	12579		RAA
☐ Nord N.1203-III Norécrin (N.1203-II)	F-BHVG	361		RA
☐ Nord N.1203-VI Norécrin (N.1203-II)	F-BBER	332		RAA
☐ Nord N.1203-VI Norécrin (N.1203-II) (N.1203-III)	F-BBES	333		RAA
☐ Piper PA-18-125 Super Cub	F-BGPT	18-1137	N1327A	RAA
☐ Zlin Z-326 Trener Master	F-BMQS	894		RAA

49 MAINE-ET-LOIRE

MUSÉE RÉGIONAL DE L'AIR (FRA95)

Address:	Aérodrome d'Angers, 49140 Marcé.
Tel:	02 41 33 04 10
Fax:	02 41 95 82 87
Email:	musee.regional.gppa@wanadoo.fr
Admission:	Daily 1400-1800.
Location:	The airfield is about 20 km north east of the town on the D.766.

The Groupement pour la Preservation du Patrimoine Aéronautique was formed in 1981 and soon began collecting gliders and light aircraft. Workshops at the old Angers airfield at Avrillé were obtained and a number of machines were restored to flying condition. The group joined the Ailes Anciennes organisation and a number of gliders were transferred from the stores of the Musée de l'Air. In 1989 a large hangar was donated by the city authorities and a museum opened. Avrillé closed in 1998 and flying moved to a new field at Marcé. Here a magnificent exhibition hall along with workshops, a library and administrative area has been constructed. The old museum building was moved from Avrillé and is now used as a store. Over one hundred and twenty aircraft and gliders are now in the collection including twenty five owned by the Réseau du Sport de l'Air. The R.S.A. is responsible for amateur aircraft construction in France. They opened a museum at Brienne-le-Château in the late 1970s but this closed a few years later. The majority of the aircraft from this display are now at Marcé. Homebuilt aircraft feature prominently in the new museum and three examples of the Mignet HM-14 Pou-du-Ciel can be seen. along with versions of the earlier HM-8. A number of post-war prototypes are on the inventory. The Chapeau JC-1 biplane first flew in 1946 and was powered by a 45 h.p. Salmson radial. Under restoration in the main hall is the Gasne RG-3 from the same year. These are two of the first original designs to appear after World War II. Max Williams built a number of small monoplanes in the late 1940s and two of these have survived. He also built a glider resembling the early Chanute model. The Max Plan PF-204 made its maiden flight at Santeuil in 1950 but was damaged and did not take to the air again for two years. The aircraft was withdrawn in 1956 and spent the rest of its life in store. Also being rebuilt is the prototype S.F.A.N. 4 which appeared in 1949 and was a visitor at several early R.S.A. rallies. This side by side two seater was developed from the S.F.A.N. 2, a licence built B.A.C. Drone. One of these is parked alongside. Lucien Tieles built the B.50 Muscadet three seater in 1946. The design was developed into the B.60 four seater which flew in 1949. Société Boisavia was formed but only forty four Mercureys were built in eight slightly different versions. Only a few have survived. The Jupiter with one engine at the front of the fuselage and one at the rear appeared in 1963. Designed by André Moynet the prototypes were built by the Matra engine company. Sud Aviation considered putting the type into production but this never happened. The oldest aircraft on show is the 1908 Gasnier biplane. René Gasnier built his first aircraft at Angers. This made a few hops on August 17th 1908 at Rochefort and was damaged. No. 1 was rebuilt and modified. This flew successfully but crashed on September 17th 1908. No.3 was completed by September 23rd 1908 but Gasnier was ill and testing stopped. The aircraft was eventually donated to the town of Angers and spent many years in store at their municipal museum. This historic machine was restored in the late 1980s. A new arrival is the relatively unknown Bidolet of 1909. This unique aircraft is poor condition after decades in store. The Gérin Varivol was built in the late 1930s. The fuselage resembled a Caudron C.450 and featured a high aspect ratio wing with rails which allowed the chord to be changed. The aircraft never flew but was apparently tested in a wind tunnel. This unique machine was found on a farm in 2000. Another new arrival is the Riout 102T which was transported to the museum in June 2005. In 1919 Riout exhibited models of an aircraft with four wings in pairs one behind the other. These were capable of being adjusted to give variable dihedral. He built a prototype in the 1930s and this was tested in a wind tunnel. The aircraft was put into store in a factory at La Couture Boussey where it remained for sixty five years. Several powered aircraft and gliders are maintained in airworthy condition. There are probably many other aircraft hidden in the country and a short distance away I know of two in a barn. A replica of the Caudron C.431 from the 1930s is under construction in the hangar. Two examples of the C.430 two seat low wing monoplane were built in the mid-1930s and achieved success in a number of races. Also on show are many engines, photographs, components and models. The displays are still being developed to present the history of aviation in the area and of amateur built designs. This superb collection includes many rarities.

TYPE	REG/SER	CON. NO.	PI/NOTES	STATUS
☐ Adam RA.14 Loisirs	F-PEVV	35bis		RA
☐ Adam RA.15/1	F-PHZC	1	F-WEPD, F-PEPD (?)	PVA
☐ Arsenal Air 102	F-CAGQ	26		PVA
☐ Arsenal Air 102	F-CABQ	31		RA
☐ Avia 152A	F-AZVI	301	F-CRLA	RAC
☐ Avialsa-Scheibe A.60 Fauconnet [L-Spatz 55]	F-CAMD	2		RA
☐ Avialsa-Scheibe A.60 Fauconnet [L-Spatz 55]	F-CCLF	10		RA
☐ Avialsa-Scheibe A.60 Fauconnet [L-Spatz 55]	F-CDBF	78K		RA
☐ Bensen B-8M	F-WYRY			PV
☐ Bidolet 1909				RAD
☐ Boisavia B.601L Mercurey				RA
☐ Boisavia B.601L Mercurey	F-BHVI	23		RA
☐ Boulay-Menin BM-1	F-CRRI	01	(F-WRRI)	RA
☐ Breguet 901S Mouette	F-CCCP	13		PVA
☐ Breguet 904S Nymphale	F-CCFN	4		PVA
☐ Breguet 904S Nymphale	F-CCFT	10		RA
☐ Carmam M.100S Mésange	OO-ZRT	13		RA
☐ Carmam M.200 Foehn	F-CDHU	44		RAD
☐ Castel C.25S	F-CRBI	141	F-CAJR	RAA
☐ Castel C.25S	F-CRJA	180	F-CBUB	RA
☐ Castel C.3010P (C.301S)	F-CRMG	1026	F-CAHR	RA
☐ Castel C.301S	F-CBVG	1063		RA

☐ Castel C.310P	F-CRJF	124	F-CALP	RA
☐ Castel C.311P	F-CALS	287/16		RA
☐ Castel-Mauboussin CM.8/15	F-CABN	269/01		RA
☐ Caudron PC.431 Rafale (R)	F-PJHB	01	.	PVC
☐ Caudron C.800 Épervier	F-CAEZ	9765/105		RA
☐ Caudron C.800 Épervier	F-CBAM	9766/106		RA
☐ Caudron C.800 Épervier	F-CAUP	9829/169		RA
☐ Caudron C.800 Épervier	F-CAHD	9890/230		PV
☐ Caudron C.800 Épervier	F-CAHE	9998/338		RA
☐ Centre Aviation GA-620 Gaucho	F-PKXH	01		RA
☐ Cessna T-50 Bobcat (UC-78B)	HB-UEF	5253	42-?????, OO-TIN	RA
☐ Chapeau EC.19 Planeum		11		RA
☐ Chapeau-Durand CXD-18	F-CRRD	01		RA
☐ Croses LC-6 Criquet	F-PJRP	100		PV
☐ Dabos JD-24 D'Artagnan	F-PJSV	01	F-WJSV	RA
☐ Druine D.31 Turbulent	F-PCZT	163		RA
☐ Durable RD-02 Edelweiss	F-PKVF	01		PV
☐ Evans VP-1 Volksplane	F-PGUI	V-1382		RA
☐ Fauvel AV.22S	F-CCGK	1		PVA
☐ Fauvel AV.36	F-CBRK	111		RA
☐ Fauvel AV.361	F-CRQX	323		RA
☐ Fere F-3	F-PYJF	01		RA
☐ Fouga CM.170R Magister	335	335		RA
☐ Fouga CM.8R/13 Sylphe IIIB	F-CRPY	1	F-PNKU – maybe ex F-WFOI, F-BFOI.	PV
☐ Gardan GY-20 Minicab	F-BFLC	3		PVA
☐ Gardan GY-80 Horizon 150	F-BJDU	01	F-WJDU	RAA
☐ Gardan GY-80 Horizon 150	F-BNYG	184		RAD
☐ Gasnier 3		01		PV
☐ Gérin Varivol V.6e				PV
☐ Guerchais-Roche SA.103 Emouchet	F-CROF	94	F-CBJB – on loan from M.A.	RA
☐ Guerchais-Roche SA.103 Emouchet	F-CRQD	176	F-CBCR	RA
☐ Guerchais-Roche SA.104 Emouchet	F-CRGE	251	F-CBDT	RA
☐ Holleville RH.1 Bambi	F-PDPZ	1	F-WDPZ	PVA
☐ Jacobs Weihe (D.F.S. 108-68)	F-CRMX	3	F-CBGT, F-CRMD – on loan from M.A.	PVA
☐ Jodel D.92 Bébé	F-PAXU	71		RAC
☐ Jodel D.113 (D.119)	F-PTXA	1276		PV
☐ Jodel D.120 Paris-Nice	F-BHFP	124		RAC
☐ Jurca MJ.5 Sirocco	F-PJBG	19	F-WJBG	RA
☐ La Guepe				RA
☐ Labit LR Gyrocopter	F-WYRY	2		PV
☐ Lachassagne AL-07	F-WBBN	01		RA
☐ Leduc RL-19	F-PAGT	01		RA
☐ Lemaire RL-1	F-PPPN	01		RA
☐ Leopoldoff L.6	F-BBCY	27		RAD
☐ Matra-Moynet M.360-6 Jupiter	F-BLKY	03	F-WLKY – on loan from M.A.	RA
☐ Maupin Woodstock				RA
☐ Max Holste MH.1521M Broussard	F-BFKL	38	38	RA
☐ Max Plan MP-204	F-PBGE	01		RA
☐ Merville S.M.31	F-CBYK	1		RAC
☐ Mignet HM-8				RA
☐ Mignet HM-8	F-PYTA	L-1		PV
☐ Mignet HM-8B				RA
☐ Mignet HM-14 Pou-du-Ciel				PV
☐ Mignet HM-14 Pou-du-Ciel				PV
☐ Mignet HM-14 Pou-du-Ciel				RA
☐ Mignet HM-290 Pou-du-Ciel				RA
☐ Morane-Saulnier MS.505 Criquet (MS.502) [Fieseler Fi 156 Storch]	F-BIPJ	149/33	F-BAOU – on loan from M.A.	PVA
☐ Morane-Saulnier MS.733 Alcyon	F-BLXL	76	76	PVA
☐ Morane-Saulnier MS.733 Alcyon	F-BMQA	144	144	RAC
☐ Morane-Saulnier MS.733 Alcyon	F-BNEI	154	154	RAC
☐ Morane-Saulnier MS.893A Commodore 180	F-BRKD	10958		RAA
☐ Nicollier HN-434 Super Ménestrel	F-PLJB	31		RAC
☐ Nord N.1201 Norécrin	F-BDSB	7		RA
☐ Nord N.1201 Norécrin	F-BDSG	12		RA
☐ Nord N.1203 Norécrin	F-BBKU	81		RA
☐ Nord N.1300 [Schneider Grunau Baby IIB]	F-CRJI	209	F-CAIC	RA
☐ Nord N.1300 [Schneider Grunau Baby IIB]	F-CAXL	239		RA
☐ Nord N.2000 [Jacobs Meise]	F-CBGB	10409/79		RA
☐ Nord N.2000 [Jacobs Meise]	F-CBVP	10423/93		RA
☐ Nord N.3400	F-AZIV	123	123	RA
☐ Nord NC.856A Norvigie	F-BNAL	56	56	RA
☐ Nord NC.856G Norvigie	F-PMBC	02	Rebuilt from NC.856N c/n 38 38	RAC
☐ Nord NC.858S (NC.854)	F-BDZP	6		PVA
☐ North American NA-88 Texan (AT-6C) (Harvard IIA)	F-BJBC	88-12326	41-33633, EX660, 7309 (South Africa), EX660, H4 (Belgium)	RAC
☐ Osterreich Aero Club Standard Austria		008		RA
☐ Piel CP.301C.1 Emeraude	F-BJFR	547		PVA
☐ Piper J-3C-65 Cub (L-4H)	F-BCPY	11531	43-30240	PVA
☐ Pitts S-1D Special	F-PYXA	7-0492		PVA
☐ Potez 60JD	F-PVQB	1		PVA

TYPE	REG/SER	CON. NO.	PI/NOTES	STATUS
☐ Pottier JP-15/34	F-CFGG	50.41		RA
☐ Pottier P.80s	F-PYEB	01		PV
☐ Rigaud (A)RD T.06	F-PXKP	06		RA
☐ Riout 102T		01		RA
☐ Rocheblave AR-01 Pou-du-Ciel Planeur		1		RA
☐ Sablier 18	F-CRMB	01		RA
☐ Saint-Germain Raz-Mut	F-PYIO	49		RA
☐ Scheibe SF-27 Zugvogel IIIB	F-CCPT	1084		PVA
☐ Schneider Grunau SG-38 (D.F.S. 108-14)		35		RA
☐ Schneider Grunau SG-38 (D.F.S. 108-14)		157		RA
☐ Schneider Grunau SG-38 (D.F.S. 108-14)	F-CAJA	172		RA
☐ Siren C.30S Edelweiss	F-CCCZ	03		RA
☐ Siren H-230	F-CCHZ	01	Wings only.	RA
☐ Siren-Bertin C.34	F-CCAZ	01		RA
☐ Société Française d'Aviation Nouvelle SFAN 2 [British Aircraft Company Drone]	F-PEEX	102		RA
☐ Société Française d'Aviation Nouvelle SFAN 4	F-PFOO	01		PV
☐ Société Industrielle Pour l'Aéronautique (SIPA) S.903 (S.901)	F-BGAA	26		RA
☐ Société Industrielle Pour l'Aéronautique (SIPA) S.903 (S.901)	F-BGAB	27		RA
☐ Société Pour l'Aviation et ses Dérivés (SPAD) VII	N4727V	248	Painted as SPAD XIII S4523	PVX
☐ Starck 07 Stabiplan				PV
☐ Starck AS.37B	F-PYLM	36		RA
☐ Starck AS.57	F-PEAY	02	F-BEAY	RA
☐ Szybowcowy Zaklad Doswiadczalny S.Z.D.24C Foka Standard	F-AZKA	W-177	OO-ZJL	PVA
☐ Tipsy T.66 Nipper II	F-PLAR	61	F-OBYV	RA
☐ Trésy 01			Incomplete.	RA
☐ Truchet TR-301 Abyssin				RA
☐ Wassmer WA.20 Javelot I	F-CBQS	9		RA
☐ Wassmer WA.21 Javelot II	F-CCEE	2		RAA
☐ Wassmer WA.21 Javelot II	F-CCEO	18		RAA
☐ Wassmer WA.21 Javelot II	F-CCHH	21		RA
☐ Wassmer WA.21 Javelot II	F-CCHJ	27		RA
☐ Wassmer WA.21 Javelot II	F-CCKE	39		RA
☐ Wassmer WA.22A Super Javelot	F-CCLZ	70		RA
☐ Wassmer WA.22A Super Javelot	F-CDCS	117		PVA
☐ Wassmer WA.26CM	F-CDUU	03		RA
☐ Wassmer WA.28 Espadon	F-CCBC	01	F-WCBC	RA
☐ Wassmer WA.28 Espadon	F-CEOD	109		RA
☐ Wassmer WA.30 Bijave	F-CCML	15		RA
☐ Wassmer WA.30 Bijave	F-CDMN	242		RA
☐ Wassmer WA.40 Super IV	F-BKJI	44		PVC
☐ Williams MW-25 Motorfly	F-WEAZ	01		RA
☐ Williams MWM-33A Chanute Glider (R)				RA
☐ Williams X-28	F-PEAT			RA
☐ Wright Flyer (R)				PV

50 MANCHE

CENTRE VOL A VOILE DE LESSAY (FRA96)

Address:	Aérodrome Charles Lindbergh, 50430 Lessay.
Tel:	02 33 46 44 22
Fax:	02 33 46 50 71
Email:	aeroclub.lessay@wanadoo.fr
Admission:	By prior permission only.
Location:	About 3 km south east of the town off the D 900.

This gliding centre still operates several classic types along with modern sailplanes. The Wassmer designs were built in substantial numbers and were for many years the backbone of most French gliding club fleets. Fewer than seventy examples of the WA.22A Javelot were built and two hundred and eight two Bijaves left the Issoire factory. The Rallye is used for towing duties. In the clubhouse there is a display of photographs tracing the history of the club. Sailplanes operated in the past are shown along with documents.

TYPE	REG/SER	CON. NO.	PI/NOTES	STATUS
☐ Morane-Saulnier MS.893E Rallye 180GT	F-GAKG	12790		RAA
☐ Schleicher ASW-15	F-CEAZ	15171		RAA
☐ Wassmer WA.22A Super Javelot	F-CDED	122		RAA
☐ Wassmer WA.22A Super Javelot	F-CACM	124	124	RAA
☐ Wassmer WA.30 Bijave	F-CCYD	101		RAA
☐ Wassmer WA.30 Bijave	F-CDJO	218		RAA

MUSÉE DES TROUPES AÉROPORTÉES (FRA97)

Address:	50480 St. Mère Église.
Tel:	02 33 41 41 35
Fax:	02 33 41 78 87
Email:	Info@airborne-museum.org
Admission:	February-March October- November daily 0930-1200 1400-1800; April daily 0900-1200 1400-1845; May-September daily 0900-1845; June-mid September daily 0900-1845.
Location:	In the centre of the town which off the N 13 about 35 km south east of Cherbourg

On the night of June 5-6th 1944 paratroopers of the 82nd and 101st U.S. Airborne Divisions landed in the area. Five hundred and twelve gliders also touched down around the town. At 4.30 am on the 6th St. Mère Église became the first town in France to be liberated. One paratrooper became entangled in the church tower and a dummy honouring this still hangs at the spot. The museum was established in the early 1980s and the first hall, shaped like a parachute, houses a C-47 painted in invasion markings. A second building, of similar design, containing a Waco Hadrian glider was added a few years later. The story of Operation Overlord is portrayed in great detail with many photographs and personal objects on show.

TYPE	REG/SER	CON. NO.	PI/NOTES	STATUS
☐ Douglas DC-3A-456 Skytrain (C-47A)	'315159'	19288	42-100825, OY-DDA, N9884F, N50V, 25 (French)	PVX
☐ Waco NZR Hadrian (CG-4A)	45-17241			PV

51 MARNE

ASSOCIATION CHAMPAGNE ARDENNE AÉROBATICS (FRA98)

Address:	L'Escale, Aérodrome Reims-Prunay, 51360 Reims.
Tel:	03 26 61 75 56
Fax:	03 26 67 75 58
Admission:	By prior permission only.
Location:	About 12 km south east of the town on the N 44.

Aircraft in airworthy condition and a Fouga Magister on static display are owned by this group. Marcel Jurca achieved success with his single seat Tempête and two seat Sirocco designs. Many have been completed by home builders. He then turned his attention to replicas of famous World War II fighters. The Jurca is a full size reproduction of the famous Supermarine Spitfire. The example in the collection, in pseudo R.A.F. colours, made its first flight in October 1994 and is now back in flying order after being damaged in a crash. The group used to operate the unique Christophe Robin CR.100 but sadly this crashed in August 2000. In the terminal building is a small display of photographs and memorabilia tracing the history of the airfield. The Max Holste company had a factory on the airfield and another in the city. The Broussard in the collection was produced here. In 1960 the Cessna company acquired a large stake in the firm and the name was changed to Reims Aviation. Since the large numbers of both single and twin engined models from the Wichita organisation have been built. Several aircraft are on loan from Escadrille du Souvenir which one had a large hangar at Étampes housing almost thirty aircraft. This building was demolished when the airfield was modernised.

TYPE	REG/SER	CON. NO.	PI/NOTES	STATUS
☐ Breguet 904S Nymphale	F-CCFK	1	On loan from Escadrille du Souvenir	RA
☐ Fouga CM.170R Magister	F-WDHG	30	30	PV
☐ Fouga CM.170R Magister	F-GIGJ	561	561, F-WIGJ	RA
☐ Jurca MJ.100D Spitfire	'BS538'	2	F-WGML, 'BS539'	RAAX
☐ Max Holste MH.1521C-1 Broussard (1521M)	F-GJBF	13	13 – on loan from Escadrille du Souvenir	RAA
☐ Nord N.3202	F-AZFT	34	34, F-WYAY – on loan from Escadrille du Souvenir	RA
☐ Nord N.3202B1B	F-AZJT	71	71, F-AZAD, F-AZJT – on loan from Escadrille du Souvenir	RAA
☐ Nord N.3202B1B	F-AZHO	95	95, (F-BNRN), 95, F-AZAC, F-WZBC – on loan from Escadrille du Souvenir	RAA
☐ Nord N.3202B1B	F-AZJO	101	101, F-BNRP, F-AZAI, F-WZBE – on loan from Escadrille du Souvenir	RAA
☐ North American NA-88 Texan (AT-6D)	'14906'	88-14510	42-44467, F-BJBM	RAAX

ASSOCIATION PARIS (FRA99)

Address:	Aérodrome Reims-Prunay, 51130 Reims.
Admission:	By prior permission only.
Location:	About 12 km south east of the town on the N 44.

This group has acquired three different versions of the twin jet communications aircraft. All three are stored in one of the hangars and restoration is planned. The prototype first flew in 1954 and was followed four years later by the Paris I four seater. The externally similar Paris II had more powerful engines and could be fitted with guns and underwing racks for bombs or rockets. The five/six seat Paris III executive transport made its maiden flight in November 1964 but only one was completed. The trio moved from the Euralair hangar at Le Bourget in the late 1990s. The type saw use with Air Forces in Argentina and Brazil.

TYPE	REG/SER	CON. NO.	PI/NOTES	STATUS
☐ Morane-Saulnier MS.760A Paris IA	F-BJET	39	39, F-WJAA	RA
☐ Morane-Saulnier MS.760B Paris II	F-BXQL	105	105, F-BJZT, PH-MSU, N760Q	RA
☐ Morane-Saulnier MS.760C Paris III	F-BLKL	01	F-WLKL	RA

MUSÉE DE LA BASE AÉRIENNE DE REIMS-CHAMPAGNE (FRA100)

Address:	Base Aérienne 112, Route D.966, 51090 Reims Cedex.
Tel:	03 26 79 51 86
Fax:	03 26 79 53 89
Admission:	By prior permission only.
Location:	About 8 km north of the city off the N 366.

The museum opened in June 2002 and traces the history of the base and of flying in the region. Highlighted in the one room is the first flight to the city carried out by Henri Farman in 1908. The famous 1909 meeting which lasted a week and the 1911 military contest are also portrayed. Many pioneer aviators brought their aircraft to these events and a number of significant flights took place. Another area is devoted to World War I with some original items of memorabilia on show. The base was constructed in the 1920s and fighter squadrons were normally in residence. Parts of an engine from a Curtiss Hawk shot down during the German invasion have been recovered. An interesting item is a banjo made from the remains of a Breguet 14.

TYPE	REG/SER	CON. NO.	PI/NOTES	STATUS
☐ Dassault Mirage IIIR	348	348		RA
☐ Dassault Mirage IIIR	350	350		RA
☐ Republic RF-84F Thunderflash	37577		53-7577	RA
☐ Sud-Ouest SO-4050 Vautour IIN	347	114		RA

MUSÉE DU TERRAIN D'AVIATION DE VRAUX 1939-1945 (FRA101)

Address:	Siege Social, 28 Rue Basse, 51150 Vraux.
Tel:	03 26 66 12 10
Admission:	August-June Saturday-Sunday 1400-1830; July daily 1400-1830.
Location:	About 12 km north west of Châlons-en Champagne on the D.1.

The association was formed in 1986 and has set up the museum as a memorial to Vraux airfield which was used by the Advanced Air Striking Force of the Royal Air Force in 1939/40. The official opening took place on July 16th 1994 and several R.A.F. veterans who had been based at the field were present. A building has been transformed into a 1930s workshop and an uncovered Pou-du-Ciel is on show. This aircraft was built in the area but was never flown due to the outbreak of World War II. The Broussard exhibited in the courtyard was constructed at nearby Reims-Prunay. The main exhibition buildings contain a fascinating range of memorabilia, photographs, documents, uniforms, vehicles, components and engines. The nose section of an Amiot 350 bomber is a rare exhibit. The brief history of the grass field, which was located north of the village, is portrayed in superb detail. The site is now farmland and there is no trace of its wartime use.

TYPE	REG/SER	CON. NO.	PI/NOTES	STATUS
☐ Jacobs D.F.S. 230C-1			Fuselage frame only.	PVD
☐ Max Holste MH.1521M Broussard	164	164		PV
☐ Mignet HM-14 Pou-du-Ciel				PV
☐ Short S.29 Stirling IV	LK142		Major fuselage sections.	PVD

52 HAUTE-MARNE

COLLECTION DE LA BASE AÉRIENNE DE ST. DIZIER (FRA102)

Address:	Base Aérienne 113, 52113 St. Dizier Air.
Tel:	03 25 07 71 13
Fax:	03 25 07 77 00
Admission:	By prior permission only.
Location:	About 2 km west of the town off the N 4.

This airfield was built as a N.A.T.O. base and opened on February 1st 1953. The first unit to arrive was EC.1 with Thunderjets which it flew until 1955 when Thunderstreaks arrived. The unit was disbanded in December 1963. A bomber wing with Mirage IVAs was formed in October 1965 and this was in residence until 1986. The current EC.7 operates Jaguars and Alpha Jets and has been at the field since May 1973. The Jaguar will be withdrawn in 2005/2006 and replaced by the Dassault Rafale. The latter type is currently being evaluated at Mont-de-Marsan and the first operational example should arrive at St. Dizier very soon. One hundred and sixty Jaguar As were flown by the Armée de l'Air along with forty of the E version. Three aircraft are now parked by the Aero Club on the other side of the field.

TYPE	REG/SER	CON. NO.	PI/NOTES	STATUS
☐ Breguet / British Aircraft Corporation Jaguar A	A113	A113		RA
☐ Breguet / British Aircraft Corporation Jaguar A	A124	A124		RA
☐ Dassault Mirage IIIR	318	318	At Aero Club.	PV
☐ Dassault Mirage IVA	16	16		RA
☐ Dassault Mirage IVP (IVA)	61	61	At Aero Club	PV
☐ Fouga CM.170R Magister	46	46		RA
☐ Lockheed 580 (T-33A)	16524	580-5856	51-6524	RA
☐ Max Holste MH.1521M Broussard	158	158	At Aero Club.	PV
☐ Republic F-84F Thunderstreak	'29094'		52-8997, 28997	PVX

53 MAYENNE

CLUB VOL A VOILE DE LA MAYENNE (FRA103)

Address:	B.P. 3979, 570 Route d'Angers, 53000 Laval Cedex.
Tel:	02 43 52 02 09
Fax:	02 43 67 03 34
Admission:	By prior permission only.
Location:	The airfield is about 6 km south of the town on the N 162.

This club operates a number of classic sailplanes. The Bölkow Phoebus was produced in three versions and well over two hundred were made. The LS-1 first flew in the late 1960s and soon achieved major successes in contests with one being placed first in the Standard Class at the 1970 World Championships. Over two hundred and twenty were built before more advanced designs were put into production. The Grob company was originally involved in making automotive machinery. Their first sailplane design the G-102 Astir appeared in 1974.

TYPE	REG/SER	CON. NO.	PI/NOTES	STATUS
☐ Bölkow Phoebus C	F-CDOT	944		RAA
☐ Carmam M.100S Mésange	F-CCPI	10		RAA
☐ Glasflügel H205 Libelle	F-CEQK	157		RAA
☐ Grob G-102 Astir CS	F-CFBO	3128		RAA
☐ Grob G-102/77J Astir Jeans	F-CFCJ	2144		RAA
☐ Morane-Saulnier MS.893A Commodore 180	F-BSCD	11486		RAA
☐ Rolladen-Schneider LS-1D	F-CEHO	228		RAA
☐ Scheibe SF-25B	F-CIBN	4803	D-KBAQ	RAA
☐ Wassmer WA.30 Bijave				RAC
☐ Wassmer WA.30 Bijave	F-CCRM	41		RAA
☐ Wassmer WA.30 Bijave	F-CCTK	85		RAA
☐ Wassmer WA.30 Bijave	F-CCTN	88		RAD
☐ Wassmer WA.30 Bijave	F-CDIL	197		RAA

54 MOSELLE

AÉROCLUB ALBERT MANGEOT – SECTION RÉTRO (FRA104)

Address:	B.P.7, 54550 Pont St. Vincent.
Tel:	03 83 47 33 54
Admission:	When the airfield is open.
Location:	Just west of the town which is about 10 km south west of Nancy.

The hill top airfield of Pont St. Vincent is home to an impressive fleet of gliders. The aeroclub and private owners maintain in flying condition a number of classic types and have several more in the workshops. The Nord company produced one hundred examples of the Jacobs Meise as the N.2000. About two hundred and fifty Castel C.301s appeared between 1945 and 1947 and three hundred Caudron C.800s from the early 1940s. Charles Fauvel developed a series of tailless gliders since the 1930s. Over one hundred AV.36s were built in the 1950s and 1960s. The powered AV.45 first flew in 1960 and only a small number appeared. The Wassmer company at Issoire constructed over fifty AV.36s in addition to its own designs.

TYPE	REG/SER	CON. NO.	PI/NOTES	STATUS
☐ Arsenal Air 100				RAC
☐ Avialsa-Scheibe A.60 Fauconnet [L-Spatz 55]	F-CCVS	66K		RA
☐ Avialsa-Scheibe A.60 Fauconnet [L-Spatz 55]	F-CDBC	75K		RA
☐ Avialsa-Scheibe A.60 Fauconnet [L-Spatz 55]	F-CDFV	119		RAA
☐ Avialsa-Scheibe A.60 Fauconnet [L-Spatz 55]	F-CDLT	142		RA
☐ Breguet 901S Mouette	F-CCCO	12		RAA
☐ Carmam M.200 Foehn	F-CCXT	5		RA
☐ Carmam M.200 Foehn	F-CDKI	51		RAA
☐ Castel C.301S				RA
☐ Castel C.301S				RA
☐ Caudron C.800 Épervier				RAD
☐ Caudron C.800 Épervier	F-CADA	9802/142	F-CACB	RAC
☐ Caudron C.800 Épervier	F-CAAJ	9967/307		RA
☐ Fauvel AV.22S	F-CAGL	2	F-CCGL	RAC
☐ Fauvel AV.36	F-CBRG	107		RA
☐ Fauvel AV.36	F-CBSM	138		RAA
☐ Fauvel AV.45				RA
☐ Fauvel AV.222	F-CRGC	07	F-WRGC	RA
☐ Grob G.102 Astir CS-77	F-CFIE	1811		RAA
☐ Guerchais-Roche SA.103 Emouchet	F-CRHH	31	F-CAXV	RA
☐ Guerchais-Roche SA.104 Emouchet	F-CCFI	288		RA
☐ Morane-Saulnier MS.893A Commodore 180	F-BSVR	11666		RAA
☐ Nord N.2000 [Jacobs Meise]				RA
☐ Nord N.2000 [Jacobs Meise]	F-CAGH	10346/16		RA
☐ Scheibe SF-28A Tandem Falke	F-CAID	5761	(D-KACN, HB-2007	RAA
☐ Scheibe SF-28A Tandem Falke	F-CFJC	57119	(D-KNAU)	RAA
☐ Schempp-Hirth Janus B	F-CCHR	03	D-3110	RAA
☐ Schleicher Ka-6E Rhönsegler	F-CDTS	4356		RAA
☐ Schleicher Ka-6E Rhönsegler	F-CDYG	4367		RAA
☐ Schleicher K.8B	F-CEJH	8956		RAA
☐ Schleicher ASK-13	F-CDYP	13323		RA
☐ Schleicher ASK-18	F-CERJ	18033		RAA
☐ Silimon IS 29D-2	F-CCJV	106		RA
☐ Wassmer WA.20 Javelot I	F-CBGZ	7		RA
☐ Wassmer WA.21 Javelot II				RAC
☐ Wassmer WA.22A Super Javelot	F-CDEE	123		RAA
☐ Wassmer WA.26P Squale	F-CDUE	40		RAA
☐ Wassmer WA.30 Bijave	F-CDJF	212		RAA

AILES DE FRANCE – (ASSOCIATION DES AMATEURS D'AÉRONEFS DE COLLECTION) (FRA105)

Address:	B.P. 62, 54300 Luneville.
Tel:	03 83 74 10 08
Admission:	By prior permission only – when the airfield is open.
Location:	At Croismaire airfield which is about 4 km east of the town on the N 4.

Established in the mid-1980s this organisation has an interesting fleet of aircraft and gliders. Some are owned by the group but the majority are the property of members. The oldest type is the Potez 600 parasol monoplane which dates from the early 1930s. Over one hundred and fifty were constructed and only a few survive. The Tiger Moth is slowly being built up from spares. The Piper Cub now resplendent in the classic yellow scheme has just been finished. Four of the five Stampes are currently active.

TYPE	REG/SER	CON. NO.	PI/NOTES	STATUS
☐ Boisavia B.601L Mercurey				RAD
☐ Boisavia B.601L Mercurey				RAD
☐ Castel C.311P	F-CAYM	294/23		RAA
☐ Caudron C.800 Épervier	F-CBYV	9891/231		RAA
☐ De Havilland D.H.82A Tiger Moth	F-AZCS		Built from spares.	RAC
☐ Fouga CM.170R Magister	F-GOGT	545	545	RA
☐ Jurca MJ.5B-1 Sirocco	F-WLKM	10		RA
☐ Max Holste MH.1521C-1 Broussard (1521M)	F-BOHP	10	10	RAA
☐ Max Holste MH.1521M Broussard	013	013		RA
☐ Morane-Saulnier MS.317 (MS.315)	F-BGKX	6518/264	264	RAA
☐ Morane-Saulnier MS.317 (MS.315)	F-BDZU	6522/268		RAC
☐ Nord N.1300 [Schneider Grunau Baby IIB]	F-CRII	203	F-CBUZ	RA
☐ Nord N.3202	19	19		RA
☐ North American NA-168 Texan (T-6G)		168-287	49-3183	RAC
☐ North American NA-168 Texan (T-6G)	F-AZGS	168-556	49-3432	RAA
☐ Piper J-3C-90 Cub (J-3C-65) (L-4H)	F-GJRC	12028	44-79732, HB-OIR, (F-GJPR)	RAA
☐ Potez 600	F-PIHA	3945	F-AOBD	RA
☐ Scheibe SF-27 Zugvogel IIIB	F-CCAX	1071		RA
☐ Stampe & Vertongen S.V.4A	F-BTXD	595	F-BDEP, CN-TTG	RAA
☐ Stampe & Vertongen S.V.4A	F-BDMI	639		RAA
☐ Stampe & Vertongen S.V.4C	F-BFLG	14	14	RAC
☐ Stampe & Vertongen S.V.4C	F-BNCU	447	F-BCXM, (F-GDXM)	RAA
☐ Stampe & Vertongen S.V.4C	F-BDJJ	516		RAA
☐ Wassmer WA.21 Javelot II	F-CCHD	8		RAA
☐ Wassmer WA.21 Javelot II	F-CCKU	59	59	RAA

COLLECTION DE LA BASE AÉRIENNE DE NANCY (FRA106)

Address:	Base Aérienne 133, B.P. 334 54133 Toul Cedex.
Tel:	03 83 52 72 72
Admission:	By prior permission only.
Location:	About 20 km south west of the town on the D 904.

The site was first used as an airfield in 1915 when a number of Breguet types flew into the grass area. In 1939 plans to construct a base were put forward and a squadron of Morane-Saulnier MS.406s operated from the site until the Germans arrived. They used the field until the end of World War II and for a short period American gliders and their tugs were in residence. In the early 1950s work started to modernise the facilities and Mystère IVAs soon arrived. The current wing was formed at Reims in May 1950 operating Vampires and Mistrals. Subsequently Thunderjets, Thunderstreaks and Super Sabres were flown. A move to Nancy took place in the mid-1960s after a period at Lahr in Germany. The Mirage IIIE then arrived and these were replaced by the 5F version in 1974. The Jaguar was then used for a period and currently the Mirage 2000D is flown.

TYPE	REG/SER	CON. NO.	PI/NOTES	STATUS
☐ Dassault Mystère IVA	185	185		RA
☐ Dassault Mirage IIIE	'512'	496	496	RAX
☐ Dassault Mirage IIIE	498	498		RA
☐ Dassault Mirage IIIE	500	500		RA
☐ Dassault Mirage IIIR	'469'	333	333	RAX

MUSÉE MILITAIRE HALL PATTON (FRA107)

Address:	Building 5271, Parc de Haye, 54840 Velaine-en-Haye.
Admission:	Saturday-Sunday 1400-1700.
Location:	About 5 km west of Nancy off the D.400.

This large area of parkland was donated to the local authority and houses many attractions including a car museum and sporting facilities. This small exhibition devoted to the famous soldier has a Bird Dog on show.

TYPE	REG/SER	CON. NO.	PI/NOTES	STATUS
☐ Cessna 305C Bird Dog (L-19E) (O-1E)	'38186'			PVX

55 MEUSE

MÉMORIAL DE VERDUN (FRA108)

Address:	1 Avenue du Corps Europeen, 55100 Fleury-devant Douaumont.,
Tel:	03 29 84 35 34
Fax:	03 29 84 45 54
Email:	memorial.documentation@wanadoo.fr
Admission:	February-mid December daily 0900-1630.
Location:	About 8 km north east of Verdun on the D 913.

The area around Verdun saw some of the bloodiest battles in World War I with horrendous loss of life. The Fort at Douaumont was overrun by the Germans in February 1916 and recaptured by the Allies eight months later. This museum portrays in vivid detail the conflict in the area. The skies above the town saw a great deal of activity and the two replicas on show were constructed by the late Jean-Baptiste Salis.

TYPE	REG/SER	CON. NO.	PI/NOTES	STATUS
☐ Fokker E III (FSM)				PV
☐ Gas Balloon			Basket only.	PV
☐ Nieuport 11 (FSM)				PV

56 MORBIHAN

AILES ANCIENNES ARMORIQUE – GROUPE JEAN MARIE LE BRIS (FRA109)

Address:	9 Rue Laennec, 56000 Vannes.
Tel:	02 48 68 17 04
Admission:	By prior permission only
Location:	At Vannes-Meucon airfield which is about 8 km north of the town off the D 778E.

This group received its first aircraft, the Noratlas, in 1984. The transport arrived by air from Evreux. A rarity is the sole prototype Nord N.2200 jet fighter which first flew in 1950. The aircraft was originally designed for the navy and was used on test work until May 1954. Many items of memorabilia, engines, models, components, photographs, documents and uniforms have been acquired and are displayed in the hangar.

TYPE	REG/SER	CON. NO.	PI/NOTES	STATUS
☐ Canadair CL-30 Silver Star 3 (CT-133) [Lockheed 580 (T-33AN)]	21009	T33-009		RA
☐ Dassault Etendard IVM	06	06		RA
☐ Dassault Super Mystère B2	179	179		RA
☐ Lockheed 580 (T-33A)	53091	580-9632	55-3091	RA
☐ Max Holste MH.1521M Broussard	70	70		RA
☐ Nord N.2200	01	01	F-WFRD – on loan from M.A.	RAC
☐ Nord N.2501 Noratlas	160	160		RA
☐ Schneider Grunau SG-38 (D.F.S. 108-14)	F-CAJB	35		RA
☐ Sud-Est SE.535 Mistral	50	50		RA
☐ Vought F-8A Crusader (F8U-1)	143719		Bu143719	RA
☐ Vought F-8P Crusader (F-8E(FN))	39	1266	Bu151770	PV

ESCADRILLE DU SOUVENIR BRETAGNE SUD (FRA110)

Address:	4 Route de Vannes, 56890 Meucon.
Tel:	02 97 60 70 94
Fax:	02 97 60 76 93
Admission:	By prior permission only.
Location:	At Meucon airfield which is about 8 km north of the town off the D 778.

Michel le Fol and his family have assembled a fleet of classic aircraft in their private hangar at Vannes. Seven examples of the Alcyon trainer were acquired and two or three of these are usually in flying condition These have now been joined by the Magister, two Broussards and a pair of Rallyes.

TYPE	REG/SER	CON. NO.	PI/NOTES	STATUS
☐ Fouga CM.170R Magister	143	143		RA
☐ Max Holste MH.1521M Broussard	F-WGBO	261	261, F-WGKN	RA
☐ Max Holste MH.1521M Broussard	F-GLMF	289	289	RA
☐ Morane-Saulnier MS.733 Alcyon	F-BNEA	15	15	RA
☐ Morane-Saulnier MS.733 Alcyon	F-BKOG	61	61	RA
☐ Morane-Saulnier MS.733 Alcyon	F-BMMR	100	100	RA
☐ Morane-Saulnier MS.733 Alcyon	F-BLYE	107	107 – contains parts of c/n 159 and c/n 183	RA
☐ Morane-Saulnier MS.733 Alcyon	F-BMMZ	130	130 – carries c/n 15 on tail.	RA
☐ Morane-Saulnier MS.733 Alcyon	F-GFZO	140	140, F-BNEE	RAA
☐ Morane-Saulnier MS.733 Alcyon	F-BNEL	159	159	RAC
☐ Morane-Saulnier MS.892A Commodore 150	F-BNXK	10610		RAA
☐ Morane-Saulnier MS.892E Rallye 150GT	F BXYP	12189		RAA

SALLES DE TRADITION DE LA BASE AÉRONAVALE DE LANN-BIHOUÉ (FRA111)

Address:	Aéronautique Navale de Lann-Bihoué, 56530 Quevan.
Tel:	02 97 12 90 00
Admission:	Wednesday 0900-1130 1330-1600 and by appointment.
Location:	About 7 km west of the town off the D 765.

An exhibition has been set up in a building in the camp. The story of the base and its units is portrayed with many photographs, models, uniforms, documents and books on view. A replica Neptune cockpit and a Link Trainer can be seen. The first type in residence was the Lancaster. This was replaced by the Neptune which served from 1953 until 1967. The Atlantic arrived in 1967 and later versions of the design are still in service. The Alizé was operated for almost thirty years by 4 Flotille which moved in from Hyères in July 1964.

TYPE	REG/SER	CON. NO.	PI/NOTES	STATUS
☐ Beech C18S Expeditor (C-45F) (UC-45F) (JRB-4)	85104	7849	(USAAF), Bu85104	RA
☐ Breguet 1050 Alizé	86	86		RA
☐ Breguet 1150 Atlantic	7	7		RA
☐ Lockheed 426-45-17 Neptune (P2V-7)	147567	726-7185	Bu147567	RA
☐ North American NA-88 Texan (AT-6D) (SNJ-5) (SNJ-7)	43981	88-16323	42-84542, Bu43981	RA
☐ Vought F-8P Crusader (F-8E (FN))	8	1225	Bu151739	

57 MEUTHE-ET-MOSELLE

COLLECTION DE LA BASE AÉRIENNE DE METZ (FRA112)

Address:	Base Aérienne 128, 57998 Metz Armées.
Tel:	03 87 63 11 15
Fax:	03 87 38 36 24
Admission:	By prior permission only.
Location:	About 6 km south west of Metz off the D 5.

A fighter unit operating the Thunderstreak was in residence from 1956 to 1965. The field has also been used by a communications squadon and this currently operates TBM. 700s and AS.555 helicopters. The Texan is painted in the markings of ELA.12/72 and was restored by members of the Ailes de France group at Luneville. The Noratlas was flown on electronic counter-measures duties from the mid-1960s until the late 1980s. The unit was then equipped with Transall C.160G's and these are still in use.

TYPE	REG/SER	CON. NO.	PI/NOTES	STATUS
☐ Nord N.2501 Noratlas	41	41		RA
☐ North American NA-182 Texan (T-6G)	114314	182-1	51-14314, F-BOEN	RA
☐ Republic F-84F Thunderstreak	28879		52-8879	RA
☐ Sikorsky S-58	170	SA-170		RA

COLLECTION DE LA BASE DE L'AVIATION LÉGÈRE DE L'ARMÉE DE TERRE DE PHALSBOURG (FRA113)

Address: B.P. 30302,
57373 Phalsbourg Cedex.
Tel: 03 87 25 23 99
Admission: By prior permission only.
Location: About 4 km west of the town off the N.4.

Phalsbourg has been one of the main bases of the service for many years. Three helicopters have been preserved with the Gazelle positioned near the main gate. The two Alouettes are located on the field.

TYPE	REG/SER	CON. NO.	PI/NOTES	STATUS
☐ Sud SA.341N Gazelle	1180	1180		RA
☐ Sud-Est SE.3130 Alouette II	2156	2156		RA
☐ Sud-Est SE.3160 Alouette III	1596	1596		RA

59 NORD

CLUB VOL A VOILE FLANDRES-ARTOIS (FRA114)

Address: Route de Blaringhem,
59173 Sercus Renescure.
Tel: 03 28 48 30 50
Admission: By prior permission only.
Location: At Calonne airfield which is about 2 km south of Merville on the D 122.

Schempp-Hirth developed a few light aircraft in the late 1950s and early 1960s and then turned its attention to sailplanes. The Janus made its maiden flight in the spring of 1974 and entered production the next year.

TYPE	REG/SER	CON. NO.	PI/NOTES	STATUS
☐ Carmam M.100S Mésange	F-CCSY	35		RAA
☐ Morane-Saulnier MS.892A Commodore 150	F-BMNS	10496		RAA
☐ Scheibe SF-28A Tandem Falke	F-CEYS	57101	(D-KDBR)	RAA
☐ Schempp-Hirth Janus A	F-CEPD	21		RAA
☐ Wassmer WA.21 Javelot II	F-CCEX	32		RAA
☐ Wassmer WA.30 Bijave	F-CCNT	70		RA
☐ Wassmer WA.30 Bijave	F-CDJM	217		RAA

COLLECTION DE LA BASE AÉRIENNE DE CAMBRAI-EPINOY (FRA115)

Address: Base Aérienne 103,
59341 Cambrai Air.
Tel: 03 27 74 75 76
Fax: 03 27 81 36 69
Admission: By prior permission only.
Location: About 8 km north west of the town off the D 340.

The 12th Fighter Wing was formed at Mont-de-Marsan in 1952 and moved to Cambrai the following year. The initial equipment was the Ouragan followed by the Mystère IVA. The wing was the first and the last to operate the Super Mystère B2. when the final examples were retired in September 1977. The Mirage F.1 was then flown for a decade until the arrival of the Mirage 2000. The Magister is at the aero club across the town.

TYPE	REG/SER	CON. NO.	PI/NOTES	STATUS
☐ Dassault Super Mystère B2	'148'	88	88	PVX
☐ Dassault Mirage IIIE	471	471		RA
☐ Fouga CM.170R Magister	213	213	At Niergnies airfield.	RA
☐ Sikorsky S-58	162	SA-162		RA

60 OISE

MUSÉE DE L'AVIATION (FRA116)

Address:	Warluis, 60430 Beauvais.
Tel:	03 44 89 28 23
Email:	jvicogne@aol.com
Admission:	Mid-march-mid October Saturday-Thursday 1400-1800.
Location:	About 5 km south east of the city just east of the N.1.

The museum owes its origins to a private collection of memorabilia started in 1945 and kept at Beauvais-Tillé airfield for many years. The exhibition at Warluis opened in 1995. World War II features prominently in the displays. On show are dioramas showing a British radar control room, the Royal Air Force in the Battle of Britain and the 322nd Bombardment Group of the U.S.A.A.F. at Beauvais airfield in 1944/5. British and American crew rooms from the conflict have been constructed with period furniture and mannequins in flying clothing. An anti aircraft post with a genuine Bofors gun is another feature of the exhibition. A large collection of photographs, documents and items of memorabilia donated by former military personnel can be seen. There are also airframe components, engines, propellers, radios etc. Many Beech 18s were used by the French Air Force on a variety of duties. The Noralpha is believed to have come from Étampes but the identity often quoted is for one known to be with a group in the Netherlands. The Broussard arrived from the closed resistance museum at Forges-les-Eaux. The V-1 was found locally and has been restored. The Mirage III, obtained from Châteaudun, is parked outside. This classic delta winged fighter was a familiar sight in the skies of northern France for many years as they were flown from several bases in the region. For a number of years a Piper Super Cub painted in false World War II American markings was kept at the airfield. This aircraft has now been sold.

TYPE	REG/SER	CON. NO.	PI/NOTES	STATUS
☐ Beech C18S Expeditor (C-45F) (UC-45F)	122	5868		PV
☐ Dassault Mirage IIIE	573	573		PV
☐ Fieseler Fi 103A-1				PV
☐ Max Holste MH.1521M Broussard	173	173		PV
☐ Nord N.1101 Noralpha (Ramier I) [Messerschmitt Me 208]			Identity doubtful.	PVX

MUSÉE DES DIRIGIBLES (FRA117)

Address:	31-33 Rue de Paris, Quartier Sud Voisinlieu, 60000 Beauvais.
Tel:	03 44 02 69 31
Admission:	February-November daily 1000-1730. (Closed first two full weeks in August)
Location:	In the south eastern part of the town.

On October 5th 1930 the R-101 crashed near Beauvais on its maiden flight from Cardington to India killing fifty of the fifty six on board. A memorial was set up on the ridge where the airship had struck the ground. In 1992 a local resident Laurent Wattlebled was concerned about the derelict state of the monument so the following February he decided to set up an association to look after the site. This work was carried out in 1994 by his family and friends and the area is regularly given attention to keep it in a good state. The idea of a museum was put forward and in 1998 a display dedicated to the R-101 was opened in part of M. Wattlebled's house. The region had been home to other pioneers of airships including Clèment Bayard so the exhibition was expanded to trace the history of dirigibles. On show are documents, models, photographs, maps, press cuttings and items of memorabilia tracing the history of airships in the "golden era" of aviation. Modern developments are also featured.

61 ORNE

AMICALE ALENÇONNAISE DES AVIONS ANCIENS (FRA118)

Address:	Aérodrome D'Alencon-Valframbert, 61000 Alencon.
Tel:	02 33 27 61 83
Fax:	02 33 31 09 62
Email:	AA.aa@carmail.com
Admission:	By prior permission only.
Location:	The airfield is about just north east of the town on the N12.

Formed in 1984 this group maintains three Flamants in flying condition. The MD-311 served with the navigational school at Toulouse and one MD-312 ended its military days at the twin engine conversion school at Avord. The first MD-312 obtained was deliberately damaged for a television show in which it represented a crashed B-25 Mitchell. After this it was rebuilt to original configuration. MD-312 F-AZDY arrived by air in 1999 from the Musée de l'Air at Le Bourget when a change in policy resulted in airworthy types either being grounded or passed on to groups. Two static examples, which may be restored, are now on the field. A fairly recent addition is the Poullin PJ-5B which is a design using Piper Cub parts. A small number were built in the late 1940s. The aircraft made its first flight at Bernay in 1949. The Beech 18 arrived from the closed museum at Brienne-le-Château. The French military used the type for training and communications duties for many years. The Texan is being built up from components acquired from a number of derelict airframes. The aeroclub at the field was formed in the early 1930s and its members own a number of classic types.

TYPE	REG/SER	CON. NO.	PI/NOTES	STATUS
☐ Beech C18S Expeditor (C-45F) (UC-45F)	8173	6250	43-35683, 1383 – c/n also reported as 8173.	RA
☐ Dassault MD-311 Flamant	F-AZER	276	276, (N276DF)	RAA
☐ Dassault MD-312 Flamant	F-AZDY	156	156	RAA
☐ Dassault MD-312 Flamant	F-AZDR	160	160 – 'damaged' for a TV show.	RAA
☐ Dassault MD-312 Flamant	215	215		RA
☐ Dassault MD-312 Flamant	235	235		RA
☐ Max Holste MH.1521M Broussard	F-GDSN	247	247	RAA
☐ North American NA-182 Texan (T-6G)			Composite airframe.	RAC
☐ Poullin PJ-5B	F-BAQC	6	F-PAQC	RAA

62 PAS-DE-CALAIS

BLOCKHAUS D'EPERLEQUES MUSEUM (FRA119)

Address: Rue du Sart,
62910 Eperleques.
Tel: 03 21 88 44 22
Fax: 03 21 88 44 84
Admission: March Sunday 1415-1800; April-May Monday-Friday 1415-1800 Sunday 1000-1900; June and September Monday-Friday 1000-1200 1415-1900 Sunday 1000-1900; July-August Sunday-Friday 1000-1900; October-November Sunday-Friday 1415-1800.
Location: About 3 km north east of the village which is about 30 km south east of Calais.

This huge bunker was built in 1943 and was used to fire V-2 rockets at Britain. There was a launch control with two firing pads. The site was capable of producing some liquid oxygen but after this was not sufficient for all the rockets so it was transported in by rail. The Allies attacked the bunker several times and on some raids 6 ton Tallboy bombs were used. Only one Tallboy fell on the bunker and this caused little damage. The railway network and other buildings were hit by the smaller bombs. The complex is now open and the visitor can see the work carried out during the latter stages of World War II in the comprehensive displays of photographs, models, rocket components and documents. The history of rocket engines is also featured.

TYPE	REG/SER	CON. NO.	PI/NOTES	STATUS
☐ Fieseler Fi 103A-1 (FSM)				PV

LA COUPOLE (FRA120)

Address: LP 284,
Helfaut,
62504 St. Omer.
Tel: 03 21 93 07 07
Fax: 03 21 39 21 45
Email: lacoupole@lacoupole.com
Admission: Daily 0900-1800 except July-August 1000-1900.
Location: About 5 km south of St. Omer off the D.195.

The complex of underground tunnels was built by Polish and Russian slave labour to assemble V-2 rockets for firing on England. The site was not completed when Allied forces captured the area in 1944. The nearby Blockhaus was damaged in bombing raids. The large concrete dome has been opened as a museum with displays of rockets, the story of building La Coupole and the history of the French Resistance. The story of the capture of the German rocket scientists by the competing Allies is also portrayed.

TYPE	REG/SER	CON. NO.	PI/NOTES	STATUS
☐ Fieseler Fi 103A-1 (FSM)				PV

64 PYRÉNÉES-ATLANTIQUES

MUSÉE DES PARACHUTISTES (FRA121)

Address:	École Troupes Aéroportées, 64082 Pau Cedex.
Tel:	05 59 40 49 18
Fax:	05 59 40 50 35
Email:	connservateur@museedesparas.com
Admission:	Tours daily at 1000, 1400,1500 and 1600.
Location:	On the N.134 to the north of the town.

This history of military parachuting is told in detail in this impressive collection. The site houses the headquarters of the Air Force parachute section. On show are models and parachutes from the early days up to the present time. Photographs of types used for the work over the years can be seen. The Noratlas, which was in service from the early 1950s until the 1980s, was used to drop many French airborne troups over the years.

TYPE	REG/SER	CON. NO.	PI/NOTES	STATUS
☐ Nord N.2501 Noratlas	161	161		PV

65 HAUTES-PYRÉNÉES

MUSÉE DU VELO (FRA122)

Address:	Route des Cols, Gerde 65200 Bagnères de Bigorre.
Tel:	05 62 95 53 11
Fax:	05 62 95 15 67
Admission:	October-April Wednesday-Monday 1000-1230 1430-1830. May-September by appointment.
Location:	About 2 km south of the town on the D.4.

The history of bicycles is told in this interactive museum which is in a town that often hosts a stage of the Tour de France. The locally built Mignet HM-290 is the only aeronautical exhibit.

TYPE	REG/SER	CON. NO.	PI/NOTES	STATUS
☐ Mignet HM-290 Pou-du-Ciel				PV

66 PYRÉNÉES-ORIENTALES

ASSOCIATION AÉRONAUTIQUE LA LAGOURE (FRA123)

Address:	Hôtel du Commerce, 66210 La Llagonne.
Tel:	04 68 04 28 02
Admission:	By prior permission only.
Location:	At Quillane airfield which is about 5 km north of Mont-Louis on the D 118.

A number of classic gliders are flown by the club from their picturesque airfield in the south of the country. Three types of Wassmer designs can be seen. The prototype Squale high performance single seater first flew in July 1967. The type entered production three years later and about eighty were built.

TYPE	REG/SER	CON. NO.	PI/NOTES	STATUS
☐ Morane-Saulnier MS.893A Commodore 180	F-BODD	10661		RAA
☐ Piper PA-25-235 Pawnee	F-GHSX	25-2387	N6765Z	RAA
☐ Schempp-Hirth Standard Cirrus G/81	F-CFDB	257	F-WFDB	RAA
☐ Wassmer WA.22A Super Javelot	F-CCRZ	97		RAA
☐ Wassmer WA.26P Squale	F-CDMQ	06		RAA

☐ Wassmer WA.30 Bijave	F-CCOQ	30	RAA
☐ Wassmer WA.30 Bijave	F-CDCE	146	RAA
☐ Wassmer WA.30 Bijave	F-CDCQ	157	RAA

MUSÉE DE L'AVIATION DU MAS PALÉGRY (FRA124)

Address:	Km 4 Route d'Elne, 66100 Perpignan.
Tel:	04 68 54 08 79
Fax:	04 68 54 08 79
Admission:	April 15th – October 15th daily 1000-1200 1500-1900.
Location:	About 4 km south of the town between the N 9 and N 114.

Charles Noetinger served as a pilot with the French Air Force. In the 1970s he began collecting aircraft and artefacts with the aim of setting up a museum on land at the family vineyard. The collection opened in the late 1970s and since the death of the founder in July 1995 the museum has been maintained by his family. The last type Charles flew with the Armée de l'Air was the Republic Thunderflash and in 1973 he bought a former Italian Air Force example from Udine. The Vampire on show was delivered to France in June 1949 and served at Dijon and Méknes in Morocco. The jet ended its service days with the Aéronavale and was rescued from a scrapyard in Brittany in 1976. Also on show are many models, components, uniforms, posters and photographs. The Boyer was built at Toulouse in 1965, modified over the next six years, and withdrawn in 1981.

TYPE	REG/SER	CON. NO.	PI/NOTES	STATUS
☐ Boyer B.II (BF.01)	F-PMXM	01	F-WMXM	PV
☐ Caudron C.800 Épervier	F-CBXF	9842/192		PV
☐ Dassault Mystère IVA			Front fuselage only.	PV
☐ Dassault Mirage F.1 (FSM)				PV
☐ De Havilland D.H.100 Vampire FB.5	VX950			PV
☐ Fouga CM.170R Magister	05	05	F-ZWSL	PV
☐ Max Holste MH.1521M Broussard	015	015		PV
☐ Morane-Saulnier MS.603	F-PHJC	1	F-WCZT (?)	RA
☐ Morane-Saulnier MS.733 Alcyon	F-BMQG	101	101	PV
☐ Republic F-84G Thunderjet	51-1077		Front fuselage only	PV
☐ Republic RF-84F Thunderflash	MM51-1928		51-1928, MM51-1928 – tail from 52-7457	PV

67 BAS-RHIN

MUSÉE DE L'ABRI (FRA125)

Address:	67690 Hatten.
Tel:	03 88 80 14 90
Fax:	03 88 80 09 25
Email:	info@maginot-hatten.com
Admission:	March-mid November Thursday-Saturday 1000-1200 1400-1800; Sunday 1000-1800. Mid-June – mid September daily 1000-1200 1400-1800; Sunday 1000-1800.
Location:	About 15 km north east of Haguenau on the D.25

This vast fort was constructed in 1930 as part of the Maginot Line. French forces were in residence from 1936-1940. In 1994 the site was opened as a museum with eight rooms of the underground bunker open to the public. The history of Hatten, the story of the many locals conscripted into the German Army and the local tank battle of January 1945 are portrayed in detail. On show in the 1944-1945 Hangar are dioramas of the battle with tanks guns and military vehicles. Outside is the Cold War area with a genuine Russian Radar Station and the aircraft, most of which came from the closed Aeropark Brandenburg in Germany.

TYPE	REG/SER	CON. NO.	PI/NOTES	STATUS
☐ Dassault Mirage IIIB	250	250		PV
☐ Mikoyan-Gurevich MiG-21SPS (MiG-21PFM)	'869'	94A4503	698 (DDR)	PVX
☐ Mil Mi-2US	501	562819043	501, (DDR-VGL), (D-HZPP) – in DDR markings.	PV
☐ Mil Mi-4				PV
☐ Mil Mi-8PS	396	0726	In DDR markings.	PV
☐ Mil Mi-8T	'698'	0623	DM-SPB, DDR-SPB, D-HOXB – in false DDR markings.	PV
☐ Mil Mi-8T	'925'	10542	925 (DDR), 93+11	PVX
☐ Yakovlev Yak-27R	35	0214		PV

69 RHÔNE

AILES ANCIENNES DE CORBAS (FRA126)

Address:	B.P., Mairie, Place Charles Jocteur, 69960 Corbas.
Tel:	04 72 50 15 89
Fax:	04 78 57 41 39
Email:	nicolas.carsoulle@wanadoo.fr
Admission:	Saturday-Sunday 1200- 1700 and in summer on most days.
Location:	The airfield is on the D 149 about 2 km south east of the town which is about 12 km south east of Lyon.

This group was formed in 1990 and soon moved into premises on the airfield. Aircraft and material were gathered and a small exhibition was set up in a hangar. Flamant 189 arrived for preservation with the local aero club in 1989 and this was taken over by Ailes Anciennes. A second airworthy Flamant followed along with a Broussard which is now resplendent in A.L.A.T. markings. These three airframes are still with the fleet. In 1994 the building was badly damaged by heavy falls of snow and a several items of memorabilia were destroyed. The group then rebuilt the hangar and started collecting again. A move has now been made to a former A.L.A.T. hangar where a museum is being set up and items of memorabilia and photographs are on show. The Cessna Bird Dog was one of the types flown on Army duties when they were in residence. These larger premises will mean that most of the airworthy fleet can now be housed under cover.

TYPE	REG/SER	CON. NO.	PI/NOTES	STATUS
☐ Cessna 305C Bird Dog (L-19E) (O-1E)	F-GDPF	24705	24705	RAA
☐ Dassault MD-312 Flamant	F-AZVG	189	189	PVA
☐ Dassault MD-312 Flamant	F-AZFS	217	217	PVA
☐ Dassault MD-312 Flamant	232	232		PV
☐ Max Holste MH.1521M Broussard	F-GGGQ	143	143, F-WGGQ	PV
☐ Max Holste MH.1521M Broussard	F-GHUO	299	299	PVA
☐ Morane-Saulnier MS.505 Criquet (MS.502) [Fieseler Fi 156 Storch]	F-AZTB	602/23	602, F-BEJN	PVA
☐ Morane-Saulnier MS.733 Alcyon	F-AZVG	67	67, F-BMMQ	PVA
☐ Morane-Saulnier MS.733 Alcyon	F-AZXU	141	141, F-BLXU	PVA
☐ Nord N.1203-III Norécrin (N.1203-II)	F-BBEO	324		RA
☐ Nord N.1203-VI Norécrin (N.1203-II) (N.1203-IV)	F-BEUS	180		PVA

70 HAUTE-SAÔNE

COLLECTION DE LA BASE AÉRIENNE DE LUXEUIL (FRA127)

Address:	Base Aérienne 116, 70301 Luxeuil-les-Bains.
Tel:	03 84 40 80 00
Email:	ba116@air.defense.gouv.fr
Admission:	By prior permission only.
Location:	About 2km south of the town off the D.270.

The site was established in 1916 and housed American units towards the end of the conflict. The base was used for exercises in the early 1930s but with the onset of World War II it was reactivated. Units flying Dewoitine D.520s and Morane-Saulnier MS.406s moved in. The Luftwaffe then flew a variety of types until early 1945. For most of its life the base has been home to fighter squadrons. The current wing was formed in July 1947 from former Thunderbolt squadrons and was equipped with Spitfires. Operational by the September it served in Indo-China. The group was later re-organised at Friedrichshafen in Germany with Thunderbolts but after a year the Vampire arrived. The base was modernised in the early 1950s to take jets. The Ouragan came into service in 1954 and in 1957 these were replaced by the Thunderstreak. After a period at Bremgarten it moved back to France in 1961. The Mirage IIIE was flown from 1968 until the late 1980s. Two squadrons of Mirage 2000Ns are currently based at the field. Also in residence is a tactical training unit using Falcon 20s. An exhibition in the headquarters building traces the history of the base and the wing.

TYPE	REG/SER	CON. NO.	PI/NOTES	STATUS
☐ Dassault Mirage IIIE	568	568		RA
☐ Dassault Mirage IIIE	572	572		RA
☐ Dassault Mirage IIIE	584	584		RA
☐ Fouga CM.170R Magister	202	202		RA

Many Dassault aircraft, including this Etendard, are part of the fleet of the Conservatoire collection at Bordeaux-Mérignac.

This superbly restored Caudron Luciole is kept in airworthy condition by the museum at La Baule.

Jean-Baptiste Salis built this Fokker E III replica for the poignant museum at Verdun.

Parked outside the Musée de l'Abri at Hatten is this Yakovlev Yak-27R painted in Soviet colours. (Keith Dexter)

The collection at Albert, which is being assembled by the Betrancourt family, includes this Dassault Mirage IIIRD.

This replica Latécoère 28 was constructed for use in a film and is now in the hangar of AMPAA at Melun-Villaroche. (Douglas Rough)

71 SAÔNE-ET-LOIRE

AÉROCLUB DU BASSIN MINIER – SECTION MUSÉE ET COLLECTION (FRA128)

Address:	B.P. 16, du Basin Minier, Aérodrome de Montceau-Pouilloux, 71301 Montceau-les-Mines.
Tel:	03 85 79 10 83
Email:	j-f.glo@tf1mail.com
Admission:	When the club is open.
Location:	The airfield is about 10 km south of the town on the D 60.

Members of the aero club are gathering a collection of military and civil types and restoring them to both flying and static condition. One Flamant is maintained in airworthy condition and two other examples of the twin engined type later arrived at the airfield. The Mignet HM-290 series appeared after World War II and a number of HM-293s are active in France. Several have been built in other countries around the world. The French government flying school at nearby St. Yan used a fleet of Alcyons for many years. The unidentified Beech 18 cockpit was obtained from this source. The origins of the Luciole are a mystery. Large numbers of this two seat biplane were built in the late 1920s and 1930s. The original identity was presumably lost when the airframe was in store for many years. The Jodel D.112 was built by members of the club in 1957 and has been based at the field ever since. The Minicab was constructed at St. Yan the following year and after several owners it arrived at the club in 1971. Designed by Yves Gardan the prototype Minicab first flew in 1949 and in addition to amateur built examples a small run was produced by the Béarn company. Some years ago two derelict Super Mystère airframes arrived from Bourges. A project to restore them into one was abandoned and they have moved on. There are plans to set up an exhibition in one of the buildings.

TYPE	REG/SER	CON.NO.	PI/NOTES	STATUS
☐ Beech D18S Expeditor (C-45G)			Front fuselage only.	RAD
☐ Caudron C.275 Luciole	F-AZCU	06		RA
☐ Dassault MD-311 Flamant	F-AZGX	290	290	RA
☐ Dassault MD-312 Flamant	191	191		RA
☐ Dassault MD-312 Flamant	F-AZFE	237	237	RAA
☐ Dassault Mirage IIIE	521	521		RA
☐ Gardan GY-201 Minicab	F-PINM	A-144		RAA
☐ Jodel D.112 Club	F-PIIM	749		RAA
☐ Max Holste MH.1521M Broussard	F-GHFG	104	104	RAA
☐ Max Holste MH.1521M Broussard	F-GKJT	106	106	RAA
☐ Mignet HM-293 Pou-du-Ciel				RA
☐ Morane-Saulnier MS.733 Alcyon	F-BNEF	145	145	RAD

ASSOCIATION POUR LA SAUVEGARDE DU PATRIMOINE AÉRONAUTIQUE EN CHAROLAIS (FRA129)

Address:	B.P.2, Aerodrome de Paray le Monail 'La Fôret', 71600 Paray-le-Monail.
Tel:	03 85 81 51 51
Admission:	Normally open at weekends.
Location:	About 2 km north of the town off the N 70.

This group has gathered a collection of classic gliders, light aircraft and components. Many French clubs have gliding sections and since World War II the local industry has produced large numbers of sailplanes. The high performance Air 100 appeared in 1945 and the 102 in 1950. Only thirty five examples of this delightful design were completed. The first Castel design, the Yanapour, flew in 1930 and over the next decade a series of prototypes was built. In the early years of World War II substantial numbers of the C.25S, C.301 series and C.310 were delivered to clubs. A regular participant at vintage rallies is the tailless AV.36. A rarity is the Prototype Sevimia 20 which first flew in 1964 and was active until 1975. The first Aero 101 two seater biplane made its maiden flight in 1950 and eleven production aircraft were subsequently delivered for club use. The Minié 4DC-32 engine of 75 h.p. or a Continental A 65 was fitted. The Nord NC.854S has been recently completed and this incorporates parts from several other aircraft. In store are major components of the second prototype of the civil version of the NC.856. The components of the Hanriot 182 are believed to be the only ones surviving of the type. Over three hundred examples of this high wing monoplane were built in the 1930s and were used for club and military tasks. No complete Caudron Goélands are known to exist and the search is on for more components so that one can emerge. Parts of several other rare types have been acquired for future rebuilds. Some components have gone to other groups to help their restoration projects. There are always a number of projects in the workshops of this enthusiastic organisation.

TYPE	REG/SER	CON. NO.	PI/NOTES	STATUS
☐ Aero 101	F-PGIC	3	F-BGIE	RA
☐ Arsenal Air 100	F-ZABY	403	Wings only – see MA.	RAD
☐ Arsenal Air 102	F-CBHG	27		RAD
☐ Arsenal Air 102	F-CABR	32		RAD
☐ Arsenal Air 102	F-CATS	35	Parts only.	RAD
☐ Avia 151A	F-CASH	8		RA
☐ Avialsa-Scheibe A.60 Fauconnet [L-Spatz 55]	F-CCLI	13		RAA
☐ Avialsa-Scheibe A.60 Fauconnet [L-Spatz 55]	F-CCPN	20	Parts only.	RAD
☐ Avialsa-Scheibe A.60 Fauconnet [L-Spatz 55]	F-CDLC	125K		RAA
☐ Beech D18S Expeditor (C-45G)			Major components.	RA
☐ Breguet 905S Fauvette	F-CCIP	12		RA
☐ Bücker Bü 181B-1 Bestmann			Parts only.	RA
☐ Carmam M.100S Mésange	F-CCXH	43	Parts only.	RA
☐ Carmam M.100S Mésange	F-CDDS	59		RA
☐ Carmam M.100S Mésange	F-CDHR	68	Wings only.	RA
☐ Castel C.25S	F-CRIN	124	F-CASS	RA
☐ Castel C.25S	F-CRDP	132	F-CBKK – parts only.	RAD
☐ Castel C.25S	F-CRPQ	136	F-CAJV – parts only.	RA
☐ Castel C.25S	F-CRKA	166	F-CAPL – Major components.	RA
☐ Castel C.3010P (C.301S)	F-CRDE	1081	F-CAKB	RA
☐ Castel C.3010P (C.301S)	F-CREC	1119	F-CBXN	RA
☐ Castel C.301S	F-CRJM	1050	F-CBLA, F-CRHQ, F-CRJM, F-WRJM	RAA
☐ Castel C.310P	F-CRNF	105	F-CBYC – parts only.	RAD
☐ Castel C.310P	F-CRFQ	122	F-CBEE	RA
☐ Caudron C.445 Goéland			Parts only.	RA
☐ Caudron C.800 Épervier	F-CBXH	9805/145	Parts only.	RA
☐ Caudron C.800 Épervier	F-CAPF	9841/181		RAA
☐ Caudron C.800 Épervier	F-CBYT	9866/206	Parts only.	RAD
☐ Cossandey Glider	71-CG	1		RA
☐ Fauvel AV.36H	F-CBRX	123		RAA
☐ Guerchais-Roche SA.103 Emouchet	F-CRQE	64	F-CBZV	RA
☐ Guerchais-Roche SA.103 Emouchet	F-CRIB	109	F-CBDD	RA
☐ Guerchais-Roche SA.103 Emouchet		116	Parts only.	RAD
☐ Guerchais-Roche SA.104 Emouchet	F-CRMJ	207	F-CBYA	RA
☐ Guerchais-Roche SA.104 Emouchet	F-CCFJ	289		RA
☐ Hanriot 182			Parts only.	RA
☐ Jodel D.92 Bébé				RA
☐ Jodel D.92 Bébé				RA
☐ Jodel D.92 Bébé	F-PYQF	725		RA
☐ Jodel D.92 Bébé	F-PDHQ	B.14		RAD
☐ Jodel D.112 Club	F-PPRB	1767	Rebuild of c/n 1078 F-BKCB using components from c/n 884 F-BHJF	RAC
☐ Jodel DR.1050 Ambassadeur		786		RAC
☐ Letov LF-107 Lunak	OK-0900	30		RA
☐ Morane-Saulnier MS.185 (MS.180)			Parts only.	RA
☐ Morane-Saulnier MS.500 Criquet [Fieseler Fi 156 Storch]			Parts only.	RA
☐ Morane-Saulnier MS.892A Commodore 150			Parts only.	RA
☐ Nord N.1002 Pingouin II [Messerschmitt Bf 108B]			Parts only.	RA
☐ Nord N.1300 [Schneider Grunau Baby IIB]	F-CRIO	136	F-CBPR – parts only.	RA
☐ Nord N.1300 [Schneider Grunau Baby IIB]	F-CRCU	249	F-CAKZ	RAD
☐ Nord N.1300 [Schneider Grunau Baby IIB]	F-CRDF	257	F-CALB	RA
☐ Nord N.2000 [Jacobs Meise]	F-CARV	10333/3	Parts only.	RAD
☐ Nord N.2000 [Jacobs Meise]	F-CBFQ	10334/4	Parts only.	RAD
☐ Nord N.2000 [Jacobs Meise]	F-CAGE	10336/6	Parts only.	RA
☐ Nord N.2000 [Jacobs Meise]	F-CAGF	10341/11	Parts only	RA
☐ Nord N.2000 [Jacobs Meise]	F-CBFR	10343/13		RAA
☐ Nord N.2000 [Jacobs Meise]	F-CAUN	10347/17		RAA
☐ Nord N.2000 [Jacobs Meise]	F-CBFO	10357/27	Parts only.	RA
☐ Nord N.2000 [Jacobs Meise]	F-CARX	10388/58	Fuselage only.	RAD
☐ Nord N.2000 [Jacobs Meise]	F-CAEJ	10417/87	Parts only.	RA
☐ Nord N.2000 [Jacobs Meise]	F-CBYH	10418/88	Parts only	RA
☐ Nord N.2000 [Jacobs Meise]	F-CACV	10428/98	Parts only.	RA
☐ Nord N.2000 [Jacobs Meise]	F-CBFX	10430/100	Parts only.	RA
☐ Nord NC.853S			Parts only.	RA
☐ Nord NC.854S (NC.853S)	F-PFYS	146	Built mainly from spares but has wings of c/n 21 F-BFIL and c/n 25 F-BFIT.	RAA
☐ Nord NC.856A Norvigie			Parts only.	RA
☐ Nord NC.856N Norclub	F-BBBY	2	Parts only.	RA
☐ Sevimia S.20	F-CRNN	01		RA
☐ Wassmer WA.21 Javelot II	F-CBYR	02		RAA
☐ Wassmer WA.21 Javelot II	F-CCEJ	16	Parts only.	RA
☐ Wassmer WA.21 Javelot II	F-CCKP	52	Parts only.	RA
☐ Wassmer WA.22 Super Javelot	F-CCLX	72	Parts only.	RA
☐ Wassmer WA.22A Super Javelot	F-CCZR	107	Parts only.	RA
☐ Wassmer WA.22A Super Javelot	F-CHRE	134	134	RA
☐ Wassmer WA.23 Super Javelot	F-CCHQ	01	Wings only.	RA
☐ Wassmer WA.30 Bijave			Parts only.	RA

73 SAVOIE

AILES ANCIENNES DE SAVOIE 'JACQUES BERTRAND' (FRA130)

Address:	131 Avenue de Turin, 73000 Chambéry.
Tel:	04 79 33 79 79
Fax:	04 79 33 79 79
Email:	ajpm@cybercable.tm.fr
Admission:	By prior permission only.
Location:	At a number of locations in the area.

This group was formed in the mid-1980s and is now part of the Ailes Anciennes organisation. For many years a workshop was in use at Chambéry-Voglans airport but the aircraft and associated material have been moved to a number of places around the town. Work to restore them to exhibition standard is being carried out by members of the organisation. The only currently active aircraft is the Minicab which was built in the Pontarlier area in the late 1950s. The museum acquired it in 1988 and keeps it at Voglans. The aim is to set up a display tracing the history of private flying in the region and a search for a suitable site is underway.

TYPE	REG/SER	CON. NO.	PI/NOTES	STATUS
☐ Gardan GY-201 Minicab	F-PIYB	A-159		RAA
☐ Morane-Saulnier MS.733 Alcyon				RAC
☐ Nord N.1101 Noralpha (Ramier I) [Messerschmitt Me 208]				RAC
☐ Nord N.1203-II Norécrin	F-BBGI	367	F-OBGI	RAC
☐ Nord N.1203-III Norécrin (N.1203-II)	F-BHVV	359		RAC
☐ Piper J-3C-65 Cub (L-4H)				RAC

74 HAUTE-SAVOIE

MUSÉE DES AILES ANCIENNES HAUTE-SAVOIE (FRA131)

Address:	3 Avenue du Général de Gaulle, 74200 Thonon les Bains.
Tel:	04 50 26 51 03
Fax:	04 50 26 51 03
Email:	pve@crossair.ch
Admission:	By prior permission only.
Location:	At Annecy-Meythet airfield which is about 3 km north west of the town off the N 508.

This group was formed in the mid-1980s and soon took on the maintenance of the Fouga Magister which was delivered to the local aero club in July 1986. A Wright Cyclone engine is being worked on along with an Artouse motor. The aim is to set up a museum at the airport. The Mystère arrived from the Alsace branch of Ailes Anciennes and the recently acquired Horizon is being rebuilt in the workshops.

TYPE	REG/SER	CON. NO.	PI/NOTES	STATUS
☐ Dassault Mystère IVA	'57'	33	33	RAX
☐ Fouga CM.170R Magister	85	85		RA
☐ Gardan GY-80 Horizon 160	F-BLVI	31		RAC

MUSÉE STERNA ET DES TROIS GUERRES (FRA132)

Address:	7 Avenue Zanaroli, 74600 Seynod.
Tel:	04 50 52 78 89
Admission:	Wednesday-Monday 0900-1200 1400-1900.
Location:	In the northern part of the town which is about 3 km south of Annecy.

This private collection, which has been in existence for more than three decades, contains many military vehicles, tanks, guns, uniforms, radios and photographs. Emphasis is placed on local battles with a number of detailed exhibitions to be seen. A wide range of weapons is also on show. The sole aircraft is the Sud Aviation built Sikorsky S-58 which served with the Air Force until the mid-1970s. After this it spent a period with C.E.L.A.G. at Grenoble before arriving at the museum in 1987.

TYPE	REG/SER	CON. NO.	PI/NOTES	STATUS
☐ Sikorsky S-58	92	SA-92		PV

75 PARIS

CITÉ DES SCIENCES ET DE L'INDUSTRIE (FRA133)

Address:	30 Avenue Corentin Carou, 75019 Paris.
Tel:	01 36 68 29 30
Fax:	01 40 05 72 22
Email:	b.benita@cite-sciences.fr
Admission:	Tuesday-Saturday 1000-1800; Sunday 1000-1700.
Location:	Near the Porte de la Villette which is in the north eastern part of the city.

Only one aircraft is displayed at this museum which traces the development of several aspects of science and its application to industry. The complex is one of the largest of its type in the world and also one of the most popular. There is a section tracing developments in medicine over the years. Many the exhibits are 'hands-on' and are specifically designed for children. Visitors can go inside the 'Argonaute' attack submarine and try their hand in an aircraft simulator. The main building is surrounded by a pleasant park and boat trips can be taken on the Ourcq Canal which passes the site. The Mirage IVA delta wing nuclear bomber made its maiden flight in June 1959 and in all sixty six were completed. The type served in this role until 1996 and the last of the photographic reconnaissance conversions were based at Mont-de-Marsan until withdrawn in late 2005. An Ariane rocket is among the hardware in the informative space hall.

TYPE	REG/SER	CON. NO.	PI/NOTES	STATUS
☐ Dassault Mirage IVA	45	45		PV

MUSÉE DES ARTS ET MÉTIERS (MUSÉE NATIONAL DES TECHNIQUES) (FRA134)

Address:	60 Rue Réamur, 75003 Paris.
Tel:	01 53 01 82 00
Fax:	01 53 01 82 01
Email:	rorato@cnav.fr
Admission:	Tuesday-Sunday 1000-1800 (Closes on Thursday at 2130)
Location:	In the northern part of the city near the merto stations of Arts et Metiérs and Réamur-Sebastopol.

The development of technology from the sixteenth century is portrayed in this fascinating museum. The collection was set up in 1794 and over a thousand items are on show. The seven main sections cover scientific instruments, materials, construction, communications, transport, energy and mechanics. The aviation department contains five early aircraft and three large scale models along with engines and components. Clément Ader started gliding experiments in 1855. On October 9th 1890 he made the first powered take off when his steam engined Éole left the ground at Armanvillers. He covered about five hundred feet a few inches above the ground but the flight was considered not to be controlled. He claimed that his 1897 Avion III flew but these were later proved to be false. The Avion III was restored by the Musée de l'Air in the 1980s. Robert Esnault-Pelterie built a copy of the 1902 Wright glider in 1904 and the first of his many monoplanes appeared three years later. The star exhibit is the Blériot XI in which the constructor made the first aerial crossing of the English Channel from Barraques to Dover on July 25th 1909. The Dufaux helicopter made a tethered flight in 1905 and succeeded in lifting 5 kg. more than its own weight. The Breguet R U1 was one of the first types to go into production for military use. In December 1911 the designer flew the aircraft across Morocco from Casablanca to Fez.

TYPE	REG/SER	CON. NO.	PI/NOTES	STATUS
☐ Ader Avion III				PV
☐ Blériot XI		01		PV
☐ Breguet R.U1		40		PV
☐ Dufaux Hélicoptère				PV
☐ Esnault-Pelterie REP A				PV

76 SEINE-MARITIME

AMICALE DES AVIONS DE COLLECTION ET SPORT (FRA135)

Address:	Route d'Hautot, Les Vatois, 76190 Aérodrome d'Yvetot.
Tel:	02 35 69 01 11
Admission:	By prior permission only.
Location:	The airfield is north west of the town off the D.5 and about 30 km north west of Rouen.

Formed in the early 1990s this organisation is assembling an interesting collection of classics at Yvetot. The first aircraft to arrive was an example of the classic Waco UPF-7 biplane. Over six hundred were produced between 1937 and 1945 with the majority going to the CPTP scheme. There are also two Bücker Jungmanns and a Jungmeister in the fleet. The Jungmanns are German built and one has been in France for many years. The Jungmeister was constructed by Hirth and Bitz in 1945 and was re-engined in the early 1990s. The Yak-3 was built in Russia in 2002 using a Yak-11 trainer airframe as the basis for the conversion. The Texan is one of many used for training by the Air Force from the 1950s up to the early 1970s.

TYPE	REG/SER	CON. NO.	PI/NOTES	STATUS
☐ Bücker Bü 131D Jungmann	F-PCSY	01	F-BCSY	RAA
☐ Bücker Bü 131D Jungmann	F-AZEM	5		RAA
☐ Bücker Bü 133E Jungmeister (Bü 133D-1)	F-AZHC	F5-2009		RAA
☐ Morane-Saulnier MS.880B Rallye 100T	F-BXMU	2589		RAA
☐ Mudry CAP.10B	F-PYIF	A.2		RAA
☐ Mudry CAP.20LS-200	F-AZUN	09	F-GAUN	RAA
☐ North American NA-182 Texan (T-6G)	F-AZIU	182-38	51-14351, 14351 (France)	RAC
☐ Waco UPF-7	F-AZJC	5495	NC29998, N29998	RAA
☐ Yakovlev Yak-3UA (Yak-11)	F-AZLY	172890		RAC

COLLECTION BOUGAREL (FRA136)

Address:	Le Hardouin, 27350 Rougemontier.
Tel:	02 32 57 34 26
Admission:	By prior permission only.
Location:	At Rouen- Boos aerodrome which is about 7 km south east of the city on the N 14.

This collection was set up to restore and fly examples of the Alcyon. The prototype of this low wing monoplane first flew in the late 1940s. One hundred and thirty were built for basic training duties by the Air Force, Navy and the government flying school at St. Yan. The group had hangarage at St. Cyr airfield but has now moved its fleet to Rouen. The Alcyons, the Morane-Saulnier MS.317 and MS.505 Criquet are regular performers at airshows in the region. The Potez 43/1 is a fairly recent acquisition. This aircraft was on show for many years at a car museum in Normandy. More than one hundred examples of this high wing design were built in the 1930s. The airframe needs a great deal of work before it can be made airworthy.

TYPE	REG/SER	CON. NO.	PI/NOTES	STATUS
☐ Max Holste MH.1521C-1 Broussard (1521M)	F-GKRO	154	154	RAA
☐ Morane-Saulnier MS.317 (MS.315)	F-BBZR	6512/258		RAA
☐ Morane-Saulnier MS.505 Criquet (MS.500) [Fieseler Fi 156 Storch]	F-BAVB	633/37	633	RAA
☐ Morane-Saulnier MS.733 Alcyon	F-BEHG	6	6	RAA
☐ Morane-Saulnier MS.733 Alcyon	F-BASJ	13	F-BDZY, (F-BDZC)	RAC
☐ Morane-Saulnier MS.733 Alcyon	F-AZKS	83	83	RAA
☐ Morane-Saulnier MS.733 Alcyon	F-BMMY	128		RAA
☐ Potez 43/1	F-AMJP	3322		RAC

GROUPEMENT ROUENNAIS D'AVIATION LÉGÈRE (FRA137)

Address:	Aérodrome de Rouen-Boos, 76520 Boos.
Tel:	02 35 80 21 30
Admission:	By prior permission only.
Location:	About 7 km south east of the city on the N 14.

This group operates both powered aircraft and gliders. There are a number of classic types in its large fleet. The oldest glider is the Nymphale which dates from 1958. This sailplane has been loaned to the club and is currently in store awaiting restoration. The airfield is also home to the Collection Bourgarel and many privately owned classic and home built aircraft. The pair of Rallyes are used as tugs.

TYPE	REG/SER	CON. NO.	PI/NOTES	STATUS
☐ Breguet 904S Nymphale	F-CCFP	6		RA
☐ Grob G.102/77J Astir Jeans	F-CFCK	2145		RAA
☐ Morane-Saulnier MS.892A Commodore 150	F-BMNO	10492		RAA
☐ Morane-Saulnier MS.893A Commodore 180	F-BSDA	11465		RAA
☐ Scheibe SF-28A Standard Falke	F-CFJA	57115	(D-KDGX)	RAA
☐ Schleicher K.8B	F-CEJQ	8977		RAA
☐ Schleicher ASK-13	F-CERA	13523		RAA
☐ Schleicher ASW-15B	F-CEJM	15349		RAA
☐ Wassmer WA.22 Super Javelot	F-CCOF	78		RAA
☐ Wassmer WA.30 Bijave	F-CDCC	144		RAA

SITE DE V1 DU VAL YGOT (FRA138)

Address:	Forêt d'Eawy, 76680 Ardouval
Tel:	02 35 93 15 04
Admission:	By prior permission only.
Location:	About 35 km north of Rouen off the D.915.

The site for firing V-1s on England was started around Christmas 1943. Although it was practically finished some months later it was never used. Several storage and assembly buildings collapsed. This was due to the slave labourers deliberately mixing the concrete so that it did not have the necessary strength. A group has restored some of these structures and tidied up the surrounding land. A replica V-1 has been built and this is mounted on a reconstruction of a launching ramp pointing towards England. Just over eight and a half thousand of these flying bombs were fired at London but less than half made it to the city.

TYPE	REG/SER	CON. NO.	PI/NOTES	STATUS
☐ Fieseler Fi 103A-1 (FSM)				PV

77 SEINE-ET-MARNE

ASSOCIATION DES MÉCANICIENS ET PILOTES D'AÉRONEFS ANCIENS (FRA139)

Address:	10 Rue Charles de Gaulle, 91070 Bondoufle.
Tel:	01 60 86 64 52
Fax:	01 64 09 36 70
Email:	ampaa@fr.fm
Admission:	By prior permission only.
Location:	At Melun-Villaroche airfield which is about 8 km north of the town off the D 57.

A group of enthusiasts at the Centre Essais en Vol started restoring a Nord N.1101 in 1980. This led to the formation of an association to collect, restore and fly vintage and classiç aircraft. Hangars and workshops were obtained at Étampes and the fleet grew rapidly. Initially mainly French designs were acquired but with the growth of the warbird movement in France foreign types appeared. When the C.E.V. vacated Melun-Villaroche in the mid-1990s one of their large hangars was taken over and the majority of the aircraft are now at this location. The Latécoère 28 floatplane was used on postal flights to South America in the 1930s and a replica built for film work is in the hangar. The last flying examples of two French types are one of the highlights of the fleet. The Hurel-Dubois high aspect wing survey aircraft was developed from the HD.31 and HD.32 tested in the mid-1950s. Eight HD.34s were ordered by the Institut Géographique National at Creil to supplant and replace their B-17 Fortresses. The Vautour twin engined jet flew in prototype form in 1952 and was ordered by the French Air Force in three versions – all weather interceptor, light attack bomber and night fighter. One hundred and forty were built including seventy of the night fighter variant. This is normally kept at Bretigny along with the Nord N.262 and one of the Broussards. Two interesting arrivals are Czech constructed Ilyushin Il-10s. At least one of these will be rebuilt to flying condition and will be the only example of the classic 'Shturmovik' design to be seen in the air. The Simoun was owned by the late Jean Blondel at Beauvais. The aircraft saw military service prior to World War II, was on the Moroccan register in 1955, and appeared in the Blondel hangar in the early 1980s. Some work was carried out on the airframe at this time. The two Bolingbrokes were acquired by Philippe Denis from the Canadian Warplane Heritage and transported to the Valence area. After his death they were purchased by the group. The Hanriot 14 is believed to be a replica and the uncovered fuselage and tail are in the main hangar. The Goumhourias have recently come from Egypt. A batch of Skyraiders was purchased from Chad in the late 1980s and a pair remain with the collection.

TYPE	REG/SER	CON. NO.	PI/NOTES	STATUS
☐ Avia B-33 [Ilyushin Il-10]	DD-39			RA
☐ Avia B-33 [Ilyushin Il-10]	1087	1087		RA
☐ Bristol 149 Bolingbroke IVT	10040			RAC
☐ Bristol 149 Bolingbroke IVT	10184			RAD
☐ Castel C.25S	F-CRHD	199	F-CAMV	RAA
☐ Caudron C.635 Simoun	F-AZBO	342	342, F-DADY	RAC
☐ Caudron C.800 Épervier	F-CAZY	9878/218		RAA
☐ Centralne Studium Samolotow (CSS) 13 [Polikarpov Po-2]	F-AZPO	49-026	5,SP-ANB	RAA
☐ De Havilland D.H.82A Tiger Moth				RA
☐ De Havilland D.H.82A Tiger Moth	F-AZDH			RA
☐ De Havilland D.H.82A Tiger Moth	'K2570'	'1935'		RAAX
☐ De Rouge-Bouvet-Vallier Elytroplan		01		RAC
☐ Douglas AD-4N Skyraider	'125716'	7609	Bu125716, 11(France), 11 (Chad),F-AZFN	RAAX
☐ Douglas AD-4NA Skyraider (AD-4N)	'126937'	7798	Bu126998, 37 (France), 37 (Chad), F-AZKY	RAAX
☐ Fauvel AV.36	F-CBRS	119		RAA
☐ Grumman G-40 Avenger (TBM-3) (TBM-3E)	F-AZJA	2688	Bu85869, N9927Z	RAA
☐ Guerchais-Roche SA.104 Emouchet				RA
☐ Hanriot HD-14 (R)				RA
☐ Heliopolis Goumhouria 6 [Bücker Bü 181D Bestmann]		158		RA
☐ Heliopolis Goumhouria 6 [Bücker Bü 181D Bestmann]		192		RA
☐ Heliopolis Goumhouria 6 [Bücker Bü 181D Bestmann]		321		RA
☐ Hurel-Dubois HD.34	F-AZNH	01	F-WHOO, F-BHOO	RAA
☐ Latécoère 28-3 (R)	'F-AJNQ'			RAX
☐ Let C-11 [Yakovlev Yak-11]	F-AZOK	25111/19		RAA
☐ Max Holste MH.1521C-1 Broussard (1521M)	F-GEDC	5	5, F-BICX	RAA
☐ Max Holste MH.1521M Broussard	F-GOMH	64	64	RA
☐ Morane-Saulnier MS.43			Wings only	RA
☐ Morane-Saulnier MS.317 (MS.315)	F-BFZH	6524/270		RA
☐ Morane-Saulnier MS.472 Vanneau				RA
☐ Morane-Saulnier MS.505 Criquet (MS.502) [Fieseler Fi 156 Storch]	F-BEJF	654/8	654	RAA
☐ Morane-Saulnier MS.733 Alcyon	F-BLYG	110	110	RA
☐ Morane-Saulnier MS.733 Alcyon	F-BMJX	194	194 – fuselage only.	RA
☐ Mudry CAP.231	F-WZCH	02		RAA
☐ Nord N.260	F-GNMH	8	8	RAA
☐ Nord N.1101 Noralpha (Ramier I) [Messerschmitt Me 208]	F-BJAA	23	23, F-BGVH	RAD
☐ Nord N.1101 Noralpha (Ramier I) [Messerschmitt Me 208]	F-WDMU	132	132	RAA
☐ Nord N.3400				RA
☐ Nord NC.856A Norvigie				RA
☐ North American NA-182 Texan (T-6G)			In Tunisian markings.	RA
☐ North American NA-182 Texan (T-6G)			In Tunisian markings.	RA
☐ North American NA-182 Texan (T-6G)	Y61305		In Tunisian markings.	RA
☐ North American NA-182 Texan (T-6G)	F-AZEF	182-74	51-14387	RAC
☐ Schneider Grunau SG-38 (D.F.S. 108-14)			Frame only	RA
☐ Stampe & Vertongen S.V.4C	F-BIHK	158		RAC
☐ Sud-Ouest SO-4050 Vautour IIN	F-AZHP	116	348	RAA
☐ Zlin Z-326 Trener Master				RA

MUSÉE SOCIÉTÉ NATIONALE D'ÉTUDE ET DE CONSTRUCTION DE MOTEURS D'AVIATION (FRA140)

Address:	Rond Pont Reny Ravaud, Etablissement de Villaroche, 77550 Moissy-Cramayel.
Tel:	01 60 59 72 58
Fax:	01 60 59 74 05
Email:	musees@snecma.com
Admission:	By prior permission only.
Location:	About 8 km north of Melun on the D 57.

This company was formed in 1945 to take over the aero engine work of the former Gnome et Rhône, Lorraine and Renault firms. In 1985 the firm decided to dispose of some of its archives and a group of volunteers took care of the material. At the same time the Musée de l'Air was contacted and the loan of several engines produced by the company was arranged. The museum was formally set up in 1990 and is housed in an historic hangar. The building was first erected at St. Chamas on the Etang du Berre near Marseilles prior to World

War II. Landplanes and seaplanes used by the Gnome et Rhône flying schools were flown from the site. The structure was moved to Villaroche in 1947. During the summer of 1999 the museum was refurbished and the displays improved. A wide range of aero engines, including many Gnome et Rhône radials and modern jets, is on view along with models of the aircraft they powered. The development of the aero engine is portrayed in detail along with the history of the company. A replica Blériot XI was constructed by Ailes Anciennes at Le Bourget for the museum. The Emouchet was used to test small rocket motors. The Vautour was used by the then locally based C.E.V. for trials and joined the collection in 1988. The Ludion one man jet lift aircraft was developed for the army in the 1960's and testing stopped in 1968. This has recently been restored for the display.

TYPE	REG/SER	CON. NO.	PI/NOTES	STATUS
☐ Blériot XI (R)				PV
☐ Dassault Mirage IIIC	21	21	On loan from M.A.	PV
☐ Guerchais-Roche SA.104 Emouchet		224	F-WGGH, F-CCCC, F-CRHF	PV
☐ Sud SA.610A Ludion		003		PV
☐ Sud-Ouest SO-4050 Vautour IIN	337	85	On loan from M.A.	PV

78 YVELINES

ASSOCIATION ARCHAEOPTERIX (FRA141)

Address:	B.P. 3002, Route de Verneuil, 78133 Les Mureaux.
Admission:	By prior permission only.
Location:	About 2 km east of Meulan.

One of the former St. Yan based Alcyons is flown by this group. The aircraft served with the Government flying school from 1965 until the early 1980's after a period of military use.

TYPE	REG/SER	CON. NO.	PI/NOTES	STATUS
☐ Morane-Saulnier MS.733 Alcyon	F-BNEC	129	129	RAA

COLLECTION DE LA BASE AÉRIENNE DE VILLACOUBLAY (FRA142)

Address:	Base Aérienne 107, 78129 Villacoublay Air.
Tel:	01 45 07 31 07
Admission:	By prior permission only.
Location:	About 8 km east of Versailles off the D 57.

A transport unit which also carries out calibration duties and a helicopter squadron are based at the field. Currently in use are TBM.700s, Dassault Falcon 50s and 900s along with Airbus A.319s which are normally to be found at Orly. The base is also the headquarters for the northern area of the country.

TYPE	REG/SER	CON. NO.	PI/NOTES	STATUS
☐ Breguet / British Aircraft Corporation Jaguar A	A99	A99	Front fuselage only.	RA
☐ Dassault Falcon 20	49	49	F-RHFA	RA
☐ Morane-Saulnier MS.760A Paris I	113	113		RA
☐ Nord N.1101 Noralpha (Ramier I) [Messerschmitt Me 208]	111	111	111, F-BLTE	RA
☐ Sud-Est SE.3130 Alouette II	104	1161		RA

GROUPE D'ÉTUDES POUR L'AVIATION SPORTIVE (FRA143)

Address:	Aérodrome de Chavenay, 78450 Villepreux.
Tel:	01 30 56 15 27 or 01 34 62 30 66 (Club)
Fax:	01 34 62 46 13
Admission:	By prior permission only.
Location:	About 12 km north west of Versailles – north of les Clayes.

This group has its own hangar at Chavenay and maintains close links with the Aéro Club Jean Bertin. The original Caudron Cyclone was designed by Marcel Riffard who was responsible for many successful racing types. The C.760 was conceived as a lightweight fighter and two prototypes were flown. These are believed to have been burnt in 1940 to stop them being captured by the Germans. Jean Noan, a development engineer at the Bertin company, started researching the project in the early 1980s. Construction started in 1987 and it made its maiden flight in June 1998. The scale replica of the Cierva C.30 autogyro is nearing completion. The parasol wing MS.317 is one of a few remaining in club use in France. The design first flew in 1930 and over three hundred were built prior to World War II. The type was put back into production at the end of hostilities.

TYPE	REG/SER	CON. NO.	PI/NOTES	STATUS
☐ Aero 45	F-AZJX	4904	I-CRES, F-GFYA	RAC
☐ Caudron JN-760 Cyclone (R)	F-AZJY	01	F-WNJY	RAA
☐ Cierva C.30A (Scale R)				RA
☐ Colomban MC-15 Cri-Cri				RA
☐ Morane-Saulnier MS.317 (MS.315)	F-BGUZ	6560/306	306 – Aéro-Club Jean Bertin.	RAA
☐ Morane-Saulnier MS.505 Criquet (MS.502) [Fieseler Fi 156 Storch]	F-BARP	496/10	Aéro-Club Jean Bertin.	RAC
☐ Morane-Saulnier MS.505 Criquet (MS.502) [Fieseler Fi 156 Storch]	F-AZDV	591	F-BDHX, (F-BMHX)	RAC
☐ Nord N.1101 Noralpha (Ramier I) [Messerschmitt Me 208]	F-BLQU	136	136	RA
☐ Nord N.1203-VI Norécrin (N.1203-III)	F-BHTF	358		RAC
☐ Nord NC.858S (NC.853S)	F-BEZX	116		RA
☐ North American NA-182 Texan (T-6G)	F-AZEZ	182-361	51-14674,114674 (France)	RAA
☐ Piel CP.80 (Mod)	F-PIFY			RA
☐ Piper PA-18-95 Super Cub (L-18C)	F-BOUF	18-1476	51-15476, 15476 (France)	RAA
☐ Piper PA-18-135 Super Cub (L-21B)	F-GFPJ	18-3188	53-4788, L-114 (Belgium), OL-L01 (Belgium), OO-HBB, OO-WIK	
☐ Scottish Aviation Bulldog 120/121 (T.1)	F-AZOB	BH120/218	XX532	RAA
☐ Stampe & Vertongen S.V.4C	F-AZOM	1146	1146,F-BAOM	RAA

79 DEUX-SÈVRES

ASSOCIATION POUR LA SAUVEGARD ET LA PRESERVATION DU PATRIMOINE AÉRONAUTIQUE NIORTAIS (FRA144)

Address:	Avenue de Limoges, 79000 Niort.
Tel:	05 49 79 40 50
Email:	mc.brechbieh@wanadoo.fr
Admission:	By prior permission only.
Location:	At Souché Aerodrome which is about 4 km east of the town off the D.848.

This recently formed group has set up workshops at the local airfield. The aims of the association are to collect and restore vintage aircraft and to preserve the aeronautical heritage of the region. Two aircraft have been obtained on loan from the Étampes based Escadrille du Souvenir. The recently restored NC.858 was built as a NC.853 powered by a 75 h.p. Minié motor but was later re-engined with a 90 h.p. Continental C90 flat four. The prototype NC.850 flew in the late 1940s and one hundred NC.853s were ordered for club use.

TYPE	REG/SER	CON. NO.	PI/NOTES	STATUS
☐ Nord N.1101 Noralpha (Ramier I) [Messerschmitt Me 208]	F-AZYV	13	13, F-BYAV – on loan from E. du S.	RAA
☐ Nord N.3202B1B	F-AZJT	71	71, F-AZAD, F-WZBT, F-WZJT – on loan from E. du. S.	RAA
☐ Nord NC.858S (NC.853S)	F-PPAN	142	F-BBRP	RAA

MUSEÉ DE NIORT (FRA145)

Address:	Le Donjon, Rue Duguesclin, 79000 Niort.
Tel:	05 49 28 14 28
Admission:	Daily 0900-1200 1400-1800 (Closes at 1700 in winter)
Location:	In the centre of the town.

The cultural history of the region is portrayed in displays in the large keep. The building was started in the twelfth century and took many years to complete. On show are costumes, agricultural implements, early weapons, furniture, documents and photographs. The Flamant was recently moved to the museum.

TYPE	REG/SER	CON. NO.	PI/NOTES	STATUS
☐ Dassault MD-312 Flamant	240	240		PV

80 SOMME

AÉROCLUB DE PICARDIE – SECTION RÉTRO (FRA146)

Address:	L.P. 0202, Aérodrome de Glisy, 80002 Glisy.
Tel:	03 22 38 10 30
Fax:	03 22 38 12 53
Email:	contact@aeroclub-picardy-amiens.com
Admission:	By prior permission only.
Location:	About 8 km south easy of Amiens on the N 29.

This aero club maintains several classic aircraft and gliders in flying condition. The Carmam Foehn is a licence built version of the M.200 designed at the Turin Polytechnic. The Vasama is one of several designs to emerge from the Polytechnic Institute in Helsinki. One Piper Cub has been painted in World War II American colours. The single seat Super Javelot first flew in 1961 and about one hundred were built in the next eight years.

TYPE	REG/SER	CON. NO.	PI/NOTES	STATUS
☐ Carmam M.200 Foehn	F-CDHC	30		RAA
☐ Glasflügel H201B Standard Libelle	F-CELR	598		RAA
☐ Glasflügel H205 Libelle	F-CEQO	162		RAA
☐ Morane-Saulnier MS.893A Commodore 180	F-BTPD	11984		RAA
☐ Piper J-3C-65 Cub (L-4J)	F-BDTT	12488	44-80192	RAA
☐ Piper J-3C-65 Cub (L-4J)	F-BCPK	13147	45-4407	RAA
☐ Polyteknikkojen Ilmailukerho PIK-16c Vasama	F-CCPS	22	F-WCPS	RAA
☐ Schempp-Hirth Nimbus IID	F-CEDK	112		RAA
☐ Wassmer WA.22A Super Javelot	F-CCTO	101		RAA

L'EPOPÉE DE L'INDUSTRIE ET DE L'AÉRONAUTIQUE (FRA147)

Address:	16 Rue de l'Industrie. 80300 Albert.
Tel:	03 22 75 09 55
Fax:	03 22 74 66 89
Email:	betrancourt @wanadoo.fr
Admission:	By prior permission only.
Location:	Off the D 920 west of the town.

The owners of this engineering company are assembling a collection of aircraft, documents, models and components. A new building to house the smaller aircraft has been constructed with a painting of an Airbus A.320 prominent on the front wall. One of the Noratlas transports was formerly on show at the now closed Avrillé airfield at Angers and did not make the move to the new museum at Marcé. The Vampire was originally with the defunct Musée Aéronautique du Champagne at Brienne-le-Château. The Indian Air Force purchased five FB.52s from de Havillands in 1950. Hindustan Aircraft Industries then assembled thirty four from British components. These were followed by almost two hundred and fifty built under licence. The jet fighter was used in a number of local conflicts and remained in service until the early 1970s. More modern combat jets from a number of countries can be compared. For several years after World War II the United States Air Force had bases in France and F-84s and F-100s would have been familiar sights A number of airframes have come from the closed museum at Nancy and the there are plans to add more machines so that a range of French post war aircraft can be seen. Types flown by other European air forces have also arrived. A second hangar was completed in early 2000 and a third is now ready. The development of French aviation will be portrayed in the exhibition which also features several engines and propellers. A display of photographs, models and components along with weapons is being set up. The Mirage F.1C is a recent arrival and joins three earlier versions of the classic fighter. The flying aircraft operate from the airfield just south of the town. Also here is an active flying club with both powered aircraft and gliders in their fleet. Nearby to this field is the factory which produced Potez designs over the years. An example of the high wing classic Potez 36 can be seen suspended in the hall of the local railway station along with some photographs.

TYPE	REG/SER	CON. NO.	PI/NOTES	STATUS
☐ Agusta-Bell 47G	046	046		RA
☐ Canadair CL-30 Silver Star 3 (CT-133) [Lockheed 580 (T-33AN)]	21255	T33-255		RA
☐ Dassault MD-311 Flamant	260	260		RA
☐ Dassault MD-311 Flamant	275	275		RA
☐ Dassault MD-312 Flamant	F-WZXA	148	148	RA
☐ Dassault MD-312 Flamant	F-AZGE	158	158	RAA
☐ Dassault MD-450 Ouragan	8	8		RA
☐ Dassault Super Mystère B2	113	113		RA
☐ Dassault Mirage IIIC	'27'	32	32	RAX
☐ Dassault Mirage IIIE	515	515		RA
☐ Dassault Mirage IIIRD	358	358		RA
☐ Dassault Mirage F.1C	20	20		RA
☐ De Havilland D.H.100 Vampire FB.52	IB427		In Indian markings.	RA
☐ Douglas DC-3A-467 Skytrain (C-47B) (Dakota IV)	'2108979'	16004/32752	44-74260, KN379, 720, F-GEOA	RAX
☐ Fiat G.91R/3	30+93	91-357	KD+347, DG+110, MA+110	RA
☐ Fouga CM.170R Magister	6	6		RA
☐ Fouga CM.170R Magister	24	24		RA
☐ Guerchais-Roche SA.103 Emouchet	F-CRGJ	103	F-CBCQ – fuselage only.	RA
☐ Guerchais-Roche SA.103 Emouchet	F-CRHI	129	F-CARA	RA
☐ Guerchais-Roche SA.103 Emouchet		26		RA
☐ Hawker P.1099 Hunter F.58A (F.6) (FGA.9)	J-4107	S4U 3339	XF462, G-9-320 – in Swiss markings.	RA
☐ Lockheed 683-10-19 Starfighter (F-104G)	21+96	683-7065	KE+365, DC+250	RA
☐ Max Holste MH.1521M Broussard	F-BGGD	290	290, F-WGGD	RA
☐ Max Holste MH.1521M Broussard	F-GIFZ	315	315	RA
☐ Mikoyan-Gurevich MiG-21SPS (MiG-21PFM)	882	94A5207	In DDR markings.	RA
☐ Morane-Saulnier MS.506L Criquet (MS.502) [Fieseler Fi 156 Storch]	F-BDXM	635	635, F-BDHM, F-WDXM	RAA
☐ Morane-Saulnier MS.733 Alcyon	F-BKOY	44	44	RA
☐ Morane-Saulnier MS.733 Alcyon	F-BMQI	116	116	RA
☐ Morane-Saulnier MS.733 Alcyon	F-BLXT	131	131	RA
☐ Morane-Saulnier MS.733 Alcyon	F-AZKN	165	165	RAC
☐ Morane-Saulnier MS.733 Alcyon	173	173	173 – with wings of c/n 186.	RA
☐ Morane-Saulnier MS.880B Rallye Club	F-BKYD	289		RA
☐ Nord N.1101 Noralpha (Ramier I) [Messerschmitt Me 208]	F-BLYU	18	18	RAA
☐ Nord N.1101 Noralpha (Ramier I) [Messerschmitt Me 208]	F-BLQF	109	109	RA
☐ Nord N.1101 Noralpha (Ramier I) [Messerschmitt Me 208]	F-BLQY	112	112	RA
☐ Nord N.1101 Noralpha (Ramier I) [Messerschmitt Me 208]	F-BLQV	143	143	RA
☐ Nord N.1203-II Norécrin	F-BBET	334		RA
☐ Nord N.1300 [Schneider Grunau Baby IIB]	F-CRNT	24	F-CBVB	RA
☐ Nord N.2501 Noratlas	54	54		RA
☐ Nord N.2501 Noratlas	97	97		RA
☐ Nord N.2501 Noratlas	125	125		RA
☐ Nord N.2501 Noratlas	184	184		RA
☐ Nord N.2501 Noratlas	189	189		RA
☐ Nord N.3400	100	100		RA
☐ Nord N.3400	20	20		RA
☐ Nord NC.856A Norvigie	26	26		RAD
☐ Nord NC.856A Norvigie	108	108		RAD
☐ North American NA-224 Super Sabre (F-100D)	'42272'	224-1	55-2734	RAX
☐ Republic F-84F Thunderstreak	'28946'		53-6536, FU-76 (Belgium)	RAX
☐ Schleicher Ka-6 Rhönsegler		333	On loan from M.A.	RA
☐ Sikorsky S-55D Chickasaw (H-19D) (UH-19D)	55-3181	55901		RA
☐ Sikorsky S-58	'80'	SA-59	59	RAX
☐ Siren C.30 Edelweiss	F-CCUA	1		RA
☐ Sud-Est SE.210 Caravelle III	F-BHRY	61		RA
☐ Sud-Est SE.3130 Alouette II	65	1070		RA
☐ Sud-Ouest SO-1221 Djinn	144	94FR144		RA
☐ Wassmer WA.21 Javelot II	F-CCEU	30		RA
☐ Wassmer WA.30 Bijave		108		RA

MUSÉE DE FRÈRES CAUDRON (FRA148)

Address:	Rue Evoque, 80120 Rue.
Tel:	03 22 25 69 94
Fax:	03 22 25 76 26
Admission:	Daily 1030-1800.
Location:	In an old church in the centre of the town which is about 20 km north west of Abbeville on the D.938.

Gaston Caudron was born in 1882 in the village of Faviers near to Rue. His brother René entered the world in July 1884. They constructed their first biplane in 1908 and two years later set up a factory at Rue and a flying school at Crotoy. The museum housed in a former church in the town opened on November 11th 1976. On show are photographs, models, documents and artefacts tracing the work of the brothers.

82 TARN-ET-GARONNE

ASSOCIATION EPSILON (FRA149)

Address:	13 Allées Montarieu, 82000 Montauban.
Tel:	05 63 91 33 05
Admission:	By prior permission only.
Location:	At an airfield in the Montauban area.

This group was formed in the 1980s and was based at the now derelict private airfield at Escatalens. A number of aircraft have left the fleet and the remainder have now moved to Montauban. Two departures are a Farman F.404 which has been rebuilt at La Ferté Alais for the Museo del Aire in Spain and a Potez 36 which hangs in the booking hall of the railway station at Albert in northern France. Marcel Brochet built a number of prototypes in the late 1940s. The single seat MB.50 Pipistrelle was developed into the tandem two seat MB.60. Evolved from this was the MB.70 series which was built in small numbers. The similar MB.80 first flew in 1951 and only ten were constructed. The MB.83 was fitted with a 90 h.p. Continental engine which replaced the original 75 h.p. Minié. A few three seat MB.100s were also constructed.

TYPE	REG/SER	CON. NO.	PI/NOTES	STATUS
☐ Brochet MB.83 (MB.80)	F-BGLG	7	On loan from M.A.	RA
☐ Dassault MD-315R Flamant	41	41		RA
☐ Max Holste MH.1521M Broussard	F-GGLZ	102	102,	RAA
☐ Nord N.1203 Norécrin				RAC
☐ Nord N.1203 Norécrin				RA
☐ Nord N.3202	F-AZFL	92	92 – on loan from M.A.	RAA
☐ Nord N.3400	140	140		RA

COLLECTION DE LA BASE DE L'AVIATION LÉGÈRE DE L'ARMÉE DE TERRE DE MONTAUBAN (FRA150)

Address:	B.P.777, 82077 Montauban Cedex.
Tel:	05 63 21 72 94
Fax:	05 63 21 72 94
Admission:	By prior permission only.
Location:	In the eastern suburbs of the town.

A variety of tasks are carried out at the field including parachute training. A small number of Pilatus PC.6Bs are operated. The collection of preserved aircraft is located behind the high wall which surrounds the base. The airfield opened in 1931 and has been home to the local aero club since that date. The site is now surrounded on all sides by houses and business premises and moves have been made to close the field.

TYPE	REG/SER	CON. NO.	PI/NOTES	STATUS
☐ Max Holste MH.1521M Broussard	93	93		RA
☐ Nord N.3202	'16'			RAX
☐ Sud SA.341F Gazelle	1629	1629		RA
☐ Sud-Est SE.3130 Alouette II	2145	2145		RA
☐ Sud-Ouest SO-1221 Djinn				RA

83 VAR

ASSOCIATION VAROISE AVIONS DE COLLECTION (FRA151)

Address:	L'Oustalet-les-Senes, 83210 Solliespont.
Tel:	04 94 33 53 24
Admission:	By prior permission only.
Location:	At Cuers-Pierrefeu airfield which is off the D14 about 5 km east of the town.

A mixture of static and active aircraft are owned by this group which has constructed a hangar/workshop to restore the airframes and engines. A Vampire arrived from Switzerland in 1991 and a Hunter followed five years later. The latter has since been sold in North America. Other types have left the collection including a Dassault Etendard, a Canadair CT-133 along with a Fouga Magister and a Zéphyr.

TYPE	REG/SER	CON. NO.	PI/NOTES	STATUS
☐ Dassault Mirage IIIE	440	440		RA
☐ De Havilland D.H.100 Vampire FB.6	F-AZHJ	668	J-1159 (Switzerland)	RAA
☐ Max Holste MH.1521C-1 Broussard (1521M)	F-GHGB	256	256	RAA
☐ Max Holste MH.1521M Broussard	251	251		RA

BREGUET HISTORIQUE CLUB (FRA152)

Address:	Route de Fréjus, 83440 Fayence.
Tel:	04 94 76 17 90
Fax:	04 94 76 13 87
Admission:	By prior permission only.
Location:	The airfield is 3 km south of the town off the D 562.

This recently formed organisation is based at the large glider field at Fayence. The Breguet company designed the 900 in the late 1940s and one of the five built flew in the 1952 World Championships which were held in Spain. In 1950 they decided to produce more advanced models capable of winning competitions. The 901 made its maiden flight in March 1954 at Toulouse-Lasbordes This type made its first championship appearance in the 1954 World contest at Camphill in England where Gérard Pierre flew it to victory. In total thirty five examples were built. The 902 was designed for training and made its maiden flight in 1957. Only two prototypes were completed. The design was one of several considered as a replacement for the Caudron C.800 in club use. The 905 Fauvette, constructed at Aire-sur-Adour, first flew on April 15th 1958. A production run of fifty was laid down and these were delivered to clubs and private owners over the next few months. The final product of the sailplane department, before it was closed down, was the sole prototype of the 906 Choucas. One aim of the group is to set up an exhibition tracing this part of the history of the famous company. One now fairly rare type under rebuild is the Hans Jacobs designed Weihe. French forces found many sailplanes in Germany after World War II and almost four hundred were taken back to France to restart the gliding movement. About a dozen Weihes were definitely acquired in this manner. Two early Avia types are prized acquisitions and these should soon be capable of flight. The Fauvel AV.361 is one of a small number of the AV.36 constructed by amateur builders.

TYPE	REG/SER	CON. NO.	PI/NOTES	STATUS
☐ Arsenal Air 100	F-CBHD	13		RAA
☐ Avia 11A				RAC
☐ Avia 152A				RAC
☐ Breguet 901S Mouette	F-CCCL	9		RAA
☐ Breguet 901S1 Mouette	F-CCGF	35		RAC
☐ Breguet 902	F-CCDR	02		RAC
☐ Breguet 905PS Fauvette	OO-ZIP	1		RAD
☐ Breguet 905S Fauvette				RAC
☐ Castel C.25S				RAC
☐ Castel C.301S	F-CRMN	1173	F-CBPE	RA
☐ Caudron C.800 Épervier	F-CBOL	9872/212		RA
☐ Caudron C.800 Épervier	F-CAFD	9935/275		RAC
☐ Centre Aéronautique Beynes KBK.10	F-CCAS	02		RA
☐ Fauvel AV.361	F-CRQX	323		RAA
☐ Guerchais-Roche SA.104 Emouchet	F-CRRN	233	F-CBJH, F-CRNJ	RAA
☐ Jacobs Weihe (D.F.S. 108-68)				RAC
☐ Nord N.1300 [Schneider Grunau Baby IIB]	F-CRNR	65	F-CAAN	RAA
☐ Rocheteau-Scheibe CRA.60	F-CDNT	05		RAA
☐ Schleicher Ka-6E Rhönsegler				RAC
☐ Siren C.30S Edelweiss	F-CDGG	48		RAA
☐ Wassmer WA.22A Super Javelot	F-CACJ	143	143	RAC
☐ Wassmer WA.22A Super Javelot	F-CAIR	145	145	RA
☐ Wassmer WA.30 Bijave	F-CDJQ	220		RAA

COLLECTION DE LA BASE AÉRONAVALE D'HYÈRES (FRA153)

Address:	Chemin Palyvestre, 83400 Hyères.
Tel:	04 94 12 45 00
Admission:	By prior permission only.
Location:	About 4 km south of the town off the D.97.

Flying from the field first took place in 1912 but it was ten years before any hangars were built. The site became a military base in 1925 and has been used by naval units for most of the last eighty years. Until recently fighter units were in residence but now the site is home to helicopter squadrons.

TYPE	REG/SER	CON. NO.	PI/NOTES	STATUS
☐ Breguet 1050 Alizé	48	48		RA
☐ Dassault Etendard IVM	13	13		RA
☐ Dassault Etendard IVM	36	36		RA
☐ Sikorsky S-58	183	SA-183		RA

COLLECTION DE LA BASE DE L'AVIATION LÉGÈRE DE L'ARMEÉ DE TERRE LE LUC (FRA154)

Address:	3 École Alphonse Dudet, 83340 Le Luc Cannet.
Tel:	04 98 11 72 45
Fax:	04 98 11 74 98
Admission:	By prior permission only.
Location:	About 5 km east of the town off the D.17.

The airfield is now home to a large advanced training school for helicopter crews. After gaining their wings at Dax the successful pilots move to Le Luc to learn to fly under operational conditions. A number of fields in the locality are used for training. The preserved Broussard recently moved from the museum at Dax. The three helicopters represent types which have flown from the field in recent years.

TYPE	REG/SER	CON. NO.	PI/NOTES	STATUS
☐ Max Holste MH.1521M Broussard	281	281		RA
☐ Sud SA.341F Gazelle	1703	1703		RA
☐ Sud-Est SE.3130 Alouette II	2066	2066		RA
☐ Vertol V.43 (H-21C)	FR-107	FR-107		RA

MUSÉE CASTEL-MAUBOUSSIN (FRA155)

Address:	Les Frais Ombruges, Traverse du 5éme Moulin, 83200 Toulon.
Admission:	By prior permission only.
Location:	At Cuers-Pierrefeu airfield which is about 5 km east of the town off the D 114.

Robert Castello was born in Spain in 1906 and moved to France five years later. He joined the Dewoitine company in 1922 and was involved in the production of several successful types. He designed a number of gliders in the 1930s and during this period he met Pierre Mauboussin who had built a range of light aircraft. After World War II the pair set up a factory at Aire-sur-Adour and their company was part of the Fouga empire. Gliders were produced along with developments powered by small jet engines. The C.25S flew in prototype form in 1942 during the occupation. Fouga built one hundred examples from 1948 and another seven were assembled from unused components in 1950. The C.301S also made its maiden flight in World War II when it took to the air in 1940. Subsequently over three hundred were constructed by Fouga and SNCAN for club and military use. A number of jet powered sailplanes, developed in the late 1940s and early 1950s, eventually led to the successful Magister trainer which served with air forces around the world. An example of the naval version, the Zéphyr, is in store for the museum and a Magister is being sought. A group of enthusiasts set up this museum to honour the work of the two designers. The exhibition hall contains a reconstruction of Castello's design office and displays tracing the history of Castel-Mauboussin aircraft and the airfield at Cuers have been set up. The French Navy have a base on the field and a unit operating training and communications aircraft is currently in residence. Two Peyret-Mauboussin XIs high wing cabin monoplanes were built and in 1931/2 the second one carried out long distance return flights from Paris to Madagascar and Paris to Saigon. The record breaking machine has been acquired but unfortunately it lacks wings. A great deal of work is needed on the fuselage which has suffered after years in store. Gliders from other manufacturers have been obtained to show the similarities in construction of machines of the period. There are not many early Mauboussin types left and a Corsaire is high on the museum's wants list. The Stampe was built from spares in the late 1990s. This biplane, owned by one of the members of the museum, is often at the nearby airfield of La Mole.

TYPE	REG/SER	CON. NO.	PI/NOTES	STATUS
☐ Castel C.25S	F-CRQO	126	F-CBJL	RA
☐ Castel C.301S				RA
☐ Castel C.301S				RA
☐ Caudron C.800 Épervier				RA
☐ Fouga CM.175 Zéphyr	12	12		RA
☐ Nord N.2501 Noratlas			Front fuselage only.	RA
☐ Nord N.1300 [Schneider Grunau Baby IIB]				RA
☐ Nord N.2000 [Jacobs Meise]				RA
☐ Nord N.2000 [Jacobs Meise]	F-CBGE	10378/48		RA
☐ Peyret-Mauboussin XI	F-AJUL	02	Less wings.	RA
☐ Stampe & Vertongen S.V.4B	F-AZLD	01-97		RAA
☐ Wassmer WA.30 Bijave	F-CCMR	20		RA
☐ Wassmer WA.30 Bijave	F-CCYJ	107		RA

MUSÉE DU SOUVENIR (FRA156)

Address:	ZA Bégude 83440 Seillens.
Tel:	04 94 84 77 93
Fax:	04 94 84 77 93
Email:	harle.sc@wanadoo.fr
Admission:	February-November daily 1400-1800
Location:	About 7 km south of Fayence on the D562.

The story of the liberation of Provence is told in the informative displays. The area saw fierce fighting in the mountainous terrain and this is highlighted in the exhibition. Also featured are the landings which took place on the coasts and the bravery of the local resistance. On show are military vehicles, armoured personnel carriers, uniforms, weapons, badges, documents and photographs and many personal items of memorabilia. There are many maps of the local conflicts. The Fouga Magister is inside the building.

TYPE	REG/SER	CON. NO.	PI/NOTES	STATUS
☐ Fouga CM.170R Magister	166	166		PV

84 VAUCLUSE

ASSOCIATION FRANCAISE D'AVIONS HISTORIQUE (FRA157)

Address:	Aérodrome d'Avignon-Caumont. 84140 Montfaret.
Tel:	04 94 90 71 77
Fax:	04 94 90 60 88
Admission:	By prior permission only
Location:	About 40 km east of Marseille on the N 8.

An interesting collection of warbirds was set up at Le Castellet in the 1990s but has now moved to Avignon. The Vought Corsair served with the Argentinean Navy from 1957 until the late 1960s. The fighter was then put on show in Buenos Aires before being sold to France in the early 1990s. The Cessna Dragonfly was operated by the Vietnamese Air Force and was one of a batch which arrived at La Ferte Alais in 1990. The Fouga CM.175 is a naval version of the Magister and thirty were used in France from 1960 until the mid-1990s. The Djinn helicopter featured rotor tip propulsion with nozzles expelling compressed air from an engine in the fuselage.

TYPE	REG/SER	CON. NO.	PI/NOTES	STATUS
☐ Cessna 318E Dragonfly (A-37B)	87958	43105	68-7958 – in Vietnamese markings.	RAC
☐ Douglas AD-4NA Skyraider (AD-4N)	F-AZHK	7802	Bu127002, 61 (France), 127002 (Gabon), (N91989)	RAA
☐ Fouga CM.175 Zéphyr	F-AZPF	28	28, F-WQCF	RAA
☐ Sud-Ouest SO-1221 Djinn	F-BIEV	1019/FR58	PB+158, PB+120	RAA
☐ Vought F4U-7 Corsair (F4U-5NL)	F-AZYS		Bu124541, 0433 (Argentina), 490	RAA

COLLECTION DE LA BASE AÉRIENNE D'ORANGE (FRA158)

Address:	Base Aérienne 115, 84871 Orange Cedex.
Tel:	04 90 11 06 26
Fax:	04 90 51 02 48
Location:	About 3 km east of the town off the D 975.
Admission:	By prior permission only.

This important base has been home to fighter units for many years and is currently used by Mirage 2000 squadrons. The 5th Fighter Wing was formed at the base in March 1951 from the old Groupement de Chasse 5 which had flown many types of piston engined fighters over the years. The new unit was first equipped with the Vampire and its French built version the Mistral. The Mystère IIC arrived in 1956 and the IVA version two years later. The Super Mystère B2 was used for a period until the wing converted to the Mirage IIIC in 1968. The Mirage F.1C was put into service in 1974 and was flown for several years. The identities of the preserved aircraft are in doubt as some carry the serials of crashed machines. There is a traditions room in the headquarters area where photographs, uniforms, documents and memorabilia are on view. Discussions are taking place as to whether the airfield will remain as an operational base so the future of the collection is uncertain.

TYPE	REG/SER	CON. NO.	PI/NOTES	STATUS
☐ Dassault MD-452C Mystère IIC	143	143		RA
☐ Dassault Mystère IVA	'68'	89	89	RAX
☐ Dassault Super Mystère B2	121	121	May be 127.	RA
☐ Dassault Mirage IIIC	38	38		RA
☐ Dassault Mirage IVA	37	37		RA
☐ De Havilland D.H.100 Vampire F.6	'10035'	633	J-1124 (Swiss)	RAX

LES AMIS DE LA 5ÈME ESCADRE (FRA159)

Address:	Zone Industrielle Sud, Avenue les Pays Bas, 84100 Orange.
Tel:	04 90 34 59 06
Fax:	04 90 34 94 10
Admission:	By prior permission only.
Location:	At Aviomodeli on the south east side of the town off the N 7.

The 5th Fighter Wing was formed at Orange on March 31st 1951 from the earlier 5th Group. The unit is still based at the airfield and operates the Mirage 2000 but the field may close in the near future. A group of former members of the unit set up this organisation to preserve its history and traditions. A collection of aircraft has been obtained and they are all stored in the grounds of a factory on the southern industrial estate. The first machine flown by EC.5 was the Vampire and a former Swiss Air Force machine has been acquired. The types which replaced it in service have also joined the display. A small number of Broussards and Magisters were used on liaison and training duties. The Czechoslovakian Air Force MiG-21F-13 was delivered in the late 1990s. The MiG-21PFM, was for a time, in the now closed Lafayette War Museum located on the other side of the town. The Hunter also arrived at this time. This aircraft was stored at Payerne for a period after it was withdrawn from use. Two ex-Swiss Vampires, a Dutch Alouette III and an Italian Fiat G.91 represent types which have visited the airfield. The Vautour is on loan from the Musée de l'Air. An archive containing photographs, documents, models and uniforms tracing the history of the unit is being assembled.

TYPE	REG/SER	CON. NO.	PI/NOTES	STATUS
☐ Dassault Etendard IVM	37	37		RA
☐ Dassault MD-452C Mystère IIC	52	52		RA
☐ Dassault Mystère IVA	28	28		RA
☐ Dassault Super Mystère B2	53	53		RA
☐ Dassault Super Mystère B2	73	73		RA
☐ Dassault Mirage IIIB	222	222		RA
☐ Dassault Mirage IIIB	241	241		RA
☐ Dassault Mirage IIIE	526	526		RA
☐ Dassault Mirage IIIRD	363	363		RA
☐ De Havilland D.H.100 Vampire FB.6	J-1183	692	In Swiss markings.	RA
☐ De Havilland D.H.115 Vampire T.55	U-1227	987	In Swiss markings.	RA
☐ Fiat G.91R/1	MM6283	49	Front fuselage from c/n 170 MM6306.	RA
☐ Fouga CM.170R Magister	350	350		RA
☐ Fouga CM.170R Magister	409	409		RA
☐ Hawker P.1099 Hunter F.58	J-4063	41H/697430	In Swiss markings.	RA
☐ Max Holste MH.1521M Broussard	5	5	5, F-GIBF	RA
☐ Mikoyan-Gurevich MiG-21F-13	0906	960906	In Czech markings.	RA
☐ Mikoyan-Gurevich MiG-21PFM	4406	94A4406	In Czech markings.	RA
☐ Nord N.1101 Ramier I [Messerschmitt Me 208]	197	197		RA
☐ Sud-Est SE.3160 Alouette III	A-267	1267	In Dutch markings.	RA
☐ Sud-Ouest SO-4050 Vautour IIN	358	128	On loan from M.A.	RA

85 VENDÉE

MUSÉE HISTORIAL DE LA VENDÉE (FRA160)

Address:	85170 Les Lucs-sur-Boulogne.
Tel:	02 51 44 28 10
Email:	conservation.musee@vendee.fr
Admission:	Opening in 2006.
Location:	In the town.

This new museum with its stunning architecture is located on the banks of the River Boulogne. The large halls have been covered with a grass roof to blend in with the landscape. The displays are being arranged to cover the history, art, culture and archaeology of the region. A Gazelle helicopter has been delivered from Dax.

TYPE	REG/SER	CON. NO.	PI/NOTES	STATUS
☐ Sud SA.341F Gazelle	1193	1193		PV

86 VIENNE

MUSÉE DE L'ART POPULAIRE CHEZ MANUEL (FRA161)

Address:	Route Nationale 10, 86000 Poitiers.
Tel:	05 49 52 70 05
Admission:	Daily 0900-1900.
Location:	About 3 km north of the town on the N 10.

The late Manuel Ribiero opened a museum in the centre of Poitiers many years ago. As more items were acquired he purchased a site on the outskirts of the city and constructed exhibition halls. The buildings are crammed with objects. Stuffed animals, furniture, clothing, kitchen and household equipment, musical instruments, vintage and modern cars, motorcycles and farm implements are just a few of the items to be found.

TYPE	REG/SER	CON. NO.	PI/NOTES	STATUS
☐ Nord N.1203 Norécrin	F-BBKX	57		PV
☐ Sikorsky S-58	142	SA-142		PV

87 HAUTE-VIENNE

ASSOCIATION LES AILES LIMOUSINE (FRA162)

Address:	Aéroport International, 87100 Limoges.
Email:	joel-grose@wanadoo.fr
Admission:	By prior permission only.
Location:	About 10 km north west of the city off the D.20.

This recently formed group aims to set up a museum of flying aircraft at the airport. The Couyaud was built at Limoges in the mid-1950s. The design was a parasol wing single seater initially powered by a Salmson radial. The aircraft was inactive for many years but was restored in the early 1990s. The pre-war Leopoldoff biplane was rebuilt at Royan in 1956 and flown for six years before being put into storage. It was restored in the mid-1980s and took to the air again in 1988. The Kaydet was built from spares by Salis Aviation.

TYPE	REG/SER	CON. NO.	PI/NOTES	STATUS
☐ Boeing-Stearman A75N1 Kaydet (PT-17)	F-AZGJ	'75-SA28'		RAA
☐ Couyaud GC-01	F-PHFG	01		RAA
☐ Leopoldoff L.4 (L.3)	F-PHQG	24	F-APZN	RAA
☐ Max Holste MH.1521C Broussard	F-GJLT	44C	F-BJLT	RAA
☐ Max Holste MH.1521C-1 Broussard (1521M)	F-GGGK	127	127, F-WGGK	RAA
☐ Max Holste MH.1521M Broussard	F-GFMN	86	86	RAC
☐ Morane-Saulnier MS.733 Alcyon				RAA
☐ Morane-Saulnier MS.733 Alcyon	F-AZSA	149	149,F-BMQK,F-GIQK	RAA
☐ Piel CP.301C Emeraude				RAC

COLLECTION NUVILLE (FRA163)

Address:	Le Ponteix, 87220 Feytiat.
Tel:	05 55 30 79 37
Admission:	By prior permission only.
Location:	At a private airfield.

The P.1 all metal high performance sailplane with fabric covering on part of the wing and tail was first flown in 1941. The glider was part of the French team which went to the U.S. National Championships in 1947. The major airframe components have survived and hopefully this rarity will be rebuilt. The SG-38 is from the large batch of gliders acquired by the French when they moved into Germany in 1945. Jacques Nuville obtained the Colomban Cri-Cri after a crash at Rocamadour and it is now flying again.

TYPE	REG/SER	CON. NO.	PI/NOTES	STATUS
☐ Castel C.310P	F-CRDC	138	F-CAOK	RA
☐ Colomban MC-15 Cri-Cri	F-PYKO	08		RAA
☐ Schneider Grunau SG-38 (D.F.S. 108-14)	F-AZBJ	19	F-CRRK, F-WRRK	RAA
☐ Sud-Ouest P.1	F-WDVD (?)		Parts only	RA

MUSÉE DE LA RÉSISTANCE ET DE LA DÉPORTATION HENRI CHADOURNE (FRA164)

Address:	Musée Municipal de l'Eveche, Place de la Cathedrale, 87100 Limoges.
Tel:	05 55 45 63 40
Admission:	July-mid September daily 1000-1145 1400- 1800; mid-September-mid June Wednesday-Monday 1400-1700; (last two weeks in June open Tuesday 1400-1700)
Location:	In the centre of the city.

The Ariete first flew in 1941 and entered service the following year. About seven hundred were completed. In 1943 forty examples were built for the Luftwaffe and flown on missions against the French Resistance. One crashed in the Limoges area on June 16th 1944 and from 1947 to 1976 the remains of the fuselage were on show in the Eveche gardens in the city. A decision was made to set up a museum tracing the history of the resistance movement and the fuselage was taken to Romanet Air Force Base. Here over four thousand hours were spent restoring it to its 1944 colours. In June 1986 the Ariete was placed on show in the museum which portrays the struggle of the fighters of the region to harass the occupying forces. Many harrowing tales are told of the capture, torture and deportation of the local maquis.

TYPE	REG/SER	CON. NO.	PI/NOTES	STATUS
☐ Caproni-Reggiane Re.2002 Ariete	'OV+BI'	1256		PVX

88 VOSGES

MUSÉE PIERRE-NOËL (FRA165)

Address:	Place George Tremouille, 88100 St. Die.
Tel:	03 29 51 60 35
Fax:	03 29 51 60 41
Email:	musee.pierre.noel@ville-saintdie.fr
Admission:	Wednesday 1000-1200 1400-1900; Thursday-Sunday 1400-1900. (Closes at 1700 October-April)
Location:	In the centre of the town.

Housed in a former episcopal palace, the displays at this museum trace all aspects of life in the region. There is an excellent archaeological section with many items recovered in the area. The city was badly damaged in World War II and Le Corbusier's models for the rebuilding programme are highlighted. The military section highlights the two world wars. Local World War I ace René Fonck is featured in a special exhibition. Born in March 1894 he first served with Army and later learned to fly. He did not become a fighter pilot until 1917 but he managed to shoot down seventy five enemy aircraft before the end of the conflict. He normally flew a SPAD VII. In the World War II area there is the airframe of a D.F.S. 230 troop carrying glider.

TYPE	REG/SER	CON. NO.	PI/NOTES	STATUS
☐ Jacobs D.F.S. 230C-1			Fuselage frame only.	PVD

PARC DU CHÂTEAU (FRA166)

Address:	54 Rue St. Michel, 88000 Epinal.
Tel:	03 29 82 53 22
Admission:	Normally during working hours.
Location:	In the eastern part of the town.

The Château was built in the thirteenth century and destroyed in 1670. The site has been opened as a tourist attraction with the ruins, a formal garden and a zoo. The Magister arrived from Châteaudun.

TYPE	REG/SER	CON. NO.	PI/NOTES	STATUS
☐ Fouga CM.170R Magister	443	443		PV

89 YONNE

CENTRE DE PLANEURS SENONAIS (FRA167)

Address:	Aérodrome de Pont sur Yonne, 89140 Gisy les Nobles.
Tel:	03 86 67 13 09
Email:	cps@planeur.sens.com
Admission:	By prior permission only.
Location:	About 10 km north of Sens on the D53.

The area has along tradition in gliding as the fifteenth French championships were held on a nearby farm in September 1930. The group is part of the Dédale organisation which co-ordinates the vintage gliding movement. An example of the M.200S built under licence in France from an Italian design is in the fleet. Under restoration is one of the Jacobs Weihe sailplanes built under licence by Victor Minié Aviation at St. Cyr in the early 1950s. Research now suggests that many of the completed airframes were in fact repaired German examples retrieved at the end of the war or built up from components.

TYPE	REG/SER	CON. NO.	PI/NOTES	STATUS
☐ Avialsa-Scheibe A.60 Fauconnet [L-Spatz 55]	F-CDGN	12K		RAA
☐ Carmam M.200 Foehn	F-CDDU	26		RAA
☐ Grob G.103 Twin Astir	F-CFBN	3158		RAA
☐ Morane-Saulnier MS.893A Commodore 180	F-BPMB	10755		RAA
☐ Piper PA-25-235 Pawnee C	F-GHTQ	25-5074	N8637L	RAA
☐ Scheibe SF-25C Falke	F-CAQX	4004	D-KAAM, F-WAQX	RAA
☐ Silimon IS 28B-2	F-CACN	224		RAA
☐ Victor Minié V.M.A. 200 Milan [Jacobs Weihe]	F-CBGM	28		RAC

MUSÉE AUTOMOBILE ET DE L'ATTELAGE D'ANCY LE FRANC (FRA168)

Address:	Le Château, 89160 Ancy le Franc.
Tel:	03 86 75 14 63
Fax:	03 86 75 10 30
Email:	Informatio@chateau-ancy.com
Admission:	April-October Daily 1000-1200 1400-1800.
Location:	On the D 905 on the east side of the town which is about 15 km south east of Tonnerre.

The château was constructed between 1546 and 1622 and houses many period relics. A major restoration programme has been started on the whole building. The outbuildings contain a range of bicycles, cars, carriages, motor cycles and farm vehicles. Around thirty cars dating from the early period can be seen and there is a collection of components and posters. A range of farm implements from hand tools to mechanical trashing machines is also on show. The sole aircraft is the locally built Pou-du-Ciel constructed in the mid-1930s and stored for many years. The aircraft is believed to have flown a few times.

TYPE	REG/SER	CON. NO.	PI/NOTES	STATUS
☐ Mignet HM-14 Pou-du-Ciel				PV

MUSÉE DE LA GUERRE 1939-1945 (FRA169)

Address:	Les Vernes, 89240 Pourrain.
Tel:	03 86 41 13 27
Admission:	Daily 0900-1200 1400-1800.
Location:	On the D 905 just west of the town which is about 15 km south west of Auxerre.

John Sontrop set up this museum several years ago. On show is a vast amount of material from the conflict. Uniforms, documents, weapons and posters can be seen, The aeronautical section has engines, instruments, propellers as well as relics recovered from crash sites. A unique item is a Pendelkasten periscope gun sight from a Junkers Ju 288 or Ju 388 and this is the only one of its type in Europe. On show in the courtyard is a Nord Norécrin modified to represent a typical World War II type. A false radial cowling and a tailwheel have been fitted. There are also a number of military vehicles outside the main building.

TYPE	REG/SER	CON. NO.	PI/NOTES	STATUS
☐ Fieseler Fi 103A-1 (FSM)				PV
☐ Nord N.1203 Norécrin		38	F-BEBH	PVX

91 ESSONNE

AMICALE ERIC NESSLER (FRA170)

Address:	Aérodrome de Cerny, 91590 La Ferté Alais.
Tel:	01 60 15 09 91
Fax:	01 60 15 09 91
Admission:	When the airfield is open – with the permission of Jean Salis.
Location:	The airfield is off the N.449 about 2 km north of the town which is about 40 km south of Paris.

In the 1930s Eric Nessler, Raymond Jarlaud and Pierre Massenet set up the Avia company. They first built training gliders but later several high performance sailplanes were produced. Nessler set many French records in the Avia 41P and in the smaller production 40P of which twenty were built between 1935 and 1945. The group was formed in the 1980 to honour the famous pilot and it now has its own hangar at La Ferté Alais. A collection of classic post-war French gliders has been obtained and several are under restoration. Fairly recent arrivals are the fuselages of two French built British Aircraft Company Drones. The pair had been stored with various groups at La Ferté Alais and Étampes for the last forty or so years. The H-3 was registered to in 1945 and is probably one of the unfinished pre-war examples stored during the conflict. Champagne Air Services at Reims obtained a permit to fly for it in 1950. The origin of the other airframe is unknown.

TYPE	REG/SER	CON. NO.	PI/NOTES	STATUS
☐ Arsenal Air 100	F-CABO	4		RA
☐ Arsenal Air 100	F-CBHC	11		RA
☐ Breguet 904S Nymphale	F-CCFM	3		RA
☐ Castel C.310P	F-CRGU	156	F-CBQF	RAC
☐ Caudron C.800 Épervier	F-CBAO	9991/331	331	RA
☐ Nord N.1300 [Schneider Grunau Baby IIB]	F-CBFE	50	F-CBFE, F-CRMC	RA
☐ Nord N.1300 [Schneider Grunau Baby IIB]	F-CRPG	163	F-CANS	RA
☐ Scheibe SF-28A Tandem Falke	F-CCJY	5763	D-KACP	RAA
☐ Société Française d'Aviation Nouvelle SFAN 2 [British Aircraft Company Drone]			Fuselage only.	RAD
☐ Société Française d'Aviation Nouvelle SFAN H-3 [British Aircraft Company Drone]	F-WBTE	01	Fuselage only.	RAD
☐ Trucavaysse GEP TCV 03	F-CRRH	1/03		RAA

AMICALE JEAN-BAPTISTE SALIS (FRA171)

Address:	Aérodrome de Cernay, 91590 La Ferté Alais.
Tel:	01 64 57 55 85
Fax:	01 64 57 44 87
Email:	bureau@ajbs.com
Admission:	Saturday-Sunday 1430-1700 (Closes at 1800 in summer.
Location:	Off the N.449 about 2 km north of the town which is about 40km south of Paris.

Jean-Baptiste Salis was born in 1896 and when he was sixteen he took a flying course at Aulnat. He served as an instructor during World War I and then used part of his gratuity to purchase some aircraft. He started restoring these to flying condition. He had a distinguished career which included establishing the first airfields in the Alps, the first flight over Mont Blanc and participating in setting up Toussus-le-Noble airfield. In 1937 he bought the Plateau d'Ardenay set on a hill top above La Ferté Alais. The woodland was cleared and a hangar, workshops and two grass runways were constructed along with a house. At the outbreak of World War II there were over thirty aircraft in the collection but during the German occupation some were confiscated and others broken up. When peace returned he was employed restoring aircraft for the Musée de l'Air and in his spare time he built replicas for films and museums. He started collecting again and scoured France for the remains of airframes hidden during the conflict. In the early 1950s he acquired the remains of a Blériot XI. This was restored and flown across the English Channel in 1954 and 1959 to commemorate the forty fifth and fiftieth anniversary of the pioneer's epic journey. A government gliding school was set up on the field in the 1950s and several modern hangars were constructed. In the Salis area many airframes, components and rotary engines were stored. Several aircraft were restored and some were sold to the U.S.A. Jean-Baptiste died in 1967 and the running of the collection was taken over by his son Jean. The gliding school moved out in 1972 and expansion of the collection began. Aircraft were acquired from all over the country and soon Jean realised that the task was too big for the family. The Amicale Aéronautique de La Ferté Alais was set up in 1972 and the present name was adopted four years later. Many of the stored aircraft were restored to flying condition and replicas were built for film and television work. There was not enough room for all the fleet so hangarage was obtained at nearby Étampes. A large museum hangar was constructed in the early 1980s and this has been gradually enlarged. Built in 1990s a line of new hangars now houses many of the privately owned aircraft based at the field. An air show is staged every Whitsun and many unique formations delight visitors. Deals with museums and collections across the world have resulted in many interesting aircraft arriving at La Ferté Alais. A Polikarpov Po-2 was obtained from the Yugoslav Aeronatical Museum in return for a Nieuport XI replica. A Breguet XIVP replica can be seen in the Thai Air Force Museum and a Grumman Bearcat came to France. This American fighter is now in California. In the mid-1980s over thirty Czechoslovakian built Yak-11s and a few Yak-18s were purchased from the Egyptian Air Force and most of these are now flying in both

Europe and the U.S.A. Many replicas have been built from scratch but several ingenious conversions have also appeared. Two Albatros C IIs were constructed from Tiger Moth airframes, a pair of Salmson 2A2s originated from Caudron Lucioles and a Noorduyn Norseman was converted to a Latécoère 17P. Some of the Texans have appeared as Grumman Hellcats and Mitsubishi Zeros for film work and two are currently flying as North American NA-68s. Many airframes are still in store and it is almost impossible to produce a totally accurate list of the Amicale, Salis family and privately owned aircraft. The one below will hopefully give the visitor an idea of what many be seen but several are stored in inaccessible areas.

TYPE	REG/SER	CON. NO.	PI/NOTES	STATUS
☐ Abraham AS-2 Iris	F-PBFV	01	F-ALHH	RAD
☐ Aeronca 11AC Chief	F-PACF	11AC-1602	OO-TWT	PVA
☐ Agusta-Bell 47G	F-BNFB	094	094	PV
☐ Albatros C II (R)	F-AZAV	005	F-WZBH – with D.H.82A parts.	PVA
☐ Alexandre-Dewoitine D.501 (Mauboussin M.129/48) (Mauboussin-Beaujard M.130)	F-PRJD	01	F-BCIZ, F-PCIZ, F-WRJD – original c/n 226.	PVA
☐ Antonov An-2T	F-AZHM	17347311	453 (DDR), DDR-SKH, D-FONH	RAD
☐ Auster J/1 Autocrat	F-BDAK	2213	VP-YHG	RAD
☐ Beech E18S	F-AZEJ	BA-359	N23J, F-BTCS	PVA
☐ Beech V35 Bonanza	F-BOSI	D-8462		PVA
☐ Bell 47G-3	F-WIPA	01		PV
☐ Blériot XI (R)	F-AZBA	1	F-WERV, F-PERV	PVA
☐ Blériot XI-2	F-AZPG	SA-29		PVA
☐ Boeing-Stearman B75N1 Kaydet (N2S-3)	F-AZGR	75-2650	Bu4320, N62418	PVA
☐ Boeing-Stearman E75 Kaydet (PT-13D)	F-AZJR	75-5656	42-17493, N5358N, (F-AZJS), F-AZJR, 'F-AEIN'	PVA
☐ Boeing-Stearman E75 L Kaydet (E-75) (PT-13D)	F-AZMZ	75-SA98	(USAAF)	PVA
☐ Breguet 14P (R)	F-AZBP	02		PV
☐ Brochet MB.72				RA
☐ Bücker Bü 131B Jungmann	F-AZBU	83	A-70 (Switzerland), HB-UTS, F-BOHF	PVA
☐ Bücker Bü 133C Jungmeister	F-AZBS	16	U-69 (Switzerland), HB-MIQ, F-BOHK	PVA
☐ Bücker Bü 133C Jungmeister	F-BEDJ	1131		RAD
☐ Bücker Bü 133C Jungmeister	F-PBRI	2008	(F-AZEU), F-AZLB	PVA
☐ Bücker Bü 181B-1 Bestmann	F-BCRE	FR-105	Fuselage only	RAD
☐ Bücker Bü 181B-1 Bestmann	F-BCRF	FR-106	(Luftwaffe), (RAF)	RAD
☐ Bücker Bü 181B-1 Bestmann	F-BCRV	FR-122	Fuselage only	RAD
☐ Caudron G.3	F-AZMB	SA-33		PVA
☐ Caudron G.3 (R)				RAC
☐ Caudron C.61bis (C.61)	F-AFAO	5305/3		RA
☐ Caudron C.69	F-AFHH			RAD
☐ Caudron C.270 Luciole	F-AMAC	6663/48	Possible identity	RA
☐ Caudron C.272 Luciole (C.270)	F-ALLL	6656/1		RAD
☐ Caudron C.275 Luciole	F-BBHX	7479/274	F-APLR	RA
☐ Caudron C.282/2 Phalène	F-AMGJ	6720/6		RAD
☐ Caudron C.601 Aiglon	F-POIT	P-2	F-BDJT	RA
☐ Centre Est Aéronautique DR.220A 2+2	F-BOZG	63		RAA
☐ Centre Est Aéronautique DR.250/160 Capitaine	F-BNVE	61		RAA
☐ Centre Est Aéronautique DR.340 Major	F-BSBZ	482		RAA
☐ Cessna 305C Bird Dog (L-19E) (O-1E)	F-WNRQ	24519	24519	RA
☐ Cessna 305C Bird Dog (L-19E) (O-1E)	F-GDPC	24728	24728, F-WDPC	PVA
☐ Colomban MC-15 Cri-Cri	F-PFHV	304		RAA
☐ Colomban MC-15R Cri-Cri				RAC
☐ Construcciones Aeronáuticas (CASA) 1.131E [Bücker Bü 131 Jungmann]	F-AZGG		E.3B-540	PVA
☐ Construcciones Aeronáuticas (CASA) 1.131E [Bücker Bü 131 Jungmann]	F-AZSE	83	E.3B-???	PVA
☐ Construcciones Aeronáuticas (CASA) 1.131SA (1.131E) [Bücker Bü 131 Jungmann]	F-PBSE	2224	E.3B-???, N52DM	PVA
☐ Construcciones Aeronáuticas (CASA) 1.131E [Bücker Bü 131 Jungmann]	F-AZTT	2241	E3B-???	PVA
☐ Construcciones Aeronáuticas (CASA) 352L [Junkers Ju 52/3m]	'N9+AA'	24	T.2B-212, G-BECL, F-AZJU	PVA
☐ Croise AC-1	F-PZRH	01		RAA
☐ Croses LC-6 Criquet	F-PYFT	72		RAA
☐ Dassault MD-311 Flamant	F-AZCB	291	291	PVA
☐ Dassault MD-312 Flamant	164	164		RA
☐ De Havilland D.H.82A Tiger Moth	OO-SOB	83283	T7025, G-AOGJ – incorporates parts of c/n 85291, DE245, G-AMUY, OO-SOD	RA
☐ De Havilland D.H.82A Tiger Moth	F-BGZT	83875	T7349, G-ANJG	RAD
☐ De Havilland D.H.82A Tiger Moth	G-ANSG	85569	DE615	RAD
☐ De Havilland D.H.82A Tiger Moth	OO-EVM	86507	NM199, T-19 (Belgium)	RA
☐ De Havilland D.H.89A Dragon Rapide (D.H.89B Dominie I)	F-AZCA	6541	X7381, G-ALZF, F-BGON	PVA
☐ De Havilland D.H.94 Moth Minor	F-PAOG	94038	G-AFNJ, AW113, G-AFNJ, F-BAOG	RA
☐ De Havilland D.H.100 Vampire FB.6	'VZ152'	624	J-1115 (Switzerland), F-AZHX – based at Le Havre.	RAAX
☐ De Havilland D.H.C.1 Chipmunk T.20	F-AZEU	C1/0299	1307 (Portugal)	PVA
☐ De Havilland D.H.C.1 Chipmunk T.20	F-AZGQ	P.15	1325 (Portugal)	RA
☐ De Havilland D.H.C.1 Chipmunk 22 (T.20)	'WB557'	C1/0702	12-132 (Denmark), P-132 (Denmark), OY-ALW, F-AZCH	PVAX

Type	Reg	C/n	Previous identities / Notes	Status
☐ Dewoitine D.26	F-AZJD	322	290 (Switzerland), U-290 (Switzerland), HB-RAC, (F-AZBC), F-AZBF – sometimes at Duxford with OFMC.	RAA
☐ Douglas AD-4NA Skyraider (AD-4N)	F-AZDP	7449	Bu124143, 14 (France), (N91909), TR-KFP, F-WZDP	PVA
☐ Douglas DC-3A-456 Skytrain (C-47A)	F-BLOZ	13142	42-93251, F-BAXG	RAA
☐ Fairchild 24R9 Forwarder (UC-61K) (Argus III)	F-AZBY	R9-923	43-14959, HB685, PH-NDH, F-BIPB	RA
☐ Fairchild 24R9 Forwarder (UC-61K) (Argus III)	F-BEXX	R9-926	43-14962, HB688	RAD
☐ Fairchild 24R9 Forwarder (UC-61K) (Argus III)	F-AZCI	R9-998	44-83037, KK380, F-BEXC	PVA
☐ Fairchild 24W41 Forwarder (C-61) (UC-61) (Argus I)	'43-14499'	W41-314(?)	42-13578, EV806, G-AKJM, VH-AVN – these identities doubtful – F-AZCF	RAAX
☐ Fairchild 24W41A Forwarder (C-61A) (UC-61A) (Argus II)	F-????	W41A-495	43-14531, FS614 – this may be F-AZCF	RA
☐ Fairchild M-62A Cornell (PT-19)				RAC
☐ Focke-Achgelis Fa 330A-1 Bachstelze	100010	100010		RA
☐ Focke-Wulf Fw 44J Stieglitz	F-AZMJ	2782	SZ-15 (Finland), OH-SZF	PVA
☐ Fokker Dr I (R)	F-AZAQ	1		PVA
☐ Fokker Dr I (R)				RA
☐ Fouga CM.170R Magister	F-GELH	102	102, F-ZVLC	RA
☐ Fouga CM.170R Magister	31	31		RA
☐ Gardan GY-80 Horizon 160	F-BLPY	63		RAA
☐ Gardan GY-80 Horizon 180	F-BNYQ	191		RAA
☐ Gardan GY-80 Horizon 180	F-BNYJ	201		RAA
☐ Hatry-Opel-Sander RAK 1 (FSM)	'D-125'		Built using parts from Castel C.310P c/n 123 F-CAIS, F-CRJJ.	PVX
☐ Hawker Sea Fury FB.10		41H/656810		RA
☐ Hirth Hi.27 Akrostar II	F-AZJF	4003	D-EBAZ, HB-MSA, F-WZJF	PVA
☐ Jodel D.92 Bébé	F-PYFS	686		RAA
☐ Jodel D.92 Bébé	F-PBOM	HR.34		RAA
☐ Jodel D.112 Club	F-PHUD	398		RAA
☐ Jodel D.112 Club	F-BMAC	1215		RAA
☐ Jodel D.120 Paris-Nice	F-BHTS	9		RAA
☐ Jodel DR.1050 Ambassadeur	F-BMGK	572		RAA
☐ Jodel DR.1051 Sicile	F-BLAY	427		RAA
☐ Kreimendahl K-10 Shoestring	F-WZPE	048		PVA
☐ Kreimendahl K-10 Shoestring	F-PYXC	054	'F-WXYC', F-WYXC	RAA
☐ Latécoère 14	F-AEIZ	189		RA
☐ Latécoère 17P (R)	F-AZBD	1	Built from Noorduyn Norseman VI c/n 448, 44-70513, F-OBTC, F-BSTC	RAD
☐ Lendepergt LP-01 Sybille	F-PYQS	01		RAA
☐ Leopoldoff L.3	F-APZP	1		RA
☐ Leopoldoff L.55	F-PRJJ	LF-01-93	F-WVZR – rebuild of L.56 c/n 3 F-BHGU	PVA
☐ Let C-11 [Yakovlev Yak-11]			In Egyptian markings.	RA
☐ Let C-11 [Yakovlev Yak-11]			In Egyptian markings.	RA
☐ Let C-11 [Yakovlev Yak-11]			In Egyptian markings.	RA
☐ Let C-11 [Yakovlev Yak-11]	704		In Egyptian markings.	RA
☐ Let C-11 [Yakovlev Yak-11]	706		In Egyptian markings.	RA
☐ Let C-11 [Yakovlev Yak-11]	708		In Egyptian markings.	RA
☐ Let C-11 [Yakovlev Yak-11]	F-AZFJ	25111/02	??? (Egypt)	PVA
☐ Let C-11 [Yakovlev Yak-11]	F-AZNN	25111/05	(Egypt)	RAA
☐ Let C-11 [Yakovlev Yak-11]	F-AZFB	25111/06	(Egypt)	PVA
☐ Let C-11 [Yakovlev Yak-11]	F-AZIR	25111/21	(Egypt)	RAA
☐ Let C-11 [Yakovlev Yak-11]	F-AZLM		(Egypt)	RAA
☐ Let L-13 Blanik	F-AZFF	026750	LX-CAH, OO-ZHG	RAA
☐ Mauboussin M.120 Corsaire	F-AMHT	104		RAD
☐ Mauboussin M.127 Corsaire	F-PBTB	92	F-BBTB	RA
☐ Max Holste MH.1521M Broussard	F-BVSU	022	22	RA
☐ Max Holste MH.1521M Broussard	F-GGKO	284	284, F-WGKO	RAD
☐ McLeod K & S Jungster I	F-PYVI	J1-760034	F-WYVI	PVA
☐ Morane-Saulnier A-1 (R)	F-AZAN	01		PVA
☐ Morane-Saulnier A-1 (R)	F-AZAP	02		PVA
☐ Morane-Saulnier H (R)	F-AZMS	Sams 22.01		PVA
☐ Morane-Saulnier MS.29C.1				RA
☐ Morane-Saulnier MS.130Et2	F-AZAA	02	F-APEK – original c/n 67	RAD
☐ Morane-Saulnier MS.138	F-AZAJ	3220/138	F-AQDN	PVA
☐ Morane-Saulnier MS.181	F-PFKX	01		RA
☐ Morane-Saulnier MS.185	F-AZAZ	3672/01	F-AJRQ	PVA
☐ Morane-Saulnier MS.230	F-AZAK	403	F-BEJO	PVA
☐ Morane-Saulnier MS.317 (MS.315)	F-BCNL	6527/273		PVA
☐ Morane-Saulnier MS.317 (MS.315)	F-BGKY	6529/275		RA
☐ Morane-Saulnier MS.317 (MS.315)	F-BGUV	6551/297		PVA
☐ Morane-Saulnier MS.317 (MS.315)	F-BCBA	6575/321		PVA
☐ Morane-Saulnier MS.341/3 (MS.342)	F-AZCX	4234/3	F-ANVS	RAC
☐ Morane-Saulnier MS.342	F-ANVT	4235/4		RA
☐ Morane-Saulnier MS.505 Criquet (MS.500) [Fieseler Fi 156 Storch]	F-BAYN	2005		RA
☐ Morane-Saulnier MS.505 Criquet (MS.502) [Fieseler Fi 156 Storch]	F-AZRA	2039/14	F-BBAT	RA

Type	Reg	c/n	Previous identities	Status
☐ Morane-Saulnier MS.505 Criquet (MS.502) [Fieseler Fi 156 Storch]	F-BBUJ	263/23		PVA
☐ Morane-Saulnier MS.505 Criquet (MS.502) [Fieseler Fi 156 Storch]	F-BEJE	699/24		RA
☐ Morane-Saulnier MS.733 Alcyon	F-BLOC	193	193	RA
☐ Morane-Saulnier MS.880B Rallye Club	F-BRRR	1403		PV
☐ Morane-Saulnier MS.880B Rallye Club	F-BKTK	215		RAA
☐ Morane-Saulnier MS.892A Commodore 150	F-BRJX	10970		RAA
☐ Mudry CAP.10 AJBS	F-PZLD	001	F-WZLD	PVA
☐ Mudry CAP.20E	F-AZOE	02	F-BOPV, F-ZWRP, F-BTAI, F-TFVV	PVA
☐ Mudry CAP.20LS	F-PZAJ	01	F-WZAJ	PVA
☐ Nicollier HN-434 Super Ménestrel	F-PRDX	29		RAA
☐ Nieuport 11 (R)	'N1538'	30	F-WZBF	RA
☐ Nord N.1002 Pingouin II [Messerschmitt Bf 108B]	F-BFUY	69	69	RA
☐ Nord N.1101 Noralpha (Ramier I) [Messerschmitt Me 208]	F-BLQQ	53	53	RA
☐ Nord N.1101 Noralpha (Ramier I) [Messerschmitt Me 208]	F-GMCY	67	67	PVA
☐ Nord N.1101 Noralpha (Ramier I) [Messerschmitt Me 208]	F-BBGA	172	172	RA
☐ Nord N.1101 Ramier I [Messerschmitt Me 208]	19	19		RA
☐ Nord N.1101 Ramier I [Messerschmitt Me 208]	120	120		RA
☐ Nord N.1101 Ramier I [Messerschmitt Me 208]	134	134		RA
☐ Nord N.1203-II Norécrin	F-BMHZ	194	194, F-BMHQ	RA
☐ Nord N.1203-II Norécrin	HB-DAR	318	(HB-DAT), OE-DAR	RAC
☐ Nord N.1203-III Norécrin (N.1201) (N.1203)	F-BBKB	3		RA
☐ Nord N.1203-VI Norécrin (N.1203-II) (N.1203-III)	F-BBEP	328		RA
☐ Nord N.3202	F-AZIY	15	15, F-WZBA	PVA
☐ Nord N.3400	37	37		RA
☐ Nord N.3400	87	87		RA
☐ Nord N.3400	121	121		RA
☐ Nord NC.854 (NC.853)	F-AZPL	10	F-BDZT, F-BZBL, F-BDZT, F-WZPL	PVA
☐ Nord NC.856A Norvigie	F-BNKT	29	29	RAD
☐ North American NA-68 (R)	F-AZHD	SA-30	Converted from NA-182 Texan c/n 182-54 51-14367, F-BVQD, F-AZBK, F-WZBK, F-AZBK	RAA
☐ North American NA-68 (R)	F-AZHE	SA-31	Converted from a NA-182 Texan (T-6G)	RAA
☐ North American NA-88 Texan (AT-6C) (Harvard IIA)	F-AZBE	88-12127	41-33606, EX633, 7349 (South Africa), H-29 (Belgium), F-BJBI, F-WJBI, F-BJBI	RAA
☐ North American NA-88 Texan (AT-6D) (SNJ-5)	F-AZRB	88-17955	42-86174, Bu90747, N3651F	RAA
☐ North American NA-122 Mustang (P-51D)	F-AZSB	122-40967	44-74427, 9252 (Canada), N9148R, N2251D – with components from c/n 122-40975 44-74435, 9221 (Canada), CF-LOQ, N130JT	PVA
☐ North American NA-168 Texan (T-6G)	F-AZMP	168-160	49-3056, AE.6-188, C.6-35	PVA
☐ North American NA-171 Trojan (T-28A)				RA
☐ North American NA-182 Texan (T-6G)	F-AZBQ	182-535	51-14848, F-BOEO	PVA
☐ North American NA-197 Texan (T-6G)	F-AZSR	197-75	53-4579, 34579	PVA
☐ Piaggio FWP.149D	F-AZKD	141	KB+118, YA+010, YA+457, D-EEWR, (G-BLOW), D-EEWR	PVA
☐ Piel CP.301C Emeraude	F-BJFN	538		RAA
☐ Piel CP.1310 Super Emeraude	TU-TFE	918	F-OBSZ	RA
☐ Pilatus P.2-06	F-AZCE	72	U-123 (Switzerland), U-152 (Switzerland)	PVAX
☐ Piper J-2 Cub	F-AZBM		F-WZBM – converted from Piper J-3C-65 Cub (L-4H) c/n 12332 44-80036, F-BDTH	PVA
☐ Piper J-3C-65 Cub (L-4H)	F-BEPJ	11182	43-29791	RA
☐ Piper J-3C-65 Cub (L-4H)	F-BMHM	11907	44-79611	RAA
☐ Piper J-3C-65 Cub (L-4H)	OO-RVA	12221	44-79925	S
☐ Piper J-3C-65 Cub (L-4J)	OO-JDC	12476	44-80180, OO-AJK	RAA
☐ Piper J-3C-65 Cub (L-4J)	F-BFQD	13028	44-80782	RAA
☐ Piper J-3C-65 Cub (L-4J)	F-BFEF	13288	45-4548, F-BFFF	RA
☐ Piper PA-18-150 Super Cub	F-BNPI	18-5396	18-5396	PVA
☐ Piper PA-23-250 Aztec	F-BOHI	27-319	N4773P, CN-TTX	RAA
☐ Pitts S-1S Special	F-AZMV	001	F-WVKB, F-BVKB	RAA
☐ Pitts S-1S Special	F-AZFH	K-027	N835, F-WZAF	RAA
☐ Pitts S-2A Special	F-GGTR	2171		RAA
☐ Polikarpov Po-2W	F-AZDB	0045	YU-CNS	RAA
☐ Royal Aircraft Factory S.E.5A (R)	F-AZCN	2	F-WZCN – converted from a S.V.4C.	RAA
☐ Royal Aircraft Factory S.E.5A (R)	'A8898'	3	F-AZCY 'F504' – converted from a S.V.4C.	RAAX
☐ Ryan Navion B	F-BHBV	NAV-4-2206	N5306K, F-OAHO, EC-AHV	RAA
☐ Salmson 2A2 (R)	F-WZBJ	006	Converted from Caudron C.275 Luciole	RA
☐ Salmson 2A2 (R)	F-WZBK	007	Converted from Caudron C.275 Luciole.	RA

TYPE	REG/SER	CON. NO.	PI/NOTES	STATUS
☐ Salmson D.6/3T2 Cri Cri	F-BDJV	1		RAD
☐ Salmson D.7-T2 Cri Cri Major	F-BEAN	02	F-WEAN	RA
☐ Salmson D.7-T2 Cri Cri Major	F-AZAB	9	F-BFNG	RA
☐ Schneider Grunau SG-38 (D.F.S. 108-14)	F-AZZG	20.24		PVA
☐ Sikorsky S-58	641	58641		RA
☐ Société Francaise de Constructions Aéronautiques-Govin Taupin	F-AZBG	10	F-APGB, F-PMEM	RAA
☐ Société Pour l'Aviation et ses Dérivés (SPAD) XIII (R)	159			RAX
☐ Soko 522	F-AZMJ	68	60168	RA
☐ Stampe & Vertongen S.V.4A	F-BFRL	1041	1041	RA
☐ Stampe & Vertongen S.V.4A	F-BHHD	1119	1119	RAA
☐ Stampe & Vertongen S.V.4A	F-BDOV	246		RA
☐ Stampe & Vertongen S.V.4C	F-BCQT	411		RAA
☐ Stampe & Vertongen S.V.4C	F-BCXD	438		RAA
☐ Stampe & Vertongen S.V.4C	F-BDCQ	546		RAA
☐ Stampe & Vertongen S.V.4C	F-BDCY	553		RA
☐ Stampe & Vertongen S.V.4C	F-BAHV	1130	1130	RAA
☐ Stampe & Vertongen S.V.4L	F-WZAZ	01		PVA
☐ Steen Skybolt	F-PASB	341		RAA
☐ Stinson 108-3 Voyager	F-BFPM	108-5080	N4080C	RAA
☐ Stinson SR-10C Reliant	F-GPJS	3/5846	F-BBCS	RA
☐ Sud-Est SE.210 Caravelle			Front fuselage only.	RA
☐ Sud-Est SE.3130 Alouette II	F-GEJC	1004	4	RAA
☐ Thunder Ax.6-56 Hot Air Balloon	F-GCZB	370		RAA
☐ Thunder Ax.7-77 Hot Air Balloon	F-GCZA	371		RA
☐ Thunder Ax.7-77 Hot Air Balloon	F-GCZF	432		RAA
☐ Vought F4U-5NL Corsair	F-AZEG		Bu124724, 600 (Honduras), NX4901E – arrived in US as FAH605.	PVA
☐ Wag Aero Sport Trainer	F-PJBS	3303		PVA
☐ Yakovlev Yak-3UTI	F-AZIM	9/04623	YR-AIF (?)	RAC
☐ Yakovlev Yak-18P				RAC
☐ Zlin XII	F-AQIE	154		RA
☐ Zlin Z-326 Trener Master	F-BNAI	905		RA
☐ Zlin Z-326 Trener Master	F-BORP	919		RA
☐ Zlin Z-326 Trener Master	F-BPNO	930		RA
☐ Zlin Z-526AFS Akrobat	D-EAPH	1230		RAA

ASSOCIATION ALBATROS (FRA172)

Address:	20 Rue Olivier Beauregard, 91380 Chilly Mazarin.
Tel:	01 69 34 59 46
Admission:	By prior permission only.
Location:	In private premises.

Captain Joseph Le Bris built a glider in 1857. He based his design on the albatross which he had observed during his time at sea. One flight was made and the machine crashed on the second. Another example was constructed in 1870 but this was not successful. This group has built a replica of the first machine with the aim of flying it. This aircraft may eventually go on show in a museum in the Paris area.

TYPE	REG/SER	CON. NO.	PI/NOTES	STATUS
☐ Le Bris Avion (R)				RA

ASSOCIATION DAKOTA ET CIE (FRA173)

Address:	4 Rue Galvani, 75838 Paris Cedex 17.
Fax:	055 63 58 39 83
Admission:	By prior permission only.
Location:	At La Ferté Alais which is off the N.449 about 2 km north of the town which is about 40 km south of Paris.

A group of enthusiasts maintain the DC-3 in airworthy condition. The aircraft has had a varied career after its U.S. military days were over. Scottish Aviation flew it from 1945 until the early 1950s and during this period it was used on trooping flights and carried a Royal Air Force serial. In the late 1970s it served as the personal transport of the President of the Central African Republic. The Dakota is often based at Orly Airport and is a regular participant at shows and meetings in the region.

TYPE	REG/SER	CON. NO.	PI/NOTES	STATUS
☐ Douglas DC-3A-456 Skytrain (C-47A) (Dakota III)	F-AZTE	9172	42-23310, G-AGZF, WZ984, G-AGZF, 141406(?) (France), F-BRGN, TL-JBB, TL-AAX, (F-ODQE), F-GDPP, F-WZTE	PVA

The Musée de l'Air has loaned this Vautour to the SNECMA Museum at Melun-Villaroche. (Douglas Rough)

Jean Salis constructed this Caudron G.3 using some original parts.

Roland Payen built a number of small delta designs including the jet powered PA.49 which is on show at the Musée de l'Air at Le Bourget.

ASSOCIATION FORTERESSE TOUJOURS VOLANT EN FRANCE (FRA174)

Address:	Aérodrome de Cernay. 91590 La Ferté Alais.
Tel:	01 64 24 41 66
Fax:	01 64 57 44 87
Email:	B.17ThePinkLady@wanadoo.fr
Admission:	By prior permission only.
Location:	The Fortress is based at Orly airport which is about 15 km south of Paris off the N 7.

This group is part of the Amicale Jean-Baptiste Salis organisation. The grass runway at La Ferté Alais is too short for safe operation of the four engined aircraft so it is normally kept at Orly. For many years the fleet of B-17s operated by the Institut Géographique National at Creil was a familiar sight in French skies. Enthusiasts were determined to keep one in flying condition in France and they acheived their aim in the mid-1980s. The aircraft was modified to B-17F configuration for use in the film 'Memphis Belle'.

TYPE	REG/SER	CON. NO.	PI/NOTES	STATUS
☐ Boeing 299-0 Fortress (B-17G) (RB-17G)	F-AZDX	8246	44-8846, F-BGSP, ZS-DXM, F-BGSP	RAA

ASSOCIATION MEMORIAL FLIGHT (FRA175)

Address:	6 Rue d'Artois, 91130 Ris Orangis.
Tel:	01 30 82 61 13
Email:	memorialflight@free.fr
Admission:	By prior permission only.
Location:	Workshops at Dugny – active aircraft at La Ferté Alais.

Originally formed to assist the Musée de l'Air in restoration projects the group acquired its first airframe when Jean Salis donated a derelict SPAD. This was restored and is now in flying condition. The Fokker Triplane was started by a private individual and completed in the organisation's workshops at Dugny. The Morane-Saulnier A is one of a trio constructed by Jean Salis and all contained some original parts. Members rebuilt an original L.V.G. C VI for the Musée de l'Air and then embarked on the construction of a faithful replica. The Albatros is being worked on in Austria. The fuselage is almost complete and will move to Dugny when the Fokker D VII is transferred to La Ferté Alais. The Blériot XI-2 has been painted in military colours as a number were used by the military before and in the early stages of World War I. This is being rebuilt after an accident. The Sopwith 1½ Strutter is a French built example and restoration of the airframe is progressing.

TYPE	REG/SER	CON. NO.	PI/NOTES	STATUS
☐ Albatros D III (R)				RAC
☐ Avro 504K (R)				RAC
☐ Blériot XI-2 (R)	F-AZNP	01.98		RAC
☐ Dassault MD-311 Flamant	F-AZFX	282	282	RAA
☐ De Havilland D.H.82A Tiger Moth				RAC
☐ Fokker D VII (R)				RAC
☐ Fokker Dr I (R)	F-AZGN	MF-01	Contains some original parts.	RAA
☐ Luft-Verkehrs-Gesellschaft (L.V.G.) C VI (R)				RAC
☐ Morane-Saulnier A-1 (R)	F-AZAO	03	On loan from M.A.	RAA
☐ Royal Aircraft Factory S.E.5A (R)	'C1096'	MF-01	F-AZBF	RAAX
☐ Société Pour l'Aviation et ses Dérivés (SPAD) XIIIC.1	F-AZFP	4377		RAA
☐ Sopwith 1½ Strutter	2897			RAC
☐ Stampe & Vertongen S.V.4A	F-BAGY	1116	1116	RAC

COLLECTION DE LA BASE AÉRIENNE DE BRÉTIGNY-SUR-ORGE (FRA176)

Address:	Base Aérienne 217, 91220 Brétigny Cedex.
Tel:	01 69 23 70 00
Admission:	By prior permission only.
Location:	Just east of the town which is about 25 km south of Paris.

The Centre d'Essais en Vol was in residence at Brétigny for many years and was involved in flight testing for all three services. A recent reorganisation of all government test centres has resulted in the establishment of the Direction des Centres d'Expertises et d'Essais. The flight test centre at Brétigny is scheduled to close and its activities relocated to Cazaux and Istres but this has not yet happened. Officer selection for the Air Force is carried out at the base along with psychological testing of serving personnel.

TYPE	REG/SER	CON. NO.	PI/NOTES	STATUS
☐ Canadair CL-30 Silver Star 3 (CT-133) [Lockheed 580 (T-33AN)]	21031	T33-031		RA
☐ Dassault Mystère IVA	245	245		RA
☐ Dassault Mirage IIIE	469	469		RA
☐ Dassault Mirage IIIR	02	02		RA
☐ Dassault Mirage IVP (IVA)	25	25		RA
☐ Sikorsky S-58	421	SKY-421		RA
☐ Sud-Ouest SO-4050 Vautour IIN	355	125		RA

ESCADRILLE DU SOUVENIR (FRA177)

Address: c/o Patrice Blin,
195 Rue de Chanval,
91690 Guillerval.
Admission: By prior permission only.
Location: At a number of locations.

Escadrille du Souvenir was set up in 1965 and obtained two hangars at Étampes. Close co-operation existed with the Musée de l'Air and some of the active aircraft of the Le Bourget collection were housed in the hangars. Branches were set up at other airfields in France and the fleet consisted of mainly post World War II types. The buildings at Étampes have been demolished and the collection dispersed A number of aircraft are still registered to the organisation and some have been loaned to other groups.

TYPE	REG/SER	CON. NO.	PI/NOTES	STATUS
☐ Breguet 904S Nymphale	F-CCFK	1	On loan to Assoc. Champagne Aérobatic.	–
☐ Castel C.311P	F-CBZM	104		RA
☐ Max Holste MH.1521C-1 Broussard (1521M)	F-GJBF	13	13 – on loan to Assoc. Champagne Aérobatic.	–
☐ Morane-Saulnier MS.504 Criquet (MS.502) [Fieseler Fi 156 Storch]	F-AZMD	600/01	F-BCME	RA
☐ Nord N.1101 Noralpha (Ramier I) [Messerschmitt Me 208]	F-AZYV	13	13, F-BYAV	RAA
☐ Nord N.3202	F-AZFT	34	34, F-WYAY - on loan to Assoc. Champagne Aérobatic.	–
☐ Nord N.3202	F-AZFU	37	37, F-WYAZ - on loan to Aéro Club at Lapalisse.	–
☐ Nord N.3202B1B	F-AZJO	101	101, F-BNRP, F-AZAI, F-WZBE – on loan to Assoc. Champagne Aérobatic.	–
☐ Nord N.3202B1B	F-AZJT	71	71, F-AZAD, F-WZBD, F-WZJT – on loan to Assoc. Champagne Aérobatic.	–
☐ Nord N.3202B1B	F-AZHO	95	95, F-BNRN, 95, F-AZAC, F-WZBC – on loan to ACDF.	–

MUSÉE DU DELTA (FRA178)

Address: 40 Avenue Jean-Pierre Bénard,
91200 Athis-Mons.
Tel: 01 69 38 83 38
Admission: September-July Wednesday and Sunday 1430-1730.
Location: At Orly Airport just south of the main terminal area off the N.7.

Roland Payen, who had designed and built several small delta aircraft, set up a group in 1986 with the aim of creating a museum which would feature designs using this distinctive wing shape. He flew a piston engined model just before World War II and his jet PA.49 from the 1950s can be seen in the Musée de l'Air. Other examples of his work were derelict at La Ferté Alais in the 1970s but these have not been seen for some time and have probably been scrapped. A replica of the PA.100 has been constructed for the collection. In 1976 the first prototype Caravelle was flown into Orly for preservation and ten years later it was joined by the second French built Concorde. Redevelopment at the airport meant that the pair had to be moved and the historic Caravelle was scrapped. The Concorde was moved to an area south of the terminal which now forms the site for the museum. There is a small exhibition in a building on the site which contains the Visair ultralight. The inside displays trace the history and development of the delta wing with models and photographs to be seen.

TYPE	REG/SER	CON. NO.	PI/NOTES	STATUS
☐ Aérospatiale / British Aircraft Corporation Concorde	F-WTSA	02		PV
☐ Dassault Mirage IIIB	245	245		PV
☐ Dassault Mirage IIIRD	352	352		PV
☐ Dassault Etendard IVM	3	3	Nearby.	PV
☐ Dassault Mercure 100	F-BTTJ	10		PV
☐ Payen PA.100 (R)				PV
☐ Sud-Est SE.210 Caravelle VI-N	F-BVPZ	218	YU-AHF	PV
☐ Visair 1		01		PV

92 HAUTS-DE-SEINE

CONSERVATOIRE CITROËN (FRA179)

Address:	La Forét Vidame, 92200 Neuilly-sur-Seine.
Tel:	01 47 48 41 41
Admission:	By prior permission only.
Location:	In the north western suburbs of Paris near the Bois de Boulogne.

The company has a collection of over two hundred and fifty historic cars at stored at premises in the Paris region. In the mid-1970s the firm constructed a light helicopter designed by Charles Marchetti. The maiden flight was made in December 1975 and testing continued for three years. The prototype is located at the company test centre along with a fuselage and other parts from what is believed to be the uncompleted second machine.

TYPE	REG/SER	CON. NO.	PI/NOTES	STATUS
☐ Citroen-Marchetti RE.2	F-WZAB	001	Maybe c/n 002.	RA
☐ Citroen-Marchetti RE.2		002	Fuselage only.	RA

93 SEINE-SAINT-DENIS

AILES ANCIENNES ÎLE DE FRANCE (FRA180)

Address:	4 Rue Brière de Boissmont, 94160 Saint Mande.
Tel:	01 43 28 31 05
Fax:	01 43 74 29 38
Email:	ailesa@free.fr
Admission:	Wednesday and Saturday 1400-1800.
Location:	On the west side of Le Bourget airport which is about 10 km north east of Paris on the A 1 and N 2.

Originally formed to assist the restoration work of the Musée de l'Air, this group has now obtained its own workshops and acquired aircraft. Amongst the aircraft rebuilt by Ailes Anciennes and now on show at the museum are the Republic F-105 and the SUC.10 Courlis. The most ambitious project undertaken was the recovery of a Lancaster from Wallis Island in the Pacific Ocean. The four engined aircraft was damaged on landing at Uti in January 1963 and after being stripped of useful parts was abandoned. The airframe arrived at Le Bourget in 1984 and is undergoing a slow restoration. The Baroudeur is the sole survivor of the type and first flew in 1953. The type was designed to operate from short fields. The Caudron C.714 fighter was acquired from a private collector in Finland. The Finnish Air Force flew six examples of this diminutive fighter.

TYPE	REG/SER	CON. NO.	PI/NOTES	STATUS
☐ Avro 683 Lancaster MR.VII (B.VII)	WU-21		NX664	RAC
☐ Beech C18S Expeditor (C-45F) (UC-45F) (JRB-4)	N61909	8608	44-87349, Bu44676, 76 – MA aircraft.	RA
☐ Caudron C.714	CA-553	8537/5	In Finnish markings.	RAC
☐ Jacobs D.F.S. 230B-2	H4+??		M.A. aircraft	RA
☐ Jacobs D.F.S. 230C-1	H4+??		M.A. aircraft.	RA
☐ Jacobs D.F.S. 230C-1	H4+??	36-16	M.A. aircraft.	RA
☐ Mauboussin M.125 Corsaire	F-BCEM	919	M.A. Aircraft	RA
☐ Nord N.2501 Noratlas	F-BCZK	44	44	RA
☐ Nord NC.856A Norvigie	111	111	M.A. aircraft.	RA
☐ Republic F-84F Thunderflash			Front fuselage only.	RA
☐ Piasecki PD-18 Retriever (HUP-2)	Bu130077		M.A. aircraft.	RA
☐ Sud-Est SE.5000 Baroudeur	3	3	Composite but mainly c/n 3 – M.A. aircraft.	RA

MUSÉE DE L'AIR ET DE L'ESPACE (FRA181)

Address:	B.P. 193, 93350 Le Bourget.
Tel:	01 49 92 71 99.
Fax:	01 49 92 70 95
Email:	musee.air@mae.org
Admission:	Monday-Friday 1000-1800.(Closes at 1700 October-April) Saturday-Sunday 1000-1200 1400-1800.
Location:	Le Bourget is about 10 km north east of Paris on the A.1 and N.2.

The museum, formed in 1919, was the first truly aeronautical collection in the world. The driving force in the early years was an engineer, General Caquot, who stored the exhibits at Issy-les-Moulineaux. In 1878 a large building was constructed for the Paris Exhibition and its dimensions were such that it was ideal for airship use. The structure was moved to Chalais-Meudon to house the dirigible 'La France'. The museum opened in the hall on November 23rd 1921 and this was in use until the mid-1990s. In 1933 a new purpose built complex was constructed on the Boulevard Victor and part of the collection was on show there from 1936. The new halls were damaged in 1940 and the collection returned to Meudon. During World War II and after the end of hostilities some restoration work was carried out. The exhibition opened again in 1950. Over sixty aircraft were displayed on the floor, on pedestals and suspended from the ceiling. The next fifteen years saw little change except for the acquisition of more material which was stored at Villacoublay and later Chartres. Chalais Meudon was inconvenient as it is located some distance from other tourist attractions and access for visitors was difficult as the museum was on a government research establishment. The airfield at Le Bourget opened in World War I and in 1919 it became the main civil airport for the capital. Many historic flights started or finished at the field including Charles Lindbergh's arrival on May 21st 1927 after his epic solo crossing of the Atlantic. The construction of Orly Airport after World War II meant a reduction in long-haul services but many European operators still favoured Le Bourget. The site became a major general aviation field and units of the Air Force and Navy used the west side installations. As airliners became larger and traffic increased the new Charles de Gaulle Airport was constructed at Roissy. Many airlines moved out and hangarage became available. The then director of the museum, General Pierre Lissarague, was quick to take advantage of the situation and aircraft were rapidly moved in. The first hall was opened in time for the 1975 Paris Air Show and the second was ready a year later. The Meudon collection was reorganised to present aircraft from the pre-1918 era. For the first time in decades there was room to stage an ordered display. As more space was acquired at Le Bourget plans were changed and when the terminal building was vacated in 1982 it was decided to modify the structure and move the Meudon exhibition to the main site. By 1981 five halls were open at Le Bourget and over one hundred and fifty aircraft were on show including several parked outside. The Air Force moved out of its Dugny base on the west side and hangars for storage and workshops were acquired. Aircraft were moved in from other sites and at one time it was planned to open a lighter than air exhibition at Meudon but this never came to fruition. On May 17th 1990 disaster struck when a fire broke out in the Dugny hangars. Over forty aircraft perished including unique prototypes and several last survivors of their type. The terminal building (Grand Gallerie) traces the story of flight from the early balloonists through the hang gliding pioneers up to World War I. The earliest machine on show is the delicate Biot glider dating from 1879 and flown at Clamart. Many French historians believe that the first powered flight took place when Clement Ader's steam powered Eole bounced briefly into the air in 1890. Seven years later the Avion III appeared but this was again not a success. The French were the world leaders in aviation in this period and exhibits include a replica of the first seaplane to fly, the Fabre Hydravion which took off from the Etang du Berre in March 1910, the Blériot in which Alphonse Pegoud performed some of the first aerobatics and the Deperdussin in which Maurice Prévost set a world air speed record of over 120 m.p.h. Up until the end of the 1990s five halls were open each with a particular theme. Hall A covered the inter-war period with several record-breaking aircraft on show. Transport, aerobatic and racing aircraft also featured. Hall B was devoted to World War II with classic fighters from five countries on show. These two areas were recently closed. Structural surveys have been carried out on the buildings in the hope of staging new exhibitions but this is looking extremely unlikely and they may have to be demolished. Hall C covers the French aviation industry since 1945. As in earlier days companies produced many innovative prototypes. Hall D deals with military aviation in the country in this period. Hall E is the largest with a spectacular arrangement of sporting aircraft and gliders suspended at many levels in the tall building. A fairly new addition is the Concorde Hall which contains the first French prototype of the supersonic airliner. Another building to house World War II types is now complete.

TYPE	REG/SER	CON. NO.	PI/NOTES	STATUS
☐ Ader Avion III (R)				PV
☐ Aero 45	F-AZCL	4927	F-OAFX, F-BGQF	RA
☐ Aero Commander 680FL	F-BRQE	1716-137	N4565E	RA
☐ Aérospatiale / British Aircraft Corporation Concorde	F-WTSS	001		PV
☐ Aérospatiale / British Aircraft Corporation Concorde 102	F-BTSD	100-013	F-WJAM, F-BTSD, N94SD	PV
☐ Agusta-Bell 47G	076	076		RA
☐ Amiot 1		01		RA
☐ Arsenal Air 100	'F-ZABY'	403	Spare wings with ASPAC.	PV
☐ Arsenal Air 102	F-CBQZ	25		RA
☐ Ateliers Aéronautiques de Colombes AAC.1 [Junkers Ju 52/3mg10e]	'334'	216	216	RAX
☐ Avia 15A				RA
☐ Avia 40P				PV
☐ Avia 41P		M3		RA
☐ Avialsa-Scheibe A.60 Fauconnet [L-Spatz 55]				RA
☐ Avialsa-Scheibe A.60 Fauconnet [L-Spatz 55]	F-CDLH	130		RAC
☐ Beech C18S Expeditor (C-45F) (UC-45F) (JRB-4)	N61909	8608	44-87349, Bu44676, 76 – with A.A. Ile de France.	RA
☐ Bell 47G-1	710	710	On loan to Musée ALAT.	–
☐ Bernard 191 Grand Raid	F-AJGP	2908/02		PV
☐ Biot Planeur				PV
☐ Blériot IX		1		RA
☐ Blériot XI				PV
☐ Blériot XI-2		686		PV
☐ Blériot XI-2		878		RA
☐ Blériot XXXVI				RA
☐ Boeing 299-O Fortress (B-17G)	F-BGSO	8289	44-8889	RA
☐ Boeing 707-328B			Front fuselage only.	PV
☐ Boeing 707-328B	F-BLCD	18941		RA
☐ Boeing 747-128	F-BPVJ	20541	N28903	PV
☐ Boeing-Stearman A75N1 Kaydet (PT-17)	41-8860	75-2419	41-8860, N61053	RA
☐ Boisavia B.601L Mercurey	F-BIRE	102		RA
☐ Breguet / British Aircraft Corporation Jaguar A	A04	A04	F-ZWRE	RA
☐ Breguet 14A2			Front fuselage only	RA

Type	Reg/Ser	C/N	PI/Notes	Status
☐ Breguet 14A2	F-WAHR	2016	2016	PV
☐ Breguet 19 Super Bidon		3		RA
☐ Breguet 19GR Grand Raid	1685	1685		RA
☐ Breguet 900	F-CAAA	6		RA
☐ Breguet 901 Mouette	F-CAJA	01	F-WAJA	PV
☐ Breguet 941S	04	04		RA
☐ Breguet 1001 Taon	02	02		RA
☐ Breguet 1050 Alizé	10	10		RA
☐ Breguet 1150 Atlantic	61	61	61, 254 (Netherlands)	RA
☐ Breguet G 111 (G 11E)	F-WFKC	1		PV
☐ Brochet MB.83 (MB.80)	F-BGLG	7	On loan to Epsilon.	–
☐ Bruel-Duhamel-Molinari Hélicoptère	F-WEPH	01	On loan to Musée ALAT.	–
☐ Bücker Bü 181C-3 Bestmann	SV+NJ	330844/FR-15	SV+NJ, F-BBNA	RA
☐ Canadair CL-215-I	F-ZBAY/23	1023	CF-TUW	RA
☐ Caquot Balloon				RA
☐ Carmam JP.15/36 Aiglon				RA
☐ Castel C.25S	F-CRFX	203	F-CBOP	RA
☐ Castel C.242		104		PV
☐ Castel C.301S	F-CBYM	1054	F-CBYM, F-CREV	RA
☐ Castel C.310P	F-CRBS	131	F-CALM	RA
☐ Castel C.311P	F-CAYN	290/19		RA
☐ Castel-Mauboussin CM.8/13	F-AZHF	01	F-CCHM	RA
☐ Caudron G.3	C.324	324		PV
☐ Caudron G.4	C.1720	1720		PV
☐ Caudron C.60	F-AINX	6184/49		PV
☐ Caudron C.109/1 (C.109)	F-PFLN	6192/6	F-AIQI	RA
☐ Caudron C.277R Luciole (C.272/4)	F-AOFX	7156/14		PV
☐ Caudron C.282/8 Phalène	F-AMKT	6770/26	On loan to A.A. Toulouse.	–
☐ Caudron C.366 Atalante		6808/4		RA
☐ Caudron C.480 Frégate				RAC
☐ Caudron C.510 Pélican	F-BDXK	6981/2	F-ANKL	RA
☐ Caudron C.600 Aiglon	F-AZCO	Peitz-3	F-BCEV	RA
☐ Caudron C.635M Simoun	'F-ANRO'	477/8519/428	T-585, CS-ADG	PVX
☐ Caudron C.714R		01		RA
☐ Caudron C.800 Épervier	F-CAFB	9865/205	On loan to M. Trad Aéronavale.	–
☐ Caudron C.800 Épervier	F-CCCA	9921/261		RAD
☐ Caudron C.800 Épervier	334	9994/334		PV
☐ Cessna 305C Bird Dog (L-19E) (O-1E)	24508	24508		RA
☐ Chaize Pilatre Balloon	F-AZDC	1	F-WZDC	RAA
☐ Chanute Glider (R)				PV
☐ Chapeau JC.1 Levrier	F-PCDQ	01	F-WCDQ	RA
☐ Charles et Robert Gas Balloon				RA
☐ Charles et Robert Gas Balloon (R)	F-GEAE	1	F-WEAE	RAA
☐ Cierva C.8L (Avro 617)	G-EBYY			PV
☐ Colomban MC-10 Cri-Cri	F-PTXJ	01		PV
☐ Comte de la Vaux Airship			Nacelle only	PV
☐ Construcciones Aeronáuticas (CASA) 2.111D (2.111A) [Heinkel He 111H-16]	BR.2I-129	123	B.2H-118 – in Spanish markings	RA
☐ Croses EC-6 Mini Criquet	F-PVQI	01		PV
☐ Curtiss-Wright CW-1 Junior	F-AZBR	1089	NC10907, N10907	RA
☐ Dassault MD-311 Flamant	280	280		RA
☐ Dassault MD-315R Flamant	130	130		RA
☐ Dassault MD-450 Ouragan	154	154		PV
☐ Dassault MD-452C Mystère IIC	104	104	On loan to CAEA	–
☐ Dassault Mystère IVA	01	01		PV
☐ Dassault Mystère IVA	1	1	On loan to A.A. Toulouse.	–
☐ Dassault Mystère IVA	23	23		RA
☐ Dassault Mystère IVA	'289'	105	105	PVX
☐ Dassault Mystère IVA	186	186	On loan to M.E. de la Chasse.	–
☐ Dassault Mystère IVA	210	210	Front fuselage only	PV
☐ Dassault Mystère IVN	01	01	On loan to CAEA.	–
☐ Dassault Super Mystère B2	'153'	11	11	PVX
☐ Dassault Super Mystère B2	59	59	On loan to M.A. du Berry.	–
☐ Dassault Super Mystère B2	90	90		RA
☐ Dassault Mirage IIIA	01	01		PV
☐ Dassault Mirage IIIB	226	226		RA
☐ Dassault Mirage IIIC	21	21	On loan to Musée SNECMA.	–
☐ Dassault Mirage IIIC	42	42		RA
☐ Dassault Mirage IIIC	74	74		RA
☐ Dassault Mirage IIIC	90	90	On loan to A.A. Toulouse.	–
☐ Dassault Mirage IIIE	460	460		RA
☐ Dassault Mirage IIIE	617	617		RA
☐ Dassault Mirage IIIR	334	334		PV
☐ Dassault Mirage IIIR	336	336		RA
☐ Dassault Mirage IIIRS	R-2115	1042	In Swiss markings.	PV
☐ Dassault Mirage IIIV	01	01		PV
☐ Dassault Mirage IVA	02	02		RA
☐ Dassault Mirage IVA	9	9		PV
☐ Dassault Mirage IVP (IVA)	62	62		RA
☐ Dassault Mirage F.1 (FSM)	'01'			PVX
☐ Dassault Mirage G.8	01	01		PV
☐ Dassault Mirage 2000C	01	01		PV
☐ Dassault Mirage 4000	01	01		RA

☐ Dassault Etendard IVM	56	56		RA
☐ Dassault Falcon 20	F-WLKB	01	F-WLKB, F-BLKB	RA
☐ Dassault Falcon 20F	F-BMSS	2/402	F-WMSS	RA
☐ Dassault Mercure 100	F-BTTD	4		PV
☐ De Havilland D.H.9	F1258			PV
☐ De Havilland D.H.80A Puss Moth	F-AZPM	2151	CH-271, F-ANRZ	RA
☐ De Havilland D.H.89A Dragon Rapide (D.H.89B Dominie I)	F-BHCD	6706	HG721, G-ALGB	PV
☐ De Havilland D.H.100 Vampire FB.6	J-1155	664	In Swiss markings	RA
☐ De Havilland D.H.112 Venom FB.1R	J-1636	846	In Swiss markings	RA
☐ De Havilland D.H.115 Vampire T.55	185	15775	In Irish markings – on loan to Musée du Château de Savigny.	–
☐ De Rouge-Chabrillan-Bouffort Elytroplan				PV
☐ Delta Atlas 14 Hang Glider				PV
☐ Deperdussin B				PV
☐ Deperdussin Monocoque		334		PV
☐ Deveque RD.700 Hot Air Balloon	F-GEDT	12		RAA
☐ Dewoitine D.520	603	603	On loan to CAEA.	–
☐ Dewoitine D.520	'277'	862	862	PVX
☐ Dewoitine D.520DC	650	650	On loan to Mus. Trad. Aéronavale.	–
☐ Dewoitine D.530	F-AJTE	06		RA
☐ Donnet-Lévêque A				PV
☐ Dornier Do 28B-1	F-ZBBF	3032	D-IBEH	RA
☐ Douglas DC-3A-456 Skytrain (C-47A)	'2100558'	12251	42-92449, F-BEFB, 92249	RAX
☐ Douglas DC-3A-456 Skytrain (C-47A) (Dakota III)	12471	12471	42-92647, KG436, EI-ACT, EI-ALT, N12471	RA
☐ Douglas DC-3A-467 Skytrain (C-47B)	43-49194	15010/26455	43-49194, OK-???, 49194, (F-OGFI) – front fuselage only.	PV
☐ Douglas DC-6B	45473	45473	N3026C, 45473, (N72534) – front fuselage only.	PV
☐ Douglas DC-7C/AMOR	45061	45061	HB-IBK, LN-MOG, F-ZBCA	RA
☐ Douglas DC-8-53 (DC-8-33)	45570	45570	F-BIUZ	PV
☐ Douglas A-26B Invader	39223	6936	41-39223, N74Y – on loan to A.A. Toulouse.	–
☐ Douglas A-26B Invader	44-34773	28052	44-34773, N67944	RA
☐ Douglas AD-4NA Skyraider (AD-4N)	53	7779	Bu126979	RA
☐ Douglas A-4SU Skyhawk (A4D-2N) (A-4C)				RA
☐ Douglas A-4SU Skyhawk (A4D-2N) (A-4C)				RA
☐ Dupuy de Lome Airship			Nacelle only	RA
☐ English Electric EA.1 Canberra B.6	763		WJ763	RA
☐ Esnault-Pelterie REP D				RA
☐ Esnault-Pelterie REP K		58		PV
☐ Fabre Hydravion (R)				PV
☐ Farman MF-7	15	446	In Belgian markings.	PV
☐ Farman HF-20	'275'			PVX
☐ Farman F.60 Goliath	F-HMFU	3	Fuselage only	PV
☐ Farman F.192	'F-AJJB'	7248/4	F-AJLU, F-AQCP, F-BAOP	RAX
☐ Farman F.455 Moustique	F-AOYL	01		PV
☐ Fauvel AV.36	F-CRRB	102	F-CBRB	PV
☐ Fauvel AV.45	F-CCHR	02	F-WCHR	RA
☐ Ferber 6bis (R)				PV
☐ Fiat G.91R/3	99+39	91-515	KD+505, EC+315, MD+315, MB+255, 32+46	RA
☐ Fieseler Fi 103A-1				PV
☐ Fieseler Fi 103A-1				RA
☐ Focke-Achgelis Fa 330A-1 Bachstelze				PV
☐ Focke-Achgelis Fa 330A-1 Bachstelze				RAD
☐ Fokker D VII	6796/18			PV
☐ Fouga CM.170R Magister	1	1		RA
☐ Fouga CM.170R Magister	23	23		PV
☐ Fouga CM.170R Magister	26	26		PV
☐ Fouga CM.170R Magister	28	28	Front fuselage only.	PV
☐ Fouga CM.170R Magister	29	29		PV
☐ Fouga CM.173 (Potez 94A)	01	01		RA
☐ Fouga CM.175 Zéphyr	17	17		RA
☐ Fouga CM.175 Zéphyr	27	27		RA
☐ Fournier RF.2	F-BJSY	02	F-WJSY	PV
☐ Gambetta Balloon				PV
☐ Gary GR.1 Gyrocopter	F-WYDD	01		PV
☐ Gasne RG-3	F-WBGN	01		RA
☐ Gloster Meteor NF.11	NF.11-1		WM296 – on loan to M.E. de la Chasse.	–
☐ Gloster Meteor NF.11	NF.11-5		WM300	RA
☐ Gloster Meteor NF.11	NF.11-8		WM303 – on loan to A.A. Toulouse.	–
☐ Gloster Meteor NF.11	NF.11-9		WM304	RA
☐ Gloster Meteor NF.11	NF.11-24		WM382 – on loan to Mus. du Château du Savigny.	–
☐ Gloster Meteor NF.14	NF.14-747	5759	WS747	RA
☐ Gourdou-Leseurre GL.25 (B.7)	F-APOZ	3		PV
☐ Grassi Ornithoptere				RA
☐ Grinvalds G-801 Orion	F-PYKF	01	F-WYKF	RA
☐ Guerchais-Roche SA.103 Emouchet	F-CRHB	69	F-CBCS	RA

☐ Guerchais-Roche SA.103 Emouchet	F-CROF	94	F-CBJB	RA
☐ Guerchais-Roche SA.103 Emouchet	F-CRPP	106	F-CBCV	RA
☐ Guerchais-Roche SA.104 Emouchet	F-CRLL	253	F-CBDV	PV
☐ Hamburger Flugzeugbau HFB.320 Hansa	F-WZIH	1024	D-CARO, YA+111, CA+111, D-9536, 16+07	PV
☐ Hanriot HD-14	F-AMBP	336		RA
☐ Hawker P.1067 Hunter F.4	ID-44	8138	In Belgian markings – on loan to Mus. du Château de Savigny.	–
☐ Hawker P.1099 Hunter F.58	J-4099	41H/697466	In Swiss markings.	PV
☐ Heinkel He 46D	846	8146	??+BL	RA
☐ Heinkel He 162A-2	'1'	120015		RAC
☐ Hiller UH12B	699	699	699, (F-BNGM)	PV
☐ Hirsch HR.100	F-WGVC	01		PV
☐ Hispano HA-1112M1L [Messerschmitt Bf 109G]	C.4K-156	172	In Spanish markings	RA
☐ Hurel Aviette	F-WTXS	01		RAD
☐ Hurel-Dubois HD.10	F-BFAN	1	F-WFAN	PV
☐ Hurel-Dubois HD.34	F-BICR	4		RA
☐ Jacobs D.F.S. 230B-2	H4+??		With A.A. Ile de France.	–
☐ Jacobs D.F.S. 230C-1	H4+??		With A.A. Ile de France.	–
☐ Jacobs D.F.S. 230C-1	H4+??	36-16	With A.A. Ile de France.	–
☐ Jacobs Habicht II (D.F.S. 108-53)	'F-CAEX'	2	F-CCAG	PVX
☐ Jacobs Meise (D.F.S. 108-70)	F-CRBT	12/259	F-CAGK	PV
☐ Jacobs Weihe (D.F.S. 108-68)	F-CRMX	3	F-CBGT, F-CRMD – on loan to M.R.A.	–
☐ Jodel D.92 Bébé	F-PEPF	01	F-WEPF	PV
☐ Jodel D.112 Club	F-BFCG	320		RA
☐ Jodel D.119	F-PINS	613		RA
☐ Junkers F 13		609	O-BACC may be c/n 600.	RA
☐ Junkers J 9 (D-1)	'5929/18'			PVX
☐ Kellner-Bechereau E.60	01	01		RA
☐ Lebaudy Airship			Nacelle only	RA
☐ Leduc 016	'03'		01 – painted as Leduc 010	PVX
☐ Leduc 022	01	01	Incorporates parts of c/n 02	PV
☐ Levasseur Antoinette				PV
☐ Lilienthal Normal-Segelapparat (R)				PV
☐ Liore et Olivier LeO C.302	F-BDAD	15		PV
☐ Lockheed 580 (T-33A)	14115	580-5409	51-4115	RA
☐ Lockheed 580 (T-33A)	35055	580-8394	53-5055	RA
☐ Lockheed 580 (T-33A)	35061	580-8400	53-5061	RA
☐ Lockheed 580 (T-33A) (RT-33A)	41553	580-9184	54-1553	RA
☐ Lockheed 683-10-19 Starfighter (F-104G)	22+40	683-7118	KE+418, DD+110 – on loan from Wehrtechnische S. GER.	RA
☐ Lockheed 726-45-17 Neptune (P2V-7)	147563	726-7177	Bu147563 – on loan to M.E. de la Chasse.	–
☐ Lockheed 726-45-17 Neptune (P2V-7)	148334	726-7262	Bu148334	RA
☐ Lockheed 726-45-17 Neptune (P2V-7)	148335	726-7264	Bu148335	PV
☐ Lockheed 749-79-22 Constellation (649-79-21)	F-ZVMV	749-2503	NC86520, XA-GOQ, NC86520, F-BAZR	RA
☐ Luft-Verkehrs-Gesellschaft (L.V.G.) C VI	9041/18			RA
☐ Martin 179G Marauder (B-26G)	44-68219	9699		PV
☐ Matra-Moynet M.360-6 Jupiter	F-BLKE	01	F-WLKE	RA
☐ Matra-Moynet M.360-6 Jupiter	F-BLKY	03	F-WLKY	RA
☐ Mauboussin M.123C Corsaire (M.129)	F-PJKQ	189	F-BCIT	RA
☐ Mauboussin M.125 Corsaire	F-BCEM	919	On loan to A.A. Ile de France.	–
☐ Max Holste MH.1521M Broussard				RA
☐ Max Holste MH.1521M Broussard	18	18		RA
☐ Max Holste MH.260	F-ZAGG	01	F-WJDV – cockpit section only	RA
☐ Messerschmitt Bf 109E-3			Front fuselage only	RAC
☐ Microlight	94-FJ			RA
☐ Microlight				RA
☐ Microlight				RA
☐ Microlight				RA
☐ Microlight				RA
☐ Mignet HM-8B				RA
☐ Mignet HM-14 Pou-du-Ciel				PV
☐ Mignet HM-280 Pou-Maquis				RA
☐ Mignet HM-320 Pou-du-Ciel	F-PHZI	01M		RA
☐ Mikoyan-Gurevich MiG-21F-13	1103	161103	In Czech markings.	PV
☐ Mikoyan-Gurevich MiG-23ML	'26'	0390324028	558 (DDR), 20+30 – in false Soviet markings.	PVX
☐ Morane-Saulnier A-1 (R)	F-AZAO	03	On loan to Memorial Flight.	–
☐ Morane-Saulnier H		156		PV
☐ Morane-Saulnier MS.30	F-ABAO	2283		RA
☐ Morane-Saulnier MS.230	1048	1048	1048, F-BGMQ	PV
☐ Morane-Saulnier MS.317 (MS.315)	F-BHHF	6566/312	F-BCBR – on loan to M.A. Presqu'ile.	–
☐ Morane-Saulnier MS.317 (MS.315)	F-BCNM	6582/328		PV
☐ Morane-Saulnier MS.406C-1 (D-3801)		15(?)	J-277 (Switzerland) – in false French markings.	RAX
☐ Morane-Saulnier MS.472 Vanneau	122	122	Front fuselage only.	PV
☐ Morane-Saulnier MS.472 Vanneau	254	254		RA
☐ Morane-Saulnier MS.500 Criquet [Fieseler Fi 156 Storch]	'D-EMAW'	1034 (?)	1034 (?)	RAX

☐ Morane-Saulnier MS.505 Criquet (MS.502) [Fieseler Fi 156 Storch]	F-BIPJ	149/33	F-BAOU	RA
☐ Morane-Saulnier MS.733 Alcyon	F-BLXS	114	114 – on loan to Ass. Orion.	–
☐ Morane-Saulnier MS.733 Alcyon	F-AZAF	190	190	RA
☐ Morane-Saulnier MS.760A Paris I	40	40		RA
☐ Morane-Saulnier MS.880B Rallye Club	F-BJSF	03	F-WJSF	RA
☐ Moto Delta G.10 Hang Glider				RA
☐ Mudry CAP.10B	03	03		RA
☐ Mudry CAP.20	F-TFVU	1	F-BTAC	RA
☐ Mudry CAP.232	F-GJGM	07		RA
☐ Nieuport 2N				PV
☐ Nieuport 11	'N.556'	976	N.976	PVX
☐ Nieuport-Delage 29C.1	'R-251'	010	N1284S	PVX
☐ Nord N.262A-44	16	16		RA
☐ Nord N.1101 Noralpha (Ramier I) [Messerschmitt Me 208]	F-GJBQ	177	177 – on loan to Mus. Presque Ile.	–
☐ Nord N.1101 Ramier I [Messerschmitt Me 208]	135	135		RA
☐ Nord N.1203-VI Norécrin	F-BICY	373		RA
☐ Nord N.1300 [Schneider Grunau Baby IIB]	F-CRBZ	26	F-CCCA – on loan to Memorial Flight.	–
☐ Nord N.1300 [Schneider Grunau Baby IIB]	F-CRRQ	40	F-CBEO, F-CREO	RA
☐ Nord N.1300 [Schneider Grunau Baby IIB]	F-CRKX	90	F-CAQL	RA
☐ Nord N.1300 [Schneider Grunau Baby IIB]	F-CRQU	159	F-CAIK, (F-CRKU)	RA
☐ Nord N.1500 Griffon II	02	02		PV
☐ Nord N.2200	01	01	F-WFRD – on loan to A.A. Arm.	–
☐ Nord N.2501 Noratlas	162	162		RA
☐ Nord N.2501 Noratlas	194	194		RA
☐ Nord N.3202	57	57		PV
☐ Nord N.3202	67	67		RA
☐ Nord N.3202	F-AZFL	92		–
☐ Nord N.3400	01	01		RA
☐ Nord N.3400	131	131		RA
☐ Nord NC.701 Martinet [Siebel Si 204D-1]			Front fuselage only	RA
☐ Nord NC.702 Martinet [Siebel Si 204A-1]	282	282	On loan to CAEA	–
☐ Nord NC.856A Norvigie	111	111	On loan to A.A. Ile de France.	–
☐ Nord NC.900A-8 [Focke-Wulf Fw 190A-8]	'7298'	62 (730924)	62	PVX
☐ North American NA-122 Mustang (P-51D)	'466318'	122-31597	44-63871, Fv26039, (Israel), N9772F	PVX
☐ North American NA-182 Texan (T-6G)	'51-14915'	182-209	51-14522	PVX
☐ North American NA-221 Sabre (F-86K)	54841	221-81	55-4841	PV
☐ North American NA-224 Super Sabre (F-100D)	52736	224-3	55-2736	PV
☐ Oemichen Helicostat 6		6		PV
☐ Omega O-84 Hot Air Balloon	F-BOHE	03		RA
☐ Ossoaviakhim Balloon			Nacelle only	PV
☐ Paramoteur Adventure F1				PV
☐ Paumier 1912				PV
☐ Payen PA.49B Katy	F-WGVA	01		PV
☐ Pfalz D XII	2690/18	3240		PV
☐ Piasecki PD-18 Retriever (HUP-2)	Bu130077		With A.A. Ile de France.	–
☐ Piccard Balloon			Nacelle only.	PV
☐ Piel CP.1310 Super Emeraude	F-BMJJ	938		PV
☐ Piper PA-18-95 Super Cub (L-18C)	'N1957C'	18-1430	51-15430	RAX
☐ Polikarpov I-153	9			RA
☐ Potez 36/13	F-ALQT	2620		PV
☐ Potez 43/7	F-APXO	3588/11		PV
☐ Potez 53		3402/10		PV
☐ Potez 58/2	F-ANYA	3875		RA
☐ Potez 842	F-BNAN	3		RA
☐ Renard et Krebs Airship 'La France'				RA
☐ Renard Hélicoptère (R)				RA
☐ Republic P-47D Thunderbolt	420371		44-20371	PV
☐ Republic F-84E Thunderjet	51-9600		0 51-9600, 9600	RA
☐ Republic F-84F Thunderstreak	28875		52-8875	PV
☐ Republic F-105G Thunderchief (F-105F)	63-8300	F-77		PV
☐ Royal Aircraft Factory B.E.2c	9969			PV
☐ Saconney Cerf Volant (R)				PV
☐ Santos-Dumont 14bis (R)				PV
☐ Santos-Dumont XX Demoiselle				PV
☐ Schleicher Ka-4 Rhönlerche II	D-7196	65/57		RA
☐ Schleicher Ka-6 Rhönsegler		333		RA
☐ Schneider Grunau SG-38 (D.F.S. 108-14)		173		PV
☐ Schneider Grunau SG-38 (D.F.S. 108-14)	'45'	31	31	PVX
☐ Schreck FBA.17HT4	F-AJOR	195		PV
☐ Short S.25 Sandringham 7 (Sunderland MR.III)	F-OBIP	SH.57C	JM719, G-AKCO, VH-APG	RA
☐ Sikorsky S-55B		55864	On loan to Musée ALAT.	–
☐ Sikorsky S-58	53	SA-53	On loan to Musée ALAT.	–
☐ Sikorsky S-58	121	SA-121		RA
☐ Siren-Bertin C.34	F-CCAY	02		PV
☐ Société d'Études et de Constructions Aéro-Navales SUC.10 Courlis	'F-BBXY'	31	F-BEKH	RAX
☐ Société National d'Étude et de Construction de Moteurs d'Aviation C400P Atar Volant	'01'	2	2	PVX
☐ Société Pour l'Aviation et ses Dérivés (SPAD) VII	S.254/2	254		PV

☐ Société Pour l'Aviation et ses Dérivés (SPAD) XIIIC.1	S5295	S5295		PV
☐ Société Pour l'Aviation et ses Dérivés (SPAD) 52	3125	3125	F-AEDD	RA
☐ Société Pour l'Aviation et ses Dérivés (SPAD) 54/1	F-AHBE	8		PV
☐ Sopwith 1 1/2 Strutter	556	556		PV
☐ SSZ-22 Airship			Nacelle only	RA
☐ Stampe & Vertongen S.V.4A	38	38	On loan to Mus. Trad. Aéronavale.	–
☐ Stampe & Vertongen S.V.4C	F-BBQL	149	149	PV
☐ Stampe & Vertongen S.V.4C	F-BMRU	643	643 – on loan to M.E. de la Chasse.	–
☐ Sud Fennec [North American NA-174 Trojan (T-28A)]	121	174-344	51-7491	RA
☐ Sud SA.3210 Super Frelon	01	01	F-ZWWE	PV
☐ Sud SA.610A Ludion				PV
☐ Sud-Est Aquilon 203 [De Havilland D.H.112]	53	53	On loan to Mus Trad. Aéronavale.	–
☐ Sud-Est SE.210 Caravelle	F-BHHI	02	F-WHHI – front fuselage only	PV
☐ Sud-Est SE.210 Caravelle 12/58T	F-GCVL	273	OY-SAE	PV
☐ Sud-Est SE.210 Caravelle III	116/F-ZACE	116	OH-LED – on loan to M.E. de la Chasse.	–
☐ Sud-Est SE.210 Caravelle III	141	141	F-WJTK, F-BJTK	RA
☐ Sud-Est SE.210 Caravelle III (IA) (I)	F-BJTR	22	F-WJTR, OH-LEB	RA
☐ Sud-Est SE.212 Durandal	01	01	Wings only	RA
☐ Sud-Est SE.535 Mistral	4	4		PV
☐ Sud-Est SE.3101	F-WFDQ	01		PV
☐ Sud-Est SE.3130 Alouette II	01	01		RA
☐ Sud-Est SE.3130 Alouette II	02	02		PV
☐ Sud-Est SE.3130 Alouette II	329	1703		RA
☐ Sud-Est SE.3130 Alouette II	787	1787		RA
☐ Sud-Est SE.3160 Alouette III				RA
☐ Sud-Est SE.5000 Baroudeur	3	3	With A.A. Ile de France.	–
☐ Sud-Ouest SO-1110 Ariel II	F-WFRQ	01		PV
☐ Sud-Ouest SO-1220 Djinn	F-WGVD	1220.02	F-WGVD, F-BGVD	PV
☐ Sud-Ouest SO-1221S Djinn	51	FR-101	On loan to A.A. Toulouse.	–
☐ Sud-Ouest SO-4050 Vautour IIB	634	109		RA
☐ Sud-Ouest SO-4050 Vautour IIB	640	119	On loan to A.A. Toulouse.	–
☐ Sud-Ouest SO-4050 Vautour IIN	304	11	On loan to Mus. du Château du Savigny.	–
☐ Sud-Ouest SO-4050 Vautour IIN	307	16		RA
☐ Sud-Ouest SO-4050 Vautour IIN	330	69		RA
☐ Sud-Ouest SO-4050 Vautour IIN	337	85	On loan to Musée SNECMA.	–
☐ Sud-Ouest SO-4050 Vautour IIN	358	128		PV
☐ Sud-Ouest SO-6000 Triton	F-WFKY	03	With parts of c/n 05 F-WFKX.	PV
☐ Sud-Ouest SO-9000 Trident	01	01		PV
☐ Sukhoi Su-22M4		30916	590 (DDR), 25+27, 98+09 – in false Soviet colours.	RAX
☐ Supermarine 361 Spitfire LF.XVIe	'TB597'	CBAF-IX-3310	RR263	PVX
☐ Svenska Aeroplan Aktiebolaget (SAAB) 29B (J 29B)	Fv29665	29665		RA
☐ Svenska Aeroplan Aktiebolaget (SAAB) 32E Lansen (32B) (J 32B) (J 32E)	Fv32515	32515		RA
☐ Svenska Aeroplan Aktiebolaget (SAAB) 35A Draken (J 35A)	Fv35069	35069		PV
☐ Svenska Aeroplan Aktiebolaget (SAAB) 37 Viggen (Sk 37) (Sk 37E)	Fv37808	37808		PV
☐ Svenska Aeroplan Aktiebolaget (SAAB) 91B Safir	F-BHAK	91296	SE-XAF	RA
☐ Szybowcowy Zaklad Doswiadczalny S.Z.D.24C Foka Standard	F-CCHX	W-150		PV
☐ Tissandier Balloon				RA
☐ Transall C-160D			Front fuselage only.	RA
☐ Trucavaysse TCV.01	F-CRPX	01		RA
☐ Vertol V.43 Shawnee (H-21C) (CH-21C)	69	FR-69	On loan to Mus. ALAT.	–
☐ Victor Minié V.M.A. 200 Milan [Jacobs Weihe]	F-CBGR	30		PV
☐ Victor Minié V.M.A. 200 Milan [Jacobs Weihe]	F-CCCD	32		RA
☐ Voisin LA 10				RA
☐ Voisin LA5 b2	V.955			PV
☐ Voisin-Farman 1 bis (R)				PV
☐ Vought F-8P Crusader (F-8E(FN))	10	1227	(Bu151741)	RA
☐ Vuia 1		1		PV
☐ Wassmer WA.21 Javelot II	58	58		RA
☐ Wassmer WA.22A Super Javelot	114	114		RA
☐ Wassmer WA.30 Bijave	F-CDIY	207		RA
☐ Wassmer WA.51 Pacific	F-BPTT	01	F-BPTT, F-WVKT	RA
☐ Westland Lysander IIIA	'N7791'	1217		RAX
☐ Wright Baby				PV
☐ Wright Flyer (R)				PV
☐ Wytwornia Sprzetu Komunikacyjnego (WSK) SM-1Wb [Mil Mi-1M]	3009	403009	In Czech markings – on loan to CELAG.	–
☐ Yakovlev Yak-3	'4'			PVX
☐ Zeppelin LZ-113			Nacelle only	PV
☐ Zlin Z-326 Trener Master	F-BORT	923		PV
☐ Zodiac MBZ-31	F-BAIZ	108		RA
☐ Zodiac ZD			Nacelle only – on loan to Mus. Trad. Aéronavale.	–

94 VAL-DE-MARNE

MUSÉE DE LA RÉSISTANCE (FRA182)

Address:	C/o M.J. Laplume, 76 Avenue Georges Gosnat, 94200 Ivry-sur-Seine.
Tel:	01 46 72 40 99
Admission:	By prior permission only.
Location:	Ivry is just south of the Boulevard Peripherique in the southern suburbs of Paris.

Several years ago the Musée de l'Air recovered a number of D.F.S. 230 troop carrying gliders. The bare frame of one of these has gone to this private museum which traces the history of the resistance movement in the Paris area. The collection contains many items of memorabilia, photographs and documents. Several personal stories of the harrowing times and the dedication to the cause are shown.

TYPE	REG/SER	CON. NO.	PI/NOTES	STATUS
☐ Jacobs D.F.S. 230C-1				PVD

95 VAL-D'OISE

COLLECTION BÉZARD (FRA183)

Address:	33 Avenue de Boran, Gouvieux, 60260 Lamorlaye.
Tel:	03 44 21 93 43
Admission:	By prior permission only.
Location:	At Persan Beaumont airfield which is about 2 km north east of Beaumont off the D 924.

Two light jets are housed in the owner's hangar at Persan-Beaumont. In the 1950s the Fouga company fitted small jet engines to airframes based on Castel-Mauboussin gliders and these eventually led to the design of the successful Magister trainer. Six Sylphes were built at Aire-sur-Adour. Charles Bézard acquired the only known survivor. After a five year restoration it flew again. The aircraft has now been donated to the Musée Régional de l'Air at Angers. Parts from the CM.8/13 were used in the rebuild. The twin boom S.I.P.A. Minijet made its maiden flight in January 1952 and only eight were completed. Two now exist, the one at Persan which has not flown for several years and one in the U.S.A. The Cobra was designed by Stelo Frati and made its maiden flight in November 1960. The first prototype of this two seat trainer crashed and the second airframe, which was never completed, will need many hours work before it takes to the air.

TYPE	REG/SER	CON. NO.	PI/NOTES	STATUS
☐ Castel-Mauboussin CM.8/13	F-CRRE	3	F-BFDJ – fuselage only.	RA
☐ Fournier RF-9	F-CAHY	02		RAA
☐ Procaer F.400 Cobra	F-AZAD	02		RA
☐ Société Industrielle pour l'Aéronautique (SIPA) S.200 Minijet	F-PDHE	7	F-BDHE	RA

RÉTRO PLANES D'ARGENTEUIL (FRA184)

Address:	12-14 Boulevard Léon Felix, 95107 Argenteuil
Tel:	01 34 23 41 00
Fax:	01 34 23 44 44 courrier@ville-argenteuil.fr
Admission:	When the town hall is open.
Location:	In the centre of the town.

Members of this group spent ten years constructing a replica Donnet-Lévêque flying boat for display in the town. It took eight people over ten thousand working hours to complete the project. The type first flew in 1912 and served with distinction in many countries. The exhibition opened on October 18th 2005. The history of the company and of the replica can be seen with photographs and models.

TYPE	REG/SER	CON. NO.	PI/NOTES	STATUS
☐ Donnet-Lévêque A (R)				RA

GERMANY

A 5, 6, 15, 23, 28, 61, 100, 119
unknown: 70
various: 54
North Sea
DENMARK
Baltic Sea
Rugen
Sassnitz
Kiel Bay
Puttgarden
Mecklenburger Bucht
Pomeranian Bay
0 50 100 km
0 50 100 miles
Kiel
Lubeck
Rostock
POLAND
Emden
Bremerhaven
Hamburg
Bremen
NETHERLANDS
Wittenberge
Berlin
Potsdam
Osnabruck
Magdeburg
Munster
Bielefeld
Dessau
Cottbus
Duisburg
Dortmund
Gottingen
Essen
Halle
Leipzig
Dusseldorf
Kassel
Dresden
Köln
Eisenach
Erfurt
Bad Hersfeld
Siegen
Aachen
Bonn
Chemnitz
Zwickau
Hof
LUX.
Wurzburg
CZECH REPUBLIC
Nurnberg
Heidelberg
Regensberg
Stuttgart
Passau
FRANCE
Ulm
Augsburg
München
Freiburg
AUSTRIA
Garmisch-Partenkirchen
Bodensee
SWITZERLAND
87, 99, 101, 91, 30, 105, 65,134, 128, 137, 96, 51, 93, 72, 77, 2, 1, 143, 131, 92, 24, 147, 20, 83,86, 149, 50, 39, 32, 89, 81, 66, 118, 69, 127, 44,67, 102, 121, 59,68, 82, 111, 35, 74, 58, 116, 146, 45, 46, 47, 49, 52, 73, 40, 132, 133, 135,136, 85, 138, 56, 113, 79, 31,109,152, 10, 98, 103, 48, 108, 130, 42, 22, 27,124, 21, 76,153, 60, 78,80, 17, 8, 88, 123, 157, 151, 112, 114, 117, 154, 150, 84, 55, 75, 38, 43, 115, 64, 122, 4, 104, 148, 7, 34, 18, 3,106, 140, 97, 53, 36, 144, 126, 14, 129, 139, 141, 33, 37,107, 11, 63, 12, 25, 41, 16,90, 19, 57, 95, 13,26,110,142, 71, 62, 9, 145, 125, 29,156, 94,120, 155

AERONAUTICUM – DEUTSCHES MARINE LUFTSCHIFF UND MARINEFLIEGER MUSEUM (GER1)

Address:	Peterstrasse Platz 3, D-27637 Nordholz.
Tel:	04741-94-1074
Fax:	04741-94-1090
Email:	info@aeronauticum.de
Admission:	Mid-March-June September-October Monday-Saturday 1300-1700; Wednesday 1300-2000, Sunday 1000-1800: July-August Daily 1000-1800.
Location:	In the south eastern part of the town which is about 25 km north of Bremerhaven.

During World War I Nordholz was an important naval airship base. The site opened in 1912 and several large hangars were constructed including one on a giant turntable. Raids on England were carried out from the field and soon after peace was declared a number of airships were destroyed by their crews so they did not fall into allied hands. The majority of the buildings were demolished over the next few years. In 1935 work started on building an airfield for Luftwaffe use and from June 1945 until August 1946 American units were in residence. Since the late 1950s the field has been home to flying squadrons of the German Navy. Members of the resident unit set up a small museum in a building on the base tracing the history of airship operations from the field. The collection grew rapidly and in 1993 a decision was taken to build a new museum which would also portray the history of naval flying in both East and West Germany. A large metal building was moved from Bremerhaven to Nordholz in 1995 and the exhibition opened in May 1997. A superb collection of models and photographs shows the construction the base and the airship operations. There is an excellent large scale representation of the airfield as it was during World War I. The use of civil airships in Germany in the inter-war period is also featured. The exhibition on naval flying since the 1950s is still being developed. Parked outside is a range of naval aircraft used by both the Bundesmarine and the Volksmarine. Missing types are being sought and a Grumman Albatross should soon be transported from Italy.

TYPE	REG/SER	CON. NO.	PI/NOTES	STATUS
☐ Bristol 171 Sycamore HR.52	'WE+543'	13473	AS+330, LC+115, 78+16, D-HALB – On loan to Focke Museum.	PVX
☐ Breguet 1150 Atlantic	61+14	28	UC+323	PV
☐ Dornier Do 28D-2 Skyservant	59+22	4197		RA
☐ Dornier Do 28D-2/OU Skyservant	59+19	4194		PV
☐ Fairey Gannet AS.4	UA+113	F9395	XG853	PV
☐ Fouga CM.170R Magister	'JC+601'	388	388 (French)	PVX
☐ Grumman G-64 Albatross (SA-16A) (HU-16A)			(USAF), (Italian A.F.) – due soon.	–
☐ Hawker P.1040 Sea Hawk 100	'VB+234'	6667	VA+234, 'VA+007', 'VA+229'	PVX
☐ Hawker P.1040 Sea Hawk 100	RB+363	6707		PV
☐ Lockheed 683-10-19 Starfighter (F-104G)	22+98	683-7181	KE+481, VA+153	PV
☐ Mikoyan-Gurevich MiG-21SPS (MiG-21PFM)	791	94A4613	In DDR markings.	RA
☐ Mil Mi-8SPS (Mi-8PS)	94+01	105100	773 (DDR)	PV
☐ Mil Mi-8TB	94+14	10575	834 (DDR)	PV
☐ Panavia PA200 Tornado IDS	43+55	4055		PV
☐ Panavia PA200 Tornado IDS	45+30	4230		RA
☐ Percival P.66 Pembroke C.54	54+08	P.66/105	CA+021, AS+560, BF+560, KS+111, SE+515	PV
☐ Piaggio FWP.149D	'91+02'	096	AS+431, DB+393, 90+77	PVX
☐ Sukhoi Su-22M4	366	25512	366 (DDR),25+05	PV
☐ Vereinigte Flugtechnische Werke – Fokker (VFW) 614	D-AXDB	G-018	(OY-RGT), 17+02	PV

AGRARHISTORISCHES MUSEUM ALT SCHWERIN (GER2)

Address:	Dorfstrasse 21, D-17214 Alt Schwerin.
Tel:	039932-49918
Fax:	039932-49917
Email:	museumaltschwerin@t-online.de
Admission:	April-October Tuesday-Sunday 1000-1700; Open on Monday May-September.
Location:	On Road 192 about 8 km north west of Malchow.

The collection was established in 1963 as part of the local museum in nearby Waren .A few years later it became an independent organisation. Historic buildings were moved to the site and the visitor can now see a farmhouse, windmill, smithy and bakery. 'Action Days' are held regularly to show how farmers worked in the past and how their lives compare with modern times. A number of farm animals can be seen in the fields of this large complex. Agricultural aviation was important in the former East Germany and two aircraft are on show along with models of a Kruk and a Dromader. The Brigadyr was in use from the mid-1950s and arrived at the Museum in 1971. The Cmelak was built at the Interflug base at Anklam from components.

TYPE	REG/SER	CON. NO.	PI/NOTES	STATUS
☐ Aero L-60 Brigadyr	DM-SLQ	151111	OK-MNA, (DDR)	PV
☐ Zlin Z-37 Cmelak		08-12	DM-SOU, DDR-SOU – composite	PV

ALBATROS FLUGMUSEUM (GER3)

Address:	Flughafen, D-70629 Stuttgart.
Tel:	0711-948-2737
Email:	info@albatros-flugmuseum.de
Admission:	April-September Daily 0800-2100; October-March Daily 0900-1800.
Location:	The airport is about 10 km south of the city just south of Autobahn A.8.

The now defunct Air Classic opened a display of aircraft in the spectator's enclosure during the 1970s. The exhibition was purchased by the owners of this museum. Building work at the site resulted in the aircraft being sold in the late 1980s to the Auto und Technik Museum at Sinsheim. The new terminal was completed in the early 1990s and the museum acquired new aircraft for the display. The Spanish built Jungmann hangs in the main hall and along the upstairs balcony are cases displaying models, uniforms and engines. The remainder of the aircraft are parked at the ends of the spectators viewing area. A replica Albatros L 73 airliner built by Manfred Pflumm has now returned to his museum at Villingen-Schwenningen.

TYPE	REG/SER	CON. NO.	PI/NOTES	STATUS
☐ Antonov An-2T	'SP-ANL'	1G 26-13	2613 (Poland) – On loan from Int. Luft. Museum.	PVX
☐ Bücker Bü 181B-1 Bestmann (Sk 25)	D-EDIB	25039	Fv25039 – on loan to Int. Luft Museum.	–
☐ Construcciones Aeronáuticas (CASA) 1.131E [Bücker Bü 131 Jungmann]	'D-EBZE'		E.3B-526	PVX
☐ Dornier Do 27A-5 (A-3)	'D-PEPO'	371	PN+103, PZ+220, 56+71, D-EDHS	PVX
☐ Junkers F 13 (FSM)	'D-1'			PVX
☐ Mil Mi-2R	SP-SAW	529021124		PV
☐ Nord N.1002 Pingouin II [Messerschmitt Bf 108B]	'D-EFAG'	163	163, HB-OAR, (D-EHUX), HB-OAR, D-EOAR, (D-EACS)	PVX
☐ North American NA-77 Texan (AT-6A)	D-FOBY	77-4176	41-217, 1608 (Portugal), G-BGGR	PV
☐ Piaggio P.149D	D-EHMG	320	AS+471, AC+471, 92+23	PV
☐ Vickers 812 Viscount	G-AVHE	363	N251V – front fuselage only	PV

ALBERT SAMMT ZEPPELIN MUSEUM (GER4)

Address:	Hauptstrasse 52, D-97996 Niederstetten.
Tel:	07932-60032
Fax:	07932-910239
Admission:	Monday 1630-1930; Tuesday 1200-1400; Wednesday-Thursday 1000-1130; Friday 1000-1130 1500-1730; Saturday-Sunday by appointment.
Location:	In the town which is about 70 km west of Nürnburg.

Albert Sammt was born in the town in 1889. He was responsible for controlling the elevators on the first Atlantic crossing by a Zeppelin in 1924. He survived the crash of the Hindenburg at Lakehurst in 1937 and was the commander of the LZ130 Count Zeppelin when the large airships were withdrawn. He died in 1982 and this museum is dedicated to his memory. On show are documents, models, photographs and memorabilia.

ALLIIERTEN MUSEUM (GER5)

Address:	Clayalle 135, D-14195 Berlin
Tel:	030-818-1990
Fax:	030-818-19991
Email:	info@AlliiertenMuseum.de
Admission:	Thursday-Tuesday 1000-1800.
Location:	In the southern part of the city centre.

Opened in June 1998, the fiftieth anniversary of the Berlin Airlift, the museum displays trace the story of the Allied involvement in the city. A former United States military site has been obtained where an old cinema and library remain. There are plans to construct a new purpose built exhibition hall. The Iroquois was used by the U.S. Army Berlin flight and the Chipmunk by the Station Flight at Gatow when it was a Royal Air Force base. The Hastings, a type used on the airlift, has recently been moved from Gatow where it spent almost twenty years parked inside the main gate. Built as the fifth production aircraft, this Hastings was delivered to Boscombe Down for trials in December 1947. The following year TG503 undertook a sales tour to the Middle and Far East and the Antipodes before being involved in further test work. In the mid-1970s it flew with the radar flight at 230 OCU. at Scampton before arriving at Gatow.

TYPE	REG/SER	CON. NO	PI/NOTES	STATUS
☐ Bell 205 Iroquois (UH-1H)	67-17305	9503		RA
☐ De Havilland D.H.C.1 Chipmunk T.10	WG466	C1/0516		PV
☐ Handley Page H.P.67 Hastings T.5 (C.1)	TG503		TG503, 8555M	PV

AUSSTELLUNG ALLIIERTE IN BERLIN (GER6)

Address:	Kurt Schumacher Damm 42-44, D-13405 Berlin.
Tel:	03397-70520
Fax:	03397-60597
Admission:	Daily 1000-1600.
Location:	In the western suburbs of the city near Tegel Airport.

The French Air Force had a display of preserved aircraft during the time they had a base at Tegel. The Fouga Magister dates from this period and was left behind when they moved out. A number of Deutsches Technikmuseum machines have spent time near the main terminal. A new military museum opened near the airport in 1999. The exhibition is run by the Association of Military Vehicle Drivers. On show are a range of military vehicles, the majority of which are owned by the members. The Varsity spent many years preserved at the former Royal Air Force base at Gatow. (Now the site of the Luftwaffen Museum). The displays are being developed and on show are several uniforms and weapons. Tegel was used in the Berlin Airlift and this features in the exhibition.

TYPE	REG/SER	CON. NO.	PI/NOTES	STATUS
☐ Fouga CM.170R Magister	52	52		PV
☐ Lockheed 683-10-19 Starfighter (F-104G)	20+04	683-2004	DA+004 (?), YA+107 – at nearby military barracks – not owned by museum.	RA
☐ Republic F-84F Thunderstreak	'DF+240'		52-6714, SE+239, DE+372, DF+126	PV
☐ Vickers 668 Varsity T.1	WF382	541	WF382, 8872M	PV

AUTO UND TECHNIK MUSEUM (GER7)

Address:	Obere Au 2, D-74889 Sinsheim.
Tel:	07261-92990
Fax:	07261-13916
Email:	info@technik-museum.de
Admission:	Daily 1000-1800.
Location:	In the town which is about 20 km south east of Heidelberg just north of Autobahn A.6.

This museum opened in the mid-1980s and occupies two vast halls and a large outside display area. Close links are maintained with the Technikmuseum Speyer and exhibits are frequently interchanged. On show at Sinsheim are cars dating from 1896 to the present day, motor cycles, railway engines, fire engines and musical instruments along with memorabilia. The museum is located next to an autobahn and several aircraft painted in false colours have been mounted in dramatic poses to attract the visitor. These machines include a former Air France Viscount, a Polish Air Force Ilyushin Il-14, two Spanish built Junkers Ju 52s, a MALEV Tupolev Tu-134 and a Sukhoi Su-22. The oldest aircraft on show is the 1911 monoplane designed by Dr. Hubner from Mossbach near Mannheim. He built two other land monoplanes and one floatplane during this period. Also on view is his 1935 ultralight Mucke. Both these types were stored for many years. A range of homebuilt aircraft and gliders can be seen. The Kaiser Ka-1 first flew at the Wasserkupe in 1952. Rudolf Kaiser later designed many types for the Schleicher company including the Rhönlerche. Several examples of the French designed flying wing Fauvel AV.36 were flown in Germany. The Friebel Aeolus uses the famous Mignet tandem wing layout. There are several other interesting homebuilts in the collection. A highlight of the exhibition is a Junkers Ju 88A rebuilt from components of an aircraft recovered from a World War II crash site. The remains of a Junkers Ju 87 raised after over fifty years in a lake can be seen nearby. The Yugoslav designed Kurir has been painted in false Luftwaffe colours. Designed by Boris Cijan this high wing monoplane was first flown in 1955 and was used by the Yugoslav Army in a variety of roles. A number of military types operated by the two German Air Forces before unification are on display. An exhibition of military vehicles and weapons has been added. Comparisons can be made between the only two supersonic airliners to see service – the Concorde and the Tupolev Tu-144. At the present time this is the only place in the world where this can be done. New exhibits, such as the Canadair CL-215, arrive regularly and more interesting types can be expected. The museum has a great deal to offer and attractions such as car rallies are often staged in the parking area.

TYPE	REG/SER	CON. NO.	PI/NOTES	STATUS
☐ Aero L-39ZO Albatros	28+27	232301	175 (DDR)	PV
☐ Aérospatiale / British Aircraft Corporation Concorde 101	F-BVFB	100-007	F-BVFB, N94FB	PV
☐ Antonov An-2T	'03'	16847305	05, HA-ANB- in false Soviet markings.	PVX
☐ Boeing 707-123B (707-123)	N3951A	17647	N7520A, C-GQBG, N777NW, 5A-DHO – front fuselage only.	PV
☐ Canadair CL-215-I	F-ZBBH/26	1026		PV
☐ Construcciones Aeronáuticas (CASA) 2.111B (2.111A) [Heinkel He 111H-16]	'5J+GN'	005	B.2H-9, B.2I-82	PVX

Type	Reg/Ser	C/n	PI/Notes	Status
☐ Construcciones Aeronáuticas (CASA) 352L [Junkers Ju 52/3m]	'RJ+NP'	50	T.2B-140, N9012P	PVX
☐ Construcciones Aeronáuticas (CASA) 352L [Junkers Ju 52/3m]	'D-AQUI'	100	T.2B-209	PVX
☐ Construcciones Aeronáuticas (CASA) 352L [Junkers Ju 52/3m]	'D-2527'	148	T.2B-257, D-CIAL, 'D-ADAM', D-CIAL	PVX
☐ De Havilland D.H.82A Tiger Moth	'DE623'	82043	N6779, D-EDON	PVX
☐ De Havilland D.H.104 Dove 7		04530	194 (Eire), G-ARUE, (OY-BSS), G-ARUE, D-IKER	PV
☐ De Havilland D.H.112 Venom FB.1	J-1603	813	In Swiss markings	PV
☐ De Havilland D.H.112 Venom FB.1R	J-1628	838	In Swiss markings	PV
☐ De Havilland D.H.112 Venom FB.4	J-1798	968	In Swiss markings	PV
☐ Delta Hang Glider				PV
☐ Dornier-Bell 205 (UH-1D)	72+97	8417		PV
☐ Douglas DC-3A-467 Skytrain (C-47B) (Dakota IV)	'D-CADE'	14005/25450	43-48189, KG773, G-AKLL, EC-AEU, T.3-62 (Spain), N8041A, 'D-CORA'	PVX
☐ Drachen Studio Kecur Tropi Hang Glider				PV
☐ Eidgenössiches Flugzeugwerke Emmen C-3605 (C-3603-1)	C-501	281		PV
☐ English Electric EA.1 Canberra B.2	99+36	R3/EA3/6644	WK130, YA+151, 00+01, D-9569	PV
☐ Fauvel AV.36	D-1202			RA
☐ Fiat G.91R/3	32+64	91-534	KD+524, DG+309, MA+309 – with tail of c/n 566, KD+556, MB+105, 32+95	PV
☐ Fieseler Fi 103A-1 (FSM)	'521121'			PVX
☐ Focke-Wulf Fw 190A-3 (FSM)	'10'			PVX
☐ Fokker E III (FSM)	'475/15'			PVX
☐ Fokker Spin III (R)				PV
☐ Frebel F5 Aeolus	D-EAPT	1		PV
☐ Friedel Windspiel 2	D-MXEL			PV
☐ Hippie H-111				PV
☐ Hispano HA-1112M1L [Messerschmitt Bf 109G]	'4'	228	C.4K-170, G-AWHS	PVX
☐ Hübner 4 Eindecker				PV
☐ Hübner Mucke				PV
☐ Hütter-Villinger-Schule Muskelkraftflugzeug				PV
☐ Ikarus Kurir L	'PT+TP'			PVX
☐ Ilyushin Il-14P		14600833	005 (Poland), 0833 (Poland)	PVX
☐ Ilyushin Il-18E	OK-PAI	181003105	OK-BYP	PV
☐ Jacobs Kranich III	D-2011	66		RA
☐ Junkers Ju 87B	1301643			PVD
☐ Junkers Ju 88A-5	'4V+UH'	881379		PVX
☐ Kaiser Ka-1	D-8117			PV
☐ Kamov Ka-26	'CCCP-26001'	7303204	CCCP-24054, D-HBAU	PVX
☐ Küffner KH92 Rotorway Executive 90	D-HAKW	92001		PV
☐ Let L-13 Blanik	D-8771			PV
☐ Lockheed 580 (T-33A)	'7'	580-1758	58-709, JE+397, JD+397	PVX
☐ Lockheed 683-10-19 Starfighter (F-104G)	22+49	683-7129	KE+429, DD+121	PV
☐ Messerschmitt-Bölkow-Blohm – Kawasaki BK 117A-1 (FSM)	'DRF 4'			PVX
☐ Mignet HM-14 Pou-du-Ciel	'D-EMIL'			PVX
☐ Mikoyan-Gurevich MiG-21SPS (MiG-21PFM)	22+33	94A5202	861 (DDR)	PV
☐ Mikoyan-Gurevich MiG-23ML	20+27	0390324018	550 (DDR)	PV
☐ Mil Mi-8T	94+18	10323	394 (DDR), (D-HOZB)	PV
☐ Morane-Saulnier MS.500 Criquet [Fieseler Fi 156 Storch]	'D-EMWF'	763	763, F-BJHX, D-EMYZ, 'D-EMIL'	PVX
☐ Noorduyn Harvard IIB [North American NA-77 (AT-16)]	'FT454'	14-555	42-12308, FE821, B-164 (Netherlands) 099 (Netherlands)	PVX
☐ Percival P.66 Pembroke C.54	D-CAKE	P.66/93	AS+552, 54+02	PV
☐ Raab Doppelraab IV	D-5374	114		PV
☐ Republic RF-84F Thunderflash	EB+302		51-1862, EB+102 – front fuselage only.	PV
☐ Scheibe L-Spatz 55	D-9187	565		PV
☐ Scheibe Mü 13E Bergfalke I	D-8299	11/5		PV
☐ Scheibe Bergfalke II/55	D-1619	374		PV
☐ Scheibe ULi-1	D-MATZ	5207		RA
☐ Schempp-Hirth Standard Cirrus	D-2102	274		RA
☐ Schleicher Ka-4 Rhönlerche II	D-1876	3036		PV
☐ Schneider ESG 31 Grunau Baby IIB	D-8055			PV
☐ Schneider Grunau SG-38 (D.F.S. 108-14) (mod)	D-8182	WBLV.89		PV
☐ Sikorsky S-58C	D-HAUF	58356	OO-SHI, B-11 (Belgium)	PV
☐ Sud-Est SE.3130 Alouette II				PV
☐ Sukhoi Su-22M4	'798'	26307	704 (DDR), 25+20	PV
☐ Tupolev Tu-134K	HA-LBH	0350925	HA-LBHHA-925	PV
☐ Tupolev Tu-144D	CCCP-77112	07-1		PV
☐ Vertol V.43 (H-21C)	83+17	WG.17	PA+212, QF+470, PX+344	PV
☐ Vickers 708 Viscount	F-BGNU	38		PV
☐ Wasp Gryphon 3 Hang Glider				PV
☐ Wilden VoWi 10E	D-EGWI	001		PV
☐ Wytwornia Sprzetu Komunikacyjnego (WSK) Lim-2 [MiG-15bis]	'12'	1B 010-06	1006	PVX
☐ Zlin Z-37 Cmelak				PV
☐ Zlin Z-381 [Bücker Bü 181D Bestmann]	HB-USE	325	OK-DRB, HB-USE, (D-EBKI)	PV

Four aircraft including this MiG-15bis are preserved at Berat-Kuçovë Air Force Base. (Bob Ruffle)

The unique Kain Helicopter is among the exhibits at the Fahrzeug-Technik-Luftfahrt Museum at Bad Ischl.

Pictured among the gliders at the Aviaticum is this German designed Dallach Sun Wheel. (Chris Chatfield)

Left: A volunteer team at the Koninklijk Legermuseum in Brussels restored this classic Percival Gull to its original markings.

Below: The superb collection of World War I aircraft at the Koninklijk Legermuseum in Brussels includes this Sopwith 1½ Strutter.

This Spitfire, which was once flown by Roger Lallement, is the highlight of the museum at Florennes.

Pictured outside the Stampe Museum hangar at Antwerp Airport is this Albatros D Va replica which was once in the Ryder's Replica Museum in Alabama. (Bob Rongé)

This superbly restored Arado Ar 196A-3 owned by the Naval Museum at Varna has been on show at Plovdiv for several years. (Bob Ruffle)

A number of aircraft, including this MiG-23MLA, have been put on show at the National History Museum in Sofia. (Bob Ruffle)

The Aero A-10 was the first Czech designed airliner. This partial replica is on show at Kbely.

The Zlin XIII, dating from 1937, carried out several long distance flights around Europe before World War II. The aircraft is in the Narodni Technicke Muzeum in Prague.

On view at the Slovacke Letecke Muzeum at Kunovice is this Aero 45.

Only two K.Z. IVs were built and both are on show in Danish museums. This, the second, was completed in 1946 and is pictured at Helsingor. (Stewart Lanham)

This superbly restored Tiger Moth in Danish military colours can be seen at Helsingor. (Stewart Lanham)

The only surviving KZ.II Sport is at the Danskveteranflysamling at Stauning Airport.

The Swiss Air Force sold off several Mirage IIIs in 2005. One was acquired by the Lennundusmuuseum. (LM)

This former Polish Air Force Sukhoi Su-22 arrived at Tartu for the Lennundusmuuseum in late 2005. (LM)

The sole surviving Bristol Bulldog was restored at Halli by a former fitter who worked on the type when it was in service with the Finnish Air Force.

The Karhulan Ilmailukerhon Lentomuseo at Kymi Airfield owns this Harakka I primary glider.

One of the rare types displayed at the Keski-Suomen Ilmailumuseo located just outside Tikkakoski Air Force Base is this Gourdou-Leseurre GL.22.

A corner of one of the halls at the Soumen Ilmailumuseo. In the foreground is a Pyry II and behind a Viima II. (Douglas Rough)

The Musée Européen de l'Aviation de Chasse at Montélimar have painted their Dassault Ouragan in 'Patrouille de France' colours.

Airbus used this Super Guppy for transporting wings. When it was retired it made the short journey to the Ailes Anciennes area at Toulouse-Blagnac.

Two Grumman Widgeons are in the superb seaplane museum at Biscarosse.

This Mignet HM-8 was built in 1985 to original 1930s plans by Emmanual Lerin at Dierre. It arrived at Musée Regional de l'Air at Angers in 2002. (Christian Ravel)

This Vampire is among the gate guards at Orange Air Force Base.

The original terminal building at Le Bourget was converted to house the early aircraft of the Musée de l'Air. This Donnet-Leveque flying boat is part of this impressive display.

The new hall of the Deutsches Technikmuseum in Berlin houses the last surviving Arado Ar 79. (DTM)

This attractively painted Mil-8PS is on show at the Aeronauticum at Nordholz.

A view of the first hall built at the Flugausstellung Junior in Hermeskeil. A former Swiss Air Force Venom is in the foreground and behind is a Super Sabre. A Hütter H 17 and a Grunau Baby hang from the roof. (Chris Chatfield)

A view of the crowded hall at the Museum für Luftfahrt und Technik at Wernigerode. A Dornier Do 27B is in the foreground. (Nigel Ponsford)

The Luftwaffe used three Canberras on a variety of duties. One is exhibited at the Luftwaffenmuseum at Gatow. (Douglas Rough)

The German Navy flew sixteen Fairey Gannets in the 1960s. This AS.4 is mounted at the Technikmuseum Speyer. (Chris Chatfield)

The Greek Air Force flew this Gulfstream I From 1964 to 1995. It is now in the Air Force Museum at Tatoi. (Trevor Stone)

This specially painted Starfighter is part of the Air Force Museum collection. (Trevor Stone)

Residing in the War Museum in Athens is this Farman replica. (Trevor Stone)

The Hungarian Air Force base at Kecskemet has an interesting museum. This MiG-21F is parked nearby.

The aeronautical hall at the Kozlekedesi Muzeum houses this restored Brandenburg B I.

The Gold Timer Foundation maintains this Lisunov Li-2 in airworthy condition. The aircraft is based at Budaors. (Stewart Lanham)

The only aircraft on show at the superb folk museum near to the waterfall at Skijor is this Quad City Challenger.

The crowded hangar of the Flugsafn Islands at Akureyri is home to this Rhönlerche glider. Behind is a Stinson SR-7B Reliant.

The unique Ognin biplane is exhibited in the terminal at Keflavik Airport.

Members of GAVS at Turin have restored this Stinson Sentinel to its original World War II colours. (GAVS-Torino)

The courtyard of the Castle at San Pelagio is used to display the aircraft of the Museo dell'Aria Nido delle Aquile. This Macchi MB.308 is parked in the cloisters area. (Douglas Rough)

The Breda Ba.19 was a popular type and one can be seen in the Caproni Museum at Trento.

This Fiat G.5bis has been restored to its original military colours and is on show at the Italian Air Force Museum at Vigna di Valle. (Douglas Rough)

Four Schneider Trophy floatplanes are on show at the Italian Air Force Museum at Vigna di Valle. This Macchi MC.72 was not ready for the last contest in 1931 but later set a World air speed record. (Douglas Rough)

Many Italian Air Force bases have collections of preserved aircraft. This Starfighter is at the home of the 51st Stormo at Istrana. (Douglas Rough)

AUTOMOBIL MUSEUM FICHTELBERG (GER8)

Address:	Nagler Weg 9, D-95686 Fichtelberg.
Tel:	09272-6066
Fax:	09272-6066
Email:	info@automobilmuseum.de
Admission:	April-October Tuesday-Sunday 1000-1800; November-March Wednesday Friday-Sunday 1000-1800.
Location:	On the eastern side of the town which is about 20 km north east of Bayreuth.

On show at this museum is a wide range of cars exhibited in two halls. Prototypes and classic types can be seen along with vehicles from the early days of motoring. Rally cars from modern times are displayed in a diorama showing the conditions encountered during contests. Motorcycles, trams, bicycles, commercial vehicles, associated equipment and models are also to be seen. The exhibition is well laid out and the vehicles are in excellent condition. Outside the buildings is the collection of aircraft. The majority are types operated by the former East German Air Force. Interflug flew two aircraft, the Kamov Ka-26 and the Zlin Cmelak, for many years on agricultural work and the West German Army used the Alouette.

TYPE	REG/SER	CON. NO.	PI/NOTES	STATUS
☐ Kamov Ka-26	D-HOAT	7303404	DM-SPT, DDR-SPT	PV
☐ Mikoyan-Gurevich MiG-21US	24+04	07685147	221 (DDR)	PV
☐ Mikoyan-Gurevich MiG-23BN	20+44	0393214212	696 (DDR)	PV
☐ Mikoyan-Gurevich MiG-23UB	20+60	A1038280	109 (DDR)	PV
☐ Mil Mi-8PS	93+60	10599	739 (DDR)	PV
☐ Sud-Est SE.3130 Alouette II	76+24	1611	PK+135, QW+742, QW+219 – on loan from Luftwaffen Museum.	PV
☐ Sukhoi Su-22UM3K	25+51	17532366510	111 (DDR)	PV
☐ Zlin Z-37A Cmelak	D-ESUH	18-26	DM-SUH, DDR-SUH	PV

AUTOMOBIL MUSEUM VON FRITZ B. BUSCH (GER9)

Address:	Am Schloss Neben Regensburg D-88364 Wolfegg.
Tel:	07527-6294
Fax:	07529-430
Admission:	Daily 0930-1800.
Location:	About 20 km east of Ravensburg on the road to Bad Wurzach.

This private car museum has many interesting vehicles, components, photographs, documents, trophies, posters, clothing and items of memorabilia on show. The collection is exhibited in five hundred year old buildings in the grounds of the castle. Cars from 1918 can be compared with classics from the 1950s and 1960s. Also on show are motor cycles, including some racing machines, and tractors. An interesting display shows how antique vehicles are sometimes found derelict in locked sheds. The only aircraft to be seen is believed to be an amateur built example of the popular French low wing single seater.

TYPE	REG/SER	CON. NO.	PI/NOTES	STATUS
☐ Druine D.31 Turbulent				PV

AUTO UND BIKER MUSEUM BERENDES (GER10)

Address:	Gewerbepark Paffendorf, Willy Messerschmitt Strasse 4, 50126 Bergheim.
Tel:	02271-41110
Admission:	Monday-Friday by appointment; Saturday-Sunday 1000-2000.
Location:	In the town which is just east of the A 16 and about 10 km west of Köln.

There is an interesting collection of cars including a Cadillac used by Elvis Presley is displayed at this museum. A number of Rolls Royce and Bentley saloons are also on show. Several racing cars are in the collection. The history of motoring is portrayed with many photographs, audio-visual displays and posters. Models from the early days up to modern times are displayed. Also to be seen are motorcycles, engines and components. The ex- Luftwaffe Starfighter, mounted, on the roof and the P.149 fuselage are the only aircraft.

TYPE	REG/SER	CON. NO.	PI/NOTES	STATUS
☐ Lockheed 683-10-19 Starfighter (F-104G)	22+65	683-7146	KE+466, DD+247	PV
☐ Piaggio P.149D			Fuselage only.	PV

The Zlin Cmelak was widely used on agricultural duties in East Germany. This example can be seen at the Agrahistorisches Museum at Alt Schwerin.

The only Tupolev Tu-144 on show outside Russia is mounted on the roof of the Auto und Technik Museum at Sinsheim. (Douglas Rough)

Four examples of the Zaunkönig were produced and one is in the main hall at Oberschleissheim. (Douglas Rough)

BALLON MUSEUM (GER11)

Address:	Bahnhofstrasse 10, D-86368 Gersthofen.
Tel:	0821-249-1506
Fax:	0821-249-1509
Email:	ballonmuseum@stadt.gersthofen.de
Admission:	Wednesday 1400-1800; Saturday-Sunday 1000-1800.
Location:	In the centre of the town which is about 8 km north west of Augsburg.

Housed in a former water tower this fascinating museum, which opened in the mid-1980s traces the history of ballooning. The first flight from the town took place in 1786 and, prior to World War I, August von Parseval built and flew his first non-rigid airship here. In 1931 Auguste Piccard used hydrogen gas made in the town on his historic stratospheric flight which took off from nearby Augsburg. The balloon field in the northern part of the town is still used. On show in the building are models, photographs, documents, instruments and memorabilia. A replica of the balloon in which Blanchard and Jeffries crossed the English Channel in January 1985 can be seen along with an original dating from the late nineteenth century.

TYPE	REG/SER	CON. NO.	PI/NOTES	STATUS
☐ Ballonfabrik Augsburg K-1050/3 Gas Balloon	D-MOBIL II			PV
☐ Blanchard and Jeffries Balloon (R)				PV
☐ Braun Balloon			Basket only.	PV

BAVARIA AIRWAYS MUSEUM (GER12)

Address:	Obere Dorfstrasse 15, D-85414 Kirchdorf a.d. Amper.
Tel:	08166-7920
Admission:	By prior permission only.
Location:	In the centre of the town which is east of the A.9 and about 35 km north east of München.

The company was formed in the late 1960s and operated a fleet of BAC 1-11s until its merger with Germanair in 1977. This private collection of memorabilia and models traces the history of the airline.

BAYERISCHE MOTOREN WERKE MUSEUM (GER13)

Address:	Petuelring 130, D-80788 München.
Tel:	089-3822-3307
Admission:	Closed until 2007. Temporary exhibition of cars in the Olympic Park.
Location:	Next to the B.M.W. factory which is in the north of the city near the Olympic Park.

The museum opened in 1973 and a decade later was completely rebuilt and modernised. On show are aero engines, cars and motorcycles produced by the company since 1916. An exhibition of trophies won by the company can also be seen. The only aircraft on view is a 1930 Klemm L 25 which was originally powered by a Daimler engine. A B.M.W. X motor was fitted in 1932. The aircraft spent some of its life in Switzerland before returning to Germany. The museum is now being refurbished and will feature many new displays incorporating the latest computer techniques. Until the museum re-opens in 2007 a number of cars are put on temporary display each day in the Olympic Park opposite the factory.

TYPE	REG/SER	CON. NO.	PI/NOTES	STATUS
☐ Klemm L 25 a VII (L 25 a)	D-1638	149	D-1638, D-EFAR	RA

BAYERISCHES ARMEEMUSEUM (GER14)

Address:	Neues Schloss, Paradeplatz 4, D-85049 Ingolstadt.
Tel:	0841-9377-0
Fax:	0841-9377-2000
Email:	sekretariat@bayerisches-armeemuseum.de
Admission:	Tuesday-Sunday 0845-1600.
Location:	In the south eastern part of the old town.

This long established museum had premises in Munich until they were destroyed in a bombing raid in World War II. The displays traced the military history of the Bavarian forces and many significant items including at least one World War I aircraft were lost. Historical documents which traced the local and political story were also destroyed. The exhibition was moved to Ingoldstadt where a wide range of weapons, uniforms, documents and photographs can be seen. In the mid-1990s one of the former redoubts, which protected the city, was restored and now houses the World War I items. This building and the associated walls are a significant part of the museum. During 1997/8 a special exhibition devoted to the Bavarian Military Aviation Corps occupied part of this structure. Many photographs, models, documents and components were seen. The operations carried out by the force in World War I were shown in great detail in informative maps. The two aircraft, representing types flown from Bavarian airfields, are currently in store along with many items from the 1920s onwards. In this area are tanks, military vehicles, radar equipment, heavy artillery and motor cycles. Long-term plans envisage a World War II display and eventually one covering the period from 1945 up to the present time.

TYPE	REG/SER	CON. NO.	PI/NOTES	STATUS
☐ Fiat G.91R/3	31+02	91-368	KD+358, DG+116, MA+116	RA
☐ Lockheed 683-10-19 Starfighter (F-104G)	21+52	683-7021	KE+321, DA+117, YA+117	RA

BÜCKER MUSEUM (GER15)

Address:	Am Strand 1, D-15834 Rangsdorf.
Tel:	033708-920066
Email:	museum@buecker-museum.com
Admission:	Wednesday, Saturday, Sunday 1300-1700. (Closes at 1600 October-February)
Location:	Just south of the E 56 and about 25 km. south of Berlin.

The Bücker company was founded at Berlin-Adlershof in 1933 and two years later moved to the new airfield and seaplane station at Rangsdorf. The factory still exists but cannot be visited at the present time. The firm built several classic designs including the Jungmann, Jungmeister and Bestmann as well as smaller numbers of the Student and Kornett. The airfield was used by Soviet forces from 1946 until 1994. The museum opened on April 1st 2001 and the displays trace the history of the airfield and the company. Large models of all Bücker types have been built along with a representation of the works as it was in 1942/3. On show are photographs, documents and artefacts tracing the development of the site and of the aircraft produced and flown from the field. In recent years fly-ins have been staged and many Bücker types have visited.

BUNDESWEHR SPORTFLIEGER GEMEINSCHAFT (GER16)

Address:	Postfach 12048, D-82242 Fürstenfeldbruck.
Tel:	08141-43370
Email:	praesident@fursty.de
Admission:	By prior permission only.
Location:	Just north of the town which is about 25 km west of Munich.

This group formed mainly by military personnel uses a fleet of classic types and gliders from the military airfield which no longer houses operational aircraft. The Dornier is often used for towing the gliders. Several Piper Super Cubs were flown by both the German Air Force and Army on a variety of duties. The prototype Motorfalke made its maiden flight in April 1963 and has since been built in large numbers. Well over one thousand have left the factory. Versions have been exported around the world and also built under licence in France, Italy and by Slingsby in England. The Rotax Falke can be fitted with an optional tricycle undercarriage.

TYPE	REG/SER	CON. NO.	PI/NOTES	STATUS
☐ Dornier Do 27A-4	D-EDMA	396	PL+426, QW+720, PS+716, 56+88	RAA
☐ Grob G.102 Astir CS	D-7368	1273		RAA
☐ Piper PA-18-95 Super Cub (L-18C)	D-ENLM	18-1592	51-15592, 15592 (France)	RAA
☐ Piper PA-18-95 Super Cub (L-18C)	D-EFBR	18-3457	54-757, AS+539, AC+539, NL+112, 96+33	RAA
☐ Rolladen-Schneider LS-4B	D-2820	4789		RAA
☐ Scheibe SF-25C Rotax-Falke	D-KTIM	44564		RAA
☐ Schleicher K.7	D-7189	7225		RAA
☐ Schleicher ASK-13	D-0824	13351		RAA

DEUTSCH-DEUTSCHES MUSEUM (GER17)

Address:	Mödlareuth 13, D-95183 Töpen.
Tel:	09295-1334
Fax:	09295-1319
Email:	museum@modlareuth.de
Admission:	March-October daily 0900-1800; Mid-January-February Monday-Friday 0900-1700 Saturday-Sunday 1000-1700.
Location:	About 5 km east of Hirschberg.

The small village of Mödlareuth was on the border between East and West Germany and here there was a small crossing post. The dividing wall split the community. The museum incorporates a one hundred metre section of the wall, the parallel fence and a former East German sentry tower. A vast amount of memorabilia and documents have been collected with the majority in store. There are plans to construct an exhibition hall. A former East German Mil-8 helicopter is on show. This type flew many border patrols.

TYPE	REG/SER	CON. NO.	PI/NOTES	STATUS
☐ Mil Mi-8TB	93+61	10553	124 (DDR)	PV

DEUTSCH-KANADISCHES LUFTWAFFENMUSEUM (GER18)

Address: Karlshruhe/Baden-Baden Airport, D-77836 Rheinmünster-Söllingen.
Tel: 07229-661340
Email: info@airforcemusemsoellingen.de
Admission: On permanent view.
Location: Just north of Rhein off Route 36 and about 15 km west of Baden-Baden.

The airfield was used by Canadian Air Forces units for many years. They returned home in the mid-1990s and one of their gate guards, a Canadair built Starfighter, was erected as a monument in the town. The site is now the new civil airport for the area. The museum is being set up in one of the former hangars at the field and displays are being assembled. The main theme will be to show the co-operation that existed between the Canadian Air Force and the region when the base was operational. Uniforms, photographs and documents are on view. The Starfighter is painted in a special red colour scheme and arrived at the museum from Memmingen. The Fiat came from Manching and the Sabre from a barracks at Lauda. The Silver Star, which was operated from the field, is currently under restoration. More aircraft are being sought to enhance the display.

TYPE	REG/SER	CON. NO.	PI/NOTES	STATUS
☐ Canadair CL-13B Sabre 6 [North American F-86E]	JB+371	1611	BB+181, BB+281	PV
☐ Canadair CL-30 Silver Star 3 (CT-133) [Lockheed 580 (T-33AN)]				PVC
☐ Canadair CL-90 Starfighter (CF-104) [Lockheed 683]	104785	683A-1085	12785 (Canada) – monument in village.	PV
☐ Fiat G.91R/3	31+21	91-388	KD+378, BD+415	PV
☐ Lockheed 683-04-10 Starfighter (RF-104G)	24+19	683-8161	KG+261, EA+249	PV

DEUTSCHE GESELLSCHAFT ZUR ERHALTUNG HISTORISCHER FLUGZEUGE (GER19)

Address: Thomas Mann Straße 3, D-89257 Illertissen.
Tel: 07303-9642-20
Fax: 07303-9642-41
Admission: By prior permission only.
Location: The airfield is just north east of the town and east of the A 7.

This group was formed to restore and fly historic aircraft. Their first acquisition was a Raab Krähe. This powered sailplane first flew in 1959 at Augsburg and was built in four versions with a variety of engines. Several other interesting aircraft are now in the fleet. Fritz Raab produced the Doppelraab as a cheap two seater training glider. Well over three hundred and fifty were constructed in seven variants. The prototype appeared at the 1951 Wasserkuppe meeting a few months after the aviation ban in Germany was lifted. The Stieglitz was built in Sweden by CVV at Hässlo near Västerås. This classic biplane saw military use before being sold on the civil market. The Yak-3 is one of a batch of twenty built in the mid-1990s at Orenburg. Original and new drawings were used as the aircraft was fitted with an Allison V-1710 engine.

TYPE	REG/SER	CON. NO.	PI/NOTES	STATUS
☐ Dornier Do 27A-1	D-EEPJ	173	AS+923, AC+923, 55+43	RAA
☐ Focke-Wulf Fw 44J Stieglitz	D-EMAX	83	Fv631, SE-AWT, D-EFUD, D-EMIL, (D-EMIG)	RAA
☐ Fouga CM.170R Magister	D-IFCC	079	(AA+179), SC+603, SB+602, 93+02 – normally at Manching.	–
☐ Jodel D.92 Bébé	D-EBOG	AB.13		RAC
☐ Raab Doppelraab IV	D-EGHR	EB.1	D-5412	RAA
☐ Raab Krähe IV	D-KOBO	102		RAC
☐ Yakovlev Yak-3M	D-FJAK	0470107	N551BH	RAA

DEUTSCHE LUFTHANSA BERLIN-STIFTUNG (GER20)

Address:	Postfach 630300, D-22313 Hamburg.
Tel:	069-696-4105
Email:	FRAZUJU52@dlh.de
Admission:	By prior permission only
Location:	At Hamburg Airport which is about 8 km north of the city centre.

Deutsche Luft-Hansa was formed on January 6th 1926 by the merger of Deutscher Aero Lloyd and Junkers Luftverkehr. Prior to World War II the airline operated a vast fleet of aircraft on internal and international services. Lufthansa was reformed in 1956 and carried on the proud traditions of its predecessor. The Deutsche Lufthansa Berlin Foundation was established on June 13th 1986 and now operates a fleet of historic aircraft. The airline bought the Ju 52 in 1984 and restored it over the next two years. The aircraft was originally delivered to the Norwegian Airline D.N.L. in the late 1930s and during a rebuild in 1947 it acquired the wings and other parts from a former Lufthansa machine, The tri-motor now carries the markings of the Lufthansa aircraft which was originally delivered in 1936. The Ju 52 is a common sight all over Europe appearing at air shows and offering rides to the public. The Messerschmitt Bf 108 was built at Regensburg in 1940 and joined the collection in 1990 after periods of service in Sicily and the U.S.A. The Dornier Do 27 was the first type to be put into production in Germany alter World War II and the example operated was donated by Conrado Dornier, son of the founder of the famous company, in 1990. Under rebuild is a Swedish built Focke-Wulf Stieglitz obtained from South Africa. Large numbers of this biplane were used for both civilian and military training in the inter-war period. This classic flew in Germany for a period before journeying south. The Lufthansa training school flew several Safirs from the mid-1950s up to the late 1960s. The aircraft in the fleet was built in Holland by the De Schelde company as the SAAB lines at Linköping were busy with military production.

TYPE	REG/SER	CON. NO.	PI/NOTES	STATUS
☐ Dornier Do 27B-3	D-EDNU	401	AC+959, JC+901, MC+901, 56+92	RAA
☐ Focke-Wulf Fw 44J Stieglitz (Sk 12)	D-EQAX	1899	Fv617, D-EFUR, ZS-WRI	RAC
☐ Junkers Ju 52/3mg8e	D-CDLH	130714	8A+?K, (LN-KAL), LN-KAF, HC-ABS, N130LW, N52JU, D-CDLH – with one wing from c/n 2982 NO+IO and the other from c/n 5489 D-AQUI, LN-DAH, D-AQUI carries D-AQUI	RAA
☐ Messerschmitt Bf 108B-1 Taifun	D-EBEI	2246	NF+MP, NX54208, N54208, N108HP	RAA
☐ Svenska Aeroplan Aktiebolaget (SAAB) 91B Safir	D-EBED	91291		RAA

DEUTSCHE RAUMFAHRTAUSSTELLUNG (GER21)

Address:	Bahnofsstrasse 8, D-08262 Mörgenrothe-Rautenkranz.
Tel:	037465-2514
Fax:	037465-2549
Email:	Raumfahrt@t-online.de
Admission:	Tuesday-Sunday 1000-1700.
Location:	Off Road 283 in the northern part of the town which is about 30 km south of Zwickau.

Sigmund Jahn became the first astronaut from the D.D.R. when he flew on a Soyuz mission in August 1978. The museum, which opened the following year, is located in his hometown and commemorates this feat. Many of his personal effects are on show in the building. The history of space flight, with particular emphasis on the Soviet contribution, is featured in the displays. The MiG-21 parked outside the building was flown by Jahn during his service in the N.V.A. There are photographs of his Air Force career and documents from this period.

TYPE	REG/SER	CON. NO.	PI/NOTES	STATUS
☐ Mikoyan-Gurevich MiG-21F-13	737	741608		PV

DEUTSCHES FEUERWEHRMUSEUM (GER22)

Address:	Saint Laurentius Strasse 3, D-36041 Fulda.
Tel:	0661-75017
Fax:	0661-241754
Email:	Deutsches-feuerwehr-museum@t-online.de
Admission:	Tuesday-Sunday 1000-1700.
Location:	In the south western part of the town.

This informative museum was established in the early 1960s and traces the history and development of the fire fighting service in the country. Displays of equipment and uniforms are on view along with photographs, models and documents. Many fire engines and other service vehicles can also be seen. Realistic dioramas show the difficult tasks encountered by firemen on active duty. The use of aircraft and helicopters by the service is portrayed in the exhibition. The former Luftwaffe Do 27 was used by the fire service from 1976 to 1984.

TYPE	REG/SER	CON. NO.	PI/NOTES	STATUS
☐ Dornier Do 27B-1	D-ELYY	222	PB+301, QM+602, JB+386, MC+386, 55+76	PV

DEUTSCHES HISTORISCHES MUSEUM (GER23)

Address:	Unter den Linden 2, D-10117 Berlin.
Tel:	030-20304-0
Fax:	030-20304-543
Admission:	Thursday-Tuesday 1000-1800. (Museum closed until 2006)
Location:	In the centre of the city.

Covering many aspects of German culture this superb museum is housed in a Baroque building, constructed between 1695 and 1706, which once served as the city arsenal. The exhibits trace the history of the country from the early days. Special exhibitions are often staged. A replica Lilienthal monoplane glider, currently in store, honours the pioneer aviator who made many flights in the region of the city between 1891 and 1896. The museum is being completely refurbished and when it re-opens it will have many new displays.

TYPE	REG/SER	CON. NO.	PI/NOTES	STATUS
☐ Lilienthal Normal-Segelapparat (R)				RA

DEUTSCHES MARINEMUSEUM (GER24)

Address:	Süsstrand 125, D-26382 Wilhelmshaven.
Tel:	04421-41061
Fax:	04421-41063
Email:	info@marinemuseum.de
Location:	In the southern part of the city.
Admission:	April-October daily 1000-1800; November-March daily 1000-1700.

The displays at this museum, which opened in 1998, trace the maritime history of the nation with several interesting dioramas depicting famous naval conflicts. On show are a torpedo boat, a minesweeper, a submarine, models, uniforms, documents and photographs. The Starfighter was for many years the frontline fighter of the Marineflieger until replaced by the Tornado, which is currently being withdrawn.

TYPE	REG/SER	CON. NO.	PI/NOTES	STATUS
☐ Lockheed 683-10-19 Starfighter (F-104G)	'22+22'	683-9035	KH+120DA+127, 25+74, '26+81'	PVX

DEUTSCHES MUSEUM – FLUGWERFT SCHLEISSHEIM (GER25)

Address:	Effnerstrasse 18, D-85764 Oberschleissheim.
Tel:	089-315714-0
Fax:	089-315714-50
Email:	fws@deutsches-museum.de
Admission:	Daily 0900-1700
Location:	About 10km north of Munich. The entrance to the airfield is just north of the Neuberberg exit on Autobahn A.99.

The airfield at Oberschleissheim opened in 1912 and was a base for the Royal Bavarian Flying Corps. An overhaul facility was later constructed and used in the inter-war period for maintenance of airliners operating out of the then Munich airport. A large flying school was also established. More hangars were built in the 1930s and after World War II American helicopters were based at the field. A flying unit of the German police and a gliding school are still in residence. The Deutsches Museum set up a store at the airfield in the 1970s to house its ever growing fleet. Plans for a new exhibition were put forward in the 1980s and this opened on September 12th 1992. The historic Flugwerft was restored to its former glory and linked to a large new display hall and restoration centre. Visitors can climb the stairs to the original control tower and from the balcony obtain a view across the airfield and of the schloss behind. An excellent display of photographs and models traces the history of the site. Exhibits showing technical developments in aviation can also be seen. Gliding has always been to the forefront in Germany and many significant sailplanes are on show. Otto Lilienthal is represented by two replicas, a Pelzner biplane replica is on show along with an original Wolfmüller built in Munich in 1909. The Mü 10 built by Akaflieg München in 1933 set several two-seat records before the outbreak of the war. A number of post-World War II sailplanes are also on view and a display of hang gliders traces the development of designs in this popular sport. Types used for private flying and aerobatics are on show Man-powered and solar-powered aircraft have also been collected. Jet aircraft used by the Luftwaffe in recent years can be seen along with designs from other countries. A team led by Kurt Tank, who was responsible for many Focke-Wulf types, designed the Indian built Marut. The prototype first flew in the early 1960s and production examples were delivered to the Indian Air Force in 1967. The Marut saw combat service in disputes with Pakistan in the 1970s. Willi Messerschmitt designed the HA-300 and prototypes were built in Spain and Egypt. Several types operated by the former East German forces have been acquired. These combat aircraft can be compared with western designs such as the Phantom and the Draken. One of the four Zaunkönig ultra light parasol monoplanes is a recent arrival. The example on show was captured by the British at Bad Harzburg. This aircraft was tested at Farnborough between 1947 and 1949. After a long civil career in England and Ireland it returned to Germany in the mid-1980s. The Do 24T-3, moved by road from Oberpfaffhofen, replaces Do-24ATT which was loaned to the exhibition for a decade. The Do 31 was on show in the courtyard of the main museum before moving for restoration. This excellent display covers many aspects of aviation and it is hoped that space can be found for the aircraft and gliders still in store in the old hangars.

TYPE	REG/SER	CON. NO.	PI/NOTES	STATUS
☐ Akaflieg München Mü 10 Milan	D-1001	5	D-14-126	PV
☐ Antonov An-2T	03	1G 59-29	In Soviet markings.	PV
☐ Bischof Muskelkraft-Flugzeug				RA
☐ Boeing-Stearman A75N1 Kaydet (N2S-4)	D-EFTX	75-3475	Bu30038, N64639, N474, G-BHUW – at museum in winter.	RAA
☐ Bohne Monoplane			Incomplete	RAD
☐ Bölkow Bö 209 Monsun 160RV	D-EFJL	134	Often at museum in winter.	PV
☐ Bölkow Phoebus C	D-2836	801	D-2836, (Austria)	PV
☐ Bücker Bü 181B-1 Bestmann	D-ECYV	331381	(Luftwaffe), SL-AAS	PV
☐ Canadair CL-13B Sabre 6 [North American F-86E]	KE+105	1659	BB+293, JD+120, YA+048, KE+105, (01+05), 'JD+105'	PV
☐ Cessna 195	N3480V	7180		PV
☐ Cody Kite (R)				PV
☐ Construcciones Aeronáuticas (CASA) 2.111B (2.111A) [Heinkel He 111H-16]	B.2I-77	025	B.2H-25, B.2I-77, G-AWHA, D-CAGI, '6J+PR', , G1+F'	PV
☐ Dittmar Condor IV/3	D-8802	24/53	On loan from SFM Gunzburg.	PV
☐ Dornier Do 24T-3	HD.5-3	5344	EC-DA?, 65-3, HR.5-3, HD.5-3, (N99222) – wings from EC-DA?, 65-4, HR.5-4, HD.5-4 – on loan from Dornier Museum.	PV
☐ Dornier Do 27A-3			Front fuselage only.	PV
☐ Dornier Do 27J-1	'D-EMMA'	2057	D-9504, D-1 (Belgium), OL-D01 (Belgium), D0-1 (Belgium), D-EGVB – on loan from Dornier Museum.	
☐ Dornier Do 31E-3	D-9531	E-3		PVC
☐ Dornier-Bell 205 (UH-1D)	D-HATU	8066	(70+36)	PV
☐ Douglas DC-3A-467 Skytrain (C-47B) (C-47D) (Dakota IV)	14+01	15544/26989	43-49728, KK209, 43-49728, GA+117, GR+117, GR+107, XA+111	PV
☐ Eurofighter EF.2000 Typhoon	98+29	DA1/01		PV
☐ Fauvel AV.36CR	D-8273	213		PV
☐ Fiat G.91R/3	99+07	91-460	KD+450, BD+239, 31+92, D-9603 – on loan from Luftwaffen Museum	RA
☐ Fiat G.91T/3 (T/1)	34+01	91-2-0001	KC+101, BD+101, MD+371 – front fuselage only.	RA
☐ Firebird Laser 12.8 Hang Glider				PV
☐ Firebird Salewa 924 Hang Glider				PV
☐ Flight Design Exxtacy 135 Hang Glider				PV
☐ Focke-Wulf Fw 44J Stieglitz	D-ECUX	91	Fv639, SE-BXN	PV
☐ Focke-Wulf Weihe 50	D-0700	01	On loan.	PV
☐ Fokker D VII	'4408/18'	3103	D-20 (Netherlands)	PVX
☐ Göppingen Gö 4 Gövier III	D-6007	406		PV
☐ Göppingen Gö 4 Gövier III	OE-0223	K-1		RA
☐ Hatry-Opel-Sander RAK 1 (FSM)				RA
☐ Heinkel He 177A-1	5J+AK	5265	Parts only.	RAD
☐ Hindustan HF-24 Marut 1	D1256		(Indian AF)	PV
☐ Hispano HA-1112K1L [Messerschmitt Bf 109G]				RAC
☐ Horten Ho IV (D.F.S. 108-251)	D-10-1451	26	D-10-1451, LA+AD	PV
☐ Huber Drachenflug Alpengleiter				PV
☐ Hütter H 17A (D.F.S. 108-67)	D-8129			RA
☐ Jacobs Kranich II (D.F.S. 108-30)	D-6171	533		PV
☐ Jacobs Meise (D.F.S. 108-70)	D-1469	001		PV
☐ Jacobs Meise (D.F.S. 108-70)	D-6336	001		RA
☐ Kaiser Ka-1	D-8362	2	On loan.	PV
☐ Kamov Ka-26	D-HOAZ	7605615	DDR-SPZ	PV
☐ Lilienthal Normal-Segelapparat (R)				PV
☐ Lockheed 483-04-08 Starfighter (F-104F)	29+03	483-5049	59-4996, BB+362	PV

Aircraft	Registration	c/n	Previous identity / notes	Status
☐ Lockheed 580 (T-33A)	94+47	580-8967	53-5628, AB+777, EA+398	PV
☐ McDonnell M.98HO Phantom II (F-4E)	67-0260	2972		PV
☐ Messerschmitt Bf 108B-2 Taifun	'D-IOIO'	2064	A-208 (Switzerland) – on loan from EADS Sammlung.	PVX
☐ Messerschmitt Bf 109G-2			Converted from HA.1109K.1L.	PVX
☐ Messerschmitt-Bölkow-Blohm 223A4 Flamingo Trainer PFM (SIAT 223A-1) (MBB 223T-1)	D-EFWC	151	EC-51A – former c/n 051	PV
☐ Mikoyan-Gurevich MiG-21MF	23+40	966215	687 (DDR)	PV
☐ Mikoyan-Gurevich MiG-23BN	20+47	0393214217	701 (DDR)	PV
☐ Müller Doppeldecker Müller Herbert 22	D-EDMH	1951		PV
☐ Pacific Kites Seagull Hang Glider				RA
☐ Parseval P.L.1			Gondola only.	RAC
☐ Pelzner Hangegleiter (R)			On loan from SFM, Gunzburg.	PV
☐ Putzer Motorraab	D-EHOG	V-3		PV
☐ Raab Doppelraab IV	D-1220			RA
☐ Raab Motorraab	D-KORL	14	D-KEDI, (D-KOPD), D-KODL	PV
☐ Republic RF-84F Thunderflash	EB+231		52-7379, EB+231, EB+331	RA
☐ Reuter UL-Arco	D-MXRM			PV
☐ Rochelt Musculair 2				PV
☐ Rochelt Schneidair				RA
☐ Rockwell / Messerschmitt-Bölkow-Blohm X-31A	Bu164585			PV
☐ Scheibe L-Spatz 55	D-1509	655		RA
☐ Scheibe L-Spatz 55M	D-KIBA	01		RA
☐ Scheibe Mü 13E Bergfalke I	D-1653	01		RA
☐ Scheibe Mü 13E Bergfalke I	D-1085	2		PV
☐ Schmidtler & Schmidtler Ranger M	D-MZSW			PV
☐ Schneider ESG 31 Grunau Baby IIB	D-1065			PV
☐ Schneider ESG 31 Grunau Baby IIB	D-1283			RA
☐ Schneider Grunau Baby III (D.F.S. 108-66)	D-1094			RA
☐ Schneider Grunau SG-38 (D.F.S. 108-14)				RA
☐ Schneider Grunau SG-38 (D.F.S. 108-14)				RA
☐ Sikorsky S-58 Seabat (HSS-1N) (SH-34J) (H-34GIIIS) (H-34GIII)	80+73	581557	Bu150808, SC+257, WD+401	PV
☐ Slingsby T.38 Grasshopper TX.1	XK824	1043		PV
☐ Stender BS-1	D-6174	2	Incorporates parts of c/n 3.	RA
☐ Sud-Est SE.3130 Alouette II	75+84	1497	QK+533, QW+224, 75+84	PV
☐ Svenska Aeroplan Aktiebolaget (SAAB) 35A Draken (J 35A)	Fv35086	35086		PV
☐ Valentin Taifun 17E	D-KLAG	1042		PV
☐ Vereinigte Flugtechnische Werke – Fokker (VFW) VAK-191B	D-9563	V-1		PV
☐ Vollmoller Motorflugzeug			Fuselage and right wing only.	PV
☐ Wasp Super Gryphon Hang Glider				PV
☐ Western-Brighton MB.65 Hot Air Balloon	D-Westfalen II	003	G-AYUK	RA
☐ Wetter Balloon				RA
☐ Winter LF-1 Zaunkönig	D-EBCQ	V-2	D-YBAR,VX190, G-ALUA, EI-AYU	PV
☐ Wolfmüller Gleiter				PV
☐ Wolfmüller-Geest Motorflugzeug				PV
☐ Wytwornia Sprzetu Komunikacyjnego (WSK) SBLim-2 (Lim-1) [MiG-15] [MiG-15UTI]	003	1A 08-003		PV
☐ Yakovlev Yak-50	DDR-WQV	781206	DM-WQV	PV
☐ Zlin Z-37A Cmelak	D-ESOZ	08-18	DM-SOZ, DDR-SOZ	PV
☐ Zlin Z-381 [Bücker Bü 181D Bestmann]	D-EBUX	186	OK-ABY	RA
☐ Zlin Z-526A Akrobat	'DDR-WKZ'	1017 (?)	DM-WKZ (?)	RAX

DEUTSCHES MUSEUM VON MEISTERWERKEN DER NATURWISSENSCHAFT UND TECHNIK (GER26)

Address:	P.O.B. 260102, Museumsinsel, D-80538 München.
Tel:	089-21791
Fax:	089-217 93 24
Email:	info@deutsches-museum.de
Admission:	Daily 0900-1700.
Location:	On the Isarinsel in the city centre.

The museum, founded by Oskar von Miller, in 1903, contains one of the major technological collections in the world. Located on an island in the Isar River, the first exhibition building opened in 1925. The Library was ready in 1932 and the Congress Building three years later. Eighty percent of the complex was destroyed in 1944/45. Many historic aircraft including an Aviatik D, a Rumpler C IV, a Siemens-Schuckert D IV, a Dornier Wal, a Heinkel He 112U, a Junkers J I and a Junkers F 13 were unfortunately lost. Reconstruction of the museum commenced in 1948 and a seven storey exhibition block with research and administrative areas resulted. The initial aeronautical display was housed in the original area rebuilt as accurately as possible to its 'pre-World War II form'. Several early aircraft, which had been saved from total destruction in the Allied raids, were put on show. Hans Grade was one of the early pioneers in Germany and his A monoplane won the Lanz prize in 1909. The aircraft was acquired from Grade in 1917. The Rumpler Taube has been with the museum since 1911, the year it flew from Munich to Berlin. The Wright A is believed to be the only genuine survivor of the seven built. World War I fighters are represented by the Fokker D VII and the Rumpler C IV. Three famous Messerschmitt types from World War II show the rapid development made in combat machines over a thirty year period. A new aviation exhibition area was completed in 1984 and the number of aircraft on show more than doubled. The sole surviving Dornier A Libelle was recovered from Fiji by the manufacturers. This flying boat was completely restored by workers at the firm. The Messerschmitt M 17 dating from 1925 can be seen. This diminutive monoplane flew over the Alps from Germany to Italy. Three examples of Junkers aircraft featuring the famous corrugated skinning are on view. The F 13 was rebuilt from two derelict airframes discovered in Afghanistan in 1969, the Junior spent most of its life in Switzerland and the Ju 52 is one of over four hundred AAC.ls built in France. The Vampyr was one of the first gliders built in the country after World War I and appeared at the Wassrekuppe in 1921. The associated displays trace historical and technical developments in aviation over the last century. The exhibition is of an extremely high standard and contains many fascinating items. In recent years the aircraft collection has grown steadily and as space was limited at the island site it was decided to open a new exhibition at the historic airfield at Oberschleissheim.

TYPE	REG/SER	CON. NO.	PI/NOTES	STATUS
☐ Agusta-Bell 47G-2	AS+058	258		PV
☐ Airbus Industrie A300B1	F-OCAZ	D.01	Major components	PV
☐ Akaflieg Hannover Vampyr				PV
☐ Akaflieg Stuttgart Fs 24 Phönix	D-9093	V-1	D-8258	PV
☐ Arado Ar 66d		1258		PVD
☐ Ateliers Aéronautiques de Colombes AAC.1 [Junkers Ju 52/3mg10e]	363	363	In French markings – c/n also reported as 1.	PV
☐ Bachem Ba 349A-1 Natter (BP-20)			Partial replica	PV
☐ Ballonfabrik Augsburg K-630/Ri Gas Balloon	D-AGIP			RA
☐ Balloon			Basket only.	PV
☐ Balloon			Basket only.	RA
☐ Balloon			Basket only	PV
☐ Balloon			Basket only.	RA
☐ Blériot XI				PV
☐ Boeing 707-123B (707-123)	N7515A	17642	Cockpit section only	PV
☐ Bölkow BO 105C (BO 105C) (BO 105HGH)	D-HAPE	V-4		PV
☐ Construcciones Aeronáuticas (CASA) 1.131E [Bücker Bü 131 Jungmann]	E.3B-555	2169		PV
☐ De Havilland D.H.104 Dove 6 (2A)	D-IFSB	04379	N4280V, G-AMXR – on loan to de Havilland HC., England.	–
☐ Dornier A Libelle II	VQ-FAB	117	On loan from Dornier Museum.	PV
☐ Dornier Do 27B-1	56+66	360	AS+939, AC+939, ? , AC+933, 56+66 'D-EHAV'	PV
☐ Dornier Do 32E	'D-HOPA'	'32004'	Composite of c/n 32001 D-HOPF c/n 32002 D-HOPS and c/n 32003 D-HOPA	PVX
☐ Entwicklungsring-Sud VJ 101C	D-9518	X-2		PV
☐ Fieseler Fi 103A-1			On loan from RAFM Reserve Collection, GB.	PV
☐ Fieseler Fi 103F-1		478374		PV
☐ Fieseler Fi 156C-3 Storch	A-96	4299	HB-ARU, A-96, HB-ARU – in Swiss markings	PV
☐ Finsterwalder Bergfex				PV
☐ Focke-Achgelis Fa 330A-1 Bachstelze				PV
☐ Fokker Dr I (R)	'425/17'		Replica containing many original parts.	PVX
☐ Grade A				PV
☐ Haase, Kensche, Schmetz H.K.S.3	D-6426		D-5426	PV
☐ Hamburger Flugzeugbau HFB.320 Hansa	D-CLOU	1002	D-CLOU, (D-CASEK)	PV
☐ Junkers A 50 ci Junior	D-2054	3575	D-2054, CH-358, HB-UXI	PV
☐ Junkers F 13 fe	'D-366'	2018		PVX
☐ Klemm L 25 e VIIIR	D-EMDU	980	D-EMDU, SE-ANF	PV
☐ Lilienthal Kleiner Doppeldecker (R)				PV
☐ Lilienthal Normal-Segelapparat				S
☐ Lilienthal Normal-Segelapparat (R)				RA
☐ Lilienthal Normal-Segelapparat (R)				PV
☐ Lockheed 683-10-19 Starfighter (F-104G)	20+90	683-6607	KC+122, JD+236, 20+90, '80+52' – front fuselage only.	PV
☐ Lockheed 683-10-19 Starfighter (F-104G)	21+53	683-7022	KE+322, DC+252	PV
☐ Messerschmitt M 17	D-779	25		PV
☐ Messerschmitt Bf 109E-3 (E-1)	'2804'	0790	C.4E-106 (Spain), AJ+YH	PVX
☐ Messerschmitt Me 163B-1a Komet	120370	120370	120370, AM210	PV
☐ Messerschmitt Me 262A-1b	500071	500071		PV
☐ Nord N.1002 Pingouin II [Messerschmitt Bf 108B]	'D-IBFW'	77	77, F-BEAI, OY-AIJ	PVX
☐ Parseval P.L.2			Gondola only.	PV
☐ Piper J-3C-65 Cub (L-4J)	D-EOMA	12622	44-80326, F-BFBI	PV
☐ Platzer Leichflugzeugbau Motte B2-B3	D-MFBB	42		PV
☐ Plauen Balloon			Basket only.	PV
☐ Preussen Balloon			Parts only.	RA
☐ Quickie Aircraft Quickie 1 (Rutan 54)	D-EEWQ	1		PV

☐ Rochelt Musculair 1				PV
☐ Rochelt Solair 1	D-MXOL			PV
☐ Rumpler C IV		310 (?)		PV
☐ Rumpler-Etrich Taube		19		PV
☐ Scheibe Spatz B			Front fuselage only.	PV
☐ Schleicher Ka-6 Rhönsegler	D-9099	378		PV
☐ Schneider Grunau SG-38 (D.F.S. 108-14)			On loan from Segelflug Museum, Gunzburg.	PV
☐ Sikorsky S-55D Chickasaw (H-19B) (UH-19B)	53-4458			PV
☐ Stark Turbulent D	D-ENEK	103 (V-3)		PV
☐ Wagner DOWA 81				PV
☐ Wright Standard Type A				PV

DEUTSCHES SEGELFLUGMUSEUM (GER27)

Address: Rhön-Wasserkuppe, D-35129 Gersfeld.
Tel: 06654-7737
Fax: 06654-7736
Email: info@segelflugmuseum.de
Admission: April-October daily 0900-1700; November- March daily 1000-1600.
Location: About 15 km east of Fulda between Roads 279 and 458.

The famous hill site of the Wasserkuppe in Rhön Mountains was first used for gliding in 1910/11. Hans Gutermuth and Berthold Fischer, two students from Darmstadt High School, first built models and then progressed to hang gliders of similar form to those flown by Otto Lilienthal twenty years earlier. After World War I Oskar Ursinius, the editor of Flugsport, launched a campaign to re-open the site. Money was raised and workshops and accommodation blocks were erected. Constructors and pilots were persuaded to gather at the hill for a meeting in the summer of 1920. The majority of the entrants were hang-gliders but one machine, Klemperer's 'Black Devil', had an enclosed fuselage. The following year forty five arrived and few were hang-gliders. Among those present was the Hannover Vampyr, now on show in the Deutsches Museum in Munich. Over the next few years the majority of the great sailplane pilots and many of the successful types from Germany and the surrounding countries came to the contests which finished in 1938. During World War II the field was used for military training. In 1951 when the ban on flying in Germany was lifted the slopes of the Wasserkuppe again saw machines soaring above them. Now modern composite high performance types are used and these contrast vividly with the vintage machines flown by the Oldtimer Club. The idea of a museum was conceived in 1970 to celebrate the fiftieth anniversary of the first meeting. Historic items were collected or brought out of store and an exhibition was staged in one of the buildings. A fund raising drive was started so that a purpose built museum could be erected. The circular structure was officially opened at the end of August 1987. Around the walls are boards tracing the history of gliding from the days of Lilienthal up to the present time. The development of sailplane and gliding equipment is also portrayed. The different methods of construction are highlighted starting with the early wooden airframes which led to the composite plastics and fibre methods used today. The work of famous designers, such as Hans Jacobs, the Hütter brothers, Wolf Hirth, Alexander Schleicher, Alexander Lippisch and Edmund Schneider, who brought Germany to the forefront of gliding in the inter-war period is displayed. Photographs of the contests from this period show many of the personalities of this time. The work of the technical university teams is highlighted. The range of gliders on exhibition highlight the strides, which have been made in sailplane design. Replicas of a number of Lilienthal's types have been constructed, as has one of the machine used by Pelzner at the 1920 meeting. This fascinating museum should be on the itinerary of anyone interested in aviation.

TYPE	REG/SER	CON. NO.	PI/NOTES	STATUS
☐ Aachen FVA 10B Rheinland (D.F.S. 108-74)	'D-12-354'		D-????, RAFGSA.521, BGA.1711	PVX
☐ Akaflieg Darmstadt D 34c	D-4644			RA
☐ Akaflieg Darmstadt H2PL Musterle (R)				PV
☐ Akaflieg Hannover Vampyr (R)				PV
☐ Akaflieg München Mü 13d	D-6293	3		PV
☐ Akaflieg Stuttgart Fs 24 Phönix	D-8353	402		PV
☐ Avialsa-Scheibe A.60 Fauconnet [L-Spatz 55]	LX-???			RA
☐ Dittmar Condor IV/3	'D-CONDOR'	23/53	D-1092	PVX
☐ Dittmar Möwe				PV
☐ Flug-Sport Vereinigung Darmstadt FSV X (R)				PV
☐ Focke-Wulf Weihe 50	D-5862	414		PV
☐ Glaser-Dirks DG.100 Elan		C-118		RA
☐ Göppingen Gö 1 Wolf (D.F.S. 108-58)	'D-15-2'		N22431	PVX
☐ Göppingen Gö 3 Minimoa	HB-282			PV
☐ Göppingen Gö 4 Gövier III	D-1084	414	On loan from SFM Gunzburg.	PV
☐ Haase, Kensche, Schmetz H.K.S.1				RA
☐ Heinkel Greif 1-A	D-6623	104		RA
☐ Horten 33				PVC
☐ Jacobs Habicht E (D.F.S. 108-53) (R)	D-8002	ABH1/OSC		PV
☐ Jacobs Kranich IIB (D.F.S. 108-30)	d-6171	533		PV
☐ Jacobs Kranich III	D-1398			RA
☐ Jacobs Kranich III	D-1398	53		RA
☐ Jacobs Meise (D.F.S. 108-70)	D-4679			PV
☐ Jacobs Rhönadler 35 (D.F.S. 108-47)			Carries false registration 'D-Gunther Groenhoff'	PV
☐ Jacobs Rhönbussard (D.F.S. 108-50)			Marked 'D-Hesselberg'	PVX
☐ Jacobs Rhönsperber (D.F.S. 108-51)	D-6262		Marked as D-Rhönsperber.	PV
☐ Lilienthal Derwitzer-Apparat (R)				PV

TYPE	REG/SER	CON. NO.	PI/NOTES	STATUS
☐ Lilienthal Grosser Doppeldecker (R)				PV
☐ Lilienthal Grosser Doppeldecker (R)				PV
☐ Lilienthal Normal-Segelapparat (R)				PV
☐ Lippisch Falke	D-FALKE		HB-16	PV
☐ Lippisch Hols Der Teufel (R)	BGA.3277			PV
☐ Pelzner Hangegleiter (R)				PV
☐ Raab Doppelraab IV	D-4389			RA
☐ Scheibe 138 Specht	D-1624			RA
☐ Scheibe Bergfalke II	D-9041	E-3		PV
☐ Scheibe L-Spatz 55	D-8278	06		RA
☐ Scheibe Mü 13E Bergfalke I	OE-0138			PV
☐ Schleicher Ka-1	D-4328			PV
☐ Schleicher Ka-3	D-6524			PV
☐ Schleicher Ka-4 Rhönlerche II	D-4385	940		RA
☐ Schleicher Ka-6BR Rhönsegler	D-4339			PV
☐ Schneider ESG 29 Grunau 9 (D.F.S. 108-10)				PV
☐ Schneider ESG 31 Grunau Baby IIB	D-1079	5/51	D-4303	PV
☐ Schneider Grunau Baby III (D.F.S. 108-66)	D-4303	05/51		PV
☐ Schneider Grunau Baby III (D.F.S. 108-66)	D-8766			RA
☐ Schneider Grunau SG-38 (D.F.S. 108-14)				PV
☐ Schneider Grunau SG-38 (D.F.S. 108-14)			Nacelle only	PV
☐ Schneider Grunau SG-38 (D.F.S. 108-14)				RA
☐ Schulz FS 3 Besenstiel (R)				PV
☐ Volkseigener Betrieb Apparatebau Lommatzsch FES-530/II Lehrmeister	DM-3308	0258		RA
☐ Volkseigener Betrieb Apparatebau Lommatzsch Lom 58/II Libelle Laminar	DM-2668	0668		PV
☐ Wolfmüller Gleiter			On loan from SFM Gunzburg.	PV

DEUTSCHES TECHNIKMUSEUM (GER28)

Address:	Trebbiner Strasse 9, D-10963 Berlin.
Tel:	030-25484-118
Fax:	030-25484-175
Email:	info@dtmb.de
Admission:	Tuesday-Friday 0900-1730; Saturday-Sunday 1000-1800.
Location:	In the city centre just south of the Tiergarten.

Allied bombing destroyed many museums in Berlin during World War II. These included the Museum of Traffic and Construction, which opened in 1906, and the Deutsche Luftfahrt Sammlung which was established in the mid-1930s and eventually had over one hundred aircraft on show. At the D.T.M. is a superb model showing the D.L.S. with its vast display dominated by the Do X flying boat. At the end of the conflict a group of enthusiasts in the then West Berlin started obtaining items for a transport and technical museum. The collection opened to the public in 1983 but lack of space meant that few of the aircraft in the collection could be displayed. Some of the former D.L.S. aircraft were discovered in Poland in 1945 and most are now in the museum at Krakow. Co-operation between the two countries resulted in a 1913 Jeannin Stahltaube and a 1917 Albatros B IIa (L 30) being restored in Berlin in the 1980s. The former remained in Germany and the latter returned to Poland. Hopefully more of the historic German aircraft stored at Krakow may return home in the future. The Halberstadt CL IV on show was one of a fleet used in the 1920s by Luftverkehr P. Strähle based at Stuttgart. Several airframes were stored at Schondorf in 1939 where they mostly remained until taken to the U.S.A. in 1982. The aircraft were obtained by the U.S.A.F. Museum which agreed that the Halberstadts moved to Berlin for restoration. One aircraft has stayed in Germany and the others have since returned to the U.S.A. A similar arrangement with the National Air and Space Museum once found a number of Horten gliders in the museum workshops but only one now remains in Germany. The rest have gone back to America. At Templehof Airport the Berlin Airlift is commemorated with a display of a C-54, in period colours. More aircraft from the collection were on show in the terminal building at Templehof and others, including the Boeing 707, can be seen at Tegel. A hangar at Gatow is used as a store and the former Argus engine works serves a depot and a restoration centre. The Eardley Billing replica was built by the late Harold Best-Devereux for the film 'Those Magnificent Men in their Flying Machines'. The aircraft was flown in the film by the German team. The prototype Arado 79 made its maiden flight in 1937 and prior to the outbreak of World War II the type set several records. Built in 1939 the example in the collection flew, in the Saar and Germany until 1967. After many years in store in the Göppingen area with Fritz Ulmer the aircraft was acquired by the museum in 1995. The pre-war Junkers Ju 52 spent a long period in Spain before returning home. The Bücker Bestmann has just been restored to its original Luftwaffe colours. The museum has now obtained two Junkers Ju 87s and a pair of Messerschmitt Bf 110s. These aircraft were brought to England from crash sites in Russia and then made their way to New Zealand before arriving in Berlin in 1997. Other World War II machines are being found. Two Gotha frames have been retreived along with a Henschel Hs 126. When restored they will be the only complete examples of these types. The Focke-Wulf Condor was designed as an airliner for Lufthansa and the four engined design entered service in the late 1930s. When war was declared the type was modified to serve as along range anti-shipping patrol aircraft. A fuselage section has been put on show and wrecks are being investigated to try and find more useful parts. Three designs by the Klemm company show the development of their monoplanes. A new exhibition hall was recently completed and many interesting types have now been put on show along with smaller items. More items are still in store and a further exhibition area is required to show these.

TYPE	REG/SER	CON. NO.	PI/NOTES	STATUS
☐ Airwave Magic IV/166 Hang Glider	D-NPKW			RA
☐ Arado Ar 79B-1	D-EMVT	0047	VA+HP, SL-AAP, D-ECUV	PV
☐ Arado Ar 96B-1	CD+DH	4081	CD+DH, 119, SE-AOB	PV

Type	Reg/Ser	Con. No.	PI/Notes	Status
☐ Baleck Muskelkraftflugzeug			At Tegel Airport.	PV
☐ Boeing 707-458	'D-ABOC'	18071	4X-ATB, N32824, N130KR	RAX
☐ Bücker Bü 131B Jungmann	A-43	55	A-43 (Switzerland), D-EBAD	PV
☐ Bücker Bü 181C-2 Bestmann	RM+HE	501659/FR-38	RM+HE, VN787, F-BBMY, 'D-ESEL'	PV
☐ De Havilland D.H.C.2 Beaver (L-20A) (U-6A)	58-2020	1350		RA
☐ Dornier Do 27B-1	D-ENKN	191	PD+101, PJ+306, AC+931, 55+58	RA
☐ Douglas DC-3A-467 Skytrain (C-47B)	A65-69	15682/27127	43-49866, A65-69, ZD215	RA
☐ Douglas DC-3A-467 Skytrain (C-47B)	45-0951	16954/34214	45-0951, N73856, T.3-54 (Spain), G-BLFL, N951CA, G-BLFL, N951CA	PV
☐ Douglas DC-4 Skymaster (C-54G)	45-0557	36010	At Tempelhof Airport.	PV
☐ Eardley-Billing 1911 (R)				RA
☐ Fieseler Fi 103A-1				RA
☐ Fieseler Fi 156C-3/trop Storch (S 14)	'F3-20'	110062	D-EXWU, Fv3810, OE-ADX, D-ENTE – carries Swedish unit code.	PVX
☐ Focke-Achgelis Fa 330A-1 Bachstelze				PV
☐ Focke-Wulf Fw 44J Stieglitz (Sk 12)	SE-CLC	51	Fv669 – wings from c/n 1904 Fv622, SE-BRZ	RA
☐ Focke-Wulf Fw 200C-3 Condor	F8+BR	0063	Fuselage section and other parts.	RAC
☐ Fokker D VII			Fuselage frame only.	PVC
☐ Fokker D VII (R)				RA
☐ Fokker Dr I (R)	'213/17'			RAX
☐ Gotha Go 145				RAD
☐ Gotha Go 242A			Fuselage frame only.	PVD
☐ Halberstadt CL IV (C-5)	D-IBAO	4205	4205/18, D-144	PV
☐ Halberstadt CLS I			Fuselage only	PV
☐ Hamburger Flugzeugbau HFB.320 Hansa				RA
☐ Heinkel He 111H-1	6N+NH	2527		RAC
☐ Henschel Hs 126B-1	TV+UB	3441		RAD
☐ Horten Ho IIL	D-10-125	6	D-10-125, T2-7, FE-7	PV
☐ Ilyushin Il-2			Fuselage only.	RAD
☐ Ilyushin Il-14P	422	14803045	921, 422, (DM-VAR), DDR-SAM – in DDR markings.	RA
☐ Jacobs D.F.S. 230C-1			Fuselage parts only.	RAD
☐ Jacobs D.F.S. 230C-2			Fuselage parts only.	RAD
☐ Jacobs Meise (D.F.S. 108-70)	D-7504	3		PV
☐ Jeannin Stahltaube	A.180/14	76	On loan from Muzeum Lotnictwa Poland.	PV
☐ Junkers J 4		803/17	Fuselage only – on loan from NMST, Italy.	PV
☐ Junkers Ju 52/3mte	D-AZAW	7220	D-AZAW, EC-CAN, EC-ABF, T.2B-108, 'D-2201' – also reported as c/n 4145.	PVX
☐ Junkers Ju 87R-2	LI+BL	5856		RAD
☐ Junkers Ju 87R-4	L1+FW	6234		PV
☐ Junkers Ju 88A-5	CF+VP			RA
☐ Junkers Ju 88G-1	2Z+BR	714628		PVC
☐ Klemm L 25 b	F-PCDA	138	D-1611, TS-AAB, EZ-AAB	RAC
☐ Klemm Kl 35D (Sk 15)	D-EDOD	1917	Fv5028, SE-BPC, D-EDOD, 'D-ELLY'	PV
☐ Klemm Kl 107C	D-ECOH	129		PV
☐ Korff Windspiel IIM				RA
☐ Lilienthal Derwitzer-Apparat (R)				PV
☐ Lilienthal Grosser Doppeldecker (R)				PV
☐ Lilienthal Kleiner Schlagflügelapparat (R)				PV
☐ Lilienthal Normal-Segelapparat (R)				PV
☐ Messerschmitt Bf 109E-4 (E-3)		1407		PV
☐ Messerschmitt Bf 110E-2	LN+CR	4502	M8+ZE	RAD
☐ Messerschmitt Bf 110F-2/trop	LN+NR	5052		PV
☐ Messerschmitt Me 262A-1	'6'	111006		RA
☐ Mignet HM-8		258		RA
☐ Nord N.1002 Pingouin II [Messerschmitt Bf 108B]	D-EKTY	257	257, F-BGIR	PV
☐ Nord N.1101 Ramier I [Messerschmitt Me 208]	106	106	F-BLOQ	RA
☐ Nord NC.702 Martinet [Siebel Si 204A-1]	331	331		PV
☐ North American NA-221 Sabre (F-86K)	'41256'	221-55	55-4815, MM55-4815	PVX
☐ Pfalz D VIII			Some components	RA
☐ Raab-Katzenstein RK 9a Grasmücke	D-1519	353	On loan from Otto Lilienthal Museum.	PV
☐ Rhein-Flugzeugbau RW 3 P75	D-EIFF	9	D-ELOL	PV
☐ Röver Eindecker			Incomplete.	PV
☐ Santos-Dumont XX Demoiselle (R)	BAPC.194	PPS/DEM/1	On loan to Hans Grade Museum.	–
☐ Scheibe Bergfalke II	D-2001	118/1		RA
☐ Schneider Grunau Baby III (D.F.S. 108-66)				RA
☐ Schneider Grunau SG-38 (D.F.S. 108-14)				RA
☐ Schneider Grunau SG-38 (D.F.S. 108-14)				RA
☐ Slingsby T.38 Grasshopper TX.1	WZ780	776		PV
☐ Temple Wing TE F-3	D-MYAP			RA
☐ Udet U 10				RAD
☐ Vickers 668 Varsity T.1	WF382	541	On loan to Aus. Alliierte.	–
☐ Wytwornia Sprzetu Komunikacyjnego (WSK) Lim-2 [MiG-15bis]	323	1B 003-23		PV
☐ Zlin Z-37 Cmelak				RA

DORNIER MUSEUM (GER29)

Address:	Neues Schloss, D-88709 Meersburg.
Tel:	07532-440-4900
Fax:	07545-84703
Admission:	April-October Daily 1000-1300 14000-1800.
Location:	In the centre of the town. Immenstaad is about 9 km west of Friedrichshafen. Oberpfaffhofen is about 20 km west of München.

Claudius Dornier was born in 1884 and joined the Zeppelin company in 1910. His first aircraft design, the Rs 1 flying boat appeared in 1915 and types bearing his name were until recently still being produced. In the inter-war period the firm became well known for its flying boats and large transport aircraft. During World War II a range of successful bombers was manufactured. Since the lifting of the ban on flying in Germany in 1955 the Munich based firm produced in some numbers the Do 27, Do 28, Do 228 and Do 328 models as well as some innovative prototypes such as the Do 31 V/STOL machine. At Meersburg on the Bodensee close to the site of the 1930s flying boat factory, the company set up a museum tracing its history. An informative display of photographs, models and documents can be seen. Components show the construction methods developed by the Dornier engineers. A Do 27 is on show at the research centre at Immenstaad. The only surviving Libelle is displayed at the Deutsches Museum. The remainder of the aircraft are at the company airfield at Oberpfaffenhofen. The site was bought from the receivers by a Swiss firm who use it for maintenance work and it is believed that they acquired the preserved aircraft as part of the deal.

TYPE	REG/SER	CON. NO.	PI/NOTES	STATUS
☐ Dornier A Libelle II	VQ-FAB	117	On loan to Deutsches Museum	–
☐ Dornier Aerodyne			At Oberpfaffenhofen.	RA
☐ Dornier Do 27A-1	'D-ELUT'	327	D-ECAK, YA+912, 56+45, D-EIRO – at Immenstaad.	RAX
☐ Dornier Do 27B-1	'D-EMMI'		Composite.	RAX
☐ Dornier Do 27J-1	'D-EMMA'	2057	D-9504, D-1 (Belgium), OL-D01 (Belgian), DO-1 (Belgium), D-EGVB, 'D-EYLE' – at Oberschleissheim.	–
☐ Dornier Do 28A-1	'D-IPAT'	3010	(D-IGES), (D-INLF), D-IATA – at Oberpfaffenhofen.	RAX
☐ Dornier Do 28D-2 Skyservant	D-IFMP	4050	D-IMOL – on loan to Flug.Junior.	–
☐ Dornier Do 28D/TNT Skyservant	D-IFNT	4330	206 (Zambia) – at Oberpfaffenhofen.	RA
☐ Dornier Do 31E-1	D-9530	E-1	At Oberpfaffenhofen.	RA
☐ Fiat G.91R/3	31+35	91-403	KD+393, DH+110, MD+252 – at Oberpfaffenhofen.	RA

EISENBAHN UND TECHNIK MUSEUM RÜGEN (GER30)

Address:	Am Bahnhof D-18609 Binz.
Tel:	03893-2366
Fax:	03893-2349
Admission:	April-October daily 1000-1700.
Location:	On the east coast of the island of Rügen.

Housed in the railway station complex this museum has on show trains, cars, fire engines and motor cycles. The small aviation section has the MiG-21 in East German colours and the Schleicher glider.

TYPE	REG/SER	CON. NO.	PI/NOTES	STATUS
☐ Mikoyan-Gurevich MiG-21MF	529	9699008	In DDR markings.	PV
☐ Schleicher K.8B	D-5091	8524		PV

ELBE FLUGZEUGWERKE SAMMLUNG (GER31)

Address:	Köningsbrücker Landstrasse, D-01109 Dresden.
Tel:	0351-8839-2177
Fax:	0351-8839-2178
Email:	efw.sales@airbus.dasa.de
Admission:	By prior permission only.
Location:	At the airport which is about 8 km north of the city centre.

In the early 1950s the German Democratic Republic set up a number of aircraft plants around the country. The Dresden factory was designated to concentrate on transport aircraft. Eighty examples of the Ilyushin Il-14P were produced with the first flying in 1956. The Type 152 jet airliner designed by Brunolf Baade made its maiden flight on December 4th 1958 but was lost in a crash soon afterwards. Work on a batch of pre-production and production airframes was started but in 1961 the East German Government decided to abandon all aircraft production and the programme was cancelled. In the early 1990s the fuselage of one of the uncompleted aircraft was found in the undergrowth at the military base at Rothenburg. This relic is now under rebuild in the factory where it was made. When complete it may go on show in the Verkehrsmuseum in Dresden if there is sufficient space. The Ilyushin Il-14 is on show outside the factory and has recently been joined by the MiG fighters.

TYPE	REG/SER	CON. NO.	PI/NOTES	STATUS
☐ Baade 152/II		011	Fuselage only.	RAC
☐ Ilyushin Il-14P	DM-SAL	14803026	DM-SAL, DDR-SAL, 'DDR-ZZB'	RA
☐ Mikoyan-Gurevich MiG-21F-13	705	741707		RA
☐ Mikoyan-Gurevich MiG-21US	24+02	08685145	218 (DDR)	RA
☐ Mikoyan-Gurevich MiG-23ML	20+35	0390324050	601 (DDR)	RA

ERINNERUNGSSTÄTTE LUFTBRÜCKE FLIEGERHORST FASSBERG (GER32)

Address:	Technische Schule der Luftwaffe 3, Postfach 916, D-29324 Fassberg.
Tel:	05055-17-212
Admission:	April-September Sunday 1400-1700: July 15th-September Tuesday-Thursday 1300-1615.
Location:	In the northern part of the town which is about 12 km south east of Munster.

Fassberg was an important airfield during the Berlin Airlift. The C-47 has been put on show as a memorial to the crews who flew across Soviet occupied territory to deliver supplies to the beleaguered city. The aircraft has been painted in the markings of one which operated from Fassberg. The exmple on show was based at Furstenfeldbruck in 1948 and was transferred to the Turkish Air Force the following year. The site is now home to a Luftwaffe Technical Training School with many instructional airframes.

TYPE	REG/SER	CON. NO.	PI/NOTES	STATUS
☐ Douglas DC-3A-456 Skytrain (C-47A)	'315208'	13880	43-100737, 6068 (Turkey)	RAX

EUROPEAN AERONAUTIC DEFENCE AND SPACE COMPANY SAMMLUNG (GER33)

Address:	Box 801109, D-81663 München.
Tel:	089-607-25711
Admission:	By prior permission only.
Location:	Finkenwerder is about 6 km west of Hamburg on the south bank of the Elbe. Manching is about 10 km south east of Ingoldstat.

The group, which controls many German Aerospace companies, took up its present name in 1996. Several aircraft have been preserved at factories in the country, A review of this policy is currently taking place and a number of airframes are likely to move. There is a possibility of a company museum being established within the next few years. Elbe Flugzeugwwerke is part of EADS but it has a separate entry until the future of its preserved aircraft has been decided. At the Finkenwerder works, near Hamburg, is a former French Air Force Noratlas which flew into the field in the mid-1980s. In 1988 workers at the Bremen plant built a replica of the prototype of the 1924 Focke-Wulf A 16 airliner and this was exhibited at some shows. The former Swiss Air Force Messerschmitt Bf 108 is on loan to the Deutsches Museum and is on show at Oberschleissheim.

TYPE	REG/SER	CON. NO.	PI/NOTES	STATUS
☐ Aero Spacelines 377SGT-F Super Guppy	F-GDSG	003	F-WDSG – at Finkenwerder.	RA
☐ Fiat G.91T/3 (T/1)	98+57	91-2-0007	BD+107, YA+021, 34+07 – at Augsburg.	RA
☐ Focke-Wulf A 16 (R)	'D-437'		At Finkenwerder.	RAX
☐ Fouga CM.170R Magister				RA
☐ Hamburger Flugzeugbau HFB.320 Hansa	D-CARA	1021	At Finkenwerder.	RA
☐ Lockheed 683-10-19 Starfighter (F-104G)	20+46	683-2054	KF+129, (DA+125), DA+110, DD+120 – at Speyer.	RA
☐ Lockheed 683-10-19 Starfighter (F-104G)	22+51	683-7131	KE+431, DD+232, BF+007 – at Manching.	PV
☐ Lockheed 683-10-19 Starfighter (F-104G)	'21+04'	683-8295	KG+395, DB+116, 25+21 – at Manching.	RAX
☐ Messerschmitt Bf 108B-2 Taifun	'D-IOIO'	2064	A-208 (Switzerland) – on loan to Flugwerft Schleissheim.	–
☐ Nord N.2501 Noratlas	F-WFJY	157	157 – at Finkenwerder.	RA

FAHRZEUGMUSEUM MARXZELL (GER34)

Address:	Albstrasse 2, D-76359 Marxzell.
Tel:	07248-6262
Email:	eintritt@fahrzeugmuseum-marxzell.de
Admission:	Daily 1400-1700.
Location:	In the centre of the town which is about 20 km south of Karlsruhe.

Set up in the 1960s this privately run museum has a wide range of exhibits. Motor vehicles, motorcycles, cycles and musical instruments feature prominently. Two large halls house the collection which includes many engines and components from a variety of types. There are also a large number of classic posters hanging on the walls of the main exhibition area. The two seat MiG-15, used by the Soviet Air Force in Germany, is mounted on top of a building in the car park. The former Luftwaffe Sycamore is painted in false civil colours. Fifty examples of the helicopter were ordered in the 1950s for use by the Luftwaffe and the Bundesmarine. The last few were withdrawn in the early 1970s. A Cessna 182 and a Stampe S.V.4 have left the collection. The Ultra Vector F 610 microlight can now be seen along with the successful Tandem Falke powered glider.

TYPE	REG/SER	CON. NO.	PI/NOTES	STATUS
☐ Bristol 171 Sycamore HR.52	'D-HELM'	13476	G-18-149, BB+178, AS+325, 78+18	PVX
☐ Mikoyan-Gurevich MiG-15UTI	75	622925		PV
☐ Scheibe SF-28A Tandem Falke	D-KHOP	5706		RA
☐ Ultra-Vector F 610	D-MAAF	1399		RA

FANIFLY RESTAURANT (GER35)

Address:	Helmstedtstrasse 1, D-39365 Harbke.
Tel:	039406-50113
Admission	On permanent view.
Location:	Just north of the town which is about 5 km south of Helmstedt on Route 245a.

This restaurant has staged a small aeronautical display. In the building are some engines, photographs and models. The former NVA MiG-21 and the ex-Interflug Il-18 are parked outside.

TYPE	REG/SER	CON. NO.	PI/NOTES	STATUS
☐ Ilyushin Il-18V	DDR-STD	180002302	493 (DDR), DM-STD	PV
☐ Mikoyan-Gurevich MiG-21SPS (MiG-21PFM)	22+35	94A5206	878 (DDR)	PV

FLIEGERWERFT (GER36)

Address:	D-75395 Ostelsheim.
Email:	hans.juergen.h.storck@daimlerchrysler.com
Admission:	By prior permission only.
Location:	About 20 km south west of Stuttgart.

This organisation has been formed to keep classic aircraft in flying condition. The Czech Meta-Sokol is an all metal derivative of the Sokol which was built before and after World War II. The Meta-Sokol made its maiden flight in 1956 and only one hundred and seven were constructed. Another Czech design is the Zlin Z.50LS all metal aerobatic single seater which made its first flight in 1975. About one hundred have now been completed. One highlight of the collection is the Swedish built Focke-Wulf Stieglitz. This two seat biplane appeared in 1932 and was built in large numbers in Germany, Argentina and Brazil. The Messerschmitt Bf 108 was built in the late 1930s. Then it served with the Luftwaffe and had several civilian owners in France and Denmark. Both Piper Cubs have more powerful engines to improve their performance.

TYPE	REG/SER	CON. NO.	PI/NOTES	STATUS
☐ Boeing-Stearman E75 Kaydet (PT-13D)	N5345N	75-5718	42-17555	RAA
☐ Dornier Do 27B-1	D-EWRG	276	AS+928, AC+928, BD+928, 56+09, D-EMAE, HB-HAG	RAA
☐ Focke-Wulf Fw 44J Stieglitz	D-EMOF	82	Fv630, SE-CBE	RAA
☐ Jacobs Kranich III				RAA
☐ Messerschmitt Bf 108B Taifun	D-EBFW	1561	D-IBHS, (Luftwaffe), F-BBRH, OY-AIH	RAA
☐ Orlican L-40 Meta-Sokol	D-EJUW	150409		RAA
☐ Piper J-3C-85 Cub (J-3C-65) (L-4H)	D-EHYM	10776	43-29485, PH-NAE, PH-NFI, D-EDIF	RAA
☐ Piper J-3C-90 Cub (J-3C-65) (O-59A) (L-4A)	D-EDUT	8962	42-38393, HB-ODM	RAA
☐ Piper PA-18-95 Super Cub (L-18C)	D-ELHM	18-1336	51-15336, 115336 (France)	RAA
☐ Rolladen-Schneider LS-3				RAA
☐ Schleicher Ka-6 Rhönsegler				RAA
☐ Schneider Grunau Baby III (D.F.S. 108-66)	D-6224	1		RAA
☐ Zlin Z-50LS	OK-WRK	0065		RAA

FLUG WERK FLIEGENDES MUSEUM (GER37)

Address:	Kothingned 4, D-85408 Gammelsdorf.
Tel:	08766-939878
Fax:	08766-939879
Email:	colling@flugwerk.de
Admission:	By prior permission only.
Location:	At Manching airfield which is about 10 km south east of Ingoldstadt just east of the A.9.

The company, set up in the mid-1990s, has produced a series of new Focke Wulf 190s. The first took to the air on October 29th 2004. Some have been supplied to museums in kit form. A new exhibition building is being constructed and this should be ready in 2006. This will house the active aircraft. In addition there will be a glass fronted area where visitors can see the work being carried out. Components are also made for other types and Messerschmitt Bf 109 rear fuselages for rebuilding projects have been produced.

TYPE	REG/SER	CON. NO.	PI/NOTES	STATUS
☐ Flug Werk FW 190A-8	D-FWWC	990001		RAA
☐ Flug Werk FW 190D-9	D-FWSC			RAA
☐ Fouga CM.170R Magister	D-IFCC	079	(AA+179), SC+603, SB+602, 93+02 – see D.G.E.H.F.	RAA
☐ North American NA-121 Texan (AT-6D) (SNJ-5)	D-FWAC	121-42032	44-81310, Bu91036, C.6-125	RAC
☐ North American NA-122 Mustang (P-51D)	D-FWNC			RAA
☐ North American NA-159 Trojan (T-28A)	D-FWBC	159-142	49-1630,N28NA	RAA

FLUGAUSSTELLUNG JUNIOR (GER38)

Address:	Hunstuckhohenstrasse, D-54411 Hermeskeil.
Tel:	06503-7693
Fax:	06503-3410
Email:	info@flugausstellung.de
Admission:	April-October Daily 0900-1800.
Location:	On Road 327 about 2 km north east of the town which is about 25 km south east of Trier.

The late Leo Junior and his wife Marika purchased a plot of land in the Eifel Mountains above the town of Hermeskeil in the early 1970s. Later assisted by their son Peter the family have developed an impressive museum with almost one hundred aircraft on show. Initially an exhibition hall was constructed along with an outside display area. The location is not near an active airfield and most aircraft have to be dismantled and transported by road. The VC-10 was flown into Saarbrucken. The autobahn, which now passes near the museum, was not built at the time and the one hundred and fifty foot fuselage was moved without being split. Airliners feature in the outside display with two former Lufthansa machines, the Super Constellation and the Viscount, an ex-Dan Air Comet and two arrivals from Augsburg – the Interflug Il-18 and Tu-134. A full size replica of Concorde was constructed by a friend in the early days of the museum and this now serves as a cafe. The first hall displays a wide range of engines, components, systems and models showing developments in technology. A second hall was built in 1984, a third in 1991 and the fourth was be ready for the 1998 season A range of light aircraft and gliders is on show in the buildings along with some of the military aircraft. More land was bought in the early 1990s and the collection expanded rapidly. Closure of British and American bases in Germany resulted in the arrival of the Canberra, Hunter, Lightning, Phantoms and Thunderchiefs. A rare exhibit is the 1935 Stettin Landmann light aircraft powered by a 25 hp Daimler engine. The airframe is mounted on a wall and the uncovered wings and tail surfaces show the wooden construction. An arrival by air was the giant Mil-6 helicopter which flew in after a journey of well over one thousand kilometres from Petschora in the Urals.

TYPE	REG/SER	CON. NO.	PI/NOTES	STATUS
☐ Aero L-39ZO Albatros	28+30	232303	180 (DDR)	PV
☐ Aérospatiale / British Aircraft Corporation Concorde (FSM)	'F-WTSA'			PVX
☐ Antonov An-26T	52+08	10706	368 (DDR), (DDR-SBB), 368 (DDR)	PV
☐ Antonov An-2T	HA-ANA	16247310	10 (Hungary)	PV
☐ Blériot XI (R)	D-EHCI	01	On loan	PV
☐ Boeing-Stearman A75J1 Kaydet (PT-18)	N56786	75-0521	40-1964	PV
☐ Bölkow BO 105C	D-HMUY	S-133	(D-HDEA)	PV
☐ Breguet / British Aircraft Corporation Jaguar GR.1A (GR.1)	XX955	S.77		PV
☐ Brantly B.2	D-HOBC	93	(N5953X), (D-HAHO), HB-XAZ	PV
☐ Bristol 171 Sycamore HR.52	78+13	13466	BB+176, CD+085, CB+02?, AS+322, GD+115 – only cockpit on show.	PV/RA
☐ Bristol 171 Sycamore HR.52	'D-HFUM'	13493	G-18-166, CB+014, LC+108, GD+117, 78+33	PVX
☐ Bücker Bü 181B-1 Bestmann (Sk 25)				RA
☐ Canadair CL-13B Sabre 6 [North American F-86E]	JC+101	1696	JC+101, JC+365	PV
☐ Construcciones Aeronáuticas (CASA) 2.111D [Heinkel He 111H-16]	'G1+FL'	145	BR.2I-14	PVX
☐ Construcciones Aeronáuticas (CASA) 352L [Junkers Ju 52/3m]	D-CIAD	016	T.2B-127	PV

☐ Convair 8-10 Delta Dagger (F-102A)	56-1125		56-61125, 61125 (Greece)	PV
☐ Dassault Super Mystère B2	173	173		PV
☐ Dassault Mirage IIIR	'304'	310	310	PVX
☐ Dassault Mirage 5BA	'BA-35'		With tail from Mirage 5F c/n 54, nose from a Mirage IIIE and wings from a Mirage IIIC – in Belgian markings.	PVX
☐ De Havilland D.H.104 Sea Devon C.20 (Dove 2A)	XJ348	04406	G-AMXX, XJ348, G-NAVY	PV
☐ De Havilland D.H.106 Comet 4	G-BDIW	6470	XR398	PV
☐ De Havilland D.H.112 Venom FB.4	J-1797	967	In Swiss markings	PV
☐ Dornier Do 27A-1	D-EFSV	339	AC+952, BF+952, EB+382, 56+53	PV
☐ Dornier Do 28D-2 Skyservant	D-IFMP	4050	D-IMOL – on loan from Dornier Museum.	PV
☐ Dornier-Bell 205 (UH-1D)	D-HATU	8066	(70+36)	PV
☐ Dornier-Breguet Alpha Jet A	40+61	0061	On loan from Luftwaffen Museum	PV
☐ Douglas DC-3A-456 Skytrain (C-47A)	111	19460	42-100997, 111 (Jordan), 42-100997, N62443	PV
☐ Eidgenössiches Flugzeugwerke Emmen C-3605 (C-3603-1)	C-541	321		PV
☐ English Electric EA.1 Canberra B(I).8	XM264	EEP71624	XM264, 8227M	PV
☐ English Electric P.25 Lightning F.2A (F.2)	XN782	95135	XN782, 8539M	PV
☐ Fairey Gannet AEW.3	XL450	F9433	XL450, 8601M	PV
☐ Fiat G.91R/3	30+86	91-350	KD+340, ED+247, MR+110 – cockpit only.	PV
☐ Fiat G.91R/3	'MM5257'	91-438	KD+428, DH+233, BD+413, KB+109, 31+70	PVX
☐ Flugtechnische Arbeitsgemeinschaft Stettin Landmann La 11	D-YLAS	9	On loan from Segelflugmuseum Gunzburg.	PV
☐ Focke-Harz Fo Ha 1		001		PVC
☐ Fokker Dr I (FSM)	'152/17'			PVX
☐ Fouga CM.170R Magister	93+03	080	(AA+180), SC+604, SB+203	RA
☐ Fouga CM.170R Magister	379	379		PV
☐ Fouga CM.170R Magister	'MT-31'	410	410 – with rear fuselage of c/n 322 MT-43 – in Belgian markings.	PVX
☐ Hawker P.1040 Sea Hawk FGA.6 (FGA.4)	XE327	6288	XE327, A2556	RA
☐ Hawker P.1099 Hunter F.58	J-4098	41H/697465	In Swiss markings.	PV
☐ Hawker P.1099 Hunter F.6A (F.6)	XF418	HABL 003284	XF418, 8842M	PV
☐ Hawker-Siddeley P.1127 Harrier GR.3	XZ998	41H/712221	XZ998, 9161M	PV
☐ Hawker-Siddeley P.1127 Harrier T.4 (T.2A)	XW927	41H/212015		RA
☐ Horten Ho XVc			On loan from SFM Gunzburg.	RAC
☐ Hunting-Percival P.84 Jet Provost T.4	XR670	PAC/W/19993	XR670, 8498M	PV
☐ Hütter H 17B	D-8045			PV
☐ Ilyushin Il-14P	3076	14803076	DM-ZXF, 010 (Poland) – in Polish markings.	PV
☐ Ilyushin Il-18V	DDR-STH	184007305	DM-STH	PV
☐ Kamov Ka-26	D-HZPS	7404609	DM-VPK, DDR-VPK	PV
☐ Lilienthal Normal-Segelapparat (R)				PV
☐ Lockheed 1049G-82-105 Super Constellation	D-ALIN	1049G-4604		PV
☐ Lockheed 580 (T-33A)	'133393'	580-1730	58-0681, BD+845, 95+17 – in false Canadian markings.	PVX
☐ Lockheed 580 (T-33A)	94+39	580-8901	53-5562, AB+763, DF+382	PV
☐ Lockheed 580 (T-33A)	BB+816	580-9115	53-5776, (AB+816) – parts only	RA
☐ Lockheed 683-04-19 Starfighter (F-104G)			Fuselage possibly ex -Canadian.	PV
☐ Lockheed 683-10-19 Starfighter (F-104G)	20+43	683-2050	KF+126, (DA+254), BF+123, (DF+113)	PV
☐ Lockheed 683-10-19 Starfighter (F-104G)	26+61	683-7407		PV
☐ Lockheed 683-10-19 Starfighter (F-104G)	FX-60	683-9103	In Belgian markings – has c/n 683-9108 on tail which is FX-65.	PV
☐ McDonnell M.98DE Phantom II (F-4C)	63-7421	358		PV
☐ McDonnell M.98DE Phantom II (F-4C)	63-7583	635		PV
☐ McDonnell M.98DF Phantom II (RF-4C)	68-0587	3566		PV
☐ Messerschmitt-Bölkow-Blohm Phoebus	D-8752	722	On loan from SFM Gunzburg.	PV
☐ Mikoyan-Gurevich MiG-21bisSAU	24+24	75058015	853 (DDR)	PV
☐ Mikoyan-Gurevich MiG-21F-13	1217	741217	In Polish markings.	PV
☐ Mikoyan-Gurevich MiG-21MF	23+44	96002003	775 (DDR)	PV
☐ Mikoyan-Gurevich MiG-21SPS (MiG-21PFM)	22+36	94A5209	889 (DDR)	PV
☐ Mikoyan-Gurevich MiG-21SPS-K (MiG-21PFM)	979	94A6505	Front fuselage only.	PV
☐ Mikoyan-Gurevich MiG-21UM	23+79	03695163	205 (DDR) – front fuselage only.	PV
☐ Mikoyan-Gurevich MiG-21US	24+08	02685139	238 (DDR)	PV
☐ Mikoyan-Gurevich MiG-23BN	698	0393214214	698 (DDR), 20+46	PV
☐ Mikoyan-Gurevich MiG-23MF	20+01	0390213095	568 (DDR)	PV
☐ Mikoyan-Gurevich MiG-23ML	20+19	0390324617	343 (DDR)	RA
☐ Mil Mi-2			Front fuselage only.	PV
☐ Mil Mi-2 (Mi-2F)	D-HZPQ	562945063	504 (DDR), (DDR-VGM)	PV
☐ Mil Mi-4A	2139	02139	In Czech markings.	PV
☐ Mil Mi-6A	RA-21133	715309	CCCP-21133	PV
☐ Mil Mi-8T	94+20	10525	909 (DDR), 94+20, (DDR-VHE) (D-HOZD)	PV
☐ Mil Mi-9 (Mi-8A)	93+95	340002	402 (DDR)	PV
☐ Mil Mi-14PL	618	B 4002	618 (DDR), 95+02	PV
☐ Mil Mi-24P	96+50	340340	480 (DDR)	PV
☐ Nord N.1002 Pingouin II [Messerschmitt Bf 108B]	'KG+EM'	91	91, F-BDUP, D-ENHO	PVX

☐ Nord N.2501D Noratlas	D-ACUT	065	GC+109, (GB+119), GB+107, YA+112, YA+572, 52+56	PV
☐ North American NA-121 Texan (AT-6F)	D-FDEM	121-42500	44-81778, D-IDEM, D-FDEM, (PH-HAR)	PV
☐ North American NA-243 Super Sabre (F-100F)	'56-3944'	243-290	56-4014 – tail of c/n 223-16 54-2136	PVX
☐ North American NA-338 Bronco (OV-10B)	99+16	338-1	Bu158292, D-9545 – on loan from Wehrtechnische Studiensammlung.	PV
☐ Panavia PA200 Tornado	XX948	P.06	XX948, 8879M	PV
☐ Percival P.66 Pembroke C.54	54+21	P.66/1013	BF+703, XA+104, 54+21, '04+21'	PV
☐ Percival P.66 Pembroke C.54		P.66/1016	SC+306, SE+520, 54+24 – in false R.A.F. colours.	PVX
☐ Piaggio P.149D	91+90	275	AS+426, BD+393, CA+ 477	PV
☐ Piper J-3C-65 Cub (L-4J)	'D-EDEW'	12620	44-80324, D-EBUR	PVX
☐ Raab Doppelraab IV	D-8572			PV
☐ Republic F-84F Thunderstreak	BF+105		52-6778, DD+382	PV
☐ Republic RF-84F Thunderflash	'EA+241'		52-7377, EB+241, EB+341	PVX
☐ Republic F-105F Thunderchief	62-4417	F-6		PV
☐ Santos-Dumont XX Demoiselle (R)				PV
☐ Saunders-Roe P.501 Skeeter AOP.12	XN354	S2/7160		PV
☐ Scheibe Bergfalke II	D-8518	02		PV
☐ Scheibe L-Spatz 55	D-1691	724		PV
☐ Schleicher Ka-4 Rhönlerche II	OO-ZOR	211	D-5499	PV
☐ Schneider ESG 29 Grunau 9 (D.F.S. 108-10) (R)			On loan from Segelflugmuseum Gunzburg.	PV
☐ Schneider ESG 31 Grunau Baby IIB	D-7160	030195		PV
☐ Sikorsky S-64A Skycrane	D-9511	64003	N306Y – front fuselage only.	PV
☐ Stamer-Lippisch Z-12 Zögling			On loan from Segelflugmuseum Gunzburg.	PV
☐ Sukhoi Su-7BM	09	5309	In Polish markings.	PV
☐ Sukhoi Su-22M4	25+16	26103	678 (DDR)	PV
☐ Svenska Aeroplan Aktiebolaget (SAAB) 37 Viggen (SF 37) (AJSF 37)	Fv37974	37974	On loan from FVM,SWE.	PV
☐ Tupolev Tu-134A	DDR-SCK	1351304	DM-SCK, 183, DM-SCK, DDR-SCK, (D-AOBB)	PV
☐ Vertol V.43 (H-21C)	83+11	WG.11	PA+206, QF+464, PX+340	PV
☐ Vertol V.43 (H-21C)	83+21	WG.21	PA+216, QF+472, PX+348	PV
☐ Vickers 1101 VC-10	G-ARVF	808		PV
☐ Vickers 814D Viscount	'814'	368	D-ANAM	PVX
☐ Vinten VJ-22 Autogyro (Vinten Wallis WA-116MC)	G-55-2	UMA-01	G-BKLZ – on loan from Wehrtechnische Studiensammlung.	PV
☐ Westland Scout AH.1	XR633	F9533	With parts from c/n F.9762 XW799, (G-BXSL)	PV
☐ Westland Scout AH.1	G-BXSL	F9762	XW799	PV
☐ Westland-Bell 47G-3B-1 Sioux AH.1	XT548	WA.437		PV
☐ Westland-Sikorsky WS-55 Whirlwind HAR.10	XP352	WA.368	XP352, 8701M – with tailboom from c/n WA.29 XD186	RA
☐ Westland-Sikorsky WS-55 Whirlwind HAR.10 (HAR.4)	XD186	WA.29	XD186, 8730M	PV
☐ Westland-Sikorsky WS-58 Wessex HC.2	XR527	WA.149		PV
☐ Westland-Sikorsky WS-58 Wessex HC.2	XT670	WA.538		PV
☐ Wytwornia Sprzetu Komunikacyjnego (WSK) SBLim-2M [MiG-15UTI]	301	3501	In Polish markings.	PV
☐ Wytwornia Sprzetu Komunikacyjnego (WSK) Lim-6M (Lim-5P) [MiG-17PF]	413	1D 04-13		PV
☐ Wytwornia Sprzetu Komunikacyjnego (WSK) SM-1Wb [Mil Mi-1M]	031	401031	In Hungarian markings	PV
☐ Zlin Z-37A Cmelak	D-ESSJ	17-28	DM-SSJ,DDR-SSJ	PV

FLUGHAFEN BREMEN AUSSTELLUNG (GER39)

Address:	Flughaffenallee 20, D-28199 Bremen.
Tel:	0421-5595-564
Fax:	0421-5595-474
Email:	contact@airport.bremen.de
Admission:	Daily 1000-1800.
Location:	At the airport which is about 5 km south of the city centre.

The Junkers W 33 'Bremen' made the first non-stop east-west crossing of the Atlantic in 1928. On April 12th, crewed by Hermann Köhl, Gunther von Hünefeld and James Fitzmaurice, the aircraft left Baldonnel in Ireland and after thirty seven hours aloft was forced to land in Labrador. The original plan was to finish the flight in New York but strong winds caused this to be abandoned. The W 33 was placed on show along with several other significant aircraft in the Henry Ford Museum in the U.S.A where it has remained until recently. The Czech built Stieglitz was delivered to Finland in 1940 and served in their Air Force.

TYPE	REG/SER	CON. NO.	PI/NOTES	STATUS
☐ Focke-Wulf Fw 44J Stieglitz	D-EHOO	2932	D-EXWL, SZ-29 (Finland), OH-SZN	PV
☐ Junkers W 33 b	D-1167	2504	On loan from Henry Ford Museum and Greenfield Village, USA.	PV
☐ Vereinigte Flugtechnische Werke – Fokker (VFW) 614	D-ASAX	G-015	D-BABN,F-GATI	PV

FLUGHAFEN LEIPZIG-HALLE BESUCHERHÜGEL (GER40)

Address:	Flughafen Leipzig-Halle, D-04029 Leipzig.
Tel:	0341-224-1155
Email:	mail.flh@leipzig-halle.de
Admission:	At all times. Visitor Centre Daily 0900-1230 1330-1800.
Location:	At Schkeuditz Airport which is about 15 km north west of Leipzig just south of Autobahn A.14.

The airport was opened in the late 1920s and many companies flew into the field. The site was bombed during World War II and most of the facilities were completely destroyed. From 1963 to 1971 one rebuilt runway was in use during the period of the Leipzig Fair. Full commercial operations resumed in 1972 and since re-unification the airport has been progressively modernised. Schkeuditz Airport now serves the cities of Halle and Leipzig and was an important base for the former East German airline Interflug. Two Soviet built types, which served with the carrier before it was absorbed into Lufthansa, are on show close to the main car parking area with a third in store. The Ilyushin Il-18 was the first of sixteen flown by Interflug and was delivered in 1960. The Tupolev Tu-134 joined the fleet in 1969 and was flown until the late 1980s. The Ilyushin Il-62 spent a period on show before moving across the field. There were plans to move the airliners to a new site and this may happen as development procedes. For a period two agricultural aircraft were on show but these have left. These were a Czech built Cmelak and a Polish designed Kruk which were flown by Interflug.

TYPE	REG/SER	CON. NO.	PI/NOTES	STATUS
☐ Ilyushin Il-18V	DDR-STA	180001905	DM-STA	PV
☐ Ilyushin Il-62	DDR-SEF	31402	DM-SEF	RA
☐ Tupolev Tu-134K	DDR-SCF	9350905	178 (DDR), DM-SCF	PV

FLUGHAFEN MÜNCHEN BESUCHERPARK (GER41)

Address:	Postfach 231755, Flughafen Franz-Josef Strauss, D-85326 München.
Tel:	089-975-00
Fax:	089-975-57906
Email:	info@munich-airport.de
Admission:	April-October daily 0900-2000; November-March daily 0900-1700.
Location:	About 30 km north east of the city centre off Autobahn A.92.

In the 1930s the civil airport for the city was located at Obersweinfeld but this was replaced by a new field at Riem in 1939. During World War II the airfield was bombed and flights did not resume until 1948. The expansion of the city meant that Riem was becoming surrounded by housing and industry so the search for a new site began. Although an area of fields was chosen there were objections and the new airport was not ready until 1992. On the night of. May 15/16th an operation to move vehicles, personnel and equipment took place so that Franz-Josef Strauss Airport was ready to open in the morning. A visitor park has been constructed and this features a large artificial hill which gives a panoramic view of the site. This affords an excellent view of operations from the busy field. At the bottom are parked three airliners, all from the defunct Air Classic collection. The Constellation, in false Lufthansa colours is open to the public. This was delivered to Air France in February 1957 and served until 1963. Air Classic put it on show at Dusseldorf Airport in the late 1970s. The Dakota is painted in an early Swissair scheme to represent the many examples of the type which flew into Munich with the national carrier. The Spanish built Junkers Ju 52/3m arrived in 1997. This classic three engined type was a regular visitor to Obersweinfeld before World War II. There is an exhibition in the park tracing the history of civil airports in the Munich area. Here the visitor can see models and photographs.

TYPE	REG/SER	CON. NO.	PI/NOTES	STATUS
☐ Construcciones Aeronáuticas (CASA) 352L [Junkers Ju 52/3m]	'D-ANOY'	54	T.2B-144, N88927, D-CIAS	PVX
☐ Douglas DC-3A-405 Skytrooper (C-53) (C-53B)	'HB-IRN'	4828	41-20058, NC34989, OY-DCA, OY-KLE, OH-VKA, LN-KLV, LN-RJA, OH-VKA, N65371, 'N569R'	PVX
☐ Lockheed 1049G-82-98 Super Constellation	'D-ALEM'	1049G-4671	F-BHML, 'D-ADAM', 'D-ALAP'	PVX

FLUGMUSEUM CÄMMERSWALDE (GER42)

Address: D-09544 Cämmerswalde
Admission: On permanent view.
Location: In the village which is about 12 km north east of Olbernhau.

In 1973 a former Interflug Il-14 was put on show in this village. The twin engined airliner was built at Dresden in 1957, served with the airline until the summer of 1970, and then preserved at Brath. Local enthusiasts have maintained the aircraft which has now been joined by a MiG-21 which was for a period on show at the Flugplatz Cottbus Museum. There are also some engines and photographs to be seen. The hills around the village are regularly used by hang gliders and this sport can be viewed from the display.

TYPE	REG/SER	CON. NO.	PI/NOTES	STATUS
☐ Ilyushin Il-14P	DM-SAB	14803008		PV
☐ Mikoyan-Gurevich MiG-21SPS-K (MiG-21PFM)	449	94A6712	In DDR markings.	PV

FLUGPIONIER GUSTAV WEISSKOPF MIT HEIMAT UND HANDWERKER MUSEUM (GER43)

Address: Plan 6,
D-91578 Leutershausen b.Ansbach.
Tel: 09823-951-0
Fax: 09823-951-50
Admission: Easter-October Sunday-Friday 1000-1200; Wednesday and Sunday also 1400-1600.
Location: In the centre of the town which is about 12 km west of Ansbach.

Gustav Weisskopf was born in Leutershausen on January 1st 1874. After an eventful early life he settled in the U.S.A. in 1895 and changed his surname to Whitehead. In 1893/4 he visited Otto Lilienthal in Germany. During the late 1890s Whitehead built an ornithopter and a glider in Boston. He continued to develop his theories and in 1899 he constructed a steam powered aircraft which according to reports crashed into a house at the level of the third floor. Two years later, then residing in Bridgeport Connecticut, he flew his monoplane No.21 a distance of about half a mile at a height of about thirty feet. The aircraft took off under its own power and the event was recorded in the 'Scientific American' magazine. He built his next aircraft No.22, powered by a diesel engine, the following year and flew about seven miles on January 17th Many people believed Weisskopf carried out the first powered flights and several books and articles have put forward their ideas. In 1980 a museum was opened in Leutershausen to honour his work. Models drawing and photographs can be seen. A replica of his No.21 has been built and underwent trials at Manching. Twenty four flights were made and the aircraft then moved to the museum. The town of Leutershausen dates from about 1000 AD and rooms in the museum building trace the history and development of the area with many interesting items displayed.

TYPE	REG/SER	CON. NO.	PI/NOTES	STATUS
☐ Bruder Weiskopf 21B (R)				PV

FLUGPLATZ FÜRSTENWALDE MUSEUM (GER44)

Address: Domstrasse 1,
D-15517 Fürstenwalde.
Tel: 03361-32037
Fax: 03361-32037
Admission: By prior permission only. (Believed to be still open)
Location: About 2 km north east of the town which is about 40 km east of Berlin.

An airfield close to the present site was built during World War I. This was closed at the end of the hostilities and the land was again farmed. A new military base was constructed in the 1930s and was used by the Luftwaffe until 1945. The Soviet forces took over the airfield and it was subsequently a major East German Air Force base. The site is now used for sport flying with flying, gliding, microlight and parachute clubs in residence. There are a number of vintage gliders in the hangars and Historicher Flugzeugbau have their workshops here. An exhibition tracing the history of the site has been set up in a building. The former East German Mil-8 arrived from Cottbus which was a major base for the type. This has recently been joined by the Dornier Do 228 static test airframe. The indoor exhibition is still believed to open to the public.

TYPE	REG/SER	CON. NO.	PI/NOTES	STATUS
☐ Dornier Do 228			Static test airframe.	PV
☐ Mil Mi-8TB	93+75	10592	938 (DDR)	PV

FLUGPLATZMUSEUM COTTBUS (GER45)

Address:	Am Fichtesportplatz, Dahlitzer Strasse, D-03046 Cottbus.
Tel:	0355-32004
Fax:	0355-32004
Email:	info@flugplatzmuseumcottbus.de
Admission:	March-October Tuesday- Saturday 1000-1600; Sunday 1000-1700: November-February Tuesday-Saturday 1000-1600.
Location:	On the south side of the airfield which is west of the city and north of Road 115.

The airfield opened in the late 1930s as the civil field for the city and some of the original buildings still stand. These include the art-deco terminal which is in reasonable condition. During World War II Focke-Wulf used the site to test aircraft built at its local factory. Substantial numbers of a number of Fw 190 variants were produced along with several Ta 152s. Most of the fuselages for the Ta 154 night fighter were constructed at Cottbus. Only about two dozen examples were completed as there were several technical problems with the design. Production of all types ceased in 1945 as the Soviet forces advanced on the city. Prior to the reunification of the country the field was home to helicopter units of the N.V.A. In recent years there were squadrons flying Bölkow BO 105s in residence but they have now moved to Holzdorf. The museum was set up by a group of enthusiasts and opened in September 1992. A site on the south side of the field with an exhibition building workshops and a large outside area was obtained. The indoor display traces the history of the airfield and units which served there with photographs, models, documents, uniforms and memorabilia on show. The development of the N.V.A is also shown. Close by is a line of military and airfield vehicles. A range of MiG types is in the collection, the earliest being a two seat version of the MiG-15. The MiG-17 was used by the Soviet Air Force. In store are two locally designed gliders used by clubs in the former East Germany. Examples of types flown by Interflug on agricultural work have also been obtained. The Antonov An-14A, moved from Dresden, is a comparative rarity. Only four examples of the type were used by the N.V.A. The Focke Wulf Fw 190 was blown up by the Luftwaffe at Furstenwalde in 1945 to prevent it being captured by the advancing Soviet forces. The airframe spent over fifty years buried by rubble before being discovered in 1997. The Yakovlev Yak-11 is currently being restored. This aircraft spent many years in a Pioneer Park in the city along with a MiG-15. Over the last decade a great deal of work has gone into developing this informative exhibition.

TYPE	REG/SER	CON. NO.	PI/NOTES	STATUS
☐ Aero L-29 Delfin	370	591535	In DDR markings.	PV
☐ Antonov An-2T	826	17908		PV
☐ Antonov An-14A	996	600904		PV
☐ Focke-Wulf Fw 190F-3/R11		670071		PVC
☐ Ilyushin Il-28	205	54006279	Front fuselage only – In DDR markings.	PV
☐ Instytut Szybownictwa IS-4 Jastrzab	DM-4000	20	SP-1394	RA
☐ Mikoyan-Gurevich MiG-15UTI	154	1615393	(Soviet) – in DDR markings – on loan from Luftwaffen Museum.	RAC
☐ Mikoyan-Gurevich MiG-17	226	54211684	22 (Soviet)	PV
☐ Mikoyan-Gurevich MiG-21bisSAU	24+21	75051407	848 (DDR) – on loan from Luftwaffen Museum.	PV
☐ Mikoyan-Gurevich MiG-21MF	653	965311	In DDR markings – on loan from Luftwaffen Museum	PV
☐ Mikoyan-Gurevich MiG-21SPS-K (MiG-21PFM)	981	94A6704	In DDR markings – on loan from Luftwaffen Museum.	PV
☐ Mikoyan-Gurevich MiG-21SPS-K (MiG-21PFM)	449	94A6712	In DDR markings – on loan from Luftwaffen Museum.	PV
☐ Mikoyan-Gurevich MiG-21SPS-K (MiG-21PFM)	986	94A6715	In DDR markings – on loan from Luftwaffen Museum	PV
☐ Mikoyan-Gurevich MiG-21US	23+99	01685134	215 (DDR) – on loan from Luftwaffen Museum.	PV
☐ Mikoyan-Gurevich MiG-23UB	20+62	A1037901	104 (DDR) – on loan from Luftwaffen Museum.	PV
☐ Mil Mi-2	32	511019039	02 – in Soviet markings – on loan from Luftwaffen Museum	PV
☐ Mil Mi-2US	380	562249032	In DDR markings – on loan from Luftwaffen Museum.	PV
☐ Mil Mi-4A	'785'	0251	561, DM-SPB, 792	PVX
☐ Mil Mi-4A	538	07142	598, (DM-WSB) – in DDR markings – on loan from Luftwaffen Museum.	RAC
☐ Mil Mi-8TB	93+68	10560	132 (DDR)	PV
☐ Mil Mi-8TB	'93+60'	10577	751 (DDR), 93+70	PVX
☐ Mil Mi-9 (Mi-8A)	93+98	340001	482 (DDR)	PV
☐ Mil Mi-24D	98+32	340278	547 (DDR), 96+39	PV
☐ Panstwowe Zaklady Lotnicze (PZL) 106A Kruk	DDR-TCA	07810140	DDR-TCA, (D-FOCA)	PV
☐ Piaggio P.149D	92+13	309	AC+460, AS+460	PV
☐ Sud-Est SE.3130 Alouette II	'76+40'	1609	PN+135, QW+740, QW+221, 76+22	PVX
☐ Sukhoi Su-22M4	25+04	25511	365 (DDR) – on loan from Luftwaffen Museum.	PV
☐ Sukhoi Su-22UM3K	98+11	17532370810	137 (DDR), 25+53	PV
☐ Volkseigener Betrieb Apparatebau Lommatzsch FES-530/II Lehrmeister	DM-3267	0217		RA
☐ Volkseigener Betrieb Apparatebau Lommatzsch Lom 58/II Libelle Laminar	DM-2660	0660		RA

TYPE	REG/SER	CON. NO.	PI/NOTES	STATUS
☐ Wytwornia Sprzetu Komunikacyjnego (WSK) Lim-5 [MiG-17F]	502	1C 09-02	On loan from Luftwaffen Museum.	PV
☐ Wytwornia Sprzetu Komunikacyjnego (WSK) Lim-5 [MiG-17F]	537	1C 09-17	In DDR markings – on loan from Luftwaffen Museum.	RA
☐ Wytwornia Sprzetu Komunikacyjnego (WSK) Lim-5P [MiG-17PF]	437	1D 02-12	437, '2009', '850', '2001'	RAC
☐ Yakovlev Yak-11	98	68210	On loan from Luftwaffen Museum	RA
☐ Zlin Z-37 Cmelak	D-EOON	06-18	DM-SNN, DDR-SNN	RA
☐ Zlin Z-37A Cmelak	D-ESLQ	14-20	DM-SLQ, DDR-SLQ	PV

FLUGPLATZMUSEUM WELZOW (GER46)

Address:	03119 Welzow.
Tel:	03571-5113833
Fax:	03571-20699
Email:	info@flugplatzwelzow.de
Admission:	By prior permission only.
Location	Just to the east of the town which is about 20 km south of Cottbus.

The first flights took place in the area in 1914 and the airfield has a varied history since then. In the 1920s and early 1930s it was used for sport and glider flying The site became part of Hitler's expansion plans and was developed into a military base. After World War II it was used by the Russians and is now a civil field. The museum traces all these phases of use with photographs, documents and flying clothing.

TYPE	REG/SER	CON. NO.	PI/NOTES	STATUS
☐ Mikoyan-Gurevich MiG-21F-13	705	741707	IN DDR markings.	PV

FLUGSPORT MUSEUM (GER47)

Address:	Flugplatz Finsterwalde, Kirchainer Strasse 58/18, D-03238 Finsterwalde.
Tel:	035311-2285
Admission:	Temporarily closed.
Location:	The airfield is about 3 km west of the town on the road to Kirchhain.

This museum was set up in the 1980s at a hangar at the then closed grass airfield. The theme of the exhibition was to trace the history of sport flying in the D.D.R. Gliders and light aircraft, several designed in the country, were on show along with models, components and photographs. The airfield was put back into use in the early 1990s and the museum fleet is either in store at the back of the hangar or in a building in the nearby town. A unique machine is the prototype of the FSS 100 monoplane built in 1962. This low wing monoplane bore a resemblance to the Piel Emeraude. There are plans to raise funds for a purpose built museum.

TYPE	REG/SER	CON. NO.	PI/NOTES	STATUS
☐ Flugsportschule Schonhagen FSS 100 Tourist	DM-WZZ	01-62		S
☐ Schneider ESG 31 Grunau Baby IIB				RA
☐ Schneider ESG 31 Grunau Baby IIB				S
☐ Schneider ESG 31 Grunau Baby IIB	DM-1627	00627		RA
☐ Schneider Grunau SG-38 (D.F.S. 108-14)				RA
☐ Schneider Grunau SG-38 (D.F.S. 108-14)				RA
☐ Volkseigener Betrieb Apparatebau Lommatzsch FES-530/II Lehrmeister				S
☐ Volkseigener Betrieb Apparatebau Lommatzsch FES-530/II Lehrmeister	DM-3277	0227		RA
☐ Volkseigener Betrieb Apparatebau Lommatzsch Lom 58/II Libelle Laminar				S
☐ Volkseigener Betrieb Apparatebau Lommatzsch Lom 58/II Libelle Laminar	DDR-2653	0653	DM-2653	RA
☐ Volkseigener Betrieb Apparatebau Lommatzsch Lom 61 Favorit V-1	DM-2700	0700		S
☐ Volkseigener Betrieb Apparatebau Lommatzsch Meise				RA
☐ Zlin Z-226 Trener 6	DDR-WEJ	243	DM-WEJ	RA

FLUGWELT ALTENBURG NOBITZ (GER48)

Address:	Flugplatz, D-04603 Altenburg Nobitz.
Tel:	03447-590301
Email:	info@flugwelt.altenburg.nobitz.de
Admission:	Monday-Friday 1000-1600 Saturday-Sunday 1000-1700 (Closes at 1600 November-March)
Location:	Just east of Nobitz which is about 3 km east of Altenburg.

In 1909 a Parseval airship visited the site in conjunction with drilling operations. Two years later the first powered aircraft used the same field. An air base was established in 1913 and in the latter stages of World War I Albatros, D.F.W., Fokker and Rumpler types were assembled in the large hangars. The terms of the 1918 Peace Treaty meant that all the buildings were dismantled and the site reverted to agricultural use. The military build up in the 1930s resulted in the construction of a new airfield. The field was ready in 1936 and was primarily a training base although a squadron of Focke Wulf Fw 190s was in residence for a period in 1942. Many night fighter pilots underwent instruction and types used included Junkers Ju 87s and 88s, Dornier Do 17s, 18s and 23s, Heinkel He 111s and Messerschmitt Bf 110s. American forces were present for a short time in 1945 before the base was handed over to the Soviet authorities. Up to 1991 it was used by fighters and in the latter period MiG-21s were flown. Now Nobitz is a civil airport with scheduled and charter flights. Flying clubs and private owners also use the airfield. The museum has been set up to trace the history of the field since the early days. On show are models, dioramas, photographs and items of memorabilia. The Russians erected a MiG-21SMT as a monument in 1985 and this has been taken down and restored. A former East German MiG-21SPS has now arrived. After storage at Rothenburg it was by a shopping mall in Zwickau for a few years.

TYPE	REG/SER	CON. NO.	PI/NOTES	STATUS
☐ Mikoyan-Gurevich MiG-21SMT	60		In Soviet markings.	PV
☐ Mikoyan-Gurevich MiG-21SPS (MiG-21PFM)	22+27	94A4303	742 (DDR)	PV

FLYING BIRDS (GER49)

Address:	Holtstrasse 39, D-44388 Dortmund.
Tel:	0231-692967
Admission:	By prior permission only.
Location:	At a private airfield in the area.

This group owns four classic gliders from the 1950s. The famous Schleicher factory at Poppenhausen started glider production in 1951 after the post-World War II ban had been rescinded. The Ka-2 and Ka-4 were designed by Rudolf Kaiser. The Greif, designed by Hans Hollfelder and Otto Funk, appeared in prototype form at the 1961 Hanover show. Only a small number of this V-tailed all metal Standard Class sailplane were constructed and the example in the collection is believed to be the only survivor. The Mü 13E Bergfalke was the first post-war German high performance glider when it appeared in 1951. The improved II/55 followed four years later.

TYPE	REG/SER	CON. NO.	PI/NOTES	STATUS
☐ Heinkel Greif 1-A	D-7074			RAC
☐ Scheibe Bergfalke II/55	OE-0413	244	D-6413	RAA
☐ Schleicher Ka-2B Rhönschwalbe	D-5213	2002		RAA
☐ Schleicher Ka-4 Rhönlerche II	D-7196	65/57		RAA

FOCKE MUSEUM (GER50)

Address:	Schwachhauser Heerstrasse, 240 D-28213 Bremen.
Tel:	0421-361-3575
Fax:	0421-361-3903
Email:	post@focke.museum.bremen.de
Admission:	Tuesday 1000-2100; Wednesday-Sunday 1000-1700.
Location:	In the eastern part of the city centre.

The organisation has its origins in two collections, a Trade Museum and an Historical Museum, which combined in the 1920s. The building was destroyed in World War II and many items were lost. Now the collection is the Federal State Museum for the area. The site contains a large botanical park, four historic buildings and purpose built exhibition halls. Urban life and culture are portrayed along with works of art. There are also many everyday items in the exhibitions. The Sycamore has recently been moved from the collection at Nordholz. Fifty examples of the helicopter were flown by both the Luftwaffe and Bundesmarine.

TYPE	REG/SER	CON. NO.	PI/NOTES	STATUS
☐ Bristol 171 Sycamore HR.52	'WE+543'	13473	AS+330, LC+115, 78+16, D-HALB – On loan from Aeronauticum.	PVX

FÖRDERKREIS LUFT UND RAUMFAHRT MECKLENBURG-VORPOMMERN (GER51)

Address:	Postfach 151946, D-18061 Rostock.
Admission:	By prior permission only.
Location:	At a workshop in the town and at Laage airfield which is about 20 km south of Rostock.

The Mecklenburg Aero Club at Rostock built a training glider in 1928. Designed by Paul Krekel the two seater was flown at one meeting at the Wasserkuppe. Ernst Heinkel donated materials for the construction of the fuselage. In 1933 Heino Funay designed a single seater which was named Jung Mecklenburg. The group is building a replica of this model using a number of original parts. A former Interflug agricultural Cmelak has also been acquired. This aircraft came from Anklam where large numbers were once stored

TYPE	REG/SER	CON. NO.	PI/NOTES	STATUS
☐ Funay Jung Mecklenburg			Partial replica.	RAC
☐ Zlin Z-37 Cmelak				RA

GEDENKSTÄTTE "MITTELBAU DORA" (GER52)

Address:	Kohnsteinweg 20, D-99734 Nordhausen-Kriderode.
Tel:	03631-4958-0
Fax:	03631-4958-13
Admission:	Daily 1000-1600.
Location:	About 5 km. north west of the town

The site with underground tunnels was used for V-2 production using slave labour from the nearby concentration camp. Over the last decade buildings have been restored and exhibitions staged tracing the history of the complex and its liberation. There are some V-2 components on show.

GERHARD NEUMANN MUSEUM (GER53)

Address:	Kainzacher 9, D-94557 Niederalteich.
Tel:	09901-202720
Email:	josef-voggenreiter@f-104.de
Admission:	By prior permission only.
Location:	About 8 km south east of Deggendorf just south of the A.3.

This private collection of mainly fighter jets was set up in the mid-1990s. In addition to the aircraft there are a number of components, models and photographs to be seen. The Lampyridae was a stealth fighter project developed in the 1980s. A three quarter scale prototype was built and its aerodynamic qualities were tested in fifteen 'flights' in a wind tunnel. The collection honours the designer Gerhard Neumann who after World War II worked for the General Electric company and was responsible for several jet engines.

TYPE	REG/SER	CON. NO.	PI/NOTES	STATUS
☐ Hamburger Flugzeugbau HFB.320 Hansa	D-COSA	1056	Fuselage only.	PV
☐ Lockheed 683-04-10 Starfighter (RF-104G)	24+49	683-8193	KG+293, BB+243 – front fuselage only.	PV
☐ Lockheed 683-04-10 Starfighter (RF-104G)	24+90	683-8240	KG+340,EB+236	PV
☐ Lockheed 683-10-19 Starfighter (F-104G)	23+73	683-8072	KG+172, JD+252, JA+107	PV
☐ Lockheed 683-10-19 Starfighter (F-104G)	25+05	683-8263	KG+363, DB+106	PV
☐ Messerschmitt-Bölkow-Blohm Lampyridae			On loan from Luftwaffen Museum.	PV
☐ Mikoyan-Gurevich MiG-21M	425	962308	425 (DDR), 22+77 – Front fuselage only.	PV
☐ Stützle SZG 10	D-GESZ			PV
☐ Panavia PA200 Tornado			Centre fuselage only.	PV

GERMAN HISTORIC FLIGHT (GER54)

Address:	Gallhöfer Weide 2, D-31715 Meerbeck.
Tel:	05721-928152
Fax:	05721-924479
Email:	info@german-historic-flight.de
Admission:	By prior permission only.
Location:	At a number of airfields.

Formed in 1999, with plans to establish a museum at Braunshweig Airport the organisation has now developed into a co-ordinating group for vintage and classic aircraft across the country. Many interesting types from several countries are owned by members and regular meetings are held. The oldest aircraft is the Fleet 1 dating from the late 1920s and other rarities include the pair of Stieglitz and the Sokol. The CH-7 is an Italian single seat kit built helicopter fitted with a Rotax engine. The example in the fleet was started in 1995 and flew several years later. A number of aircraft are based in neighbouring countries but one which is a long way away is the Kudu resident in its native South Africa. It is owned by a German resident in the country.

TYPE	REG/SER	CON. NO.	PI/NOTES	STATUS
☐ Aero 145	D-GASA	19-014	OK-NHF, G-AROE, (D-GONE), G-AROE	RAA
☐ Aero C-104 [Bücker Bü 131D Jungmann]	CF-UWE	203	(Czech AF), OK-BFW, (D-EFZU), N817S	RAA
☐ Aeromere F.8L Falco Series 2	G-OCDS	114	I-VEGL, OO-MEN, G-VEGL	RAA
☐ Antonov An-2S	D-FAIR	17247305	450 (DDR), 54+02	RAA
☐ Antonov An-2T	D-FJKA	19318	839 (DDR), DDR-WJP	RAA
☐ Atlas C.4M Kudu	ZS-WZO	30	980	RAA
☐ Beech 35 Bonanza	N2778V	D-170		RAA
☐ Beech 35 Bonanza	D-EHIM	D-499	NC90580, HB-ECI, OO-ECI, D-EHIM, OO-NDH	RAA
☐ Beech G35 Bonanza	D-EKUF	D-4713	N12B	RAA
☐ Boeing-Stearman A75N1 Kaydet (PT-17)	'346'	75-710	41-910,N55097	RAAX
☐ Boeing-Stearman A75N1 Kaydet (PT-17)				RAA
☐ Boeing-Stearman A75N1 Kaydet (PT-17)				RAA
☐ Boeing-Stearman A75N1 Kaydet (PT-17)				RAA
☐ Boeing-Stearman A75N1 Kaydet (PT-17)				RAA
☐ Bölkow BO 208C Junior				RAA
☐ Bölkow BO 209 Monsun				RAA
☐ Bölkow BO 209 Monsun				RAA
☐ Bücker Bü 133D-1 Jungmeister	G-BSZN	2002	D-ECAY, N8103	RAA
☐ Bücker T-131PA Jungmann	SP-YDX	102	SP-SPX	RAA
☐ Bücker T-131PA Jungmann	SP-YDY	103	SP-FUY	RAA
☐ Bücker T-131PA Jungmann	SP-YDK	112	(SP-KDK), (D-EKDK)	RAA
☐ Cessna 140				RAA
☐ Cessna 170				RAA
☐ Cessna 170				RAA
☐ Cessna 195A	N3446V	7136	NC3446V	RAA
☐ Cessna F172G	D-ECNE	F1720234	HB-CBP	RAA
☐ Cessna F172H	D-EBVA	F1720419	(D-EDGE)	RAA
☐ Cessna P210N	N660JG	P2100657		RAA
☐ Champion 7EC Traveler (7FC Tri-Traveler)	D-EUUU	7FC-404	N9829Y, D-EBMQ	RAA
☐ Colomban MC-15 Cri-Cri				RAA
☐ Construcciones Aeronáuticas (CASA) 1.131E [Bücker Bü 131 Jungmann]	D-EIWW	2028	E.3B-432, D-ENHD	RAA
☐ Construcciones Aeronáuticas (CASA) 1.131E [Bücker Bü 131 Jungmann]	D-EFQP	2046	E.3B-442	RAA
☐ Construcciones Aeronáuticas (CASA) 1.131E [Bücker Bü 131 Jungmann]	D-EGBM	2062	E.3B-415	RAA
☐ Construcciones Aeronáuticas (CASA) 1.131E [Bücker Bü 131 Jungmann]	D-EEGN	2095	E.3B-351	RAA
☐ Construcciones Aeronáuticas (CASA) 1.131E [Bücker Bü 131 Jungmann]	D-EDWJ	2136	E.3B-453	RAA
☐ Construcciones Aeronáuticas (CASA) 1.131E [Bücker Bü 131 Jungmann]				RAA
☐ Construcciones Aeronáuticas (CASA) 1.131E [Bücker Bü 131 Jungmann]				RAA
☐ De Havilland D.H.82A Tiger Moth	D-ESPS	83683	T7213, G-ANGD, D-EKAL, (D-EAKP), D-EHAL, HB-UCX	RAA
☐ De Havilland D.H.C.1 Chipmunk 22 (T.10)	D-EPAK	C1/0328	WD388, G-BDIC	RAA
☐ De Havilland D.H.C.2 Beaver				RAA
☐ Dornier Do 27A-1	D-EGFR	160	PC+113, QM+606, SC+718, SE+521, 55+36	RAA
☐ Dornier Do 27A-4	D-EOAD	459	KD+???, QM+015, PL+105, PK+222, 57+30	RAA
☐ Dornier Do 28D-2 Skyservant	D-ICDY	4164	58+89	RAA
☐ Eidgenössiches Flugzeugwerke Emmen C-3605 (C-3603-1)	D-FOOT	274	C-494, HB-RDB	RAA
☐ Elisport CH-7 Angel	D-HOUV	3511		RAA
☐ Ercoupe 415D				RAA
☐ Ercoupe 415D	D-EZII	1769	NC99146, N99146	RAA
☐ Ercoupe 415D	D-EOPI	541	N887368, D-EBUP, (D-EBUY)	RAA
☐ Fairchild 24R9 Forwarder (UC-61K) (Argus III)	D-EFML	R9-947	43-14983, HB709, HB-EIR	RAA
☐ Fleet 1	NC8616	28	NC8616, N8616	RAA
☐ Focke-Wulf Fw 44J Stieglitz (Sk 12)	SE-BWM	37	Fv655	RAA
☐ Focke-Wulf Fw 44J Stieglitz (Sk 12)	D-ENAY	45	Fv663, SE-BWH, D-EGAM	RAA
☐ Globe GC-1B Swift	N3327K	1320	N3327K, D-EJYB	RAA
☐ Heliopolis Goumhouria 6 [Bücker Bü 181D Bestmann]	D-EGZR	185	SU-347	RAA
☐ Heuer FW 190	D-EIFW	333/86AB		RAA
☐ Heuer FW 190				RAA
☐ Jodel D.150 Mascaret				RAA
☐ Jodel DR.1050 Ambassadeur				
☐ Klemm Kl 35D (Sk 15)	D-EHKO	1854	Fv5020, SE-BHR, D-EBIB	RAA
☐ Luscombe 8E Silvaire	D-EQUS	5651	NC2924K, N2924K, G-BSHJ	RAA
☐ Max Holste MH.1521M Broussard	F-GJJM	292	292	RAA
☐ Meyers 200D				RAA
☐ Mraz M-1D Sokol	D-EGWP	304	OK-DIX, HB-TBG, (D-EFTB), D-EGWP, G-BWRG	RAA
☐ Noorduyn Harvard IIB [North American NA-77 (AT-16)]	D-FRCP	14A-868	43-15269, FS728, R-104 (Netherlands), PH-SKL, G-BAFM, HB-RCP	RAA

☐ Oberlerchner JOB 15-150/2	D-EJOB	070	(D-EKEM), OE-DOB	RAA
☐ Panstwowe Zaklady Lotnicze (PZL) 106A Kruk	D-FOAB	48040	DM-TAB, DDR-TAB	RAA
☐ Piaggio FWP.149D	D-EGME	183	KB+145, AS+022, BF+420, 91+61	RAA
☐ Piaggio P.149D	D-EGIT	260	AS+411, AC+411, 91+78	RAA
☐ Piel CP.301C Emeraude				RAA
☐ Pilatus P.3-05				RAA
☐ Piper J-3C-85 Cub (J-3C-65) (L-4H)	D-ECIV	11364	43-30073, (France), SL-AAK	RAA
☐ Piper PA-18-95 Super Cub (L-18C)				RAA
☐ Piper PA-18-95 Super Cub (L-18C)	D-EGFG	18-3420	54-720, AS+509, AC+501, NL+107, 96+02	RAA
☐ Piper PA-18-95 Super Cub (L-18C)	D-ELNI	18-456	50-1800, (Greece)	RAA
☐ Piper PA-22-108 Colt				RAA
☐ Piper PA-22-150 Tri-Pacer	OY-DMG	22-5337	SE-CEI	RAA
☐ Piper PA-28-140F Cherokee	D-EFOK	28-7325289	N11C	RAA
☐ Piper PA-28-181 Cherokee Archer II	D-ELAQ	28-7890432	N9567N	RAA
☐ Piper PA-28R-200 Cherokee Arrow II	D-EESO	28R-7435189	N41478	RAA
☐ Procaer F.15B Picchio				RAA
☐ Putzer Elster B	D-ELKY	032		RAA
☐ Putzer Elster B	D-EGFH	043	D-ELBD, 97+20	RAA
☐ Robin DR.400/180 Regent	D-EFKV	1549		RAA
☐ Scheibe SF-25B Falke	D-KLBA	4621	D-KEGI, OE-9341	RAA
☐ SIAI-Marchetti SF.260	'ST-26'	1-10	OO-HAP, F-BRUR, OO-RUR, D-EDUR	RAAX
☐ Stampe & Vertongen S.V.4C	D-ERLA	101	F-BBVA, D-EBHL	RAA
☐ Steen Skybolt	N250SB	SW27		RAA
☐ Svenska Aeroplan Aktiebolaget (SAAB) 91B-2 Safir				RAA
☐ Wassmer WA.40 Super IV	D-EJAE	30		RAA
☐ Yakovlev Yak-18A	D-EYTG		307 (Soviet Union), G-BVVX	RAA
☐ Yakovlev Yak-52	LY-AON	822812	143 (DOSAAF)	RAA
☐ Yakovlev Yak-52	LY-AGI	845202		RAA
☐ Yakovlev Yak-52	LY-BAL	878207	DOSAAF 139, 139 (Ukraine)	RAA
☐ Yakovlev Yak-52	LY-SUN	9010408	DOSAAF 20, 20 (Ukraine)	RAA
☐ Zlin Z-126 Trener				RAA
☐ Zlin Z-226T Trener 6	D-EEKA	195	OK-MGW, OE-CKA	RAA

GRENZMUSEUM RHÖN "POINT ALPHA" (GER55)

Address:	Hummelsberg 1, D-36169 Rasdorf.
Tel:	06651-919030
Fax:	06651-919031
Email:	PointAlpha@t-online.de
Admission:	Daily 1000-1700.
Location:	On the road between Rasdorf and Geisa.

This is one of several museums which have been set up along the former border between East and West Germany. The activities which took place in the region during the partition of the country are highlighted. The Alouette was one of several helicopters used by the West German forces to patrol the area.

TYPE	REG/SER	CON. NO.	PI/NOTES	STATUS
☐ Sud-Est SE.3130 Alouette II				PV

GRENZMUSEUM SCHIFFLERSGRUND (GER56)

Address:	D-37318 Asbach /Sickenberg.
Tel:	036087-98407
Fax:	036087-98414
Email:	GreMu1991@aol.com
Admission:	March-October daily 1400-1700; November-February Monday-Friday 1000-1600, Saturday-Sunday 1300-1600.
Location:	About 5 km east of the town which is about 30 km south of Göttingen.

This fascinating museum, which opened on October 3rd 1991, is housed at a former East German border post high in the hills above the town. Remnants of the ditches, gun towers and fences constructed to stop people fleeing to the west can be seen. An exhibition has been mounted tracing the history of the border defences.

TYPE	REG/SER	CON. NO.	PI/NOTES	STATUS
☐ Mil Mi-2	D-HZPH	563821114	307 (DDR), , DDR-VGC	PV
☐ Mil Mi-8TB	93+84	10578	752 (DDR)	PV
☐ Mil Mi-24V	01	3532422810014	In Soviet markings.	PV

GROB MUSEUM (GER57)

Address:	Lettenbachstrasse 9, D-88674 Tussenhausen-Mattsies.
Tel:	082-68-998-0
Fax:	082-68-998-114
Email:	grob_aerospace.info@online.de
Admission:	By prior permission only.
Location:	About 8 km north of Mindelheim.

The company was formed in 1971 and initially produced a range of fibreglass high performance gliders. The first powered design the G.109 motor glider flew in 1980. The company is setting up a museum at its factory airfield and five types have so far been allocated for display. In conjunction with a Texas company a number of high altitude surveillance designs were produced. Six Egrets were built. The sole Strato is the largest wing span composite aircraft and in 1995 reached over sixty thousand feet. The story of the company and its innovative work will be portrayed when a purpose built exhibition hall is constructed. More types will be added so that the whole range of designs will be exhibited along with test models and photographs.

TYPE	REG/SER	CON. NO.	PI/NOTES	STATUS
☐ Grob G.103C Twin III Acro	D-5325	34115		RA
☐ Grob G.104 Speed Astir IIC	D-4222	4501		RA
☐ Grob GF.200	D-EFKH	20001		RA
☐ Grob G.520 Egrett Strato I	D-FGRO	10005		RA
☐ Grob G.850 Strato 2C	D-CDLR	30001		RA

HANS GRADE MUSEUM (GER58)

Address:	Am Flugplatz, D-14822 Borkheide.
Tel:	033845-40210/40369
Email:	info@belzig-online.de
Admission:	April-October Wednesday,Saturday 1400-1700; Sunday 1000-1700.
Location:	At the airfield which is just north of the village. Borkheide is about 25 km south west of Potsdam.

Hans Grade was born in 1879 and flew his first aircraft, a triplane, at Magdeburg in 1908. The following year he set up a factory at Bork which, prior to World War I, produced over fifty aircraft. His monoplanes, the Libelle and the A, brought him to the forefront of aviation in Germany but by the outbreak or World War I production had stopped. When peace returned Grade built cars in the factory. In 1990 a former Interflug Il-18 flew into the sport airfield at Borkheide to become the centrepiece of a museum devoted to the pioneer aviator. Along one side of the cabin is a collection of memorabilia including the first aerial telegram carried by him on August 11th 1912. Interflug used the field as a base for crop spraying and examples of types used have been collected.

TYPE	REG/SER	CON. NO.	PI/NOTES	STATUS
☐ Ilyushin Il-18V	DDR-STE	182005101	499 (DDR), DM-VAY, DM-STE	PV
☐ Kamov Ka-26	D-HOAJ	7404804	DM-SPJ, DDR-SPJ	PV
☐ Santos-Dumont XX Demoiselle (R)	BAPC.194	PPS/DEM/1	On loan from DTM.	PV
☐ Zlin Z-37 Cmelak	DM-SQI	09-05		PV
☐ Zlin Z-37 Cmelak	DDR-SQL	09-08		RA
☐ Zlin Z-37 Cmelak	DDR-SQM	10-16	DM-SQM	RA
☐ Zlin Z-37A Cmelak	DDR-SST	18-10	DM-SST	PVD
☐ Zlin Z-37A-2 Cmelak			One wing from c/n 19-04 DM-SRZ, DDR-SRZ, D-EOYX	PVD

HEERESFLIEGER BASE BÜCKEBURG SAMMLUNG (GER59)

Address:	Heeresfliegerwaffenschule, D-31675 Bückeburg.
Tel:	05722-940
Admission:	By prior permission only.
Location:	The airfield is just north of the town.

Bückeburg is the main helicopter training base for the German Army. The Heeresflieger was established in 1957 with Dornier Do 27s, Piasecki H-21s and Sikorsky S-58s. Over one hundred helicopters are in use at the field and the test squadron is also in residence. A growing collection of preserved aircraft has been assembled. Some of those listed also serve as instructional airframes for the trainee mechanics.

TYPE	REG/SER	CON. NO.	PI/NOTES	STATUS
☐ Dornier Do 27A-1	'QW+712'	284	SC+704, SE+526, 56+16	RA
☐ Dornier-Bell 205 (UH-1D)	71+98	8318		RA
☐ Dornier-Bell 205 (UH-1D)	73+25	8445		RA

TYPE	REG/SER	CON. NO.	PI/NOTES	STATUS
☐ Dornier-Breguet Alpha Jet A	41+06	0106		RA
☐ Fiat G.91R/3	99+45	91-499	KD+489, EC+318, MD+318, BD+276, MC+129, 32+30	RA
☐ Mil Mi-8PS	93+80	10597	732 (DDR)	RA
☐ Mil Mi-24P	96+49	340339	464 (DDR)	RA
☐ North American NA-338 Bronco (OV-10B)	99+17	338-2	Bu158293, D-9546	RA
☐ North American NA-338 Bronco (OV-10B)	99+29	338-14	Bu158305, D-9558	RA
☐ Piaggio FWP.149D	91+62	184	KB+150, AS+023, BF+421	RA
☐ Sikorsky S-58	'QA+471'	SA-101	101 (France)	RAX
☐ Sud-Est SE.3130 Alouette II	75+55	1406	PF+134, PF+202 – at nearby barracks.	RA
☐ Sud-Est SE.3130 Alouette II	76+09	1563	PC+139, PC+208	RA
☐ Sud-Est SE.3130 Alouette II	76+92	1834	PF+144, PF+211	RA

HEERESFLIEGER BASE MENDIG SAMMLUNG (GER60)

Address:	HFVAS 300, D-56743 Mendig.
Tel:	02652-94-0
Admission:	By prior permission only.
Location:	About 20 km west of Koblenz.

The base has been home to Army helicopters for many years. Currently the resident unit flies Bölkow BO 105Ps but the future of the field is under discussion. The Vertol is near the gate with the other two inside the camp.

TYPE	REG/SER	CON. NO.	PI/NOTES	STATUS
☐ Dornier-Bell 205 (UH-1D)	72+16	8336		RA
☐ Sud-Est SE.3130 Alouette II	76+76	1760	PE+138, PE+207	RA
☐ Vertol V.43 (H-21C)	83+32	WG.32		RA

HEIMATMUSEUM BERLIN-TREPTOW (GER61)

Address:	Sterndamm 102, D-12487 Berlin,
Tel:	030-625-2301-129
Fax:	030-635-1685
Admission:	Thursday-Sunday 1400-1800.
Location:	In the south eastern part of the city.

Johannistal Airport opened in 1909 and was the location of many early meetings. Large numbers of pioneer aviators took their aircraft to the field for their maiden flights. Over twenty factories including Albatros, LVG and Rumpler were built at the site. There was also a hangar which could take Zeppelins. The airfield remained in use until the end of World War II and many wrecked aircraft were present. The museum traces the story of this historic airfield. There is a superb collection of photographs taken during the airfield's existence.

HELI DROME MUSEUM (GER62)

Address:	Leonardi da Vinci Abigastrasse 2, D-88662 Überlingen.
Tel:	07551-8004028
Admission:	April-October Wednesday-Friday 1400-1730; Saturday-Sunday 1000-1700.
Location:	In the town just north of Route N.31.

Set up by a former helicopter pilot the museum traces the history of rotary wing flight with a comprehensive display of models and photographs. The former East German Mi-9 is the only full size machine on show.

TYPE	REG/SER	CON. NO.	PI/NOTES	STATUS
☐ Mil Mi-9 (Mi-8A)	'93+09'	340008	426 (DDR), 93+94	PVX

HERMANN-KÖHL-MUSEUM (GER63)

Address:	Rathaus, D-89284 Pfaffhofen a.d. Rort.
Tel:	07302-960011
Admission:	Monday-Friday 0900-1200 1500-1700 (Closes on Thursday at 1800).
Location:	About 15km south east of Ulm on Road U 97.

Hermann Kohl was the chief Lufthansa night flying pilot. In 1928 he piloted the Junkers W 33 'Bremen' on a flight from Baldonnel in Ireland to Canada. The aircraft was aloft for thirty six and a half hours and made the first east-west crossing of the Atlantic. This small museum in his hometown traces the story of his life.

HERMANN-OBERTH-RAUMFAHRTMUSEUM (GER64)

Address:	Pfinzinger Strasse 2-12, D-90537 Feucht.
Tel:	09128-3502
Fax:	09128-14920
Admission:	Saturday-Sunday 1400-1700 or by appointment.
Location:	About 12 km south east of Nürnburg.

Hermann Oberth was one of the pioneers of rocket motors and he concentrated on the use of liquid fuels. This museum traces his life and the scientific advances he made. There are photographs and models to be seen.

HISTORISCH-TECHNISCHES INFORMATIONSZENTRUM (GER65)

Address:	Bahnhofstrasse 28, D-17449 Peenemunde.
Tel:	038371-505-0
Fax:	0388371-505-111
Email:	HTI@Peenemunde.de
Admission:	April-October daily 0900-1800; November-March Tuesday-Sunday 1000-1600.
Location:	In the centre of the village which is about 10 km north of Wolgast.

Peenemunde was the main rocket research centre in Germany between 1936 and 1945. In late 1935 Werner von Braun was spending a holiday with relations near Anklam. He had been detailed to find a large site for weapons research. He chose the north west tip of Usedom Island. The Army bought the area and the local residents were forcibly moved out. The Messerschmitt Me 163 rocket fighter was also flown from the site and the test unit for the type was set up at the airfield. Until 1990 the base was home to N.V.A. fighter units. The works and part of the surrounding area now serve as a museum tracing the history of weapons developed at Peenemunde. The displays are steadily developing and already present a fascinating picture of this once secret site.

TYPE	REG/SER	CON. NO.	PI/NOTES	STATUS
☐ Aero L-39ZO Albatros	28+01	731001	139 (DDR)	PV
☐ Antonov An-2TD	D-FONB	1G 180-41	799 (DDR), DDR-SKB	PV
☐ Fieseler Fi 103A-1				PV
☐ Kamov Ka-26	D-HOAW	7001404	404 (Hungary), DDR-SPW	PV
☐ Mikoyan-Gurevich MiG-17	'009'	54211959	402 (DDR) – on loan from Luftwaffen Museum.	PVX
☐ Mikoyan-Gurevich MiG-21F-13	677	741619	In DDR markings – on loan from Luftwaffen Museum.	RA
☐ Mikoyan-Gurevich MiG-21F-13	693	74210815	In DDR markings – on loan from Luftwaffen Museum.	RA
☐ Mikoyan-Gurevich MiG-21PFM	'992'	760604	821 – in DDR markings – on loan from Luftwaffen Museum.	PVX
☐ Mikoyan-Gurevich MiG-21PFM	934	761205	On loan from Luftwaffen Mus.	RA
☐ Mikoyan-Gurevich MiG-23MF	20+04	0390213098	584 (DDR) – on loan from Luftwaffen Museum.	RA
☐ Mikoyan-Gurevich MiG-23ML	332	0390324625	In DDR markings – on loan from Luftwaffen Museum.	PV
☐ Mil Mi-2S	94+57	564411105	348 (DDR) – on loan from Luftwaffen Museum.	PV
☐ Mil Mi-8T	911	10527	In DDR markings – on loan from Luftwaffen Museum.	RAX
☐ Sukhoi Su-22M4	25+02	25509	362 (DDR)	PV
☐ Zlin Z-37A Cmelak	D-ESUJ	18-28	DM-SUJ, DDR-SUJ	PV

HISTORISCHER FLUGZEUG (GER66)

Address:	In Steinfeld 3, D-48465 Suddendorf.
Tel:	0172-534-6267
Email:	ben@rumpf.net
Admission:	By prior permission only.
Location:	At Klausheide airfield which is about 6 km north east of Nordholn off Route 213.

This group operates a fleet of classic aircraft which includes six Stampe S.V.4s. They regularly attend meetings in the area and provide aerobatic routines at shows along with the Pitts Specials.

TYPE	REG/SER	CON. NO.	PI/NOTES	STATUS
☐ Cessna 195B	D-EFTH	16087	N2102C, N195MB	RAA
☐ Pitts S-2B Special	D-EHIL	5203	N317JK	RAA
☐ Pitts S-2S Special	N156CB	3011		RAA
☐ Stampe & Vertongen S.V.4C	D-EODN	113	F-BCFY	RAA
☐ Stampe & Vertongen S.V.4C	D-EROB	151	151, F-BNDI, D-ECDI	RAA
☐ Stampe & Vertongen S.V.4C	D-EBUT	304	F-BCLD	RAA
☐ Stampe & Vertongen S.V.4C	D-EFPS	415	F-BCQY	RAA
☐ Stampe & Vertongen S.V.4C	D-EDCK	540	F-BDCK	RAA
☐ Stampe & Vertongen S.V.4C	D-ERDA	599	F-BDET, D-EOWS	RAA

HISTORISCHER FLUGZEUGBAU (GER67)

Address: Buchholzer Chaussee 1a,
D-15517 Fürstenwalde.
Tel: 03361-34449975
Fax: 03361-349976
Email: fpfw@aol.com
Admission: By prior permission only.
Location: About 2 km north east of the town which is about 40 km east of Berlin.

The organisation was set up in 1998 with the aim of creating a period airfield. The first project was the construction of the Etrich Taube. This monoplane with its distinctive wing shape was completed in 2001. A second Taube was recxently destroyed in a crash. The first example plus an Albatros B II have been sold in New Zealand to finance the construction of the remaining types.

TYPE	REG/SER	CON. NO.	PI/NOTES	STATUS
☐ Blériot XI (R)				RAC
☐ Farman III (R)	D-EFAR	1969		RAC
☐ Fokker D III (R)				RAC
☐ Fokker D VII (R)				RAC
☐ Grade Eindecker (R)				RAC
☐ Harlan Eindekker (R)				RAC
☐ Jeannin Stahltaube				RAC
☐ Santos-Dumont XX Demoiselle (R)				RAC
☐ Staaken R VI (Scale R)				RAC

HUBSCHRAUBER MUSEUM (GER68)

Address: Postfach 1310,
Sableplatz,
D-31675 Bückeburg.
Tel: 05722-5533
Fax: 05722-71539
Email: dieter.bals@hubschraubermuseum.de
Admission: Daily 0900-1700.
Location: In the centre of the town which is about 50 km west of Hannover on Road 65.

Werner Noltemeyer started collecting documents, photographs and models relating to rotary wing flight when he was stationed with the German Army at the nearby airfield. In 1971 the town donated a house for the establishment of the first museum in the world devoted to this form of flight. In 1980 a large modern extension was added to provide covered exhibition space for the growing number of helicopters and autogyros. An extensive archive and research centre is located at the museum. Space is once again at a premium and the main exhibition area is becoming crowded. The story of rotary wing flight is told from the earliest days in a series of informative displays. Photographs, documents, models and memorabilia are on view. Rotary winged aircraft from several countries can be seen and these range from prototypes and one off homebuilt machines to types which have been widely used in both civil and military roles. Germany was one of the first countries to realise the potential of this form of flight and produced some of the first successful helicopters but sadly little survives from this period. In the early 1970s a replica of the Focke-Wulf Fw 61 was built. The twin rotor design first flew in 1936 and Hanna Reitsch piloted one inside the Deutschlandhalle in Berlin to show the control that could be achieved. Most of the aircraft on show have been built after 1950 and demonstrate the variety of designs used to achieve stability. The rotor configurations which can be seen include main and tail, twin, intermeshing, tandem, coaxial and reaction driven. A number of autogyros are also on view.

TYPE	REG/SER	CON. NO.	PI/NOTES	STATUS
☐ Aerotechnik WGM-21	D-HIDI	V-1		PV
☐ Air and Space 18A	D-HOBB	18-26	N6120S	PV
☐ Bell 47G-2 Sioux (H-13H) (OH-13H)	58-5348	2361		PV
☐ Bensen B-8M Gyrocopter				PV
☐ Bölkow BO 46	'D-9514'	V-2	D-9515	PVX
☐ Bölkow BO 102B Helitrainer		4502		PV

☐ Bölkow BO 103	D-9505	V-1	D-9505, D-HECA	PV
☐ Bölkow BO 105V	D-HAJY	V-3		PV
☐ Bölkow BO 108A-1	D-HBEC	VT 002		PV
☐ Bölkow Flying Jeep				PV
☐ Bölkow P 166/3			Parts only.	PV
☐ Bristol 171 Sycamore HR.52	78+20	13478	G-18-151, SC+201, WE+546, LC+101	PV
☐ Derschmitt Autogyro				PV
☐ Dornier Argus I				PV
☐ Dornier Argus I				PV
☐ Dornier Do 32K	98+23	004		PV
☐ Focke-Achgelis Fa 330A-1 Bachstelze	100406	100406		PV
☐ Focke-Borgward BFK 1 Kolibri	D-HOCE	102(V-2)	Dynamic components only.	PV
☐ Focke-Wulf Fw 61 (R)	'D-EBVU'		'D-EKRA'	PV
☐ Georges G 1 Papillon				PV
☐ Georges G 2		V-1		PV
☐ Gosslich Pedalcopter			On loan from Deutsches Museum	PV
☐ Havertz HZ 5	D-HAJU	5		PV
☐ Helmbaecher 4				PV
☐ Hiller UH12C Raven (H-23C) (OH-23C)	55-4109	814	On loan from U.S. Army Museum	PV
☐ Hughes 269C Osage (TH-55A)	67-16955	19106		PV
☐ Kaman K-600-3 Huskie (H-43B) (HH-43B)	62-4547	173	Also reported as c/n 174.	PV
☐ Kamov Ka-26	D-HOAL	7505201	DM-SPL, DDR-SPL	PV
☐ Krauss TRS.1 Hummel	D-HOCY	V-1		PV
☐ Merckle SM 67	'D-9506'	V-3	Incorporates parts of V-2 the original D-9506.	PVX
☐ Messerschmitt-Bölkow-Blohm – Kawasaki BK 117A-1	D-HBKA	P-2		PV
☐ Mil Mi-2	556	543624074	556 (DDR), (DDR-VGO)	PV
☐ Nagler-Rolz NR 54		V2	On loan from N.A.S.M. USA.	PV
☐ Saunders-Roe P.501 Skeeter AOP.12	XN348	S2/7154	XN348, 8042M	PV
☐ Schilling HSX-2 Cierva	'D-HOKY'		D-HOHS	PVX
☐ Siemetzki Asro 4		V-1		PV
☐ Sikorsky S-58 Seabat (HSS-1N) (SH-34J)	81+09	581679	Bu150807, QK+584, PZ+023, QW+112	PV
☐ Sud-Est SE.3130 Alouette II	75+05	1193	PA+138, PQ+137, PP+136, PX+202 – cabin only.	PV
☐ Sud-Est SE.3130 Alouette II	77+17	1871	AS+364	PV
☐ Sud-Ouest SO-1221 Djinn	7	1019FR58	F-BNAY – but may be c/n 1016FR52 PB+119 PB+157	PV
☐ Vereinigte Flugtechnische Werke – Fokker (VFW) H-2	D-HIBY	V-1		PV
☐ Vereinigte Flugtechnische Werke – Fokker (VFW) H-3E Sprinter	D-9543	E-1		PV
☐ Vertol V.43 (H-21C)	83+06	WG.06	PA+201, QK+561, PX+335 – parts as demonstration of controls.	PV
☐ Vertol V.43 (H-21C)	83+07	WG.07	PA+202, QF+461, PX+336	PV
☐ Wagner Rotocar 3		V-1		PV
☐ Wytwornia Sprzetu Komunikacyjnego (WSK) SM-1/600Sz [Mil Mi-1A]	CCCP-05712			PV
☐ Zierath Z 1		V-1		PV

INTERESSENGEMEINSCHAFT Ju 52 (GER69)

Address:	Ziegeleiweg 50, D-31832 Springe.
Tel:	05041-81428
Email:	JHereld@tglw.de
Admission:	April-October Tuesday, Saturday-Sunday 1000-1800.
Location:	At Wunstorf Air Force Base which is about 5 km north west of the town.

Wunstorf opened as a Luftwaffe base in 1934 and from 1945 until 1958 housed units of the Royal Air Force. Since then it has been one of the major transport bases of the new Luftwaffe. One of four Junkers Ju 52/3ms recovered from a lake in Norway in 1985 was presented to the Luftwaffen Museum. The airframe was transported to Wunstorf where restoration was started by members of the resident LTG62. Funds were raised to construct an exhibition hall which opened in the early 1990s. The superbly rebuilt Ju 52 is the centrepiece of this interesting display. The story of the landing of the Ju 52 fleet on the frozen Norwegian lake and the recovery of the airframes are portrayed with dioramas and photographs. The history of the base and its units can also be seen in a display of memorabilia, photographs, uniforms and documents. The Focke-Wulf built Piaggio P.149 is mounted by the base gate which is a short distance from the museum building. A flyable Czech built Fieseler Storch is normally based in the hall during the winter and a replica D.F.S. 230 glider has been completed. Two other sailplanes are in the exhibition. The Lehrmeister an original design produced in the former East Germany and large numbers of SG-38s were used for primary training.

TYPE	REG/SER	CON. NO.	PI/NOTES	STATUS
☐ Dornier Do 28D-2 Skyservant	58+95	4170		PV
☐ Dornier-Bell 205 (UH-1D)	70+68	8128		PV
☐ Jacobs D.F.S. 230A-2		120-02		PV
☐ Junkers Ju 52/3mg4e	DB+RD	6693	On loan from Luftwaffen Museum	PV

TYPE	REG/SER	CON. NO.	PI/NOTES	STATUS
☐ Mil Mi-8T	93+03	10511	400 (DDR)	PV
☐ Mraz K-65 Cap [Fieseler Fi 156C-3 Storch]	D-EMAV	741	OK-DF?, HB-IKA, D-EKUS – on loan	PVA
☐ Nord N.2501 Noratlas	'GR+248'	66	66 (France)	PVX
☐ Piaggio FWP.149D	'AS+4'	049	DA+392, AC+404, 90+35, '30+51' – on gate.	PVX
☐ Schneider Grunau SG-38 (D.F.S. 108-14)				PV
☐ Volkseigener Betrieb Apparatebau Lommatzsch FES-530/II Lehrmeister	DM-3324	0274	DM-3324, DDR-3324	PV

INTERNATIONALES FLUGBOOT MUSEUM (GER70)

Address: –
Location: Unknown.

This group has put forward ambitious plans to build a full size replica of the Dornier Do X which was destroyed in the allied raid on the Deutsche Luftfahrt Sammlung in Berlin in 1943.

TYPE	REG/SER	CON. NO.	PI/NOTES	STATUS
☐ Dornier Do-X (R)				RAC

INTERNATIONALS LUFTFAHRTMUSEUM MANFRED PFLUMM (GER71)

Address: Spittellsonnar Weg 78, D-78056 Villingen-Schwenningen.
Tel: 07720-66302
Admission: Daily 0900-1900
Location: The airfield is about 3 km east of Schwenningen off Road 27.

Manfred Pflumm has built a large number of replicas for museums across Germany. Examples of his work can be seen at Frankfurt, Gatow, Laatzen and Stuttgart. In the mid-1980s he decided to set up a museum at the airfield where he had his workshops. The main hangar displays the light aircraft, hang gliders and gliders along with a range of models, engines, parachutes, components and engines. The outside park is being developed with a number of small hangars and landscaping of the site. The post-war Luftwaffe is represented by the Sabre, Canberra, Starfighter, T-33 and Fiat G.91 and a number of former East German types have arrived. Microlights, including some built by Manfred, can be seen. A number of his replicas are also on view. One of the two surviving Zaunkönig parasol monoplanes is a rarity. Four examples of the parasol wing design were constructed, two during World War II and two in the mid-1950s. The prototype Fischer RW 3 flew in 1955 and manufacturing rights were acquired by the Rhein Flugzeugbau company in 1957. Powered by a Porsche engine driving a propeller mounted in a slot between the fin and the rudder only a few production examples appeared. The concept was developed into the Fantrainer. The Albatros L 73 replica has returned after a long period at Stuttgart airport. This interesting collection has many types on view which cannot be seen in other museums.

TYPE	REG/SER	CON. NO.	PI/NOTES	STATUS
☐ Adam Mifka Mi-1	'D-HMIA'			PVX
☐ Aero L-60 Brigadyr	OK-LGL	150401	OK-LGL, OE-BVL	PV
☐ Akaflieg Stuttgart Fs 26 Moseppl	D-KFFS	V-1		PV
☐ Albatros L 73 (FSM)	'D-961'			PVX
☐ Antonov An-2T	2613	1G 26-13	2613 (Poland) – On loan to Albatros FM.	–
☐ Antonov An-2TP (An-2R)	SP-AOG	1G 148-07	SP-WLS	PV
☐ Bölkow BO 105CBS	D-HMMM	S-151	N90746, D-HDES	PV
☐ Bücker Bü 181B-1 Bestmann (Sk 25)	D-EDIB	25039	Fv25039 – on loan from Albatros FM.	PV
☐ Canadair CL-13A Sabre 5 [North American F-86E]	'JB+111'	840	23050, BB+141, BB+239	PVX
☐ De Havilland D.H.100 Vampire F.6	J-1068	V0186 (979)	In Swiss markings.	PV
☐ Dornier Do 27A-1	D-EPEA	272	LC+158, YA+914 (?), D-EDBR – Possible identity.	PVX
☐ Dornier Do 27A-3	D-ELTT	430	LC+156, CB+003, 57+04	PV
☐ Dornier Do 27B-1	D-EMKA	152	PD+103, PF+108, PG+216, 55+32	PV
☐ Dornier Do 27B-1	D-EJJJ	192	PD+107, PF+106, PF+219, 55+59	PV
☐ Dornier Do 27B-1	D-EHOX	269	D-EHOX, YA+910, 56+02	PV
☐ Dornier Do 27B-2 (Do 27B-1)	D-EFFA	113	PA+106, QW+713, QW+103, 55+09	PV
☐ Dornier Do 335A-1 (FSM)				PVC
☐ Dornier-Breguet Alpha Jet A	40+74	0074	On loan from Luftwaffen Museum.	PV
☐ English Electric EA.1 Canberra B.2	99+34	R3/EA3/6651	WK137, YA+152, 00+02, D-9566 – on loan from Luftwaffen Museum.	PV

☐ Evans VP-1 Volksplane	D-EEVP	1		PV
☐ Fauvel AV.36	D-8290			PV
☐ Fiat G.91R/3	31+95	91-463	KD+453, BD+245 – tail from c/n 526 KD+516, EC+101, MD+101, BD+277, 32+56	PV
☐ Fokker Dr I (FSM)				PVX
☐ Fokker E III (FSM)	'36/15'		'98/15'	PVX
☐ Funk FK 9TG	D-MNLG	077		PV
☐ Grover J-3 Kitten	D-MZAG	AL-1		PV
☐ Hawker P.1040 Sea Hawk 100	'MS+001	6686	VB+136	PVX
☐ Junkers J 10 (FSM)				RAC
☐ Junkers Ju 87B-2 (FSM)	'TG+KL'			PVX
☐ Lemberger Grade Monoplane (R)	D-EKLB	7 (V-1)		PV
☐ Lockheed 580 (T-33A)	94+64	580-9152	54-1535, AB+798, EB+393	PV
☐ Lockheed 583-10-20 Starfighter (TF-104G)	27+28	583D-5730	61-3059, DA+059, DA+364, JA+374 – fuselage only.	PV
☐ Lockheed 683-10-19 Starfighter (F-104G)	20+47	683-2055	KF+130, DA+103	PV
☐ Messerschmitt Bf 109E (FSM)	'6'			PVX
☐ Messerschmitt Me 262A-1a (FSM)	'5+'			PVX
☐ Mikoyan-Gurevich MiG-15UTI			Due soon.	–
☐ Mikoyan-Gurevich MiG-21F-13	'1981'	741225	1225 (Hungary)	PVX
☐ Mooney M.20E	HB-DEG	345		PV
☐ Nickel Falter I	D-MXOX			PV
☐ North American NA-338 Bronco (OV-10B)	99+18	338-3	Bu158294, D-9547	PV
☐ Panstwowe Zaklady Lotnicze (PZL) 104 Wilga 35A	D-EWRW	118407	DM-WRW, DDR-WRW	RAD
☐ Pflumm Tragschrauber				PV
☐ Piaggio FWP.149D	D-EEHG	065	DD+389, 90+50	PV
☐ Pilatus P.3-03	HB-RBV	468	A-830 (Switzerland)	PV
☐ Piper PA-23-160 Apache	D-GHWW	23-1816	N4351P	PV
☐ Quickie Aircraft Quickie 1 (Rutan 54)	D-EGWW	001		PV
☐ Rhein-Flugzeugbau RW 3 P75	D-EDEV	004		RA
☐ Saunders-Roe P.501 Skeeter AOP.12				PV
☐ Schneider ESG 31 Grunau Baby IIB	D-9209	03		PV
☐ Schneider Grunau SG-38 (D.F.S. 108-14)	D-7033			PV
☐ Siebelwerke ATG (SIAT) 223K-1 Flamingo	D-EHVD	20	D-ENBR, HB-EVD	PV
☐ Sperling / Pflumm Berblinger 2000				PV
☐ Sud-Est SE.3130 Alouette II	75+46	1363	PG+135, PA+135, PA+206	PV
☐ Tahlhofer Flamingo 1 Hang Glider				PV
☐ Tahlhofer Quicksilver				PV
☐ Weigel Harz-Fink	D-EADL	01		PV
☐ Winter LF-1 Zaunkönig	D-EBCG	V-4	D-ECER	PV
☐ Wytwornia Sprzetu Komunikacyjnego (WSK) Lim-2 [MiG-15bis]		1B 010-19	1019 – in false Soviet markings.	PVX
☐ Yakovlev Yak-18T	RA-44446	22202030258	CCCP-44446	PV
☐ Zlin Z-226 Trener 6	D-EYTT	171	OK-MFZ, D-EHSE, HB-TRT	PV
☐ Zlin Z-37A Cmelak	D-ESRV	10-26	DM-SRV, DDR-SRV – with parts of c/n 16-20 the original DM-SRV.	PV

KREIS AGRAR MUSEUM (GER72)

Address:	Rambower Weg, D-23972 Dorf Mecklenburg.
Tel:	038341-790020
Fax:	038341-790114
Admission:	April-October daily 1000-1600; November-March Monday-Friday daily 1000-1600.
Location:	Off the A20 between Lubeck and Rostock.

Exhibits at this museum trace the developments in agriculture and the way of life in the region. There are many farm implements and items of machinery to be seen. Large numbers of Cmelaks were used for crop spraying in the former East Germany and several were based in the region. Parts of the Bf 109 were recovered from a local crash site. An exhibition tracing the history of this aircraft can be seen.

TYPE	REG/SER	CON. NO.	PI/NOTES	STATUS
☐ Messerschmitt Bf 109			Major components.	PVD
☐ Zlin Z-37 Cmelak	DDR-SNM	06-17	DM-SNM	PV

KREISMUSEUM BITTERFELD (GER73)

Address:	Kirchplatz 3, D-06749 Bitterfeld.
Tel:	03493-23295
Fax:	03493-23295
Email:	Kreismuseum-bitterfeld@gmx.de
Admission:	Tuesday-Friday 0900-1200 1300-1700, Sunday 1000-1600.
Location:	In the town which is about 30 km north east of Halle.

The area has regular balloon meetings and a section of the local museum traces the history of the sport. On show are a basket and an envelope along with items of memorabilia.

TYPE	REG/SER	CON. NO.	PI/NOTES	STATUS
☐ Balloon			Basket only.	PV
☐ Balloon			Envelope only.	PV

KULTURHISTORISCHES MUSEUM (GER74)

Address:	Otto von Guericke Strasse 68-73, D-39104 Magdeburg.
Tel:	0391-53650-0
Fax:	0391-53650-10
Email:	museum@magdeburg.de
Admission:	Tuesday-Sunday 0900-1700.
Location:	In the city centre.

Hans Grade was the first German to fly an aircraft designed in the country. He set up a factory at Magdeburg in 1905 before moving to Bork in four years later. A replica of the model with which he gained a prize in 1909 is on view. This museum has on show a wide range of items tracing local history and culture.

TYPE	REG/SER	CON. NO.	PI/NOTES	STATUS
☐ Grade Eindecker (R)				PV

LANDESMUSEUM FÜR TECHNIK UND ARBEIT (GER75)

Address:	Museumstrasse 1, D-68165 Mannheim.
Tel:	0621-42989
Fax:	0621-4298-754
Email:	lta@ltamannheim.de
Admission:	Tuesday,Thursday 0900-1700; Wednesday 0900-2000; Friday 0900-1300; Saturday 1000-1700; Sunday 1000-1800.
Location:	In the estern part of the city centre.

This regional museum for technology and work traces developments in the area over the last two and a half centuries. Examples of industrial machinery are featured. The only aircraft on show is a replica of the rocket powered HAK-1 which was piloted by Fritz von Opel on its maiden flight on September 30th 1929. This took place near Frankfurt-am-Main. The aircraft was aloft for about seventy five seconds and travelled about one and a half kilometres. Some damage occurred during the landing and the project was abandoned.

TYPE	REG/SER	CON. NO.	PI/NOTES	STATUS
☐ Hatry-Opel-Sander RAK 1 (FSM)				PV

LANDESMUSEUM KOBLENZ (GER76)

Address:	Festung Ehrenbreitstein, Hohe Ostfront, D-56077 Koblenz.
Tel:	0261-6675-0
Fax:	0261-701-1989
Email:	info@landesmuseumkoblenz.de
Admission:	March 21st-November 0900-1700.
Location:	In the western part of the city.

Carl Clemens Bücker was born near Koblenz on February 1lth. 1895. During World War I he was a pilot in the German Marine Flying Corps. After a period in Sweden where he founded the firm of Svenska AB he returned to Germany to set up his own factory at Johannisthal in 1933. A move was made to Rangsdorf in 1935 and the company achieved fame with its superb Jungmann and Jungmeister aerobatic biplanes. The museum, located in the historic fortress overlooking the city, obtained a Czech built Jungmann in 1983 and later an Egyptian Goumhouria. The displays trace the history and development of the region and have many interesting items on show in the building which dominates the area above the town and the river.

TYPE	REG/SER	CON. NO.	PI/NOTES	STATUS
☐ Aero C-104 [Bücker Bü 131D Jungmann]	'D-ECCB'	222	OK-BJK, OE-ACN	SX
☐ Heliopolis Goumhouria 6 [Bücker Bü 181D Bestmann]	D-EFUW	186	SU-350	RA

LANDWIRTSCHAFTS-UND-FORSTMUSEUM (GER77)

Address:	An der Muhle, D-19243 Wittenburg.
Admission:	Tuesday, Thursday, Friday 0900-1700; Wednesday 0900-2000; Saturday 1000-1700; Sunday 1000-1800.
Location:	In the southern part of the town which is just north of the A 24.

The displays at this museum trace the history of agriculture and country life in the former East Germany from 1945 until 1989. The exhibition was set up in 1998. The only aircraft in the collection is the Cmelak.

TYPE	REG/SER	CON. NO.	PI/NOTES	STATUS
☐ Zlin Z-37 Cmelak	DDR-SQR	10-20	DM-SQR	PV

LUFTBRÜCKENGEDENKANLAGE (GER78)

Address:	Rhein-Main Air Force Base, D-60549 Frankfurt.
Tel:	069-699-7804
Admission:	On permanent view – park open Sunday 1000-1800.
Location:	By the military gate to the airport which is about 10 km south of the city off Autobahn A.5.

Rhein-Main was an important base during the Berlin Airlift. From here American aircraft flew hundreds of missions to the beleaguered city. To honour these achievements two transport aircraft have been placed in a memorial park. The C-47 and C-54 were the mainstay of the U.S.A.A.F. transport fleet at the time. Both aircraft are painted in period colours. The closure of the base has recently been announced and all land will be turned over to the airport authority. The future of the memorial is not known.

TYPE	REG/SER	CON. NO.	PI/NOTES	STATUS
☐ Douglas DC-3A-467 Skytrain (C-47B)	43-49081	14897/26342	43-49081, EC-ASF, T.3-64 (Spain), (G-BMIR), N1350M	PV
☐ Douglas DC-4 Skymaster (C-54E)	44-9063	27289	44-9063, NC88887, N88887, HB-ILU, EI-ARS, LN-TUR, EI-ARS, N88887, FAR-91, N88887, ZS-LMH, N88887, EL-AJP, N88887	PV

LUFTFAHRT UND TECHNIK MUSEUMSPARK (GER79)

Address:	Kasataienpromenade 50, D-06217 Merseburg.
Tel:	03461-525776
Fax:	03461-525778
Email:	info@luftfahrt-technik-museum-de
Admission:	Tuesday-Friday 0900-1700; Saturday-Sunday 1000-1800.
Location:	At the former military airfield which is in the north western suburbs of the town.

Established in the late 1990s this museum is housed in a large hangar on the former Soviet Air Force base close to the town. The history of the field is portrayed with an exhibition of photographs, documents and models. Several aircraft came from the now closed Luftfahrtmuseum Köln-Butzerweilerhof which was forced to vacate its premises in 1997. Engines and components, including some recovered from crash sites, have been put on show. Three replicas of successful Fokker designs from the World War I period can be seen. The collection includes a number of unique types including the Knechtel KN I powered glider and the Schuffenhauer autogyro. Seven helicopters are in the collection. The former Belgian Army Alouette served at Butzweilerhof for many years and was donated to the museum there when its unit returned home. The others flew with the German Army. There is a large apron outside the hangar where some aircraft are parked.

TYPE	REG/SER	CON. NO.	PI/NOTES	STATUS
☐ Aerodyne Vector 600	D-MXOB			PV
☐ Akaflieg Hannover AFH-26	D-5526	1		RA
☐ Antonov An-2R	HA-MHL	1G 123-02		PV
☐ Ballonfabrik Augsburg K-1260/3-Ri Gas Balloon	D-CLOUTH-IX	8763		PV
☐ Bell 47G-2			Fuselage frame only.	PV
☐ Bölkow BO 105M				PV
☐ Cameron N-105 Hot Air Balloon	D-RHEINGAS	2790		PV
☐ Comco Ikarus Fox-C22	D-MSGF			PV
☐ Curtiss D Pusher (R)				PV

Type	Reg./Ser.	Con. No.	PI/Notes	Status
☐ De Havilland D.H.104 Devon C.2/2 (C.1)	WB533	04269	WB533, G-DEVN	PV
☐ Dornier Do 27A-4 (A-3) (A-5)	D-EGEA	377	PK+103, PD+112, PD+338, 56+74	PV
☐ Dornier Do 27B-1	D-EFHO	177	AS+907, AC+907, 55+47	PV
☐ Fiat G.91R/3	31+78	91-446	KD+436, DH+241, MC+121	PV
☐ Fiat G.91R/3	32+11	91-479	KD+469, EC+306, MD+306, MR+116, MB+2?? – front fuselage only – on loan from Luftwaffen Museum.	PV
☐ Fieseler Storch Ultralight	D-MXFI			PV
☐ Fire Balloons G Hot Air Balloon	D-Epson	035		PV
☐ Flightship Ground Effects Airfish				PV
☐ Fokker D VI (FSM)	'17'			PVX
☐ Fokker D VII (FSM)	'5290/18'			PVX
☐ Fokker Dr I (FSM)				PV
☐ Glasflügel Mosquito			Fuselage only.	PV
☐ Ilyushin Il-14P	3065	14803065	In Polish markings.	PV
☐ Ilyushin Il-62	DM-SEC	10903	DM-SEC, DDR-SEC	RA
☐ Knechtel KN-1	D-KNPF	V-1		PV
☐ Lippisch Aerofoil				PV
☐ Lockheed 683-04-10 Starfighter (RF-104G)	24+54	683-8202	KG+302, BB+250 – on loan from Luftwaffen Museum.	PV
☐ Lockheed 683-10-19 Starfighter (F-104G)	21+56	683-7025	KE+325, DB+104, DC+104 – on loan from Luftwaffen Museum.	RA
☐ Messerschmitt Me 163B-1a Komet (FSM)	'VD+ER'		'54'	PVX
☐ Mikoyan-Gurevich MiG-21MF	670	966206	In DDR markings – on loan from Luftwaffen Museum.	PV
☐ Mikoyan-Gurevich MiG-21MF	673	966207	In DDR markings – on loan from Luftwaffen Museum.	PV
☐ Mikoyan-Gurevich MiG-21SPS (MiG-21PFM)	725	94A4212	In DDR markings – on loan from Luftwaffen Museum.	PV
☐ Mikoyan-Gurevich MiG-21SPS (MiG-21PFM)	779	94A4502	In DDR markings – on loan from Luftwaffen Museum.	PV
☐ Mikoyan-Gurevich MiG-21SPS (MiG-21PFM)	829	94A4705	In DDR markings – on loan from Flugausstellung Hangelar.	PV
☐ Mil Mi-8T	390	0223	In DDR markings – on loan from Luftwaffen Museum.	PV
☐ Republic RF-84F Thunderflash	'ED+119'		51-1869, EB+368, EB+119, EB+319 – on loan from Luftwaffen Museum.	PVX
☐ Scheibe Bergfalke II/55	D-1552	279		PV
☐ Scheibe Bergfalke III				PV
☐ Schneider Grunau Baby III (D.F.S. 108-66)	D-4019	34		PV
☐ Schneider Grunau SG-38 (D.F.S. 108-14)				PV
☐ Schuffenhauer SG-3	D-HGYR	SG-3		PV
☐ Sud-Est SE.3130 Alouette II	75+28	1310	PD+134, PH+238, PH+207 – on loan from Luftwaffen Museum	PV
☐ Sud-Est SE.3130 Alouette II	75+86	1511	PE+131, PE+202 – on loan from Luftwaffen Museum.	PV
☐ Sud-Est SE.3130 Alouette II		1514	PQ+933, PQ+133, QA+208, 25+78 – pod only.	PV
☐ Sud-Est SE.3130 Alouette II	A-16	1595	In Belgian markings – composite.	PV
☐ Tupolev Tu-134K	DDR-SCZ	9350913	177 (DDR)(DM-VBB), DM-SCZ	PV
☐ Wildente 2	D-MBNN			PV
☐ Wytwornia Sprzetu Komunikacyjnego (WSK)	06	W05006 SM-1W [Mil Mi-1M]	In Hungarian markings.	PV
☐ Yakovlev Yak-52	LY-AKD	811908		RAD
☐ Zlin Z-326 Trener Master				PV
☐ Zlin Z-37A Cmelak	D-ESRF	16-03	DM-SRF, DDR-SRF – on loan from LM Köln.	PV
☐ Zlin Z-526 Trener Master	F-BSEI	1051	OK-XRG, OO-PTZ	PV

LUFTFAHRTHISTORISCHE SAMMLUNG DER FLUGHAFEN FRANKFURT AG (GER80)

Address:	Flughafen Rhein/Main A.G., Luftfahrthistorische Sammlung Kl 3, D-60549 Frankfurt/Main.
Tel:	069-690-66076
Admission:	Daily 0800-2100.
Location:	The airport is about 8 km south of the city off Autobahn A.3.

A group was formed in 1981 with the aim of tracing the history of the airport. A large collection of photographs and documents has been assembled and this archive also covers the development of airliners and airline history. Hanging in the terminal complex are several gliders and replica powered aircraft with others in store. In 1991, the centenary of Lilienthal's first flight was celebrated and a replica of one of his designs constructed. The fourteen year old Peter Riedel took his PR.2 glider to the first Wasserkuppe meeting in 1920. The aim of the group was to set up a museum at the airport but these ambitious plans have been shelved for the time being.

TYPE	REG/SER	CON. NO.	PI/NOTES	STATUS
☐ Fauvel AV.36	D-8373		On loan from OSG Wasserkuppe.	RA
☐ Hütter H 17A (D.F.S. 108-67)	D-1012			PV
☐ Jacobs Meise (D.F.S. 108-70)	'D-1956'	EB-66	On loan from OSG Wasserkuppe.	PVX
☐ Junkers F 13 (FSM)				PV
☐ Lilienthal Grosser Doppeldecker (R)				RA
☐ Riedel PR.2 Rhönbaby (R)				PV
☐ Schneider Grunau SG-38 (D.F.S. 108-14) (R)				PV
☐ Spalinger S-18-III	D-9329			RA

LUFTFAHRTHISTORISCHE SAMMLUNG FINOW (GER81)

Address:	Am Flugplatz 1, D-16227 Eberswalde.
Tel:	03335-7233
Fax:	03335-326224
Email:	webmaster@luftfahrt-museum-finowfurt.de
Admission:	April-October Tuesday-Friday 1000-1700, Saturday-Sunday 1100-1700.
Location:	At the north west corner of the airfield which is just south of Finowfurt.

The airfield at Finow opened as a Luftwaffe base in 1938 and from the summer of 1944 was the home of KG200 which flew captured Allied bombers on clandestine missions. The unit was involved in the Mistel programme in which a twin engined bomber packed with explosives was taken aloft by a fighter mounted above it. On approaching the target the bomber was released. The Soviet Air Force moved in fighters during 1950 and before the units returned to Russia in May 1993 the base was home to MiG-29s. The project to start a museum was initiated in October 1991 and a former dispersal area with ten hard shelters and associated buildings is now in use. The display covers the history of the field and its units with many interesting items on show. The former Interflug Tu-134 was transported by road from Schonefeld Airport. The first Mil Mi-8T, delivered to Interflug in 1966 and flown by the company for twenty five years, is a prized exhibit. The main aim of the museum is to trace the history of flying during the period of existence of the D.D.R. One hangar is fitted out as a typical Soviet maintenance shop complete with tools and equipment along with a MiG-23 on overhaul. More types are expected in the near future. An arrival a few years ago is the wreck of a Focke-Wulf Fw 190A-8 recovered from a lake near Alt-Zeschdorf. A special display has been staged to trace the combat history of this aircraft, which will not be restored, and the work of the team in obtaining it for the exhibition. The collection of the late Helmut Hubner joined the museum in the mid-1990s.

TYPE	REG/SER	CON. NO.	PI/NOTES	STATUS
☐ Aero L-29 Delfin	340	591526	In DDR markings.	PV
☐ Antonov An-2T	D-FONF	117447319	811 (DDR), DDR-SKF	PV
☐ Antonov An-2T	RA-05825	1G 63-32	05 (Soviet), CCCP-05825, RA-05825, D-FMGM	PV
☐ Fauvel AV.36C	D-4058	159	On loan.	PV
☐ Focke-Wulf Fw 190A-9/R2	12	560024		RAD
☐ Hamburger Flugzeugbau HFB.320 Hansa	D-CARE	1022	On loan from Luftwaffen Museum.	PV
☐ Ilyushin Il-14P	482	14803035	482, DM-VAD – in DDR markings.	PV
☐ Kamov Ka-26	D-HOAU	7303405	DM-SPU, DDR-SPU	PV
☐ Let L-200D Morava	DDR-WLA	171213	OK-RFH, DM-WLA	PV
☐ Mikoyan-Gurevich MiG-15UTI	135	722650	(Soviet) – in DDR markings – on loan from Luftwaffen Museum.	PV
☐ Mikoyan-Gurevich MiG-17F	'08'	0630	In DDR markings – on loan from Luftwaffen Museum.	PVX
☐ Mikoyan-Gurevich MiG-21F-13	708	741611	In DDR markings.	PV
☐ Mikoyan-Gurevich MiG-21M	22+87	960514	589 (DDR)	PV
☐ Mikoyan-Gurevich MiG-21SPS (MiG-21PFM)	836	94A4706	In DDR markings – front fuselage only.	PV
☐ Mikoyan-Gurevich MiG-21SPS (MiG-21PFM)	22+38	94A5509	897 (DDR)	PV
☐ Mikoyan-Gurevich MiG-21UM	23+61	516915006	233 (DDR)	PV
☐ Mikoyan-Gurevich MiG-23BN	20+55	0393215732	720 (DDR)	PV
☐ Mikoyan-Gurevich MiG-23S	08	220001013	01 (Soviet) – on loan from Luftwaffen Museum.	PV
☐ Mikoyan-Gurevich MiG-23UB	20+57	A1038506	103 (DDR)	PV
☐ Mil Mi-2	D-HZPL	569342085		PV
☐ Mil Mi-8T	D-HOXA	0211	DM-SPA, DDR-SPA	PV
☐ Mil Mi-8T	395	0423	In DDR markings – on loan from Luftwaffen Museum.	PV
☐ Panstwowe Zaklady Lotnicze (PZL) M-18 Dromader	D-FOLO	1Z 019-23	DM-???	PV
☐ Platzer Leichflugzeugbau Motte B2-B3	D-MOOI			PV
☐ Silberfalter Ultralight				RA
☐ Sud-Est SE.3130 Alouette II	76+80	1765	PH+242, PO+135, PY+206 – on loan from Luftwaffen Museum.	PV
☐ Temple Wing TE F-3	D-MXDX			PV
☐ Tupolev Tu-134	DDR-SCH	9350906	DM-SCH	PV

☐ Wytwornia Sprzetu Komunikacyjnego (WSK) M-18 Dromader	D-FOLO	1Z 019-23	DDR-TLO, DM-TLO	RAC
☐ Yakovlev Yak-28R	'91'	8961310	09, 25	PVX
☐ Yakovlev Yak-52	RA-70977		CCCP-70977	PV
☐ Zlin Z-37 Cmelak				RA
☐ Zlin Z-37 Cmelak	D-ESLZ	15-14	DDR-SLZ, DM-SLZ	PV
☐ Zlin Z-37A Cmelak	D-ESVT	20-23	DDR-SVT, DM-SVT	PV
☐ Zlin Z-526 Trener Master	DM-WKY	1016		PVC
☐ Zlin Z-526A Akrobat	DM-WKX	1041		PV

LUFTFAHRTMUSEUM LAATZEN-HANNOVER (GER82)

Address:	Ulmer Strasse 2, D-30880 Laatzen.
Tel:	0511-8791791/2
Fax:	0511-879-1793
Admission:	Tuesday-Sunday 1000-1700 (Closed Dec 20th-January 5th).
Location:	In the north eastern part of the town which is just south of Hannover.

This impressive museum opened on November 15th 1992 in a specially constructed building with two exhibition halls. The owner of the collection, Günter Leonhardt, started acquiring items more than thirty five years ago. The aim is to show the aircraft in a period setting so that people of all ages and interests will benefit from a visit. The first hall shows mainly replica aircraft from the early period. Also in this area are vehicles, models and engines along with photographs and documents. Significant developments in aviation are featured with informative displays. The work of Otto Lilienthal is highlighted in the pioneers section. The story of World War I is portrayed vividly with particular emphasis on German aces such as Manfred von Richthofen. The growth of air transport from the Junkers F 13 up to the Graf Zeppelin can be traced. Record breaking flights are also featured. These include the crossing of the Atlantic by Lindbergh and the first east-west flight by the crew of the Junkers W 33 'Bremen'. The line of machines starts with a Lilienthal glider and next to it is a Horvath Monoplane. Erno Horvath was one of the pioneer aviators in Hungary and built his first aircraft in 1910 with two later versions appearing the following year. A Klemm 25 built in the 1980s by the Oldtimer Group at the Wasserkuppe and a Junkers F 13 are in this hall. Four World War I fighters and the Ryan N.Y.P. used for Lindbergh's famous flight from Long Island to Paris complete the replica display. An exciting project completed in 2000 was the rebuild of a Focke-Wulf Fw 190. Large sections of a D-9 model were raised from the Schweriner See and usable components have been restored. This has been joined by a Flug Werk newly built example. Crash sites been investigated and many parts recovered. The second hall covers the period from World War I to the present day. A Messerschmitt Bf 109 was raised from the Mediterranean and restored. This famous fighter is next to a Spitfire bought in England. The Ju 52 front fuselage came from Czechoslovakia. The second hall also contains a large exhibition of engines and components. The Hansa and the MiG-21 are displayed outside with the former spectacularly mounted on poles. The standard of the exhibits and their imaginative presentation makes this museum a must for both enthusiasts and the public.

TYPE	REG/SER	CON. NO.	PI/NOTES	STATUS
☐ Akaflieg Braunschweig SB-6 Nixope			Wing only.	PV
☐ Antonov An-2R	HA-MHM	1G 123-03		PV
☐ Dornier Do 28D-2 Skyservant	58+68	4143		PV
☐ FFB Flamingo I	D-MXFB			PV
☐ Filter Schwan 1				PV
☐ Flug Werk FW 190A/N		999000		RA
☐ Focke-Wulf Fw 44J Stieglitz	SZ-30	2933	D-EXWK, SZ-30, OH-SZC	PV
☐ Focke-Wulf Fw 190A-8		'170393'	Composite from several aircraft.	PVX
☐ Fokker Dr I (R)	'425/17'		Replica containing original parts.	PVX
☐ Fokker E III (FSM)				PVX
☐ Grade Eindecker (R)	'31'			PVX
☐ Hamburger Flugzeugbau HFB.320 Hansa	D-CARY	1026	D-CARY, N890HJ, N71CW, N71DL, TC-FNS	PV
☐ Horvath III (R)				PV
☐ Ikarus Windspiel 2 Hang Glider				PV
☐ Junkers F 13 (FSM)				PV
☐ Junkers Ju 52/3mge			Fuselage section only.	PV
☐ Klemm L 25 d (R)	D-EOJK	AB-1		PV
☐ Lilienthal Normal-Segelapparat (R)				PV
☐ Lockheed 683-10-19 Starfighter (F-104G)	20+45	683-2053	KF+128, (DA+124), DA+109 – with parts of c/n 683-8031 KG+131, JA+118, 23+52	PV
☐ Messerschmitt Bf 109G (FSM)			Fuselage only.	PV
☐ Messerschmitt Bf 109G-2/trop	3+	'14753'		PV
☐ Mikoyan-Gurevich MiG-15bis	022	31530712		PV
☐ Mikoyan-Gurevich MiG-21F-13	688	741006		PV
☐ Nieuport 11 (FSM)				PV
☐ Piaggio FWP.149D	90+68	086	AC+453, AS+495	PV
☐ Ryan N.Y.P. (FSM)	'N-X-211'			PVX
☐ Schneider ESG 31 Grunau Baby IIB	OE-0129	007		PV
☐ Schneider Grunau SG-38 (D.F.S. 108-14)				PV
☐ Sopwith F.1 Camel (R)	'B7220'			PVX
☐ Stampe & Vertongen S.V.4C	'863'		In false French markings.	PVX

☐ Sud-Est SE.3130 Alouette II	75+02	1180	PA+133, PQ+134, QW+737, PE+133, PE+201	PV
☐ Supermarine 379 Spitfire FR.XIVc	MV370		MV370, HS??? (India), T-44 (Indian), G-FXIV	PV
☐ Tipsy T.66 Nipper I	D-EJOF	18	OO-NIE	PV
☐ Volkseigener Betrieb Apparatebau Lommatzsch Lom 57/I Libelle	DM-2559	059		PV
☐ Volkseigener Betrieb Apparatebau Lommatzsch Meise	DM-2188	0188		PV
☐ Yakovlev Yak-18	5418	5418	In Hungarian markings.	PV

LUFTFAHRTMUSEUM RECHLIN-LÄRZ (GER83)

Address:	Flugplatz, D-17248 Lärz.
Tel:	03983-326692
Admission:	Summer daily 1000-1600; Winter Thursday-Sunday 1000-1800.
Location:	At Rechlin-Lärz Airfield which is about 3 km south of the town, south of Road 198.

The Russians built this new airfield south of famous Rechlin test centre. The site remained operational until the early 1990s when the Soviet units returned home. At the present time civilian aircraft and gliders use part of the field. The museum has been set up in a building and has on show a fascinating collection of relics recovered from the area. Components from crash sites, uniforms, photographs, documents and ammunition can be seen.

TYPE	REG/SER	CON. NO.	PI/NOTES	STATUS
☐ Ilyushin Il-2			Fuselage only.	RAC
☐ Messerschmitt Bf 109G-2	2	14658	KG+WF – front fuselage only.	PV
☐ Mikoyan-Gurevich MiG-17	'07'	54212054	25 (Soviet) – on loan from Luftwaffen Mus.	PVX
☐ Mikoyan-Gurevich MiG-21U-600	292	664719	292 (DDR), 23+96	PV
☐ Mil Mi-8TB	94+10	10572	827 (DDR)	PV
☐ Mil Mi-24V			Front fuselage only.	PV

LUFTFAHRTSAMMLUNG SANNER (GER84)

Address:	P.O. Box 30 05, D-64625 Bensheim-Auerbach.
Tel:	062-519380
Fax:	062-25174672
Admission:	By prior permission only.
Location:	In the northern part of the town which is about 25 km north east of Mannheim

This private collection has been assembled by a local factory owner. The aim is to open a museum tracing the history of military flying in post-war Germany. At the present time the majority of the aircraft are stored.

TYPE	REG/SER	CON. NO.	PI/NOTES	STATUS
☐ Let L-410MA Turbolet	0402	750402	In Czech markings.	RA
☐ Mikoyan-Gurevich MiG-17F				RA
☐ Mikoyan-Gurevich MiG-21UM	'238'	10695162	207 (DDR), 23+81	RAX
☐ Mikoyan-Gurevich MiG-23UB	20+61	A1037826	102 (DDR)	RA
☐ Mil Mi-2	SP-SAI	512622101		RA
☐ Mil Mi-8T	94+23	10529	913 (DDR)	RA
☐ Panstwowe Zaklady Lotnicze (PZL) TS-11 Iskra 100bisB	324	1H 03-24	In Polish markings.	RA
☐ Sukhoi Su-20R	6137	74727	In Czech markings.	RAX
☐ Sukhoi Su-22M4	25+28	30917	598 (DDR)	RA

LUFTFAHRTTECHNISCHER MUSEUMVEREIN ROTHENBURG (GER85)

Address:	Friedenstrasse 113, D-02929 Rothenburg.
Tel:	035891-47-0
Fax:	03591-47-205
Email:	n.kalz@web.de
Admission:	May-October Daily 1000-1800.
Location:	In the town which is about 100 km north east of Dresden.

The airfield was built in 1953/4 for use by the Soviet forces. Rothenburg became an important N.V.A. base with fighters and trainers in use. The history of the airfield and its units is portrayed along with the test flying carried out at the site. Upon the reunification of Germany many redundant airframes were stored at the field. Several were allocated to the museum and these have been put on show. There is also a company dealing with these aircraft on the field and there are always former military types here. The Fiat G.91 is a rarity in the former East Germany. Photographs, models, components, radar items, radios, uniforms and documents have been collected over the last few years. There is an interesting collection of jet engines featuring nearly all the types fitted to N.V.A. aircraft in recent years. A Baade 152 fuselage was found dumped on the airfield in the late 1990s. This had been hidden by scrub for over thirty years. This is now being rebuilt at the Elbe works in Dresden. The museum has an engine from this type plus some small parts.

TYPE	REG/SER	CON. NO.	PI/NOTES	STATUS
☐ Aero L-29 Delfin	339	692061	In DDR markings.	PV
☐ Aero L-39ZO Albatros	143	731005	143 (DDR), 28+05	PV
☐ Fiat G.91R/3	30+74	91-336	KD+326, ED+240, MR+113	PV
☐ Mikoyan-Gurevich MiG-21bisSAU	838	75051378	838 (DDR), 24+18	PV
☐ Mikoyan-Gurevich MiG-21F-13	623	741916	In DDR markings.	PV
☐ Mikoyan-Gurevich MiG-21M	581	960508	581 (DDR), 22+85	PV
☐ Mikoyan-Gurevich MiG-21MF	784	96002170	784 (DDR), 23+49	PV
☐ Mikoyan-Gurevich MiG-21SPS-K (MiG-21PFM)	545	94A7215	545 (DDR), 22+21	PV
☐ Mikoyan-Gurevich MiG-21U-600	296	664818	296 (DDR), 23+98	PV
☐ Mikoyan-Gurevich MiG-21US	236	05685134	236 (DDR), 24+07	PV
☐ Mikoyan-Gurevich MiG-23BN	20+38	0393211085	689 (DDR)	PV
☐ Mil Mi-2S	94+60	562633112	383 (DDR)	PV
☐ Mil Mi-14PL	95+04	B 4004	620 (DDR)	PV
☐ Sukhoi Su-22M4	25+42	26817	757 (DDR)	PV

LUFTFAHRTTECHNISCHES MUSEUM (GER86)

Address:	Am Claasee 1, D-17248 Rechlin.
Tel:	039823-20424
Fax:	039823-27966
Email:	museum.rechlin@t-online.de
Admission:	February-April Monday-Thursday 1000-1600; May-October daily 1000-1700
Location:	At Rechlin-Nord which is just north of the village.

This museum aims to trace the history and technical developments in aviation that have taken place at the site. Flying first took place in 1918 and from 1934 to 1945 the complex was the main Luftwaffe flying test centre. The museum, housed in three buildings surviving from this era, traces the history of Rechlin and the airfield at nearby Lärz built by the Soviet forces. On show are many models, photographs and documents along with components and engines. The aircraft collection includes one of the Ilyushin Il-2 fuselages found nearby.

TYPE	REG/SER	CON. NO.	PI/NOTES	STATUS
☐ Ilyushin Il-2m3			Fuselage only.	PVD
☐ Mil Mi-8T	93+34	10530	902 (DDR)	PV
☐ Sukhoi Su-22UM3K	25+48	17532367002	119 (DDR)	PV
☐ Zlin Z-37A Cmelak	D-ESSD	17-22	DM-SSD, DDR-SSD	PV

LUFTSPORTVEREIN SÜDENTONDEREN (GER87)

Address:	P.O. Box 1221, D-25912 Aventoft.
Tel:	04662-2524
Admission:	By prior permission only.
Location:	The airfield is just south of the village which is about 5 km south of Tonder, Denmark.

This organisation has in its fleet a number of classic sailplanes. The Weihe 50 was developed in the 1950s from the original Hans Jacobs design and the Focke Wulf company produced a small number. The type influenced types built in several European countries in the 1940s and 1950s. The delightful gull wing Minimoa first flew in 1935 and went into production the following year. About one hundred were built before World War II. A number were exported including one transported to Argentina in a Zeppelin. The type set a number of records prior to the outbreak of World War II. Several modern types are also in use by this enthusiastic group.

TYPE	REG/SER	CON. NO.	PI/NOTES	STATUS
☐ Focke-Wulf Weihe 50	D-0084	8		RAA
☐ Göppingen Gö III Minimoa	D-8064	184	D-8094, HB-???, N2664B	RAA
☐ Scheibe SF-25B Falke	D-KEAT	46253		RAA
☐ Scheibe SF-25C Rotax-Falke	D-KIEK	44638		RAA
☐ Schleicher Ka-6CR Rhönsegler				RAA
☐ Schleicher ASK-13	D-0095	13126		RAA

LUFTWAFFE BASE BÜCHEL SAMMLUNG (GER88)

Address:	Jagdbombergeschwader 33, Postfach 33, D-56809 Cochem.
Tel:	026-71231
Admission:	By prior permission only.
Location:	About 10 km north west of Cochem on Road 259. The Fliegerkaserne is just west of the town on Road 259.

The first fighter bomber wing (JBG31) was formed at Büchel in late 1957. Equipped with Thunderstreaks the wing moved to Norvenich the following year and was replaced by JBG33 which is still in residence. The new unit also operated Thunderstreaks and these served until 1964 when the Starfighter arrived. Most Luftwaffe combat units were allocated a small number of T-33s for communication, liaison and training duties. Piaggio P.149s were also used on these tasks. The Tornado was introduced in the early 1980s and is still flown. A Thunderstreak is preserved at the Fliegerkaserne which is some distance from the airfield on the road to Cochem.

TYPE	REG/SER	CON. NO.	PI/NOTES	STATUS
☐ Lockheed 580 (T-33A)	JD+395	580-1657	58-0688, JD+395, JE+395	RA
☐ Lockheed 580 (T-33A)	'DC+382'	580-8198	52-9967, AB+733, BD+733, 94+34	RAX
☐ Lockheed 683-10-19 Starfighter (F-104G)	'40+33'	683-7036	KE+336, DA+244, DD+253, 21+67	PVX
☐ Lockheed 683-10-19 Starfighter (F-104G)	26+26	683-9178	KH+177, DF+245	RA
☐ Republic F-84F Thunderstreak	'DC+101'		52-6707, DD+354 , DD+354	RAX
☐ Republic F-84F Thunderstreak	DC+319		53-7045, DD+242, DR+???, DC+373, DC+251 – at Fliegerkaserne Cochem.	PV

LUFTWAFFE BASE FASSBERG SAMMLUNG (GER89)

Address:	Technische Schule der Luftwaffe 3, Postfach 916, D-29324 Fassberg.
Tel:	05055-171015
Fax;	05055-171019
Email:	TSLw3presseoffizier@bubdeswehr.org
Admission:	By prior permission only.
Location:	In the northern part of the town which is about 12 km south east of Munster.

At the current time the airfield is home to a Luftwaffe technical training school which has a large number of instructional airframes. Airframe and engine fitters learn their skills here and there is also a section which deals with the repair of battle damaged airframes. There are currently four aircraft preserved on the base.

TYPE	REG/SER	CON. NO.	PI/NOTES	STATUS
☐ Dornier-Bell 205 (UH-1D)	72+85	8405		RA
☐ Fiat G.91R/3	99+08	91-467	KD+457,BD+251, 31+99, D-9604	RA
☐ Fiat G.91R/3	'31+05'	91-501	KD+491,DC+302,MR+302, MA+302,32+32	PVX
☐ Sud-Est SE.3130 Alouette II	76+02	1547		PV

LUFTWAFFE BASE FÜRSTENFELDBRUCK SAMMLUNG (GER90)

Address:	Offizierschule der Luftwaffe, Postfach 1264B, D-82256 Fürstenfeldbruck.
Tel:	081-419621
Admission:	By prior permission only.
Location:	Just north of the town which is about 25 km west of Munich.

In recent years the base has housed the Alpha Jet training wing but this closed in 1997. The Luftwaffe Officer Training School remains in residence and a traditions room has been set up in one of their buildings. The history of the airfield in the period prior to and during World War II is portrayed in detail. There are also sections devoted to its time as an American base. The display cabinets contain many models, photographs, documents and trophies. The preserved aircraft are located around the vast site.

TYPE	REG/SER	CON. NO.	PI/NOTES	STATUS
☐ Dornier-Breguet Alpha Jet A	41+57	0157		RA
☐ Fiat G.91R/3	31+98	91-466	KD+456, EC+122, EC+102, MD+108	RA
☐ Fiat G.91R/3	32+52	91-521	KD+511, EC+237, MD+237	RA
☐ Fiat G.91T/3 (T/1)	34+02	91-2-0002	BD+102, YA+020, MB+374	RA
☐ Lockheed 580 (T-33A)	'AB+773'	580-7981	52-9930, AB+728, BD+728, 94+22	RAX
☐ Lockheed 683-10-19 Starfighter (F-104G)	'22+36'	683-7143	KE+443, DD+244, 22+62	RAX
☐ McDonnell M.98NQ Phantom II (F-4F)	37+71	4520	72-1181	RA
☐ Panavia PA200 Tornado IDS	44+84	4184		RA
☐ Piaggio FWP.149D	90+94	114	(AS+438), AS+073, DA+389, 90+94, D-EOGE	RA
☐ Republic F-84F Thunderstreak	DD+244/ '51-1665'		52-6737, DD+244, DD+344 –	RAX
☐ Republic RF-84F Thunderflash	'BD+119'		51-17041, EB+243, EB+343	RAX

LUFTWAFFE BASE HOHN SAMMLUNG (GER91)

Address:	Lufttransportgeschwader 63, Hugo Junkers Kaserne, D-24806 Hohn b Rendsburg.
Tel:	04335-940
Admission:	By prior permission only.
Location:	About 10 km. west of Rendsburg off Route 202.

Hohn is one of the major Luftwaffe transport bases housing Transalls and a helicopter squadron. The French built former Portuguese Air Force Junkers 52 has been painted in typical World War II colours.

TYPE	REG/SER	CON. NO.	PI/NOTES	STATUS
☐ Ateliers Aéronautiques de Colombes AAC.1 [Junkers Ju 52/3mg10e]	'1Z+IK'	053	6320 (Portugal)	RAX
☐ Dornier Do 28D-2 Skyservant	58+34	4109	At Kaserne.	RA
☐ Nord N.2501D Noratlas	'52+55'	185	KA+196, GB+249, 53+55	RAX

LUFTWAFFE BASE JEVER SAMMLUNG (GER92)

Address:	Jagdbombergeschwader 38, Upjeversche Strasse 1 D-26419 Schortens.
Tel:	04461-180
Admission:	By prior permission only.
Location:	About 5 km south of Jever south of Road 210.

This Luftwaffe base, built in 1936, was used by the Danish Army from 1946 until 1948 and by the Royal Air Force between 1952 and early 1961. A display of memorabilia is in the entrance hall of the gatehouse and plans have been put forward to establish a traditions room which will enable the history of the wing to be shown.

TYPE	REG/SER	CON. NO.	PI/NOTES	STATUS
☐ Canadair CL-13B Sabre 6 [North American F-86E]	'BB+103'	1730	JB+114	RA
☐ Dornier-Breguet Alpha Jet A	41+24	0124		RA
☐ Fiat G.91R/3	32+58	91-528	KD+518, EC+311, MD+311, MD+256	RA
☐ Lockheed 483-04-08 Starfighter (F-104F)	29+09	483-5059	59-5006, BB+372	RA
☐ Lockheed 683-10-19 Starfighter (F-104G)	26+67	683-7413		RA

LUFTWAFFE BASE LAAGE SAMMLUNG (GER93)

Address:	Jagdgeschwader 73, Daimler-Benz Allee 2 B3, D-18299 Kronskamp.
Tel:	038459-622300
Admission:	By prior permission only.
Location:	About 3 km west of the town which is about 20 km south of Rostock off Road 103.

The airfield was an important East German Air Force fighter base for many years and was home to the MiG-29s acquired when the country was unified. The majority of these went to the Polish Air Force in 2004. In the late 1990s a unit flying the Phantom moved to the base. This commenced conversion to the Eurofighter Typhoon in 2004. A number of aircraft have been put on display to reflect the history of the site. Jagdgeschwader 73 was formed at Oldenburg in 1959 and in the 1960s operated Canadair Sabres and Fiat G.91s before being disbanded in 1964. The three MiG fighters have all flown from Laage.

TYPE	REG/SER	CON. NO.	PI/NOTES	STATUS
☐ Canadair CL-13B Sabre 6 [North American F-86E]	JC+102	1691	Possible identity.	RAX
☐ Fiat G.91R/3	33+03	91-574	KD+564	RA
☐ Lockheed 683-04-10 Starfighter (RF-104G)	'BB+105'	683-8255	KG+355, EB+247, 25+02	RAX
☐ McDonnell M.98HO Phantom II (F-4E)	'35+73'	4951	75-0631	RAX
☐ Mikoyan-Gurevich MiG-21F-13	'335'	741004	619 (DDR)	RAX
☐ Mikoyan-Gurevich MiG-23ML	20+11	0390324619	330 (DDR)	RA
☐ Mikoyan-Gurevich MiG-29G (MiG-29)	29+03	2960525110/3414	615 (DDR)	RA
☐ Sukhoi Su-22M4	734	31205	734 (DDR), 25+38	RA

LUFTWAFFE BASE LANDSBERG SAMMLUNG (GER94)

Address:	Lufttransportgeschwader 61, D-86929 Penzing.
Tel:	08181-2021
Admission:	By prior permission only.
Location:	About 5 km north east of Landsberg.

A flying training school equipped with Harvards and Magisters was established at Landsberg in 1956 and disbanded ten years later. In 1964 a helicopter transport unit was set up at the base. The current occupying wing is LTG 61, formed in 1956 at Neubiberg with C-47s. The Noratlas arrived in 1958 and the Transall, which is still flown, in 1971. The five preserved aircraft are located around the base. The Harvard and Magister were put on display in the mid-1960s. The former French Air Force Noratlas was presented to the unit in September 1987. The Sycamore was completely rebuilt by volunteers from the wing. There is a possibility that the wing will disband and its UH-1Ds will move to Holzdorf so the future of the display is uncertain.

TYPE	REG/SER	CON. NO.	PI/NOTES	STATUS
☐ Bristol 171 Sycamore HR.52	LB+105	13503	CB+019, LC+112, SC+202, 78+37	RAX
☐ Canadian Car & Foundry Harvard 4 [North American NA-186 (T-6J)]	AA+666	CCF4-458	52-8537	RA
☐ Dornier-Bell 205 (UH-1D)	71+10	8170		RA
☐ Fouga CM.170R Magister	AA+152	052	AA+152, CA+024, AA+024	RA
☐ Nord N.2501 Noratlas	'GA+125'	128	128 (France)	RAX

LUFTWAFFE BASE LECHFELD SAMMLUNG (GER95)

Address:	Jagdbombergeschwader 32, Schwabstadl Kaserne, D-86836 Klosterlechfeld.
Tel:	08232-2011 ext 331.
Admission:	By prior permission only.
Location:	About 25 km south of Augsburg east of Road 17.

The Lechfeld Wing was formed in 1958 and flew Thunderstreaks until 1962. Starfighters were operated for twenty years until the arrival of the Tornado which is likely to remain in residence for some time. A group of volunteers is setting up a display at the Schwabstadl Kaserne located just south of the airfield. This traces, in detail, the history of the site and its units. During World War II the field was used for test flying Messerschmitt Me 262s built at nearby Augsburg. A few components found on the field have been recovered and there is an informative photographic display showing the development of the type. JBG32 operated over Bosnia and in another room an exhibition showing the work of the unit during this operation has been staged. Also on show are photographs and models of the types flown from Lechfeld along with uniforms and badges.

TYPE	REG/SER	CON. NO.	PI/NOTES	STATUS
☐ Lockheed 580 (T-33A)	DB+396	580-1410	57-0681, AB+820, DB+396, 94+82	RA
☐ Lockheed 683-10-19 Starfighter (F-104G)	'20+02'	683-7004	KE+304, DA+112, BF+112, 21+36	RAX
☐ Percival P.66 Pembroke C.54	54+26	P66/1018	At Ulrich Kaserne.	RA
☐ Republic F-84F Thunderstreak	'DB+132'		52-6764, DD+375, BF+	RAX
☐ Republic F-84F Thunderstreak	'DB+232'		51-1645, DB+032, DE+364, DD+367	RAX

Many classic gliders can be seen in the Deutsches Segelflugmuseum on the famous Wasserkuppe. Pictured here is a Jacobs Rhönsperber.

This Horten Ho IIL was restored by the staff at the Deutsches Technikmuseum in Berlin. (DTM)

Parked outside the secret World War II factory at Peenemunde is this former East German air Force MiG-17.

This replica Focke-Wulf Fw 61 is at the Hubschrauber Museum in Buckeburg.

One hall at the Luftfahrtmuseum at Laatzen houses many replicas of early aircraft. The nose of the Horvath III can be seen in front of a Fokker EIII and a Fokker Dr I.

Three Mig fighters are show near one of the hard shelters at the museum at Finow. On the left are a MiG-17F and a MiG-15UTI. On the right is a MiG-23S. (Douglas Rough)

LUFTWAFFE BASE NEUBRANDENBURG SAMMLUNG (GER96)

Address:	Kasernenkommandant, Fliegerhorst Neubrandenburg, D-17039 Trollenhagen.
Tel:	0395-4630
Admission:	By prior permission only.
Location:	About 5 km. north of the town just east of Route 96.

The airfield was an important East German fighter base with MiG-21s in residence. Since unification the Luftwaffe have had a site on the southern side and a civil terminal has been constructed on the northern boundary. Three former NVA machines were joined by a Starfighter which came from the naval arsenal at Wilhelmshafen.

TYPE	REG/SER	CON. NO.	PI/NOTES	STATUS
☐ Lockheed 683-04-10 Starfighter (RF-104G)	21+12	683-6661	KC+146, VB+207	RA
☐ Mikoyan-Gurevich MiG-21PFM	825	760606		RA
☐ Mikoyan-Gurevich MiG-23ML	20+29	0390324027	554 (DDR)	RA
☐ Wytwornia Sprzetu Komunikacyjnego (WSK) Lim-5 [MiG-17F]	'003'	1C 07-15	781 (DDR)	RAX

LUFTWAFFE BASE NEUBURG SAMMLUNG (GER97)

Address:	Jagdeschwader 74 'Molders', Wilhelm-Frankl-Kaserne, D-86633 Neuburg/Donau.
Tel:	02231-2091
Admission:	By prior permission only.
Location:	About 2 km west of the town off Route 16.

The resident unit JG74 was formed at Ahlhorn in 1961 and absorbed JG75 equipped with F-86Ks. The wing moved to Neuburg in 1965 and re-equipped with F-104Gs. Since 1974 it has operated the F-4F and Eurofighter Typhoons will arrive in due course. One Sabre is preserved at the gate to the airfield and two aircraft are at the nearby Wilhelm Frank Kaserne. The Phantom will be put on show in the future.

TYPE	REG/SER	CON. NO.	PI/NOTES	STATUS
☐ Lockheed 683-10-19 Starfighter (F-104G)	23+57	683-8037	KG+137, JD+129, JA+233 – at Kaserne.	RA
☐ McDonnell M.98HO Phantom II (F-4E)	75-0633	4956		RA
☐ North American NA-232 Sabre (F-86K)	'JD+119'	232-168	55-4928	RAX
☐ North American NA-232 Sabre (F-86K)	'JG-74'	232-172	55-4932 – possible identity – at Kaserne.	RAX

LUFTWAFFE BASE NÖRVENICH SAMMLUNG (GER98)

Address:	Jagdbombergeschwader 31 'Boelcke', Boelcke-Kaserne, D-50171 Kerpen.
Tel:	02231-2091
Admission:	By prior permission only.
Location:	About 10 km. south west of Kerpen east of Route 477.

The wing was established on September 1st 1957 at Büchel and later moved to Nörvenich. The initial equipment was the F-84F which was replaced by the F-104G in 1961. The Tornado arrived in 1981 and is still in use. The Eurofighter Typhoon will equip the unit in the next few years. A Thunderstreak and a Starfighter are at the nearby Kaserne and some of the aircraft on the airfield also serve in the training role.

TYPE	REG/SER	CON. NO.	PI/NOTES	STATUS
☐ Dornier Do 28D-2 Skyservant	58+41	4116		RA
☐ Dornier-Breguet Alpha Jet A	40+85	0085		RA
☐ Fiat G.91R/3	99+11	91-518	KD+508, XB+103, 32+49, D-9607	RA
☐ Lockheed 483-04-08 Starfighter (F-104F)	'21+21'	483-5070	59-5017, BB+383, 29+17	RAX
☐ Lockheed 483-04-08 Starfighter (F-104F)	DA+101'	483-5073	59-5020, BB+386, 29+19 – at Kaserne.	RAX

☐ Lockheed 683-10-19 Starfighter (F-104G)	'DA+235'	683-8231	KG+331, JD+249, 24+81 – tail from c/n 683-8199 KG+299, JD+101, 24+52	RA
☐ Piaggio P.149D	91+86	270	AS+421, AC+421, D-EBCO	RA
☐ Republic F-84F Thunderstreak	'DA+127		53-7102, DA+127,BF+108 – at Kaserne.	RAX

LUFTWAFFE BASE SCHLESWIG-JAGEL SAMMLUNG (GER99)

Address:	Aufklürungsgeschwader 51, Bennebeker Chausse, D-24848 Kropp.
Tel:	04624-300
Admission:	By prior permission only.
Location:	About 10 km south of Schleswig east of Road 77.

The wing was formed at Erding in July 1959 and equipped with the RF-84F Thunderflash. In 1960 the unit moved to Manching and three years later the RF-104G Starfighter arrived. A transfer to Bremgarten took place in 1971 and the RF-4E Phantom was introduced. The current equipment is the Tornado and the unit transferred to Jagel a few years ago. One of the Starfighters is preserved at the nearby barracks.

TYPE	REG/SER	CON. NO.	PI/NOTES	STATUS
☐ Dornier-Breguet Alpha Jet A	40+23	0023		RA
☐ Dornier-Breguet Alpha Jet A	40+44	0044		RA
☐ Lockheed 580 (T-33A)	'EB+396/EB+397'	580-9140	54-1523, AB+797, JD+383, EC+377, MD+377, DD+397, 94+59	RAX
☐ Lockheed 683-10-19 Starfighter (F-104G)	'23+81'	683-2094	KF+169, DC+245, 20+81	PVX
☐ Lockheed 683-10-19 Starfighter (F-104G)	'24+77'	683-7159	KE+459, VA+135, 22+77 – at Kaserne.	PVX
☐ Panavia PA200 Tornado IDS	44+53	4153		RA
☐ Republic RF-84F Thunderflash	EB+250		52-7355	PV

LUFTWAFFEN MUSEUM (GER100)

Address:	General Steinhoff Kaserne, Kladower Damm 182-188, D-14089 Berlin.
Tel:	030-3687-2601
Fax:	030-3687-2610
Email:	LwMuseumBw@snafu.de
Admission:	Tuesday-Sunday 0900-1630.
Location:	At Gatow Airfield which is in the western suburbs of Berlin.

The museum has its origins in a collection of Luftwaffe and general aviation material acquired by members of the service. The first display opened in 1963 in two hangars at the base at Uetersen, north of Hamburg. Over the years aircraft and material were steadily acquired. When the country was reunified the collection from the former L.S.K. Officers School at Bautzen near Dresden was moved to Uetersen. Gatow was built in 1935 and housed a Luftwaffe Aerial Warfare School. The Red Army occupied the site for a period in 1945 and soon after it was turned over to the British hard runways were laid. Gatow was the main airfield in the British Zone of the city and played an important role in the Berlin Airlift. The Royal Air Force left the site in 1994 and the museum began transferring its vast fleet of aircraft and memorabilia across the country. One hangar is now open to the public and a well laid out display been set up. About twenty aircraft are normally on view and these represent different periods in the development of military aviation in the country. Two wars on German soil and the policy adopted by the Allies after each conflict meant that most aircraft which had survived were either scrapped or taken home for testing. During World War I Germany had a vast number of aircraft flying over the Western Front. A number of replicas of early types have been constructed to fill the void and at the current time four are exhibited. More types from the inter-war period are in the planning stages and some of these replicas will be built soon. Military flying was bannned in 1918 but in 1934 Hitler ordered the establishment of the Luftwaffe which quickly became a potent fighting force. Sadly little has survived from this period. The World War II section includes a replica of a D.F.S. 230 troop carrying glider and a Grunau Baby in period colours. The development of the modem Luftwaffe is shown along with that of the former East German Air Force. West Germany was allowed to set up its new Air Force in 1956 and in a short time more than twenty wings with a complement of more than thirteen hundred aircraft were in use. In East Germany a small police flying unit was established in 1950. Five years later the official Air Force came into being and up to the re-unification of the country used mainly Soviet designed aircraft. The majority of types flown by the two forces have been preserved. More than fifty aircraft are parked outside and a further five hangars are used for storing airframes, engines and the vast amount of associated material. Another serves as a restoration workshop. The airfield headquarters building is also scheduled to be part of the display as are some of the storage hangars. The British and French Air Forces had bases in Germany for many years after World War II and the Harrier, Hunter, Lighning and Super Mystère B2 reflect this period. As types are withdrawn from service they are being added and more are expected in the near future. A large collection of memorabilia, uniforms, components and engines is in store. There is potential for a superb exhibition and hopefully it will not be too long before the next stages are ready to open to the public.

TYPE	REG/SER	CON. NO.	PI/NOTES	STATUS
☐ Aero L-29 Delfin	338	591525	In DDR markings.	PV
☐ Aero L-29 Delfin	311	692053	In DDR markings.	PV
☐ Aero L-39V Albatros	28+48	630705	170 (DDR)	PV
☐ Aero L-39ZO Albatros	144	731006	144, (28+06) – in DDR markings.	RA
☐ Albatros B I (FSM)				RAC
☐ Antonov An-2	822	117047312	In DDR markings.	PV
☐ Antonov An-2	'8120'	18147320	812 (DDR),.DM-WCZ	PV
☐ Antonov An-14A	995	601005	In DDR markings.	PV
☐ Antonov An-26SM	52+09	11402	369 (DDR), (DDR-SBL), 369 (DDR)	PV
☐ Avro 504K (R)	'E3349'	RPL 6832		PVX
☐ Bölkow BO 105M (BO 105C) (BO105D)	98+20	S-90	D-HDCO, D-9596	RA
☐ Bölkow BO 105P	'98+37'	V-3	Boom from c/n S-7 98+07	RA
☐ Breguet 1150 Atlantic	61+17	34	UC+326	PV
☐ Bristol 171 Sycamore HR.52	78+04	13442	G-18-???, BA+176, CD+082, SC+207, WE+541, LC+116	RA
☐ Bücker Bü 181B-1 Bestmann (Sk 25)	'NF+1R'	25017	Fv25017, D-EGUF	PVX
☐ Canadair CL-13A Sabre 5 [North American F-86E]	BB+150	895	23105, BBV+150, BB+250	PV
☐ Canadair CL-13B Sabre 6 [North American F-86E]	01+01	1591	BB+361 (?), BB+262 (?), BB+161, YA+005	PV
☐ Canadair CL-13B Sabre 6 [North American F-86E]	D-9539	1603	BB+173	PV
☐ Canadair CL-13B Sabre 6 [North American F-86E]	'JA+111'	1625	JC+368	PVX
☐ Canadair CL-13B Sabre 6 [North American F-86E]	JB+110	1643	JD+238, BB+382, JB+374	RA
☐ Canadair CL-13B Sabre 6 [North American F-86E]	'JA+106'	1664	BB+186, JD+112, YA+044, 01+06 – on loan to Richt. Mus	–
☐ Canadair CL-13B Sabre 6 [North American F-86E]	'JB+110'	1734	JC+110 – on loan to Militar HM.	–
☐ Canadair CL-13B Sabre 6 [North American F-86E]	D-9542	1740	JC+103, BB+266, JB+373, JB+103, YA+???, 01+10	PV
☐ Canadair CL-13B Sabre 6 [North American F-86E]	'JA+111'	1775	JB+112, 'JA+110' – on loan to Mus Wernigerode.	–
☐ Canadian Car & Foundry Harvard 4 [North American NA-186 (T-6J)]	AA+615	CCF4-465	52-8544, AA+615, D-FABU	PV
☐ Construcciones Aeronáuticas (CASA) 2.111B (2.111A) [Heinkel He 111H-16]	'G1+AD'	125	B.2H-109, B.2I-117	RAX
☐ Dassault Super Mystère B2	72	72		PV
☐ Dassault Mirage IIIE	587	587		PV
☐ Dornier Do 27A-3	D-EJUX	464	AA+933, (LB+155), AA+933, GD+155, 57+35	RA
☐ Dornier Do 27A-4	57+38	467	D-EGAQ, YA+004, YA+904	RA
☐ Dornier Do 28D-2 Skyservant	59+20	4195		RA
☐ Dornier Do 29	'YA+101'	V-1	YD+101	RAX
☐ Dornier DS 10 Fledermaus 2	D-9534	2		RA
☐ Dornier-Bell 205 (UH-1D)	D-HATE	8063	(70+33)	PV
☐ Dornier-Bell 205 (UH-1D)	71+42	8202		PV
☐ Dornier-Bell 205 (UH-1D)	73+13	8433		PV
☐ Dornier-Breguet Alpha Jet A	40+26	0026		PV
☐ Dornier-Breguet Alpha Jet A	40+61	0061	On loan to Flugausstellung Junior.	–
☐ Dornier-Breguet Alpha Jet A	40+74	0074	On loan to Int. Luft. Mus.	–
☐ Dornier-Breguet Alpha Jet A	41+50	0150		PV
☐ English Electric EA.1 Canberra B.2	WP515	EEP71054	Front fuselage only.	RA
☐ English Electric EA.1 Canberra B.2	99+34	R3/EA3/6651	WK137, YA+152, 00+02, D-9566 – on loan to Int.Luft. Mus.	–
☐ English Electric EA.1 Canberra B.2	99+35	R3/EA3/6652	WK138, YA+153, 00+03, D-9567	PV
☐ English Electric P.25 Lightning F.2A (F.2)	XN730	95107	XN730, 8496M	PV
☐ Fairey Gannet AS.4	'UA+106'	F9391	XG849, UA+110	RAX
☐ Fiat G.91R/3	'37+39'		Fuselage only.	PVX
☐ Fiat G.91R/3	99+07	91-460	KD+450, BD+239, 31+92, D-9603 – on loan to Flugwerft Schleiss.	–
☐ Fiat G.91R/3	32+11	91-479	KD+469 – front fuselage only – on loan to LM Merseburg.	–
☐ Fiat G.91R/3	32+15	91-483	KD+473, EC+316, MD+316, MB+128	PV
☐ Fiat G.91R/3	32+72	91-542	KD+532, XB+113, YA+018	RA
☐ Fiat G.91R/3	99+12	91-554	KD+544, DG+324, MR+324, BD+272, 32+84, D-9608	PV
☐ Fiat G.91R/3	'35+99'	91-570	KD+560, ER+???, MC+108, 32+99 – front fuselage only.	PVX
☐ Fiat G.91R/4	'35+41'	91-4-0113	BD+239, BR+239	PVX
☐ Fiat G.91T/3 (T/1)	34+13	91-2-0015	BD+115, MA+374 – front fuselage only	RA
☐ Fiat G.91T/3 (T/1)	99+41	91-2-0027	BD+126, MA+373, 34+25	PV
☐ Fiat G.91T/3 (T/1)	34+52	91-2-0612	Nose only	RA
☐ Fiat G.91T/3 (T/1)	99+40	91-2-0621	34+61	PV
☐ Fieseler Fi 103A-1				PV
☐ Flug Werk FW 190A/N		990003		RA
☐ Focke-Wulf Fw 190A-8			Wing only.	RA
☐ Focke-Wulf Fw 190D-9/R11	'8'	210968		RAC
☐ Fokker D VII (FSM)	'7775/18'			PVX
☐ Fokker Dr I (FSM)	'152/17'			PVX
☐ Fokker E III (FSM)	'603/15'			RAX
☐ Fouga CM.170R Magister	AA+014	229		RA

☐ Gloster Meteor NF.11	NF.11-14		WM369 – in French markings.	PV
☐ Göppingen Gö 4 Gövier III	D-6623	410	On loan to MFG.5 at Kiel-Holtenau.	–
☐ Gotha Go 242			Parts only.	RA
☐ Hamburger Flugzeugbau HFB.320 Hansa	D-CARE	1022	On loan to LHS Finow.	–
☐ Hamburger Flugzeugbau HFB.320 Hansa	16+06	1048	D-CISI	PV
☐ Hamburger Flugzeugbau HFB.320ECM Hansa (HFB.320)	16+26	1063	D-CANU	PV
☐ Hawker P.1040 Sea Hawk FGA.6 (FGA.4)	WV865	6110	WV865, A2554	PV
☐ Hawker P.1099 Hunter F.6A (F.6)	XG152		XG152, 8843M	PV
☐ Hawker-Siddeley P.1127 Harrier GR.1	XV278			PV
☐ Henschel Hs 293A-1				RA
☐ Hispano HA-1112K1L [Messerschmitt Bf 109G]	'4'	'10575'	C.4J-??	PVX
☐ Ilyushin Il-28B	208	55006448	(Soviet) – in DDR markings.	PV
☐ Jacobs D.F.S. 230A-2	'KA+1-52'		Partial replica.	PVX
☐ Junkers J 9 (D-1) (FSM)				PV
☐ Junkers Ju 52/3mg4e	DB+RD	6693	On loan to Interess. Ju 52.	–
☐ Let L-410UVP(S) Turbolet	53+10	800525	OK-164, 318 (DDR)	PV
☐ Lilienthal Normal-Segelapparat (R)				RA
☐ Lockheed 483-04-08 Starfighter (F-104F)	BB+368	483-5055	59-5002, BB+368, 29+06	RA
☐ Lockheed 580 (T-33A)	'ND+204'	580-7374	51-17480, AB+703, BD+703, BB+802, 94+02	RAX
☐ Lockheed 580 (T-33A)	94+44	580-8960	53-5621, AB+772, JA+399, JB+399, EA+397	RA
☐ Lockheed 580 (T-33A)	'94+55'	580-9120	53-5781, AB+805, BD+805, 94+56	PVX
☐ Lockheed 580 (T-33A)	EB+399	580-9257	54-1568, (AB+825), BD+825, EB+399 (94+69)	PV
☐ Lockheed 583-10-20 Starfighter (TF-104G)	27+90	583F-5920	KF+220, EB+373, 27+90	PV
☐ Lockheed 583-10-20 Starfighter (TF-104G)	28+01	583F-5931	KF+231, BB+122 – front fuselage only.	PV
☐ Lockheed 683-04-10 Starfighter (RF-104G)	24+54	683-8202	KG+302, BB+250 – on loan to LM Merseburg.	–
☐ Lockheed 683-04-10 Starfighter (RF-104G)	25+07	683-8265	KG+365, EB+251 – front fuselage only.	RA
☐ Lockheed 683-10-19 Starfighter (F-104G)	20+37	683-2044	KF+120, DA+248, DD+233	PV
☐ Lockheed 683-10-19 Starfighter (F-104G)	21+56	683-7025	KE+325, DB+104, DC+104 – on loan to LM Merseburg.	–
☐ Lockheed 683-10-19 Starfighter (F-104G)	22+06	683-7076	(DC+255), KE+376	PV
☐ Lockheed 683-10-19 Starfighter (F-104G)	26+43	683-7303	On loan to MHM, Dresden.	–
☐ Lockheed 683-10-19 Starfighter (F-104G)	26+49	683-7309		–
☐ Lockheed 683-10-19 Starfighter (F-104G)	26+51	683-7311		PV
☐ Lockheed 683-10-19 Starfighter (F-104G)	26+17	683-9159	KH+168, DF+236	RA
☐ Lockheed 683-10-19 Starfighter ZELL (F-104G)	DB+127	683-2002	DA+102, DB+127, 20+02	PV
☐ McDonnell M.98LG Phantom II (RF-4E)	35+62	4144	69-7509	RA
☐ McDonnell M.98NQ Phantom II (F-4F)	38+34	4705	72-1244	PV
☐ Messerschmitt Me 163B-1a Komet	191904	191904	191904, AM.217, 8480M	PV
☐ Messerschmitt Me 262A-1 (FSM)				RA
☐ Messerschmitt-Bölkow-Blohm Europa Jet (Mock-up)	'97+01'		On loan to Int. Luft. Mus.	–
☐ Messerschmitt-Bölkow-Blohm Lampyridae			On loan to G. Neumann Museum.	–
☐ Mikoyan-Gurevich MiG-15bis	3905	623905	In Czech markings.	RA
☐ Mikoyan-Gurevich MiG-15UTI	154	1615393	(Soviet) – in DDR markings – on loan to FM Cottbus.	–
☐ Mikoyan-Gurevich MiG-15UTI	135	722650	In DDR markings – on loan to LHS Finow.	–
☐ Mikoyan-Gurevich MiG-15UTI	163	922257	In DDR markings.	PV
☐ Mikoyan-Gurevich MiG-17	'009'	54211959	404 (DDR) – in DDR markings – on loan to HTI Peenemunde.	–
☐ Mikoyan-Gurevich MiG-17	'07'	54212054	25 (Soviet) – in DDR markings – on loan to Luft. Mus Rechlin.	–
☐ Mikoyan-Gurevich MiG-17F	'08'	0630	(Soviet) – in DDR markings – on loan to LHS Finow.	–
☐ Mikoyan-Gurevich MiG-19PM	391	65210901		RA
☐ Mikoyan-Gurevich MiG-19PM	335	65210929	In DDR markings.	PV
☐ Mikoyan-Gurevich MiG-21bisSAU	24+53	75035841	990 (DDR)	PV
☐ Mikoyan-Gurevich MiG-21bisSAU	24+21	75051407	848 (DDR) – on loan to FM Cottbus.	–
☐ Mikoyan-Gurevich MiG-21F-13	693	740815	In DDR markings – on loan to HTI Peenemunde.	–
☐ Mikoyan-Gurevich MiG-21F-13	677	741619	In DDR markings – on loan to HTI Peenemeude.	–
☐ Mikoyan-Gurevich MiG-21F-13	645	741924	In DDR markings.	PV
☐ Mikoyan-Gurevich MiG-21M	596	960708	In DDR markings.	PV
☐ Mikoyan-Gurevich MiG-21MF	653	965311	In DDR markings – on loan to FM Cottbus.	–
☐ Mikoyan-Gurevich MiG-21MF	670	966206	In DDR markings – on loan to LTM Merseburg.	–
☐ Mikoyan-Gurevich MiG-21MF	673	966207	In DDR markings – on loan to LTM Merseburg.	–
☐ Mikoyan-Gurevich MiG-21MF	686	966301	In DDR markings.	RA
☐ Mikoyan-Gurevich MiG-21PFM	'992'	760604	821 – in DDR markings – on loan to HTI Peenemunde.	–

☐ Mikoyan-Gurevich MiG-21PFM	934	761205	In DDR markings – on loan to HTI Peenemunde.	–
☐ Mikoyan-Gurevich MiG-21PFM	950	761402	In DDR markings.	PV
☐ Mikoyan-Gurevich MiG-21SPS (MiG-21PFM)	725	94A4212	In DDR markings – on loan to LTM Merseburg.	–
☐ Mikoyan-Gurevich MiG-21SPS (MiG-21PFM)	779	94A4502	In DDR markings – on loan to LTM Merseburg.	–
☐ Mikoyan-Gurevich MiG-21SPS-K (MiG-21PFM)	981	94A6704	In DDR markings – on loan to FM Cottbus.	–
☐ Mikoyan-Gurevich MiG-21SPS-K (MiG-21PFM)	449	94A6712	In DDR markings – on loan to FM Cottbus.	–
☐ Mikoyan-Gurevich MiG-21SPS-K (MiG-21PFM)	986	94A6715	In DDR markings – on loan to FM Cottbus.	–
☐ Mikoyan-Gurevich MiG-21SPS-K (MiG-21PFM)	989	94A6804	989, 22+19 – front fuselage only.	PV
☐ Mikoyan-Gurevich MiG-21SPS-K (MiG-21PFM)	472	94A7005	Front fuselage only.	RA
☐ Mikoyan-Gurevich MiG-21SPS-K (MiG-21PFM)	22+09	94A7009	479 (DDR)	PV
☐ Mikoyan-Gurevich MiG-21UM	23+77	02695156	256 (DDR)	PV
☐ Mikoyan-Gurevich MiG-21US	23+99	01685134	215 (DDR) – on loan to FM Cottbus.	–
☐ Mikoyan-Gurevich MiG-23BN	20+51	0393214225	710 (DDR)	PV
☐ Mikoyan-Gurevich MiG-23MF	20+04	0390213098	584 (DDR) – on loan to HTI Peenemunde.	–
☐ Mikoyan-Gurevich MiG-23MF	574	0390213294	In DDR markings.	RA
☐ Mikoyan-Gurevich MiG-23MF	20+02	0390213299	577 (DDR)	PV
☐ Mikoyan-Gurevich MiG-23ML	20+13	0390324624	333 (DDR)	PV
☐ Mikoyan-Gurevich MiG-23ML	332	0390324625	In DDR markings – on loan to HTI Peenemunde.	–
☐ Mikoyan-Gurevich MiG-23S	08	220001013	01 (Soviet) – on loan to LHS Finow.	–
☐ Mikoyan-Gurevich MiG-23UB	20+62	A1037901	104 (DDR) – on loan to FM Cottbus.	–
☐ Mikoyan-Gurevich MiG-23UB	20+63	A1037902	105 (DDR)	PV
☐ Mikoyan-Gurevich MiG-29G (MiG-29)	29+03	2960525110	615 (DDR)	PV
☐ Mil Mi-2	32	511019039	02 – in Soviet markings – on loan to FM Cottbus.	–
☐ Mil Mi-2S	94+63	563148103	393 (DDR)	RA
☐ Mil Mi-2S	94+57	564411105	348 (DDR) – on loan to HTI Peenemunde.	–
☐ Mil Mi-2US	380	562249032	In DDR markings – on loan to FM Cottbus.	–
☐ Mil Mi-4A	538	07142	538, (DM-WSB) – in DDR markings – on loan to FM Cottbus.	–
☐ Mil Mi-4A	569	13146	In DDR markings.	PV
☐ Mil Mi-8PS	93+51	105104	914 (DDR)	PV
☐ Mil Mi-8T	390	0223	In DDR markings – on loan to LTM Merseburg.	–
☐ Mil Mi-8T	93+01	031233	398 (DDR)	PV
☐ Mil Mi-8T	395	0423	In DDR amrkings – on loan to LHS Finow.	–
☐ Mil Mi-8T	911	10527	In DDR markings – on loan to HTI Peenemunde.	–
☐ Mil Mi-8T	93+14	10543	927 (DDR)	PV
☐ Mil Mi-9 (Mi-8A)	93+92	340006	411 (DDR)	PV
☐ Mil Mi-14PL	95+01	B 4001	617 (DDR)	RA
☐ Mil Mi-24D	521	110171	521 (DDR), '5211'	PV
☐ Mil Mi-24P	96+43	340333	387 (DDR)	PV
☐ Morane-Saulnier MS.500 Criquet [Fieseler Fi 156 Storch]	'7A+WN'	637	637 (France), F-BJQG, (EI-AUU), G-AZMH	PVX
☐ Nord N.1101 Ramier I [Messerschmitt Me 208]	81	81	On loan to Museum für Luftfahrt und Technik und T.	–
☐ Nord N.2501D Noratlas	99+14	152	KA+163, GC+235, GB+104, 53+30, D-9580	RA
☐ Nord NC.701 Martinet [Siebel Si 204D-1]	57	57	Contains parts of c/n 93	RAD
☐ North American NA-232 Sabre (F-86K)	'JD+249'	232-121	55-4881	PVX
☐ North American NA-338 Bronco (OV-10B)	99+33	338-18	Bu158309, D-9562	PV
☐ Panavia PA200 Tornado IDS	44+56	4156		RA
☐ Percival P.66 Pembroke C.54	'XA+109'	P.66/102	AS+558, YA+558, 54+07	PVX
☐ Piaggio FWP.149D	90+78	097	AS+432, BF+408, 90+78, D-EFLGA	R
☐ Piaggio FWP.149D	91+03	124	KB+101, AS+011, BF+412	PV
☐ Piper PA-18-95 Super Cub (L-18C)	AS+525	18-3443	54-0743, AS+525, AC+525, NL+118, 96+20	PV
☐ Putzer C.1	D-EBUC	V-1	D-EBUT – on loan to MLT Wernigerode.	–
☐ Putzer Elster B	D-ECFM	005	D-EJIH, 97+03	PV
☐ Raab Doppelraab IV	D-3547			RA
☐ Republic F-84F Thunderstreak	'DF+240'		52-6714, DE+239, DE+372, DE+126	RA
☐ Republic F-84F Thunderstreak	'DD+313'		52-6746, DD+239, DD+339 – also carries '52-6774'	PVX
☐ Republic F-84F Thunderstreak	BF+106		52-6804, DR+???, DE+377, BF+382	PV
☐ Republic F-84F Thunderstreak	DF+316		53-7058, DA+114, DF+114	RA

☐ Republic RF-84F Thunderflash	'ED+119'		51-1869, EB+119, EB+319 – on loan to LM Merseburg.	RA
☐ Republic RF-84F Thunderflash	EB+344		52-7346, EB+244	PV
☐ Rumpler Taube (R)				PV
☐ Saunders-Roe P.501 Skeeter AOP.12	XM556	S2/5110	XM556, 7870M – G-HELI allocated – fitted with boom of c/n S2/5105 XM529, 7979M.	RA
☐ Schneider ESG 31 Grunau Baby IIB	WL+VIII-21	3	D-1979	PVX
☐ Schneider ESG 31 Grunau Baby IIB	'D-0025'	4	D-6058 – at Appen.	RAX
☐ Siemens-Schuckert D IV (FSM)				RAC
☐ Sikorsky S-58 (H-34GII)	80+34	581099	CA+351	RA
☐ Sikorsky S-65 (CH-53G)	84+20	V018		RA
☐ Slingsby T.38 Grasshopper TX.1	"D-4037'	761	WZ765, BGA.3662, D-0314	PVX
☐ Slingsby T.38 Grasshopper TX.1	WZ829	810	WZ829, BGA.3662	RA
☐ Sud-Est SE.3130 Alouette II	75+28	1310	PD+134, PH+238, PH+207 – on loan to LM Merseburg.	–
☐ Sud-Est SE.3130 Alouette II	75+83	1496	QK+532, QW+225	RA
☐ Sud-Est SE.3130 Alouette II	75+86	1511	PE+131, PE+202 – on loan to LM Merseburg.	–
☐ Sud-Est SE.3130 Alouette II	76+03	1548	PK+132, PL+201	RA
☐ Sud-Est SE.3130 Alouette II	76+24	1611	PK+135, QW+742, QW+219 – on loan to AM Fichtelberg.	–
☐ Sud-Est SE.3130 Alouette II	76+66	1732	PP+141, PX+210 – on loan to Mototechnica.	–
☐ Sud-Est SE.3130 Alouette II	76+80	1765	PH+242, PO+135, PY+206 – on loan to LHS Finow.	–
☐ Sukhoi Su-20R	98+61	72412	(Egypt)	RA
☐ Sukhoi Su-22M4	613	25018	613 (DDR), (25+11)	PV
☐ Sukhoi Su-22M4	25+04	25511	365 (DDR) – on loan to FM Cottbus.	–
☐ Sukhoi Su-22M4	25+40	26715	741 (DDR) – at Appen.	RA
☐ Sukhoi Su-22M4	798	31406	798 (DDR), 25+44	RA
☐ Sukhoi Su-22M4	5	72412	98+61 – in Egyptian markings.	PV
☐ Sukhoi Su-22UM3K	25+52	17532367001	112 (DDR)	PV
☐ Vertol V.43 (H-21C)	83+08	WG.08	PA+203, PG+208, QF+462, PX+337	PV
☐ Wytwornia Sprzetu Komunikacyjnego (WSK) Lim-5 [MiG-17F]	346	1C 07-23		RA
☐ Wytwornia Sprzetu Komunikacyjnego (WSK) Lim-5 [MiG-17F]	905	1C 08-20	In DDR markings.	RA
☐ Wytwornia Sprzetu Komunikacyjnego (WSK) Lim-5 [MiG-17F]	502	1C 09-02	On loan to FM Cottbus.	–
☐ Wytwornia Sprzetu Komunikacyjnego (WSK) Lim-5P [MiG-17PF]	'091'	1D 02-08	615 (DDR) – in DDR markings.	PVX
☐ Wytwornia Sprzetu Komunikacyjnego (WSK) SM-1/300 [Mil Mi-1]			Cockpit only.	RA
☐ Wytwornia Sprzetu Komunikacyjnego (WSK) SM-1/600 [Mil Mi-1A]	'001'	S1A01002	506 (DDR)	RAX
☐ Wytwornia Sprzetu Komunikacyjnego (WSK) SM-1W [Mil Mi-1M]	529	W05016		RA
☐ Yakovlev Yak-11	225	68203	In DDR markings.	PV
☐ Yakovlev Yak-11	98	68210	In DDR markings – on loan to FM Cottbus.	–
☐ Yakovlev Yak-18A	25	0516	25, DM-WGW, '42' – in DDR markings.	PV

LUFTWAFFENKASERNE HEIDE SAMMLUNG (GER101)

Address:	Kasernenkommandant, Wulf Isebrand Kaserne, D-25746 Heide.
Tel:	0481-900-0
Admission:	By prior permission only.
Location:	In the town which is about 100 km. north west of Hamburg just north of A 23.

This Luftwaffe barracks has assembled a collection of preserved aircraft to show the airmen some of the traditions and history of the service. In the main building there is also a collection of memorabilia. Basic training of recruits takes place at the site. The newcomers to military life spend twelve weeks at the camp before moving on to learn special skills. All the types have served in numbers since the new Air Force was formed in 1956. The Bell UH-1D is from the large batch manufactured by the Dornier company.

TYPE	REG/SER	CON. NO.	PI/NOTES	STATUS
☐ Dornier-Bell 205 (UH-1D)	73+09	8429		RA
☐ Fiat G.91R/4	'35+41'	91-4-0124	BD+362, BR+362, 'BD+250'	RAX
☐ Piaggio FWP.149D	91+49	171	KB+147, BF+705, BD+391, 91+49, D-EAXT	RA

LUFTWAFFENKASERNE HOPSTEN MUSEUM (GER102)

Address:	General Wever Kaserne, Schorlemerstrasse 80, D-48432 Rheine
Tel:	05971-91070
Admission:	By prior permission only.
Location:	In the south eastern suburbs of the town.

A museum has been set up in the General Wever Kaserne in the town of Rheine. This barracks is named after the first Chief of Staff of the Luftwaffe when it was formed in the mid-1930s. The initial airfield at Hopsten was completed in 1939 and in the early days of World War II it used by a number of day and night fighter units who were in residence for short periods. Later in the conflict it was home to squadrons operating the Messerschmitt Bf 109, the Messerschmitt Me 262 and the Arado Ar 234. Allied forces took control of the base in April 1945 and soon turned it over to the local population for agricultural use. In 1959 work on a new airfield was started on the old site and JBG 36 moved in two years later with F-84F Thunderstreaks. Starfighters arrived in 1965 and these were replaced by the F-4F Phantom II ten years later. The wing was disbanded in December 2005 and the last operational aircraft flew out. A museum was set up in the nearby barracks and this is believed to be still there. The displays trace the history of the site, its units and personnel. There are photographs, documents, uniforms, components, badges and models on show. The preserved F-84F which was first on show at the barracks and later at the airfield has moved to the Luftwaffen Museum at Gatow.

TYPE	REG/SER	CON. NO.	PI/NOTES	STATUS
☐ Lockheed 683-10-19 Starfighter (F-104G)	'DF+101'	683-7140	KE+440, DD+241, DA+254, 22+59	RAX
☐ Lockheed 683-10-19 Starfighter (F-104G)	25+30	683-8307	KG+407, DB+125, DC+117 – front fuselage only.	RA

LUFTWAFFENKASERNE KÖLN-BONN MUSEUM (GER103)

Address:	Kaserne Wahn, Flughafen Strasse 1, D-51147 Köln.
Tel:	02203-9080
Admission:	By prior permission only
Location:	At the airport which is about 15 km. south east of the city.

The Luftwaffe have an administrative base on one side of the civil airport which serves the former capital of the old West Germany. This was once an important camp which saw the arrival of many foreign leaders and military personnel. The G.91 is by the gate and the remaining preserved aircraft are in the grounds. In one of the buildings there is a small museum tracing the history of the area which was first used by the military in the early nineteenth century. On show are many paintings from this period along with uniforms. The development of the airfield is also portrayed with photographs, uniforms and models on show.

TYPE	REG/SER	CON. NO.	PI/NOTES	STATUS
☐ Dornier-Bell 205 (UH-1D)	70+43	8103	KL+109	RA
☐ Fiat G.91R/3	31+29	91-396	KD+386, DH+103, MD+255	RA
☐ Lockheed 483-04-08 Starfighter (F-104F)	'BB+374'	483-5061	59+5008, BB+374, 29+11, 'DA+101'	RAX
☐ Lockheed 683-04-10 Starfighter (RF-104G)	23+98	683-8124	KG+224, EA+114	RA

LUFTWAFFENKASERNE ROTH SAMMLUNG (GER104)

Address:	Kasernenkommandant, Otto Lilienthal Kaserne, D-91154 Roth.
Tel:	09171-832614
Admission:	By prior permission only.
Location:	Just west of the town which is about 25 km south of Nürnburg.

Roth has housed fixed and rotary wing units of the Heeresflieger for many years A Luftwaffe barracks and training school is also located at the site. Four aircraft are parked along the road from the main gate to the airfield. The Thunderstreak has been present since 1965 and the Sabre, which arrived for instructional duties in 1959, was put on show in the late 1960s as was the Thunderflash. The Starfighter appeared in the late 1980s.

TYPE	REG/SER	CON. NO.	PI/NOTES	STATUS
☐ Canadair CL-13A Sabre 5 [North American F-86E]	'JA+130'	838	23048, BB+140, BB+130	RAX
☐ Lockheed 683-10-19 Starfighter (F-104G)	'23+99'	683-8011	KG+111, (JA+102), JA+125, BF+125, 23+36	RAX
☐ Republic F-84F Thunderstreak	'DA+379'		51-1796, DE+109, DE+361, DE+126, DD+370, DD+379	RAX
☐ Republic RF-84F Thunderflash	'EA+105'		53-7693, BD+115, EA+115, EA+315	RAX
☐ Sud-Est SE.3130 Alouette II	75+20	1286	PB+131, PA+131, PA+201	RA
☐ Sud-Est SE.3130 Alouette II	75+98	1543	PQ+939, PQ+139, QA+211	RA

MARINEMUSEUM DÄNHOLM (GER105)

Address: Zur Sternschanze 7, D-18439 Stralsund.
Tel: 03831-297327
Fax: 03831-280060
Admission: Tuesday-Sunday 1000-1700.
Location: In the northern part of the island which is just east of Stralsund.

This collection is a branch of the local cultural museum and is located on the small island of Dänholm. The story of life over the ages is told and the exhibitions show how conditions have changed since people first settled the area. The history and development of water transport and industry is portrayed. There are many shipwrecks in the area and items recovered can be seen. A site on the island was used for training purposes both in World War II and during the time it was part of the German Democratic Republic. The work of this garrison is portrayed in detail and many personal items have been put on show. The Mil Mi-8 was used in the area by the East German Navy.

TYPE	REG/SER	CON. NO.	PI/NOTES	STATUS
☐ Mil Mi-8TB	94+12	10574	831 (DDR)	PV

MERCEDES-BENZ MUSEUM (GER106)

Address: Mercedesstrasse 137a, Untertürkheim, D-70327 Stuttgart.
Tel: 0711-172-2578
Fax: 0711-175-1173
Email: mb.museum@daimlerchrysler.com
Admission: Tuesday-Thursday Saturday- Sunday 0900-1700. (When ready)
Location: At the car factory which is about 4 km east of the city centre.

Gottleib Daimler produced his first car in 1885 and was followed the next year by Karl Benz. The museum has more than one hundred vehicles in its collection which trace the progress made by the company over the last century. Commercial and saloon models can be seen along with the famous sports and racing designs which won many trophies for Germany. The aeronautical section has a range of engines produced by the firm. A partial replica of a 1928 KIemm L 20 powered by a 20 h.p. two cylinder Daimler-Benz engine is on show. A new museum is being built outside the factory gates and this complex should soon be ready. This will allow better public access, as previously visitors had to wait for transport from the main factory gate.

TYPE	REG/SER	CON. NO.	PI/NOTES	STATUS
☐ Klemm L 20 B 1	D-1433	14	Partial replica	PV

MESSERSCHMITT STIFTUNG (GER107)

Address: Pienzenauerstrasse 17, D-81679 München.
Tel: 089-981830
Fax: 089-98290126
Admission: By prior permission only.
Location: At Manching which is about 10 km south east of Ingoldstadt just east of the A.9.

This group is dedicated to keeping in flying condition examples of types designed by Willy Messerschmitt. A hangar and workshops have been constructed at Manching to house the fleet. A replica of the M 17 of 1925 has been built and this has appeared at several shows. The Taifun was the first all metal design produced by the company. The prototype flew in June 1934 and production aircraft achieved success in a number of contests prior to World War II. Two of the Bf 109s have all been converted from Spanish airframes and fitted with Daimler-Benz engines. The Me 163 was first flown as a glider in the spring of 1941 when it was towed behind a Bf 110. The prototype was then taken to Peenemunde to have its rocket motor fitted. The replica sailplane in the collection was built by Josef Kurz in the late 1990s. After a number of flights at the Wasserkuppe it was sold to the foundation. The Me 262 is the second of the newly built batch from America to fly and after testing it arrived at Manching on January 19th 2006. After World War II Willy Messerschmitt worked in Spain where he designed the Saeta and later in Egypt to produce the HA-300 and examples of these designs have been acquired.

TYPE	REG/SER	CON. NO.	PI/NOTES	STATUS
☐ Helwan HA-300	51-100	V-1		RA
☐ Hispano HA.200D Saeta	D-IWMS	20/73	E.14B-67, C.10B-67, A.10B-67, EC-648, EC-FVU	RAA
☐ Messerschmitt M 17 (R)	D-887/D-ERTA	1994/1		RAA
☐ Messerschmitt Bf 108B-1 Taifun	D-ESBH	370114	D-IJHW, AW167, G-AFZO, HB-ESM	RAA RAA
☐ Messerschmitt Bf 109G-2 [Hispano HA-1112K1L]	C.4J-??	54		RA
☐ Messerschmitt Bf 109G-6 (Hispano HA-1112M1L)	D-FMBB	156	C.4K-87	RAC
☐ Messerschmitt Bf 109G-10	D-FDME	151591	(Luftwaffe), D-FEHD, ZK-CIX	RAA
☐ Messerschmitt Me 163B (R)	D-1634	1788	D-ESJK	RAA
☐ Messerschmitt Me 262A/B-1c	D-IMTT	501244	N262MS	RAA

MIGMUSEUM SÖMMERDA (GER108)

Address:	Flugplatz Dermsdorf, Am Flugplatz, D-99625 Dermsdorf.
Tel:	03635-482388.
Fax:	03635-482884
Email:	flugservicesoemmerda@t.online.de
Admission:	By prior permission only.
Location:	About 6 km north east of Sömmerda.

Flying training, charter and overhaul work are carried out by the company at this grass airfield. Five former N.V.A. aircraft were acquired as an attraction for visitors and four are displayed in a compound near the control tower. A MiG-21SPS was on display for a time but this has moved to Bindersleben airfield near Erfurt.

TYPE	REG/SER	CON. NO.	PI/NOTES	STATUS
☐ Mikoyan-Gurevich MiG-21M	560	960410	In DDR markings.	PV
☐ Mikoyan-Gurevich MiG-21U-400	23+88	661016	251 (DDR)	PV
☐ Mikoyan-Gurevich MiG-21U-600	23+95	664620	289 (DDR)	PV
☐ Sukhoi Su-22M4	25+17	26204	682 (DDR)	PV

MILITARHISTORISCHES MUSEUM (GER109)

Address:	Olbrichtplatz 3, D-01099 Dresden.
Tel:	0351-592-3250
Fax:	0351-592-3263
Admission:	Tuesday-Sunday 0900-1700
Location:	In the northern part of the city centre.

Set up in 1961 with the title 'Armeemuseum der Deutschen Demokratischen Republik' the exhibition traced German military history from 1400 to the present time. Many of the early items came from the former Saxony Army Museum which, at one time, had a genuine Fokker E III on show. The displays are arranged chronologically. In the 1918-1945 hall a Polish built Po-2 in false Soviet colours is on view along with the remains of a Mustang recovered from a local lake. The post-1945 hall has been reorganised to trace the history of the forces of both East and West Germany prior to reunification. The number of former N.V.A. aircraft on view has been reduced and several Luftwaffe types have been added. The Fiat G.91 and the Bronco were delivered slung under helicopters in August 1992. Over two hundred models tracing the development in aircraft design, from the Rumpler Taube to modern military and civil types, are on show. Dioramas of famous battles can be seen in all the halls. The collection includes many uniforms, photographs, documents and military vehicles.

TYPE	REG/SER	CON. NO.	PI/NOTES	STATUS
☐ Aero L-29 Delfin	313	692054		PV
☐ Canadair CL-13B Sabre 6 [North American F-86E]	JB+110	1734	JC+110	PVX
☐ Centralne Studium Samolotow (CSS) 13 [Polikarpov Po-2]	'250'	420-32	SP-AFN, DM-WAA – in false Soviet markings.	PVX
☐ Dornier-Bell 205 (UH-1D)	73+11	8431		PV
☐ Fiat G.91R/3	99+01	91-060	BF+015, BR+015, 30+07, D-9597	RA
☐ Fieseler Fi 103A-1				PV
☐ Lockheed 683-10-19 Starfighter (F-104G)	26+43	683-7303	On loan from Luftwaffen Museum.	PV
☐ Mikoyan-Gurevich MiG-21F-13	'268'	741620	671 (DDR), '1801'	PVX
☐ Mikoyan-Gurevich MiG-21PFM	868	761103		RA
☐ Mil Mi-4			Cockpit section only	PV
☐ North American NA-122 Mustang (P-51D)			Parts only.	PVD
☐ North American NA-338 Bronco (OV-10B)	99+21	338-6	Bu158297, D-9550	RA
☐ Schneider Grunau SG-38 (D.F.S. 108-14)	525	83		RA
☐ Sud-Est SE.3130 Alouette II	75+24	1298	PH+133, PH+237, PH+206	PV
☐ Udet U 10	D-452		Left wing only.	PV
☐ Wytwornia Sprzetu Komunikacyjnego (WSK) Lim-5 [MiG-17F]	300	1C 006-30		PV
☐ Yakovlev Yak-18	'13'	6015	DM-WBG	RAX

MOTOREN UND TURBINEN UNION MUSEUM (GER110)

Address:	Dachauer Strasse 665 D-80995 München.
Tel:	089-154992
Admission:	By prior permission only.
Location:	In the north western outskirts of the city of the road to Dachau.

The company is the largest aero engine manufacturer in the country. A collection of motors has been set up in a building at the factory. These range from a Daimler D IIIa of 1919 up to the RB 199 used to power the Tornado. Over twenty superbly restored engines are on show with about forty in store. An interesting exhibit is a B.M.W. VI from von Gronau's Dornier Wal. The flying boat was destroyed in the 1944 bombing raid on the Deutsches Museum in the city. Aircraft were on show in the early 1990s but these have now moved on.

MOTORTECHNICA MUSEUM (GER111)

Address:	Weserstrasse 225, D-32547 Bad Oeynhausen.
Tel:	05731-9960
Fax:	05731-92412
Admission:	Daily 0900-1800.
Location:	Off the road to Vlotho just south off Autobahnkreuz Bad Oeynhausen.

A motor museum has been in existence for many years but the original exhibition closed in 1988. New owners took over in 1992. The halls, containing a large number of cars, commercial vehicles, motor cycles and industrial machinery, were reorganised and many items added. The display is one of the largest in Germany with over four hundred and fifty vehicles on show. Also on view are engines, posters, trophies and associated motoring items. Many examples of large industrial engines can be seen in one hall. Three aircraft survive from the original exhibition, the Sycamore, Dornier Do 27 and Piaggio P.149. The Sycamore was used by the fire service after its military days were over and the helicopter is exhibited in their red colours. Germany ordered seventy six Piaggio P.149s from Italy in the late 1950s and one hundred and ninety were built by Focke-Wulf. Most of the survivors were sold on the civil market. The Dornier Do 27 was the first type to be put into production in Germany when the ban on flying and aircraft manufacture was lifted in the 1950s. The wreck of the Thunderbolt was recovered from a crash site and is displayed in the condition in which it was found. There are no plans to restore the airframe. The remains of a Junkers Ju 88 have also been found. A number of former East German military aircraft, including four versions of the classic MiG-21 and a two seat Sukhoi Su-22, have been acquired. The majority of these are stored in a compound at the rear of the car park. The Starfighter, painted in a special scheme, is on long term loan from the Military Aviation Museum in the Netherlands.

TYPE	REG/SER	CON. NO.	PI/NOTES	STATUS
☐ Aero Commander 680E	D-IBIB	805-58		PV
☐ Antonov An-2R	SP-WWF	1G 173-57		PV
☐ Bristol 171 Sycamore HR.52	D-HAHN	13445	BA+178, CD+084, SC+208, WE+542, LC+120, 78+06, D-HOPF	RA
☐ Dornier Do 27B-1	D-EIKW	289	SC+709, SE+531, 56+21, (D-EIWP)	RA
☐ Junkers Ju 88A-1				PVD
☐ Lockheed 583-10-20 Starfighter (TF-104G)	D-5804	583E-5804	In Dutch markings – on loan from MLM, Netherlands.	PV
☐ Mikoyan-Gurevich MiG-21MF	'22+28'	96002112	782 (DDR), 23+48	PVX
☐ Mikoyan-Gurevich MiG-21SPS (MiG-21PFM)	'353'	94A6408	953 (DDR), 22+44	PVX
☐ Mikoyan-Gurevich MiG-21U-600	23+91	662619	272 (DDR)	PV
☐ Mikoyan-Gurevich MiG-21UM	23+83	07695156	266 (DDR)	PV
☐ Mikoyan-Gurevich MiG-23UB	20+58	A1038034	106 (DDR)	PV
☐ Mil Mi-2				PV
☐ Mil Mi-8PS	93+39	10551	966 (DDR)	PV
☐ Mil Mi-8PS	93+19	10552	970 (DDR)	RA
☐ Piaggio P.149D	D-EHIT	257	AS+408, AC+408, KB+201, AS+094, D-EJCA, 91+75	RA
☐ Republic P-47D Thunderbolt	42-27924			PVD
☐ Sud-Est SE.3130 Alouette II	76+66	1732	PP+141, PX+210 – on loan from Luftwaffen Museum.	PV
☐ Sukhoi Su-22UM3K	25+50	17532371002	146 (DDR)	PV

MUSEUM CICHORIUS (GER112)

Address:	Max Planck Strasse 47, D-63500 Seligenstadt.
Tel:	061-82-68320
Admission:	By prior permission only.
Location:	On Road 45 about 20 km south east of Frankfurt.

This private museum has two aircraft on show along with memorabilia, photographs, documents, uniforms, posters, components and engines. The Bücker Bestmann is one of a batch of one hundred and twenty built by Hagglund and Söner at Örnsköldsvik in Sweden between 1944 and 1946 for military use. The survivors were replaced by the SAAB Safir in 1952/3 and then sold on the civil market. A number were exported to Germany in the 1950s. The aircraft was withdrawn from use in the mid-1970s. Designed by Edmund Schneider vast numbers of SG-38 primary gliders were built in the 1930s and 1940s and used for basic flying training in many countries. Many were also built under licence in several European states and a few examples are still active.

TYPE	REG/SER	CON. NO.	PI/NOTES	STATUS
☐ Bücker Bü 181B-1 Bestmann (Sk 25)	D-EKOB	25096	Fv25096	RA
☐ Schneider Grunau SG-38 (D.F.S. 108-14)				RA

MUSEUM FÜR ASTRONOMIE UND TECHNIKGESCHICHTE (GER113)

Address:	Postfach 410420, Orangerie, An der Karlsaue 20c, D-34121 Kassel.
Tel:	0561-701320
Fax:	0561-7013211
Email:	info@museum-kassel.de
Admission:	By prior permission only.
Location:	In the town.

Gerhard Fieseler came to the area in the 1920s to work for the Raab-Katzenstein company and he later set up a firm which bore his own name. His most famous design, the Storch, was built in large numbers and gave excellent service for many years. A former Swedish Air Force example was acquired in 1977 and the aircraft has been slowly restored over the last two decades. A replica Lilienthal glider hangs in the entrance hall.

TYPE	REG/SER	CON. NO.	PI/NOTES	STATUS
☐ Fieseler Fi 156C-3/trop Storch (S 14)	D-EKLU	110061	Fv3809	RAC
☐ Lilienthal Kleiner Doppeldecker (R)				PV

MUSEUM FÜR FLUGZEUGTECHNIK UND GESCHICHT (GER114)

Address:	Heylstrasse 28, D-63571 Gelnhausen Hailer,
Email:	flugzeugtechnikmuseum@t.online.de
Admission:	By prior permission only.
Location:	In the town which is about 30 km east of Frankfurt-am-Main

This private collection contains many components, models, engines, uniforms and documents. A reconstruction of a Messerschmitt Me 262 cockpit is underway and is being fitted with original instruments.

TYPE	REG/SER	CON. NO.	PI/NOTES	STATUS
☐ Messerschmitt Me 262A-1 (R)			Cockpit section only.	RA

MUSEUM FÜR HISTORISCHE WEHRTECHNIK (GER115)

Address:	Heinrich Diehl Strasse, D-90552 Röthenbach-Pegnitz.
Tel:	09120-9168
Fax:	09120-181472
Email:	info@wehrtechnikmuseum.de
Admission:	First Saturday in month 1400-1700.
Location:	About 5 km north east of Nürnburg.

This museum has a large collection of military vehicles and equipment on show. The aeronautical section includes guns, gunsights, components and engines. The only aircraft remaining at the site is an example of the Fieseler Fi 103 (V-1) flying bomb. The Arado 96 is currently in the Munich area for restoration. It may also serve as the pattern aircraft for a possible series of newly built machines. The type was built in France and Czechoslovakia after the end of World War II but no complete examples have survived. The last French built SIPA 121, owned by Jean Salis, crashed in 1978 and was totally destroyed.

TYPE	REG/SER	CON. NO.	PI/NOTES	STATUS
☐ Arado Ar 96B-1	PD+EJ	4210		RAC
☐ Fieseler Fi 103A-1				PVC

MUSEUM FÜR LUFTFAHRT UND TECHNIK (GER116)

Address:	Giessenweg 1, D-38855 Wernigerode.
Tel:	03943-632791
Fax:	03943-632793
Email:	info@luftfahrtmuseum-wernigerode.de
Admission:	Monday-Tuesday 1000-1300, Wednesday-Sunday 1000-1700.
Location:	In the northern part of the town centre,

Clemens Aulich started planning this museum in 1992. Buildings close to the town centre were converted into exhibition halls and workshops. The display opened in 1999 and has gathered an interesting collection over the last few years. Several of the initial airframes arrived from Hermeskeil. The displays are concerned with the technical side of aviation and on show are models, components, flying clothing, rotor blades, ejector seats and engines. A mobile radar station can also be seen. Visual displays are being installed to show the developments which have occurred in airframe and engine technology. Aircraft have been acquired from around Europe and the Hunter was purchased in England in 2005. A unique exhibit is the C.1 prototype dating from the mid-1970s. The Putzer company started building sailplanes in 1953. In the early 1960s several experimental light aircraft prototypes were constructed including one example of the C.1. The Aero 45 was once on show at the Hungarian Agricultural Service headquarters at Kapolsujlak airfield. When the organisation ran into financial difficulties the collection was dispersed. In 1984 the Queen Air was flying from Africa to England for overhaul. After leaving Graz one engine failed and it made a forced landing at Nürnburg. The aircraft was auctioned in the early 1990s to repay some of the landing and parking fees owing and was acquired by the museum. The two Dornier aircraft were obtained from a technical school in Braunschweig.

TYPE	REG/SER	CON. NO.	PI/NOTES	STATUS
☐ Aero Super 45S	'DM-SGF'	04-013	HA-OMD	PVX
☐ Antonov An-2				PV
☐ Beech 65-80 Queen Air	5X-SAM	LD-102	(G-ASIC), G-ASIU, (5H-MSL)	PVX
☐ Bölkow BO 105CB	D-HDEG	S-139		PV
☐ Canadair CL-13B Sabre 6 [North American F-86E]	'FU-972'	1775	JB+112, JA+110, 'JA+111' – on loan from Luftwaffen Museum.	PVX
☐ De Havilland D.H.112 Venom FB.1R	J-1635	845	In Swiss markings	PV
☐ Dornier Do 27B-1 (A-1)	D-EITE	286	SC+706, SE+528, 56+18	PV
☐ Dornier Do 28D-1 Skyservant	D-IBSW	4033		PV
☐ Dornier-Bell 205 (UH-1D)				RAD
☐ Dornier-Bell 205 (UH-1D)	72+59	8379		PV
☐ Dornier-Bell 205 (UH-1D)	73+01	8421		PV
☐ Fiat G.91R/3			Rear fuselage only.	RA
☐ Fiat G.91R/3	31+00	91-366	KD+356, DG+114, MA+114, MA+244 – front fuselage only.	PV
☐ Fiat G.91R/3	31+39	91-407	KD+397, DH+114, MC+251	PV
☐ Fiat G.91R/4	'75+00'	'91-4-0122'	'BD+248' – reported as such but this aircraft was destroyed in a fatal crash in 1963 and broken up at Erding.	PVX
☐ Fiat G.91T/1				RA
☐ Hang Glider				PV
☐ Hawker P.1067 Hunter F.4	WV276	41H/670778	WV276, 7847M	PV
☐ Hunting-Percival P.84 Jet Provost T.4	XS217	PAC/W/23894		PV
☐ Lockheed 580 (T-33A)	'140153'	580-1653	58-0684, JC+395, MB+391, 95+20	PVX
☐ Lockheed 683-10-19 Starfighter (F-104G)	20+07	683-2007	DA+104, BF+008	PV
☐ Lockheed 683-10-19 Starfighter (F-104G)	22+45	683-7123	KE+423, DD+115	PV
☐ Lockheed 683-10-19 Starfighter (F-104G)	23+09	683-7192	KE+492, VB+235	PV
☐ Lockheed 683-10-19 Starfighter (F-104G)	25+29	683-8306	KG+406, DB+124 – front fuselage only.	PV
☐ Lockheed 683-10-19 Starfighter (F-104G)	25+68	683-9014	KH+114, JA+250 – fuselage only – identity doubtful.	PV
☐ Mikoyan-Gurevich MiG-21SPS (MiG-21PFM)	703	94A4006	703 (DDR), 22+22	PV
☐ Mikoyan-Gurevich MiG-23MF	20+06	0390213096	586 (DDR)	PV
☐ Mil Mi-2S	555	543620074	555, (DDR-VGN)	PV
☐ Nord N.1101 Ramier I [Messerschmitt Me 208]	81	81	On loan from Luftwaffen Museum.	PVC
☐ Putzer C.1	D-EBUC	V-1	D-EBUT – on loan from Luftwaffen Museum.	PV
☐ Sikorsky S-65A (CH-53G)	84+12	V010	Front fuselage only.	PV
☐ Sud-Est SE.3130 Alouette II	77+10	1862	AS+357	PV
☐ Sukhoi Su-22M4	25+43	26818	769 (DDR) – front fuselage only.	PV
☐ Westland-Sikorsky WS-55 Whirlwind HAR.10	XP339	WA.355	On loan from Wehrtecnhnische Studiensammlung.	PV
☐ Zlin Z-37A Cmelak	DM-SUW	19-20	DM-SUW, DDR-SUW, D-ESUW	PV

MUSEUM FÜR MILITAR UND ZEITGESCHICHTE (GER117)

Address:	Waldweg 3, D-97509 Stammheim.
Tel:	09381-9225
Fax:	09381-9850
Email:	info@g-weissenseel.de
Admission:	February-mid December Tuesday-Sunday 1000-1800.
Location:	About 15 km south of Schweinfurt.

A superb collection of military vehicles and weapons is on show at this privately run museum. The exhibits come from several countries. Included in the display are searchlights, ambulances, fire engines, amphibious vehicles, track laying machines and missiles. There is an excellent display of tanks from the World War II period up to fairly modern times. Inside the buildings are displays of uniforms, models, components, radios and equipment. The only aircraft on show is the Thunderstreak mounted spectacularly above the entrance to the grounds. Four hundred and fifty examples of the jet fighter were delivered by sea to Germany for the new Luftwaffe. They served until the late 1960s when most were replaced by the Starfighter.

TYPE	REG/SER	CON. NO.	PI/NOTES	STATUS
☐ Republic F-84F Thunderstreak	'DE+175'		51-1724, DE+127, DE+363, DE+107	PVX

MUSEUM FÜR TECHNIK NATUR UND VERKEHR (GER118)

Address:	Bichwedde 10, D-49577 Ankum.
Tel:	05464-1345
Fax:	05464-1629
Email:	info@schulte-handel.de
Admission:	By prior permission only.
Location:	In the town which is on Route 214 about 30 km north of Osnabrück.

The owner of this collection has a factory in the town. He has put forward plans for a military museum on a nearby site. The exhibition will trace the development of the services and weapons over the centuries. The aircraft are nearly all stored in containers at a number of locations at the present time. All the types have seen service with the Luftwaffe and there are a number of former East German machines. A small number have moved on from here and are on show in the museums at Usedom and Wernigerode. There are also military vehicles and tanks in the collection along with uniforms, engines, components and items of memorabilia.

TYPE	REG/SER	CON. NO.	PI/NOTES	STATUS
☐ Aero L-39ZO Albatros	28+31	232304	182 (DDR)	RA
☐ Fiat G.91R/3	99+02	91-068	BD+108, EC+108, ER+108, BD+271, 30+13	RA
☐ Mikoyan-Gurevich MiG-21F-13	'696'	740901	679 (DDR)	RAX
☐ Mikoyan-Gurevich MiG-21SPS (MiG-21PFM)	22+23	94A4209	717 (DDR)	RA
☐ Mikoyan-Gurevich MiG-21SPS (MiG-21PFM)	22+28	94A4309	760 (DDR)	PV
☐ Mikoyan-Gurevich MiG-21U-600	23+90	662617	265 (DDR)	RA
☐ Mikoyan-Gurevich MiG-21US	24+09	04685139	242 (DDR)	RA
☐ Mikoyan-Gurevich MiG-21US	24+01	07685145	217 (DDR)	RA
☐ Mikoyan-Gurevich MiG-23ML	20+33	0390324038	569 (DDR)	RA
☐ Piaggio FWP.149D	D-EFWP	118	AS+459, D-EKLI, 90+98	RA
☐ Piaggio FWP.149D	D-EGSG	282	AS+433, AC+433, 91+46	RA
☐ Sukhoi Su-22M4	25+07	25714	546 (DDR)	RA
☐ Sukhoi Su-22M4	25+08	25715	574 (DDR)	RA
☐ Sukhoi Su-22M4	25+46	31508	824 (DDR)	RA

MUSEUM HAUS AM CHECKPOINT CHARLIE (GER119)

Address:	Friedrichstrasse 43/44, D-10969 Berlin.
Tel:	030-253725-0
Fax:	030-2512075
Email:	info@mauermuseum.de
Admission:	Daily 0900-2200.
Location:	In the centre of the city.

The Berlin Wall evoked many emotions during the time it divided the city. An exhibition opened in 1962 in the Bernauer Strasse and another in the Friedrichstrasse the following year. The two combined in 1971 and the display was enlarged in 1987. During the 'Iron Curtain' period many people tried to escape from the Communist regimes in Eastem Europe. Their successes and failures are documented in the exhibition. The story of the construction and downfall of the wall is portrayed in vivid detail. Three hot air balloons and three ultralight aircraft which were used in successful flights across the borders are on view. Another pair of ultralights is in store. Two of the aircraft were used by Czech escapers. The third, painted in Soviet markings, made a two way journey from the west to free a brother of the pilot. The family had been divided by the wall for many years and the mission was completed by a landing in the centre of West Berlin.

TYPE	REG/SER	CON. NO.	PI/NOTES	STATUS
☐ Balloon				PV
☐ Balloon				PV
☐ Balloon			Basket only	PV
☐ Bethke Ultralight				PV
☐ Heptner Ultralight				RA
☐ Hlavaty Ultralight				PV
☐ Naxera Ultralight				RA
☐ Zdarsky Ultralight				PV

NEUES STADTMUSEUM LANDSBERG (GER120)

Address:	Von-Helfenssteingasse 425, D-86899 Landsberg Am Lech.
Tel:	08191-942326
Fax:	08191-943237
Email:	neues.stadtmuseum@landsberg.de
Admission:	April-January Tuesday-Sunday 1400-1700.
Location:	In the town which is just south of the A.96.

This local history museum traces all aspects of life in the community. Local trades are featured with replicas of the workshops of goldsmiths and silversmiths and a 1900 pharmacy. Alois Wolfmüller built a glider in the town in 1907 and made some successful flights. A scale replica of this machine has been built for the display. The story of his aeronautical experiments can be seen in a photographic display along with items of memorabilia.

TYPE	REG/SER	CON. NO.	PI/NOTES	STATUS
☐ Wolfmüller Gleiter (Scale R)				PV

OLDTIMER CLUB ACHMER (GER121)

Address:	P.O. Box 3452 D-49024 Osnabruck.
Tel:	05461-4000
Email:	info@flugplatzachmer.de
Admission:	By prior permission only.
Location:	The airfield is about 15 km. north west of the town near Wackum.

The club is assembling an interesting collection of vintage gliders. The former Swedish Air Force Stieglitz is used as the tug along with the Robin DR.400. Heini Dittmar built the prototype Condor in 1932. Prior to World War II three versions appeared and they had an outstanding record in competitions.

TYPE	REG/SER	CON. NO.	PI/NOTES	STATUS
☐ Cumulus	D-6068			RAA
☐ Dittmar Condor IV/3	D-6043	13	LV-EHB	RAA
☐ Focke-Wulf Fw 44J Stieglitz (Sk 12)	D-EDYV	2549	Fv667, SE-BWN, D-ECAN possibly c/n 2814 Fv5771.	RAA
☐ Jacobs Kranich IIB-1 (D.F.S. 108-30) (SE-103)	D-6048	065	Fv8204, SE-SPN, BGA.1092 and wings from c/n ? RAFGSA.271, BGA.1258	RAA
☐ Jacobs Kranich III	D-6044	64		RAA
☐ Jacobs Reiher III (D.F.S. 108-60) (R)				RAC
☐ Jacobs Meise (D.F.S. 108-70)	D-6046	1/95	D-6220, BGA.2080	RAA
☐ Jacobs Weihe (D.F.S. 108-68)	BGA.1297	224	Fv8306, SE-STN, G-ASCV, BGA.1297	RAC
☐ Robin DR.400/180 Remorqueur	D-EBZP	1418		RAA
☐ Scheibe SF-25C Falke	D-KTIY	44681		RAA
☐ Scheibe SF-25C Rotax-Falke	D-KEAZ	44578		RAA
☐ Schleicher K.7	D-6304	888		RAA
☐ Schleicher K.8B	D-6305	5/142/59		RAA
☐ Schleicher K.8B	D-6261	589		RAA
☐ Schneider ESG 31 Grunau Baby IIB	D-5221	6		RAA

TYPE	REG/SER	CON. NO.	PI/NOTES	STATUS
☐ Schneider Grunau Baby III (D.F.S. 108-66)	D-6054	1	RAFGSA.???, BGA.1754	RAA
☐ Szybowcowy Zaklad Doswiadczalny S.Z.D.24A Foka 4	D-6373	W-241		RAA
☐ Vögt Lo 100 Zwergreiher				RAC
☐ Vögt Lo 100 Zwergreiher	D-3100	AB/117		RAA

OLDTIMER FLIEGERCLUB (GER122)

Address:	Glockenstrasse 35, D-40476 Dusseldorf.
Tel:	0211-441207
Admission:	By prior permission only.
Location:	At a private airfield in the Saarbrucken area.

The organisation is part of the Flugsportverien Saarbrucken. Currently two vintage gliders dating from the 1950s are in flying condition and the fleet may well be enlarged in the future.

TYPE	REG/SER	CON. NO.	PI/NOTES	STATUS
☐ Delfin	D-5600	V-1		RAA
☐ Kaiser Ka-1	D-3025	0101		RAA

OLDTIMER SEGELFLUG CLUB MAINZ (GER123)

Address:	Flugplatz, D-55116 Mainz.
Email:	kontakt@oscmainz.de
Admission:	By prior permission only.
Location:	The airfield is about 8 km. west of the town.

The club has recently restored the Focke Wulf built Kranich to flying condition. Two other sailplanes are in their workshops and these should soon be airworthy. There are several modern gliders at the field.

TYPE	REG/SER	CON. NO.	PI/NOTES	STATUS
☐ Jacobs Kranich III	D-7002	57		RAA
☐ Raab Doppelraab IV				RAC
☐ Scheibe SF-27 Zugvogel IIIA				RAC
☐ Schleicher K.7				RAA

OLDTIMER SEGELFLUGCLUB WASSERKUPPE (GER124)

Address:	Flugplatz Wasserkuppe, D-35129 Gersfeld.
Tel:	06654-8284
Email:	Info@osc.wasserkuppe.de
Admission:	By prior permission only.
Location:	The airfield is about 15 km east of Fulda between Roads 279 and 458.

The group was formed in the early 1980s and is housed in the former museum building at the famous hill site. The first project was the construction of a replica Habicht glider. Hans Jacobs designed the type for the 1936 Olympic Games and four examples flew in the contest. The collection includes a number of classic gliders which were inhabitants of the site for many years. A replica KIemm L 25 was built in the early 1990s but this was sold to the Luftfahrtmuseum at Laatzen near Hannover. Now flying is a replica of the Udet U 12 Flamingo biplane. First flown in 1925 the type was the last product of the Udet company. Substantial numbers were built by B.F.W. (later to become Messerschmitt) and under licence in Hungary and Latvia. The Siebel Si 202 replica was built by Josef Kurz and this should soon join the collection.

TYPE	REG/SER	CON. NO.	PI/NOTES	STATUS
☐ Fauvel AV.36	D-8373		On loan to LHS – Frankfurt.	-
☐ Jacobs Meise (D.F.S. 108-70)	'D-1956'	EB-66	On loan to LHS – Frankfurt.	-
☐ Jacobs Reiher III (D.F.S. 108-60) (R)	D-7033	AB R1/OSC		RAA
☐ Jacobs Rhönbussard (D.F.S. 108-50)	D-7059	485	BGA.395, G-ALKY, BGA.395 – on loan from SFM Gunzburg.	RAA
☐ Rieseler R.III (R)	D-EIJK	N01/1848		RA
☐ Schleicher Ka-2 Rhönschwalbe	D-7039	229		RAA
☐ Schneider ESG 31 Grunau Baby IIB	D-3856	03		RAA

☐ Schneider Grunau SG-38 (D.F.S. 108-14)				RA
☐ Schneider Grunau SG-38 (D.F.S. 108-14)	D-7055	AB001/OSC		RAA
☐ Schneider ES.49	D-5069	15/52		RAA
☐ Siebel Si 202 Hummel (R)	D-EPJK	1		RAA
☐ Udet U 12/K Flamingo (R)	D-EOSC	01		RAA

OLDTIMER SEGELFLUGVEREIN MÜNCHEN (GER125)

Address:	Bauseweinalle 123, D-80999 München.
Tel:	089-601-1190
Email:	osvmunich@aol.com
Admission:	By prior permission only.
Location:	At Greiling Airfield which is about 3 km east of Bad Tölz off Road 472.

Based at the former U.S. Army airfield the group operates a fleet of vintage and classic gliders from four countries. Egon Scheibe was the leader of the Akaflieg München in the 1930s. The group designed and built the Mü 10 in 1934. The design was successful but only one was built. The Mü 13 was a single seat development and the design was improved. The successful Polish Bocian flew in prototype form in 1952 and a substantial number were constructed over the next few years. The group built a replica of the 1920s Udet Flamingo biplane fitted with an original Siemens Sh-14 radial. This biplane was completed in the late 1990s.

TYPE	REG/SER	CON. NO.	PI/NOTES	STATUS
☐ Akaflieg München Mü 13d				RAA
☐ Glasflügel H201B Standard Libelle	D-2160	436		RAA
☐ Göppingen Gö 4 Gövier III	D-7061	411	D-9009, OE-0891	RAA
☐ Jacobs Kranich IIB-2 (D.F.S. 108-30)	BGA.1147	821	RAFGSA.215	RAC
☐ Jacobs Meise (D.F.S. 108-70)				RAC
☐ Jacobs Meise (D.F.S. 108-70)				RAC
☐ Jacobs Meise (D.F.S. 108-70)	D-1059	0240	OE-0052	RAC
☐ Musger Mg 19a Steinadler	D-1078	026	OE-0373	RAA
☐ Musger Mg 23SL	OE-0661	16		RAA
☐ Scheibe Bergfalke II/55	D-0004	239		RAA
☐ Scheibe L-Spatz 55	D-1019			RAA
☐ Schleicher Ka-2B Rhönschwalbe	D-5253			RAA
☐ Schleicher K.8B	D-1840	8334/A		RAA
☐ Schneider ESG 31 Grunau Baby IIB	D-1018	005	OE-0250	RAA
☐ Schneider ESG 31 Grunau Baby IIB	D-1073	101		RAA
☐ Schneider Grunau SG-38 (D.F.S. 108-14)	D-7051	ABX/OSC		RAA
☐ Schneider Grunau SG-38 (D.F.S. 108-14)	D-8985	E-1		RAA
☐ Slingsby T.21B Sedbergh TX.1	BGA.4833	1159	XN155	RAA
☐ Szybowcowy Zaklad Doswiadczalny S.Z.D.9bis Bocian 1D	D-1079	P-364	OE-0499	RAA
☐ Udet U 12/S Flamingo (R)	'D-1202'	1785	D-EOSM	RAAX

OLDTIMERFREUNDE-DONAUWÖRTH-STILLBERGHOF (GER126)

Address:	Gempfingenstrasse 9, D-86666 Burgheim.
Tel:	0160-152-1510
Email:	bausetter@gmx.de
Admission:	By prior permission only.
Location:	At Donauwörth airfield which is about 5 km. south east of the town on Route 16.

This group was set up in 1995 after six years planning. Now almost thirty gliders are in the fleet with about a dozen in airworthy condition. Three workshops are in use along with a hangar for the completed machines. The Kranich II is from a batch produced in Spain. One of the Grunau Baby IIBs was assembled in England in 1948 by Hawkridge Aircraft at Dunstable from German parts. Only about ten examples of the Ka-1 were completed. Erwin Köhler produced kits under licence in Fulda and sold them to amateur builders for completion. Kaiser by this time was employed by Egon Scheibe at Dachau. Two former Air Training Corps types are in the collection. Branches have been set up at other airfields in the area and some of the fleet are detached to these.

TYPE	REG/SER	CON. NO.	PI/NOTES	STATUS
☐ Akaflieg München Mü 13d				RAC
☐ Dittmar Condor IV/3	D-5087	21/53		RAA
☐ Dornier Do 27A-1	D-EEPJ	173	AS+923, AC+923, 55+43	RAA
☐ Jacobs Kranich IIB-2 (D.F.S. 108-30)	D-8504	24		RAA
☐ Jacobs Kranich III	D-4007	56		RAA
☐ Jacobs Meise (D.F.S. 108-70)	D-1348	1		RAC
☐ Kaiser Ka-1				RAC

TYPE	REG/SER	CON. NO.	PI/NOTES	STATUS
☐ Piper PA-18-95 Super Cub (L-18C)	D-EBXF	18-3456	54-756, AS+528, AC+528, NL+110, 96+32	RAA
☐ Raab Doppelraab IV				RAC
☐ Raab Doppelraab IV				RAC
☐ Rock Geier II	D-9129	1		RAA
☐ Scheibe Bergfalke II/55	D-1500	255		RAA
☐ Scheibe L-Spatz 55				RAC
☐ Scheibe L-Spatz 55				RAA
☐ Scheibe Mü 13E Bergfalke I				RAC
☐ Scheibe SF-27 Zugvogel IIIB				RAC
☐ Scheibe SF-27A Zugvogel V				RAC
☐ Schleicher Ka-2B Rhönschwalbe	D-5481	213		RAA
☐ Schleicher Ka-4 Rhönlerche II				RAA
☐ Schleicher Ka-6CR Rhönsegler	D-5854	6637		RAA
☐ Schneider ESG 31 Grunau Baby IIB				RAC
☐ Schneider ESG 31 Grunau Baby IIB	BGA.615	G-4848	BGA.615, G-ALMM	RAC
☐ Schneider Grunau Baby III (D.F.S. 108-66)				RAC
☐ Schneider Grunau SG-38 (D.F.S. 108-14)				RAC
☐ Schneider Grunau SG-38 (D.F.S. 108-14)				RAC
☐ Schneider Grunau SG-38 (D.F.S. 108-14)				RAC
☐ Schneider ES.49				RAC
☐ Slingsby T.21B Sedbergh TX.1	BGA.3235	1155	XN151	RAA
☐ Slingsby T.31B Cadet TX.3				RAC
☐ Vögt Lo 100 Zwergreiher	D-5406	17		RAA
☐ Volkseigener Betrieb Apparatebau Lommatzsch FES-530/II Lehrmeister	OE-0575			RAA

OTTO LILIENTHAL GEDENKSTÄTTE STÖLLN (GER127)

Address:	Lilienthal-Verein Stölln, Otto Lilienthal Strasse 56, D-14728 Stölln.
Tel:	033875-32020
Admission:	April-October Tuesday-Thursday 1000-1700, Friday-Sunday 1000-1800; November-March Saturday-Sunday 1100-1600.
Location:	At Stölln airfield which is just east of the village and about 20 km north of Rathenow.

The pioneer aviator Otto Lilienthal was killed on August 9th 1896 whilst gliding from a hill close to Stölln. His glider suffered structural failure and he fell to his death. At the nearby airfield a former Interflug Il-62 has been set up as a museum honouring his achievements with particular reference to those in the local area. A display of documents and photographs can be seen tracing his flights region along with models of his gliders. A replica of the monoplane in which he met his death has been constructed.

TYPE	REG/SER	CON. NO.	PI/NOTES	STATUS
☐ Ilyushin Il-62	DDR-SEG	31403	DM-SEG	PV
☐ Lilienthal Normal-Segelapparat (R)				PV

OTTO LILIENTHAL MUSEUM (GER128)

Address:	Ellbogenstrasse 1, D-17389 Anklam.
Tel:	03971-245500
Fax:	03971-245580
Email:	LilienthalMuseum@t-online.de
Admission:	May-September Tuesday-Friday 1000-1700; Saturday-Sunday 1400-1700: October-April Tuesday-Friday 1000-1600; Sunday 1400-1700.
Location:	In the centre of the town – the airfield is about 3 km south west of the town on Road 197.

Otto Lilienthal was born in Anklam on May 23rd 1848 and he flew his first glider in 1891. Over the next five years he built and flew at least sixteen versions. He was killed in a crash near Stölln on August 9th 1896. His home in Anklam was destroyed in World War II and a monument now stands on the site. A regional museum was established in a house in the town and items relating to his life were part of the display. The building was closed in the late 1980s and rebuilt for an exhibition devoted solely to the work of the pioneer aviator. This new museum opened on July 13th 1991. In 1925 the town asked Hans Richter to build a replica of the Normal Segelapparat using some original parts. In 1985 the museum commissioned Stephan Kitsch of Magdeburg to build replicas of the models which no longer existed. A new hall has now been erected at the rear of the house to display these aircraft. A fascinating exhibition tracing the work of Lilienthal can now be seen. The airfield at Anklam opened in 1935 and was a Luftwaffe base until 1944. Interflug re-opened the site in 1959 for use by their vast fleet of agricultural aircraft. Four types used in this work have been put on display near the entrance to the field to show this period of Anklam's aviation history. A recent acquistion is the inventory of the hang gliding museum. The collection was started in 1982 by hang-glider pilot Günther Berghardt who set up the museum in April 1988. More than one hundred and fifty hang-gliders and para-gliders from around the world were acquired along with instruments, documents harnesses and photographs.

TYPE	REG/SER	CON. NO.	PI/NOTES	STATUS
☐ Acklebein Standard 84/90 Hang Glider				RA
☐ Aerial Arts Gliding Clubman C164 Hang Glider				RA
☐ Airwave Magic 3 Hang Glider				RA
☐ Airwave Magic 4 Hang Glider				RA
☐ Antonov An-2TP	D-FONG	112247308	863 (DDR), DDR-SKG	PV
☐ Avon Kites Sonic Hang Glider				RA
☐ Bach Skybird 2 Hang Glider				RA
☐ Ballonfabrik Stuttgart K-1000/3-Stu Gas Balloon	D-STADT MUNSTER	286	Basket only.	RA
☐ Bamboo Butterfly Hang Glider (R)				RA
☐ Bamboo Butterfly Hang Glider (R)				RA
☐ Baumann BM III Hang Glider				RA
☐ Bautek Fafnir Hang Glider				RA
☐ Bautek Milan Hang Glider				RA
☐ Bautek Pamir Hang Glider				RA
☐ Bautek Weltrekordgerat Fafnir Hang Glider				RA
☐ Bennett Delta Wing 210 Hang Glider				RA
☐ Bennett Delta Wing Lazor 170 Hang Glider				RA
☐ Bennett Delta Wing Mariah 170 Hang Glider				RA
☐ Bennett Delta Wing Phoenix 6B Hang Glider				RA
☐ Bennett Delta Wing Phoenix SX Hang Glider				RA
☐ Bennett Delta Wing SC Hang Glider				
☐ Bicla Adler Hang Glider				RA
☐ Bicla Adler Hang Glider				RA
☐ Bicla Bergstar 1 Hang Glider				RA
☐ Bicla Bergstar 2 Hang Glider				RA
☐ Bicla Comet Hang Glider				RA
☐ Bicla Flugdrachen Bicla Eagle 1 Hang Glider				RA
☐ Bicla Flugdrachen Bicla Eagle 2 Hang Glider				RA
☐ Bicla Flugdrachen Bicla Standard Hang Glider				RA
☐ Bicla Flugdrachen Bicla Standard Hang Glider				RA
☐ Bicla Maxi Hang Glider				RA
☐ Bicla Radonneuse Maxi Hang Glider				RA
☐ Butterfly				RA
☐ Chanute Glider (R)				RA
☐ Chargus Cyclone Hang Glider				RA
☐ Chargus Midas Hang Glider				RA
☐ Chucks Glider Supplies Falcon V Hang Glider				RA
☐ Corinne Delta Eagle Cloud Hang Glider				RA
☐ Czech Floater Hang Glider				RA
☐ Czech World Cup Hang Glider				RA
☐ Danis Manta Hang Glider				RA
☐ Danis Manta Hang Glider				RA
☐ Delta Wing Tyrol Concord II Hang Glider				RA
☐ Dorfner Aquila 3 Hang Glider				RA
☐ Ebert Condor Hang Glider				RA
☐ Edel Corvette 21 Hang Glider				RA
☐ Eipper Antares Hang Glider				RA
☐ Eipper MX Quicksilver				RA
☐ Electra Flyer Cirrus 1 Hang Glider				RA
☐ Electra Flyer Cirrus 3 Hang Glider				RA
☐ Electra Flyer Nimbus Hang Glider				RA
☐ Electra Flyer Olympus 180 Hang Glider				RA
☐ Electra Flyer Sunflower Hang Glider				RA
☐ Engel Bora 100 Hang Glider				RA
☐ Engel Bora Mosquito Hang Glider				RA
☐ Engel Bora Swallowtail Hang Glider				RA
☐ Engel/Treichler Bora Pirat Hang Glider				RA
☐ Falhawk Excel 151 Hang Glider				RA
☐ Finsterwalder Bergfex Hang Glider				RA
☐ Finsterwalder Minifex Hang Glider				RA
☐ Finsterwalder Superfex Hang Glider				RA
☐ Firebird 2 Hang Glider				RA
☐ Firebird C12 Hang Glider				RA
☐ Firebird CX 17 Hang Glider				RA
☐ Firebird Ex Tase 22 Hang Glider				RA
☐ Firebird Ex Tase 30 Hang Glider				RA
☐ Firebird Fox 24 Hang Glider				RA
☐ Firebird Fox 26 Hang Glider				RA
☐ Firebird Laser 12.8 Hang Glider				RA
☐ Firebird Sierra Hang Glider				RA
☐ Firebird Spirit Hang Glider				RA
☐ Flight Design Alpin Caddy Hang Glider				RA
☐ Flight Design Dream 2 Hang Glider				RA
☐ Flight Design Easy 2 Hang Glider				RA
☐ Flug und Fahrzeugwerke (FFA) Swiss Delta Hang Glider				RA
☐ Forster Hawk 77 Hang Glider				RA
☐ Guggenmos Bullet Racing Hang Glider				RA
☐ Guggenmos Hang Glider			Wings only.	RA
☐ Guggenmos Hang Glider			Wings only.	RA
☐ Gygax Swiss Lancer 4 Hang Glider				RA

☐ Gygax Zephyr Hang Glider				RA
☐ Gygax Zephyr Hang Glider				RA
☐ Harker/Schweiger Harker World Cup 90 Hang Glider				RA
☐ Highster Aircraft Highster Hang Glider				RA
☐ Hiway Super Scorpion Hang Glider				RA
☐ Hocke Skyglider Hang Glider				RA
☐ Hocke Skyliner Hang Glider				RA
☐ Hocke Skysurfer Hang Glider				RA
☐ Holzer Savoie Diamant Hang Glider				RA
☐ Huber Dreisitzer Hang Glider				RA
☐ Huber Standard Hang Glider				RA
☐ Hudson Happy Duck Hang Glider				RA
☐ Ikarus Deltabau 100 Hang Glider				RA
☐ Ikarus Deltabau 200 Hang Glider				RA
☐ Ikarus Deltabau 300 Hang Glider				RA
☐ Ikarus Deltabau 300s Hang Glider				RA
☐ Ikarus Deltabau 600b Hang Glider				RA
☐ Ikarus Deltabau 800 Hang Glider				RA
☐ Ikarus Windspiel 2 Hang Glider				RA
☐ Kamov Ka-26	D-HOAG	7705908	DM-SPG, DDR-SPG	PV
☐ Knittel Stern Hang Glider				RA
☐ Knuth Falke 2 Hang Glider				RA
☐ Knuth Standard Hang Glider				RA
☐ Knuth Standard Hang Glider				RA
☐ Knuth Swallowtail Hang Glider				RA
☐ Krabbemayer Hekra K2 Hang Glider				RA
☐ La Mouette Atlas 14 Hang Glider				RA
☐ La Mouette Atlas 16 Hang Glider				RA
☐ La Mouette Atlas 18 Hang Glider				RA
☐ La Mouette Azur 15 Hang Glider				RA
☐ La Mouette Hermes 16 Hang Glider				RA
☐ La Mouette Jet Hang Glider				RA
☐ La Mouette Profil Sport Hang Glider				RA
☐ Lilienthal Derwitzer-Apparat (R)				PV
☐ Lilienthal Grosser Doppeldecker (R)				PV
☐ Lilienthal Grosser Doppeldecker (R)				PV
☐ Lilienthal Kleiner Doppeldecker (R)				PV
☐ Lilienthal Kleiner Schlagflügelapparat (R)				PV
☐ Lilienthal Kleiner Schlagflügelapparat (R)				PV
☐ Lilienthal Maihöhe-Rhinow Apparat (R)				PV
☐ Lilienthal Normal-Segelapparat (R)				PV
☐ Lilienthal Normal-Segelapparat (R)				PV
☐ Lilienthal Stürmflugelmodell (R)				PV
☐ Lilienthal Südende-Apparat (R)				PV
☐ Lilienthal Vorflügelapparat (R)				PV
☐ Manta Fledge 2b Hang Glider				RA
☐ Mayer Mydra Standard				RA
☐ Moyes GTR 162 Hang Glider				RA
☐ Moyes GTR 162 Hang Glider				RA
☐ Moyes Maxi Hang Glider				RA
☐ Moyes Mega Hang Glider				RA
☐ Moyes Stingray Hang Glider				RA
☐ Nase 4 Hang Glider				RA
☐ Niebler/Schmidt Falke 3 Hang Glider				RA
☐ Orion Deltabau Fun 14 Hang Glider				RA
☐ Orion Deltabau Swiss Super Scorpion Hang Glider				RA
☐ Orion Deltabau Swiss Super Scorpionli Hang Glider				RA
☐ Pacific Gull HA 19 Hang Glider				RA
☐ Pacifik Wings Express Racing Hang Glider				RA
☐ Panstwowe Zaklady Lotnicze (PZL) 106BR Kruk	D-FOED	10880212	DDR-TED	PV
☐ Parasail Jet Hang Glider				RA
☐ Peregrine Aviation OWL Hang Glider				RA
☐ Raab-Katzenstein RK 9a Grasmücke	D-1519	353	On loan to Deutsches TM.	–
☐ Rademacher Mono-Fly Hang Glider				RA
☐ Reyer Bavaria Delta Hang Glider				RA
☐ Reyer Bavaria Hang Glider				RA
☐ Rogallo Eigenbau Hang Glider				RA
☐ Rogallo Lump Hang Glider				RA
☐ Schatzinger Delta Hang Glider				RA
☐ Schicke Turmloser Standard Hang Glider				RA
☐ Schmidt Bergfalke Hang Glider				RA
☐ Schmidt Bergfalke Hang Glider				RA
☐ Schmidtler Ranger A Hang Glider				RA
☐ Schmidtler Scout Hang Glider				RA
☐ Schmidtler Stratos N Hang Glider				RA
☐ Schwarze Ente Hang Glider				RA
☐ Seagull Aircraft Seagull 7 Hang Glider				RA
☐ Sky Sports Merlin Hang Glider				RA
☐ Skylider Hang Glider				RA
☐ Soarmaster PP-106 Hang Glider				RA
☐ Solar Wings Typhoon S4 Hang Glider				RA
☐ Soundhaus DDR-Rogallo Hang Glider				RA

☐ Steger Delta-Wing SC Hang Glider				RA
☐ Steger Hornet 15 Hang Glider				RA
☐ Steinbach Delta Brasil 1976 Hang Glider				RA
☐ Steinbach Delta Euro 1 Hang Glider				RA
☐ Steinbach Delta Euro 2 Hang Glider				RA
☐ Steinbach Delta Hai Hang Glider				RA
☐ Steinbach Delta Spot Hang Glider				RA
☐ Steinbach Delta WM 90 Hang Glider				RA
☐ Stiller Hang Glider				RA
☐ Sun Sail Sun Standard Hang Glider				RA
☐ Sun Sail Sun Swift Hang Glider				RA
☐ Sun Sail Sun Swift Hang Glider				RA
☐ Sunbird Nova Hang Glider				RA
☐ Szybowcowy Zaklad Doswiadczalny S.Z.D.24A Foka 4				RA
☐ Tecma Air Sport Spirale 23 Hang Glider				RA
☐ Thalhofer Cloud 2 Hang Glider				RA
☐ Thalhofer Condos Hang Glider				RA
☐ Thalhofer Condos Hang Glider				RA
☐ Thalhofer Flamingo 1 Hang Glider				RA
☐ Thalhofer Flamingo 1 Hang Glider				RA
☐ Thalhofer Flamingo Sport Hang Glider				RA
☐ Thalhofer Junior Hang Glider				RA
☐ Thalhofer Rhönadler Hang Glider				RA
☐ Tragschauber Giro Hang Glider				RA
☐ Ultralite Products Comet Hang Glider				RA
☐ Ultralite Products Dragonfly 1 Hang Glider				RA
☐ Ultralite Products Dragonfly 2b Hang Glider				RA
☐ Ultralite Products Redtail Hang Glider				RA
☐ Ultralite Products Spyder Hang Glider				RA
☐ Ultralite Products Super Redtail Hang Glider				RA
☐ Uni-Praha Holz Fledge Hang Glider				RA
☐ Vega MX II Hang Glider				RA
☐ Voithofer 1.Pinzgauer Hang Glider				RA
☐ Warnke Ultralight				RA
☐ Wasp Falcon 3 Hang Glider				RA
☐ Wasp Falcon 4 Hang Glider				RA
☐ Wasp Gryphon 3 Hang Glider				RA
☐ Wasp Laser 190 Hang Glider				RA
☐ Wasp Super Gryphon Hang Glider				RA
☐ Wills Wing New Wave 15 Hang Glider				RA
☐ Zetka Aar Hang Glider				RA
☐ Zetka Taifun Hang Glider				RA
☐ Zlin Z-37A Cmelak	D-ESOT	21-02	DM-SWC, DM-SOT, DDR-SOT – original c/n 08-11 composite.	PV

RATHAUS STADT BÖBLINGEN (GER129)

Address:	Rathaus, D-71032 Böblingen
Tel:	07031-669700
Fax:	07031-669719
Email:	buergeramt@boeblingen.de
Admission:	By prior permission only.
Location:	In the centre of the town near the Market Place.

Just after World War I Hans Klemm designed several light aircraft for the Daimler company in Stuttgart. In 1926 he set up his own company at Böblingen and the first product was the L 25. Over six hundred examples of the low wing monoplane were built using a variety of engines. The Kl 35 was also constructed in large numbers and served as a trainer with airforces in several countries. In the town hall there is a small exhibition, honouring the work of Klemm. Photographs, memorabilia, documents and models can be seen. The L 25, dating from the mid-1930s, is currently in store in the building and there are plans for a building to exhibit it. This aircraft was restored in the 1960s and flew for a time from Berneck and Bezgenreit.

TYPE	REG/SER	CON. NO.	PI/NOTES	STATUS
☐ Klemm L 25 d VII R	D-EJOL	798	D-ELAH	RA

RAUMFAHRTMUSEUM MITTWEIDA (GER130)

Address:	Rochlitzer Strasse 62, D-09648 Mittweida.
Tel:	03727-90811
Fax:	03727-90821
Email:	Space.service@t-online.de
Admission:	Last Sunday in month 1600-1800.
Location:	In the town which is about 15 km. north of Chemnitz.

This privately run collection traces the history and development of rockets. This type of engine has been fitted to aircraft both as the main power plant and for assisted take off. This work is featured in the displays. There are several photographs and models of rocket-powered types and details of their use.

RICHTHOFEN MUSEUM (GER131)

Address:	Isumser Strasse 20a, D-26409 Wittmund.
Tel:	04462-5091 ext.202.
Admission:	By prior permission only.
Location:	The barracks is in the southern part of the town. The airfield is about 10 km west on Road 210.

Jagdgeschwader 71 has set up a museum, dedicated to Manfred von Richthofen, in the barracks in the town. The wing is named after the famous pilot. On show is an excellent collection of models, photos, documents, medals, posters, trophies, components, flying clothing and uniforms tracing the life of Richthofen and his family along with the history of the units bearing his name. A replica Fokker Triplane in its famous red colours is on show. Also exhibited at the barracks are a Sabre and a Starfighter. At the airfield the wing has restored and modified a Spanish built Messerschmitt Bf 109 to represent a G model in typical World War II markings. The unit was set up at Ahlhorn in June 1959 and equipped with Canadair Sabres. The wing moved to its current home in 1964 and transferred to the Starfighter. These served until the arrival of the Phantom in 1973.

TYPE	REG/SER	CON. NO.	PI/NOTES	STATUS
☐ Canadair CL-13B Sabre 6 [North American F-86E]	'JA+106'	1664	BB+186, JD+112, YA+044, 01+06 – on loan from LM.	RAX
☐ Fokker Dr I (FSM)	'102/17'			RAX
☐ Hispano HA-1112M1L [Messerschmitt Bf 109G]	'12'	194	C.4K-134	RAX
☐ Lockheed 683-04-10 Starfighter (RF-104G)	24+85	683-8235	KG+335, EB+232	RA
☐ Lockheed 683-10-19 Starfighter (F-104G)	20+86	683-6602	KC+118, JD+232, JA+234	RA
☐ McDonnell M.98NQ Phantom II (F-4F)	37+11	4373	72-1121	RA

RUBESAN'S DA CAPO OLDTIMERMUSEUM (GER132)

Address:	Karl Heine Strasse 105, Plagwitz, 04229 Leipzig.
Tel:	0341-9260137
Fax:	03419260147
Email:	events@rubensansdacapo.de
Admission:	Tuesday-Saturday 1100-1600; Sunday 1000-1800.
Location:	In the western part of the city.

On show are a large collection of cars, motorcycles, aircraft propellers and items of memorabilia. The Ilyshin Il-18, which used to be at the airport, is on the roof of the complex.

TYPE	REG/SER	CON. NO.	PI/NOTES	STATUS
☐ Ilyushin Il-18V	DDR-STB	180002001	DM-STB	PV

SÄCHSISCHES FEUERWEHRMUSEUM (GER133)

Address:	Hauptstrasse 30, D-01619 Zeithain.
Tel:	03525-762062
Fax:	03525-763334
Email:	patz_co@t.online.de
Admission:	By prior permission only.
Location:	In the centre of the town which is about 5 km. north east of Reisa.

Set up in 1997 the museum traces the history of the fire fighting service in Saxony. On show are fire engines and pumps which show the development of the machinery over the years.

TYPE	REG/SER	CON. NO.	PI/NOTES	STATUS
☐ Mil Mi-2See	94+83	552649122	386 (DDR)	PV

SAMMLUNG AEROCLUB PEENEMUNDE (GER134)

Address: Flugplatz,
D-17449 Peenemunde.
Tel: 038371-20350
Fax: 038371-20352
Admission: On permanent view.
Location: Just north of the town.

Four aircraft have been parked near the aero club for some time. The East German Air Force flew nine Ilyushin Il-28s on target towing duties and in addition had one Il-28U which is now in a rather poor condition.

TYPE	REG/SER	CON. NO.	PI/NOTES	STATUS
☐ Ilyushin Il-28U	193	610311	In DDR markings.	PVD
☐ Mikoyan-Gurevich MiG-21US	24+06	04685134	230 (DDR)	PV
☐ Mil Mi-8TB	93+63	10555	126 (DDR)	PV
☐ Mil Mi-14PL	95+05	B 4005	625 (DDR)	PV

SAMMLUNG GROSSENHAIN (GER135)

Address: Zum Fliegerhorst 25,
D-01558 Grossenhain.
Tel: 03522-527950
Fax: 03522-527951
Email: info@flugplatz-grossenhain.com
Admission: By prior permission only.
Location: About 30 km. north west of Dresden.

The airfield was an important Soviet Air Force base during the 'Cold War' period. The site is now home to flying clubs, overhaul companies and Josef Koch's fleet of historic aircraft. The MiG-17 was left behind by the departing Russians and was once flown by units operating from the field.

TYPE	REG/SER	CON. NO.	PI/NOTES	STATUS
☐ Mikoyan-Gurevich MiG-17F	47		In Soviet markings.	PV
☐ Mikoyan-Gurevich MiG-21SPS (MiG-21PFM)	780	94A4310	780 (DDR), 22+30	PV
☐ Mikoyan-Gurevich MiG-21U			Front fuselage only.	PV

SAMMLUNG KOCH – HISTORISCHE FLUGZEUG (GER136)

Address: Zum Fliegerhorst 13,
D-01558 Grossenhain.
Tel: 03522-527527
Fax: 03522-528001
Email: info@fliegendes-museum.de
Admission: By prior permission only.
Location: About 30 km. north west of Dresden.

Josef Koch set up the Fliegendes Museum at Augsburg in the 1990s. A purpose built hangar complex was erected and many interesting aircraft were obtained. Development at the airfield necessitated a move. The static airliners were transported to Hermeskeil and many of the flying types moved to the Front Line Museum at Sandown in England in 1996. When this exhibition closed the fleet returned to Germany where they led a nomadic existence before arriving at Grossenhain. The Dragon Rapide which spent most of its life in Switzerland was restored at Augsburg. The Klemm L 25 was imported in to England in 1927 and after a long period in store was rebuilt by Roy Nerou at Coventry in the early 1970s.

TYPE	REG/SER	CON. NO.	PI/NOTES	STATUS
☐ Antonov An-2T	D-FOFM	12847302	802 (Soviet), 802 (DDR), (54+11)	RAA
☐ Blériot XI (R)	G-BWRH	01	N25WM, D-EFTE	RAA
☐ Bölkow BO 207	D-ESMA	259		RAA
☐ Bücker Bü 131B Jungmann	D-EAZO	52	A-41 (Switzerland), HB-UTK	RAA
☐ Canadian Car & Foundry Harvard 4 [North American NA-186 (T-6J)]	D-FABE	CCF4-499	52-8578, AA+624	RAA
☐ De Havilland D.H.82A Tiger Moth	'T6390'	(84764)	T6390, G-ANIX, D-ELOM, D-EFTF, G-ANIX, D-EFTN – composite which assumed this identity.	RAAX
☐ De Havilland D.H.89A Dragon Rapide (D.H.89B Dominie I)	D-ILIT	6879	NR803, G-AMAI, EC-AGP, 'G-RCYR', D-ILIT, G-AMAI	RAA

TYPE	REG/SER	CON. NO.	PI/NOTES	STATUS
☐ Fokker Dr I (R)	'426/17'	003	D-EFTN, G-BWRJ, D-EFTJ	RAA
☐ Klemm L 25 a Ia	D-EFTE	152	G-AAHW, D-ELFK, G-AAHW	RA
☐ Klemm Kl 35D (Sk 15)	D-EFTY	1642	SE-AIP, Fv5081, SE-AIP, D-EHUX, D-EFTG, G-BWRD	RA
☐ Lockheed 683-10-19 Starfighter (F-104G)	21+55	683-7024	KE+324, DB+103	RA
☐ Mignet HM-19C Pou-du-Ciel	G-BWRI	01	HB-SPG	RAA
☐ Morane-Saulnier MS.505 Criquet (MS.500) [Fieseler Fi 156 Storch]	G-BWRF	73	73, F-BAUV, D-EFTY	RAA
☐ Mraz M-1D Sokol	G-BWRG	304	OK-DIX, HB-TBG, (D-EFTB), D-EGWP	RAA
☐ Panstwowe Zaklady Lotnicze (PZL) 101A Gawron	SP-CHD	74134		RAC
☐ Piper PA-18-95 Super Cub	D-EKYL	18-4452	N8014R	RAA
☐ Schneider ESG 31 Grunau Baby IIB				RA
☐ Stampe & Vertongen S.V.4A	D-EJKA	396	396, F-BDOT, D-EJKA, G-BWRE	RAA

SAMMLUNG NEUENKIRCHEN (GER137)

Address: D-17039 Neuenkirchen.
Admission: Not yet open.
Location: About 8 km north east of Neubrandenburg.

Over the last few years several aircraft have arrived in the village for a proposed museum. The site is a short distance from the former military airfield at Neubrandenburg. Almost all in the collection were operated in the former East Germany and the history of flying in that country will be highlighted.

TYPE	REG/SER	CON. NO.	PI/NOTES	STATUS
☐ Fiat G.91R/3	31+62	91-430	KD+420, DG+236, MA+236	RA
☐ Kamov Ka-26	D-HOAQ	7404618	DM-SPQ, DDR-SPQ	RA
☐ Mikoyan-Gurevich MiG-21M	22+52	963209	438 (DDR) – Front fuselage only.	RA
☐ Mikoyan-Gurevich MiG-21MF	781	96002037	781 (DDR), 23+47 – in DDR markings.	RA
☐ Mikoyan-Gurevich MiG-23ML	20+10	0390324623	329 (DDR)	RA
☐ Mil Mi-8T	93+85	10580	763 (DDR)	RA
☐ Panstwowe Zaklady Lotnicze (PZL) 104 Wilga 35AD	DDR-VPT	61108	DDR-WBC	RA
☐ Sukhoi Su-7U	91	1807	In Soviet markings (?).	RA
☐ Zlin Z-142	D-EWOM	0131	DM-WOM, DDR-WOM	RAD
☐ Zlin Z-37A Cmelak	D-ESLW	15-12	DM-SLW, DDR-SLW	RA
☐ Zlin Z-37A Cmelak	D-ESSP	18-06	DM-SSP, DDR-SSP	RA

SAMMLUNG TIPPMAN (GER138)

Address: D-02627 Baschütz.
Admission: By prior permission only.
Location: About 5 km. east of Bautzen.

Bautzen was an important East German Air Force base they had a collection of preserved aircraft which is now at the Luftwaffe Museum at Gatow. Herr Tippman has put three types on show at his property.

TYPE	REG/SER	CON. NO.	PI/NOTES	STATUS
☐ Mikoyan-Gurevich MiG-21SPS (MiG-21PFM)	22+43	94A5606	948 (DDR)	PV
☐ Zlin Z-37A Cmelak	DDR-SUD	18-22	DM-SUD, DDR-SUD, (D-ESUD)	PV
☐ Zlin Z-42MU	D-EMWJ	0020	DM-WMJ, DDR-WMJ	PV

SAMMLUNG ULMER (GER139)

Address: Flug Ltr. Waldeck 15/5, D-73035 Göppingen.
Tel: 07161-73673
Admission: By prior permission only.
Location: The Bücker aircraft are at the above address – the remainder are at Bezgenreit airfield which is about 2 km east of the village and 5 km south of Göppingen.

Fritz Ulmer assembled an interesting collection over many years. Initially housed at Berneck airfield the fleet moved to Bezgenreit in the mid-1970s. The small hangar was crammed with many machines dismantled or hanging from the rafters. Plans to construct a second building were thwarted by the local authorities. As a result the 'Bücker Studio' was established at the family home. The company produced just six types during its existence and examples' of three are on show along with models, photographs and documents tracing the history of the firm. The classic Jungmann and Jungmeister acrobatic biplanes were produced in large numbers and are highly sought after machines. The Student is very rare with the one in the collection and possibly one other in Switzerland being the only examples left. At the airfield there was a significant collection of classic gliders but the majority were unfortunately destroyed in arson attack on hangar on January 19th 2001.

TYPE	REG/SER	CON. NO.	PI/NOTES	STATUS
☐ Bücker Bü 131B Jungmann	D-EGHC	25	A-16 (Switzerland), HB-USR	RA
☐ Bücker Bü 133C Jungmeister	D-ENOW	6	U-59 (Switzerland), HB-MII	RA
☐ Bücker Bü 180B-1 Student	HB-EFO	2106		RA
☐ Glasflügel BS-1				RA
☐ Jacobs Meise (D.F.S. 108-70)	HB-514			RA
☐ Spalinger S-15K	HB-489		Major components.	RA

SCHWÄBISCHES BAUERN UND TECHNIKMUSEUM (GER140)

Address:	Markstrasse 5, Seifertshofen D-73569 Eschach b. Schwäbisch Gmünd.
Tel:	07975-360
Fax:	07975-5486
Admission:	Daily 0900-1800.
Location:	In the village which is about 4 km north of Eschach and about 12 km north of Schwäbisch-Gmund.

Eugen Kiemele and his family have run a scrap business in the village for years. Many interesting and antique items came into his possession and this led to the idea of a museum. Two halls display a variety of agricultural machinery, cars, cycles, motor cycles, railway engines, tractors, military vehicles and tanks. Household items, toys and costumes can also be seen. There is a section devoted to furniture and clocks. Thousands of artefacts are on show with many more in store. The yard has handled a number of military aircraft from countries around Europe and some of these have been displayed and others scrapped. The S-58, Thunderstreak, Noratlas, Workhorse and Super Sabre are long term residents. The Skeeters were flown by the Army Air Corps from their bases in northern Germany for many years. Airframes are processed regularly and some have been sold to other museums and collections both in Germany and neighbouring countries.

TYPE	REG/SER	CON. NO.	PI/NOTES	STATUS
☐ Antonov An-26SM	52+10	14208	373 (DDR), (DDR-SBM), 373 (DDR) – front fuselage only.	RA
☐ Antonov An-26T	52+05	10509	376 (DDR), (DDR-SBD), 376 (DDR)	RA
☐ Lockheed 683-04-10 Starfighter (RF-104G)	24+11	683-8151	KG+251, EA+239	RAD
☐ Lockheed 726-45-14 Neptune (P2V-7) (P2V-7S) (SP-2H)	144685	726-7136	Bu144685 – front fuselage only – in French markings.	PVD
☐ McDonnell M.36CM Voodoo (F-101C)	'85-0701'	526	57-0348 – front fuselage only.	PVX
☐ Microlight	D-MXRG			PV
☐ Mikoyan-Gurevich MiG-15bis	'1973'		707 – in Hungarian markings.	RA
☐ Mikoyan-Gurevich MiG-21F-13	'1981'	741905	905 – in Hungarian markings.	PV
☐ Mikoyan-Gurevich MiG-21MF	23+41	96001012	767 (DDR)	PV
☐ Mikoyan-Gurevich MiG-21SPS (MiG-21PFM)	22+34	94A5204	869 (DDR)	PV
☐ Mikoyan-Gurevich MiG-23BN	20+42	0393214210	694 (DDR)	PV
☐ Mikoyan-Gurevich MiG-23MF	20+08	0390213351	592 (DDR)	RA
☐ Mil Mi-2S	94+50	563401044	301 (DDR)	PV
☐ Mil Mi-8T	94+21	10526	910 (DDR), 94+21, (D-HOZE)	PV
☐ Nord N.1300 [Schneider Grunau Baby IIB]	618	618		PV
☐ Nord N.2501D Noratlas	53+43	173	KA+184, GB+237	PV
☐ North American NA-223 Super Sabre (F-100D)	54-2136	223-16	Composite with c/n 223-65 54-2185	PV
☐ Panstwowe Zaklady Lotnicze (PZL) 106A Kruk	SP-WUS	37016		PV
☐ Republic F-84F Thunderstreak	FU-160		53-6899 – in Belgian markings	PV
☐ Saunders-Roe P.501 Skeeter AOP.12	XM563	S2/7061		RA
☐ Saunders-Roe P.501 Skeeter AOP.12	XN343	S2/7068		RA
☐ Saunders-Roe P.501 Skeeter AOP.12	XN339	S2/7145		RA
☐ Scheibe Bergfalke II	D-5383			PV
☐ Sikorsky S-58 Seabat (HSS-1N) (SH-34J)	143	581153	Bu147634, H-7 (Netherlands), 8-4 (Netherlands) – in Dutch markings.	PV
☐ Sukhoi Su-22M4	25+13	25020	641 (DDR)	PV
☐ Vertol V.43 (H-21C)	83+18	WG.18	PA+213, QK+563, PX+345 – with tail fins from c/n WG.10 and WG.15.	PV

SEGELFLUGSAMMLUNG WELZHOFER (GER141)

Address:	c/o Hotel zum Hirsch, Marktplatz 18, D-89312 Günzburz.
Tel:	082-21-5610
Admission:	By prior permission only.
Location:	At Günzburg airfield which is about 3 km north east of the town on Road 16.

This private collection of mainly gliders has been in existence for many years. An old hangar at the local airfield stores many of the airframes. The search for a suitable exhibition building continues. Several classic sailplanes from the inter-war period have been obtained and a number have been loaned to the Deutsches Segelflugmuseum at the famous Wasserkuppe and to other organisations in the country. The Wolf was the first type produced by Schempp and Hirth at Göppingen. A small number were built in the mid-1930s and three are known to survive. One of these has been passed to the Segelflug Museum. Primary gliders were used by many clubs in the 1920s and 1930s. One of the earliest was the Besenstiel designed and built by Ferdinand Schulz in 1922. The only powered aircraft owned is the La 11 parasol designed in Stettin. This machine dating from 1935, powered by a 25hp Daimler engine, has been loaned to Flugausstellung Junior.

TYPE	REG/SER	CON. NO.	PI/NOTES	STATUS
☐ Dittmar Condor IV/3	D-8802	24/53	On loan to F. Schleissheim.	–
☐ Flugtechnische Arbeitsgemeinschaft Stettin Landmann La 11	D-YLAS	9	On loan to Flugausstellung Junior.	–
☐ Horten Ho XVc			On loan to Flugausstellung Junior.	–
☐ Hütter H 17A (D.F.S. 108-67)				PV
☐ Hütter H 17A (D.F.S. 108-67)				S
☐ Jacobs Kranich II (D.F.S. 108-30)	PH-103	15	D-9019, PH-999 – in Holland.	RA
☐ Jacobs Meise (D.F.S. 108-70)				PV
☐ Jacobs Meise (D.F.S. 108-70)				RAC
☐ Jacobs Rhönbussard (D.F.S. 108-50)	D-7059	485	BGA.395, G-ALKY, BGA.395 – on loan to OSC Wasserkuppe.	–
☐ Messerschmitt-Bölkow-Blohm Phoebus	D-8752	722	On loan to Flugausstellung Junior.	–
☐ Pelzner Hangegleiter (R)			On loan to F. Schleissheim.	–
☐ Schneider ESG 29 Grunau 9 (D.F.S. 108-10) (R)			On loan to Flugausstellung Junior.	–
☐ Schneider ESG 31 Grunau Baby IIB				RA
☐ Schneider ESG 31 Grunau Baby IIB				PV
☐ Schneider Grunau SG-38 (D.F.S. 108-14)			On loan to Deutsches Museum.	–
☐ Schneider Grunau SG-38 (D.F.S. 108-14)				PV
☐ Stamer-Lippisch Z-12 Zögling			On loan to Flugausstellung Junior.	–
☐ Wolfmüller Gleiter			On loan to DSM.	–

SIEMENS-MUSEUM MÜNCHEN (GER142)

Address:	Prannerstrasse 10, D-80333 München.
Tel:	089-234-2660
Admission:	Monday-Friday 0900-1600, Saturday-Sunday 1000-1400.
Location:	In the city.

The company set up a museum in Berlin in 1916. A transfer to Munich occurred in 1954 and since then the exhibition has been steadily improved. On show are examples of aero-engines made over the years.

SPORTFLUGGRUPPE NORDHOLZ-CUXHAVEN (GER143)

Address:	Postfach 42, D-27633 Nordholz.
Tel:	04741-8384
Fax:	04741-603-0371
Email:	info@sfg-nordholz.de
Admission:	By prior permission only.
Location:	In the south eastern part of the town which is about 25 km north of Bremerhaven.

The group has an interesting fleet of gliders and powered aircraft. A pilot training school is also in operation. The Goumhouria is one of several purchased by German owners from Egypt. The type was put into production at Heliopolis in the early 1950s. About three hundred were built in six versions. The Mark 1 was powered by a Walter Minor engine and the others were fitted with a Continental flat four. The Do 27 is mainly used as the glider tug. Some of the aircraft are also operated as part of the German Historic Flight.

TYPE	REG/SER	CON. NO.	PI/NOTES	STATUS
☐ Cessna F150K	D-ECFP	F1500588		RAA
☐ Cessna F172M	D-ELFN	F17201499		RAA
☐ Cessna 182N Skylane	D-ELFP	60301	N92663	RAA
☐ Dornier Do 27A-1	D-EGFR	160	PC+113, QM+606, SC+718, SE+521, BD+??, 55+36 – also part of German Historic Flight.	RAA
☐ Heliopolis Goumhouria 6 [Bücker Bü 181D Bestmann]	D-EGZR	185	SU-347 – also part of German Historic Flight.	RAA
☐ Piaggio FWP.149D	D-EGME	183	KB+145, AS+022, BF+420, 91+61 – also part of German Historic Flight.	RAA
☐ Piper PA-18-135 Super Cub (L-21B)	D-ENFC	18-3830	54-2430, R-140 (Netherlands)	RAA

☐ Piper PA-18-95 Super Cub (L-18C)	D-EGFG	18-3420	54-720, AS+509, AC+501, NL+107, 96+02 – also part of German Historic Flight.	RAA
☐ Piper PA-28-140D Cherokee	D-EMCB	28-7125520	N1849T	RAA
☐ Putzer Elster B	D-EGFH	043	D-ELBD, 97+20 – also part of German Historic Flight.	RAA
☐ Rolladen-Schneider LS-4	D-5758	4630		RAA
☐ Scheibe SF-25C Falke 1700	D-KDBL	44266		RAA
☐ Schleicher Ka-6CR Rhönsegler	D-6319	1044		RAA
☐ Schleicher K.8B				RAA
☐ Schleicher ASK-13	D-0535	13236		RAA

STADTMUSEUM SCHORNDORF – GALLERIE FÜR TECHNIK (GER144)

Address: Arnold-Strasse 1,
D-73614 Schorndorf.
Tel: 07181-602157
Email: mail@stadtmuseum.schorndorf.de
Admission: Tuesday-Friday 1400-1700; Saturday 1000-1200 1400-1700; Sunday 1000-1700.
Location: In the town which is about 25 km east of Stuttgart south of Route 29.

This town museum was originally set up in the 1930s and the displays trace the history of the locality. On show are many everyday items showing life in the area and the development of the region over the years. A new technical gallery was recently opened in a former furniture factory. The work of local engineers Gottlieb Daimler and Ersnt Heinkel is portrayed along with machines from local industries. The only aircraft displayed is a Halberstadt CL IV which was one of a fleet used by Luftverkehr Paul Strähle on charter flights in the 1920s. He also operated a scheduled service from Stuttgart to Konstanz for a short period. Several aircraft were placed in store at Schorndorf in the late 1930s and apart from the example on show in this museum they remained in the village until taken to the U.S.A. in 1982. The CL IV was exhibited at the Daimler-Benz Museum in Stuttgart for many years before moving to the motor museum at Langenburg in the early 1980s.

TYPE	REG/SER	CON. NO.	PI/NOTES	STATUS
☐ Halberstadt CL IV (C 24)	D-71	1447		PV

STARFIGHTER STAFFEL (GER145)

Address: Garlenstrasse 19,
D-87746 Erkheim.
Tel: 08336-9392
Admission: By prior permission only.
Location: At Memmingen airfield which is about 3 km east of the town.

The airfield was operational during World War II and Messerschmitt Me 262s were among the types flown. JBG 34 was formed at Memmingen in 1955 and equipped with the F-84F. The first Starfighters arrived in 1964 and the wing was the last to fly the type when they were finally withdrawn in October 1987. The Tornado was in use from late 1987 until the end of 2002 when the wing disbanded and the base closed. The group has been formed to keep alive the traditions of the wing and its aircraft. The F-84F and the RF-104G were the gate guardians to the field. The F-104G has arrived from Erding where it was an instructional airframe. The TF-104G crashed at Memmingen in 1984 but survived. Three variants of the infamous type can be compared. The airfield is now used for civil flights, especially by the low cost carriers, and is marketed as 'Munich-West' even though it is about one hundred and fifty kilometers from the Bavarian capital.

TYPE	REG/SER	CON. NO.	PI/NOTES	STATUS
☐ Lockheed 583-10-20 Starfighter (TF-104G)	27+26	583D-5727	61-3056, DA+056, EB+372	RA
☐ Lockheed 683-04-10 Starfighter (RF-104G)	'23+34'	683-8158	KG+258, EA+246, 24+17	RA
☐ Lockheed 683-10-19 Starfighter (F-104G)	22+58	683-7139	KE+439, DD+240	RA
☐ Republic F-84F Thunderstreak	'DD+113'		52-6669, DR+043, DD+120, DD+320	RAX

TECHNIK-MUSEUM HUGO JUNKERS (GER146)

Address: Kühnauerstrasse 161a,
D-06812 Dessau.
Tel: 0340-6611982
Fax: 0340-6611193
Email: Technik-Museum-Dessau@t-online.de
Admission: Monday-Friday 1000-1700, Sunday 1000-1600.
Location: About 3 km west of the city centre.

Hugo Junkers was born on February 3rd 1859 and in 1895 he founded a company in Dessau to produce boilers, cooling and ventilation equipment. In 1910 he patented an aerofoil section with metal skinning and carried out tests in a wind tunnel he built near Aachen. Five years later an experimental wing using steel tube construction with a spot welded sheet iron skin was built for static tests. Engineers Otto Mader and Otto Reuter designed and built a low wing monoplane the J 1 using these techniques. Six developed J 2s followed and the strength of the airframe led to Reuter designing the J 4 biplane, which featured a corrugated light dural alloy skin for the wings and tail surfaces. This structure was also used for the fuselages of subsequent designs for the next fifteen years. At the end of World War I the company turned its attention to commercial aircraft and on June 25th 1919 the prototype F 13 flew. More than three hundred examples were produced over the next thirteen years and it became one of the most important transport designs of the period. A range of successful aero engines was also developed along with both small and large aircraft. The company expanded in the inter-war period and by 1938 had factories in more than a dozen locations. Many successful types appeared including the famous Ju 52/3m, the Ju 86, the Ju 87 'Stuka' and the Ju 88. At the end of the war the Junkers empire was broken up. Several of its leading designers were taken to the Soviet Union and continued work on jet powered bombers. The museum was established in the early 1990s and a small display tracing the history of the company and its designs has been set up in the building which also serves as offices. On show are models, photographs, paintings, uniforms, posters and components. A library with many original company documents has also been set up. A large hangar from the post-World War II era has been restored to house the aircraft. Under rebuild in the nearby workshops is a Ju 52/3m, one of the batch recovered from a lake in Norway. A collection of aircraft used in the former East Germany has also been assembled to show flying in the area from the 1950s. The prototype Ilyushin Il-14 first flew in the Soviet Union in July 1950 and was put into production in Moscow and Tashkent. Eighty were built in Dresden between 1955 and 1959. The example in the collection was damaged in a forced landing at Leipzig in November 1967. The airframe was on show near the Halle Ice Stadium until the early 1990s when it was moved to Pulsforde where it was rebuilt. The airliner arrived at the museum in 1999.

TYPE	REG/SER	CON. NO.	PI/NOTES	STATUS
☐ Antonov An-2T	D-FWJD	1G 98-51	DM-WJD, DDR-WJD, (D-FCJD)	PVA
☐ Ilyushin Il-14P	DM-SAF	14803016		PV
☐ Junkers Ju 52/3mg4e	CO+EI	6134	IZ+BY	RAC
☐ Kamov Ka-26	'DDR-VPK'	7404108	DM-VPR, DDR-VPR, D-HZPT	PVX
☐ Mikoyan-Gurevich MiG-15UTI	16	461810	In Soviet markings.	RA
☐ Mikoyan-Gurevich MiG-21U-400	23+89	661118	258 (DDR)	PV
☐ Mikoyan-Gurevich MiG-23MF	20+05	0390213100	585 (DDR)	PV
☐ Mil Mi-2	D-HZPE	539811066	DDR-VPJ	PV
☐ Mil Mi-2P	D-HZPC	538839114	DDR-VPG	PV
☐ Panstwowe Zaklady Lotnicze (PZL) 106BR Kruk	D-FOEJ	10880223	DDR-TEJ	PV
☐ Scheibe Spatz A	D-0280	01		RA
☐ Sud-Est SE.3130 Alouette II	'PQ+131'	1300	PC+131, PA+138, PA+202, 75+26 – fuselage only.	RA
☐ Sukhoi Su-22M4	25+09	25916	600 (DDR)	PV
☐ Sukhoi Su-22UM3K	25+49	17532367003	127 (DDR)	PV
☐ Volkseigener Betrieb Apparatebau Lommatzsch Meise	DM-2052	0052		RA
☐ Yakovlev Yak-27R	28	0708	In Soviet markings.	RA
☐ Zlin Z-37 Cmelak	D-ESMX	05-12	DM-SMX, DDR-SMX	PV
☐ Zlin Z-37A Cmelak	DDR-SUC	18-21	DM-SUC, DDR-SUC, (D-ESUC)	PV

TECHNIK-UND VERKEHRSMUSEUM STADE (GER147)

Address:	Freiburgerstrasse 60, D-21682 Stade.
Tel:	04141-2888
Fax:	04141-43898
Email:	tuvmstade@aol.com
Admission:	Tuesday-Friday 1000-1600; Saturday- Sunday 1000-1800 (Closes at 1700 on Saturday-Sunday October-April.
Location:	In the eastern part of the town which is about 30 km west of Hamburg.

The museum is the largest in its field in Lower Saxony. Local industry from the 1850s is portrayed in the exhibition. On show are bicycles, motor cycles, cars, railway engines, steam rollers and agricultural machinery. Several period workshops have been constructed to show the advances made over the years. Two small galleries are devoted to aviation. One traces the history of the former military airfield at Stade. On show are models and memorabilia. Construction commenced in the early 1930s, it opened in 1934 and three hard runways were laid in 1937. Types based during this period included Junkers Ju 52s and Ju 86s, Dornier Do 17s and Focke-Wulf Fw 56s and Fw 58s. During World War II many operational units were in residence. The British forces blew up the runways in the late 1940s and the site served as a Luftwaffe and Heer barracks for many years. Now it is home to factories and a nature reserve. In the second, items recovered from local crash sites can be seen. There is a Napier Sabre from Hawker Tempest SN205 which force landed near the town on May 1st 1945 and a Merlin from a downed Lancaster. Period photographs enhance both displays. The Rhönlerche is suspended inside the building along with the hang glider. In the late 1990s four former East German military aircraft were on show outside the building but these have moved to other collections.

TYPE	REG/SER	CON. NO.	PI/NOTES	STATUS
☐ Drachen Studio Kecur Tropi Hang Glider				PV
☐ Schleicher Ka-4 Rhönlerche II	D-6202			PV

TECHNIKMUSEUM SPEYER (GER148)

Address:	Geibstrasse 2, D-67346 Speyer.
Tel:	06232-67080
Fax:	06232-670820
Email:	speyer@technik.museum.de
Admission:	Daily 0900-1800.
Location:	In the southern part of the town near the cathedral.

The museum opened on April 11th 1991 in the 1913 Liller Hall. This large industrial building has been given protected status. Around it more exhibition halls, workshops and outside display areas have been constructed. The exhibitions feature aircraft, railway engines, rolling stock, cars, motor cycles, steamrollers, industrial engines, fire engines and boats. Nearby is an associated collection with a large number of mechanical musical instruments and period costumes on view. Several of the exhibits came from the Auto und Technik Museum in nearby Sinsheim and there is still movement between the two organisations. The high vaulted roof of the hall assists in providing an excellent well lit display area. There are almost thirty fire engines dating from 1880 on view. In common with Sinsheim aircraft are mounted outside in dramatic poses to attract the visitor. The Dakota, Mercure, Noratlas and VFW 614 stand guard whilst a T-33 slowly rotates at the top of a pylon. At one end of the hall is a collection of German military aircraft dominated by one of the Junkers Ju 52s recovered from a Norwegian Lake. Jet trainers on show include a Fouga Magister, which can be compared with a development, the Potez-Heinkel CM 191B. An Aero L-29 Delfin in Czech test markings and a full size model of an Alpha Jet painted in a Royal Air Force 'Red Arrows' scheme can also be seen! Only twelve Dassault Mercure airliners were produced with eleven being operated by Air Inter. The prototype made its maiden flight in May 1971 and the type was withdrrawn from service in the early 1990s. The museum achieved a coup with the arrival of a giant Tashkent built Antonov An-22. The aircraft on show is the first production example and was delivered to the designers at Kiev in the mid-1960s. Bought from the Antonov Design Bureau it flew into Speyer on December 29th 1999. Another large type on show is a former Lufthansa Boeing 747. Very few examples of the type which made a significant change to air travel have been preserved. The fuselage of the Dornier Do 24 flying boat joined the exhibition in the late 1990s. It is believed to either a former Spanish Air Force machine or one recovered from a crash site. A recent arrival is one of the former French Government fleet of Canadair CL-215 water bombers which flew in from Marseille. The Luftwaffe flew eighteen Broncos from 1971 until the mid-1990s. These carried out a number of duties including target towing. The centre section of the Zero was put on show a few years ago and may be original. Replicas of early types including some from the World War I period have been obtained to present the story of aviation since Lilienthal's era. This impressive collection contains many rarities and is still acquiring aircraft and vehicles.

TYPE	REG/SER	CON. NO.	PI/NOTES	STATUS
☐ Aero Commander 680F	D-ILUX	1087-65	N6245X	PV
☐ Aero L-29 Delfin	OK-02	290805	0805	PV
☐ Aero L-39ZO Albatros	28+08	731010	147 (DDR)	PV
☐ Antonov An-2TP	RA-41343	1G 65-18	CCCP-41343	PVX
☐ Antonov An-22 (AN-22) (An-22PZ)	UR-64460	6340103	CCCP-56391, 03, CCCP-56391, 41, CCCP-64460, LZ-SGB, LZ-SFD	PV
☐ Antonov An-26S	52+04	10409	375 (DDR), DDR-SBN, 375 (DDR)	PV
☐ Beech E50 Twin Bonanza	D-ITMS	EH-56	HB-HOU, A-711 (Switzerland), N211EL	PV
☐ Boeing 747-230B	D-ABYM	21588		PV
☐ Canadair CL-13B Sabre 6 [North American F-86E]	'23042'	1613	BB+183, BB+283, YA+042, (01+04)	PVX
☐ Canadair CL-215-I	F-ZBAR/21	1021		PV
☐ Dallach Sunrise II	D-MNIW	007		RA
☐ Dassault Mirage IIIE	432	432		PV
☐ Dassault Mirage IIIRD	'33'	355	355	PVX
☐ Dassault Mercure 100	F-BTTB	2		PV
☐ De Havilland D.H.100 Vampire FB.6	J-1081	992	In Swiss markings.	PV
☐ Dornier Do 24T-3			Fuselage section only.	PVD
☐ Dornier-Breguet Alpha Jet A (FSM)	'33'			PVX
☐ Douglas DC-3A-457 Skytrooper (C-53D)	F-BFGX	11722	42-68795, SE-BAW, F-BFGX, (HB-ISF)	PV
☐ Drachen Studio Kecur Tropi Hang Glider				PV
☐ Eidgenössiches Flugzeugwerke Emmen C-3605 (C-3603-1)	D-FOXY	315	C-535, N7129V	PV
☐ Fairey Gannet AS.4		F9394	XG852, UA+112	PV
☐ Fiat G.91R/3		91-415	KD+445, DG+231, MA+231, 31+47 – in false Italian markings.	PVX
☐ Fieseler Fi 156C-3 Storch (S 14)	D-EZZZ	4370	CK+KI, Fv3805, (D-EAXY), D-EBGY – composite incorporating parts of c/n 1143 NL+UU, Fv3821, OE-ADZ, D-EADZ	RAA
☐ Fieseler Fi 156C-3/trop Storch (S 14)	'H3+BF'	110254	Fv3819, OE-ADS	PVX
☐ Fokker Dr I (FSM)	'152/17'			PVX
☐ Fokker Dr I (FSM)	'240/17'			PVX
☐ Fokker E III (FSM)	'204/17'	1924	'417/15'	RAX
☐ Fouga CM.170R Magister	387	387	In French markings.	PV
☐ Hawker P.1099 Hunter F.6	XE656	41H/680000		PV
☐ Jacobs Meise (D.F.S. 108-70)	D-1948	9		PV
☐ Junkers Ju 52/3mg4e	'VB+JA'	6821	VB+UB, 'CA+JY'	PVX

Jurca MJ.5 Sirocco	D-EJHD	D-29		PV
Lilienthal Normal-Segelapparat (R)				PV
Lockheed 580 (T-33A)	'63659'	580-7365	51-17471, AB+716, BD+716, BB+801, 94+01	PVX
Lockheed 583-10-20 Starfighter (TF-104G)	28+27	583F-5957	KF+257, KE+115, KE+215, BB+127	PV
Lockheed 683-10-19 Starfighter (F-104G)	'26+63'	683-7070	KE+370, DC+125, 22+01	PVX
Lockheed 683-10-19 Starfighter (F-104G)	'KG+181'	683-6620	KC+131, JD+245, 20+99, '23+81' – possible identity.	PVDX
Lockheed 683-10-19 Starfighter (F-104G)	25+66	683-9012	KH+122, JA+248	PV
McDonnell M.36BA Voodoo (F-101B)	58-0265	637		PV
McDonnell M.98DE Phantom II (F-4C)	'Bu153072'	364	63-7423	PVX
McDonnell M.98DE Phantom II (F-4C)	63-7446	413		PV
McDonnell M.199-1A Eagle (F-15A)	74-0109	A070		PV
Messerschmitt Bf 109G-4	3+	19310	BH+XN	PVX
Messerschmitt Bf 110D-0	NO+DS	3154	Parts only.	PVC
Mikoyan-Gurevich MiG-15UTI	18	0415320		PV
Mikoyan-Gurevich MiG-21M	22+80	960407	553 (DDR) – front fuselage only.	PV
Mikoyan-Gurevich MiG-21SPS (MiG-21PFM)	'C993'	94A4301	738 (DDR), 22+25 – in false Indian markings.	PVX
Mikoyan-Gurevich MiG-23BN	'22+02'	0393211087	690 (DDR), 20+39	PVX
Mikoyan-Gurevich MiG-23BN	'98+25'	0393214219	705 (DDR), 20+49	PVX
Mil Mi-2	45	511622100		PV
Mil Mi-8T	'CCCP-06181'	3135	33	PVX
Mil Mi-14PL	637	B 4006	637 (DDR), 95+06	PV
Mil Mi-24P	'13'	340337	442 (DDR), 96+47, 98+34	PVX
Mitsubishi A6M5 Zero Sen Model 52 (FSM)	'B1-05'		Centre section only.	PVX
Mraz M-1D Sokol	D-EJZO	336	OK-???, I-VARI, HB-TAS	PV
Nord N.2501 Noratlas	154	154	In French markings.	PV
North American NA-338 Bronco (OV-10B)	99+28	338-13	Bu158304, D-9557	PV
Panstwowe Zaklady Lotnicze (PZL) 106BR Kruk	SP-ZBH	07810145		PV
Pilatus P.3-03	A-808	325		PV
Potez-Heinkel CM 191B	D-9532	191-002		PV
Raab Krähe II	D-KONY	222	D-KAFA, OE-9008	PV
Republic F-84F Thunderstreak			52-6816, DD+108, DD+308, 'BA+102' -in false Italian markings.	PVX
Republic F-105F Thunderchief	63-8265	F-45		RA
Scheibe L-Spatz 55	D-8580	3		RA
Scheibe L-Spatz 55	D-1980	535		PV
Schleicher Ka-4 Rhönlerche II	D-8594	762		PV
Schleicher K.7	D-1952	7110		PV
Stampe & Vertongen S.V.4C (R)	'IF'	'1010'		RAX
Sud-Est SE.3130 Alouette II	75+35	1327	PE+136, PL+133, PK+203	PV
Sukhoi Su-22M4	25+14	26001	644 (DDR)	PV
Temple Wing TE F-3	D-MYAP			PV
Vereinigte Flugtechnische Werke – Fokker (VFW) 614	OY-TOR	G004	D-BABD	PV
Wright Flyer (R)				PV
Zlin Z-37A Cmelak	D-ESUU	19-18	DM-SUU, DDR-SUU	PV

TRADITIONSGEMEINSCHAFT JAGDBOMBERGESCHWADER 43 (GER149)

Address:	Flugabwehrraketengruppe 24, Fliegerhorst, D-26127 Oldenburg.
Tel:	0441-96173-110
Fax:	0441-96173-109
Admission:	By prior permission only.
Location:	In the western part of the city

Oldenburg has been a military town since the 1870s. In 1933 work started on converting a former drill field into an airfield. The first hangar was completed later in the year and a pilot training school moved in. During World War II fighter units were normally in residence. In 1944 the airfield suffered major damage in a bombing raid. Canadian forces captured the base in 1945 and soon after British troops used the airfield as a vehicle repair facility. Later the runways were repaired and extended for use by the Royal Air Force. In 1957 it was handed over to the new Luftwaffe who moved in a weapons training unit with Sabres. JBG 43 was formed at Oldenburg in 1966 and operated the Fiat G.91 for many years. The wing was disbanded in 1993 and the field became home to an air defence missile wing. This unit is due to move out shortly and parts of the airfield will be turned over to the community. The Traditions Room was set up to trace the history of the airfield and on outside display are three aircraft. It is hoped that the exhibition will remain on the site under local control.

TYPE	REG/SER	CON. NO.	PI/NOTES	STATUS
Canadair CL-13B Sabre 6 [North American F-86E]	JB+371	1813	BB+193, JB+377	RA
Dornier-Breguet Alpha Jet A	40+43	0043		RA
Fiat G.91R/3	31+01	91-367	KD+357, DG+115, MA+115	RA

UNITED STATES AIR FORCE BASE SPANGDAHLEM COLLECTION (GER150)

Address:	United States Air Force Base, Flugplatz 125, D-54529 Spangdahlem.
Tel:	06565-944602
Admission:	By prior permission only.
Location:	About 15 km. east of Bitburg.

The airfield opened in 1953 and the 10th Tactical Reconnaissance Wing moved in from Toul in France. This unit remained until 1959 when the 49th Tactical Fighter Wing arrived from Etain. The current occupant the 52nd TFW was formed at the field in December 1971. Spangdahlem is now the only remaining U.S.A.F. fighter base in Germany. Types flown are the General Dynamics F-16 and the Fairchild-Republic A-10A. A collection of types formerly flown by the unit has been preserved around the site.

TYPE	REG/SER	CON. NO.	PI/NOTES	STATUS
☐ Fairchild-Republic A-10A Thunderbolt II	77-0264	A10-189		PV
☐ General Dynamics 401 Fighting Falcon (F-16A)	'85-1552'	61-53	78-0057	PVX
☐ McDonnell M.98HO Phantom II (F-4E)	66-0308	2505		PV
☐ McDonnell M.199-1A Eagle (F-15A)	'85-552'	A046	74-0085	PVX
☐ Republic F-105G Thunderchief (F-105F)	62-4446	F-35		PV

UNITED STATES ARMY HANAU BASE MUSEUM (GER151)

Address:	Fliegerhorst Kaserne, Hanau Army Air Field, D-63452 Hanau.
Tel:	06183-513227
Admission:	By prior permission only.
Location:	About 15 km. east of Frankfurt-am-Main.

The airfield was built for the Luftwaffe in 1937 and officially opened on March 19th 1939. A squadron equipped with Heinkel He 111s moved in but their stay was short. For most of World War II a glider school used the facilities. D.F.S. 230s were used for instruction and he tug aircraft included Heinkel He 45s and He 46s. In the latter stages of the conflict Junkers 88s were flown on night missions. Bombing raids in late 1944 badly damaged the site. Intelligence had revealed that the Luftwaffe had plans to establish a Messerschmitt Me 262 unit and the runway had been extended for this purpose. American forces took over airfield but it was not until 1952 that it was fully operational. Many original buildings still survive around the site. The U.S. Army has flown helicopters and fixed wing types for many years. A small museum has been set up in one of the buildings. For a time a former Dutch Super Cub was on show but this has been replaced by the Kiowa.

TYPE	REG/SER	CON. NO.	PI/NOTES	STATUS
☐ Bell 206A Kiowa (OH-58A) (OH-58C)	70-15622	41173		PV

VERKEHRSMUSEUM (GER152)

Address:	Augustusstrasse 1, D-01067 Dresden.
Tel:	0351-8644-0
Fax:	0351-8644-110
Email:	vmuseum@verkehrsmuseum.sachsen.de
Admission:	Tuesday-Sunday 0900-1700
Location:	In the city centre just south of the River Elbe.

The museum was, for many years, the main transport and communications museum of the D.D.R. Unification of the country has resulted in a few changes to the displays which are all well laid out and informative. Sections devoted to motoring and the railways have many early vehicles on show. The development of public transport is portrayed with trams and buses on view. Shipping on the Elbe is also shown in detail. The aviation section highlights the work of pioneer aviators and has a number of models on show. In 1960 Frau Käthe Grade donated the major components of an original Eindecker to the museum and a restoration was carried out incorporating several new parts. This monoplane had been stored by the family for around half a century. The Aero 45 was imported into East Germany in 1957 for use by the national airline. The aircraft then served on liaison duties at Dessau with the Air Force from 1962 until donated to the museum two years later. Ballooning took place in the area in the pioneer days and a replica basket is on show. The development of air travel and control is shown and a large working model of an airport is on display. Gliding was a very popular sport in East Germany and many clubs were set up. Pre-war designs were put back into production, sailplanes were imported from Poland and Czechoslovakia and new indigenous models appeared. The Lom Meise first flew in 1956 and almost one hundred and fifty appeared over the next two years. The Motte is an ultralight dating from 1994.

TYPE	REG/SER	CON. NO.	PI/NOTES	STATUS
☐ Aero Super 45S	'DM-VMD'	04-002	OK-???, DM-SGE, 555, DM-NVA'	PVX
☐ Balloon			Basket only	PV
☐ Blériot XI (R)				PV
☐ Friedel Motte	D-MAIL			PV
☐ Grade Eindecker		2	Partial replica	PV
☐ Lilienthal Normal-Segelapparat (R)				PV
☐ Volkseigener Betrieb Apparatebau Lommatzsch Meise	DM-2075	0075		RA

WEHRTECHNISCHE STUDIENSAMMLUNG (GER153)

Address:	Bundesamtes für Wehrtechnik und Beschaffung, Mayener Strasse 87, Postfach 73 60, D-56057 Koblenz.
Tel:	0261-400-1423
Fax:	0261-400-1424
Email:	WTS@BWB.ORG
Admission:	Daily 0930-1630 ; Closed December 24 – January 2.
Location:	In the Lützel area of the city just just north of the Europa Bridge.

This display of military equipment opened on November 12th 1982 and consisted mainly of weapons, ammunition, wheeled and tracked vehicles, naval equipment, communications, optical devices and clothing. The policy was, initially, to obtain aircraft which made significant contributions to the advancement of technology. This has now been widened to include a range of military types. The first to arrive at the museum was the second prototype VAK-191B VTOL experimental jet which first flew in 1971. In August 1982 the aircraft was moved from Bremen to Koblenz suspended under a CH-53G helicopter. The Starfighter on show is fitted with an additional small wing for fly-by-wire tests of a control vehicle. The Firebird ultralight was used in a series of trials at Manching. The SG.1162 was also used on this work and this type is on show. Fairly recent arrivals are three former East German Air Force machines and the Alpha Jet. In the 1960s and 1970s the Dornier company produced a number of remotely controlled helicopters for battlefield surveillance. Examples of these can be seen in the display. In the early 1980s the Vinten company built examples of the Wallis autogyro with the eventual aim of putting the type into production. Only two were completed and flown. Both are in the collection with the first prototype out on loan to Flugausstellung Junior. Also on view are many instruments, control systems etc. showing the rapid advances made in the technology associated with military aircraft. Some types have left the exhibition and replaced with more modern designs whilst others have been loaned out.

TYPE	REG/SER	CON. NO.	PI/NOTES	STATUS
☐ Dassault Mirage IIIC	27	10		PV
☐ Dornier Do 32K	005	005		PV
☐ Dornier Do 34 Kiebitz	98+24	P02		PV
☐ Dornier-Breguet Alpha Jet A	98+55	03	F-ZWRV, 40+01	PV
☐ Fiat G.91R/3	32+06	91-474	KD+464, BD+262	PV
☐ Lockheed 580 (T-33A)	94+39	580-8901	53-5562, AB+763, DF+382 – on loan to Flugausstellung Junior.	–
☐ Lockheed 683-10-19 Starfighter (F-104G)	22+40	683-7118	KE+418, DD+110 – on loan to Musée de l'Air, France.	–
☐ Lockheed 683-10-19 Starfighter (F-104G) (F-104CCV)	98+36	683-8100	KG+200, JA+244, JD+256, 23+91	PV
☐ Mikoyan-Gurevich MiG-21bisSAU	'2'	75051402	846 (DDR), 24+20 – in false Soviet markings.	PVX
☐ Mikoyan-Gurevich MiG-23BN	'7'	0393214218	702 (DDR), 20+48 – in false Soviet markings.	PVX
☐ Mil Mi-24P	98+33	340330	357 (DDR), 96+40	PV
☐ Nord N.2501 Noratlas	199	199		PV
☐ Schwebegestell SG.1162		5		PV
☐ Schweiger Firebird M 1	98+56	065108		RA
☐ Sud-Est SE.3130 Alouette II	75+52	1402	PB+133, YA+031	PV
☐ Vereinigte Flugtechnische Werke – Fokker (VFW) VAK-191B	D-9564	V-2		PV
☐ Vinten VJ-22 Autogyro (Vinten Wallis WA-116MC)	G-55-2	UMA-01	G-BKLZ – on loan to Flugausstellung Junior.	–
☐ Vinten VJ-22 Autogyro (Vinten Wallis WA-116MC)	G-55-1	UMA-02		PV
☐ Westland-Sikorsky WS-55 Whirlwind HAR.10	XP339	WA.355	On loan to MLT Wernigerode.	–

WÜRZBURG MUSEUM (GER154)

Address:	D-97070 Würzburg.
Admission:	-
Location:	In the town which is just north of the E 43.

Some time ago there was a report of a museum containing the wreckage excavated from more than a dozen sites around Germany. These were mainly from the World War II period. Components and engines from German and Allied aircraft were recovered. Efforts to trace the collection have proved unsuccessful. The former East German Air Force two seat MiG-21 was also supposed to be going to an exhibition in Würzburg. I have been informed that plans for a local technical museum were drawn up. Are these three stories connected? I would welcome any further information in order to clear up the confusion.

TYPE	REG/SER	CON. NO.	PI/NOTES	STATUS
☐ Mikoyan-Gurevich MiG-21UM	23+80	04695163	206 (DDR)	PV

ZEPPELIN MUSEUM FRIEDRICHSHAFEN (GER155)

Address:	Seestrasse 22, D-88045 Friedrichshafen.
Tel:	07541-3801-0
Fax:	07541-3801-81
Email:	zeppelin@zeppelin-museum.de
Admission:	May-June,October Tuesday-Sunday 1000-1700; June-September daily 1000-1700; November-April Tuesday-Sunday 1000-1700.
Location:	In the centre of the town by the lake.

Ferdinand von Zeppelin was born on July 8th 1838 in the Bodensee area. After a successful military career he retired in 1890. Five years later he applied for a patent for large airship. Construction of a floating hangar on the Bodensee began in June 1899 and just over a year later LZ 1 airship flew. Public donations and lottery money enabled the construction of several more machines and commercial and military successes followed. In the inter-war period the 'Graf Zeppelin' and 'Hindenburg' made many long distance flights. The first museum in the area opened in 1912 and featured the work of Zeppelin in its displays. After World War II a Zeppelin Museum was set up with models and memorabilia on show. A move was made to the restored Harbour Railway Station and this new display opened on July 2nd 1996. A superb exhibition tracing the history and development of the Zeppelin has been staged. The work of other airship constructors is also featured. The highlight is a one hundred and eight foot long replica of part of the LZ-129 'Hindenburg'. The visitor can view passenger and crew areas and marvel at the complexity of the construction Engines, components, models, photographs, instruments, uniforms. Crockery and cutlery used on airships can also be seen.

TYPE	REG/SER	CON. NO.	PI/NOTES	STATUS
☐ Zeppelin LZ-129 (R)			Partial section.	PV

ZEPPELIN MUSEUM MEERSBURG (GER156)

Address:	Schlossplatz 8, D-88708 Meersburg.
Tel:	07532-7909
Admission:	March-November daily 1000-1800.
Location:	In the centre of the town.

Hans Urban began collecting Zeppelin items several years ago. He moved to Meersburg on Lake Constance which is near to the site of the airship factory. On show are many photographs and models along with documents and personal items. There are small components from several Zeppelins to be seen. The development of Zeppelin's airships from the LZ-1 up to the LZ-130 is traced in this infomative exhibition.

ZEPPELIN MUSEUM NEU-ISENBURG (GER157)

Address:	Kapitän-Lehmann-Strasse 2, D-63263 Neu-Isenburg.
Tel:	069-694390
Fax:	069-692016
Admission:	Friday 1300-1700, Saturday-Sunday 1000-1700.
Location:	About 10 km. south of Frankfurt-am-Main just south of the A.3.

This museum opened in 1988 in a specially designed building. The roof replicates the structure of a Zeppelin showing in detail the methods of construction used by the builders. On show are many models, documents, uniforms, components and photographs tracing the history and development of these large airships. A reconstruction of a small part of the promenade deck of the LZ-129 Hindenburg is one of the highlights of this excellent display. This shows the luxury which the wealthy passengers could expect.

TYPE	REG/SER	CON. NO.	PI/NOTES	STATUS
☐ Zeppelin LZ-129 (R)			Partial section.	PV

The unique F-104G ZELL Starfighter which was fitted with a rocket motor for ramp launching. The aircraft is at the Luftwaffenmuseum at Gatow.

The main hall at the Otto Lilienthal Museum at Anklam contains replicas of all his designs. Shown here is the Grosser vDoppeldecker.

This giant Antonov An-22 dominates one part of the outside area at the Technikmuseum Speyer. (Douglas Rough)

Parked outside in the Greek Air Force Museum area at Tatoi is this Grumman Albatross. (Trevor Stone)

The collection at Sedes Air Force Base includes this Republic Thunderflash.

The Greek Air Force flew many Starfighters and one is now outside the War Museum in Athens. (Douglas Rough)

GREECE

ANDRAVIDA AIR FORCE BASE COLLECTION (GRE1)

Address:	117 Pterix Makhis, Andravida Air Force Base.
Admission:	By prior permission only.
Location:	About 5 km north east of the town

The field is home to a Phantom wing, the Operational Conversion Unit for the type and the Air Force Gunnery School. Squadrons from other bases are frequent visitors to Andravida for weapons training. The site has been home to fighter units for many years and also serves as the civil airport for the popular holiday region. The four preserved aircraft represent types which have been based at the field in the past or those which used the nearby ranges. A small display park has been set up just inside the main gate.

TYPE	REG/SER	CON. NO.	PI/NOTES	STATUS
☐ Canadair CL-13 Sabre 2 [North American F-86E]	19243	143	19243 (Canada)	RA
☐ Lockheed 683-10-19 Starfighter (F-104G)	22304	683D-6003	62-12304	RA
☐ Northrop N-156A Freedom Fighter (F-5A)	89053	N.6424	68-9053, 89053 (Jordan)	RA
☐ Republic F-84F Thunderstreak	37145		53-7145	RA

ARAXOS AIR FORCE BASE MEMORIAL PARK (GRE2)

Address:	116 Pterix Makhis, Araxos Air Force Base.
Admission:	By prior permission only.
Location:	About 30 km south west of Patria.

The wing currently operates Vought Corsairs in the fighter bomber role. These ex-U.S. Navy aircraft replaced the Starfighter in the early 1990s. In addition there is a search and rescue detachment in residence. A memorial park has been set up on the parade ground close to the main gate.

TYPE	REG/SER	CON. NO.	PI/NOTES	STATUS
☐ Lockheed 580 (T-33A)	58646	580-1615	58-0646	RA
☐ Lockheed 683-10-19 Starfighter (F-104G)	5961	583-5961	KF+261, KE+119, 28+31	RA
☐ Lockheed 683-10-19 Starfighter (F-104G)	7097	683-7097	KE+397, VA+117, 22+22	RA
☐ Lockheed 683-10-19 Starfighter (F-104G)	'12307'	683D-6006	62-12307,22307	RAX
☐ Lockheed 683-10-19 Starfighter (F-104G)	32708	683D-6060	63-12708	RA
☐ Republic F-84F Thunderstreak	37230		53-7230	RA

ASKIFOU WAR MUSEUM (GRE3)

Address:	Askifou Skafia, Crete
Admission:	By prior permission only.
Location:	On the south coast of the island about 50 km south of Chania.

This private collection of memorabilia has been assembled by George Hatzidakis. There is large part of the fuselage frame of a D.F.S. 230 glider along with components from other aircraft.

TYPE	REG/SER	CON. NO.	PI/NOTES	STATUS
☐ Jacobs D.F.S. 230C-1			Fuselage frame only.	RAD

BATTLESHIP AVEROFF NAVAL MUSEUM (GRE4)

Address:	Trocadero Marina, Neo Faliro, Athens.
Tel:	2109836539
Admission:	Monday Wednesday-Friday 1100-1300 1500-1700; Saturday-Sunday 1100-1500.
Location:	In the southern part of the city.

The ship played a key role in the 1912-1913 Balkan War against the Ottoman Empire. It then had a long and distinguished career in both peacetime and other conflicts. Now it is parked at the marina and on board are displays tracing the maritime history of the country. The story of life aboard a warship in battle conditions is portrayed in detail. The Freedom Fighter is parked on the quayside nearby.

TYPE	REG/SER	CON. NO.	PI/NOTES	STATUS
☐ Northrop N-156A Freedom Fighter (F-5A)	97175	N.6492	69-7175	PV

ELEFSIS AIR FORCE BASE HERITAGE PARK (GRE5)

Address:	112 Pterix Mahis, Elefsis Air Force Base.
Admission:	By prior permission only.
Location:	Just north of the town which is about 20 km north west of Athens.

This important base close to Athens houses the Orions operated by the Naval Air Service, transport units of the Air Force and an Air Sea Rescue helicopter detachment. The Canadair CL-215 and CL-415 water bombers are also in residence. The Heritage Park has recently been set up near the main gate. The types preserved all have connections with the field. The Navy flew the Grumman Albatross from the late 1970s until the mid-1990s. The Noratlas was once the mainstay of the transport fleet and a small number of Dornier Do 28s remain in use.

TYPE	REG/SER	CON. NO.	PI/NOTES	STATUS
☐ Convair 8-10 Delta Dagger (F-102A)	'61052'		56-1059, 61059	RA
☐ Convair 8-12 Delta Dagger (TF-102A)	62326		56-2326	RA
☐ Dornier Do 28D-2 Skyservant	4138	4138	58+63	RA
☐ Douglas DC-3A-467 Skytrain (C-47B)	92626		49-2626	RA
☐ Grumman G-111 Albatross (G-64) (SA-16A) (SA-16B) (HU-16B)	510070	G-149	51-0070	RA
☐ Grumman G-111 Albatross (G-64) (SA-16A) (SA-16B) (HU-16B)	517203	G-272	51-7203 – at 253 Mira area.	RA
☐ Lockheed 580 (T-33A)	54951	580-9911	55-4951	RA
☐ Nihon Kokuki Seizo Kabushiki Kaisha (NAMC) YS-11A-220	2137	2137	SX-BBH	RA
☐ Nord N.2501D Noratlas	52-128	030	GB+106, (GA+106), GA+246, 52+28	RA
☐ Nord N.2501D Noratlas	53-234	157	KA+168, AS+594, 53+34	RA
☐ Northrop N-156A Freedom Fighter (F-5A)	69136	N.6240	66-9136 – at north gate.	RA

HELLINIKI AEROPORIA MOUSSIO (GRE6)

Address:	Dekelia Air Force Base, 1010 Athens.
Tel:	01-246-1661
Admission:	By prior permission only.
Location:	About 10 km north east of the of the city

In 1912 the Greek Army established a flying unit at Larissa with four Farman biplanes and two years later a Naval Aviation Service was set up. Over the next twenty years the two forces operated mainly British and French types. The State Aircraft Factory was established and in 1926 its first aircraft, a licence built Blackburn Velos, flew. In 1935 the Royal Hellenic Air Force was formed and new types were ordered. Fighter units operated the Polish P.Z.L. 24F. Bristol Blenheim and Fairey Battle bombers were ordered from Britain. France supplied Bloch M.B.151 fighters and Potez 63 bombers. After the country was liberated in October 1944 Britain and the U.S.A. supplied aircraft to the new Air Force. In 1952 Greece joined NATO and American jets were delivered in considerable numbers. Initially Canadair Sabres, T-33s and F-84G Thunderjets flew with the service. These were later replaced by the F-84F Thunderstreak, F-104 Starfighter and F-5 Freedom Fighter. In 1985 a decision was made to assemble items for a museum. A large quantity of historical artefacts, photographs and documents was collected. A hangar has been allocated at Dekelia and aircraft are undergoing restoration. The Spitfire, which was for many years on show at the War Museum in Athens, has now been rebuilt. The rare Curtiss Helldiver, the only example of its type in Europe, also moved from the city. A small number of these were used in the war against the Communists in the late 1940s. Under restoration at Ellinikon is a Junkers Ju 52 which was recovered from Alinta Bay in October 2003. The aircraft came down in the sea after a paratroop dropping mission attacking the island of Leros on November 12th 1943. This aircraft may eventually be displayed in a new war museum proposed for Leros. Also raised from the deep is the Rootes built Bristol Blenheim which was shot down near Retimo on April 28th 1941. Over fifty German built Nord Noratlases were delivered in the late 1960s and early 1970s. They were operational until 1986. The aircraft in the collection was for many years an instructional airframe at a technical school on the base and it is due to be restored in the near future. Greece was one of the few European countries to use the Convair F-102 and a pair of two seaters has been saved. Two Starfighters are resplendent in special schemes. One is in 'Tiger Meet' colours and the other has an eagle painted along its fuselage with a background of snow topped mountains. As types are withdrawn from use examples will be allocated to the collection. The museum is still classified as an active unit so is only open one day a year. Plans are being drawn up to allow access on a more regular basis and hopefully this will occur soon.

TYPE	REG/SER	CON. NO.	PI/NOTES	STATUS
☐ Agusta-Bell 47J-2	066	2060	Boom from c/n 2064.	RA
☐ Bell 47G-2 Sioux (H-13H) (OH-13H)	5322	2335	58-5322	RA
☐ Bell 47G-2 Sioux (H-13H) (OH-13H)	5385	2398	58-5385	RA
☐ Bell 47G-3B-2 Sioux (TH-13T)	ΕΣ-713	4006	69-19626	RA
☐ Bristol 149 Blenheim IV	L9044			RAD
☐ Canadair CL-13 Sabre 2 [North American F-86E]	'12910'	68	19168	RAX
☐ Canadair CL-13 Sabre 2 [North American F-86E]	'19202'	69	19169	RAX
☐ Canadair CL-13 Sabre 2 [North American F-86E]	19199	99		RA
☐ Cessna 318B Tweety Bird (T-37B)	74742	40997	67-14742	RA
☐ Cessna 318C Tweety Bird (T-37C)	01959	42014	70-1959	RA
☐ Consolidated 28-5A Canso A	5B-PBY	CV-333	11042 (Canada), CF-PQF, C-FPQF – privately owned.	RAAX
☐ Convair 8-12 Delta Dagger (TF-102A)	54035		55-4035	RA
☐ Convair 8-12 Delta Dagger (TF-102A)	62335		56-2335	RA
☐ Curtiss 84G Helldiver (SB2C-5)	83321		Bu83321	RA
☐ De Havilland D.H.82A Tiger Moth	G776	85063	T6776	RA
☐ Douglas DC-3A-467 Skytrain (C-47B) (Dakota IV)	KJ960	14807/26252	43-48991	RA
☐ Douglas DC-3A-467 Skytrain (C-47B)	43-49111	14927/26372		RA
☐ Douglas DC-3A-467 Skytrain (C-47B) (Dakota IV)	KK169	15415/26860	43-49599	RA
☐ Grumman G-111 Albatross (G-64) (SA-16A) (SA-16B) (HU-16B)	15289	G-171	51-5289	RA
☐ Grumman G-111 Albatross (G-64) (SA-16A) (SA-16B) (HU-16B)	51-7190	G-250		RA
☐ Grumman G-111 Albatross (G-64) (SA-16A) (SA-16B) (HU-16B)	51-7204	G-274		RA
☐ Grumman G-159 Gulfstream I	P9	120		RA
☐ Junkers Ju 52/3mg3e	DI+KG	7607	4V+BT – at Ellinikon AFB.	RAC

TYPE	REG/SER	CON. NO.	PI/NOTES	STATUS
☐ Lockheed 580 (T-33A)	58519	580-1568	58-0519	RA
☐ Lockheed 580 (T-33A)	16714	580-6046	51-6714, 14693 (Canada)	RA
☐ Lockheed 580 (T-33A)	29805	580-8065	52-9805	RA
☐ Lockheed 580 (T-33A)	35029	580-8368	53-5029	RA
☐ Lockheed 580 (T-33A)	35328	580-8667	53-5328	RA
☐ Lockheed 580 (T-33A)	41614	580-9350	54-1614	RA
☐ Lockheed 580 (T-33A)	35890	580-9366	53-5890	RA
☐ Lockheed 583-10-20 Starfighter (TF-104G)	22278	583C-5523	62-12278,CE.8-1 (Spain)	RA
☐ Lockheed 583-10-20 Starfighter (TF-104G)	5908	583F-5908	KF+208, TB+261, TA+164, 27+79	RA
☐ Lockheed 683-10-19 Starfighter (F-104G)	'2691'		Front fuselage only.	RA
☐ Lockheed 683-10-19 Starfighter (F-104G)	32720	683-6072	63-12720, C.8-5 (Spain)	RA
☐ Lockheed 683-10-19 Starfighter (F-104G)	6699	683-6699	D-6699 (Netherlands)	RA
☐ Lockheed 683-10-19 Starfighter (F-104G)	7151	683-7151	KE+451, VA+127, 22+70	RA
☐ Lockheed 683-10-19 Starfighter (F-104G)	7415	683-7415	26+69	RA
☐ Mignet HM-14 Pou-du-Ciel				RA
☐ North American NA-88 Texan (AT-6D)	751		49-2751	RA
☐ North American NA-168 Texan (T-6G)	830			RA
☐ North American NA-168 Texan (T-6G)	49-3424	168-548		RA
☐ North American NA-168 Texan (T-6G)	49-3409	182-533		RA
☐ North American NA-168 Texan (T-6G)	93514	168-658	49-3514	RA
☐ North American NA-190 Sabre (F-86D)	'998'			RA
☐ North American NA-190 Sabre (F-86D)	52-10067	190-792		RA
☐ Nord N.2501D Noratlas (N.2508)	53-258	001A (02)	F-WJDZ, YA+035, 53+58	RA
☐ Northrop N-156A Freedom Fighter (F-5A)	38405	N.6042	63-8405	RA
☐ Northrop N-156A Freedom Fighter (F-5A)	10541	N.6202	65-10541, 3-536 (Iran)	RA
☐ Northrop N-156A Freedom Fighter (RF-5A)	97170	RF.1050	69-7170	RA
☐ Piper PA-18-135 Super Cub	SX-AGU	18-5066	(Greek A.F.), SX-ADS	RA
☐ Piper PA-18-135 Super Cub (L-21B)	246		Fuselage frame only.	RA
☐ Republic F-84F Thunderstreak	26743		52-6743, (DR+126), DD+126, DD+326	RA
☐ Republic F-84F Thunderstreak	'26595'		52-6822 or 52-6361	RAX
☐ Republic F-84F Thunderstreak	26919		52-6919	RA
☐ Republic RF-84F Thunderflash	17011		51-17011, EB+237, EB+337	RA
☐ Republic F-84G Thunderjet	'998'		51-11082	RAX
☐ Sikorsky S-55D Chickasaw (H-19B) (UH-19B)	13952		51-3952	RA
☐ Supermarine 361 Spitfire LF.IXc	'TA854'		MJ755	RAX
☐ Wytwornia Sprzetu Komunikacyjnego (WSK) Lim-2 [MiG-15bis]	'925'	1B 018-03	1803 (Poland), '301'	RAX

IRAKLION AIR FORCE BASE COLLECTION (GRE7)

Address:	126 Sminarkia Makhis, Iraklion Air Force Base, Crete.
Admission:	By prior permission only.
Location:	About 5 km east of the town.

This field is currently home to a Mirage F.1CG squadron. Forty were delivered in 1974 when tension with Turkey was high and the U.S.A. would not supply combat types. Five aircraft are preserved around the base.

TYPE	REG/SER	CON. NO.	PI/NOTES	STATUS
☐ Canadair CL-226 Freedom Fighter (NF-5B) [Northrop N-156B]	4027	4027	K-4027 (Netherlands)	RA
☐ Northrop N-156A Freedom Fighter (F-5A)	69133	N.6237	66-9133	RA
☐ Northrop N-156A Freedom Fighter (F-5A)	13371	N.7004	63-13371, 371 (Norway)	RA
☐ Republic F-84F Thunderstreak	??745			RA
☐ Republic RF-84F Thunderflash	27468		52-7468	RA

LARISSA AIR FORCE BASE COLLECTION (GRE8)

Address:	110 Pterix Makhis Larissa Air Force Base Larissa.
Admission:	By prior permission only.
Location:	About 4 km east of the city off the E75.

Larissa is the site of the Tactical Air Command Headquarters of the Hellenic Air Force. The 110 Pterix Museum opened in September 1993 and its displays trace the history of the unit and its aircraft. Models, components, uniforms, photographs and memorabilia can be seen. The types on show have all been flown from the field in recent years and the majority are parked outside the exhibition building.

TYPE	REG/SER	CON. NO.	PI/NOTES	STATUS
☐ Canadair CL-13 Sabre 2 [North American F-86E]	19409	309	19409 (Canada)	RA
☐ Convair 8-10 Delta Dagger (F-102A)	61232		56-1232	RA
☐ Lockheed 580 (T-33A)	29913	580-7884	52-9913	RA
☐ Lockheed 580 (T-33A)	35494	580-8833	53-5494	RA
☐ Lockheed 683-04-10 Starfighter (RF-104G)	6692	683-6692	KC+165, VB+226, 21+31	RA
☐ Lockheed 683-10-19 Starfighter (F-104G)	6668	683-6668	D-6668 (Netherlands) – at HQ.	RA
☐ Northrop N-156A Freedom Fighter (F-5A)	38430	N.6067	63-8430 – on gate.	RA
☐ Northrop N-156A Freedom Fighter (F-5A)	89083	N.6454	68-9063 – at HQ.	RA
☐ Northrop N-156A Freedom Fighter (F-5A)	69209	N.7032	66-9209, 209 (Norway)	RA
☐ Republic F-84F Thunderstreak	37050		53-7050, DB+252, DB+383	RA
☐ Republic RF-84F Thunderflash	28728		52-8728	RA
☐ Republic RF-84F Thunderflash	37588		53-7588 – on gate.	RA
☐ Republic F-84G Thunderjet	19752		51-9752	RA

MACEDONIAN AERO CLUB COLLECTION (GRE9)

Address:	Mikra Airport, Thessaloniki.
Tel:	02310-476000
Email:	aeroclub-tsle@otnet.gr
Admission:	By prior permission only.
Location:	The airfield is about 10 km south of the city.

The aero club has set up a display outside its buildings. Many C-47s and Canadair Sabres were operated by the Air Force from the field and one of each has been preserved. The F-84F is at the gate to the military base.

TYPE	REG/SER	CON. NO.	PI/NOTES	STATUS
☐ Canadair CL-13 Sabre 2 [North American F-86E]	19294	194	At nearby petrol station.	PV
☐ Douglas DC-3A-456 Skytrain (C-47A)	92613		(USAAF), 49-2613	PV
☐ Republic F-84F Thunderstreak	26686		52-6686 – on military base.	RA

MALEME COLLECTION (GRE10)

Address:	Maleme, Chania, Crete.
Admission:	By prior permission only.
Location:	About 15 km west of Hania.

A collection of preserved aircraft is being assembled for a proposed museum. The history of the Air Force on Crete will be shown. The base is used as a relief field for Souda and F-16s can often be seen training here. German paratroops landed at Maleme in their 1941 invasion and many bitter conflicts took place in the area.

TYPE	REG/SER	CON. NO.	PI/NOTES	STATUS
☐ Bell 205 Iroquois (UH-1H)				RA
☐ Lockheed 580 (T-33A)	17549	580-7694	51-17549	RA
☐ Lockheed 683-10-19 Starfighter (F-104G)	7088	683-7088	KE+388, VA+108, 22+17	RA
☐ Northrop N-156A Freedom Fighter (F-5A)	13366	N.6135	64-13366	RA
☐ Republic F-84F Thunderstreak	37218		53-7218	RA
☐ Republic RF-84F Thunderflash	28740		52-8740	RA

MESSOLONGI MOUSSIO (GRE11)

Address:	Messolongi.
Admission:	Aircraft on permanent view.
Location:	In a park in the town which is about 40 km north west of Patra.

A museum is being established at the location of the famous battle. During World War II the town was almost completely destroyed and the story of the conflict will be portrayed in detail. More types are expected.

TYPE	REG/SER	CON. NO.	PI/NOTES	STATUS
☐ Lockheed 580 (T-33A)	35265	580-8604	53-5265	PV
☐ Lockheed 683-10-19 Starfighter (F-104G)	32730	683D-6082	63-12730, C.8-7 (Spain)	PV
☐ Northrop N-156A Freedom Fighter (F-5A)	70376	N.6498	70-1376, (Iran), 01376 (Jordan)	PV
☐ Republic F-84F Thunderstreak	26914		52-6914	PV
☐ Republic RF-84F Thunderflash	37575		53-7575, BD+251, EA+365, EB+325	PV

MOUSSIO SCHOLIS IKARON (GRE12)

Address:	Dekelia Air Force Base, 1010 Athens.
Admission:	By prior permission only.
Location:	About 10 km north east of the city

The Ikarus School trains officers for the Air Force. A small museum in the building traces the history of the establishment. A collection of preserved aircraft is displayed in the grounds of the academy.

TYPE	REG/SER	CON. NO.	PI/NOTES	STATUS
☐ Canadair CL-13 Sabre 2 [North American F-86E]	19146	46		RA
☐ Cessna 318C Tweety Bird (T-37C)	25970	40763	62-5970	RA
☐ Convair 8-10 Delta Dagger (F-102A)	61233		56-1233	RA
☐ Lockheed 580 (T-33A)	16717	580-6049	51-6717	RA
☐ Lockheed 580 (T-33A)	36129	580-9750	53-6129	RA
☐ Lockheed 583-10-20 Starfighter (TF-104G)	5958	583F-5958	KF+258, KE+116, KE+216, EB+376, 28+28	RA
☐ North American NA-168 Texan (T-6G)				RA
☐ Northrop N-156A Freedom Fighter (RF-5A)	97166	RF.1046	69-7166	RA
☐ Republic F-84F Thunderstreak				RA
☐ Republic F-84F Thunderstreak	26837		52-6837 – on base gate.	PV
☐ Republic RF-84F Thunderflash	37665		53-7665, BD+243, EA+243, EA+343, EB+328	RA

NEA ANKHIALOS AIR FORCE BASE COLLECTION (GRE13)

Address:	111 Pterix Makhis, Nea Ankhialos Air Force Base.
Admission:	By prior permission only.
Location:	South of the town which is about 20 km south west of Volos.

This important base is home to F-16 units and a helicopter detachment. The Canadian built Sabre is mounted on a pole near the station headquarters alongside one of the F-5s.

TYPE	REG/SER	CON. NO.	PI/NOTES	STATUS
☐ Canadair CL-13 Sabre 2 [North American F-86E]	19448	348	19448 (Canada)	RA
☐ Lockheed 580 (T-33A)	34916	580-8255	53-4916	RA
☐ Northrop N-156A Freedom Fighter (F-5A)	38416	N.6053	63-8416	RA
☐ Northrop N-156A Freedom Fighter (F-5A)	689072	N.6443	68-9072	RA
☐ Northrop N-156A Freedom Fighter (F-5A)	689073	N.6444	68-9073, (Jordan), (Iran)	RA
☐ Northrop N-156A Freedom Fighter (F-5A)	689077	N.6448	68-9077, (Iran), 89077 (Jordan)	RA
☐ Republic F-84F Thunderstreak	26831		52-6831	RA

POLEMICO MOUSSIO (GRE14)

Address:	Vasilissis and 2 Rizari Street, Athens 139.
Tel:	01-729-0543
Admission:	Tuesday-Saturday 0900-1400; Sunday and Public Holidays 0930-1400.
Location:	In the city centre near the Hilton Hotel

The Hellenic War Museum opened in July 1975 and its displays trace the development of military history and technology up to the present day. All three branches of the Greek services are portrayed. The aviation section highlights military flying in the country since 1912. Four Farman biplanes were used in the 1912/3 Balkan War and the first mission was flown by Lieutenant D. Caberos from Larissa. The replica on show was built by the State Aircraft Factory in 1968. After World War II Britain and the U.S.A. supplied a number of aircraft to assist in the rebuilding of the Air Force. A campaign against Communist fighters started soon after. The Air Force bombed several targets and the rebellion was quashed by 1949.

TYPE	REG/SER	CON. NO.	PI/NOTES	STATUS
☐ Bell 47-3B-1 Sioux (OH-13S)	ΕΣ-709	4002	69-19622	PV
☐ Farman MF-7 (R)				PV
☐ Lockheed 683-10-19 Starfighter (F-104G)	6695	683-6695	D-6695 (Netherlands)	PV
☐ North American NA-168 Texan (T-6G)	'32803'	168-644	41-32803, 49-3500	PVX
☐ North American NA-173 Sabre (F-86D)	'51-6171'	173-537	51-8404 – tail from c/n 171-315 51-6171.	PVX
☐ Northrop N-156A Freedom Fighter (F-5A)	89071	N.6442	68-9071, (Iran), (Jordan)	PV
☐ Piper J-3C-65 Cub (L-4H)	241		(USAAF)	RA
☐ Republic F-84F Thunderstreak	37216		53-7216, DB+244, DB+344	PV

SEDES AIR FORCE BASE MUSEUM (GRE15)

Address:	355 Mira, Sedes Air Force Base, Thessaloniki.
Admission:	By prior permission only.
Location:	About 10 km south of the city.

Flying from the field is a detachment of 355 Mira who still operate several C-47s with the last scheduled to retire in 2007. They also use the nearby airfield at Mikra. A former Royal Air Force Dakota is on show along with an ex-German Noratlas. A Greek Army Aviation unit is also in residence. Fighter aircraft flew with 113 Pterik Makhis which was disbanded in 2001. The museum traces the long history of the base and its units. On show are photographs, documents, models, uniforms and badges along with components and instruments.

TYPE	REG/SER	CON. NO.	PI/NOTES	STATUS
☐ Boeing-Stearman E75 Kaydet (PT-13D) (N2S-5)	SX-AGI	75-8499	42-109466, Bu43505, N43505	RA
☐ Canadair CL-30 Silver Star 3 (CT-133) [Lockheed 580 (T-33AN)]	21367	T33-367		RA
☐ Canadair CL-226 Freedom Fighter (NF-5A) [Northrop N-156A]	'05'	3031	K-3031 (Netherlands), 3031	RAX
☐ Convair 8-10 Delta Dagger (F-102A)	61031		56-1031	RA
☐ Douglas DC-3A-467 Skytrain (C-47B) (Dakota IV)	KN542	16398/33146	44-76814	RA
☐ Lockheed 580 (T-33A)	16713	580-6045	51-6713	RA
☐ Lockheed 580 (T-33A)	35629	580-8968	53-5629, AB+778, BD+778, 94+48	RA
☐ Lockheed 583-10-20 Starfighter (TF-104G)	5708	583D-5708	61-3037, DA+037, BB+107, DA+370, 27+07	RA
☐ Nord N.2501D Noratlas	53-241	164	KA+175, GB+234, 53+41	RA
☐ Northrop N-156A Freedom Fighter (F-5A)	89065	N.6436	68-9065, 89065 (Iran)	RA
☐ Republic RF-84F Thunderflash	37682		53-7682, BD+113, EA+113, EA+313, EB+334	RA

SOUDA AIR FORCE BASE COLLECTION (GRE16)

Address:	115 Pterix Makhis, Souda Air Force Base, Hania, Crete.
Admission:	By prior permission only.
Location:	On the north side of the island of Crete about 15 km east of Hania.

General Dynamics F-16Cs and F-16Ds moved into this airfield, located on the island of Crete, in 2003. They replaced the Vought A-7 Corsairs which transferred to Araxos. The site is often visited by aircraft from other European forces and three aircraft are displayed in the 'NATO Air Park'. The resident wing, 115 Pterix, flew Thunderjets, Thunderstreaks and Thunderflashes in the past. T-33s were once used for target towing.

TYPE	REG/SER	CON. NO.	PI/NOTES	STATUS
☐ Canadair CL-30 Silver Star 3 (CT-133) [Lockheed 580 (T-33AN)]	21596	T33-596		RA
☐ Lockheed 580 (T-33A)	58683	580-1732	58-0683	RA
☐ Lockheed 580 (T-33A)	36000	580-9532	53-6000	RA
☐ Republic F-84F Thunderstreak	'815'		53-7218, 37218	RAX
☐ Republic F-84F Thunderstreak	26744		52-6744	RA
☐ Republic F-84F Thunderstreak	36745		53-6735	RA

STEFANOVIKION ARMY BASE COLLECTION (GRE17)

Address:	Scholi Aeroporias Stratou, Stefanavikion.
Admission:	By prior permission only.
Location:	Near Larissa AFB.

The aviation branch of the Greek Army was formed in 1956 and operates a small number of fixed wing aircraft and a variety of helicopters. The first types used were Cessna U-17s and a solitary Beaver. Later Bell 47 helicopters were added. Three bases are now in use and types flown include the Nardi-Hughes 300C, Chinook and Apache. Several aircraft, including the three Aero Commanders used, are now preserved. One of the Bell 47s has been painted in the markings of the first helicopter flown by the service. There is a small display tracing the history of Army flying in one of the buildings.

TYPE	REG/SER	CON. NO.	PI/NOTES	STATUS
☐ Aero Commander 680FL	EΣ-288	1383-144	N6318U	RA
☐ Aero Commander 680FL	EΣ-316	1815-155		RA
☐ Aero Commander 680FL	EΣ-315	1837-154	(N9012N)	RA
☐ Bell 47G-3B Sioux (OH-13S)	'EΣ-101'	3994	69-19614, E--701	RAX
☐ Bell 47G-3B Sioux (OH-13S)	EΣ-706	3999	69-19619	RA
☐ Piper PA-18-135 Super Cub (L-21B)	EΣ-253			RA

TANAGRA AIR FORCE BASE COLLECTION (GRE18)

Address:	114 Pterix Makhis, Tanagra Air Force Base.
Admission:	By prior permission only.
Location:	About 40 km north west of Athens south of the E75.

In addition to the resident Air Force defence wing operating Mirage 2000s Tanagra is home to Hellenic Aerospace Industries major overhaul facility and technical school. One of the Starfighters is located at the base gate and the Mirage 2000 is mounted in the 331 Mira area. The Mirage F.1CG was noted on display recently but it is not known whether this is a permanent addition to the collection.

TYPE	REG/SER	CON. NO.	PI/NOTES	STATUS
☐ Canadair CL-13 Sabre 2 [North American F-86E]	19235	135		RA
☐ Convair 8-10 Delta Dagger (F-102A)	61101		56-1101	RA
☐ Convair 8-10 Delta Dagger (F-102A)	61106		56-1106	RA
☐ Convair 8-10 Delta Dagger (F-102A)	61140		56-1140	RA
☐ Dassault Mirage 2000EG	215	115	Front fuselage and wings only.	RA
☐ Dassault Mirage F.1CG	115	96		RA
☐ Lockheed 580 (T-33A)	58516	580-1485	58-0516	RA
☐ Lockheed 683-04-10 Starfighter (RF-104G)	6662	683-6662	KC+147, VB+208, 21+13	RA
☐ Lockheed 683-04-10 Starfighter (RF-104G)	6691	683-6691	KC+164, VB+225, 21+30	RA
☐ Northrop N-156A Freedom Fighter (F-5A)	689081	N.6452	68-9081 89081 (Jordan)	RA
☐ Northrop N-156A Freedom Fighter (F-5A)				RA

THESSALONIKI POLEMICO MOUSSIO (GRE19)

Address:	Grigoriou-Lambraki, Pedio Aereos 3, Thessaloniki.
Tel:	2310-249803
Fax:	2310-249803
Admission:	Tuesday-Friday 0900-1400; Saturday-Sunday 1000-1400.
Location:	In the centre of the town.

The museum opened in 2000 in a villa built in 1900. The displays trace the military history of the region with emphasis on local conflicts as well as the major wars. Specially featured are the two World Wars, the Balkan Wars, the conflict between Greece and Italy and the Asia Minor War. In effect this is the northern branch of the main War Museum in Athens. The F-5 is painted in the colours of the 'Aegean Blue' aerobatic team.

TYPE	REG/SER	CON. NO.	PI/NOTES	STATUS
☐ Northrop N-156A Freedom Fighter (F-5A)	13353	N.6122	64-13353, 13353 (Norway)	PV

TRIPOLIS AIR FORCE BASE COLLECTION (GRE20)

Address:	124 Pterix, Tripolis Air Force Base, Tripolis.
Admission:	By prior permission only.
Location:	In the north eastern suburbs of the town which is about 120 km south west of Athens.

Conscripts to the Air Force receive their basic training at this establishment. A display of preserved aircraft designed to show the traditions of the service has been set up near the main parade ground. Convair F-102s were operated in the 1960s and 1970s. Many F-84Fs and RF-84Fs were flown for several years. A number of C-47s are still flown by the Air Force including one based at Larissa for V.I.P. use.

TYPE	REG/SER	CON. NO.	PI/NOTES	STATUS
☐ Cessna 318C Tweety Bird (T-37C)	01957	42012	70-1957	RA
☐ Convair 8-10 Delta Dagger (F-102A)	'61205'		56-1025, 61025	RAX
☐ Douglas DC-3A-456 Skytrain (C-47A)	'92532'		49-2632	RAX
☐ Lockheed 580 (T-33A)	36131	580-9752	53-6131	RA
☐ Lockheed 683-10-19 Starfighter (F-104G)	32715	683D-6067	63-12715, C.8-1 (Spain)	RA
☐ Nord N.2501D Noratlas	53-240	163	KA+174, GB+233, 53+40	RA
☐ Republic F-84F Thunderstreak	26900		52-6900	RA
☐ Republic RF-84F Thunderflash	37660		53-7660, BD+107, EA+107, EA+307, EB+362	RA

VARIA MOUSSIO (GRE21)

Address:	Varia, Lesbos.
Admission:	–
Location:	In the centre of the town which is about 5 km south of Mytilini.

A municipal military museum is being set up in the town. The Texan, which needs a full restoration, was acquired from a scout camp at Kastania. Two Northrop Freedom Fighters have been promised.

TYPE	REG/SER	CON. NO.	PI/NOTES	STATUS
☐ North American NA-168 Texan (T-6G)	493414	168-538	49-3414	PVD
☐ Northrop N-156A Freedom Fighter (F-5A)			Due soon.	RA
☐ Northrop N-156B Freedom Fighter (F-5B)			Due soon.	RA

HUNGARY

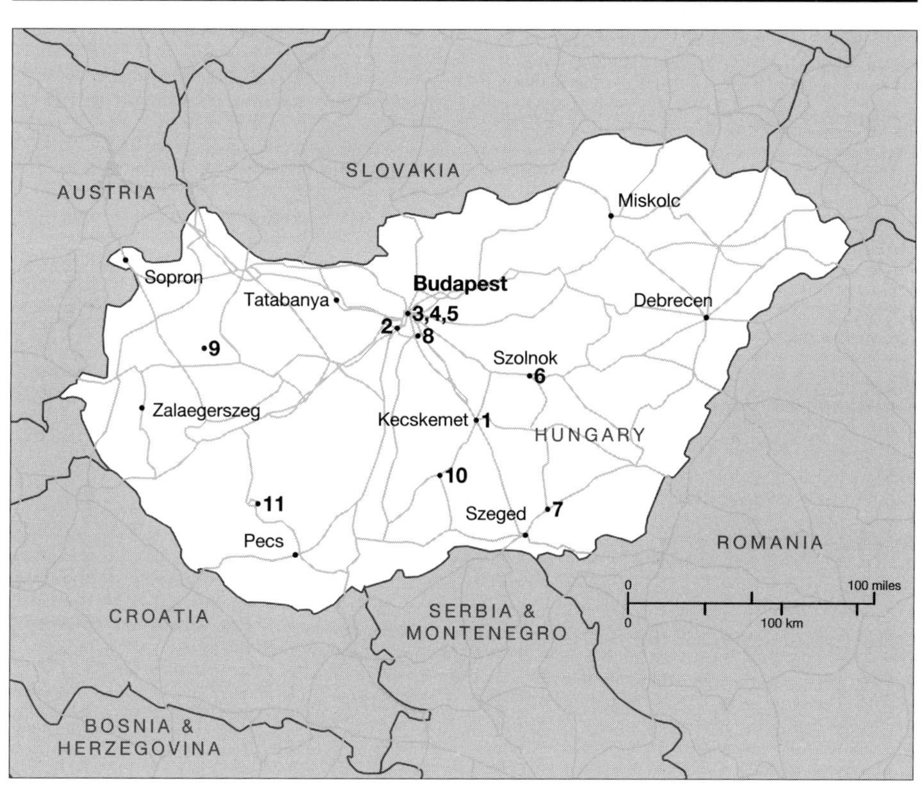

CSAPAT MÚZEUMA (HUN1)

Address:	Repteriut P.F.320, 6000 Kecskemét.
Tel:	076-483511
Admission:	By prior permission only.
Location:	About 6 km south east of the town on Route 44.

The museum traces the military history of the region and of the base. A regiment was formed in the town in 1725 and a cavalry unit in 1871. Construction of the airfield started in the late 1930s and Fiat CR.32s, CR.42s, Caproni-Reggiane Re 2000s and Heinkel He 70s were operated. The Germans took over the site during World War II and photos from this period show a Messerschmitt Me 323 parked in front of the hangars. The airfield was bombed by the Royal Air Force in 1944. The small museum has many personal items on show including some once owned by Dezso Szenfgyorgi, a military and airline pilot, after whom the base in named.

TYPE	REG/SER	CON. NO.	PI/NOTES	STATUS
☐ Ilyushin Il-28	47	55006047		RAD
☐ Mikoyan-Gurevich MiG-15bis	'1977'	2684	684	RA
☐ Mikoyan-Gurevich MiG-15bis	'1976'	31530725	725	RAX
☐ Mikoyan-Gurevich MiG-17PF	'1976'	0401	401	RAX
☐ Mikoyan-Gurevich MiG-19PM	'1976'			RAX
☐ Mikoyan-Gurevich MiG-21F-13	'25'	741301	301	PVX
☐ Mikoyan-Gurevich MiG-21F-13	'1978'	741909	909	RAX
☐ Mikoyan-Gurevich MiG-21F-13	915	741915		RA
☐ Wytwornia Sprzetu Komunikacyjnego (WSK) SBLim-2 (Lim-1) [MiG-15] [MiG-15UTI]	'1951'	1A 06-002	002	RADX

GOLD TIMER ALAPÍTVÁNY (HUN2)

Address:	Koeberki ut 36, 1112 Budapest XI.
Tel:	01-249-9518
Email:	info@goldtimer.hu
Admission:	By prior permission only – Monday-Friday 0600-1500.
Location:	At Budaors Airport which is in the south western suburbs of the city and at the Kossuth Lajos TTS.

The aircraft service of the Hungarian Agricultural Ministry was set up in 1959 with a fleet of six Polikarpov Po-2s and by the 1980s had over one hundred aircraft and helicopters. The organisation started collecting airframes for preservation in 1974 and display was staged at the main pilot training school at Kaposujlak. A second exhibition site was established at the historic Farkashegy gliding centre which opened in 1929 in the hills above old Buda. Many record breaking flights were made from the field which was damaged during World War II. The site was rebuilt and used from 1947 until 1959. In the early 1990s the privatised organisation now known as Air Service Hungary sold the Farkashegy site and most of the aircraft on display. The Kaposujlak exhibition had closed a few years earlier. A foundation has now been set up to maintain the aircraft some of which are flying.

TYPE	REG/SER	CON. NO.	PI/NOTES	STATUS
☐ Aero L-60 Brigadyr	HA-BRB	150910		RA
☐ Centralne Studium Samolotow (CSS) 13 [Polikarpov Po-2]	HA-PAO	448	48 (Hungary) – on loan from KM.	RAA
☐ Lisunov Li-2P [Douglas DC-3 modified]	HA-LIX	18433209	(S104), 209, HA-LIX, 209	RAA
☐ Panstwowe Zaklady Lotnicze (PZL) 101A Gawron	HA-PXA			RA
☐ Rubik R-07B Vocsok (R)	HA-2336			RAA
☐ Rubik R-08B Pilis	HA-3508			RA
☐ Rubik R-11 Cimbora (R)	HA-5035			RAA
☐ Rubik R-15 Metal-Koma (R-15 Koma)				RA
☐ Rubik R-18C Kanya	HA-RUF	E-779	On loan from KM	RA
☐ Wytwornia Sprzetu Komunikacyjnego (WSK) M-15-01 Belphegor	CCCP-15187	1S 019-10	On loan to MRMA.	–
☐ Wytwornia Sprzetu Komunikacyjnego (WSK) SM-1W [Mil Mi-1M]	037	W04037		RA
☐ Zlin Z-37 Cmelak	DDR-SNB	06-03		RA

KOSSUTH LAJOS MÚSZAKI (HUN3)

Address:	Kossuth Lajos ut. 12, Csepel, 1211 Budapest.
Tel:	01-427-2700
Fax:	01-427-2702
Admission:	By prior permission only.
Location:	On Csepel Island in the city.

This large technical school which trains airframe and engine fitters has a collection of preserved aircraft. Some of these also serve as instructional airframes. Several were part of the now defunct Hungarian Agricultural Service collection. In a number of rooms in the buildings engines, components and photographs can be seen.

TYPE	REG/SER	CON. NO.	PI/NOTES	STATUS
☐ Antonov An-2M	HA-MHG	601220		RA
☐ Kamov Ka-26	408	7001408		RA
☐ Kamov Ka-26	510	7001510	510, HA-MRQ	RA
☐ Mikoyan-Gurevich MiG-21MF	4407	964407		RA
☐ Mil Mi-8T	CCCP-25625	9775212		RA
☐ Panstwowe Zaklady Lotnicze (PZL) 101A Gawron	HA-PXB			RA
☐ Wytwornia Sprzetu Komunikacyjnego (WSK) SM-1W [Mil Mi-1M]	31	W04031		RA
☐ Wytwornia Sprzetu Komunikacyjnego (WSK) SM-1W [Mil Mi-1M]	033	W04033		PV
☐ Zlin Z-226MS Trener	HA-TRL	370	Fuselage frame only.	RA
☐ Zlin Z-526F Trener Master	HA-TRN	1243		RA

KÖZLEKEDÉSI MÚZEUM (HUN4)

Address: Varosligeti Korut 11,
1146 Budapest.
Tel: 01-273-3846
Fax: 01-363-7822
Email: folgazgato@kozmuz.hu
Admission: Tuesday-Sunday 1000-1800.
Location: In the north east of the city near the ring road.
Ferihegy Airport is about 15 km south east of the city off Route 4.

Opened in 1896 the Hungarian Museum of Transport is one of the oldest of its type in Europe. The first aeronautical items to be obtained were three broken propellers from the 1910 Budapest aviation meeting. Aircraft were gradually added but a bombing raid in 1944 destroyed most of the collection. The museum was slowly rebuilt but did not open to the public until April 2nd 1966. An excellent collection of railway and public transport vehicles is on show along with cars, cycles and motorcycles. There is a large outside area housing these. One of the highlights is a display of models of all the Danube bridges in the city. Two of the first aircraft to join the museum were constructed by Hungarian pioneer aviators. The Zselyi II monoplane first appeared in February 1910 at Rakosmezo airfield near Budapest and incorporated several advanced ideas for the time. These included a piano wire braced wooden fuselage and steel bracing rods in the wings. After a crash the aircraft was modified. Erno Horvath built his first aircraft in 1910 and two later versions appeared the following year. Both were destroyed in the 1944 raid. The engine from the Zselyi was salvaged and a replica airframe built. In the mid-1980s a new hall close by was acquired and this became home to the aeronautical section. The Junkers F 13 on show was leased in 1921 by two Hungarians who were part of a plot to restore the Habsburg dynasty. The aircraft was seized and used by Regent Horthy. In 1968 the F 13, which survived the 1944 raid, was restored at Ferihegy Airport by Erno Rubik, father of the designer of the dreaded cube! Erno founded the Aero Ever company at Esztergom in 1938 and over the years a range of gliders and light aircraft has been produced. The museum has examples of many of these on show. The Lampich L 2 set a number of records in the late 1920s and 1930s and made many long distance flights around Europe. The aircraft was badly damaged by the bombs which fell on the museum. In the early 1970s a team led by Antal Banhidi, who along with Arpad Lampich, had taught Erno Rubik at Budapest Technical University restored the L 2. The tiny monoplane was placed on show on September 4th 1975, the fiftieth anniversary of its first flight. The museum in co-operation with the airport authorities has set up an outside airpark close to Terminal 2 at Ferihegy Airport. Mostly transport types are displayed here and as aircraft are withdrawn more will be added.

TYPE	REG/SER	CON. NO.	PI/NOTES	STATUS
☐ Aero L-60 Brigadyr	HA-BRA	150909		PV
☐ Aero Super 45S	HA-REC	171310		PV
☐ Alagi-Kozponti Kiserleti A-08 Siraly I	HA-7017			PV
☐ Alagi-Kozponti Kiserleti A-08B Siraly II	HA-7018			RA
☐ Andrew Szep HFC.125	G-BCPX	PFA/12-10019 and AS.001		PV
☐ Antonov An-2			Front fuselage only	PV
☐ Antonov An-2M	HA-MHI	701647	At Ferihegy Airport.	PV
☐ Antonov An-2TP	HA-ABH	1G 28-01	CCCP-44998, RA-44988	PV
☐ Banhidi Gerle 13 (R)	HA-AAI	F-04		PV
☐ Beniczky E-31 Esztergom	HA-4000			RA
☐ Beniczky E-31 Esztergom	HA-3417	E-1287		PV
☐ Beniczky M-30 Super Fergeteg	HA-7013	A-010		RA
☐ Beniczky M-30/c.1 Fergeteg	HA-5147	A-08		PV
☐ Brandenburg B I	H-MAHE			PV
☐ Brugger MB.2 Kolibri	HA-YAA			PV
☐ Centralne Studium Samolotow (CSS) 13 [Polikarpov Po-2]	HA-PAO	448	48 (Hungary) - on loan to Gold Timer Foundation.	–
☐ Fabian Levente II	HA-LEB			PV
☐ Ganz Aero GAK-22 Dino	HA-YACT	001-93	HA-XBP	PV
☐ Griffon Hang Glider				PV
☐ Homebuilt Biplane	HA-XAH			PV
☐ Ilyushin Il-14G	04	147001821	48 - at Ferihegy Airport.	PV
☐ Ilyushin Il-18V	HA-MOA	180001903	At Ferihegy Airport.	PV
☐ Jacobs Meise (D.F.S. 108-70)	HA-4154			PV
☐ Janka Gyongyos 33	H-C 05.01			PV
☐ Junkers F 13 b	CH-59	574	Wings of CH-66	PV
☐ Kesselyák Mihaly KM-400	HA-X001			PV
☐ Lampich L-2 Roma	H-MAFD			PV
☐ Lilienthal Normal-Segelapparat (R)				PV

☐ Lisunov Li-2T [Douglas DC-3 modified]	HA-LIQ	23441206	206, HA-LIQ, 206 - at Ferihegy Airport.	PV
☐ Lloyd 40.01	40.01			PV
☐ Microlight	40-02			PV
☐ Mikoyan-Gurevich MiG-21PF	'14'	761514	514 - front fuselage only.	PV
☐ Mil Mi-2	HA-BCB	516302099	At Ferihegy Airport.	PV
☐ Mraz M-1C Sokol	HA-REA	209		PV
☐ Polikarpov Po-2	HA-POA	1203	On loan from Magyar Mezogadasagi Muzeum. Possibly c/n 0083 YR-POA.	PV
☐ Rosmaring Mustang Hang Glider				PV
☐ Rubik R-02 Vocsok	HA-2254	E-714		PV
☐ Rubik R-08D Pilis	HA-3319			PV
☐ Rubik R-08D Pilis	HA-3181	E-1059		RA
☐ Rubik R-08D Pilis	HA-3136	E-624		RA
☐ Rubik R-15B Koma	HA-5096	E-845		PV
☐ Rubik R-16B Lepke	HA-1039	E-1000		PV
☐ Rubik R-18C Kanya	HA-RUG	E-778		PV
☐ Rubik R-18C Kanya	HA-RUF	E-779	On loan to Gold Timer Foundation.	-
☐ Rubik R-22S Junius 18	HA-4123			RA
☐ Rubik R-22S Junius 18	HA-4085	E-815		PV
☐ Rubik R-22S Super Futar	HA-4213			RA
☐ Rubik R-22S Super Futar B	HA-4208			PV
☐ Rubik R-22SV Junius 18	HA-4141			PV
☐ Rubik R-25 Mokany	HA-4300			PV
☐ Rubik R-26S Gobé	HA-5355	E-1204		PV
☐ Rubik R-26S Gobé	HA-5397	E-1226		RA
☐ Samu-Geonczy SG-2 Kek Madar	HA-BKF	001		PV
☐ Tupolev Tu-134	HA-LBE	9350802	At Ferihegy Airport.	PV
☐ Tupolev Tu-154B-2 (Tu-154B)	HA-LCG	75A-127	At Ferihegy Airport.	PV
☐ Wytwornia Sprzetu Komunikacyjnego (WSK) SM-1Wb [Mil Mi-1M]	30	401030		RA
☐ Yakovlev Yak-18	HA-FAA	4312	HA-FAA, 12	PV
☐ Yakovlev Yak-40E	HA-YLR	9541044	At Ferigehy Airport.	PV
☐ Zlin Z-37 Cmelak				PV
☐ Zlin Z-226 Trener 6	HA-TRG	348-22		PV
☐ Zlin Z-326 Trener Master	HA-TRO	829		PV
☐ Zsebo-Bohn Z.03b Ifjusag	HA-5211	A-094		PV
☐ Zselyi II (R)				PV

MAGYAR MEZÖGAZDASÁGI MÚZEUM (HUN5)

Address:	Varosliget, Szechenyi-sziget, 1146 Budapest.
Tel:	01-363-1117
Fax:	01-363-2711
Email:	info@mmgm.hu
Admission:	Tuesday-Sunday 1000-1700.
Location:	In the north east of the city near the ring road.

Agriculture has always played an important part in the economy of the country. The museum displays trace the development of machinery used to work the land and show the variety of crops grown. Aircraft and helicopters have been employed for seeding, spraying and dusting for several years. The museum has loaned a Polikarpov Po-2 to the Kozlekedesi Muzeum. The famous Soviet biplane was first flown in the agricultural role in the 1930s and carried on these tasks for many years. The Antonov An-2 was operated in large numbers for the last fifty years by the agricultural service and several remain in flying condition with clubs in Hungary.

TYPE	REG/SER	CON. NO.	PI/NOTES	STATUS
☐ Antonov An-2R				RA
☐ Polikarpov Po-2	HA-POA	1203	Possibly c/n 0083 YR-POA – on loan to KM.	–

MAGYAR REPÜLÉSTÖRTENÉTI MÚZEUM ALAPÍTVÁNY (HUN6)

Address:	P.F.1, 5008 Szolnok.
Tel:	056-505100
Email:	zubo@freemail.hu
Admission:	Monday-Thursday 0900-1430; Friday 0900-1300.
Location:	About 4 km south east of the town on Route 424.

Opened in 1973 on the base, entry to the museum was restricted. In 1994 a move was made to an area close to the main gate with full public access. A foundation has been set up with the aim of constructing a large display hall and developing the collection. Szolnok is home to a military technical college and a unit flying helicopters. The aircraft on show are mainly military types but three airliners once flown by Malev can also be seen. The Lisunov Li-2 was operated by Malev and its predecessor Maszvolet before being taken over by the military. Restoration of this aircraft and the Ilyushin Il-14 are planned. The ground instructional airframes which are technically part of the museum collection are listed here. The museum hopes that more foreign aircraft will soon join the inventory. A collection of archive material has been gathered and the college has many engines and components which will join the display once premises have been constructed

TYPE	REG/SER	CON. NO.	PI/NOTES	STATUS
☐ Aero 45	'G-007'		23	PVX
☐ Aero L-29 Delfin	379	591379		PV
☐ Aero L-39ZO Albatros	S2	731011	160 (DDR), 28+19	PV
☐ Aero L-39ZO Albatros	'016'	731016	153 (DDR), 28+13	RAX
☐ Aero L-39ZO Albatros	S1	731018	155 (DDR), 28+15	PV
☐ Antonov An-2R	'10'	1G 181-38	HA-MDG	PVX
☐ Antonov An-24B	907	77303907		PV
☐ Antonov An-26	202	02202		PV
☐ Canadair CL-90 Starfighter (CF-104) [Lockheed 683-04-12]	63-893	683A-1193	12893, 104893 – in Turkish markings.	PV
☐ Centralne Studium Samolotow (CSS) 13 [Polikarpov Po-2]	HA-PAU	0443	43	PV
☐ Hawker P.1099 Hunter F.58	J-4022	41H/697389	In Swiss markings.	RA
☐ Ilyushin Il-14P	'426'	14803022	403, 426 (DDR, (DM-VAL) – in false Hungarian markings.	PVX
☐ Ilyushin Il-18Grm (Il-18V)	HA-MOE	182005505		PV
☐ Ilyushin Il-2				PVD
☐ Ilyushin Il-28	55	56455		PV
☐ Kamov Ka-26	505	7001505		PV
☐ Let L-200D Morava	R-05	171128		RA
☐ Let L-410UVP Turbolet			Due soon.	–
☐ Lisunov Li-2T [Douglas DC-3 modified]	HA-LIU	18439306	306, HA-LIU, 306 – Composite with Li-2T c/n 23441301 301 HA-LIS	RAC
☐ Lockheed 683-10-19 Starfighter (F-104G)	21+64	683-7033	KE+333, DC+???, DA+238	PV
☐ Mikoyan-Gurevich MiG-15	'1951'		Also carries '1977'	RAX
☐ Mikoyan-Gurevich MiG-15	424	???424		PV
☐ Mikoyan-Gurevich MiG-15	838	???838		RA
☐ Mikoyan-Gurevich MiG-15bis			On base gate.	PV
☐ Mikoyan-Gurevich MiG-15bis	25		In North Korean markings.	PV
☐ Mikoyan-Gurevich MiG-15bis	724	31530724	On base gate.	PV
☐ Mikoyan-Gurevich MiG-15bisZ	'912'	4512	512	PVX
☐ Mikoyan-Gurevich MiG-15UTI	203	3203		PV
☐ Mikoyan-Gurevich MiG-17PF	405	0405		PV
☐ Mikoyan-Gurevich MiG-19PM	28	651028		PV
☐ Mikoyan-Gurevich MiG-21bisA	3537	75033537		RA
☐ Mikoyan-Gurevich MiG-21bisA	3732	75033732		RA
☐ Mikoyan-Gurevich MiG-21bisA	3745	75033745		RA
☐ Mikoyan-Gurevich MiG-21bisA	3945	75033945		PV
☐ Mikoyan-Gurevich MiG-21F-13	224	741224		RA
☐ Mikoyan-Gurevich MiG-21F-13	814	741814		RA
☐ Mikoyan-Gurevich MiG-21F-13	819	741819		RA
☐ Mikoyan-Gurevich MiG-21F-13	822	741822		RA
☐ Mikoyan-Gurevich MiG-21F-13	911	741911		RA
☐ Mikoyan-Gurevich MiG-21F-13	2311	742311		RA
☐ Mikoyan-Gurevich MiG-21F-13	2316	742316		RA
☐ Mikoyan-Gurevich MiG-21MF	4605	964605		RA
☐ Mikoyan-Gurevich MiG-21MF	4606	964606		RA
☐ Mikoyan-Gurevich MiG-21MF	9306	969306		RA
☐ Mikoyan-Gurevich MiG-21MF	9309	969309		PV
☐ Mikoyan-Gurevich MiG-21MF	9512	969512		PV
☐ Mikoyan-Gurevich MiG-21PF	1512	761512		RA
☐ Mikoyan-Gurevich MiG-21U-600	4419	664419		PV
☐ Mikoyan-Gurevich MiG-21UM	0465	04695165		RA
☐ Mikoyan-Gurevich MiG-21UM	3041	516903041		PV
☐ Mikoyan-Gurevich MiG-23MF	06	0390217165	12405 (Soviet)	PV
☐ Mikoyan-Gurevich MiG-23MF	12	0390217173	12501 (Soviet)	RA
☐ Mil Mi-2	7831	517831092		RA
☐ Mil Mi-2	8911	518911104		PV
☐ Mil Mi-2	R-10	535431127		RA
☐ Mil Mi-4A	'27'	04146	534 (DDR), (DM-WSC), '13'	PVX
☐ Mil Mi-8S	416	10416		PV
☐ Mil Mi-8T	328	0328		RA
☐ Mil Mi-8T	10417	10417		RA
☐ Mil Mi-8T	10420	10420		RA
☐ Mil Mi-8T	10422	10422		RA
☐ Mil Mi-8T	036	20136		RA
☐ Mil Mi-24D	96+27	110162	434 (DDR)	RA
☐ Mil Mi-24D	114	K20114		PV
☐ Mil Mi-24D	117	K20117		PV
☐ Rubik R-16B Lepke	HA-1308			PV

TYPE	REG/SER	CON. NO.	PI/NOTES	STATUS
☐ Rubik R-22S Junius 18	HA-4112			RA
☐ Rubik R-26S Gobé	HA-5410	E-1261		PV
☐ Sukhoi Su-22M3K	12	51612		PV
☐ Sukhoi Su-22M3K	03	52303		RA
☐ Svenska Aeroplan Aktiebolaget (SAAB) 32E Lansen (32B) (J 32B) (J 32E)	Fv32607	32607		RA
☐ Svenska Aeroplan Aktiebolaget (SAAB) 37 Viggen (JA 37) (JA 37D) (JA 37DI)	Fv37347	37347	On loan from FVM,SWE.	PV
☐ Tupolev Tu-134	HA-LBF	0350923		PV
☐ Wytwornia Sprzetu Komunikacyjnego (WSK) SM-1W [Mil Mi-1M]	19	W02019		RA
☐ Wytwornia Sprzetu Komunikacyjnego (WSK) SM-1W [Mil Mi-1M]	36	W04036		RAD
☐ Wytwornia Sprzetu Komunikacyjnego (WSK) SM-1W [Mil Mi-1M]	09	W05009	09, R-009	PV
☐ Wytwornia Sprzetu Komunikacyjnego (WSK) SM-1Wb [Mil Mi-1M]	032	401032	032, R-032, R-008, 1032	RA
☐ Yakovlev Yak 11	'1941'		11	RAX
☐ Yakovlev Yak-12R				RA
☐ Yakovlev Yak-18				RA
☐ Zlin Z-142			Due soon.	–
☐ Zlin Z-326 Trener Master	HA-TRI	627		RA

ÓPUSZTASZERI NEMEZETI TÖRTÉNETI EMLÉKPARK (HUN7)

Address:	Szoborkert 68, H-6767 Ópusztaszeri.
Tel:	062-275257
Fax:	062-275007
Email:	info@pusztaszer.hu
Admission:	April-October daily 0900-1800; November-March daily 0900-1600.
Location:	About 20 km north of Szeged.

The national historical memorial park occupies a large site with many attractions including buildings moved to the complex. There are a few military vehicles and the Antonov An-2 in one area.

TYPE	REG/SER	CON. NO.	PI/NOTES	STATUS
☐ Antonov An-2M	HA-MHH	601301		PV

OZIGETVAR MÚZEUM (HUN8)

Address:	H-2351 Alsónémedi.
Tel:	0630-443018
Admission:	By prior permission only.
Location:	About 15 km south of Budapest on Route 5.

Sandor Foldi started collecting ex-military aircraft in the mid-1990s. These were stored at his premises at Vecsés. He built a new home at Alsónémedi and over the next few years the majority of the airframes were moved to this location. There are not many Yak-28s preserved in Europe so this aircraft is something of a rarity. The aircraft were acquired from towns and military bases in the country.

TYPE	REG/SER	CON. NO.	PI/NOTES	STATUS
☐ Antonov An-2	HA-MHB	601215		RA
☐ Kamov Ka-26	HA-MPI	7706307		RA
☐ Mikoyan-Gurevich MiG-15bis	'14'	2666	666 – in false Soviet markings.	RAX
☐ Mikoyan-Gurevich MiG-15bis	708	31530708	'1975'	RA
☐ Mikoyan-Gurevich MiG-15bis	713	31530713	'1983'	RA
☐ Mikoyan-Gurevich MiG-15bis	981	31530981	'1983'	RA
☐ Mikoyan-Gurevich MiG-15UTI	754	612754	'1975'	RA
☐ Mikoyan-Gurevich MiG-15UTI	771	922771		RA
☐ Mikoyan-Gurevich MiG-17PF	403	0403	'1975'	RAX.
☐ Mikoyan-Gurevich MiG-17PF	'17'	0404	404, '1975'	RAX
☐ Mikoyan-Gurevich MiG-19PM	33	651033	'1975'	RA
☐ Mikoyan-Gurevich MiG-19PM	36	651036	'1978'	RA
☐ Mikoyan-Gurevich MiG-21F-13	0220	560220	In Czech. markings.	RA
☐ Mikoyan-Gurevich MiG-21F-13	218	741218		RA
☐ Mikoyan-Gurevich MiG-21U-400	1320	661320		RA
☐ Panstwowe Zaklady Lotnicze (PZL) 101A Gawron	HA-PZK	21012		RA
☐ Wytwornia Sprzetu Komunikacyjnego (WSK) SBLim-2 (Lim-1) [MiG-15] [MiG-15UTI]	011	1A 06-011	'1975'	RA
☐ Wytwornia Sprzetu Komunikacyjnego (WSK) SM-1W [Mil Mi-1M]	13	W02013		RA
☐ Yakovlev Yak-28R	20	7961004	In Soviet markings.	RA

The Közlekedési Múzeum has opened a display compound at Ferihegy Airport. Among the former MALEV airliners is this Tupolev Tu-134. (Stewart Lanham)

Jozef Pinter's excellent museum at Kecel houses this Antonov An-24V. (Stewart Lanham)

This Yakovlev Yak-11 is on show at Jozef Pinter's museum at Kecel. (Stewart Lanham)

PÁPA AIR FORCE BASE HERITAGE PARK (HUN9)

Address:	H-8500 Pápa.
Admission:	By prior permission only.
Location:	About 5 km north east of the town.

Papa has been an important fighter base for many years. The resident units disbanded in August 2000. The Heritage Park has been set up just inside the main gate to honour the field's past glories. The three aircraft on show were all flown from the airfield and some more modern types may join the exhibition. In common with many preserved Hungarian military aircraft dates of significance have been applied. The airfield is now used to store withdrawn aircraft any many MiG-21s, MiG-23s and Sukhoi Su-22s are parked awaiting their fate. Some have moved on to other museums in the country and hopefully others will escape being scrapped.

TYPE	REG/SER	CON. NO.	PI/NOTES	STATUS
☐ Mikoyan-Gurevich MiG-15UTI	'1950'		779	RAX
☐ Mikoyan-Gurevich MiG-19PM	'1975'			RA
☐ Mikoyan-Gurevich MiG-21F-13	'1976'	741806	806	RA

PINTER MŰVEK HADTÖRTÉNETI MÚZEUM (HUN10)

Address:	Rákóczi uti ipartelep, 6737 Kecel
Tel:	078 321 444
Fax:	078 321 600
Email:	hadtorteneti.kecel@museum.huhu
Admission:	November-February daily 0800-1600; March-October daily 0800-1800.
Location:	In the town which is about 15 km south west of Soltvadkert on Route 54.

Founded in 1918 the military museum is housed in superbly restored buildings in the citadel in Old Buda. There were impressive collections of documents, uniforms, medals, small arms, badges, decorations and dioramas. Aircraft were on display in the courtyard but were placed in store almost twenty years ago. Plans for a new aircraft exhibition site near Rakosmezo, which was the first airfield in the area, failed to materialise. The aircraft collection was acquired by József Pintér who has substantially added to it. On show at Kecel are large numbers of weapons, missiles, military vehicles and radar equipment. A tree filled park with walkways has been constructed. The aircraft are types which have been used by the Hungarian Air Force in recent years. Only two Antonov An-24Bs were used by the air force. The majority of the MiG variants flown have been acquired. New additions to the collection have come from the Air Force bases at Kecsemét, Pápa and Szolnok and more modern machines are sure to follow. The majority of the exhibits have been restored to display condition.

TYPE	REG/SER	CON. NO.	PI/NOTES	STATUS
☐ Aero L-29 Delfin	376	591376		PV
☐ Aero L-39ZO Albatros	'28'	731008	145 (DDR), 28+07, S-3	PVX
☐ Antonov An-24B	908	77303908		PV
☐ Mikoyan-Gurevich MiG-15bis	677	2677		PV
☐ Mikoyan-Gurevich MiG-15bis	064	3064	'1963'	PV
☐ Mikoyan-Gurevich MiG-15bisR	061	3061		PV
☐ Mikoyan-Gurevich MiG-17PF	315	0315		PV
☐ Mikoyan-Gurevich MiG-17PF	847	0847		PV
☐ Mikoyan-Gurevich MiG-19PM	'027'	651027	27, '1974'	PVX
☐ Mikoyan-Gurevich MiG-21bisAP	1953	75061953		PV
☐ Mikoyan-Gurevich MiG-21F-13	'1907'	741907	907	PVX
☐ Mikoyan-Gurevich MiG-21MF	8202	968202		PV
☐ Mikoyan-Gurevich MiG-21MF	9311	969311		PV
☐ Mikoyan-Gurevich MiG-21U-400	1418	661418		PV
☐ Mikoyan-Gurevich MiG-21UM	0158	01695158		PV
☐ Mikoyan-Gurevich MiG-23MF	07	0390217166	12407 (Soviet)	PV
☐ Mikoyan-Gurevich MiG-23UB	20	19015091		PV
☐ Mil Mi-2	8912	518912104		PV
☐ Mil Mi-2	8916	518916104		PV
☐ Mil Mi-8T	10424	10424		PV
☐ Mil Mi-24D	104	K20104		PV
☐ Sukhoi Su-7BKL			In false North Korean markings.	RA
☐ Sukhoi Su-22M3K	11	51611		PV
☐ Svenska Aeroplan Aktiebolaget (SAAB) 35D Draken (J 35D)	Fv35371	35371	On loan from FVM, Sweden.	PV
☐ Wytwornia Sprzetu Komunikacyjnego (WSK) SM-1/300 [Mil Mi-1]	33	W01033		PV
☐ Wytwornia Sprzetu Komunikacyjnego (WSK) SM-1W [Mil Mi-1M]	32	W01032		RA
☐ Yakovlev Yak-11	63			PV
☐ Yakovlev Yak-18				RA
☐ Zlin Z-43	078	0078		PV

TASZÁR AIR FORCE BASE COLLECTION (HUN11)

Address:	H-7261 Taszár
Admission:	By prior permission only.
Location:	Just north east of the town which is about 10 km east of Kaposvar.

Fighter units of the Hungarian Air Force were stationed at this field for many years. During the Balkan crisis in 1996 the United States Air Force based combat aircraft at Taszar. There are no squadrons currently in residence but the airfield is maintained in a state of readiness. One of the MiG-19s is preserved at the nearby barracks and the rest of the collection is parked outside the headquarters building.

TYPE	REG/SER	CON. NO.	PI/NOTES	STATUS
☐ Mikoyan-Gurevich MiG-15bis	'7104'	31530817	817	RA
☐ Mikoyan-Gurevich MiG-15UTI	'1978'			RA
☐ Mikoyan-Gurevich MiG-19PM	34	651034		RA
☐ Mikoyan-Gurevich MiG-19PM	37	651037		RA
☐ Mikoyan-Gurevich MiG-21bisAP	5721	75035721		RA
☐ Mikoyan-Gurevich MiG-21bisSAU	1904	75061904		RA
☐ Mikoyan-Gurevich MiG-21F-13	801	741801	'1975'	RA
☐ Mikoyan-Gurevich MiG-21PF	409	760409	'1989'	RA
☐ Mikoyan-Gurevich MiG-21PF	505	760505	'1989'	RAX
☐ Sukhoi Su-22M3K	01	52101		PV

ICELAND

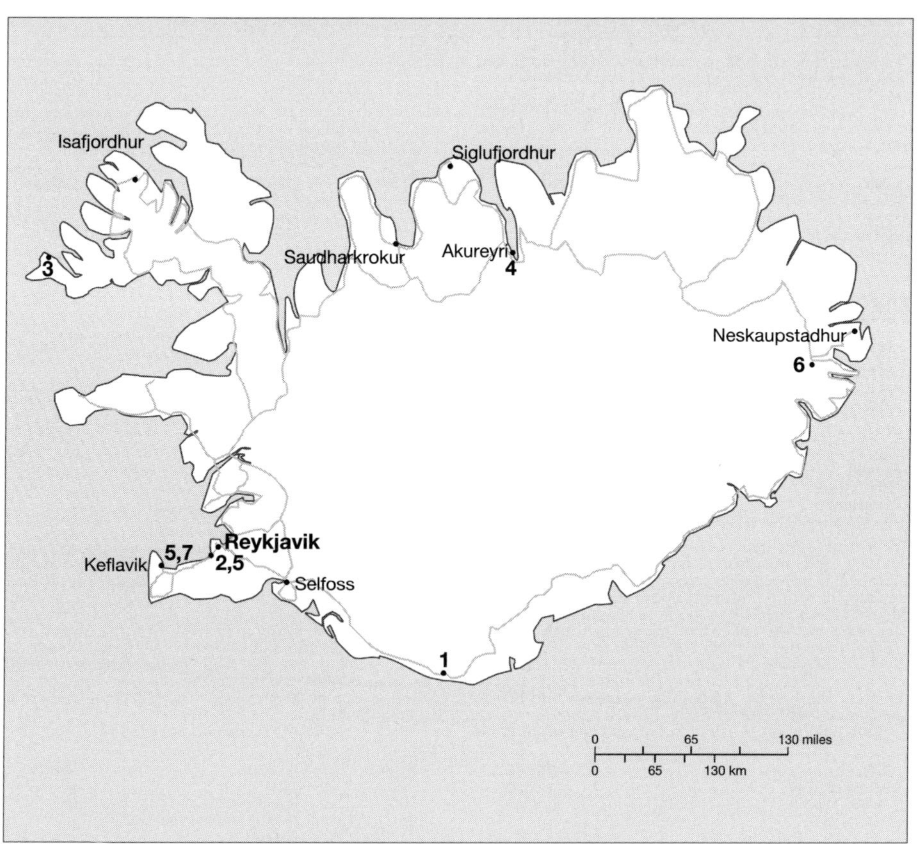

BYGGDASFNID SKOGUM (ICE1)

Address:	Skogar, IS-861 Hvolsvöllur.
Tel:	487-8845
Fax:	487-8858
Email:	skogasafn@simnet.is
Admission:	June-August daily 0900-1900; May and September daily 1000-1700; October-April daily 1100-1600.
Location:	In the village which is about 120 km south east of Reykjavik on Route 1.

There are many waterfalls in the country and the one at Skogar is visited by most tourist groups travelling along the southern coast. The region was settled in the twelfth century and the informative folk museum traces the history of the locality. In 2000 work started on a new building to house the Technology and Transport collection. This exhibition opened in 2002 and suspended from the roof is a locally built Quad City Ultralights Challenger. Designed in Iowa the type made its debut at the 1983 Sun'n'Fun meeting in Florida. Also here is a large photograph of the first aircraft flown in Iceland, Avro 504K H2545.

TYPE	REG/SER	CON. NO.	PI/NOTES	STATUS
☐ Quad City Ultralights Challenger				PV

DC-3 FRIENDS ASSOCIATION (ICE2)

Address:	Landgrædsla Rikisins, Gunnarslotti, IS-851 Hellu.
Tel:	488-3000
Fax:	488-3010
Email:	dc3@land.is
Admission:	By prior permission only.
Location:	At Reykjavik Airport which is in the south western suburbs of the city.

The group was formed to operate a DC-3 which had been flown by the Icelandic Soil Conservation service since 1972. The aircraft is now painted in the colours of Flugfelag Islands who used it from 1947 until 1972. Prior to this it was based at Keflavik with the North Atlantic transport service of the U.S.A.A.F. The DC-3 has already visited shows in Europe and now has flown for over twenty six thousand hours since it left the Long Beach production line in October 1943. A second unairworthy example is housed at the airport and this may be rebuilt in the future although a great deal of time will be required for this project.

TYPE	REG/SER	CON. NO.	PI/NOTES	STATUS
☐ Douglas DC-3A-456 Skytrain (C-47A) (Dakota III)	TF-ISB	9860	42-23998, FD939, G-AIBA, FD939, G-AKSM	RA
☐ Douglas DC-3A-456 Skytrain (C-47A)	TF-NPK	13861	43-30710, TF-ISH	RAA

EGILS OLAFSSONAR MINJA-OG FLUGMINJASAFN (ICE3)

Address:	Hnjotur, Orlygshofn, IS-451 Patreksfjördur.
Tel:	456-1569
Email:	museum@hnjotur
Admission:	June-August daily 1000-1800.
Location:	About 22 km east of Cape Bjargtangar.

The Latrabjarg cliffs rise over four hundred feet from the sea and are home to many birds. Here at Bjargtangar is the westernmost point in Europe. This is reached by a dirt road and about half way along the peninsula is the Egil Olafsson Folk Museum at Hnjotur. The museum was set up in the early 1980s and its exhibits trace the development of life in the region. On show are costumes, cooking utensils, stuffed birds, fossils and many other items tracing the harsh conditions of the area. The founder died a few years ago and before his demise his plans included the setting up of an aviation exhibition. Airfield buildings from small fields in the region were moved to the site and photographs, models, components and posters can be seen. In the early 1990s the Antonov An-2 was on flight from Russia to America where it was refused landing permission. The biplane returned to Reykjavik and was eventually purchased by the museum in 1994. Unfortunately it was parked outside and had to endure the harsh climate. A former seaplane hangar used by the Junkers fleet of Flugfelag Islands was moved to the museum and the Antonov can be seen inside. The C-117 moved from Keflavik in 2003.

TYPE	REG/SER	CON. NO.	PI/NOTES	STATUS
☐ Antonov An-2TP	RA-50502	1G 88-29	CCCP-50502	PV
☐ Douglas Super DC-3 (R4D-8) (C-117D)	Bu17191	43379	Rebuilt from DC-3A-456 (C-47A) (R4D-5) c/n 12980 42-93105, Bu17191.	RA

FLUGSAFN ISLANDS (ICE4)

Address:	Hringteigi, IS-600 Akureyri.
Tel:	0863-2835/0462-2835
Fax:	0462-2835
Email:	flugsafn@flugsafn.is
Admission:	June-August Thursday-Sunday 1400-1700; September-May Saturday 1400-1700.
Location:	At Akureyri Airport which is about 2 km south of the town.

The Flugsafnid a Akureyri was established more than a decade ago and soon obtained a building at the field. This had been vacated by a bankrupt company and was transferred to the society for museum use. In the last ten years a superb exhibition of photographs has been set up on a balcony at the rear of the hall. The history of flying in the region and of the companies, clubs and individuals at Akureyri is portrayed in great detail. There are about a dozen aircraft currently on show but the society has obtained permission to extend the building to about three times its current size and funds are being sought. The name change took place recently to reflect the fact that it is the major aviation museum in the country. Possibly a nearby hangar will also be acquired. The collection hopes to obtain a Boeing 747 from Atlanta Air and the photographic exhibition will be moved into the aircraft. The aircraft will probably be TF-ATF which took a party from the Icelandic chapter of the E.A.A. as well as some aircraft to Oshkosh in 2002. This ambitious project is still under negotiation. The oldest aircraft on show is a Stinson SR-7B which was purchased in the U.S.A. and restored by Loftleider to represent one flown by them in their early days. The original TF-AZX was imported in March 1944 and was test flown from the Vatnagardar seaplane port which is now the main cargo harbour for Reykjavik. The first passenger flight took place on April 7th 1944 and the Stinson was wrecked in September 1944. The aircraft was waiting to take off from Miklavatn when it was blown over by the wind and sank. This high wing design was stored at Reykjavik for many years before moving north. Gliding has been carried out at Akureyri for over half a century and several sailplanes are in the collection. Pride of place goes to the Grunau 9 built in the town over the winter of 1937/8. The first flight was made in the spring from the hill behind what is now the site of the airport. This aircraft was in use until 1989 and has been completely restored with the exception of the nacelle which rests at the side of the hangar. The gliding club now operates from the former World War II field at Modruvellir about fifteen miles south of the town. Also on show is a Schleicher Rhonlerche II. Three other sailplanes are awaiting restoration and are currently stored in the building. These are a Grunau Baby built by members of the club in 1950, an Elliott Olympia 1 constructed at Newbury in 1947 and imported into Iceland three years later and a Schweizer TG-3A. As sailplanes are withdrawn by the club they will join the collection. Homebuilt aircraft also feature. Two types built by Hunn Snaedal can be seen. The Bensen B-8 was constructed in 1971 and first flew the following year. The VP-1 was started in 1975, made its maiden flight in 1981, and operated for four years. The prototype Arctic Raven is a new addition. The local EAA have an active chapter and this part of the collection should expand as space becomes available. Flyable aircraft also reside in the hall and when the building is extended more will move in from the adjacent hangars. Currently on show is an Auster 5 which made the first ambulance flight in Iceland. This has recently been rebuilt and fitted with a more powerful engine in new cowlings. The original components can be seen in a nearby workshop. A Piper Cub in the traditional yellow scheme and a Cessna 140 are next door. Under restoration is a Canadian built Tiger Moth which should be completed soon. A flyable DC-3 has recently arrived from South Africa after serving in many parts of the world. The front fuselage of a former Iscargo DC-6B is outside the hangar. The aircraft was scrapped at the field some time ago. A wreck of another Northrop N-3PB has recently been located at the bottom of a bay in the south west of the country and this enterprising group would like to raise it and acquire it for the exhibition.

TYPE	REG/SER	CON. NO.	PI/NOTES	STATUS
☐ Arctic Raven 2XS	TF-ABD	1		PVA
☐ Auster J 5A (AOP.5)	TF-LBP	1577	TJ592	PVA
☐ Beech D18S Expeditor (C-45H)	TF-JFA	AF-602	52-10672, TF-JME, TF-JMB – likely to join collection.	RAA
☐ Beech D50B Twin Bonanza	TF-ESD	DH-204	N302P, TF-FSD	PV
☐ Bensen B-8M Gyrocopter	TF-EAA			PV
☐ Cessna 140	TF-AST	9359	(NC72186), N72186, TF-JET	PVA
☐ De Havilland D.H.82C Tiger Moth (PT-24)	TF-KBD	DHC.1407	(42-1068), FE204, 1204	RAC
☐ Dornier Do 28B-1	TF-LOW	3091	TF-CWE, TF-DOV, TF-DOW	PVA
☐ Douglas DC-3A-360 Skytrain (R4D-1)	TF-AVN	4363	Bu4703, C-900, N69D, N166M, N234Z, HZ-TA3, N234Z, ZS-MRU	PV
☐ Douglas DC-6A	TF-IUB	44907	N37592, LN-FOL – front fuselage only.	PV
☐ Elliott AP.5 EoN Olympia 1	TF-SBB	EoN/0/023	BGA.555, TF-SDB	PV
☐ Evans VP-1 Volksplane	TF-KEA	2341		PV
☐ Piper J-3C-65 Cub (L-4H)	TF-CUB	10606	42-29315, N51550, TF-JMF	PVA
☐ Piper J-3C-65 Cub (L-4H)	TF-KAP	12328	44-80032, 44-80545, G-ALGH	PVA
☐ Piper PA-18-135 Super Cub (L-21B)	TF-ABM	18-3919	54-2519, MM54-2519, I-EIXJ, EI-175, N9949Q, TF-RBE, TF-FKM – c/n quoted as 18-3562 so a fuselage change may have occurred.	PVA
☐ Piper PA-23-150 Apache	TF-JMH	23-1027	N3107P	PVA
☐ Pitts S-1J Special	TF-ABJ	02	C-GSMP	PVA
☐ Schleicher Ka-4 Rhönlerche II	TF-SBE	3006		PV
☐ Schneider ESG 29 Grunau 9 (D.F.S. 108-10)				PV
☐ Schneider ESG 31 Grunau Baby IIB	TF-SBD			PV
☐ Schweizer SGS.2-12 (TG-3A)	TF-SBA		42-53120	PV
☐ Skandinavisk Aero Industri (SAI) KZ III U-2	TF-KZA	86	Likely to join collection.	RA
☐ Stinson SR-7B Reliant	'TF-AZX'	9685	NC16123, N16123	PVX
☐ Waco YKS-7	TF-SGL	5237	Fuselage frame only.	PV

The Icelandic Aviation Historical Society has premises at Reykjavik Airport. Assembled in the storage area is this Grunau 9 primary glider.

The airstrip near San Possidonio houses a collection of mainly ex-military aircraft. The SIAI-Marchetti SM.1019E is among the exhibits.

The Museo del Genio in Rome is home to this Blériot XI which is believed to be the aircraft which made the first flight in Libya in October 1911.

ISLENSKA FLUGOGUFELAGID (ICE5)

Address:	P.O. Box 3108, IS-123 Reykjavik.
Admission:	By prior permission only.
Location:	Reykjavik Airport is in the south western suburbs of the city. Keflavik Airport is about 50 km south west of Reykjavik off Route 41.

Formed in 1977 the Icelandic Aviation Historical Society has been active in the preservation field for many years. Members have assisted in the recovery of the Fairey Battle now on show in the Royal Air Force Museum at Hendon and the Northrop N-3PB at Gardermoen in Norway. Plans were put forward for the construction of a museum at Reykjavik Airport but these have been put on hold. Icelandair restored a Waco YKS-6 to represent their first aircraft, a YKS-7 floatplane, flown by their predecessor 'Flugfelag Akureyrar'. This classic biplane has been donated to the society who plans to rebuild it to flying condition. The airfield, built by the British in 1942, is now very close to residential areas and there are discussions taking place about possible closure which will set back the museum project still further. The society has workshops and a store among the large number of private hangars on the west side of the field. Assembled in the storage building is a Grunau 9, which was rebuilt and flown on June 14th 1992 to celebrate the fifteenth anniversary of the founding of the society. The glider dates from the early 1930s. Other sailplanes in this area are a locally built Olympia Meise constructed in 1948 and a Brieglieb BG-12 fitted with a 16 metre wing. A frame of an SG-38 is also present along with a wing from a de Havilland Fox Moth and a damaged Brantly 305 helicopter. There are many components, some recovered from crash sites, in this building. Awaiting restoration is an Auster Autocrat which arrived in the country in September 1955 and has been stored for many years. On arrival at Keflavik passengers can see, suspended from the terminal roof, the first, and until recently the only, Icelandic designed aircraft. The Ognin, powered by a de Havilland Gipsy I engine, was designed by Gunnar Jonasson and Bjorn Olsen. The aircraft was built in 1932 but did not fly until November 23rd 1940 due to the lack of a suitable motor. This biplane made four flights before private flying was banned by the British authorities. This unique machine was stored in a loft at Reykjavik Airport until 1977. A group, which included Gunnar Jonasson, rebuilt the aircraft to flying condition in the mid-1980s. Engine runs were carried out in February 1987 and the aircraft taxied around at Reykjavik airport. Also at Keflavik is a Klemm L 25 which arrived in the country in 1938 as part of a German gliding expedition.

TYPE	REG/SER	CON. NO.	PI/NOTES	STATUS
☐ Auster J/1 Autocrat	TF-ACC	2207	G-AIGV	RAC
☐ Brantly 305	TF-DIV	1037		RAD
☐ Breglieb BG-12/16	TF-SON	HP-01		RAA
☐ Jacobs Meise (D.F.S. 108-70)	TF-SAI	X/48/Rvk		RAD
☐ Jonasson & Olsen Ognin	TF-OGN		At Keflavik Airport.	PV
☐ Klemm L 25 e VII R	TF-SUX	847	D-ESUX – at Keflavik – owned by Iceland Aero Club.	RA
☐ Schneider ESG 29 Grunau 9 (D.F.S. 108-10)				RA
☐ Schneider Grunau SG-38 (D.F.S. 108-14)			Fuselage frame only.	RA
☐ Waco YKS-6	'TF-ORN'	4505	NC15613	RACX

ISLENSKA STRIDSARASAFNID (ICE6)

Address:	Heidarvegur, IS-730 Reydarfjördur.
Admission:	Mid June-August daily 1300-1800.
Location:	In the northern part of the town off Route 92.

On the eastern side of the country is the town of Reydarfjordur, which was an important naval base in World War II. On the hillside above the town is the Icelandic Wartime Museum located on the site of a former hospital. A number of Nissen huts survive and the museum is situated in buildings modified from this period. A fascinating display of photographs and artefacts can be seen. The aeronautical interest comprises components from crashed aircraft, instruments, uniforms and photographs.

KEFLAVIK NATO BASE COLLECTION (ICE7)

Address:	IS-235 Keflavik.
Tel:	425-4552
Admission:	By prior permission only.
Location:	About 50 km south west of Reykjavik off Route 41.

During World War II a number of airfields were constructed by the British and Americans for their military use. Keflavik has remained in use ever since and in addition to being a major NATO base it now serves as the major international airport for the country. On the military side of the field is a display of photographs in the Public Affairs Office tracing the history of the site. The 57th Fighter Squadron was in residence for a period but now small numbers of aircraft are detached to the field on rotation. Honouring the unit is an F-4E Phantom painted in the colours of the wing. A Convair F-102 was formerly on show but this was scrapped over ten years ago. A C-117 moved to the folk museum at Hnjotur in 2003. In the summer of 2005 an Orion which had displayed for years also succumbed to the breaker's axe. Many visiting types can usually be seen on the ramp.

TYPE	REG/SER	CON. NO.	PI/NOTES	STATUS
☐ McDonnell M.98HO Phantom II (F-4E)	'66-300'	4398	72-1407	RA

ITALY

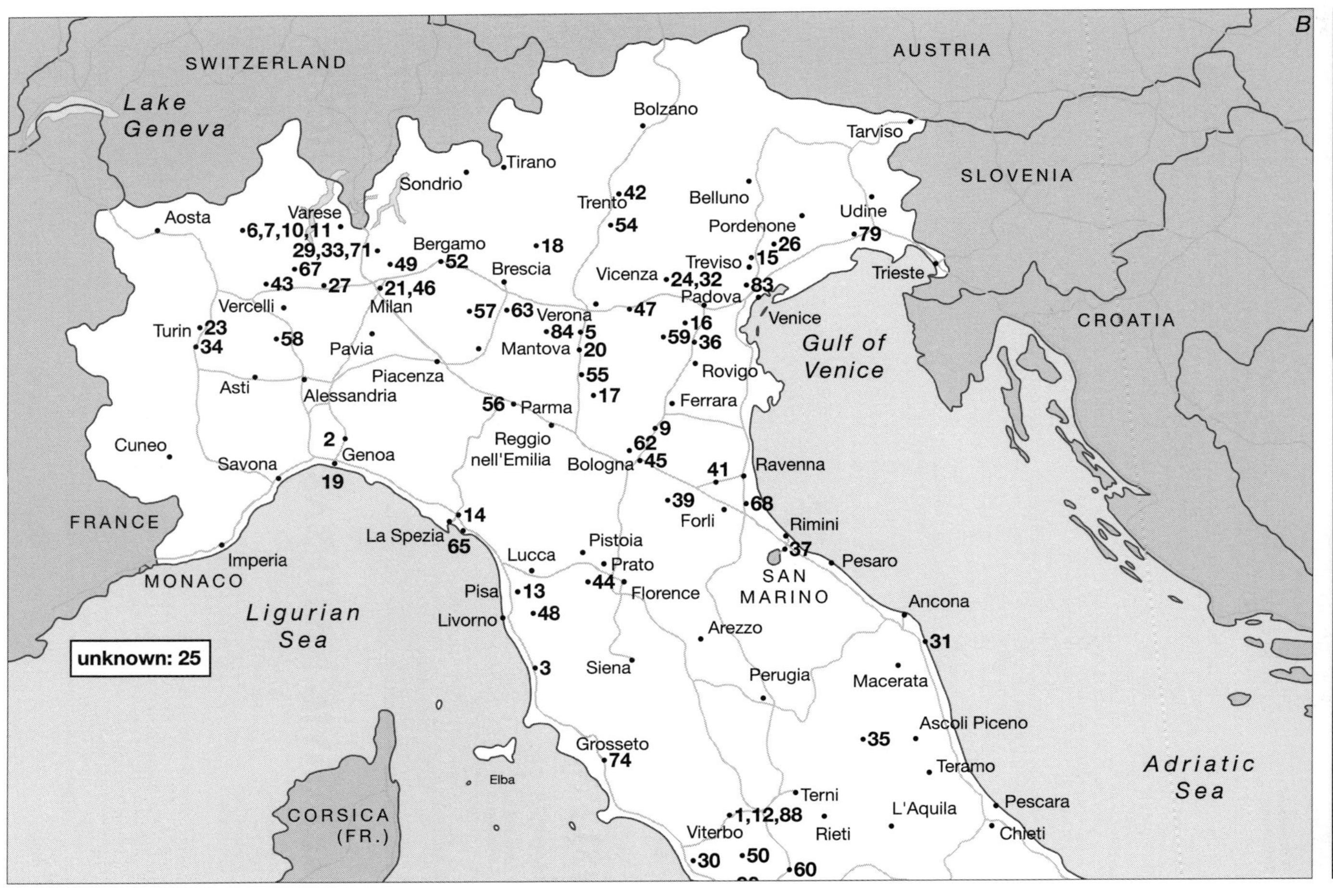
B
SWITZERLAND
AUSTRIA
Lake Geneva
SLOVENIA
CROATIA
FRANCE
MONACO
SAN MARINO
CORSICA (FR.)
Gulf of Venice
Ligurian Sea
Adriatic Sea
Elba
Bolzano
Tarviso
Tirano
Sondrio
Trento •42
•54
Belluno
Udine
•79
Pordenone
Aosta
Varese
•6,7,10,11
29,33,71
Bergamo
•18
•26
•15
Treviso
Trieste
•49
•52
Brescia
•67
Vicenza
•24,32
•83
Padova
•43
•27
•21,46
Milan
Vercelli
•57
•63
Verona
•47
Venice
•16
Turin •23
•34
•58
Pavia
•84
•5
Mantova
•20
•59
•36
Rovigo
Piacenza
Asti
Alessandria
•55
•17
Ferrara
56
Parma
•9
Cuneo
2
Genoa
Savona
19
Reggio nell'Emilia
Bologna
•62
•45
41
Ravenna
•39
Forlì
•68
•14
La Spezia
65
Rimini
•37
Pesaro
Imperia
Lucca
Pistoia
Prato
•44
Florence
Pisa
•13
•48
Livorno
Ancona
Arezzo
•31
unknown: 25
•3
Siena
Perugia
Macerata
Ascoli Piceno
•35
Grosseto
•74
Teramo
Terni
•1,12,88
Viterbo
Rieti
L'Aquila
Pescara
Chieti
•30
•50
•60

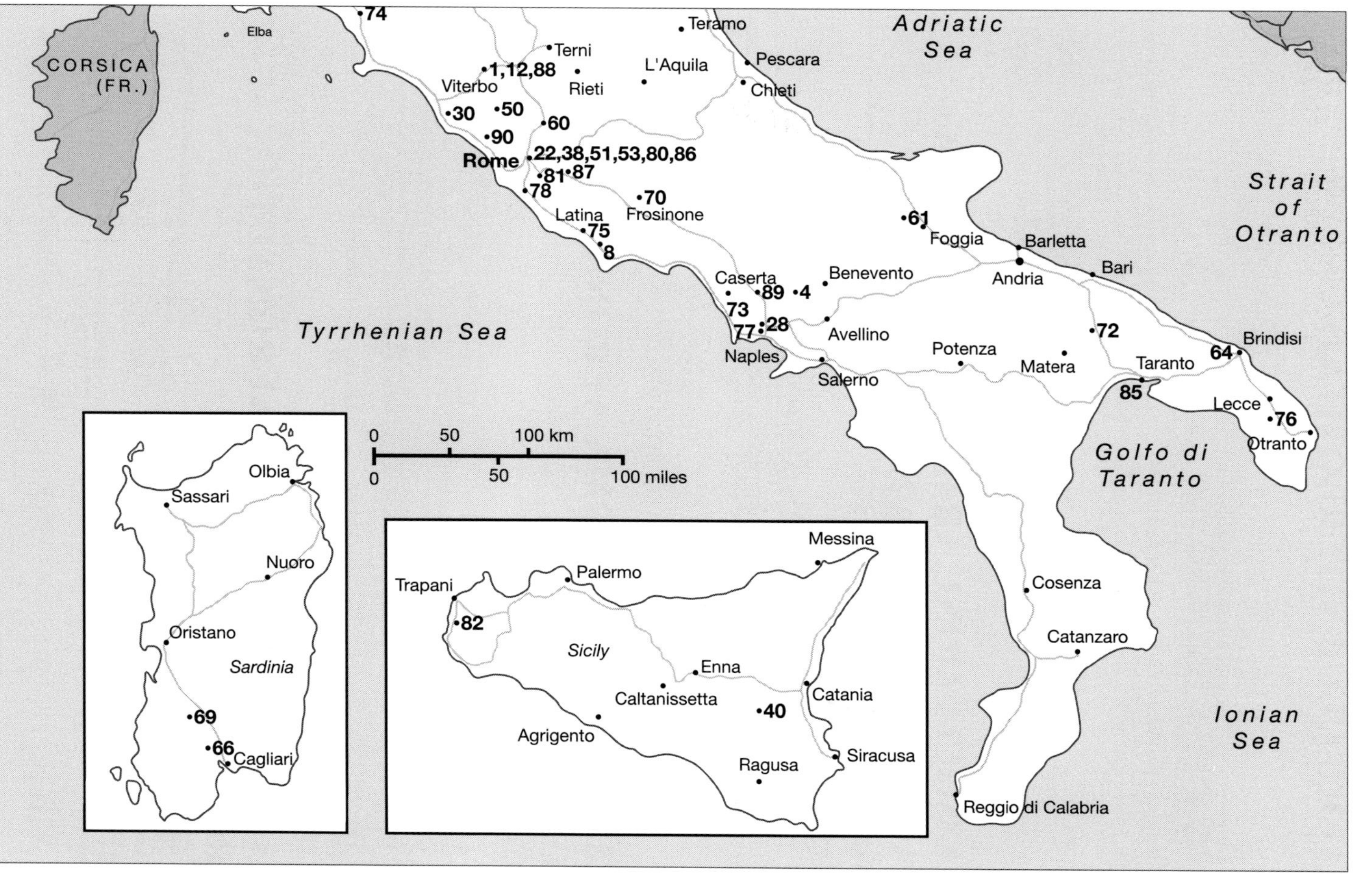
CORSICA (FR.)
Elba
•74
Teramo
Adriatic Sea
Terni
•1,12,88
Rieti
L'Aquila
Pescara
Chieti
Viterbo
•30
•50
•60
•90
Rome
•22,38,51,53,80,86
•81
•87
•78
•70
Frosinone
Latina
•75
8
Strait of Otranto
•61
Foggia
Barletta
Andria
Bari
Caserta
•89
•4
Benevento
73
77
•28
Avellino
Tyrrhenian Sea
•72
Brindisi
64
Potenza
Matera
Taranto
Naples
Salerno
85
Lecce
•76
Otranto
Golfo di Taranto
0 50 100 km
0 50 100 miles
Olbia
Sassari
Nuoro
Oristano
Sardinia
•69
•66
Cagliari
Messina
Trapani
Palermo
•82
Sicily
Enna
Catania
Caltanissetta
•40
Agrigento
Siracusa
Ragusa
Cosenza
Catanzaro
Ionian Sea
Reggio di Calabria

AERO CLUB VITERBO (ITA1)

Address: Strada Occhi Bianchi, 01100 Viterbo.
Tel: 0761-250510
Fax: 0761-352942
Email: info@aeroclubviterbo.com
Admission: By prior permission only.
Location: About 4 km north west of the town off Route 204.

Members of the Viterbo Aero Club, established in 1961, have set up a vintage section which has three aircraft. The Stinson Sentinel was used in large numbers by the Italian Air Force in the immediate post-war period. In the 1950s most of the survivors were transferred to aero clubs. The L-5 has been restored to American World War II markings. Many Super Cubs were used by the Army at Viterbo for liaison and training.

TYPE	REG/SER	CON. NO.	PI/NOTES	STATUS
☐ Piper PA-18-95 Super Cub (L-18C)	I-ZUMA	18-1993	52-2393, MM522393, I-EILU	RAA
☐ Piper PA-18-95 Super Cub (L-18C)	I-LABO	18-2018	52-2418, MM522418, I-EIRI	RAA
☐ Stinson V-76 Sentinel (L-5)	I-AEFU		42-98596, MM52873	RAA

ASSOCIAZIONE ARMA AERONAUTICA – ACQUI TERME (ITA2)

Address: Piazza S. Francesco 1, 15011 Acqui Terme.
Tel: 0144-57064
Admission: By prior permission only.
Location: At Acqui Terme airfield which is about 30 km south west of Alessandria.

Members of this organisation of former Italian Air Force personnel have restored the T-6 for display. Large numbers of both American and Canadian built versions of the type served in Italy for almost thirty years.

TYPE	REG/SER	CON. NO.	PI/NOTES	STATUS
☐ Canadian Car & Foundry Harvard 4 [North American NA-186 (T-6H-4M)]	MM53766	CCF4-???		PV

ASSOCIAZIONE ARMA AERONAUTICA – CECINA (ITA3)

Address: c/o Casa del Mutilato, Via Fattori, 57023 Cecina.
Admission: On permanent view.
Location: Off Route 1 about 34 km south of Livorno.

The local branch of the A.A.A. has been presented with a Macchi MB.326. They have restored the aircraft for display at their premises in the town and staged a photographic display in the building.

TYPE	REG/SER	CON. NO.	PI/NOTES	STATUS
☐ Aermacchi MB.326	MM54283	6448/189		PV

ASSOCIAZIONE ARMA AERONAUTICA – ROTONDI (ITA4)

Address: 83017 Rotondi.
Admission: On permanent view.
Location: In the town which is about 20 km east of Caserta.

The Italian Air Force operated fifty Piaggio P.166s on a number of duties between 1961 and 1996. The branch has obtained the first one delivered and placed it on show in the town.

TYPE	REG/SER	CON. NO.	PI/NOTES	STATUS
☐ Piaggio P.166ML1	MM61871	379		PV

ASSOCIAZIONE ARMA AERONAUTICA – ROVERBELLA (ITA5)

Address:	46048 Roverbella.
Admission:	On permanent view.
Location:	In the town which is about 10 km north of Mantova on Road 249.

The local A.A.A. branch has received an Aermacchi MB.326 which they will restore and place in a park in the town to serve as part of a war memorial to residents who lost their lives in battles.

TYPE	REG/SER	CON. NO.	PI/NOTES	STATUS
☐ Aermacchi MB.326	MM54246	6334/104		PV

ASSOCIAZIONE ARMA AERONAUTICA – VARESE (ITA6)

Address:	26 Via S. Francesco d'Assisi, 21000 Varese.
Tel:	0332-238347
Admission:	On permanent view.
Location:	In the town.

The Aermacchi MB.326 was built locally and served with the Italian Air Force from 1961 until 1990. This example maintained by the A.A.A. has been on show in the town since 1996.

TYPE	REG/SER	CON. NO.	PI/NOTES	STATUS
☐ Aermacchi MB.326	MM54209	6288/58		PV

ASSOCIAZIONE RESTAURO AERONAUTICO (ITA7)

Address:	Via Matteotti 11, 21040 Venegono Superiore.
Tel:	02-8953-1716
Fax:	02-8953-1716
Admission:	By prior permission only.
Location:	At a private workshop just south of Venegono Airfield.

This group has been formed to restore aircraft for other museums. The first project was a Messerschmitt Bf 109 which can now be seen in the Technik Museum at Speyer in Germany. This aircraft ditched in the Black Sea due to engine failure in March 1943. The team has just finished a Fiat CR.42 for the museum at Vigna di Valle. The example for The Fighter Collection at Duxford was delivered in February 2006 The derelict airframe of a Messerschmitt Bf 110 is in store and this project should soon be started.

TYPE	REG/SER	CON. NO.	PI/NOTES	STATUS
☐ Messerschmitt Bf 110C-4		3577	8H+FM	RAD

CENTRO ESPOSIZIONI STORICHE DELLE ORME (ITA8)

Address:	Via Migliara 43,5, Borgo Faiti, 04010 Latina
Tel:	0773-258708
Fax:	0773-255000
Email:	info@pianadelleorme.it
Admission:	Monday-Friday 0900-1700; Saturday-Sunday 0900-1700.
Location:	About 8 km south east of Latina on Route 7.

The Curtiss P-40 is on show in the condition in which it was recovered after crashing in the sea in January 1944. The wreck was lifted in 1995. The Italian Air Force operated over sixty C-119s between 1953 and 1979. Also on show are many weapons, uniforms, military vehicles, documents etc. in this large museum.

TYPE	REG/SER	CON. NO.	PI/NOTES	STATUS
☐ Curtiss 87-A4 Warhawk (P-40E) (Kittyhawk IA)	42-10857			PVD
☐ Fairchild 110 Flying Boxcar (C-119G) (EC-119G)	MM53-8146	249	53-8146	PV

CENTRO POLIFUNZIONALE FERRUCCIO LAMBORGHINI (ITA9)

Address:	Via Statale 342, 40040 Dosso.
Tel:	0333-441-7356
Admission:	By prior permission only.
Location:	About 25 km south west of Ferrara.

This museum was opened in May 1995 by Tonino Lamborghini as a tribute to his father, Ferruccio, who designed the prototype helicopter on show. Also many of the famous sports cars are exhibited.

TYPE	REG/SER	CON. NO.	PI/NOTES	STATUS
☐ Aer-Lualdi L.59	MM576			RA

COLLEZIONE AERMACCHI (ITA10)

Address:	Via Foresio 1, 21040 Venegono Superiore.
Tel:	0331-813111
Fax:	0331-827595
Email:	Info@aermacchi.it
Admission:	By prior permission only.
Location:	At Venegono airfield which is about 5 km south of the city on Route 233.

Founded in 1912 as Nieuport-Macchi the company has remained in the aviation industry and is still producing high quality designs which are in service around the world. In the 1920s the firm constructed a series of floatplane racers which flew with success in the Schneider Trophy. During World War II the MC.200 range of fighters operated in large numbers with the Air Force. In the post war era the MB.308 lightplane flew with the Air Force, many aeroclubs and private owners. The MB.326 jet trainer, which made its maiden flight in December 1957, has been a great success and has served with air forces around the world. The company has gathered examples of some of its designs at the factory airfield along with an archive of photographs and documents. Several aircraft were donated to the Air Force Museum in 1998.

TYPE	REG/SER	CON. NO.	PI/NOTES	STATUS
☐ Aermacchi MB.326E	MM571	6153/3	MM572, I-MAHI	PV
☐ Macchi MC.205V Veltro	MM92166		1243 (Egypt)	PV
☐ Macchi MB.308	I-FABR	????/001		PV

COLLEZIONE CAPRONI (ITA11)

Address:	Villa Caproni, 21040 Venegono Superiore.
Admission:	By prior permission only
Location:	Just north of the village.

The Caproni family had a museum at Vizzola Ticino airfield and other aircraft were stored at their villa. The majority of the collection moved to Trento when the museum there opened in 1992. Some aircraft have remained at the villa including Gianni Caproni's first powered machine the Ca.1 dating from 1910. The Ca.18 shoulder wing monoplane was the first Italian designed and built aircraft to serve with army. Six were flown by an observation squadron at Piacenza. The parasol wing Ca.22, powered by an 80 h.p. radial, set several world and Italian records. The attractive Ca.113 biplane made its maiden flight in 1931 and was one of the most famous aerobatic aircraft of the period. One piloted by Mario de Bernardi took part in the U.S. National Air Races meeting at Cleveland, Ohio in 1931. After World War II Bernardi restored the aircraft in the collection for display work and it was later used as a glider tug. The Gabardini monoplane first flew in 1913 and proved to be ideal for training pilots. A works and school were established at Cameri. Two airframes are in the collection.

TYPE	REG/SER	CON. NO.	PI/NOTES	STATUS
☐ Caproni Ca.1				RA
☐ Caproni Ca.18	231			RA
☐ Caproni Ca.22				RA
☐ Caproni Ca.113	I-MARY	3473		RA
☐ De Havilland D.H.85 Leopard Moth	I-ACIH	7074	G-ACTH – front fuselage only	RAD
☐ Gabardini 2				RA
☐ Gabardini 2 Idro				RA

COLLEZIONE CAVALLERIA DELL'ARIA (ITA12)

Address:	Comando Cavalleria dell'Aria Piazza S. Francesco 5, 01100 Viterbo.
Tel:	0761-307716
Admission:	By prior permission only from the Air Cavalry Headquarters in Rome 06-4735-8682.
Location:	The museum will be at Caserma Palmanova in the town. Until it opens the aircraft are at the military airfield 4 km north west of the town off Route 2.

Italian Army Aviation was formally established in 1951 and the first pilots were trained at Fort Rucker in Alabama. In 1952 Piper Super Cubs were delivered to Bracciano. Army officers receive their basic pilot training with the Air Force at Latina and then move to the Army Aviation Centre at Viterbo. Types used by the Army have been collected for display. A museum will be set up at a barracks in the town to trace the history of the service and an historic flight will be based at the airfield. At the present time the majority of the aircraft are in store at the field. The base gate guardians are part of the collection and will probably stay at this site.

TYPE	REG/SER	CON. NO.	PI/NOTES	STATUS
☐ Agusta-Bell 204B	MM80320	3086	Carries EI-220.	RA
☐ Agusta-Bell 204B	MM80322	3091	Carries EI-222.	RA
☐ Agusta-Bell 47G-3B-1	'MM80573'	1527	MM80273 – carries EI-33.	PV
☐ Agusta-Bell 47G-3B-1	MM80345	1567	Carries EI-41.	PV
☐ Agusta-Bell 47G-3B-1	MM80351	1601	Carries EI-47	RA
☐ Agusta-Bell 47G-3B-1	MM80420	1603	Carries EI-49.	PV
☐ Cessna 305C Bird Dog (L-19E) (O-1E)	MM61-2964	305M0010	61-2964 – carries EI-27.	RAA
☐ Cessna 305C Bird Dog (L-19E) (O-1E)	MM61-3000	305M0050	61-3000 – carries EI-14.	RA
☐ Piper PA-18-135 Super Cub (L-21B)	MM53-7736	18-3336	53-7736, I-EIHG – carries EI-117.	RA
☐ Piper PA-18-135 Super Cub (L-21B)	MM54-2552	18-3952	54-2552, I-EIUA – carries EI-252	RAA
☐ Piper PA-18-95 Super Cub (L-18C)	'I-EIMU'	18-1978	52-2378, MM52-2378	PVX
☐ Piper PA-18-95 Super Cub (L-18C)	MM52-2415	18-2015	52-2415, I-EIRO – carries EI-85	RAA
☐ Piper PA-18-95 Super Cub (L-18C)	MM52-2425	18-2025	52-2425, I-EITE – carries EI-94	RA

COLLEZIONE INSTITUTO TECNICO DI STATO LEONARDO DA VINCI (ITA13)

Address:	Via Matilde Contessa 27, 56123 Pisa.
Tel:	050-888-4111
Admission:	By prior permission only.
Location:	In the city.

This large polytechnic trains airframe and engine fitters among many other trades. Some aircraft are used as instructional airframes and others are preserved for exhibition purposes. The Savoia-Marchetti SM.79 is one of three recovered after many years storage in Lebanon and will hopefully be rebuilt.

TYPE	REG/SER	CON. NO.	PI/NOTES	STATUS
☐ Aermacchi MB.326	MM54153	6129/2		RA
☐ Autogyro				RA
☐ Canadair CL-13 Sabre 4 [North American F-86E]	MM19782	682	19782 (Canada), XB894	RA
☐ Fiat G.91R/1B	MM6413	217		RA
☐ Fiat G.91Y	MM580	2002	On loan from Mus. AMI.	RA
☐ Glider				RAC
☐ Lockheed 580 (T-33A)	MM51-9249	580-7315	51-9249	RA
☐ Lockheed 583-10-20 Starfighter (TF-104G)	MM54257	583H-5208	Front fuselage only.	RA
☐ Lockheed 683-10-19 Starfighter (F-104S) (F-104S/ASA)				RA
☐ Savoia-Marchetti SM.79	L-111		MM21150, LR-AMA – bare frame only – on loan from Mus .AMI.	RAD
☐ SG Aviation SG280 Storm				RA
☐ Zenair CH-200 Zenith	I-GCAB			RA

COLLEZIONE MARISTAELI LUNI (ITA14)

Address:	Comando Maristaeli Luni, 19038 Sarzana.
Tel:	0187-671354
Email:	distaerop.sarzana@aeronautica.difesa.it
Admission:	By prior permission only.
Location:	About 5 km east of La Spezia off Route 62.

The base opened on November 1st 1968 and houses Naval helicopter units. Examples of types used by the service have been preserved around the site. The first to be operated was the Agusta-Bell 47G, which entered service in 1956, and one has been mounted by the main gate to the camp.

TYPE	REG/SER	CON. NO.	PI/NOTES	STATUS
☐ Agusta-Bell 204AS	MM80371	3140		RA
☐ Agusta-Bell 47G-2	'MM83087'		MM80087	PVX
☐ Agusta-Bell 47J-3	MM80360	2073	'MM80306' on left side.	RA
☐ Eurocopter EH-101	MMX605	PP6	i-RAIA	RA
☐ Sikorsky S-58 Seabat (HSS-1N) (SH-34J)	MM153622	581775	Bu153622	RA

COLLEZIONE PETRIN (ITA15)

Address:	Petrimetal, SS. Pontebbana, Castrette di Villorba, 31050 Treviso.
Tel:	0422-919687
Admission:	By prior permission only.
Location:	About 6 km north of Treviso on Route 13.

The firm has assembled a collection of former Air Force aircraft in front of its factory. Over sixty examples of the C-119 served in Italy between 1953 to 1979. Thunderstreaks and Thunderflashes entered service in 1956 and remained in use for almost twenty years. The Fiat assembled F-86K Sabre was delivered to the Air Forces of France, Germany, Holland and Norway as well as Italy. In Italian service the type flew from late 1955 to July 1973. A number of the Harvards are in a poor condition as they have been outside for years.

TYPE	REG/SER	CON. NO.	PI/NOTES	STATUS
☐ Canadian Car & Foundry Harvard 4 [North American NA-186 (T-6H-2M)]	'MM54135'	CCF4-???		RAX
☐ Canadian Car & Foundry Harvard 4 [North American NA-186 (T-6H-4M)]	MM53819	CCF4-???	Frame only.	RAD
☐ Canadian Car & Foundry Harvard 4 [North American NA-186 (T-6H-4M)]	MM53849	CCF4-???		RAD
☐ Canadian Car & Foundry Harvard 4 [North American NA-186 (T-6H-4M)]	MM54117	CCF4-???		RAD
☐ Fairchild 110 Flying Boxcar (C-119G) (C-119J)	MM51-8121	124	51-8121 may be c/n 131 51-8128.	RA
☐ Fiat G.91R/1A	MM6311	175	Tail from c/n 191 MM6387.	RA
☐ Fiat G.91R/1B	MM6396	200	Tail from c/n 213 MM6409.	RA
☐ Fiat G.91R/1B	MM6401	205	Tail from c/n 155 MM6291.	RA
☐ Fiat G.91R/1B	MM6415	219	Tail from c/n 194 MM6390	RA
☐ North American NA-88 Texan (AT-6D)				RA
☐ North American NA-88 Texan (AT-6D)	MM53869			RA
☐ North American NA-221 Sabre (F-86K)	MM55-4869	221-109	55-4869 – tail from c/n 213-58 54-1288.	RA
☐ Republic F-84F Thunderstreak	MM53-6619		53-6619 – tail from 52-10524.	RA
☐ Republic RF-84F Thunderflash	MM53-7585		53-7585 – tail from 52-6972.	RA

COLLEZIONE SORLINI (ITA16)

Address:	Sorlini srl, Via Marconi 3, 25080 Calvagese della Riviera.
Tel:	030-601031
Email:	avio@sorlini.com
Admission:	By priorv permission only.
Location:	At Montegaldella which is about 5 km from the Grisignano exit of the A4.

A fleet of classic aircraft is being acquired by Mr. Sorlini. The oldest is the Avia FL.3 which first flew in late 1939. Both open and closed cockpit versions of the side-by-side two seat low wing monoplane were produced. Well over three hundred were built during World War II. The type was put back into production in 1945 and several were constructed over the next two years. The Macchi MB.308 first flew in January 1947 and served with the Air Force and flying clubs for many years. The Safir has been in Mr. Sorlini's ownership since 1955.

TYPE	REG/SER	CON. NO.	PI/NOTES	STATUS
☐ Avia FL.3	I-AVIG	A.1		RAC
☐ Canadian Car & Foundry Harvard 4 [North American NA-186 (T-6H-4M)]	I-TSIX		MM53785, I-LSBA	RAA
☐ Canadian Car & Foundry Harvard 4 [North American NA-186 (T-6H-4M)]	MM53815			RA
☐ Fiat G.46-4B-5	I-AEKA	180	MM53304, I-AEKA, I-LSBA	RAA
☐ Macchi MB.308	I-BIOH	5894/121	MM53074	RA
☐ Piper PA-18-150 Super Cub	I-LSBC	18-8109006		RAA
☐ Svenska Aeroplan Aktiebolaget (SAAB) 91C Safir	I-LUXI	91319	SE-XBF	RA

DELTALAND – PARCO VELIVOLI STORICI (ITA17)

Address:	Via Matteotti 323, 41039 San Possidonio.
Tel:	0535-36005 / 0348-7277-4055
Email:	lucianafer@libero.it
Admission:	Daily 0900-1800.
Location:	Just south of the village on the road to Carpi.

A collection of mainly military aircraft was set up in the early 1990s at this airstrip which is used by microlights and light aircraft. Examples of recently withdrawn types have been acquired and restored for static display. The SM.1019E was designed to replace the Cessna Bird Dog in Army service. SIAI-Marchetti developed the Bird Dog airframe and fitted an Allison turboprop engine. The first deliveries were made in the spring of 1976 and eighty were built. The two Fiat G-46 trainers are awaiting restoration, as is the Stinson Sentinel.

TYPE	REG/SER	CON. NO.	PI/NOTES	STATUS
☐ Aermacchi MB.326E (MB.326)	MM54168	6172/18		PV
☐ Aermacchi MB.339CD				RA
☐ Aermacchi MB.339CD			Static test airframe.	RA
☐ Agusta A.109A-1	MM81255	7408		RAD
☐ Agusta-Bell 47J	MM80188	1101		RAD
☐ Agusta-Bell 204B	MM80382	3104		PV
☐ Agusta-Bell 205A-1	I-VFET	4503		RAD
☐ Agusta-Bell 206A-2 Jet Ranger	MM80568	8211		RAD
☐ Beech C18S Expeditor (C-45F) (UC-45F)	MM61754	6964	44-47086, HB276	RA
☐ Bell 47G-2 Sioux (H-13H) (OH-13H)	MM80793			RA
☐ Bell 47G-2 Sioux (H-13H) (OH-13H)	MM80796	2139	57-6210	RA
☐ Bell 47G-2 Sioux (H-13H) (OH-13H)	MM80812	2312	58-1548	PV
☐ Bell 47G-2 Sioux (H-13H) (OH-13H)		2338	58-5325	PV
☐ Bell 47G-2 Sioux (H-13H) (OH-13H)	MM80784	2352	58-5339	RA
☐ Fiat G.46-3B	I-AEHR	179	MM53303	RA
☐ Fiat G.46-3B	I-ADRO	46	MM52803	RA
☐ Fiat G.91R/1A	MM6305	169		PV
☐ Fiat G.91Y				RA
☐ Fiat G.91Y	MM6466	2028		PV
☐ Fiat G.91Y	MM6472	2034		PV
☐ Fiat G.91Y	MM6958	2065		RA
☐ Lockheed 580 (T-33A)	MM51-9141	580-6925	51-9141	PV
☐ Lockheed 683-10-19 Starfighter (F-104G)				RA
☐ Lockheed 683-10-19 Starfighter (F-104G)	MM6595	683-6595		PV
☐ Lockheed 683-10-19 Starfighter (F-104G)	MM6598	683-6598	Rear fuselage only.	RA
☐ Lockheed 683-10-19 Starfighter (F-104G)	MM6647	683-6647	Tail from c/n 683-6520 MM6520.	RA
☐ North American NA-168 Texan (T-6G)	MM53665		(USAF)	PV
☐ North American NA-168 Texan (T-6G)	MM53669		(USAF)	RA
☐ North American NA-168 Texan (T-6G)	MM54110		(USAF)	PV
☐ Piaggio P.166ML1	MM61911	423	MM61911, I-PIAA	PV
☐ SIAI-Marchetti SM.1019E	MM57195	1-002		PV
☐ SIAI-Marchetti SM.1019E	MM57226	1-034		RA
☐ SIAI-Marchetti SM.1019E	MM57250	1-058		RA
☐ SIAI-Marchetti SM.1019E	MM57259	1-069		RA
☐ SIAI-Marchetti SM.1019E	MM57263	1-073		RA
☐ SIAI-Marchetti SM.1019E	MM57264	1-074		RA
☐ Stinson V-76 Sentinel (L-5B)				RAD

FONDAZIONE VITTORIALE DEGLI ITALIANI (ITA18)

Address:	Vittoriale degli Italiani, 25083 Gardone Riviera.
Tel:	0365-296511
Fax:	0365-296512
Email:	vittoriale@vittoriale.it
Admission:	Daily 0830-1230 1400-1800.
Location:	On Road No.45bis about 30 km north east of Brescia.

The estate is devoted to the memory of poet and aviator Gabriele D'Annunzio. The story of his life is portrayed in detail with many personal items on show. In August 1918 he led a raid from San Pelagio to Vienna. The flight lasted seven hours and flew over enemy territory for more than five hundred miles. Ten single seat Ansaldo SVA 5s plus a modified two seater took part. The two seater was piloted by Natale Palli with D'Annunzio as observer.

TYPE	REG/SER	CON. NO.	PI/NOTES	STATUS
☐ Ansaldo SVA 10	12736	29		PV

FONDAZIONE ANSALDO (ITA19)

Address:	Villa Cattaneo dell'Olmo, Corso F.M. Perrone 118, 16161 Genova.
Tel:	010-655-8556
Fax:	010-655-8484
Email:	lombardo@ansaldo.it
Admission:	Aircraft on permanent view at the airport entrance.
Location:	In the south western part of the city.

The Ansaldo company moved into aviation during World War I and the successful SVA biplanes were produced in large numbers. A factory and airfield was constructed near the city for this purpose. The company was absorbed into the FIAT empire in 1926. Designed by Umberto Savoia and Rodolfo Verduzio the SVA 1 first flew in 1917. The SVA 5 appeared the following year and was powered by a 220 h.p. Piemontese Automobile PA.6 engine. The last flying examples of the type were used on police work up to 1929. A replica SVA 5 was built for the Ansaldo company by Felice Gonalba between 1987 and 1990. The biplane, with its distinctive fuselage shape, was put on show in a glass building at Genova Airport in 2001. A vast amount of archive material is in store in the city and hopefully this will form part of a museum tracing the history of the company.

TYPE	REG/SER	CON. NO.	PI/NOTES	STATUS
☐ Ansaldo SVA 5 (R)	'11720'			PVX

GALLERIA STORICA DEL CORPO NAZIONALE DEI VIGILI DEL FUOCO (ITA20)

Address:	Commando Provinciale Vigili del Fuoco. Viale Risorgimento. 46100 Mantova.
Tel:	0376-221222
Fax:	0376-322222
Email:	comando.mantova@vigilifuoco.it
Admission:	Saturday-Sunday 0900-1200 1530-1830.
Location:	In the Piazza Arche in the city near the castle.

This excellent museum traces the history of fire fighting from the early days. On show are superbly restored fire engines ranging from simple water carrying carts to modern vehicles. The display includes an amphibious vehicle used to travel along waterways and a superb collection of metal helmets. Equipment used by the service along with many photographs and documents are exhibited. In recent times helicopters have played an important role in the service and a Bell 47 flown for several years can be seen in the building.

TYPE	REG/SER	CON. NO.	PI/NOTES	STATUS
☐ Agusta-Bell 47G-3B-1	I-VFEN	1597		PV

GRUPPO AMICI VELIVOLI STORICI – MILANO (ITA21)

Address:	Via Vespucci 11. 20093 Cologno Monzese.
Tel:	02-2539-1118.
Email:	Claudio.Basile@rasnet.it
Admission:	By prior permission only.
Location:	At a private workshop in the city.

This chapter was set up in April 1990 and members are working on several projects. A Macchi MB.308 floatplane is being rebuilt from the components of several aircraft. The prototype first flew in 1946 and was produced in large numbers for both civil and military use. The type was also built under licence in Argentina. The unique Saltafossi is a high wing homebuilt dating from 1946 and this has been restored to flying condition. Designed by Ermeneglido Preti, who also built a number of cars, the aircraft was found in a local college. The original Aermacchi MB.2 engine has been replaced by an 850 c.c. DAF motor. The polytechnic at Milan has designed many gliders. The Canguro first flew in 1941 and over fifty were built. Initially serving with the military a number of these sailplanes were later used by flying clubs. Members of the group recently completed the rebuild of the tail section of the Re.2005 stored at the Caproni Museum.

TYPE	REG/SER	CON. NO.	PI/NOTES	STATUS
☐ Centro Volo a Vela del Politecnico di Milano C.V.V.6 Canguro				RAC
☐ Macchi MB.308			Composite.	RAC
☐ Preti PM.2 Saltafossi				RAA

GRUPPO AMICI VELIVOLI STORICI – ROMA (ITA22)

Address:	P.O. Box 7138, 00100 Roma-Nomentano.
Tel:	06-3972-7717
Fax:	06-392-7717
Email:	gavsita@libero.it
Admission:	By prior permission only.
Location:	At a private workshop in the city.

Formed in 1983 the group has collected a considerable amount of historical material. In 1986 a Nardi FN.305 was acquired and restored. This aircraft is now on loan to the Museo Storico A.M.I. Currently in store is a rare Saiman 202 which will be rebuilt. Work is now concentrated on the components of the Ro.41.

TYPE	REG/SER	CON. NO.	PI/NOTES	STATUS
☐ Industrie Meccaniche e Aeronautiche Meridionali (IMAM) Ro 41B			Parts only on loan from Mus. A.M.I.	RAC
☐ Nardi FN.305	MM52757	766	MM52757, I-DASM – on loan to Mus. AMI.	–
☐ Societa Anonima Industrie Meccaniche Aeronautiche Navali (SAIMAN) 202M	I-BIOM	7	MM52193	S

GRUPPO AMICI VELIVOLI STORICI – TORINO (ITA23)

Address:	Via Gioberti 25. 10128 Torino.
Tel:	011-779-4815
Fax:	011-779-4815
Email:	gavs.italia@libero.it
Admission:	By prior permission only.
Location:	At a private workshop in Leini which is about 10 km north of the city.

Founded in 1985 the Turin Chapter has been involved in many projects. The first restoration to be carried out was the Ansaldo SVA 10 which once belonged to Gabriele d'Annuzio. This biplane has been exhibited at the Gardone Museum for many years. In 1990 work started on the SPAD VII for the Baracca Museum. This superbly restored biplane can now be seen at Lugo. A completed Stinson Sentinel is now resplendent in original World War II configuration. Discussions are taking place with other local organisations to set up an aviation museum.

TYPE	REG/SER	CON. NO.	PI/NOTES	STATUS
☐ Avia FL.3	I-BIOU		MM56233	RA
☐ Beech C18S Expeditor (C-45F) (UC-45F)	MM61714	6976	44-47094, KJ493	RAC
☐ Canadian Car & Foundry Harvard 4 [North American NA-186 (T-6H-4M)]	MM53820	CCF4-???	(USAF)	RA
☐ Centro Volo a Vela del Politecnico di Milano C.V.V.8 Bonaventura	I-MCPV	011		RA
☐ Centro Volo a Vela del Politecnico di Torino M-300	I-CNVU	2		RA
☐ Fiat G.91PAN (G.91)	MM6265	31		RA
☐ Piaggio P.136L1	I-FRLV	212	I-SASO	RAC
☐ Republic F-84G Thunderjet			Composite.	RAC
☐ SIAI-Marchetti S.205C (S.205-20)	I-IBAE	06-005		RAC
☐ Stinson V-76 Sentinel (L-5)			Fuselage frame only.	RAD
☐ Stinson V-76 Sentinel (L-5)	42-99119	76-1538	42-99119, MM52882, I-AEEL	RA
☐ Vignoli Autogyro	I-SART		I-STAR	RA

GRUPPO AMICI VELIVOLI STORICI – VICENZA (ITA24)

Address:	Via Gaetano Maccà, 36100 Vicenza.
Tel:	0444-511747
Email:	gversola@tin.it
Admission:	By prior permission only.
Location:	At a private workshop in the city.

This branch of G.A.V.S. does not have any aircraft allocated at the present time. However they have carried out restoration of aircraft and components for a number of museums.

HISTORIC AIRCRAFT GROUP (ITA25)

Address: ?
Location: Unknown.

There have been reports in magazines of this group which has obtained a number of aircraft and plans to restore them to flying condition. No mention has been made of their location.

TYPE	REG/SER	CON. NO.	PI/NOTES	STATUS
☐ Aeronáutica M.100S Mesange				RA
☐ Avia FL.3				RAC
☐ Fiat G.46-3B				RA
☐ Macchi MB.308	D-EJCH	5844/71	I-NCOM, D-EJUP	RAA
☐ Stinson V-76 Sentinel (L-5)	I-AECP		(USAAF), MM52839	RAC

JONATHAN COLLECTION – AEREI STORICI FAMOSI (ITA26)

Address: Via Cadore 12,
31015 Conegliano.
Tel: 0438-33916/60887
Admission: Flying days Saturday-Sunday – otherwise by prior permission only.
Location: The airfield is on an island in the River Piave at Cimadolmo about 10 km north of Treviso.

This small grass airfield houses an interesting collection of flyable aircraft. During the summer air shows are held at weekends. Three replicas highlight the early period of aviation. The start of powered flight is shown by the Wright Flyer, a two seat Blériot XI portrays the pre-1914 period and the Fokker Dr I shows the rapid advances in design brought about by World War I. The Tiger Moth trained many pilots around the world for more than a quarter of a century. The Piper Cub has been painted in World War II colours.

TYPE	REG/SER	CON. NO.	PI/NOTES	STATUS
☐ Blériot XI-2 (R)	I-PONI	02		PVA
☐ Centro Volo a Vela del Politecnico di Torino M-100SS	I-AGOS	056		PVA
☐ De Havilland D.H.82A Tiger Moth	I-GATO	85253	DE193	PVA
☐ Fokker Dr I (R)	I-LYNC	01/84M		PVA
☐ Piper J-3C-65 Cub (O-59A) (L-4A)	'236433'	10905	43-29614, I-NITA	PVAX
☐ Piper PA-18-135 Super Cub (L-21B)	I-BTRE	18-3339	53-7339, MM53-7339, I-EIKR, EI-120	PVA
☐ War Aircraft P-51 Mustang	I-MUST	93/004		RAC
☐ Wright Flyer (R)		03		PVA

MONUMENTO ALL'AVIATORE (ITA27)

Address: 28066 Galliate.
Admission: On permanent view.
Location: In the town which is about 5 km north east of Novara.

The aircraft was dedicated on February 25th 2002 as a memorial to all local aviators who had lost their lives in service. The F-104S variant was operational from mid-1969 until late-2004.

TYPE	REG/SER	CON. NO.	PI/NOTES	STATUS
☐ Lockheed 683-10-19 Starfighter (F-104S) (F-104S/ASA)	MM6840	683-6840		PV

MONUMENTO DELL'AVIATORE (ITA28)

Address: Pineta Communale San Antonio,
80021 Afragola.
Admission: On permanent view.
Location: In the town which is about 5 km north of Napoli.

The so far unidentified Aermacchi MB.326 has been put on show as a memorial to flyers born in the town. The trainer served in large numbers in both Italy and other countries.

TYPE	REG/SER	CON. NO.	PI/NOTES	STATUS
☐ Aermacchi MB.326				PV

MONUMENTO DI GUERRA (ITA29)

Address:	Viale di Remembrance, 21015 Lonate Pozzolo
Admission:	On permanent view.
Location:	In the western part of the town which is just south east of Malpensa Airport and about 30 km north west of Milano.

The Fiat G.59 has been here for many years and now only a derelict fuselage and one wing remain. This advanced trainer first flew in 1948 and one hundred and seventy five were produced.

TYPE	REG/SER	CON. NO.	PI/NOTES	STATUS
☐ Fiat G.59-2B	MM53136	45		PVD

MONUMENTO DI GUERRA (ITA30)

Address:	01016 Tarquinia.
Admission:	On permanent view.
Location:	In the town which is about 70 km north west of Roma.

Recently put on show as a memorial to local aviators who lost their lives in war, the Fiat G.91 was transported from Améndola. The aircraft was stored at the base after being withdrawn from use in the mid-1990s.

TYPE	REG/SER	CON. NO.	PI/NOTES	STATUS
☐ Fiat G.91T/1	MM54392	119		PV

MUSEO AERONAUTICO AIRPARK (ITA31)

Address:	SS 16 Loreto Porto Recanati, 60025 Loreto.
Tel:	071-9797260
Admission:	Monday-Friday 1830-1930; Saturday- Sunday 1730-1930.
Location:	On Route 16 between Loreto and Porto Recanati.

This open-air museum used to contain a number of interesting aircraft. Several have gone to other museums in the country. The Caravelle, now the only one remaining, was part of the Air Inter fleet in France before arriving in Italy in 1982 for use by Altair who operated it for three years.

TYPE	REG/SER	CON. NO.	PI/NOTES	STATUS
☐ Sud-Est SE.210 Caravelle III	I-GISE	208	F-WNKB, F-BNKB	PV

MUSEO AEROPORTO MILITARE T. DAL MOLIN (ITA32)

Address:	Via Ferrarin 138 36100 Vicenza.
Tel:	0444-511747
Admission:	Guided tours first Saturday of month 0930-1130 – book with GAVS Vicenza.
Location:	In the north western suburbs of the city

Warrant Officer T. Dal Molin piloted the Macchi M.52R which was second in the 1929 Schneider Trophy race held at Calshott. On January 18th 1930 he was killed in the Savoia Marchetti S.65 which plunged into Lake Garda. This unusual design, featuring one tractor and one pusher engine in a short nacelle with the pilot housed in between, was attempting to set a new world air speed record. The aircraft had been taken to Calshott for the 1929 contest but cooling and fuel problems prevented it from starting. The small museum set up at the base honours his contribution to aviation and has a few small parts of the S.65 in the collection. The history of the airfield and the resident units is portrayed. Types recently used by the military are also on show.

TYPE	REG/SER	CON. NO.	PI/NOTES	STATUS
☐ Agusta-Bell 204B	MM80357	3085		RA
☐ Canadian Car & Foundry Harvard 4 [North American NA-186 (T-6H-4M)]	MM53821	CCF4-???		RAC
☐ Fiat G.91R/1A	MM6292	156		RA
☐ Fiat G.91R/1B	MM6388	192	Front fuselage only.	RA
☐ Lockheed 683-10-19 Starfighter (F-104G)	MM6577	683-6577		RA
☐ North American NA-213 Sabre (F-86K)	MM54-1288	213-58	54-1288, Q-288 (Netherlands) fin from c/n 221-98 55-4858.	RA

MUSEO AGUSTA (ITA33)

Address:	Via Giovanni Agusta 500, 21017 Cascina Costa di Samarate.
Tel:	0331-220545
Email:	museo@glaagusta.com
Admission:	Tuesday-Wednesday 1400-1800; Sunday 1000-1230 1400-1800.
Location:	Just south of Malpensa Airport and which is about 30km north west of Milano.

Giovanni Agusta formed a company in 1907 and this built a small number of aircraft. Then the firm constructed the famous MV Agusta line of motor cycles. In 1952 Giovanni's son Domenico took out a licence for the manufacture and distribution of Bell helicopters in Europe. The first Agusta-Bell 47G made its maiden flight in May 1954 and large numbers of several Bell models have been built. Indigenous designs followed with the A.101G flying in 1964. Also Sikorsky and Vertol types have been produced. In 1981 the Breda-Nardi company was bought by Agusta and their plant constructed Hughes 300s and 500s under licence. The company saved many of its prototypes and the collection was stored with the Caproni Museum from 1991 for about ten years. This new museum opened in 2004 and on show are several helicopters, motor cycles and many other items tracing the history of the Agusta company. The remaining helicopters are in store in the area. The Bell 48 was imported to serve as the development prototype for the A.102. Hopefully the other helicopters can soon be exhibited so that the range of types produced can be seen in full.

TYPE	REG/SER	CON. NO.	PI/NOTES	STATUS
☐ Agusta A.101G	MM80358			RA
☐ Agusta A.102				RA
☐ Agusta A.102	I-AGUT	1	I-AGUT, MM573	RA
☐ Agusta A.103				PV
☐ Agusta A.104				RA
☐ Agusta A.104B				RA
☐ Agusta A.105A	MM80415			RA
☐ Agusta A.105B	MM80416			PV
☐ Agusta A.109A	I-AGUL	7103		PV
☐ Agusta A.112				RA
☐ Agusta A.113				RA
☐ Agusta A.114				RA
☐ Agusta A.115	I-AGUC			RA
☐ Agusta A.129A Mangusta	MMX598	29005		PV
☐ Agusta EMA.124	I-EMAF	7501		RA
☐ Agusta-Bell 47G-2	I-VFEC			PV
☐ Agusta-Bell 47J-3B-1	MM80728	2123		PV
☐ Bell 48 (YR-12B) (YH-12B)	46-0217			RA

MUSEO DEL POLITECNICO – SEZIONE AERONAUTICA (ITA34)

Address:	Corso Duca Degli Abruzzi 24, 10129 Torino.
Tel:	011-564-6825/6602.
Fax:	011-564-6899
Admission:	By prior permission only.
Location:	In the centre of the city.

The Turin Polytechnic has a large museum tracing then history and development of many aspects of technology. The college has been active in glider design since the 1950s. The CVT-2, dating from 1954, designed by Alberto and Piero Morelli set Italian height and distance records and competed in two National Championships. Only one was built and it was probably the first sailplane to feature a 'T-tail'. The sole CVT-4 Strale has also been saved. This incorporated improved features learned from the comprehensive testing of the Veltro. The Morelli designed M-100 was produced in Italy. In France Carmam built the M.100 and the two seat M.200. Alberto designed the M-300 and four prototypes were built by the Polytechnic. Over forty aero engines from early times up to modern jets are displayed. There are also pieces of apparatus used in aeronautical research. Discussions are taking place with other local groups regarding the establishment of an aviation museum in the area.

TYPE	REG/SER	CON. NO.	PI/NOTES	STATUS
☐ Aviamilano-Caproni A-2	I-ERCO	604		RA
☐ Centro Volo a Vela del Politecnico di Milano C.V.V.2 Asiago	I-GVGA			RA
☐ Centro Volo a Vela del Politecnico di Torino CVT-2 Veltro	I-CVTB	1		RA
☐ Centro Volo a Vela del Politecnico di Torino CVT-3				RA
☐ Centro Volo a Vela del Politecnico di Torino CVT-4 Strale	I-CNVU	1		RA
☐ Centro Volo a Vela del Politecnico di Torino M-100	I-LOTI	1		RA
☐ Centro Volo a Vela del Politecnico di Torino M-100SS	I-CVTD	026		RA
☐ Centro Volo a Vela del Politecnico di Torino M-300	I-CVTG	001	Parts only	RA
☐ Centro Volo a Vela del Politecnico di Torino M-300	I-CVTE	1		RA

MUSEO DEL VOLO LIBERO (ITA35)

Address:	06046 Castelluccio di Norcia .
Admission:	By prior permission only.
Location:	Just north of the town which is about 35 km west of Ascoli Piceno.

This museum was set up in the late 1990s and currently has two aircraft on display. One is an as yet unidentified hang glider and the other the front fuselage of a Fiat G.91. There is a hang gliding school in the area.

TYPE	REG/SER	CON. NO.	PI/NOTES	STATUS
☐ Fiat G.91R/3			Front fuselage only.	PV
☐ Hang Glider				PV

MUSEO DELL'ARIA 'NIDO DELLE AQUILE' (ITA36)

Address:	Castello di San Pelagio. Via San Pelagio 42. 35020 Carrara San Giorgio.
Tel:	049-912-5008
Fax:	049-912-5929
Email:	info@museodellaria.it
Admission:	Tuesday-Sunday 0930-1230 1430-1900. (1400-1800 in winter). Closed December-January.
Location:	About 12 km south west of Padova, east of the A.13.

San Pelagio Castle was used by Gabriele D'Annuzio as the headquarters for his famous raid on Vienna on August 8th 1918. The Zaborra family have owned the estate since 1726 and the current Contessa is married to an architect, Alberto Avesarni, who has set up several theme and wild life parks in Italy. He decided to establish the museum in the early 1980s and he received a great deal of help from Contessa Maria Fede Caproni. The history of aviation is portrayed in twenty rooms, each depicting a particular theme with emphasis on the Italian contribution. The first is devoted to Leonardo da Vinci with models and drawings on show. There is a display of D'Annunzio's briefing with full scale wax figures seated around a table. Gabardini's historic crossing of the Alps in 1914 is commemorated. Nobile's airship flight over the North Pole is highlighted. Italy's record in the Schneider Trophy is featured, as are Balbo's famous formation flights across the Atlantic with Savoia-Marchetti flying boats. In the courtyard of the castle are displayed the light aircraft and helicopters. The Fauvel tailless glider was produced in some numbers in France. Adriano Mantelli designed a series of twin boom pusher lightplanes and the AM.10 prototype is on show. The Avia FL.3 was produced in large numbers for civil and military use.

TYPE	REG/SER	CON. NO.	PI/NOTES	STATUS
☐ Aermacchi MB.326	MM54243	6329/99		PV
☐ Agusta-Bell 47J	MM80227	1122		PV
☐ Agusta-Bell 204B	MM80281	3049	Also reported as MM80467	PV
☐ Ansaldo SVA 5 (FSM)	'24525'			PVX
☐ Avia FL.3	I-AIAD	A-10		PVX
☐ Brugger MB.2 Kolibri	I-CAPI	0001		PV
☐ Canadian Car & Foundry Harvard 4 [North American NA-186 (T-6H-4M)]	MM53823	CCF4-???		PV
☐ Centro Volo a Vela del Politecnico di Milano C.V.V.6 Canguro	I-TRIW	0003	MM100005, I-AECE	PV
☐ Construzione Aero Taliedo CAT.20	I-LAUS			PV
☐ Fairchild 24R9 Forwarder (UC-61K) (Argus III)	I-FRIF	R9-1036	44-83075, KK418	PVX
☐ Fauvel AV.36	I-DAWN	42		PV
☐ Grumman G-111 Albatross (G-64) (SA-16A) (SA-16B) (HU-16B)	MM51-7253	G-343	51-7253	PV
☐ Hang Glider				PV
☐ Macchi MB.308	I-ATAA	5851/78	MM52931	PV
☐ Mantelli AM.10	I-CARD	001	C/n may be 004	PV
☐ Partenavia P.66B Oscar 100	I-LOLE	11		PV
☐ Republic RF-84F Thunderflash	MM52-7339		52-7339 – incorporates parts from 53-6730 and 53-6827.	PV
☐ Sezione Sperimentale EC38-56C Uribel	I-AVMM	008		PV

MUSEO DELL'AVIAZIONE (ITA37)

Address:	Via San Aquilina 58, Cerbaiola, 47900 Rimini.
Tel:	0541-7756696
Fax:	0541-905148
Email:	museoaviazione@libero.it
Admission:	Daily 1000-1600.
Location:	Off the Route 72 from Rimini to San Marino about 1 km from the border.

This privately owned museum opened on April 2nd 1995. A landscaped terraced area on the side of a hill overlooking the road from San Marino to Rimini is the site of the display. The area was formerly used for agriculture. The aircraft are clearly visible to the many tourists who visit the tiny republic. The exhibition hall houses uniforms, medals, photographs and components. The history of aviation is portrayed in the displays. In 2000 the museum dedicated a memorial to those who lost their lives at Ramstein on August 28th 1988 when Aermacchi MB.339s of the Frecce Tricolore collided in mid-air during their display. The wrecks of the three aircraft are on show. A rare machine is one of the few surviving Saiman 202 liaison aircraft dating from the early 1940s. Successful trainers are the Texan, the Fiat G.46, the Aermacchi MB.326 and the Iskra. The Thunderstreak has been painted in the colours of the 50th Stormo who operated the type from Piacenza San Giorgio. Several jets have been acquired from former Warsaw Pact countries and a number of these have been painted in false markings to add variety for the tourist. The Swearingen types are not common in museums. The designs have served as feeder liners and executive transports in many countries. The Javelin was acquired from the now closed museum at Bochum in Germany and is now a rare type.

TYPE	REG/SER	CON. NO.	PI/NOTES	STATUS
☐ Aeritalia G.222TCM	MM583	4002		PV
☐ Aermacchi MB.326	MM54194	6199		PV
☐ Aermacchi MB.326E	MM54216	6299/69		PV
☐ Aermacchi MB.339A/PAN	MM54474	6669/062		PVD
☐ Aermacchi MB.339A/PAN	MM54481	6676/071		PVD
☐ Aermacchi MB.339A/PAN	MM54552	6773/168		PVD
☐ Agusta-Bell 47G-2	MM80479	302		PV
☐ Agusta-Bell 47G-3B-1	MM80492	1638		PV
☐ Agusta-Bell 204B	MM80286	3036		PV
☐ Antonov An-2R	SP-TCD	1G 173-03		PV
☐ Antonov An-2R		1G 188-60	SP-TTC, SP-TCG – in false markings	PVX
☐ Antonov An-2T	'SP-EGA'		Front fuselage only.	PVX
☐ Douglas DC-3A-360 Skytrain (C-47)	MM61826	4380	41-18342, I-LIRA, MM61826, I-RIBE	PV
☐ Douglas DC-3A-456 Skytrain (C-47A) (R4D-5)	'N242AG'	12679	42-92834, Bu17174, N242AG, N123H, N7124, N711TD, I-COFR	PV
☐ Fiat G.46-3A	MM52805	69	MM52805, I-AEKE	PV
☐ Fiat G.91PAN (G.91)	MM6249	15		PV
☐ Fiat G.91R/1B	MM6389	193	Tail from G.91R/1A c/n 166 MM6302	PV
☐ Fiat G.91T/1	MM54403	130		PV
☐ Fiat G.91T/1	MM54405	132		PV
☐ Fiat G.91T/1	MM54407	134		PV
☐ Fokker Dr I (FSM)				PV
☐ Gloster Javelin FAW.9 (FAW.7)	'XH707'		XH768, 7929M, XH768	PVX
☐ Hawker P.1099 Hunter F.58	J-4057	41H/697424	In Swiss markings.	PV
☐ Ilyushin Il-28	7	2207	In Polish markings.	PV
☐ Let L-410M Turbolet	OK-FDC	750408		PV
☐ Lockheed 580 (T-33A)	MM54-1602	580-9338	54-1602	PV
☐ Lockheed 683-10-19 Starfighter (F-104G)	26+28	683-9180	KH+179, DF+247	PV
☐ McDonnell M.98DJ Phantom II (F-4C)	64-0757	1047		PV
☐ Mikoyan-Gurevich MiG-15UTI	127	022532	In DDR markings.	PV
☐ Mikoyan-Gurevich MiG-19S	'7110'	150316	0316 (Czech) – in false Pakistani markings.	PVX
☐ Mikoyan-Gurevich MiG-21MF	23+42	96001039	772 (DDR)	PV
☐ Mikoyan-Gurevich MiG-21PFM	'3-0914'	760914	870 (DDR) – in false Iranian markings.	PVX
☐ Mikoyan-Gurevich MiG-21UM	23+82	516915011	231 (DDR)	PV
☐ Mikoyan-Gurevich MiG-21UM	285	516999436	Front fuselage only – in DDR markings.	PV
☐ Mikoyan-Gurevich MiG-23BN	718	0393215729	718 (DDR), 20+54	PV
☐ Mil Mi-2	SP-TSB	543042123	CCCP-20141, SP-SDN	PV
☐ Mil Mi-2P	'155'	535437127	SP-SAE – in false Latvian markings.	PV
☐ Mil Mi-9 (Mi-8A)	93+96	340003	405 (DDR)	PV
☐ North American NA-88 Texan (AT-6C)	'MM53042'		MM53145	PVX
☐ Panstwowe Zaklady Lotnicze (PZL) TS-8 Bies	'0309'	1E 07-16 (?)		PVX
☐ Panstwowe Zaklady Lotnicze (PZL) TS-11 Iskra 200bisD	W1757	3H 19-16	1915 – in Indian markings – original c/n 3H 14-32.	PV
☐ Piaggio P.148	'MM53740'	175	MM53727	PVX
☐ Piaggio P.166ML1	MM61913	425		PV
☐ Republic F-84F Thunderstreak	MM53-6970		53-6970 - front fuselage only.	PV
☐ Republic F-84F Thunderstreak	'5-36591'		53-6646, MM53-6646	PVX
☐ Republic RF-84F Thunderflash	MM52-7459		52-7459	PV
☐ SIAI-Marchetti S.205-18F	I-SIAD	235		PV
☐ Societa Anonima Industrie Meccaniche Aeronautiche Navali (SAIMAN) 202M	MM52161	3	MM52161, I-FALK	PV
☐ Sukhoi Su-7BM	5308	5308	In Czechoslovakian markings.	PV
☐ Sukhoi Su-22M4	'27'	25307	360 (DDR), 25+01	PVX
☐ Swearingen SA.226AT Merlin IV	I-NARW	AT-058	N500YM, OY-AST, D-ICFB	PV
☐ Swearingen SA.226TC Metro III	I-SWAB	TC-402	N10129, OE-LSD, OO-XCI, F-GFJX	PV
☐ Vought A-7E Corsair II	Bu158830	E-319		PV
☐ Wytwornia Sprzetu Komunikacyjnego (WSK) Lim-6bis (Lim-5M) [MiG-17F]	212	1F 02-12		PV

MUSEO DELL'ISTITUTO STORICO DI CULTURA DELL'ARMA DEL GENIO (ITA38)

Address:	Lungotevere Della Vittoria 31, 00195 Roma.
Tel:	06-372-5446
Admission:	Monday-Friday 0830-1330 ; Sunday 0830-1130. Often closed check before visiting.
Location:	In the northern part of the city near the Ponte del Risorgimento.

The history of Italian military transport is portrayed in this excellent museum. Sections of the display are devoted to military engineering, including bridge building, and communications. The Blériot XI is believed to be the aircraft which made the first flight in the war in Libya in October 1911.

TYPE	REG/SER	CON. NO.	PI/NOTES	STATUS
☐ Blériot XI		412		PV

MUSEO DELLA GUERRA (ITA39)

Address:	Palazzo Alidosi, 40022 Castel Del Rio.
Tel:	0542-95554
Fax:	0542-95554
Email:	museo@museoguerra-casteldelrio.it
Admission:	Sunday 1500-1800.
Location:	About 25 km south west of Imola on Route 610.

On show at this museum is a former Italian Air Force Texan which has been painted in United States military markings. The displays trace the history of warfare with particular emphasis on local battles.

TYPE	REG/SER	CON. NO.	PI/NOTES	STATUS
☐ Canadian Car & Foundry Harvard 4 [North American NA-186 (T-6H-2M)]	'28449'	CCF4-???	MM54146	PVX

MUSEO DELLA PIAZZAFORTE (ITA40)

Address:	Sant Giacomo del Castello Severo, 96011 Augusta.
Tel:	0931-522284
Admission:	Monday-Saturday 0930-1230.
Location:	In the centre of the town which is about 20 km south of Catania.

The museum is housed in an old fortress close to the harbour. Relics from several aircraft, including a float from a Cant Z.506, and engines from a Ju 88 and a Fiat RS.14, are on show along with uniforms and memorabilia. The Agusta A.106 helicopter is one of two used in trials at Pratica and later operated from Catania.

TYPE	REG/SER	CON. NO.	PI/NOTES	STATUS
☐ Agusta A.106	MM5001N			PV

MUSEO FRANCESCO BARACCA (ITA41)

Address:	Via Baracca 65, 48022 Lugo di Romagna.
Tel:	0545-24821/38556
Email:	museobaracca@racine.ra.it
Admission:	Tuesday-Sunday 1000-1200 1600-1800.
Location:	In the centre of the town which is on Route 253 about 20 km west of Ravenna.

Francesco Baracca was born in Lugo in 1888 and was one of the pioneers of Italian aviation. During World War I he flew SPAD VIIs and XIIIs and was killed in 1918. A museum honouring his exploits was established in the town. The SPAD VII in which he scored his thirtieth victory near Asiagio in December 1917 is on show. This aircraft was transported to Vigna di Valle in 1967 for restoration. In 1990 the biplane was moved to G.A.V.S. Turin for a major rebuild and it emerged resplendent in Baracca's original markings. The new museum opened on June 20th 1993. The story of Baracca's life is told with many photographs and personal items on show.

TYPE	REG/SER	CON. NO.	PI/NOTES	STATUS
☐ Fiat G.91Y	MM6444	2006		PV
☐ Société Pour l'Aviation et ses Dérivés (SPAD) VII	S.2489			PV

MUSEO G. CAPRONI (ITA42)

Address:	Via Lidorno 3, 38100 Trento.
Tel:	0461-944888
Fax:	0461-944800
Email:	caproni@mtsn.tn.it
Admission:	Tuesday-Friday 0900-1300 1400-1700; Saturday-Sunday 1000-1300 1400-1800.
Location:	At Trento Airport which is about 5 km south of the town off Route 12.

In 1908 Gianni Caproni became the first Italian to set up an aircraft factory. The works were located at Taliedo near Milan and a flying school was established at Vizzola Ticino where in the 1930s another factory was built. By the outbreak of World War II the company had taken over several other firms. Up to 1939 over one hundred different designs had been produced. During World War I the firm became well known for its bombers. In the inter-war period several giant aircraft were built including the Ca.60 flying boat and the Ca.90 biplane, which in 1929 was the largest aircraft in the world. The Caproni Museum was set up in 1929 by Gianni and his wife Timina. Several early Caproni airframes had been saved and an archive of historical documents and photographs was started. The aircraft were put on show in a large hangar at the Taliedo factory. During World War II the collection was stored in a number of locations but some material was lost. A factory occupation by workers in late 1949 resulted in the burning of a Ca.4 triplane and the destruction of other items. The family moved many airframes to their villa at Venegono Superiore and the papers were kept in Rome. During the 1960s some aircraft were taken to two hangars at Vizzola Ticino and these were opened to the public. During this period the collection expanded with the acquisition of several more modern types. Gianni's daughter Maria Fede never gave up the dream of a new purpose built museum dedicated to her parent's efforts. In 1988 the Province of Trento came to an agreement with the Caproni family. The local authority would provide the funds for the restoration of the aircraft and build a museum. The majority of the airframes were moved to the area and Masterfly at Rovereto commenced the task of rebuilding several machines. The first phase of the museum was opened on October 3rd 1992 with around twenty aircraft on show. The museum displays many rare types and all have been restored to a high standard. Eventually it is proposed to have on show all the sixty plus aircraft owned by the museum and two more exhibition halls are planned. Several examples of Caproni's products can be seen and there are models of many of his designs. The Ca 6 biplane is the earliest on show whilst one of his successful Ca 100 biplanes from the 1930s is exhibited on floats. The only Fokker D VIII known to exist is on view, sadly the wings were lost many years ago. Three examples of the SM 79 were reported in Lebanon many years ago. One was brought back to Italy in the late 1960s and is now on show at Vigna di Valle. Negotiations with the Lebanese authorities started in the late 1980s for a second example. In early 1993 an Air Force team went to an airfield in the Bekaa Valley where the SM.79 had been stored for over twenty five years. The trimotor arrived at Trento in the summer of 1993 and has been restored in period markings for the display.

TYPE	REG/SER	CON. NO.	PI/NOTES	STATUS
☐ Aerolombarda GP.2 Asiago	I-DASI		MM30098	RA
☐ Aerolombarda GP.2 Asiago	I-ZUME		MM30096	RA
☐ Aerolombarda GP.2 Asiago	I-VERG	02/GS/04		RA
☐ Agusta-Bell 47G-4	I-FLAM	2501	MM80426	PV
☐ Ansaldo A-1 Balilla	16552			RA
☐ Ansaldo SVA 5	11777			PV
☐ Avia FL.3	I-AIAE	A-16		PV
☐ Breda Ba.19	'I-ABCT'		MM70019	PVX
☐ Bristol-Coanda Monoplane		154		PV
☐ Bücker Bü 131B Jungmann	A-45	57	A-45 (Switzerland), HB-UTN, I-CERM	PV
☐ Caproni Ca.6				PV
☐ Caproni Ca.9				PV
☐ Caproni Ca.53				RA
☐ Caproni Ca.60			Front fuselage and other small parts	RA
☐ Caproni Ca.100 Caproncino	I-GTAB	1	On loan to Museo Storico AMI.	–
☐ Caproni Ca.100 Caproncino	MM56237	3752	MM56237, I-DISC	PV
☐ Caproni Ca.163			Possibly I-WEST.	PV
☐ Caproni Ca.193	I-POLO	5736	MM56701	PV
☐ Caproni-Reggiane Re.2000 Falco I	MM8287		On loan from Museo Storico AMI	RA
☐ Caproni-Reggiane Re.2005 Sagittario	MM92351		On loan from Museo Storico AMI.	RA
☐ Caproni-Trento F.5	MM553		I-RAIA, MM553 – on loan from Museo Storico AMI.	PV
☐ Caproni-Vizzola A-3	I-RIFF	63		RA
☐ Caproni-Vizzola C.22J (Mock up)				PV
☐ Costruzioni Aeronautiche Novaresi (CANSA) C.6b Falchetto	MM475			RAD
☐ Da Vinci Flying Machine (FSM)				PV
☐ De Havilland D.H.104 Dove 6	I-ANIC	04495		RA
☐ Dornier Do 27B-1	I-EMFG	275	AS+927, AC+927, 56+08, D-EMFG	PV
☐ Fairchild 24 C8C	I-GENI	2662		RA
☐ Fiat G.91Y	MM6470	2032		RA
☐ Fokker D VIII	MM194	2916 (?)	MM194, I-FRAK or I-ELIA – 275/18 or 293/18 – fuselage only.	PV
☐ Gabardini G.51bis	I-AXAQ	805	'MM04306'	PV
☐ Homebuilt Helicopter	'I-MODI'			RA
☐ Hughes 269A	N8870F			RA
☐ Jurca MJ.5 Sirocco	I-RUMM	67		PV
☐ Lockheed 683-10-19 Starfighter (F-104G)	MM6609	683-6609		PV
☐ Macchi M.20	5		I-AABO	PV

TYPE	REG/SER	CON. NO.	PI/NOTES	STATUS
☐ Macchi MC.200 Saetta			Major fuselage components only	RAD
☐ Macchi MB.308	I-ACSN	5885/112	MM53065	PV
☐ Mantelli AM.6				RA
☐ Manzolini Libellula I	I-MANN	1		RA
☐ Manzolini Libellula II	I-MANZ	1		RA
☐ Manzolini Libellula III				RA
☐ Nardi-Hughes NH-500				RA
☐ Noorduyn Harvard IIB [North American NA-77]	MM54142	07/73	Possible identity	RA
☐ North American NA-207 Sabre (F-86K)	MM53-8300	207-28	53-8300	RA
☐ Partenavia P.53 Aeroscooter (MdB.02)	I-SELI	002		RA
☐ Republic RC-3 Seabee	I-SIBI	331	HB-SEA	RA
☐ Savoia-Marchetti SM.79	L-113		MM24499, LR-AMC – in Lebanese markings.	PV
☐ Savoia-Marchetti SM.80 Bis	I-ELIO	30003	I-TATI	PV
☐ Savoia-Marchetti SM.102	I-AEVO	20	MM61829	RA
☐ Silvercraft SH-4	I-SILY	006		RA
☐ Societa Aeronautica Italiana – Ambrosini S.2S	I-LANC			RA
☐ Societa Anonima Industrie Meccaniche Aeronautiche Navali (SAIMAN) 202M	MM52163	'5'	MM52163, I-BIOL	PV
☐ Viberti Musca 1	I-DIAN	12		RA
☐ Vizzola II	I-RENI	003		RA

MUSEO GOTTAR PARK (ITA43)

Address: 28053 Castelleto Sopra Ticino
Admission: Daily 1000-1600.
Location: South east of Arona near the junction of SS32 and SS33.

This private transport museum has a number of vehicles and trains on show. Four aircraft are in the collection. The Partenavia company produced several light designs from the early 1950s. The Oscar made its maiden flight in 1965 and over three hundred P.66 variants were produced over the next decade by Partenavia and Aviolight.

TYPE	REG/SER	CON. NO.	PI/NOTES	STATUS
☐ Agusta-Bell 47J-3	MM80296	2047	With parts of Agusta-Bell 47G-2 c/n 248 MM80166.	PV
☐ Fiat G.91T/1	MM54415	142		PV
☐ Lockheed 683-10-19 Starfighter (F-104S) (F-104S/ASA)	MM6836	683-6836	Composite with parts from c/n 683-6833 MM6833 and c/n 683-6768 MM6768.	PV
☐ Partenavia P.66B Oscar 100	I-BRIN	06		PV
☐ Piaggio P.166ML1	MM61875	383		PV

MUSEO LEONARDO DA VINCI (ITA44)

Address: Castello dei Conti Guidi,
50053 Vinci.
Tel: 0571-56055
Email: leonardiano@leonet.it
Admission: Daily 0930-1800.
Location: About 25 km west of Firenze.

This museum was set up more than twenty five years ago to honour the work of the famous local inventor and painter. The collection is housed in a tower in the historic city walls. Some original material can be seen along with copies of his papers and drawings. The story of his life is portrayed in detail. A replica of one of his glider designs has been built. It is intended to carry out flight tests with the machine before it goes on display.

TYPE	REG/SER	CON. NO.	PI/NOTES	STATUS
☐ Da Vinci Glider (R)				RA

MUSEO MEMORIALE DELLA LIBERTÁ (ITA45)

Address: Via Guiseppe Dozza 24,
40139 Bologna.
Tel: 051-461100
Fax: 051-462172
Email: arturoansaloni@virgilio.it
Admission: May-September Tuesday-Sunday 0930-1230 1500-1700; October-April Tuesday-Saturday 0930-1230 Sunday 1530-1830.
Location: In the eastern part of the town.

The main exhibition consists of five large dioramas detailing significant events in the liberation of the town and the surrounding area in 1945. The visitor can walk through these areas and see the events unfold. The Piaggio P.166 has been on show for several years. The other pair have been allocated and should have arrived.

TYPE	REG/SER	CON. NO.	PI/NOTES	STATUS
☐ Canadian Car & Foundry Harvard 4 [North American NA-186 (T-6H-4M)]				PV
☐ Lockheed 683-10-19 Starfighter (F-104S) (F-104S/ASA)	MM6836	683-6836	Rear fuselage only.	PV
☐ Piaggio P.166ML1	MM61914	426		PV

MUSEO NAZIONALE DELLA SCIENZA E DELLA TECNICA (ITA46)

Address:	Via San Vittore 21, 20123 Milano.
Tel:	02-485551
Fax:	02-4801-0016
Email:	museo@museoscienza.it
Admission:	Tuesday-Sunday 0930-1200 1400-1730. Part of the Aeronautical Section is often closed – check with the museum.
Location:	In the city centre near the Piazza del Duomo.

The museum was established in February 1953 when an exhibition was staged honouring Leonardo da Vinci. The great gallery of the museum houses many of his original drawings and documents. The aeronautical section was opened in May 1973 and in addition to the aircraft there is a wide range of engines, models, components and associated equipment on show tracing the technical development of flight. The early era is portrayed by two replicas. The Farman biplane was built in 1956 and flown at Fiumicino. From World War I is the Macchi built Nieuport biplane. Sporting flying between the wars is well represented and includes a replica of the diminutive Ricci 6 triplane of 1918. When built it was the smallest aircraft in the world. Designed for a competition for touring aircraft the Ricci was powered by a six cylindner Anzani engine. After evaluation by the military it was scrapped. The replica was built in 1967 for the museum. The high wing Breda 15 first flew in 1929 and was one of the outstanding touring aeroplanes of the 1930s. The type was also flown on military duties. The largest aircraft is the sole Caproni TM.2 glider. First flown in the spring of 1943 it was badly damaged when a tow cable broke. After repairs it was tested for a short period and then the project was abandoned. After the war Caproni planned to fit two engines but this never happened. The Veltro was one of the most successful Italian aircraft of World War II. The Puss Moth was delivered new to Italy in 1931, finally retired in 1957, and then presented to the museum. The sole prototype of the Magni PM.3/4 Vale features swept wings and a ply covered monocoque fuselage. This high wing monoplane was exhibited at the 1937 Salone Aeronautico in Milan. Another unique machine is the Frati designed F.9 built by Pasotti. The type was a single engined version of the F.6 Airone and it made its maiden flight in July 1956. A rarity is the Hungarian designed M.24 built in 1939. This low wing two seat cabin monoplane is powered by a 100 hp.Hirth HM.504 engine. A small number were used by the Egyptian Air Force. The design came from the team at the Technical University in Budapest who built several original types in the inter-war period. The Avro built Cierva autogyro was delivered to Italy in 1935 and later evaluated by the Air Force. It was finally withdrawn in 1948 and presented to the museum. The Zögling replica was built and flown in 1946 by members of the Milan Gliding Association. Plans for a large new exhibition building at a site near Malpensa Airport have been put forward and this should enable more of the stored material to be put on show.

TYPE	REG/SER	CON. NO.	PI/NOTES	STATUS
☐ Blériot XI (R)				PV
☐ Breda Ba.15				PV
☐ Caproni-Campini CC.2			Fuselage only	PV
☐ Cierva C.30A (Avro 671)	I-CIER	753	G-ACXA, MM30030	PV
☐ Costruzioni Aeronautiche Taliedo TM.2	MM511	2		RA
☐ De Havilland D.H.80A Puss Moth	I-FOGL	2114		PV
☐ De Havilland D.H.100 Vampire FB.52A	MM6112	291		PV
☐ Farman HF-4 (R)	I-FARM			PV
☐ Fiat G.91R/1B	MM6382	186	Tail from c/n 224 MM6420.	PV
☐ Junkers J 4		803/17	Fuselage only – On loan to DTM, Germany.	–
☐ Macchi MC.205V Veltro	'MM92215'	6665	MM91818, I-MCVE	PVX
☐ Macchi-Nieuport Ni.10-18mq	I-BORA		15179	PV
☐ Magni PM.3/4 Vale	MM253			PV
☐ Muegyetemi Sportrepulo Egyesulet M.24	'I-TITI'		HA-RAN (?)	PVX
☐ Nardi FN.333 Riviera				PV
☐ North American NA-182 Texan (T-6G)	MM54114		(USAF)	PV
☐ North American NA-221 Sabre (F-86K)	MM55-4812	221-52	55-4812	PV
☐ Pasotti F.9 Sparviero	I-HAWK	D02		PV
☐ Republic F-84F Thunderstreak	MM53-6805		53-6805	PV
☐ Ricci 6 (R)				PV
☐ Savoia-Marchetti SM.102	I-GION	17	MM61810	PV
☐ Societa Aeronautica Italiana – Ambrosini Super S.7	I-PAIN	1/01		PV
☐ Societa Anonima Industrie Meccaniche Aeronautiche Navali (SAIMAN) 202M	I-CUPI		MM52162	RA
☐ Stamer-Lippisch Z-12 Zögling 33 (R)				PV

MUSEO NICOLIS (ITA47)

Address:	Viale Postumia 65, 37069 Villafranca di Verona.
Tel:	045-630-3281
Fax:	045-797-9493
Email:	museonicolis@museonicolis.com
Admission:	Tuesday-Sunday 1000-1800.
Location:	About 15 km south west of Verona off Route 62.

This museum has a large collection of cars, motor cycles, bicycles and military vehicles. Many of the cars were restored to working order by Luciano Nicolis. The earliest on show is a 1903 Cottereau Populaire and also from this period are a 1909 Bianchi and a 1914 Benz/8/20. Londoners can feel at home when they see an example of the famous Austin Heavy Taxi. One highlight is a superbly restored Bugatti 49, built in 1931, and used in the 1966 film 'Grand Prix'. The Starfighter has been painted in a special scheme applied to an F-104S. The aviation section also includes models, engines and components.

TYPE	REG/SER	CON. NO.	PI/NOTES	STATUS
☐ Fiat G.46-3B				PV
☐ Lockheed 580 (T-33A)	MM51-9145	580-6929	51-9145	PV
☐ Lockheed 683-10-19 Starfighter (F-104G)	'MM6827'	683-6514	MM6514	PVX

MUSEO PIAGGIO (ITA48)

Address:	Viale Rinaldo Piaggio 7, 56025 Pontedera.
Tel:	0587-291935
Email:	museo@museopiaggio.it
Admission:	Monday-Saturday 1000-1800.
Location:	In the town which is about 15km south east of Pisa off Route 555.

Piaggio constructed ships and railway carriages before entering aviation in 1916. The first aircraft made were Caproni bombers. In 1923 the Pegna Company was taken over and the P.2 fighter appeared. Since then many original and successful designs have been built. The Pontedera plant has produced aero engines and during World War II aircraft, including the four engined P.108 bomber. After the end of the conflict motor vehicles were made at the site. The museum opened in the mid-1990s and has on show a range of Gilera motor cycles and examples of the Vespa motor scooter designed by a member of the Piaggio family. Photographs, models and documents show all the activities of the firm since it was set up. The P.148 trainer first flew in 1951 and the type was used by the air force until the mid-1970s. A few were then sold into civilian ownership. The type was in competition with the Macchi M.416 which proved to be superior in the primary role. Several were then used for liaison and glider towing duties. An ex-Luftwaffe P.149D is under restoration. One prototype was built in Italy and this was later used by the Italian Air Attache in Bonn. A production run for the Luftwaffe and licence building by Focke Wulf followed. Examples of other Piaggio types are being sought.

TYPE	REG/SER	CON. NO.	PI/NOTES	STATUS
☐ Piaggio P.148	MM53562	138		PV
☐ Piaggio P.149D				RAC

MUSEO STORICO ALFA ROMEO (ITA49)

Address:	Fiat Auto, Viale Alfa Romeo, Centro Direzionale, 20020 Arese.
Tel:	02-444-29303
Admission:	Monday-Friday 0930-1330 1430-1630.
Location:	At the factory which is off Road No.233 about 12 km north west of Milano.

Alfa Romeo was set up in 1910 and has gained a world-wide reputation for quality cars. The museum has over fifty superbly restored vehicles on view including several racers in the famous Italian red. The exhibits trace the development of Alfa Romeo cars from 1910 to the present day. There is an excellent display of models and a cabinet showing the many trophies won in competition. The company was a leading manufacturer of aero engines and a range of their motors is exhibited. The only aircraft in the collection is an Ambrosini Grifo powered by an Alfa Romeo engine. The monoplane is painted in the colours of the one flown across the South Atlantic by Bonzi and Lualdi. Their aircraft was on show in the National Museum in Buenos Aires until December 1973 when it returned to Italy. The airframe was in poor condition so a reconstruction was carried out using another aircraft as the basis with some original parts incorporated in the rebuild. The Grifo, the first post-war product of the Ambrosini company, was a development of their 1930s series of low wing cabin monoplanes. A few were evaluated by the Air Force who used the similar S.7 for training and liaison duties.

TYPE	REG/SER	CON. NO.	PI/NOTES	STATUS
☐ Societa Aeronautica Italiana – Ambrosini S.1001 Grifo	'I-ASSI'	11	I-RANN	PVX

MUSEO STORICO DELL'AERONAUTICA MILITARE ITALIANA (ITA50)

Address:	Aeroporto di Vigna di Valle, 00062 Vigna di Valle.
Tel:	06-902-4034
Email:	musam@aeronautica.difesa.it
Admission:	June-September Tuesday-Sunday 0900-1800; October-May Tuesday-Sunday 0900-1600.
Location:	About 25 km north west of Roma on the south side of Lago di Bracciano. Guidonia is about 20 km north west of Roma.

Major Giulio Doughet first suggested in 1913 that material from the early days of ballooning and flying should be collected but it was more than sixty years later that the Italian Air Force Museum found a permanent home. Fortunately historic aircraft had been saved by military units, commercial organisations and individuals around the country. In 1956 a small display was staged in Rome and this led to more aircraft and other items being acquired. An International Exhibition was held in Turin in the early 1960s and a few aircraft were put on show. The idea of a museum was put forward and one of the pavilions was taken over. The venture was not a success and by the early 1970s had virtually closed. A restoration centre had been set up at Vigna di Valle to prepare aircraft for the Turin display. Political pressure for the exhibition site to be in the Rome area led to the choice of Vigna di Valle for the museum. The site on the shores of Lake Bracciano was an important seaplane station for many years. In 1908 the first flight of an Italian airship took place there. Three hangars survived and there was a large outside hard standing area. Two historic hangars, the large Badoni and the smaller Austro-Hungarian, were restored and connected by a modern structure which provided extra exhibition space as well as housing the administrative and research areas. The museum opened in May 1977 and since then has been re-organised. The Military Aviation Service was established in November 1912 but Blériot monoplanes had been used the previous year against Turkey. The Austro-Hungarian hangar houses the early aircraft. Dominating this area is a Caproni Ca 33 bomber. Italy was one of the first countries to use heavy bombers. The aircraft on show was built in 1916 and in 1921 was bought and stored by a private individual for thirty eight years. Nobile's polar flights in the airship Norge with Amundsen in 1926 and in 1928 in his Italia are featured. The Ansaldo company produced many successful fighters and three products of the company are in the collection. The biplane SVA series was used in large numbers in World War I. Over one hundred examples of the parasol-wing AC 2 were operated from the mid-1920s. This design was based on the French Dewoitine D 1. Italy competed in many Schneider Trophy contests and a line of four floatplanes in the distinctive red national colours evokes memories of a vanished era. The quartet are a Fiat C.29, the Macchi M.39, a Macchi M 67 and the Macchi MC 72. In the 1926 race one of the M.39s piloted by de Bernardi won at Hampton Roads in Virginia. Four days later he set a world air speed record. The C.29 made its maiden flight at Lake Garda in August 1929 but was damaged on a test flight and did not compete in the contest at Calshot. The Badoni houses aircraft from 1935 to 1966 and includes many unusual and unique types including two trimotors, the Cant Z.506 and the Savoia-Marchetti SM.79. The Z.506 is exhibited on floats and the prototype first flew in 1935. Over the next few years the type set speed, altitude and distance records for seaplanes. The Savoia-Marchetti company became famous when the SM.55 flying boat made several trans-Atlantic flights. In 1933 twenty four made a formation journey to the Chigago World Fair. This epic flight with Marshall Balbo in command is highlighted in a special display. The firm turned its attention to three engined transports and several models soon appeared. Three SM.79s were discovered in Lebanon many years ago and protracted negotiations eventually resulted in all returning to Italy. One of the aircraft rebuilt at Lecce is the Lohner L-1 flying boat. Designed in Austria the type first flew in the early years of World War I. The example in the collection was for many years on show in the historical museum in Bari. The Caproni-Campini CC.1 has been modified to CC.2 configuration. This aircraft had a conventional piston engine mounted in its fuselage and was driven by the channelling of exhaust gases and airflow from the nose intake. The CC.1 was Italy's first jet aircraft and its maiden flight was made on August 28th 1940 with 1926 Schneider Trophy winner Mario de Bernardi at the controls. A rare aircraft which is rarely on show is the Weber A VII Etiopia. Dating from the mid-1930s this low wing monoplane was built and flown in Ethopia. As types are withdrawn from service examples are arriving at the museum. Almost all types flown by the Air Force in recent years are now in the collection. Products of the post-war Italian aircraft industry are also well represented.

TYPE	REG/SER	CON. NO.	PI/NOTES	STATUS
☐ Aerfer Ariete	MM569	2		PV
☐ Aerfer Sagittario II	MM561	2		RA
☐ Aermacchi MB.326	MM572	6153/3	MM572, I-MAHI	RA
☐ Aermacchi MB.326E	MM54389	6502/243		PV
☐ Aermacchi MB.326K	MM54290	6403/172	I-FAZE – at Guidonia.	RA
☐ Aermacchi MB.326K	MM54390	6477/218	MM54390, I-AMKK, I-IVAO	RA
☐ Agusta A.102	I-ECIN	004	MM80201	RA
☐ Agusta-Bell 47G-2	MM80113	196		PV
☐ Agusta-Bell 47J	MM80187	1100		PV
☐ Agusta-D'Ascanio				PV
☐ Ansaldo AC 2	MM1208			PV
☐ Ansaldo SVA 5	11721			PV
☐ Ansaldo SVA 9				RA
☐ Avia FL.3	I-ADOD	A34-28		PV
☐ Bazzocchi EB-4				RA
☐ Beech C18S Expeditor (C-45F) (UC-45F)	MM61734	6566	43-35830, (RAF)	RA
☐ Blériot XI (R)				RA
☐ Blériot XI-2	'BL-246'		Probably BL-160	PVX
☐ Bonomi BS.17 Allievo Cantù				PV
☐ Breda Ba.19			Fuselage only.	SD
☐ Canadair CL-13 Sabre 4 [North American F-86E]	MM19792	692	19792 (Canada), XB915	PV
☐ Cantieri Riuniti dell'Adriatico (CANT) Z.501 Gabbiano			Parts from lake	RAD

☐ Cantieri Riuniti dell'Adriatico (CANT) Z.506S Airone	'MM45422'		MM45425	PVX
☐ Caproni Ca.36 (Ca.3)	'4166'		23174	PVX
☐ Caproni Ca.100 Caproncino	I-GTAB	1	On loan from Museo Caproni.	RA
☐ Caproni Ca.100 Idro	I-DISC	3752	MM56273	RAC
☐ Caproni Ca.100 Idro	I-ABOU	3992	MM65156	RA
☐ Caproni-Campini CC.1	MM487	4850	Exhibited in CC.2 form	PV
☐ Caproni-Reggiane Re.2000 Falco I	MM8287		On loan to Museo Caproni.	–
☐ Caproni-Reggiane Re.2001 Falco II	MM08071			RAC
☐ Caproni-Reggiane Re.2002 Ariete		126		RAC
☐ Caproni-Reggiane Re.2005 Sagittario	MM92351		On loan to Museo Caproni.	–
☐ Caproni-Trento F.5	MM553		I-RAIA, I-FACT – on loan to Museo Caproni.	–
☐ Centro Volo a Vela del Politecnico di Milano C.V.V.6 Canguro	I-AECG		MM100007	RA
☐ Centro Volo a Vela del Politecnico di Milano C.V.V.6 Canguro Palas	MM100028	2-131		PV
☐ Centro Volo a Vela del Politecnico di Milano C.V.V.8 Bonaventura	MM100042	001		RA
☐ Curtiss A1 (R)				RA
☐ Curtiss A1 (R)				RA
☐ D'Ascanio-Trojani DAT.3 (FSM)				RA
☐ Da Vinci Flying Machine (FSM)				PV
☐ De Havilland D.H.100 Vampire FB.52A			Composite of c/n 6088/50 MM602, MM6014; c/n 5987/20 MM6042; c/n 6120/82 MM6083; c/n 6122/84 MM6125 and others – on loan to Racc. Amendola.	–
☐ De Havilland D.H.100 Vampire FB.6	J-1107	616		RA
☐ De Havilland D.H.113 Vampire NF.54	MM6152	13094		PV
☐ Dornier Do 217	XM+?M		Rear fuselage only – at Guidonia	RAD
☐ Douglas DC-3A-360 Skytrain (C-47)	MM61894	4261	41-7774, I-LIDA – at Guidonia	RA
☐ Douglas DC-3A-456 Skytrain (C-47A)	MM61776	19194	42-100731, PH-TBH	PV
☐ Eurowing Cirrus 2 Hang Glider				PV
☐ Fairchild 110 Flying Boxcar (C-119F) (C-119J)	MM51-8128	131	51-8128	RA
☐ Fairchild 110 Flying Boxcar (C-119G)	MM52-6029	11030		RA
☐ Fairchild 24R9 Forwarder (UC-61K) (Argus III)	I-FAMA	R9-1055	44-83094, KK437, MM56698	RA
☐ Fiat G.5 Bis	I-BFFI	5	MM290	RA
☐ Fiat C.29	MM130bis	2		PV
☐ Fiat CR.42	'MM4653'	917	Fv2539, SE-AOP	PVX
☐ Fiat G.46-1B	I-AEHP	11	MM52778	RA
☐ Fiat G.46-1B	MM52795	28	MM52795, 'I-IVAN'	RA
☐ Fiat G.46-3B	MM53090	140	MM53090, I-AEKM, I-AEHF.	RA
☐ Fiat G.46-4A	MM53283	189		PV
☐ Fiat G.46-4A	MM53286	192	MM53286, I-AELM	PV
☐ Fiat G.46-4A	MM53292	198		RA
☐ Fiat G.46-4A	MM53295	201		RA
☐ Fiat G.49-2	MM556	2	MM556, I-FIAT	RA
☐ Fiat G.55	MM53265	74	Rebuilt from G-59-2A	PV
☐ Fiat G.59-4B	MM53276	61		PV
☐ Fiat G.59-4B	MM53778	185		RA
☐ Fiat G.80-3B	MM53882	2		PV
☐ Fiat G.82	MM53885	2		RA
☐ Fiat G.82	MM53886	3		RA
☐ Fiat G.82	MM53888	5		RA
☐ Fiat G.91PAN (G.91)	MM6250	16		PV
☐ Fiat G.91R/1	MM6280	46		PV
☐ Fiat G.91R/1B	MM6405	209		PV
☐ Fiat G.91T/1	MM6344	74		PV
☐ Fiat G.91Y	MM580	2002	On loan to Coll ITIS.	–
☐ Fiat G.91Y	MM6959	2066		PV
☐ Fiat G.212CA	MM61804	19		PV
☐ Fieseler Fi 156C-3/trop Storch	MM12822	5802	MM12822, I-FAGG, 20, D-EDEC, G-FIST	PV
☐ Garnerin Balloon				PV
☐ Grumman G-64 Albatross (SA-16A) (HU-16A)	MM50-179	G-68	50-0179	PV
☐ Grumman G-89 Tracker (S2F-1) (S2F-1S1) (S-2F)	MM136556	465	Bu136556	PV
☐ Grumman G-89 Tracker (S2F-1) (S-2A)	MM148295	734	Bu148295 – front fuselage only.	PV
☐ Gruppo Velivoli SIAI 3-VI Eolo	I-BIGI	001		PV
☐ Hanriot HD-1	19309	515		PV
☐ Helio H-395B Super Courier	MM91001	529	N4178D	RA
☐ Hispano HA.132L [Fiat CR.32]	'MM4666'	328	C.1-328	PVX
☐ Industrie Meccaniche e Aeronautiche Meridionali (IMAM) Ro 41B				PV
☐ Industrie Meccaniche e Aeronautiche Meridionali (IMAM) Ro 43	MM27050			RA
☐ Lockheed 15-27-01 Harpoon (PV-2)	N7486C	15-1385	Bu37419	RA
☐ Lockheed 580 (T-33A) (RT-33A)	MM53-5594	580-8933	53-5594	PV
☐ Lockheed 683-10-19 Starfighter (F-104G)	MM6599	683-6599		PV
☐ Lockheed 683-10-19 Starfighter (F-104G)	MM6501	683-9998		PV
☐ Lockheed 683-10-19 Starfighter (F-104S) (F-104S/ASA)	MM6741	683-6741	Front fuselage only.	PV

☐ Lohner L-1	L-127			PV
☐ Macchi AL.60C5				RA
☐ Macchi M.39	MM76	5		PV
☐ Macchi M.67	MM105	3	Fuselage only.	PV
☐ Macchi MC.72	MM181			PV
☐ Macchi MC.200 Saetta	'MM7707'		MM8307 – at Istrana.	–
☐ Macchi MC.202 Folgore	'MM7844'		MM9667	PVX
☐ Macchi MC.205 Veltro (MC.202)	'MM9345'		MM9546	PVX
☐ Macchi MB.308	I-DONT	2		RA
☐ Macchi MB.308	I-GORI	5878/105	MM53058	PV
☐ Macchi MB.308G Idro	I-EMAM	5872/99	MM53053	RAA
☐ Macchi MB.323	MM554		I-RAIE	PV
☐ Macchi M.416 [Fokker S-11]	MM53244	1042	MM53244, I-GIAB	RA
☐ Macchi M.416 [Fokker S-11]	I-AELI	1058	MM53761	RA
☐ Macchi M.416 [Fokker S-11]	I-AELY	1059	MM53762	PV
☐ Macchi M.416 [Fokker S-11]	I-AEPF	6005/61	MM53444 – at Guidonia.	RAD
☐ Macchi M.416 [Fokker S-11]	I-AELS	6013/69	MM53457	RAD
☐ Meteor MS-30L Passero [Scheibe L-Spatz]	I-FOLK	50.008		RA
☐ Militi MB.3 Leonardo	I-MIBO			PV
☐ Nardi FN.305				RAD
☐ Nardi FN.305	MM52757	766	MM52757, I-DASM – on loan from G.A.V.S.	PVX
☐ North American NA-122 Mustang (P-51D)	MM4323	122-39910	44-73451	PV
☐ North American NA-182 Texan (T-6G)	MM54097			PV
☐ North American NA-221 Sabre (F-86K)	MM55-4868	221-108	55-4868,	RA
☐ Panavia PA200 Tornado IDS	MM7001	P.14	MM588	RA
☐ Panavia PA200 Tornado F.3	MM7210	3333	ZE836	PV
☐ Partenavia P.53 Aeroscooter (MdB.01)	I-REDI	1		PV
☐ Piaggio P.108B	MM22003		Parts only	PV
☐ Piaggio P.136F	MM80005	110	At Guidonia.	RA
☐ Piaggio P.136L1	MM80078	204	At Guidonia.	RA
☐ Piaggio P.136L1	MM80083	213	At Guidonia.	RAD
☐ Piaggio P.148	MM53584	160		RA
☐ Piaggio P.150	MM555	170/1	I-PIAR	RA
☐ Piaggio P.166ML1	MM61874	382		RA
☐ Piaggio P.166ML1	MM61933	443		RA
☐ Piaggio-Douglas PD-808GE1	MM61961	518		PV
☐ Republic P-47D Thunderbolt	MM4653		44-89746	RA
☐ Republic F-84F Thunderstreak	MM53-6892		53-6892	RA
☐ Republic F-84G Thunderjet	MM111049		51-11049	PV
☐ Republic RF-84F Thunderflash	MM52-7458		52-7458	PV
☐ Savoia-Marchetti SM.56	I-AEDA	5611		PV
☐ Savoia-Marchetti SM.79	L-111		MM21150, LR-AMA – bare airframe only – on loan to ITIS.	–
☐ Savoia-Marchetti SM.79	'MM24327'		MM45508, LR-AMB, L-112 (Lebanon)	PVX
☐ Savoia-Marchetti SM.82PW Marsupiale	'MM61850'		MM61187	PVX
☐ SIAI-Marchetti S.211 (FSM)				PV
☐ Societa Aeronautica Italiana – Ambrosini S.1001 Grifo			Fuselage only	PV
☐ Societa Aeronautica Italiana – Ambrosini Super S.7	MM53851		Incomplete – possible identity	RA
☐ Societa Aeronautica Italiana – Ambrosini Super S.7	MM53852		Incomplete – possible identity	RA
☐ Societa Aeronautica Italiana – Ambrosini Super S.7	MM53853		Incomplete – possible identity	RA
☐ Societa Aeronautica Italiana – Ambrosini Super S.7	MM558	2	I-RAIN	PV
☐ Societa Anonima Industrie Meccaniche Aeronautiche Navali (SAIMAN) 202M	I-SARD	508	MM51497	RA
☐ Société Pour l'Aviation et ses Dérivés (SPAD) VII	S.1420			PV
☐ Société Pour l'Aviation et ses Dérivés (SPAD) VII		S.1383 (?)		RA
☐ Stinson V-76 Sentinel (L-5)	I-AEEU		(USAAF), MM52848	PV
☐ Stinson V-76 Sentinel (L-5)	I-AEFQ		(USAAF), MM56693	SD
☐ Supermarine 361 Spitfire LF.IXc	MK805	CBAF-IX-1780	MK805, MM4084, 'MM4079'	PV
☐ Svenska Aeroplan Aktiebolaget (SAAB) 29F (29B) (J 29B) (J 29F)	Fv29543	29543	At Guidonia.	RA
☐ Weber A VII Etiopia 1				RA
☐ Westland-Sikorsky WS-51 Dragonfly 1A	MM80118	WA/H/6	G-ALMB, I-MCOM – at Guidonia.	RAC
☐ Wright Flyer 4 (R)				PV

MUSEO STORICO DELL'ARMA DEI CARABINIERI (ITA51)

Address:	Piazza Risorgimento, 00136 Roma.
Tel:	06-654-1020
Email:	cqmuseodv@carabinieri.it
Admission:	Currently closed
Location:	In the city centre near the Vatican. The aircraft are stored at Pratica di Mare.

The museum traces the history of the State Police with uniforms, weapons, documents, photographs and memorabilia on view. There are also several vehicles, motor cycles, and radios in the collection. A major refurbishment of all the galleries is taking place. The aircraft are currently stored in a hangar at Pratica di Mare. The SPAD replica was built at Vigna di Valle and incorporates a few original parts. The biplane is painted to represent the aircraft flown by Carabinieri pilot Ernesto Cabruno who flew with 77 Squadron. His original aircraft is on display at Vigna di Valle. The Carabinieri operate a large fleet of helicopters from bases around the country and other types are expected to join the display in the near future.

TYPE	REG/SER	CON. NO.	PI/NOTES	STATUS
☐ Agusta-Bell 47G-3B-1	MM80482	1615		RA
☐ Agusta-Bell 47J-3	MM80294	2039		RA
☐ Société Pour l'Aviation et ses Dérivés (SPAD) VII (R)	'S.1420'			RAX

MUSEO STORICO DELLA CITTA DI BERGAMO (ITA52)

Address:	Piazza Mercato del Fieno, 6a, 24129 Bergamo.
Tel:	035-247116
Fax:	035-219128
Email:	info@museostoricobg.org
Admission:	Tuesday-Sunday 0900-1200 1500-1800.
Location:	In the old town which is north of the town centre. Bergamo is about 15 km north east of Milano.

Housed in a fortified monastery by the old city walls the museum has on show items from the unification of the country in 1815 up to World War I. Several weapons and uniforms can be seen. The industrial development which took place between 1815 and 1867 is highlighted with particular reference to the production of goods made of silk. In the middle of the 19th century the town developed significantly and the plans from this period have been saved. The Balilla was used by the famous pilot Antonio Locatelli from 1918 to 1920. He flew the biplane to the local airfield on August 24th 1920 and soon afterwards presented it to the museum along with items of memorabilia. He was born in the area in 1895 and killed in action in Ethiopia in June 1936. About one hundred and fifty A-1s were built and only two survive. The type was fitted with two machine guns firing through the propeller blades. In late 2000 the Balilla was removed from the museum and transported to the G.A.V.S. workshops near Turin. Large parts of the wooden structure were found to be in poor condition after the fabric had been removed. This was done carefully to preserve the paintings, insignia and camouflage. Over six thousand man hours were put in by the volunteer team. The 220 hp SPA 6A engine was also rebuilt and this is now on display near the aircraft. A mock up motor made from wood and plastic is fitted to the airframe.

TYPE	REG/SER	CON. NO.	PI/NOTES	STATUS
☐ Ansaldo A-1 Balilla	16553	64		PV

MUSEO STORICO DELLA MOTORIZZAZIONE MILITARE (ITA53)

Address:	Viale Dell'Esercito 170, Caserna Rosetti-Cecchignola, 00143 Roma.
Tel:	06-501-1885
Fax:	06-501-1885
Admission:	Saturday 0900-1200 or by appointment.
Location:	In the southern suburbs of the city just inside Exit 25 of the ring road.

The largest display of military vehicles in the country is on show in the museum along with uniforms, documents and memorabilia. There are tanks, motor cycles, lorries tracked vehicles and specialised machines to be seen. The history of motorised transport and military engineering is told in the exhibition. There are models of bridges and other structures constructed by the army. The Piper Super Cub was the first type to he flown by the Italian Army in the 1950s and helicopters were introduced into the service in 1956.

TYPE	REG/SER	CON. NO.	PI/NOTES	STATUS
☐ Agusta-Bell 47J-3B	MM80263	2026		PV
☐ Agusta-Bell 204B	MM80390	3120		PV
☐ Bell 47G-2 Sioux (H-13H) (OH-13H)	MM80811	2299	58-1538	PV
☐ Piper PA-18-135 Super Cub (L-21B)	EI-206	18-3597	54-2397, I-EIJA – this aircraft is also registered in the USA as N27295. One of them could be c/n 18-3596 54-2396, I-EIYZ, EI-205.	PV
☐ SIAI-Marchetti SM.1019E	MM57246	1-054		PV
☐ Piper PA-18-95 Super Cub (L-18C)	'EI-00'		54-2396, MM54-2396	PVX

MUSEO STORICO ITALIANO DELLA GUERRA DI ROVERETO (ITA54)

Address:	Castello di Rovereto, Via Castelbarco 7, 38068 Rovereto.
Tel:	0464-438100
Fax:	0464-423410
Email:	camillozadra@museodellaguerra.it
Admission:	Daily 0900-1200 1500-1700. Closed during December.
Location:	In the centre of the town which is about 20 km south of Trento off Route 12.

A fifteenth century castle is home to the museum which displays a mainly World War I collection. There are many poignant reminders of the harsh conditions endured. The aeronautical section has many superb models showing aircraft used by the Italian military from 1916 to the outbreak of World War II. Uniforms, documents, medals are also on view. The museum owns a Macchi built Nieuport presented by local resident Emilio Stafelini. The biplane moved to the Caproni Museum store near Trento a few years ago. Now restored to original configuration it will return to Rovereto in the near future and again be exhibited in the museum.

TYPE	REG/SER	CON. NO.	PI/NOTES	STATUS
☐ Macchi-Nieuport Ni.12	13469		Due back soon.	PV

MUSEO VORREI VOLARE (ITA55)

Address:	Via S. Francesco D'Assisi 18, 46020 Pegonagna.
Tel:	0376-550024
Admission:	Monday-Friday 1500-1900; Saturday-Sunday 0930-1230 1500-1900.
Location:	About 40 km north of Modena.

On show at this private museum set up by Enzo Bottura is a large collection of models tracing the history of aviation with particular emphasis on the Italian contribution. The displays contain photographs, documents, memorabilia and flying clothing and are being developed to present a comprehensive review of flying.

TYPE	REG/SER	CON. NO.	PI/NOTES	STATUS
☐ Aermacchi MB.326	MM54186	6190/21		PV
☐ Fiat G.91Y	MM6955	2062		PV

NUCLEO AEREO AEROBATICO PARMENESE (ITA56)

Address:	Starda della Repubblica 58, 43100 Parma.
Tel:	0521-293721
Admission:	By prior permission only.
Location:	At Parma airport which is about 5 km west of the town.

Star of this private collection of warbirds owned by Pino Valenti is one of only two Fiat G.59s currently flying. The G.59 was a development of the World War II G.55 and indeed the first twelve were converted from the earlier model. The G.55 was powered by a Daimler Benz DB 605 and the G.59 was fitted with the Rolls Royce Merlin. The G.59 entered Service in February 1950 and was withdrawn from use in the mid-1960s. One hundred and eighty eight were built and some were exported to Argentina and Syria. Pino Valenti acquired the G.59 in 1983 and major rebuild was needed to bring the fighter to airworthy condition. The first flight took place in May 1992 with the owner of the Australian example, the now deceased Guido Zuccoli, at the controls. One of the Fiat G.46s is airworthy and a second example is in the workshops.

TYPE	REG/SER	CON. NO.	PI/NOTES	STATUS
☐ Aero L-29 Delfin	I-SEXI	591235	1235, OK-TYP	RAA
☐ De Havilland D.H.82A Tiger Moth	G-AJHU	83900	T7471	RAC
☐ Fiat G.46-3B	I-AEHI	43	MM52800	RAC
☐ Fiat G.46-4A	I-AEKT	216	MM53491	RAA
☐ Fiat G.59-4B	I-MRSV	181	MM53774	RAA
☐ Noorduyn Harvard IIB [North American NA-77 (AT-16)]	G-BWUL	14A-1415	43-13116, FT375	RAA
☐ North American NA-88 Texan (AT-6C)	MM53863			RAC
☐ North American NA-182 Texan (T-6G)	MM54102			RA
☐ North American NA-182 Texan (T-6G)	MM54109			RA
☐ Pitts S-2A Special	I-MLAT	2226		RAA
☐ Zlin Z-50LS	I-SHOW	0054	OK-TRN	RAA

PLAZA DELL'AERONAUTICA (ITA57)

Address: 25034 Orzinouvi.
Admission: On permanent view.
Location: In the southern part of the town which is about 25 km south west of Brescia on Route 235.

The Thunderflash has been on show in the town since June 1977. The aircraft served at Villafranca-Verona from the mid-1950s until the mid-1970s. It was then in store at Ghedi for a short time. Seventy eight examples of the RF-84F flew with the Italian Air Force until they were replaced by the RF-104G Starfighter.

TYPE	REG/SER	CON. NO.	PI/NOTES	STATUS
☐ Republic RF-84F Thunderflash	MM52-7397		52-7397	PV

PLAZA DELL' AERONAUTICA (ITA58)

Address: Via Guiseppe Saragat, 13039 Trino.
Admission: On permanent view.
Location: About 18 km south west of Vercelli on Route 455.

This small park commemorates local aviators and a Fiat G.91 has been put on show. The aircraft was flown by 2 Stormo at Treviso from the mid-1960s until it was withdrawn in the early 1990s. The G.91T was developed from the G.91R fighter as an operational conversion and weapons trainer.

TYPE	REG/SER	CON. NO.	PI/NOTES	STATUS
☐ Fiat G.91R/1	MM6274	40		PV

RACCOLTA AERO CLUB MONTAGNANA (ITA59)

Address: Via Rottavecchia, CP 114, 35054 Montagnana.
Tel: 0429-804212
Fax: 0429-878287
Admission: By prior permission only.
Location: About 6 km west of the town at Bevilacqua.

This active club operates a fleet of powered aircraft and gliders from its field. There is a display of photographs, documents and memorabilia in the clubhouse. The three former Air Force machines arrived for display on the field in the late 1990s. The T-33 has now been painted in false U.S.A.F. colours.

TYPE	REG/SER	CON. NO.	PI/NOTES	STATUS
☐ Aermacchi MB.326	MM54189	6194/39		PV
☐ Fiat G.91R/1A	MM6290	154		PV
☐ Lockheed 580 (T-33A)	'391'	580-9617	55-3076, MM53-3076	PVX

RACCOLTA DELLA BASE D'ORTE (ITA60)

Address: 11 Deposito Centrale AM, Voc Lucignano 13, 01028 Orte
Tel: 0761-403264
Admission: By prior permission only.
Location: About 20 km south west of Terni off Route 204.

At this site is a large barracks along with a storage depot. The five aircraft are parked around the camp and represent types which have made significant contributions to Italian military aviation.

TYPE	REG/SER	CON. NO.	PI/NOTES	STATUS
☐ Aermacchi MB.326	MM54381	6494/235		RA
☐ Agusta-Bell 47J	MM80191	1104		RA
☐ Canadian Car & Foundry Harvard 4 [North American NA-186 (T-6H-4M)]				RA
☐ Fiat G.91R/1B	MM6391	195		RA
☐ Lockheed 683-04-10 Starfighter (RF-104G)	MM6633	683-6633	Tail from F-104G c/n 683-6561 MM6561.	RA

RACCOLTA DELLA BASE DI AMÉNDOLA (ITA61)

Address: 32 Stormo CBR,
SS.89 per Manfredonia,
70023 Améndola.
Tel: 0881-702111
Email: 32st-com@aeronautica.difesa.it
Admission: By prior permission only.
Location: About 20 km north west of Foggia just south of Route 89.

The 32nd Stormo was formed at Brindisi in September 1967 operating the Fiat G.91R. Later the G.91Y was flown. The wing moved to Améndola in the 1990s and converted to the AMX. In 1951 a unit was formed to train Italy's first jet pilots and this initially flew Vampires and T-33s from the base.

TYPE	REG/SER	CON. NO.	PI/NOTES	STATUS
☐ Aermacchi MB.326E				RA
☐ De Havilland D.H.100 Vampire FB.52A	'MM6156'		Composite of c/n 6088/50 MM602, MM6014; c/n 5987/20 MM6042; c/n 6120/82 MM6083; c/n 6122/84 MM6125 and other airframes – on loan from Mus. Stor. AMI.	RAX
☐ Fiat G.91T/1	MM6341	71		RA
☐ Fiat G.91T/1	MM6348	78		RA
☐ Fiat G.91T/1	MM6363	93		RA
☐ Fiat G.91Y	MM6952	2059		RA
☐ Lockheed 580 (T-33A)	'MM54-1951'	580-9451	54-2951, MM54-2951	RAX
☐ Macchi M.416 [Fokker S-11]	MM53749	6051/106	MM53749, I-AEMQ	RAD

RACCOLTA DELLA BASE DI BORGO PANIGALE (ITA62)

Address: Via Triumvirate,
40132 Bologna.
Admission: By prior permission only.
Location: About 5 km north west of the city.

This army helicopter base houses two groups each with three squadrons. Types in use are the Agusta-Bell 205, the Agusta 109CM and the A.129. Two of the preserved aircraft are by the main gate and the other is in the camp.

TYPE	REG/SER	CON. NO.	PI/NOTES	STATUS
☐ Agusta-Bell 204B	MM80300	3047		RA
☐ Agusta-Bell 204B	MM80307	3050		RA
☐ Agusta-Bell 204B	MM80381	3100		RA

RACCOLTA DELLA BASE DI BRESCIA-GHEDI (ITA63)

Address: 6 Stormo CB,
Aeroporto Militare,
Staada Castenedolo 85,
25016 Ghedi.
Tel: 030-90421
Email: 6st-com @aeronautica.difesa.it
Admission: By prior permission only.
Location: About 15 km south of Brescia and just north of the village.

The 6th Stormo flew the Messerschmitt Bf 109 in North Africa in 1943 but was disbanded soon afterwards. The unit was reformed at Treviso on January 1st 1951 and moved to Ghedi five months later. Since then it has flown P-51Ds, F-84Gs, F-84Fs, F-104Gs and currently operates the Tornado IDS.

TYPE	REG/SER	CON. NO.	PI/NOTES	STATUS
☐ Aermacchi MB.326	MM54284	6449/190		RA
☐ Lockheed 683-10-19 Starfighter (F-104G)	MM6522	683-6522		RA
☐ Lockheed 683-10-19 Starfighter (F-104G)	MM6601	683-6601		PV
☐ Republic F-84F Thunderstreak	'MM53-6855'		53-6740, MM53-6740	RAX

This former Aeroflot Kamov Ka-26 can be seen in the museum compound at Riga. (Mort Stanley)

Several versions of the MiG-21 are on show at Riga. Pictured here is a MiG-21ST. (Bob Ruffle)

This Antonov An-24B is on show at the Lithuanian Aviation Museum at Kaunas. (Mort Stanley)

This flyable replica of a Bellanca CH-300 is on show in the Lithuanian Aviation Museum at Kaunas.

Members of the Malta Aviation Museum constructed this replica Pou-du-Ciel. (MAM)

This superbly restored Spitfire is in the hangar of the Malta Aviation Museum. (MAM)

This Fokker F II replica is on show in the Aviodrome at Lelystad. (Willem Honders)

Pictured outside the replica 1930s Schiphol terminal at the Aviodrome at Lelystad are a Lockheed Constellation and a Dakota. (Willem Honders)

The second Fokker Friendship built is owned by the F-27 Friendship Association and is kept in the Aviodrome at Lelystad. (Klaas-Reinder Sluijs)

Members of the Koolhoven Foundation rebuilt this BAT Bantam which had spent many years in store in England. (Willem Honders)

This replica Fokker D.XXI resides in the General Snijdershal at the Militaire Luchtvaart Museum at Kamp Van Zeist.

This Fleet 2 is operated by the 'Early Birds' group at Lelystad and is shown visiting a local show.

This replica Valtion Saaski was built in the workshops of the Norsk Luftsfartsmuseum at Bodø. (Sven Scheiderbauer)

The oldest aircraft on show at the Forsvarets Flysamling at Gardermoen is this Rumpler Taube. (Douglas Rough)

The indigenous Norge C is pictured above a Bell 47J in the Norsk Teknisk Museum in Oslo. (Douglas Rough)

A small collection of preserved aircraft is located inside the main gate of Radom Air Force Base. Shown here is a MiG-21M in a special colour scheme.

This Yak-23 was for many years on show in the main Army Museum in Warsaw. The aircraft was recently moved to their other site at Fort Sadyba. (Douglas Rough)

A general view of part of the aircraft park at the Army Museum in Warsaw. In the foreground is a Yak-9P.

This Portuguese built Chipmunk is maintained in airworthy condition by the Aero Fénix organisation. (Rui Ferreira)

Parked outside the Museu do Ar hangar at Sintra is this Hornet Moth which was brought back to Portugal from Angola. (Rui Ferreira)

This Fiat G.91 in 'Tiger' colours is part of the Museu do Ar collection at Sintra. (Rui Ferreira)

On show at the Muzeul Aviatei at Otopeni is this MiG-17PF. (Alex Trandafir)

This replica Vuia 1 was constructed for exhibition at the Muzeul Aviatei at Otopeni. (Alex Trandafir)

On show in the Central Military Museum in Bucharest is this Nardi FN.305. (James Hunter)

This Antonov An-12BK-PPS is on show at the 610 Combat and Conversion Training Centre Museum at Ivanovo-North. (Keith Dexter)

A superb collection of helicopters, including this Mil Mi-18, are at the Army Conversion Training Museum at Torzhok. (Keith Dexter)

This rare Kochyerigin DI-6 is on show at the Central Museum of the Great Patriotic War in Victory Park, Moscow. (Douglas Rough)

Large numbers of American aircraft were supplied to the Soviet Union during Word War II. On show at Monino is this Douglas Havoc. (Douglas Rough)

The civil aviation museum at Ulyanovsk houses this Tupolev Tu-114D. (Bob Ruffle)

Parked at the Road of Life Museum near St. Petersburg is this Lisunov Li-2. (Paul Kernot)

Above: This indigenous Ikarus S-49C is on show in the Belgrade museum. (Keith Dexter)

Right: This Zlin HC-102 Heli Baby moved from the Kbely store to be put on show in the aviation section of the Slovakian Technical Museum at Kosice. (Jozef Andal)

Below: This KB-14 glider is shown at a vintage meeting at Postojna. The sailplane will be preserved in the future. (Tomas Meze)

This Miles Falcon returned to England for restoration. It is now part of the Fundacion Infante de Orleans fleet. This collection will soon move from Cuatro Vientos to Getafe.

The only remaining Dornier Wal is in Argentina. When it returned to Spain for restoration the factory at Cadiz built a faithful replica for the Museo del Aire.

The museum at Malaga has painted this DC-3 in the colours of the first example of the type operated by Iberia. (MAENA)

The oldest aircraft at the F15 Flygmuseum at Söderhamn is this SAAB J 21. (F15 Museum)

The Swedish Air Force used this Norseman on ambulance duties. It is now in the Flygvapen Museum at Malmslatt.

The RFN Museum at Vidsel has put on display this de Havilland Venom which was used at the field. (RFN Museum)

Three Hafeli replicas are show in the Swiss Air Force Museum at Dubendorf. The DH-5 was in service from 1929 to 1940.

The diminutive Rosgen EPR.301 is in the fleet of the Birrfeld based Veterano.

This Moth Major has served with the Historic Aircraft Group at Lausanne for many years.

This Grigorovich M.5 flying boat was forced down off the Turkish coast in World War I. The aircraft is now in the Turkish Air Force Museum at Yesilkoy near Istanbul.

On show in the Rahmi H. Koc Museum in Istanbul is this Pitts Special. (Stewart Lanham)

The Turkish Air Force used many Phantoms and this example is preserved in the museum at Eskisehir. (MDeniz Ayvaz)

Two Antonov An-71s were completed and one is at the company airfield at Svyatoshino. (Dimitriy Komissarov)

On show at the State Aviation Museum at Kiev-Zhuliany is this MiG-27K. (Dimitriy Komissarov)

This VTOL Yak-38 is at the State Aviation Museum at Kiev-Zhuliany. (Dimitriy Komissarov)

RACCOLTA DELLA BASE DI BRÍNDISI (ITA64)

Address:	Via U Maddalena 54, 72010 Bríndisi.
Tel:	0831-412163
Admission:	By prior permission only.
Location:	Just north of the town.

A Fiat G.91 wing was formed at the base it 1967 but this moved to Amèndola in the 1990s and has since converted to the AMX. Several G.91s were scrapped at the site along with other types. The G.91PAN was flown by the 'Frecce Tricolore' for a period and was later transferred to normal duties.

TYPE	REG/SER	CON. NO.	PI/NOTES	STATUS
☐ Aermacchi MB.326	MM54211	6290/60		RA
☐ Fiat G.91PAN (G.91)	MM6242	8		RA
☐ Fiat G.91Y	MM6455	2017		RA

RACCOLTA DELLA BASE DI CADIMARE (ITA65)

Address:	Aeroporto di Cadimare, Via della Marina 15, 19131 Cadimare.
Tel:	0187-733400
Email:	cadimare.euroform@aeronautica.difesa.it
Admission:	By prior permission only.
Location:	About 5 km south west of La Spezia.

This old seaplane base is still used by the Air Force as a school and training centre. In the interwar period many floatplanes and flying boats served with the military. During the early stages of World War II a unit flying the Cant Z.501 carried out reconnaissance patrols in the area. Over two hundred examples of the single engine flying boat were in service around the country. The seaplane station closed in the late 1950s.

TYPE	REG/SER	CON. NO.	PI/NOTES	STATUS
☐ Aermacchi MB.326	MM54240	6324/94		RA
☐ Agusta-Bell 47G				RA
☐ Fiat G.91Y	MM6447	2009		RA
☐ Piaggio P.166ML1	MM61925	435		RA
☐ Piaggio-Douglas PD-808TA	MM61948	506		RA

RACCOLTA DELLA BASE DI CAGLIARI-ELMAS (ITA66)

Address:	Aeroporto Militare, 09122 Elmas.
Tel:	070-2110382
Fax:	070-240641
Admission:	By prior permission only.
Location:	About 5 km north west of the city.

Opened in 1937 the airfield also serves as the civil airport for the city of Cagliari. The air force has a base on the field which is often used for NATO exercises. The preserved aircraft are positioned around the camp. The Harvard is normally in the hangars and two aircraft are located with the aero club. In the 1930s seaplanes also used the site. The long distance flights made by fleets of Savoia-Marchetti SM.55s achieved world-wide acclaim but prior to this a number of individual journeys were made. The first journey by the type took place in 1927 when the 'Santa Maria' piloted by Colonel de Pinedo took off from Elmas on February 13th. He carried out a twenty eight thousand mile tour around the Atlantic. Tragedy occurred at Phoenix, Arizona when a cigarette carelessly thrown away set fire to the SM.55. A second aircraft the 'Santa Maria II' was shipped out and the epic resumed. The flight was completed on June 16th via the eastern U.S.A., Canada, the Azores and Portugal. The T-33 is parked outside the aeroclub and the Harvard normally resides in a military hangar.

TYPE	REG/SER	CON. NO.	PI/NOTES	STATUS
☐ Aermacchi MB.326	MM54278	6443/184	At aero club.	PV
☐ Agusta-Bell 47G-2	MM80098	215		RA
☐ Agusta-Bell 47J-3	MM80502	2119		RA
☐ Canadian Car & Foundry Harvard 4 [North American NA-186 (T-6H-4M)]	MM53799	CCF4-296	51-17114	RA
☐ Grumman G-89 Tracker (S2F-1) (S-2A)	MM144716	677	Bu144716	RA
☐ Lockheed 580 (T-33A) (RT-33A)	MM53-5668	580-9007	53-5668 – at aero club.	PV

RACCOLTA DELLA BASE DI CAMERI (ITA67)

Address:	Aeroporto Militare, SS Bellinzago, 28060 Cameri.
Tel:	0321-616222
Admission:	By prior permission only.
Location:	About 10 km north of Novara between Cámeri and Bellinzago.

Formed on April 1st 1967 the 53rd Stormo was based at Cámeri until it disbanded in 1999. A display room showing mementos and photographs is situated in the headquarters building. The history of the base and its units is portrayed. The initial equipment operated was the F-104G Starfighter. The F-104S was added in the early 1970s. The unit has also flown a number of liaison and training types. The aircraft exhibition has been set up alongside the station headquarters. The pre-production Tornado is used as a travelling exhibit. At the current time a maintenance unit is in residence and this carries out all work on the Tornado.

TYPE	REG/SER	CON. NO.	PI/NOTES	STATUS
☐ Aeritalia AMX	MM7090	IX002		RA
☐ Aermacchi MB.326	MM54274	6439/180		RA
☐ Agusta-Bell 47J-3	MM80257	2038		RA
☐ Canadair CL-13 Sabre 4 [North American F-86E]	MM19668	568	19668 (Canada), XB814	RA
☐ Fiat G.91T/1	MM54397	124		RA
☐ Grumman G-64 Albatross (SA-16A) (HU-16A)	MM50-174	G-62	50-0174	RA
☐ Lockheed 580 (T-33A)	MM51-17534	580-7594	51-17534	RA
☐ Lockheed 683-04-10 Starfighter (RF-104G)	MM6634	683-6634		RA
☐ Lockheed 683-10-19 Starfighter (F-104G)	MM6504	683-6504		RAX
☐ North American NA-182 Texan (T-6G)	'MM53802'	182-183	51-14492, MM54106	RAX
☐ North American NA-207 Sabre (F-86K)	MM53-8316	207-44	53-8316, MM6228	RA
☐ Panavia PA200 Tornado	MM-X-587	P.09		RAX
☐ Piaggio P.166ML1	MM61927	437		RA
☐ Republic RF-84F Thunderflash	MM52-7390		52-7390	RA

RACCOLTA DELLA BASE DI CÉRVIA – SAN GIORGIO (ITA68)

Address:	5 Stormo Caccia, Via Confine snc, 48015 Cérvia.
Tel:	0544-962511
Email:	5st-com@aeronautica.difesa.it
Admission:	By prior permission only.
Location:	About 20 km south of Ravenna off Route 16 and just south west of the village.

5 Stormo served in World War II and during this time flew the Caproni-Reggiane Re.2001 and Re.2002 as well as the Macchi MC.200. In the immediate post-war years it was based at Bergamo and Vincenza flying Spitfires, Mustangs and Thunderbolts. The first jet type, the F-84G Thunderjet, arrived in the early 1950s and the unit led a nomadic existence before taking up residence at Rimini in 1965. F-84F Thunderstreaks and F-104G and RF-104G Starfighters were subsequently flown. The wing moved to Cérvia in the mid-1990s and operated the F-104S Starfighter which has now been replaced by the F-16. A communications squadron with S.208Ms is in residence.

TYPE	REG/SER	CON. NO.	PI/NOTES	STATUS
☐ Fiat G.91Y	MM6459	2021		RAD
☐ Fiat G.91Y	MM6956	2063		RA
☐ Lockheed 683-10-19 Starfighter (F-104S) (F-104S/ASA) (F-104S/ASAM)	MM6716	683-6716		RA
☐ Lockheed 683-10-19 Starfighter (F-104S) (F-104S/ASA) (F-104S/ASAM)	MM6880	683-6880		RA
☐ North American NA-207 Sabre (F-86K)	MM53-8291	207-19	53-8291	RA
☐ Republic F-84F Thunderstreak	MM52-10524		52-10524 – with tail from 53-6619, MM53-6619	RA

RACCOLTA DELLA BASE DI DECIMOMANNU (ITA69)

Address:	Aeroporto Militare, 09033 Decimomannu.
Tel:	070-96621
Email:	rssta-com@aeronautica.difesa.it
Admission:	By prior permission only.
Location:	About 15 km north west of Cagliari off Route 130 and north of the town.

Decimomannu is home to an Italian Air Force unit flying helicopters and trainers. Fighters from other N.A.T.O. forces are regularly detached to the field. The base serves as an Air Weapons Training Installation using the nearby ranges. The Starfighter is in Luftwaffe colours and the Harrier in R.A.F. markings. Both types were fairly common sights at the field. The other aircraft on show represent those which have either been based at Decimomannu or served on detachment. Normally the only permanent residents are a small number of Aermacchi MB.339As and Agusta-Bell AB.212s used on communication and rescue duties.

TYPE	REG/SER	CON. NO.	PI/NOTES	STATUS
☐ Aermacchi MB.326	MM54376	6489/230		PV
☐ Agusta-Bell 47J-3	MM80256	2035		PV
☐ Hawker-Siddeley P.1127 Harrier GR.3 (GR.1) (GR.1A)	XV758	41H/712021		RA
☐ Lockheed 580 (T-33A)	MM51-17455	580-7148	51-17455	PV
☐ Lockheed 683-04-10 Starfighter (RF-104G)	25+14	683-8278	KG+378, EB+257	PV
☐ Lockheed 683-10-19 Starfighter (F-104S) (F-104S/ASA) (F-104S/ASAM)	MM6887	683-6887		RA

RACCOLTA DELLA BASE DI FROSINONE (ITA70)

Address:	72 Stormo Elicotteri, Aeroporto Militare, Via Armando Fabi 192, 03100 Frosinone.
Tel:	0775-2621
Email:	72st-com@aeronautica.difesa.it
Admission:	By prior permission only.
Location:	Just south west of the town which is about 85 km south east of Roma off the A1.

The airfield was constructed in 1939 and for four years was home to the pilot training school for non-commissioned officers. The Germans were in residence for a time and the site was damaged by allied bombing. The current school was formed in the 1950s and has undergone several name changes. The first helicopters used were the Agusta-Bell 47G and the Sikorsky S-55. These were replaced by Agusta-Bell 47Js and 204s. Now the Nardi-Hughes NH.500E is the type used. Rotary wing pilots for all services are trained at this Air Force Base. The helicopters are also used for liaison and communications duties and often detached to other airfields. A collection of types formerly used by the unit is preserved around the site.

TYPE	REG/SER	CON. NO.	PI/NOTES	STATUS
☐ Agusta-Bell 47G-2 (47G)	MM80052	287	Original c/n 009.	RA
☐ Agusta-Bell 47G-2	MM80474	297		RA
☐ Agusta-Bell 47J	MM80208	1113		RA
☐ Agusta-Bell 204B	MM80282	3053		RA
☐ Bell 47G-2 Sioux (H-13H) (OH-13H)	MM80790	2262	58-1498	RA

RACCOLTA DELLA BASE DI GALLARATE (ITA71)

Address:	2 Deposito Centrale A.M., Viale Milano 85, 21013 Gallarate.
Tel:	0331-793541
Admission:	By prior permission only.
Location:	In the south eastern suburbs of the town which is about 40 km north west of Milano off Route 33.

A large storage unit is housed at this site. Helicopters occasionally fly into the barracks. The collection of aircraft has been assembled to give the airmen a taste of the traditions of the Air Force. The famous 'Frecce Tricolori' aerobatic team, based at Rivolto, used the Fiat G.91PAN from 1964 to 1981 and the example on show is in their colours. The Sabre is one of a batch built by North American and supplied in kit form to Fiat who assembled them for use by NATO forces. The majority of the preserved aircraft are positioned among the warehouses along the drive from the gate to the headquarters building.

TYPE	REG/SER	CON. NO.	PI/NOTES	STATUS
☐ Aermacchi MB.326H	MM54268	6294/64		RA
☐ Agusta-Bell 47G-2	MM80477	300		RA
☐ Agusta-Bell 47J	MM80224	1139		RA
☐ Canadian Car & Foundry Harvard 4 [North American NA-186 (T-6H-2M)]	MM54143	CCF4-???		RA
☐ Fiat G.91PAN (G.91)	MM6239	5		RA
☐ North American NA-207 Sabre (F-86K)	MM53-8299	207-27	53-8299, MM6211	RA
☐ Piaggio P.166ML1	MM61882	390		RA

RACCOLTA DELLA BASE DI GIOIA DEL COLLE (ITA72)

Address:	36 Stormo CB, Aeroporto Militare, Via Provenciale Taranto 1533, 70023 Gioia del Colle.
Tel:	080-348-7111
Email:	36st-com@aeronautica.difesa.it
Admission:	By prior permission only.
Location:	About 40 km south of Bari on Route 100 and just south of the town.

The field is currently home to the 36th Stormo which operates the Panavia Tornado and the Aermacchi MB.339CD. The Eurofighter Typhoon will be based at the field. A communications squadron is also in residence flying the Piaggio P.180 Avanti. The wing was formed as a transport unit at Guidonia in late 1948 and disbanded seven years later. Among the types used were the Savoia-Marchetti SM.82 and the Saiman 202. These were later supplemented by Fiat G.12s and G.212s along with the Beech C-45. The unit was reformed with fighters at Gioia in 1966 flying the F-86K and the F-84F. The F-104S arrived in 1971 and these served until the mid-1980s.

TYPE	REG/SER	CON. NO.	PI/NOTES	STATUS
☐ Aermacchi MB.326	MM54199	6204/49		RA
☐ Aermacchi MB.326	MM54281	6446/187		RA
☐ Lockheed 580 (T-33A) (RT-33A)	MM53-5430	580-8769	53-5430	RA
☐ Lockheed 683-10-19 Starfighter (F-104S) (F-104S/ASA)	MM6835	683-6835		RA
☐ North American NA-207 Sabre (F-86K)	MM53-8308	207-36	53-8308, MM6220	RA
☐ Piaggio P.166ML1	MM61903	405		RA
☐ Republic F-84F Thunderstreak	MM53-6653		53-6653	RA
☐ Republic F-84F Thunderstreak	MM53-6858		53-6858	RA

RACCOLTA DELLA BASE DI GRAZZANISE (ITA73)

Address:	9 Stormo Caccia, Aeroporto Militare, Via dell'Aeroporto, 81046 Grazzanise.
Tel:	0823-964572
Email:	9st-com@aeronautica.difesa.it
Admission:	By prior permission only.
Location:	About 20 km west of Caserta off Route 264.

The 9th Stormo was set up at this base in September 1967 flying F-104G Starfighters. These were replaced by the F-104S in 1972/3 and this variant remained operational until 2005 when they moved to Trapani Bergi and withdrawn from use. Small numbers of SIAI-Marchetti S.208Ms and Agusta-Bell 212s remain but the long term future of the base is under discussion. The Canadair built Sabre is preserved at the nearby barracks.

TYPE	REG/SER	CON. NO.	PI/NOTES	STATUS
☐ Aermacchi MB.326	MM54378	6491/232		RA
☐ Canadair CL-13B Sabre 6 [North American F-86E]	MM19523	423	19523 (Canada), XB620	RA
☐ Lockheed 583-10-20 Starfighter TF-104G)	MM54235	583F-5783		RA
☐ Lockheed 683-10-19 Starfighter (F-104S) (F-104S/ASA) (F-104S/ASAM)	MM6914	683-6914		RA
☐ Lockheed 683-10-19 Starfighter (F-104S) (F-104S/ASA) (F-104S/ASAM)	MM6930	683-6930		RA
☐ North American NA-182 Texan (T-6G)	MM54098			RA

RACCOLTA DELLA BASE DI GROSSETO (ITA74)

Address:	4 Stormo Caccia, Aeroporto Militare, Via Castiglionese 70, 58100 Grosseto.
Tel:	0564-4451
Email:	4st-com@aeronautica.difesa.it
Admission:	By prior permission only.
Location:	On the western outskirts of the town.

Grosseto is home to the 4th Stormo which operates Eurofighter Typhoons. These replaced the Starfighter in 2004. The wing was based at Gioia in 1944 and flew a number of piston engined fighters in the period after the armistice. Among the types used were the Macchi MC.202 and MC.205V. Later Bell P-39 Airacobras and Lockheed P-38 Lightnings were flown. Vampires and Canadair Sabres were also operated. After a number of moves the unit arrived at its current home in the early 1960s and the first Starfighter was assigned in June 1963. The unit has a collection of preserved aircraft around the base. A virtually new airfield has been developed and part of the old site is now incorporated in the civil terminal area.

TYPE	REG/SER	CON. NO.	PI/NOTES	STATUS
☐ Aermacchi MB.326E (MB.326)	MM54190	6195/40		RA
☐ Canadair CL-13 Sabre 4 [North American F-86E]	'MM19694'	741	19841 (Canada), XB954, MM19841	RAX
☐ Lockheed 583-10-20 Starfighter (TF-104G)	MM54231	583F-5778	63-12690	RA
☐ Lockheed 683-10-19 Starfighter (F-104G)	MM6505	683-6505		RA
☐ Lockheed 683-10-19 Starfighter (F-104S) (F-104S/ASA) (F-104S/ASAM)	MM6740	683-6740	In the town.	RA
☐ North American NA-168 Texan (T-6G)	MM54101	168-149	49-3045 - Maybe MM53694	RA

RACCOLTA DELLA BASE DI LATINA (ITA75)

Address:	70 Stormo, Aeroporto Militare, Via dell'Aeroporto, 04013 Latina.
Tel:	0773-630211
Email:	70st-com@aeronautica.difesa.it
Admission:	By prior permission only.
Location:	About 5 km north of Latina Scalo railway station.

207 Gruppo was formed at Latina in May 1955 and initially had the role of a multi-engine crew training school. In use were Beech C-45s and Douglas C-47s. These were gradually replaced by the SIAI-Marchetti SF.260AM and Piaggio P.166M. The SF.260 is still in use and has been joined by the Macchi MB.339A. The Bell 47, Fiat G.91Y and Piaggio P.166 are preserved by the main gate and the others are parked around the field. The Starfighter is outside the nearby Headquarters. The airfield also serves as the civil airport for the area.

TYPE	REG/SER	CON. NO.	PI/NOTES	STATUS
☐ Bell 47G-2 Sioux (H-13H) (OH-13H)	MM80791	2405	58-5392	RA
☐ Fiat G.91T/1	MM6339	69		RA
☐ Fiat G.91Y	MM6491	2053		RA
☐ Lockheed 580 (T-33A)	MM55-2980	580-9477	55-2980	RA
☐ Lockheed 683-10-19 Starfighter (F-104G)	MM6589	683-6589	At Base Headquarters in nearby Borgo Piave.	RA
☐ Piaggio P.148	MM53740	188		RAD
☐ Piaggio P.166ML1	MM61873	381		RA

RACCOLTA DELLA BASE DI LECCE-GALATINA (ITA76)

Address:	61 Stormo, Aeroporto Militare, Str. St. 476SW, 73100 Lecce.
Tel:	0832-265090
Email:	61st-com@aeronautica.difesa.it
Admission:	By prior permission only.
Location:	About 15 km south of Lecce east of Road 101.

This long established base has seen many changes over the years. During World War II it was home to many units. Fighter types in use included Macchi MC.200s, 202s, 205s and Caproni-Reggiane Re.2002s. Bombers and transports flown were the Martin Baltimore, Savoia-Marchetti SM.79, SM.82, SM.84, Caproni Ca.314 and Cant Z.1007. At the end of the conflict a United States Air Base Group was in residence. When the site was returned to Italian control a school training fighter pilots moved in and then one covering basic flying training arrived. Now the 61st. Stormo operates from the field using Aermacchi MB.339As and MB.339CDs. The restoration centre for the Italian Air Force Museum has rebuilt many types here.

TYPE	REG/SER	CON. NO.	PI/NOTES	STATUS
☐ Aermacchi MB.326	MM54154	6130/3		RA
☐ Aermacchi MB.339A/PAN	MM54439	6598/005		RA
☐ Canadian Car & Foundry Harvard 4 [North American NA-186 (T-6H-4M)]	MM53831	CCF4-???		RA
☐ Lockheed 683-10-19 Starfighter (F-104S) (F-104S/ASA) (F-104S/ASAM)				RA

RACCOLTA DELLA BASE DI NAPOLI-CAPODICHINO (ITA77)

Address:	Comando Aeroporto Militare, Via Gabriele D'Annunzio 39, 80141 Napoli.
Tel:	081-705-5111
Email:	capodichino@aeronautica.difesa.it
Admission:	By prior permission only.
Location:	In the military area of the airport which is just north of the town.

The Air Force has a base at the field which also serves as the international airport for the city. In the 1940s and early 1950s the airfield was an important Air Force fighter base with squadrons flying P-51D Mustangs and later de Havilland Vampires. The site housed Italian Navy units for many years and a few helicopters remain along with an overhaul facility. United States naval aircraft are often in residence. The Financial Guard also has a helicopter base here. The T-33 is by the main gate and the remaining trio are stored on the site awaiting display. The MB.326 was preserved in the Aeritalia complex and is believed to still be there.

TYPE	REG/SER	CON. NO.	PI/NOTES	STATUS
☐ Aermacchi MB.326	MM54170	6174/20		RA
☐ Grumman G-89 Tracker (S2F-1) (S-2A)	MM133180	151	Bu133180	RA
☐ Grumman G-89 Tracker (S2F-1) (S-2A)	MM144710	671	Bu144710	RA
☐ Lockheed 580 (T-33A)	MM51-17536	580-7596	51-17536	RA

RACCOLTA DELLA BASE DI PRATICA DI MARE (ITA78)

Address:	14 Stormo, Aeroporto Militare, 00040 Pratica di Mare.
Tel:	06-910921
Email:	9ba-com@aeronautica.difesa.com
Admission:	By prior permission only.
Location:	Close to the coast about 30 km south west of Roma off Route 148.

In the 1930s the Regia Aeronautica set up a research establishment. In 1948 a similar organisation was formed at Guidonia. The unit later moved to Ciampino and finally took up residence at Pratica in 1957. All types selected for military service are evaluated and development trials are carried out. In the 1956 a wing flying the Canadair Sabre was formed and this moved to Grosetto in the summer of 1961. The base is also home to the radio and radar calibration unit of the Air Force. The Reparto Radiomisure was formed in 1964 flying T-33s, C-45s and C-47s on these duties. A C-119J was later added for ECM work. This unit was disbanded in 1976 and its duties moved to the newly formed 14 Stormo. Since then types flown have been the aircraft transferred plus variants of the PD-808 and, Aermacchi MB.326s. Currently in use are Fiat G.222s, Boeing 707s, Piaggio P.166s, Piaggio P.180 Avantis and Aermacchi MB.339s. A search and rescue unit flying Agusta-Bell 212s and Sikorsky HH-3Fs is also in residence. In addition the Carabinieri and the Guardia di Finanza keep helicopters at the field. The collection of preserved aircraft is displayed around the vast site. The last Aeritalia built F-104G served with the 5th Stormo at Rimini before being returned to Lockheed for conversion into one of the development aircraft for the F-104S programme. Almost two hundred and fifty of this improved version were produced in Italy. The Piaggio-Douglas PD.808 was a joint venture between the two companies. The prototype made its maiden flight in August 1964 but failed to break into the civil market.

TYPE	REG/SER	CON. NO.	PI/NOTES	STATUS
☐ Aermacchi MB.326	MM54201	6191/22		RA
☐ Aermacchi MB.326K	MM54385	6498/239		RA
☐ Agusta-Bell 47G-2	'MM80084'	248	MM80166	RAX
☐ Agusta-Bell 47G-2	MM80476	299		RA
☐ Agusta-Bell 47G-2 (Bell 47D-1)	MM80043	288	I-PLVT – original c/n 626.	RA
☐ Agusta-Bell 47J	MM80157	1054		RA
☐ Agusta-Bell 47J	MM80212	1120		RA
☐ Agusta-Bell 204B	'PS-001'			RA
☐ Bell 47G-2 Sioux (H-13H) (OH-13H)	MM80804	2270	58-1506	RA
☐ Canadian Car & Foundry Harvard 4 [North American NA-186 (T-6H-4M)]	MM53828	CCF4-???		RAA
☐ Fiat G.91PAN (G.91)	MM6248	14		RA
☐ Fiat G.91T	MM6288	1		RA
☐ Fiat G.91Y	MM579	2001		RA
☐ Lockheed 580 (T-33A)	MM51-4514	580-5809	51-4514	RA
☐ Lockheed 683-10-19 Starfighter (F-104G)	MM6527	683-6527		RA
☐ Lockheed 683-10-19 Starfighter (F-104G) (F-104S)	MM6660	683-6660		RA
☐ Lockheed 683-10-19 Starfighter (F-104S) (F-104S/ASA)	MM6827	683-6827		RA
☐ Nardi-Hughes NH-500MC	MM80961	0236		RA
☐ Piaggio-Douglas PD-808GE1	MM61958	505		RA

The Science Museum in Milan has many interesting types on show including this de Havilland Puss Moth which has spent over seventy five years in Italy.

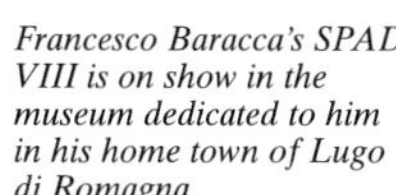

Francesco Baracca's SPAD VIII is on show in the museum dedicated to him in his home town of Lugo di Romagna.

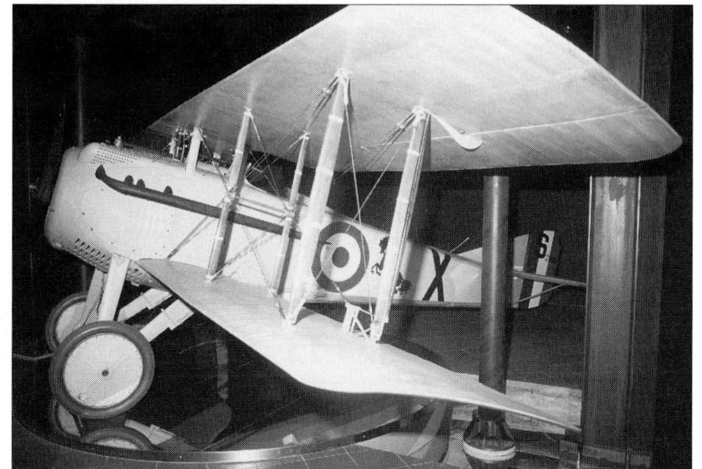

A number of aircraft have been painted in aerobatic team colours at Rivolto. Shown here is a Canadair built Sabre in a black 'Lanceri Neri' scheme.

RACCOLTA DELLA BASE DI RIVOLTO (ITA79)

Address:	2 Stormo, Aeroporto Militare, Via Udine 56, 33033 Rivolto.
Tel:	0432-906777
Email:	2st-com@aeronautica.difesa.it
Admission:	By prior permission only.
Location:	About 15 km south west of Udine and north east of the village on Road 13.

A decision was made in 1961 to create a unit to serve as the official Air Force aerobatic team. Prior to this a number of Stormo had formed teams and flown for short periods. Officially known as the 'Pattuglia Acrobatica Nazionale' the team became better known as the 'Frecce Tricolore'. The 313 Gruppo came into being on March 1st 1961 and ten Canadair built Sabres were transferred from the 4th Aerobrigita. In 1964 the Fiat G.91PAN arrived. These were replaced by the Macchi MB.339A in 1982. The first post war Italian team was the 'Cavallino Rampante' using Vampires from 1950 to 1952. A former Swiss machine has been painted in their colours. The two Sabres represent the 'Cavallino Rampante' and 'Lanceri Neri' teams of the late 1950s. The F-84F is in the markings of the 'Diavoli Rossi' unit. The blue G.91 PAN was flown by the 'Frecce Tricolore'.

TYPE	REG/SER	CON. NO.	PI/NOTES	STATUS
☐ Canadair CL-13 Sabre 4 [North American F-86E]	'MM19685'	564	19664 (Canada), XB810 – with parts of c/n 423 19523, XB620	RAX
☐ Canadair CL-13 Sabre 4 [North American F-86E]	MM19680	580	19680 (Canada)	RA
☐ Canadair CL-13 Sabre 4 [North American F-86E]		624	19724 (Canada), XD723, MM19724	RAX
☐ Canadian Car & Foundry Harvard 4 [North American NA-186 (T-6H-4M)]	MM53822			RA
☐ De Havilland D.H.100 Vampire FB.6		679	J-1170 (Switzerland)	RAX
☐ Fairchild 110 Flying Boxcar (C-119G)	MM52-6020	10950	52-6020	RA
☐ Fiat G.91PAN (G.91)	MM6241	7		RA
☐ Fiat G.91R/1B	MM6381	185		RA
☐ Fiat G.91R/1B	MM6416	220		RA
☐ Fiat G.91T/1	MM6360	90		RA
☐ Lockheed 580 (T-33A)	MM55-3080	580-9621	55-3080	RA
☐ Lockheed 580 (T-33A) (RT-33A)	MM53-5795	580-9134	53-5795	RA
☐ North American NA-213 Sabre (F-86K)	'MM55-4818'	213-62	54-1292 – fitted with tail of c/n 221-5 55-4818, MM55-4818.	RAX
☐ Republic F-84F Thunderstreak	MM53-6845		53-6845	RA
☐ Republic RF-84F Thunderflash	MM52-7474		52-7474 – with parts of 52-7463.	RA

RACCOLTA DELLA BASE DI ROMA-CENTOCELLE (ITA80)

Address:	Aeroporto Militare, Via Papiria 365, 00175 Roma.
Tel:	06-24291
Email:	esa-pi@aeronautica.difesa.it
Admission:	By prior permission only.
Location:	In the south eastern suburbs of the city near Junction 21 of the ring road.

This former airfield is now the headquarters of Comando 2 Regio Aerea which controls units in the central part of the country. Three aircraft are now preserved at the site with the Starfighter mounted by the main gate.

TYPE	REG/SER	CON. NO.	PI/NOTES	STATUS
☐ Aermacchi MB.326	MM54222	6305/75		RA
☐ Fiat G.91T/1	MM54399	126		RA
☐ Lockheed 683-10-19 Starfighter (F-104S) (F-104S/ASA)	MM6916	683-6916		RA

RACCOLTA DELLA BASE DI ROMA-CIAMPINO (ITA81)

Address:	Via Appia Nuova 1651, 00040 Roma.
Tel:	06-7934-0695
Email:	31st-com@aeronautica.difesa.it
Admission:	By prior permission only.
Location:	About 15 km south east of the city on Route 7.

Formed as a helicopter unit at Pratica di Mare in 1965 the 31st Stormo flew Agusta Bell 47G-2s, 47Js and 204Bs. In 1976 the unit took on the responsibility of V.I.P. transport, gained a fixed wing fleet, and moved to Ciampino. The wing is collecting aircraft for a proposed museum and has also acquired documents and photographs. The Albatross is parked near to the main gate of the military camp.

TYPE	REG/SER	CON. NO.	PI/NOTES	STATUS
☐ Agusta-Bell 204B	MM80278	3030		RA
☐ Agusta-Bell 47J	'MM80137'			RAX
☐ Grumman G-64 Albatross (SA-16A) (HU-16A)	MM51-035	G-110	51-035	RA
☐ Piaggio-Douglas PD-808RM	MM61950	508		RA

RACCOLTA DELLA BASE DI TRAPANI-BIRGI (ITA82)

Address:	37 Stormo, S.N. Contra Marausa, 91100 Trapani.
Tel:	0923-843132
Email:	37st.com@aeronautica.difesa.it
Admission:	By prior permission only.
Location:	About 12 km south of the town.

The 37 Stormo was formed in the late 1930s as a bomber unit and operated Fiat BR.20s. First flown in 1936 this twin engined aircraft served with many units and around two hundred and seventy five were delivered. The BR.20 flew in the Spanish Civil War and took part in the campaign against Greece. A fighter wing operating General Dynamics F-16s is in residence. The first of the type arrived in mid-2003. The F-104S, a type formerly flown by the wing, is by the main gate and several others are stored on the field.

TYPE	REG/SER	CON. NO.	PI/NOTES	STATUS
☐ Lockheed 683-10-19 Starfighter (F-104G)	MM6544	683-6544		RA
☐ Lockheed 683-10-19 Starfighter (F-104S) (F-104S/ASA)	MM6910	683-6910		RA
☐ Republic RF-84F Thunderflash	MM52-7466		52-7466	RA

RACCOLTA DELLA BASE DI TREVISO-ISTRANA (ITA83)

Address:	51 Stormo CBR, Aeroporto Militare, Via Monte Grappa 83, 31036 Istrana.
Tel:	0482-833111
Email:	51st-com@aeronautica.difesa.it
Admission:	By prior permission only.
Location:	About 12 km west of Istrana off Route 53

Originally formed as a night flying transport unit at Lecce in 1944 the 2nd Stormo flew Savioia-Marchetti SM.82s and Cant Z.1007s. The wing was reformed with fighters in 1951 and over the next decade led a nomadic existence. Vampires and several liaison aircraft were flown. A permanent home at Treviso was acquired in 1961. On show around the base is a collection of types recently flown by the Air Force. The unit operated Canadair Sabres in the late 1950s and to represent this a Fiat F-86K is on show. The Fiat G.91R entered service in 1961. All fighter units were allocated T-33s for training and general duties and three can he seen.

TYPE	REG/SER	CON. NO.	PI/NOTES	STATUS
☐ Aermacchi MB.326E (MB.326)	MM54217	6300/70		PV
☐ Fiat G.91R/1B	MM6417	221		RA
☐ Lockheed 580 (T-33A)	MM51-9037	580-6821	51-9037	RA
☐ Lockheed 580 (T-33A)	MM52-9898	580-7794	52-9898	RA
☐ Lockheed 580 (T-33A) (RT-33A)	MM53-5322	580-8661	53-5322	RA
☐ Lockheed 683-10-19 Starfighter (F-104G)	MM6529	683-6529		RA
☐ Lockheed 683-10-19 Starfighter (F-104S) (F-104S/ASA)	MM6750	683-6750		RA
☐ Lockheed 683-10-19 Starfighter (F-104S) (F-104S/ASA)	MM6804	683-6804		RA
☐ Macchi MC.200 Saetta	'MM7707'		MM8307 – on loan from Mus. AMI	RAC
☐ North American NA-207 Sabre (F-86K)	MM53-8278	207-6	53-8278, MM6190, – with parts from c/n 221-103 55-4863, MM55-4863	RA
☐ Republic F-84F Thunderstreak	MM53-6704		53-6704	RA

RACCOLTA DELLA BASE DI VILLAFRANCA (ITA84)

Address:	Aeroporto Militare, Località Caluri, 37069 Villafranca.
Tel:	045-633-2111
Email:	rms-com@aeronautica.difesa.it
Admission:	By prior permission only.
Location:	About 15 km south west of Verona and just north of the village.

The 3rd Stormo was active as a fighter unit in World War II. After the armistice it flew Savoia-Marchetti SM.79s and SM.82s along with several light aircraft from Lecce. Reformed again at Bari in 1948 P-38 Lightnings and P-51D Mustangs were used. The wing moved into Villafranca in 1954. Since then it has flown the F-84G, RF-84F, RF-104G and F-104G. The AMX arrived in the early 1990s and was in use for a few years. Currently no operational aircraft are in residence. One of the Starfighters is preserved at the nearby barracks in the town and two others are located at the former squadron headquarters.

TYPE	REG/SER	CON. NO.	PI/NOTES	STATUS
☐ Lockheed 683-10-19 Starfighter (F-104G)	MM6513	683-6513		RA
☐ Lockheed 683-10-19 Starfighter (F-104G)	MM6514	683-6514		RA
☐ Lockheed 683-10-19 Starfighter (F-104G)	MM6547	683-6547	At barracks in town.	RA
☐ Lockheed 683-10-19 Starfighter (F-104G)	MM6579	683-6579		RA
☐ Republic RF-84F Thunderflash	MM52-7403		52-7403	RA

RACCOLTA DELLA BASE SCUOLA SARAM DI TÁRANTO (ITA85)

Address:	Comando Scuola SARAM, Via Rondinella Contrada Pizzone, 74100 Taranto.
Tel:	099-779-6372
Email:	saram-euroform@aeronautica.difesa.it
Admission:	By prior permission only.
Location:	Off Road 172 by the bridge into the city.

The site was first used by military seaplanes in 1914/15 and in the 1920s housed an Air Force squadron. Over the years a number of schools have used the camp. The current establishment provides basic military training for entrants to the services. The gate is guarded by two aircraft a Fiat G.91 and a Macchi MB.326.

TYPE	REG/SER	CON. NO.	PI/NOTES	STATUS
☐ Aermacchi MB.326	MM54152	6128/1		RA
☐ Agusta-Bell 204AS	MM80363	3082		RA
☐ Fiat G.91R/1	MM6275	41		RA
☐ Lockheed 580 (T-33A) (RT-33A)	MM53-5396	580-8735	53-5396	RA

RACCOLTA DELLA BRUNO BENTIVOGLIO (ITA86)

Address:	Via della Bufolatta 1015, 00138 Roma.
Tel:	06-8712-2398
Admission:	By prior permission only
Location:	Just outside the ring road by Junctions 10 and 11.

The owner of this scrapyard has bought and processed many aircraft and put a number of types on show. Large numbers of G.91s were acquired from Améndola and Brindisi in the late 1990s.

TYPE	REG/SER	CON. NO.	PI/NOTES	STATUS
☐ Agusta-Bell 204B	'PS-001'			RAX
☐ Fiat G.91T/1	MM54408	135		RA
☐ Fiat G.91T/1	MM6315	45	At Via Prenestina.	RA
☐ Lockheed 580 (T-33A)	MM51-9033	580-6817		RA
☐ Lockheed 683-10-19 Starfighter (F-104G)	MM6551	683-6551	Tail from c/n 683-6578 MM6578.	RA
☐ North American NA-207 Sabre (F-86K)	MM53-8297	207-25	53-8297	RA
☐ Republic F-84F Thunderstreak	MM53-6733		53-6733	RA
☐ Republic RF-84F Thunderflash	MM52-7395		52-7395	RA

RACCOLTA DELLA RISTORANTE ZI PIETRO (ITA87)

Address:	Via Tuscanola 1713, 00044 Vermicino.
Admission:	On permanent view.
Location:	About 15 km south east of Roma on Route 215.

The Agusta Bell 47 and Beech 18 are on display in front of this restaurant. The other three airframes are stored dismantled behind the buildings. They will hopefully soon be put on show.

TYPE	REG/SER	CON. NO.	PI/NOTES	STATUS
☐ Agusta-Bell 47J	MM80136	1035		PV
☐ Beech C18S Expeditor (C-45F) (UC-45F)				PV
☐ Lockheed 580 (T-33A)	MM51-17488	580-7468	51-17488	RA
☐ Piaggio P.148				RA
☐ Piaggio P.166ML1	MM61904	407		RA

RACCOLTA DELLA SCUOLA SARVAM DI VITERBO (ITA88)

Address:	Comando Scuola SARVAM, Stada Toscanese 71H, 01100 Viterbo.
Email:	sarvam-com@aeronautica.difesa.it
Admission:	By prior permission only.
Location:	About 5 km north west of the town off Route 204.

The Air Force has a barracks located on the north side of the main Italian Army airfield. A collection of preserved aircraft has been put on display at this site. The school trains airfield defence forces.

TYPE	REG/SER	CON. NO.	PI/NOTES	STATUS
☐ Aermacchi MB.326	MM54155	6131/4		RA
☐ Canadian Car & Foundry Harvard 4 [North American NA-186 (T-6H-2M)]	MM54139	CCF4-???		RA
☐ Canadian Car & Foundry Harvard 4 [North American NA-186 (T-6H-4M)]	MM53818	CCF4-???		RA
☐ Fiat G.91T/1	MM6368	98		RA
☐ Lockheed 580 (T-33A)	MM55-3033	580-9574	55-3033	RA
☐ Lockheed 683-10-19 Starfighter (F-104G)	MM6590	683-6590		RA
☐ Piaggio P.166ML1	MM61910	422		RA

RACCOLTA DELLA SCUOLA SOTTUFFICIALI (ITA89)

Address:	Scuola Sottufficiali AM, Palazzo Reale, Via Nazionale Appia 2, 81100 Caserta.
Tel:	0823-210052.
Email:	ssam-com@aeronautica.difesa.it
Admission:	By prior permission only.
Location:	In the northern part of the town.

The Scuola Specialisti of the Air Force has moved from premises at Caserta to a new site at Capua. The remaining training unit has a number of preserved aircraft at the site as well as several instructional airframes. The two Starfighters were built by Aeritalia and entered service in the mid-1960s. The Tornado in the collection is the first Italian example which made its maiden flight at Caselle on December 5th 1975.

TYPE	REG/SER	CON. NO.	PI/NOTES	STATUS
☐ Aeritalia AMX	MM7102	IX014		RA
☐ Aermacchi MB.326	MM54220	6303/73		RA
☐ Aermacchi MB.339A	MM54438	6597/004		RA
☐ Lockheed 683-10-19 Starfighter (F-104G)	MM6507	683-6507		RA
☐ Lockheed 683-10-19 Starfighter (F-104G)	MM6552	683-6552		RA
☐ Panavia PA200 Tornado	MM-X-586	P.05		RA
☐ Piaggio P.166ML1	MM61921	433		RA

RUSTY ANGELS (ITA90)

Address:	Loc. Pizzoprato, 00061 Anguillara.
Tel:	06-996-8947
Email:	crowsnest@tin.it
Admission:	By prior permission only.
Location:	At Santo Stefano airfield near Anguillara Sabazia which is about 30 km north west of Roma.

Members of the group have set up a flying museum at their private airfield. The former Italian Army Super Cub is painted in military colours. The Macchi MB.308 first flew in 1947 and eighty one were used by the Air Force.

TYPE	REG/SER	CON. NO.	PI/NOTES	STATUS
☐ De Havilland D.H.82A Tiger Moth	I-JENA	84682	T6256, G-APLR	RAC
☐ De Havilland D.H.82A Tiger Moth	I-BANG	85482	DE486, G-APRY	RAA
☐ De Havilland D.H.82A Tiger Moth	I-RIBI	86231	NL760, G-APJK	RAC
☐ De Havilland D.H.82A Tiger Moth	I-JJOY	86550	PG641, EI-AHH, EI-AHM, G-APGM	RAA
☐ De Havilland D.H.82A Tiger Moth	I-EDAI	86560	PG651, (Fr.Mil), F-BDOQ, G-AYUX	RAA
☐ Fokker Dr I (R)	I-JENI	0819170		RAC
☐ Piper PA-18-135 Super Cub (L-21B)	I-OMAT	18-3299	53-7756, MM53-7756, EI-134,	RAA

LATVIA

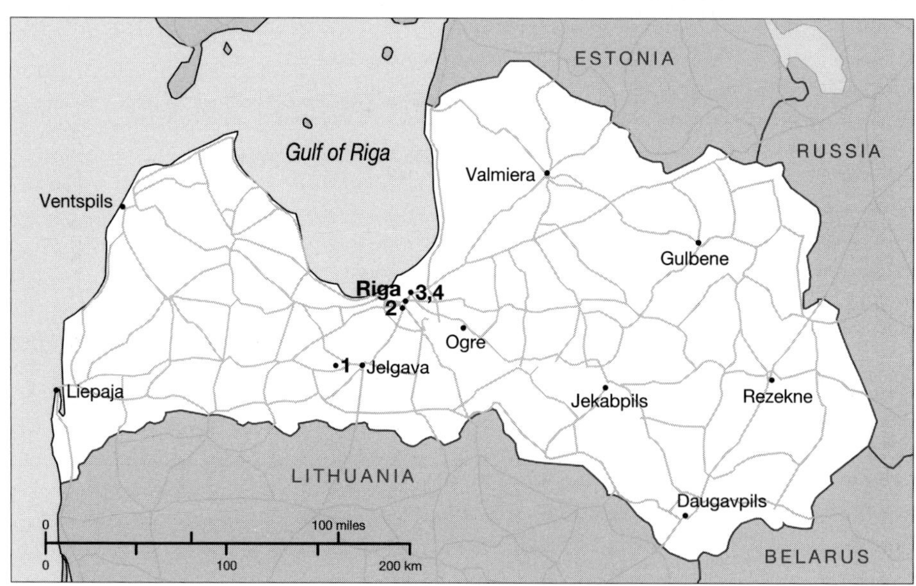

KOLKHOZ NAKOTNE MUZEJS (LAT1)

Address:	Nakotne.
Admission:	By prior permission only.
Location:	About 15 km west of Jelgava.

Several years ago a report in a German magazine mentioned that a Tupolev Tu-104 had been donated to a local group for preservation. The airliner was to serve as a museum at a sport aviation airfield. The aircraft was delivered to Aeroflot in March 1957 and served mainly with their Siberian division. After being withdrawn from use it spent some time as an instructional airframe at the Riga Institute. Is it still at the field?

TYPE	REG/SER	CON. NO.	PI/NOTES	STATUS
☐ Tupolev Tu-104A	CCCP-42328	66600202	CCCP-L5422	PV

LATVIJAS AVIACIJAS TEHNIKES MUZEJS (LAT2)

Address:	SmilsuIela 20, LV-1013 Riga.
Tel:	0686-2707
Admission:	When the staff are present.
Location:	At the International Airport which is about 5 km south west of the city.

The collection was started in 1969 by an engineer, then employed by Aeroflot, and his son. The types on show have nearly all been used by the Soviet Air Force and include examples of fairly recent front line models. In addition to the aircraft, ejector seats and an airfield beacon can be seen. The Tu-134 nose serves as an office for the museum. The MiG-15UTIs were gate guards at Soviet bases in Latvia and obtained when the units returned to Russia. Many other Soviet aircraft were left behind and the museum moved quickly to obtain some of these. There is an impressive line up of fighters. Several versions of the classic MiG-21 are on show along with the later MiG-23, 25, 27 and 29. These types are joined by Sukhoi designs. All gave excellent service from the military airfields which were used by the Soviet Air Force. DOSAAF also flew from a number of locations and the Blaniks and the Yak-18 were in their large fleet in Latvia. The Tu-22 is parked just outside the museum compound. The swing-wing Tu-22M appeared in 1967 and well over three hundred were built in several versions. The Antonov An-14 light transport was designed in the mid-1950s to fill an Aeroflot requirement. The prototype first flew in March 1958 and about two hundred were built for civil and military use. The Yakovlev Yak-28 twin engined tactical bomber entered service in the early 1960s and interceptor versions were also built. The Tu-154 is a recent arrival. The airliner was delivered to Aeroflot in October 1981 and was normally based at Riga. When Latvia gained its independence the Tu-154 joined Latavio and later Latpass Airlines. It is hoped the necessary funds can be found to keep the museum open.

TYPE	REG/SER	CON. NO.	PI/NOTES	STATUS
☐ Aero L-29 Delfin	22	290421		PV
☐ Aero L-29 Delfin	92	291109		PV
☐ Aero L-29 Delfin	38	294966		PV
☐ Aero L-29 Delfin	26	691847		PV
☐ Antonov An-2	22	110547307		PV
☐ Antonov An-2	CCCP-32418	1G 101-36		PV
☐ Antonov An-2R	CCCP-02660	1G 123-26	Fuselage only.	PV
☐ Antonov An-14A	01	903007		PV
☐ Antonov An-24B			Front fuselage only.	PV
☐ Antonov An-24B	YL-LCD	77303902	CCCP-46400	PV
☐ Cessna 150A	D-EMEH	59081	N6681T	PV
☐ Kamov Ka-26	CCCP-24057	6900401		PV
☐ Let L-13 Blanik	47			PV
☐ Let L-13 Blanik	72	1511		PV
☐ Mikoyan-Gurevich MiG-15UTI	58	022611		PV
☐ Mikoyan-Gurevich MiG-15UTI	14	022638		PV
☐ Mikoyan-Gurevich MiG-21SMT	10	50023100		PV
☐ Mikoyan-Gurevich MiG-21ST	76	50027021		PV
☐ Mikoyan-Gurevich MiG-21ST	40	50029804		PV
☐ Mikoyan-Gurevich MiG-21UM	94	516939011		PV
☐ Mikoyan-Gurevich MiG-21US	06	02685133		PV
☐ Mikoyan-Gurevich MiG-23	15	18715/0719	Front fuselage only.	PV
☐ Mikoyan-Gurevich MiG-23M	74	0390207525		PV
☐ Mikoyan-Gurevich MiG-23MF	16	0390206503		PV
☐ Mikoyan-Gurevich MiG-25R	34	84027607		PV
☐ Mikoyan-Gurevich MiG-25U	30	020SM03	Front fuselage only.	PV
☐ Mikoyan-Gurevich MiG-27	60	3910601		PV
☐ Mikoyan-Gurevich MiG-29UB	52	952		PVD
☐ Mil Mi-2	21	513219103		PV
☐ Mil Mi-2	22	513832104		PV
☐ Mil Mi-4	CCCP-31449			PV
☐ Mil Mi-6A	09	10680704		PV
☐ Mil Mi-8T			Front fuselage only.	PV
☐ Mil Mi-8T	17	9710615	Tail boom from c/n 9710819.	PV
☐ Mil Mi-24A		2201108	Rear fuselage only.	PV
☐ Mil Mi-24A	20	2201407		PV
☐ Mil Mi-24V			Front fuselage only.	PV
☐ Sukhoi Su-7BKL	27	5710		PV
☐ Sukhoi Su-7UM	43	2318		PV
☐ Sukhoi Su-17M4		4219	Front fuselage only.	PV
☐ Sukhoi Su-24		0515318	Front fuselage only.	PV
☐ Sukhoi Su-24		0915306	Front fuselage only.	PV
☐ Sukhoi Su-27			Front fuselage only.	PV
☐ Tupolev Tu-22M2	53			RA
☐ Tupolev Tu-104A			Front fuselage only.	PV
☐ Tupolev Tu-134A			Front fuselage only.	PV
☐ Tupolev Tu-134B			Front fuselage only.	PV
☐ Tupolev Tu-154B-2	YL-LAB	81A515	CCCP-85515	PV
☐ Wytwornia Sprzetu Komunikacyjnego (WSK) SM-1W [Mil Mi-1M]	17			PV
☐ Yakovlev Yak-18T	CCCP-38342	4200803		PV
☐ Yakovlev Yak-28R	22	7960808		PV

Four Aero L-29 Delfins are displayed at the museum at Riga Airport. (Bob Ruffle)

This former Soviet Air Force MiG-21PF is on show at the Lithuanian Aviation Museum at Kaunas. (Bob Ruffle)

The Wine Museum in Luxembourg has this Djinn on show in its grounds

LATVIJAS KARA MUZEJS (LAT3)

Address:	Smilsu iela 20, LV-1868 Riga.
Tel:	7228147
Fax:	7223287
Email:	administrajica@karamuzejs.lv
Admission:	October-April Wednesday-Sunday 1000-1700; May-September Wednesday-Sunday 1000-1800.
Location:	In the northern part of the city centre.

Started in 1916 as the Latvian Riflemen's Museum, the collections traced the history of the regiment. In 1919 the name was changed to the Latvian War Museum and it moved into one of Riga's twenty five fourteenth century fortification towers. During World War II and the Soviet occupation many items were lost or transferred to other museums and the building was closed from 1940 until 1990. Since independence a large number of objects have been recovered and individuals donated memorabilia and weapons which they had concealed for years. The military history of the country is portrayed in detail. There is a small area devoted to aviation.

TYPE	REG/SER	CON. NO.	PI/NOTES	STATUS
☐ Mikoyan-Gurevich MiG-15			Front fuselage only.	RA

RIGAS MOTORRUMUZEJS (LAT4)

Address:	Sergejsa Eizenstena 6, LV-1079 Riga.
Tel:	7097170
Fax:	7515694
Email:	rmm@apollo.lv
Admission:	Tuesday-Sunday 1000-1800.
Location:	In the north eastern suburbs of the city.

This museum has on show a wide range of cars and commercial vehicles. Among the highlights of the exhibition is one of the famous Auto Union racing models of the late 1930s. The small aviation section contains large models of the Ilya Muromets and the locally designed VEB I-12 as well as engines.

LITHUANIA

LIETUVOS AVIACIJOS MUZIEJUS (LIT1)

Address:	Veiveriu 132, LT-3018 Kaunas.
Tel:	390357
Fax:	295547
Email:	lam@lam.lt
Admission:	Tuesday-Saturday 0900-1700.
Location:	At Aleksotas airfield which is about 3km north east of the town centre.

The Sport Aviation Museum was formed in 1983 by a number of enthusiasts and began acquiring aircraft and associated equipment along with photographs, documents and memorabilia. On February 19th 1990 the Ministry of Culture set up the Lithuanian Technical Museum which took over the collection. A further change of name to the Lithuanian Aviation Museum occurred on February 1st 1995. The museum is located at the old Kaunas airfield constructed by the Germans in 1915 when they occupied the region. Between the wars the field was the main base for the Lithuanian Air Force. The Germans again took over the site in World War II. At the end of the conflict the airfield served as the airport for the city until 1989 and also housed Soviet helicopter units. The aircraft include a number of types used by DOSAAF during the Soviet occupation of the country and many locally designed light aircraft and gliders. In 1969 the Litovskaya Aviatsionaya Konstruktsiya was formed and it started producing the BRO-11 glider. Designed by Bronyus Oshkinis, who had earlier built several other sailplanes, the BRO-11 first flew in 1954. Several products of the group can be seen. When the country regained its independence the name of the organisation was changed. The Kensgalia Lituanica is a replica of the Bellanca CH-300 and was built in 1982.

TYPE	REG/SER	CON. NO.	PI/NOTES	STATUS
☐ Aero L-29 Delfin	08	591382		PV
☐ Antonov An-2			Front fuselage only.	PV
☐ Antonov An-2P	4184	1G 141-84	In Polish markings.	RA
☐ Antonov An-2TP	CCCP-92816	1G 53-25	CCCP-65873	PVD
☐ Antonov A-13		5215		RA
☐ Antonov An-14A	34	903112		RA
☐ Antonov An-24B	06	87304405	CCCP-46444, LY-AAI	PV
☐ Beksta RB-17				RA
☐ Kamov Ka-26	LY-HBQ	7202603	CCCP-19403,LY-HAG	PV
☐ Kensgaila Lituanica (R)	LY-XAA			RA
☐ Let L-13 Blanik			Front fuselage only.	RA
☐ Lietuviska Aviacine Konstrukcija LAK-1 (Karvelis BK-7)				RA
☐ Lietuviska Aviacine Konstrukcija LAK-2 (Oskinis BRO-11M Zyle 2)		1713		PV
☐ Lietuviska Aviacine Konstrukcija LAK-5 Nemunas		0001		PV
☐ Lietuviska Aviacine Konstrukcija LAK-9M	CCCP-6409			RA
☐ Lietuviska Aviacine Konstrukcija LAK-10	CCCP-0501			PV
☐ Lietuviska Aviacine Konstrukcija LAK-11 Nida		007		PV
☐ Lietuviska Aviacine Konstrukcija LAK-12E	01			PV
☐ Lietuviska Aviacine Konstrukcija LAK-14 Strazdas		0305		PV
☐ Lietuviska Aviacine Konstrukcija LAK-15	004			RA
☐ Lietuviska Aviacine Konstrukcija LAK-16MM	LY-23			PV
☐ Mikoyan-Gurevich MiG-21PF	95	76212110		RA
☐ Mil Mi-2T	'06'	510543127	543 (Poland), 0543 (Poland)	PV
☐ Motor Skraidykle T-2				PV
☐ Oskinis BRO-12		6052		PV
☐ Oskinis BRO-18 Boruze				RA
☐ Oskinis BRO-20 Pukelis				RA
☐ Oskinis BRO-23				RA
☐ Panstwowe Zaklady Lotnicze (PZL) TS-11 Iskra 100bisB	612	1H 06-12	0612 – in Polish markings.	PV
☐ Szybowcowy Zaklad Doswiadczalny S.Z.D.30 Pirat	8-18	S-0635		RA
☐ Szybowcowy Zaklad Doswiadczalny S.Z.D.36A Cobra 15	8-10	W-728		RA
☐ Vaineikiai Motorglider				RA
☐ Valunas Helicopter				PV
☐ Yakovlev Yak-18A	11	1162214		RA
☐ Yakovlev Yak-18A	06	1163201		RA
☐ Yakovlev Yak-18PM	01	700102		RA
☐ Yakovlev Yak-50	03	740109		RA
☐ Yakovlev Yak-50	02	770901		PV
☐ Yakovlev Yak-52	21	822009		RA
☐ Zlin Z-326 Trener Master	02	823-4		RA
☐ Zlin Z-326A Akrobat	201	585-05		RA

VYTAUTO DIDZIOJO KARO MUZIEJUS (LIT2)

Address:	Donelaicio 64, 3000 Kaunas.
Tel:	320939
Admission:	May – September Wednesday-Sunday 1000-1800; October – April Wednesday-Sunday 0900-1700.
Location:	In the centre of the city.

In the fifteenth century Duke Vytautas stopped the advance of the crusaders into the country and made Lithuania one of the most important states in the region. The museum traces the military history of the nation with many impressive displays. In the inter-war period the Kaunas Aircraft Workshops produced several indigenous machines. The low wing Anbo 1 designed by A. Gustaitis dates from 1925. Many more Anbo designs followed and several used by the Lithuanian Air Force were taken over by the Soviet military when they invaded the country. On July 15th 1933 Stephen Darius and Stanley Girenas took off in a Bellanca CH-300 from Floyd Bennett Field in New York and headed across the Atlantic. In the early hours of the 17th they crashed in what was then Germany but is now Poland. They were both born in Lithuania and emigrated to the U.S.A. as youngsters. Darius returned in 1920 and served in the Lithuanian Air Force before going back to America in 1927. The wreckage of the aircraft is on show along with personal effects of both pilots. A replica of the aircraft built in 1982 by Valdez Kensgaila is in the collection of the Lithuanian Aviation Museum.

TYPE	REG/SER	CON. NO.	PI/NOTES	STATUS
☐ Bellanca CH-300 Pacemaker	NR688E	137		PVD
☐ Gustaitis Anbo 1		17		PV

VYTAUTO LAPENO AVIACIJOS MUZIEJUS (LIT3)

Address:	Istros Aerodromas, Staniiniu Kalmas, Panavezioraj, LT-5300 Panevezys.
Tel:	45 554332
Email:	avia.istros@panevezys.post.omnitel.lt
Admission:	By prior permission only.
Location:	About 5 km east of the town.

Members of the local aero club are setting up a museum which will trace the history of aviation in the region. During the Soviet occupation of the country there were several military bases in the area. The first aircraft have now arrived and the displays are being developed. The Ukrainian authorities donated the Sukhoi Su-15.

TYPE	REG/SER	CON. NO.	PI/NOTES	STATUS
☐ Aero L-29 Delfin	14	691916		PV
☐ Mikoyan-Gurevich MiG-21SM	35	150C001		PV
☐ Mikoyan-Gurevich MiG-23ML	05	0390317527		PV
☐ Mil Mi-2		543725084		PV
☐ Sukhoi Su-15	82		In Ukrainian markings.	PV

LUXEMBOURG

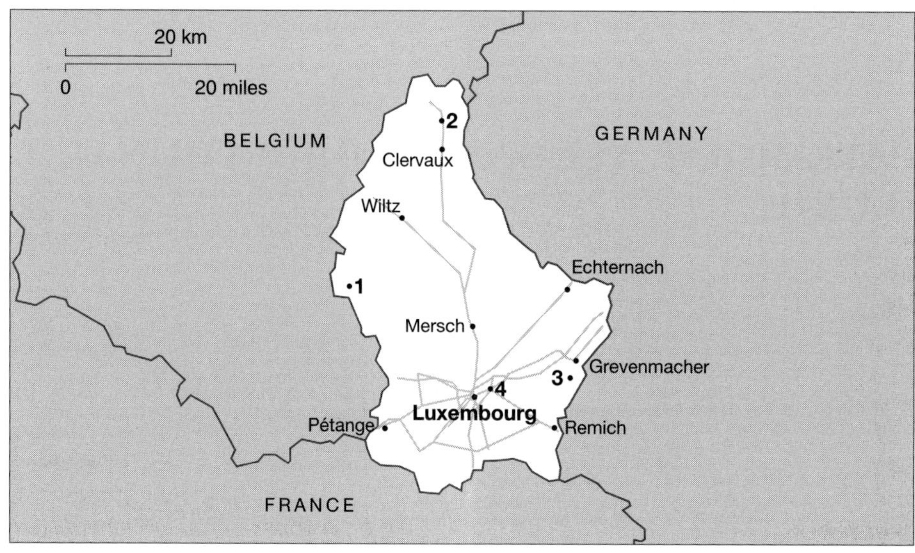

385TH BOMB GROUP MUSEUM (LUX1)

Address:	c/o 44 Rue Principal, L-8833 Wolwelange.
Tel:	023-649565
Email:	Horo@pt.lu
Admission:	By prior permission only.
Location:	In Rue de l' Église in Perlé which is about 12 km north of Arlon, Belgium.

The 385th Bomb Group was activated in December 1942 at Davis-Monthan Field in Arizona but was not formed until the following February at Geiger Field in Washington state. The unit moved to Great Ashfield in Suffolk in July 1943 and stayed until August 1945. Two of the B-17s flown by the wing collided near Perlé on July 12th 1944 and eighteen of the twenty aircrew were killed. Of the pair that survived one was captured by the Germans and the other made his way into Belgium where he was saved by the local Resistance. Three rooms in the local school were allocated in 1998 to serve as a memorial. Crash sites of B-17s have been investigated and many items of memorabilia have been donated. The exhibition has grown over the last few years.

MONUMENT BELGE-BRITANNIQUE (LUX2)

Address:	Mairie, L-9974 Maulusmühle.
Email:	info@maulusmuhle .com (Town Hall)
Admission:	On permanent view
Location:	About 5 km north of Clervaux on Route 335.

The aircraft was shot down on March 21st 1945 after retrieving three Belgian SOE agents. All six on board perished in the crash. The remains consisting of both engines, both wings and the centre section of the fuselage have been set up as the memorial. The graves of those who were killed are also at the site.

TYPE	REG/SER	CON. NO.	PI/NOTES	STATUS
☐ Lockheed 414-56-11 Hudson IIIA (A-29A)	FK803	414-7579	42-47359	PVD

MUSEÉ DU VIN (LUX3)

Address:	115 Route du Vin, L-5416 Ehnen.
Tel:	76 00 26
Admission:	Tuesday-Sunday 0930-1130 1400-1700
Location:	On Route 16 about 10 km north of Remich.

This museum, located in an old vineyard house, presents a significant collection of tools and utensils, photographic documents on work related to vine growing. On site are an authentic vineyard, a cooperage, a forging mill and a gauging office. The history of wine making in the region is portrayed in the exhibition. The Djinn, which is parked at the rear of the building, represents the use of helicopters in pest control in vineyards.

TYPE	REG/SER	CON. NO.	PI/NOTES	STATUS
☐ Sud-Ouest SO-1221 Djinn				PV

PATRIMOINE AÉRONAUTIQUE NATIONAL (LUX4)

Address:	c/o Guillaume Heiderscheid, 19 Rue de Strassen, L-8156 Briedel.
Tel:	24641 (Airport Office)
Admission:	By prior permission only.
Location:	The airport is about 6 km east of the city centre.

Five former Spanish Air Force Texans were bought by the group in the mid-1980s. Three were sold almost immediately and the other two slowly restored to flying condition. One remains with the organisation. An ex-Dutch Air Force Super Cub was later acquired. Two former French Army Bird Dogs are now airworthy. The O-1A underwent a lengthy restoration in the hangar at the airport.

TYPE	REG/SER	CON. NO.	PI/NOTES	STATUS
☐ Cessna 305A Bird Dog (L-19A) (O-1A)	LX-PAB	23312	23312 (France)	RAA
☐ Cessna 305C Bird Dog (L-19E) (O-1E)	LX-PAC	24566	24566 (France), F-GHDK	RAA
☐ North American NA-168 Texan (T-6G)	LX-PAE	168-587	49-3453, E.16-106 (Spain)	RAA
☐ Piper PA-18-135 Super Cub (L-21B)	LX-PAA	18-3615	54-2415, R-125 (Netherlands)	RAA

MALTA

MALTA AVIATION MUSEUM FOUNDATION (MAL1)

Address:	BRT13, Ta'Qali.
Tel:	2141-6095
Fax:	2141-9374
Email:	info@maltaaviationmuseum.com
Admission:	Daily 0900-1700
Location:	About 7 km west of Valletta.

The foundation, formed on November 1st 1994, obtained permission to set up a museum at the disused Ta'Qali airfield. This site was a pre-World War II civil airport used by Italian airliners until 1940. The field was taken over by the Royal Air Force in November 1940 and remained operational until the early 1960s. A workshop is in use at the site and a display opened on April 26th 1996 in this building. In addition to the aircraft on view photographs, documents, memorabilia, engines and components can be seen. Members of the group have recently completed the restoration of a Spitfire IX. The fuselage was found in a local scrap yard and other parts have been obtained from many sources. Also finished is a Hurricane recovered from the sea. Many hours of work was put in on this restoration. The Swordfish is one of the airframes stored by the late Ernie Simmonds at Tillsonburg in Canada from 1946 until 1970. The Pou-du-Ciel replica was built a few years ago by museum members and has been fitted with a Citroen 2CV engine. The Sea Venom arrived from the Jet Age Collection in Gloucestershire in late 2005. On September 28th 2005 the second phase was ready with the completion and opening of 'The Air Battle of Malta Memorial Hangar'.

TYPE	REG/SER	CON. NO.	PI/NOTES	STATUS
☐ Agusta-Bell 47G-2			Due soon.	–
☐ Beech D18S Expeditor (C-45H)	N495F	AF-888	52-10958, (N8176H), N3114G, N114G	PVC
☐ Cessna 305C Bird Dog (L-19E) (O-1E)	9H-ACB	305M0029	61-2983	PV
☐ De Havilland D.H.82A Tiger Moth	G-ANFW	85660	DE730	PVC
☐ De Havilland D.H.112 Sea Venom FAW.22	XG691	121110		PVC
☐ De Havilland D.H.115 Vampire T.11	WZ550	15109	WZ550, 7902M	PV
☐ Douglas DC-3A-456 Skytrain (C-47A)	C-FITH	20228	43-15762, NC9033H, ZS-DLX, N9033H, ZS-DLX, CF-ITH	PV
☐ English Electric P.1B Lightning F.2	XN769	95122	XN769, 8402M – front fuselage only – on loan.	PV
☐ Fairey Swordfish II	HS491			PVC
☐ Fairey Firefly AS.5			Major components.	PVD
☐ Fiat G.91R/1B	MM6387	191	Tail from c/n 181 MM6377.	PVX
☐ Hawker Hurricane IIA	Z3055		Rear fuselage from Z3571.	PV
☐ Hawker P.1040 Sea Hawk FGA.6 (FGA.4)	WV826	6071		PV
☐ Mignet HM-14 Pou-du-Ciel (R)				PV
☐ Supermarine 361 Spitfire LF.IXc	EN199	3677	Parts from BR108 and BR368	PV

NATIONAL WAR MUSEUM (MAL2)

Address:	Drill Hall, Lower Fort Saint Elmo, Valletta.
Tel:	2122-2430
Fax:	2123-8480
Email:	Eem.magno-conti@gov.mt
Admission:	Daily 0900-1700.
Location:	At the end of Republic Street.

For over a century a museum covering the conflicts which took place in the area between 1530 and 1798 has been located in the Palace Armoury. The National War Museum Association opened a display in 1975 in the waterfront fort and this dealt with later times. The restored fuselage of 'Faith' one of three Sea Gladiators which heroically defended Malta in the early days of the Mediterranean campaign is a prized exhibit. The aircraft was presented to the island on September 3rd 1943. Components from crash sites on the island and in coastal waters have been found and restored for display with others still to be put on show.

TYPE	REG/SER	CON. NO.	PI/NOTES	STATUS
☐ Gloster Sea Gladiator	'N5520'		N5519 – 'Faith' – less wings	PVX
☐ Junkers Ju 87D	16970	16970	Components only	PVD
☐ Messerschmitt Bf 109F-1			Wing only	PVD
☐ Supermarine 349 Spitfire F.Vc/Trop	BR108		Cockpit and engine only.	PVD
☐ Supermarine 357 Seafire F.IIc	MB293			RAD

NETHERLANDS

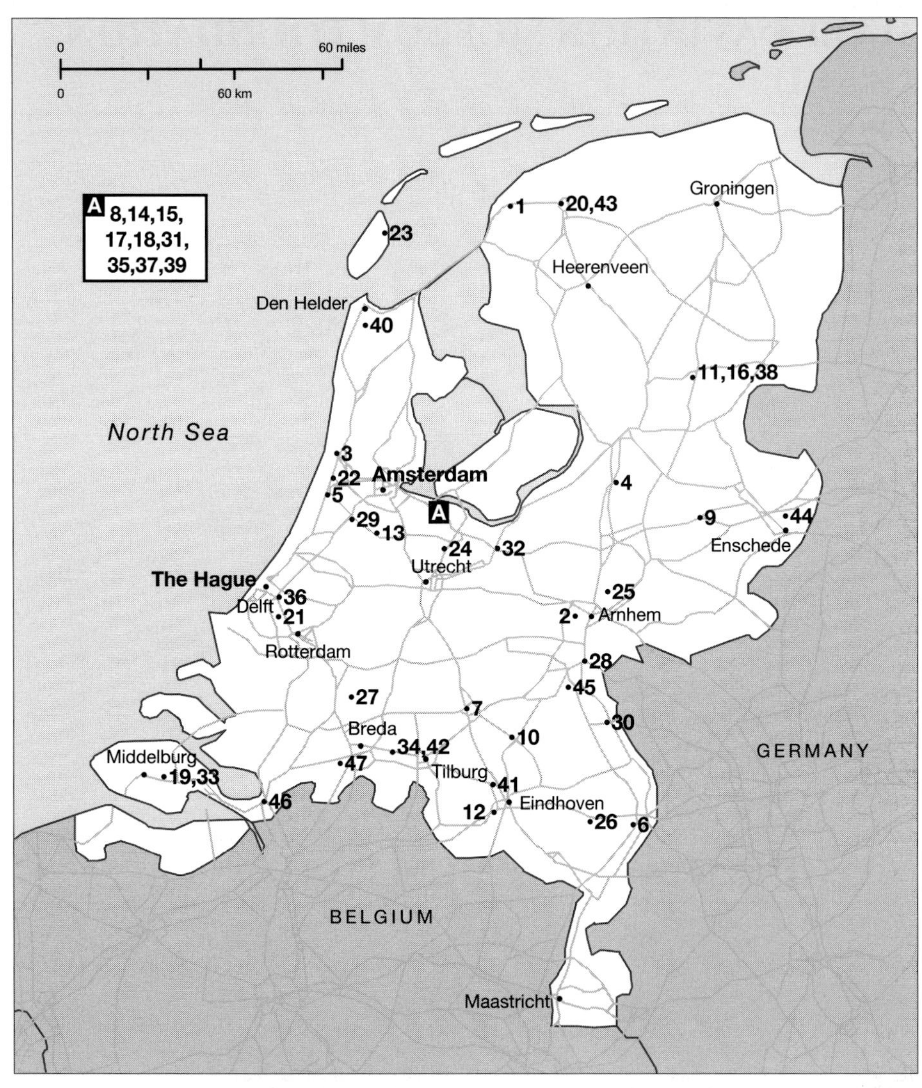

AEOLUS PARK (NET1)

Address:	Hearewei 249, 8855 AZ Sexbierum.
Tel:	0517-591144
Email:	info@aeolusfriesland.nl
Admission:	Daily 1000-1900.
Location:	On the N.393 in the town which is about 7 km north east of Harlingen.

This children's adventure and learning centre has many attractions including several transport items. The former Polish MiG-21 two seater arrived recently and is the only aviation exhibit.

TYPE	REG/SER	CON. NO.	PI/NOTES	STATUS
☐ Mikoyan-Gurevich MiG-21UM	6509	09695165	In Polish markings.	PV

AIRBORNE MUSEUM 'HARTENSTEIN' (NET2)

Address:	Utrechtsweg 232, 6862AZ Oosterbeek.
Tel:	026-337710
Fax:	026-3391785
Email:	info@airbornemuseum.org
Admission:	April – OctobeMonday-Saturday 1000-1700; Sunday 1200-1700. November-March Monday-Saturday 1100-1700; Sunday 1200-1700.
Location:	About 5 km west of Arnhem on the N.225.

Displays here trace the airborne landings which were an essential part of the liberation of the Netherlands. There are many dioramas showing the roles of the troops after they had disembarked in 'Operation Market Garden'.

AIRCRAFT RECOVERY GROUP 1940-1945 MUSEUM (NET3)

Address:	Fort Veldhuis, Genieweg 1, 1967 PS Heemskerk.
Tel:	0251-230670
Email:	info@org194-1945.nl
Admission:	May-September Sunday 1000-1700.
Location:	Off the A.9 south of the town which is about 15 km north of Haarlem.

The group has investigated many crash sites and excavated several components and engines. The museum displays many of these along with other items relating to World War II.

TYPE	REG/SER	CON. NO.	PI/NOTES	STATUS
☐ Heinkel He 115B		2732	Crash remains	PVD
☐ Short S.29 Stirling I	N3654		Crash remains.	PVD
☐ Short S.29 Stirling IV (R)			Front fuselage only.	PV

AMERICAN MOTORCYCLE MUSEUM (NET4)

Address:	Zwolsestraat 63C, 8101 AB Raalte.
Tel:	0572-364187
Email:	info@harley-indian-museum.nl
Admission:	Daily 1100-1700.
Fax:	0572-364383
Location:	In the centre of the town which is about 20 km south east of Zwolle on the N.348.

Over one hundred and forty classic American motorcycles can be seen in this museum along with items of memorabilia. The collection moved from Zwolle in 2004 to a purpose built hall. The Piaggio was on show at the Antik Museum in Kalkar in Germany for many years before joining the exhibition.

TYPE	REG/SER	CON. NO.	PI/NOTES	STATUS
☐ Antonov An-2T	SP-FAX	1G 26-20	2620 (Poland), SP-UXD	PV
☐ Mikoyan-Gurevich MiG-21F-13			Due from Poland.	–
☐ Mil Mi-2R	SP-TSC	524738046		PV
☐ Piaggio FWP.149D	D-EADK	023	DD+393, AC+435, 90+13	PV

ATLANTIKWALL MUSEUM (NET5)

Address:	Wilhelminastraat 43, 2201 KB Noordwijk aan Zee.
Tel:	071-361-5785
Admission:	Saturday-Sunday 1000-1700.
Location:	On the coast about 20 km north east of Den Haag.

These vast fortifications were built on a golf course by the Germans in 1940. The Atlantikwall society is slowly restoring parts of the complex and now has an exhibition in one of the bunkers. The history of the site is portrayed. The wreck of the Messerschmitt which was piloted by Oberleutnant Eugine-Ludwig Zweger was recovered from its crash site. The aircraft was shot down by a Spitfire V of 118 Squadron.

TYPE	REG/SER	CON. NO.	PI/NOTES	STATUS
☐ Messerschmitt Bf 109G-6	'7'	15678		PVD

AUTOBEDRIJF PIET SMEDTS COLLECTIE (NET6)

Address:	Napoleonsbaan Zuid 27, 5991 NB Baarlo.
Tel:	077-477-2154
Fax:	077-477-3931
Admission:	By prior permission only but unlikely to be given.
Location:	About 5 km south west of Venlo on the N.273. Kessel is about 4 km south of Baarlo.

Over the last few years the owner of this B.M.W. garage has acquired a large numbers of ex-military aircraft from Germany, the Czech Republic and Poland. Another yard at Kessel has recently come into use. Some aircraft have gone to other display sites both in the Netherlands and Belgium. Two Starfighters and a pair of MiG-21s were recently sold to private collectors. More land has been acquired and there are plans to open a museum.

TYPE	REG/SER	CON. NO.	PI/NOTES	STATUS
☐ Canadair CL-13A Sabre 5 [North American F-86E]	BB+237	1111	23321 (Canada), BB+131	RA
☐ Canadair CL-13B Sabre 6 [North American F-86E]	JC+240	1704	At Kessel.	RA
☐ Canadair CL-226 Freedom Fighter (NF-5A) [Northrop N-156A]	K-3063	3063	At Kessel.	RA
☐ Dassault Mirage IIIE				RA
☐ Dassault Mirage IIIRS	R-2107	1037	In Swiss markings.	RA
☐ Dornier-Breguet Alpha Jet A	40+18	0018		RA
☐ Dornier-Breguet Alpha Jet A	40+52	0052		RA
☐ Dornier-Breguet Alpha Jet A	40+65	0065		RA
☐ Dornier-Breguet Alpha Jet A	40+95	0095	At Kessel.	RA
☐ English Electric P.25 Lightning F.2A (F.2)	'XN781'	95137	XN784, 8540M	RAX
☐ Fiat G.91R/3	99+05	91-378	BD+405, 31+12, D-9601	RA
☐ Fiat G.91R/3	99+38	91-437	KD+437, DH+232, MD+301, 31+69	RA
☐ Fokker F.27 Friendship 400MPA (100)	PH-FCX	10183	PH-FCX, TC-TEK	RA
☐ Let L-410A Turbolet	OK-ADQ	700003	OK-176, OK-AKG, OK-AZA	RA
☐ Lockheed 483-04-08 Starfighter (F-104F)	29+17	483-5070	59-5017, BB+383 – at Kessel.	RA
☐ Lockheed 583-10-20 Starfighter (TF-104G)	28+13	583F-5943	KE+201	RA
☐ Lockheed 583-10-20 Starfighter (TF-104G)	28+22	583F-5952	KE+210, DC+364 – on loan to Belgisch Mil. Rad. Mus, BEL	–
☐ Lockheed 683-04-10 Starfighter (RF-104G)	23+92	683-8102	KG+102, EA+106 – at Mill, NET.	RA
☐ Lockheed 683-04-10 Starfighter (RF-104G)	24+89	683-8239	KG+339, EB+235	RA
☐ Lockheed 683-10-19 Starfighter (F-104G)	21+60	683-7029	KE+329, DA+121 – tail from c/n 8270 KG+370, EB+253, 25+09 – at Kessel.	RA
☐ Lockheed 683-10-19 Starfighter (F-104G)	21+71	683-7040	KE+340, DA+251, DD+257	RA
☐ Lockheed 683-10-19 Starfighter (F-104G)	21+78	683-7047	KE+347 - At Kessel.	RA
☐ Lockheed 683-10-19 Starfighter (F-104G)	22+39	683-7117	KE+417, DD+109 –	RA
☐ Lockheed 683-10-19 Starfighter (F-104G)	23+01	683-7184	KE+484 – tail from c/n 683-8102 KG+106, EA+107, 23+92 – at Kessel.	RA
☐ Lockheed 683-10-19 Starfighter (F-104G)	26+72	683-7418	At Kessel.	RA
☐ Lockheed 683-10-19 Starfighter (F-104G)	23+51	683-8030	KG+130, JA+117, BF+126	RA
☐ Lockheed 683-10-19 Starfighter (F-104G)	'BB+371'	683-8075	KG+175, JA+123, JA+106, 23+76.	RAX
☐ Lockheed 683-10-19 Starfighter (F-104G)	'D-8212'	683-8212	KG+312, 24+63 – tail from c/n 683-8226 KG+326, 24+77	RAX
☐ Lockheed 683-10-19 Starfighter (F-104G)	25+61	683-9007	KH+107, JA+243 – at Kessel.	RA
☐ Lockheed 683-10-19 Starfighter (F-104G)	26+30	683-9182	KH+181, DF+249 – at Kessel.	RA
☐ McDonnell M.98DJ Phantom II (F-4C)	64-0745	1028		RA
☐ Mikoyan-Gurevich MiG-21M	1809	961809	In Polish markings – at Kessel.	RA
☐ Mikoyan-Gurevich MiG-21M	1812	961812	In Polish markings.	RA
☐ Mikoyan-Gurevich MiG-21M	1909	961909	In Polish markings.	RA
☐ Mikoyan-Gurevich MiG-21M	1914	961914	In Polish markings.	RA
☐ Mikoyan-Gurevich MiG-21M	2007	962007	In Polish markings.	RA
☐ Mikoyan-Gurevich MiG-21MF	8909	968909	In Polish markings.	RA
☐ Mikoyan-Gurevich MiG-21SPS (MiG-21PFM)	22+45	94A6410	963 (DDR) – at Zwanenburg , NET.	PV
☐ Mikoyan-Gurevich MiG-21US	24+11	06685139	248 (DDR)	RA
☐ Mikoyan-Gurevich MiG-23ML	2423	0390322423		RA
☐ Mikoyan-Gurevich MiG-23UB	20+59	A1038221	107 (DDR) on loan to Belgisch Mil. Rad. Mus, BEL	RA
☐ Mil Mi-2	OK-FIU	534542125	B-2542	RA
☐ Mil Mi-2	B-2910	536010019	In Czech markings.	RA
☐ Mil Mi-8T	OK-FXA	10539	923 (DDR), 93+09	RA
☐ Republic F-84F Thunderstreak	FU-10		52-7115 – in Belgian markings.	RA
☐ Republic F-84F Thunderstreak	P-263		53-6780	RA
☐ Rolladen-Schneider LS-4A	PH-941	4845	D-3599	RA
☐ Sukhoi Su-22UM-3K	98+16	17532371001	138 (DDR), 25+54 – at Kessel.	RA
☐ Sukhoi Su-22M4	25+41	26716	743 (DDR)	RA
☐ Svenska Aeroplan Aktiebolaget (SAAB) 91D Safir	PH-RLH	91375		RA
☐ Szybowcowy Zaklad Doswiadczalny S.Z.D.30 Pirat	D-1553	B-357		RA

AUTOTRON ROSMALEN (NET7)

Address:	Graafsebaan 133, 5248 NL Rosmalen.
Tel:	073-5233300
Fax:	073-5216795
Email:	info@autotron.nl
Admission:	Easter-October 24th daily 1000-1700
Location:	Off the N.50 about 7 km east of s'Hertogenbosch.

The town of Drunen was the first location for this collection then known as Lips Autotron. In 1987 a large complex was constructed on a site on the outskirts of Rosmalen. Regarded as one of the best automobile museums in Europe there are more than four hundred vehicles available for display. Also on show are many photographs, documents, posters and trophies to portray the history of motoring. Suspended in the main hall are the Nieuport 11 replica and the Stampe. The Zeppelin gondola was acquired in 1987. Over the last decade a number of aircraft have been loaned to the collection by the Militaire Luchtvaart Museum at Kamp van Zeist.

TYPE	REG/SER	CON. NO.	PI/NOTES	STATUS
☐ Farman HF-20 (R)	'LA-2'		Was painted as HF-22 'LA-16' – on loan to MLM.	–
☐ Nieuport 11 (R)	'N220'		'N1540'	PVX
☐ Republic F-84F Thunderstreak	P-263		53-6780 – on loan from MLM.	PV
☐ Stampe et Vertongen S.V.4C				PV
☐ Zeppelin LZ-???			Gondola only	PV

AVIODROME (NET8)

Address:	Pelikaanweg 50, 8218 NT Lelystad Airport.
Tel:	0320-289840
Fax:	0320-289841
Email:	info@aviodrome.nl
Admission:	Daily 1000-1700.
Location:	About 7 km south of the town off the N.302

The first plans for a Dutch Aeronautical Museum were put forward in 1916 but it was another twenty years before a building was acquired at Schiphol Airport. Germany attacked the country on May 10th 1940 and when the airfield was bombed part of the collection was damaged. The surviving airframes were taken to the Fokker works and some of the more interesting types were transported to Berlin for exhibition in the famous Deutsche Luftfahrt Sammlung. On November 16th 1955 the Dutch National Air Museum Foundation was established and the collection of material commenced. A museum with nine aircraft on show opened in a former Fokker flight test hangar on May 17th 1960 but was forced to close seven years later due to airport redevelopment. The airport authorities, Fokker, and K.L.M. put up money for a new building. The geodetic aluminium clad domed structure was designed by Professor Fuller of the Temcor Corporation in the U.S.A. and handed over to the museum in 1969. The exhibition opened to the public on July 10th 1971. The airport expanded and the museum was forced to move. A new complex at Lelystad opened on November 26th 2003. The site has been developed as an 'Aviation Theme Park' which includes a replica of Schiphol Airport's 1928 terminal building. In this area visitors will be able to visit the control tower, see period films and book pleasure flights. The main hall contains around twenty aircraft and further buildings will be erected. A large hangar houses many aircraft and this can also be visited. A number of organisations carry out work in the complex. Dutch built aircraft feature prominently and the displays trace the development of the aviation industry in the country. The famous Fokker company set up a plant in Amsterdam in 1919 and later moved to Schiphol. This remained the main factory for the company until its collapse. A replica of the Spin was built by the manufacturers in 1936 to commemorate the twenty fifth anniversary of the type. A Dr I replica was started by volunteers at the museum in 1977 and completed twelve years later. The fuselage of a 1925 S.IV trainer was obtained from Delft Technical University in the 1950s and there are long term plans to construct new wings. A replica of the 1920 F.II is nearing completion. The prototype of this design was built in Germany and escaped to Holland by taking off directly from the hangar at Schwerin. In 1955 Fokker and K.L.M. bought from Denmark a F.VIIa, originally delivered to Balair in Switzerland in 1928. This aircraft is now resplendent in the colours of the first F.VII used by K.L.M. which was destroyed in the initial German raid on Schiphol. On long term loan from the Western Canada Aviation Museum is the fuselage of a F.XIa (B.IVA) amphibian. The fuselages for this type were made in Holland and the wings were constructed in the U.S.A. where final assembly took place. The C.VD biplane also came from Delft and has been restored to its original markings. Post war products from Fokker include the S.11 Instructor, the sole S.12 built in Europe, and the Friendship. The remains of three Brewster Buffalo fighters have been salvaged. Hopefully one display aircraft can be built from these parts. Over seventy examples of the type served in the Dutch East Indies. A number of types including the Constellation are maintained in airworthy condition. Also at Lelystad are other collections where a variety of types, many airworthy, can be seen.

TYPE	REG/SER	CON. NO.	PI/NOTES	STATUS
☐ Agusta-Bell 204B	221	3012		RA
☐ Anselma Sagitta 013	PH-308	006		RA
☐ Anselma Sagitta 013	PH-319	013		RA
☐ Antonov An-2R	'562'	1G 172-48	CCCP-40776, LY-ACQ, 19	PVX
☐ Auster J/1 Autocrat	PH-NFH	1845	PH-NAA, PH-LPS	RA
☐ Avro 652A Anson C.19	'D-26'		VM352	RAX
☐ Beech D18S Expeditor (C-45G)	G-BKRG	AF-522	51-11665, N9072Z, N75WB	PVX

☐ Birdman Cherokee				RA
☐ Blackburn B-103 Buccaneer S.2	XV163	B3-04-66	Front fuselage only.	PV
☐ Blériot XI (R)			BAPC.105	PV
☐ Boeing 747-206B	PH-BUK	21549		PV
☐ Bowers Fly Baby 1A	PH-CVH	3		RA
☐ Brewster B.339D Buffalo	'304'		Parts only.	RA
☐ Brewster B.339D Buffalo	B3-174	375	Parts only.	RAC
☐ Brewster B.339D Buffalo	B3-178	379	Parts only.	RA
☐ British Aerial Transport FK.23 Bantam	K-123	FK.23/15	F1654, K-123, (G-EACN) – on loan from Koolhoven Foundation.	PV
☐ Butterfly				RA
☐ Butterfly				RA
☐ Cessna F172N Skyhawk	PH-OTK	F17201963	PH-AXY	RA
☐ Cierva C.30A (Avro 671)	SE-AFI	735	LN-BAD, 99 (Norway) – c/n also quoted as 706 which was G-ACVC sold from GB in 1934 – perhaps a composite.	RA
☐ De Havilland D.H.82A Tiger Moth	A-38	83101	R5242	PV
☐ De Havilland D.H.104 Dove 6 (1)	OO-SCD	04117	VP-KDE, G-AMFU – front fuselage only.	RA
☐ De Havilland D.H.104 Sea Devon C.20	'PH-MAD'	04453	XJ350	PVX
☐ De Havilland D.H.C.2 Beaver	'JZ-PAD'	1288	N7904C – fuselage only.	RAX
☐ Douglas DC-2-112	'PJ-AJU'	1288	NC13738, A30-14, VH-CRH – on loan from DDA.	RAX
☐ Douglas DC-2-142 (R2D-1)	'PH-AJU'	1404	Bu9993, NC39165	PVX
☐ Douglas DC-3A-456 Skytrain (C-47A)	N47FK	9700	42-23838, NC49538, N7V, N3W, N3PG, N308FN, CF-EEX, C-FEEX, N2669A	PVA
☐ Douglas DC-3A-456 Skytrain (C-47A) (Dakota III)	'PH-TCB'	9836	42-23974, FD938, 6867 (South Africa), ZS-NJE, G-BVOL – composite	PVX
☐ Douglas DC-3A-467 Skytrain (C-47B) (Dakota IV)	'PH-ALR'	16218/32966	44-76634, KN487, G-AMCA	PVX
☐ Douglas DC-4 Skymaster (C-54A)	PH-DDY	7488	42-107469, NC53103, PI-C102, HS-POE, 107469 (Thailand), VQ-ZEF, A2-ZEF, ZS-IPR, 6906 (South Africa), ZS-IPR – on loan from DDA.	PVX
☐ Douglas DC-9			Cabin section only.	RA
☐ Engel Bora Hang Glider				RA
☐ Evans VP-1 Volksplane	'PH-VPI'	NVAV-10	'PH-AVG', PH-GOO	RAX
☐ Fieseler Fi 103A-1 (FSM)				RA
☐ Firebird Tri-CX	PH-1L1	063-83		RA
☐ Fokker Spin III	PH-WEY		On loan from Fokker H.T.	PV
☐ Fokker Spin III (R)				RA
☐ Fokker D VII			Wing only.	PV
☐ Fokker Dr I (FSM)	'152/17'			PVX
☐ Fokker E III (R)				RA
☐ Fokker C.VD	634		312, 634, '618'	RA
☐ Fokker F.II (R)	'H-NABC'	1598		RACX
☐ Fokker F.VIIa	'H-NADP'	5054	CH-159, OY-DED, SE-ASE, OY-ASE, 'H-NACT'	PVX
☐ Fokker F.VIIa	PJ-AJS	5312	Front fuselage only.	RAD
☐ Fokker F.VIII/2m	PJ-AID	5041	H-NAED, PH-AED, PJ-AED	RAC
☐ Fokker F.XIA (B IVA)	CF-AUV	906	On loan from WCAM, MB, Canada.	RAC
☐ Fokker S.IV	PH-SIV	'NVAV-74'	108 – new wings being built.	PVC
☐ Fokker S.11.1 Instructor (S.11)	PH-UEU	6194	PH-NED – fuselage frame only.	RA
☐ Fokker S.11.1 Instructor (S.11)	E-9	6200		PV
☐ Fokker S.11.1 Instructor (S.11)	PH-AFS	6205	E-14, (PH-HOO)	PVA
☐ Fokker S.11.1 Instructor (S.11)	PH-HOK	6272	E-29	PVA
☐ Fokker S.11.1 Instructor (S.11)	PH-HOG	6275	PH-NFA, E-39, 199, (PH-HOH) – parts of c/n 6193 E-4	PVA
☐ Fokker S.11.1 Instructor (S.11)	PH-ACG	6279	E-36, 179	PVA
☐ Fokker S.12	PH-NDC	6287	PH-NDC, (E-41)	RA
☐ Fokker S.14.2 Mach Trainer (S.14.1)	PH-XIV	6289	(PH-NDY), 'K-1' – on loan from Fokker H.T.	RA
☐ Fokker F.27 Friendship 100	PH-NIV	10101	On loan from Fokker H.T.	RA
☐ Fokker F.27 Friendship 100	PH-NVF	10102	PH-NVF, D-BAKI – on loan from F-27 Association.	PV
☐ Fokker F.27 Friendship 100	PH-FHF	10105	EI-AKA, ZK-NAH, VH-NLS	PVA
☐ Fokker F.27 Friendship 400MPA (100)	PH-FCX	10183	PH-FCX, TC-TEK	RA
☐ Fokker F.28-1000 Fellowship	PH-MKH	11242	(PH-KRK), (PH-KLM) – on loan from Fokker H.T.	RA
☐ Fokker 50			Fuselage only.	RA
☐ Fokker 50	PH-OSI	10688	On loan from Fokker H.T.	PV
☐ Fokker 100			Fuselage only – on loan from Fokker H.T.	RA
☐ Gas Balloon			Basket only.	RA
☐ Göppingen Go 4 Govier III	PH-211	421		RA
☐ Grumman G-89 Tracker (S2F-1) (S-2N) (US-2N)	159	720	Bu148281	PV
☐ Hawker Sea Fury FB.50	6-43	6310	On loan to MLM.	–
☐ Hawker P.1040 Sea Hawk FGA.6 (FGA.4)	'118'	7474	WV828 – in false Dutch markings – on loan to TK Mar.	–

Type	Reg/Ser	C/N	PI/Notes	Status
☐ Hawker P.1067 Hunter F.51	'WV395'	41H/680269	47-410 (Denmark), E-410 (Denmark) G-9-438 – incorporates tail of F.4 c/n 41H/670841 WV395, 8001M, G-9-428	PVX
☐ Hunting-Percival P.84 Jet Provost T.3A (T.3)	XN600	PAC/W/13885	Front fuselage only.	PV
☐ La Mouette Cobra Hang Glider				RA
☐ La Mouette Hang Glider				RA
☐ Lambach HL II (R)	PH-APZ			RA
☐ Lilienthal Normal-Segelapparat (R)				PV
☐ Lockheed 683-10-19 Starfighter (F-104G)	22+90	683-7173	KE+473, DD+125	RA
☐ Lockheed 726-45-14 Neptune (P2V-7B) (P2V-7S) (SP-2H)	210	726-7263		RA
☐ Lockheed 749A-79-38 Constellation (C-121A) (VC-121A)	N749NL	749A-2604	48-0612, N9465, C-GXKR, N749VR	RAA
☐ Mignet HM-14 Pou-du-Ciel	'PH-POU'			RAX
☐ Mignet HM-14 Pou-du-Ciel	'G-AEOF'	WM.1	BAPC.22	RAX
☐ Mikoyan-Gurevich MiG-21SPS-K (MiG-21PFM)	473	94A7006		PV
☐ Monnett Monerai		NVAV-43	Incomplete.	PV
☐ Mudry CAP.328	PH-RVH	NVAV-75		RA
☐ Nederlandse Helicopter Industrie (NHI) H-3 Kolibrie	PH-NHI	3001	Contains parts of c/n 3013	PV
☐ Nieuport 28C.1 (R)	N6256	1		RA
☐ Noorduyn Harvard IIB [North American NA-77 (AT-16)]	B-73	14A-1268	43-12969, FT228	RA
☐ Noorduyn Norseman VI (C-64A) (UC-64A)	F-AZBN	774	44-70509, I-AIAK, YE-AAD, I-AIAK, EC-ANO, CN-TEE – on loan from Noorduyn Foundation.	PVC
☐ North American NA-100 Mitchell (B-25D)	2-9	100-20754	42-87261, FR199, A-22, M-9, B-9 – front fuselage only.	RA
☐ Pinguin 1 Hang Glider				RA
☐ Piper J-3C-65 Cub	NC16623	4740		PV
☐ Rienks R-1B Gyroglider			Uses parts of Koolhoven FK-43 c/n 4311 PH-ASN, 965, MX459, K-54, (PH-TCN), PH-NAU and an unidentified Schneider Grunau Baby.	RA
☐ Schleicher Ka-4 Rhönlerche II	PH-237	155		RA
☐ Schleicher Ka-4 Rhönlerche II	PH-242	160		RA
☐ Schleicher Ka-4 Rhönlerche II	PH-251	226		RA
☐ Schleicher Ka-4 Rhönlerche II	PH-375	3078/BR		PV
☐ Schleicher K.8B	PH-393	8768		PV
☐ Schneider ESG 31 Grunau Baby IIB	PH-152	6034		RA
☐ Schneider ESG 31 Grunau Baby IIB	PH-153	6035		RA
☐ Schneider ESG 31 Grunau Baby IIB	PH-170	6052		PV
☐ Sikorsky S-55D (HO4S-3)	076		Bu133777	PV
☐ Slingsby T.30A Prefect	PH-193	736		RA
☐ Slingsby T.34 Sky	PH-232	673	BGA.691, G-673	RA
☐ Slingsby T.34A-1 Sky	PH-203	821		RA
☐ Slingsby T.41 Skylark 2	PH-227	1005		RA
☐ Slingsby T.41 Skylark 2	PH-231	1009		RA
☐ Slingsby T.43 Skylark 2C	PH-249	1033		RA
☐ Sobeh H-2	PH-NFT	2001		PV
☐ Sud SA.365C-1 Dauphin	'PH-SAW'	5053	N3610B, PH-SSC, LV-APO, PH-SSC, EC-DYU	PV
☐ Stamer-Lippisch Z-12 Zögling (R)	'PH-1'			RAX
☐ Sud-Est SE.210 Caravelle III	PH-TRO	33	F-WJAM, HB-ICW – front fuselage only.	PV
☐ Supermarine 361 Spitfire LF.IXc	'H-53'	CBAF-IX-970	MJ271, H-8	PVX
☐ Supermarine 361 Spitfire LF.IXc (FSM)	'3W-K'			PVX
☐ Svenska Aeroplan Aktiebolaget (SAAB) 37 Viggen (SH 37) (AJSH 37)	Fv37901	37901	On loan from FVM, SWE	PV
☐ Svenska Aeroplan Aktiebolaget (SAAB) 91D Safir	PH-RLN	91379	At T.S. in Zwolle.	–
☐ Van Ommeren Vo-3	PH-1A6	NVAV/29-1		RA
☐ Viking Dragonfly 2	PH-SYS	288/NVAV-60	(PH-APS)	RA
☐ Westland-Sikorsky WS-51 Dragonfly HR.3	'8-1'	WA/H/62	WG752	RA
☐ Wright Flyer (R)				PV

AVOG'S CRASH MUSEUM (NET9)

Address:	Europaweg 34, 7137 HN Lievelde.
Tel:	0544-461480
Admission:	First Sunday in month 1300-1700.
Location:	About 10 km north west of Winterswijk.

This private collection of components was started in 1972 and opened in 1981. Members of the group have investigated many crash sites in the local area. The history of each recovery is told with documents, photographs and maps. The Napier Sabre engine from Hawker Typhoon IIB MN206 which was shot down and crashed near Winterswijk is displayed. The exhibition concentrates mainly on the large numbers of Allied aircraft downed in the region but parts from German types can also be seen.

BEVRIJDENDE VLEUGELS (NET10)

Address:	Sonseweg 39, 5681 BH Best.
Tel:	0499-329722
Fax:	0499-329930
Email:	wingslib@tref.nl
Admission:	Mid April-October Tuesday-Friday 1000-1700 Sunday 1200-1700.
Location:	About 3 km east of the town which is about 10 km north of Eindhoven.

On September 17th 1944 United Slates troops in Waco Hadrian gliders landed behind German lines near Veghel as part of the 'Market Fields' operation. Bitter fighting took place around the town. The museum was opened in 1984 by Prince Bernhard in a disused factory in Veghel. A move to a former Army barracks near Best took place and the new exhibition opened on July 15th 1997. The displays highlight the area around Veghel and the fighting which occurred. On show are many tanks, military vehicles, motor cycles and guns. A typical Dutch street scene with military vehicles, citizens going about their business and a large painting showing the gliders overhead was the main feature of the old display and this has been transferred to the new site. A wing section from a Waco CG-4A glider which took part in the raid has was found on a local farm.

TYPE	REG/SER	CON. NO.	PI/NOTES	STATUS
☐ Douglas DC-3A-453 Skytrooper (C-53C)	'290321'	4978	(NC30025), 43-2022, NC33315, N89SA, N894A, N32MS	PVX
☐ Douglas DC-3A-467 Skytrain (C-47B)	'2100847'	16371/33119	42-76787, F-BAIF	PVX
☐ Fieseler Fi 103A-1 (FSM)	'521121'			PVX
☐ Lockheed 583-10-20 Starfighter (TF-104G)	D-5805	583E-5805	On loan from MLM.	PV
☐ Mikoyan-Gurevich MiG-21F-13			Front fuselage only.	PV
☐ Mikoyan-Gurevich MiG-21PFM	5612	94A5612	Front fuselage only.	PV
☐ Mikoyan-Gurevich MiG-21UM	3036	516903036	In Hungarian markings.	PV
☐ Piper J-3C-65 Cub (L-4J)	'32-S'	12772	44-80476, OO-GEI, OO-AVL, PH-NLA	PVX
☐ Supermarine 361 Spitfire LF.IXc (FSM)	'P7981'			PVX
☐ Waco NZR Hadrian (CG-4A)			Wing section only.	PV
☐ Waco NZR Hadrian (CG-4A) (FSM)	319726'			PVX

CLASSIC INDEPENDENT AVIATORS (NET11)

Address:	Plesmanlaan 2, 7903 BE Hoogeveen.
Tel:	03096451
Fax:	031503122818
Email:	Klaas-doornbos@htnel.nl
Admission:	By prior permission only.
Location:	The airfield is in the north eastern suburbs of the town.

This group, which currently has three aircraft in its fleet, is now based at Hoogeveen although they may spend time at Teuge. The Argus is for sale or for exchange with an interesting project. This aircraft has been restored to World War II colours, as has the Sentinel. More aircraft are expected to join the collection.

TYPE	REG/SER	CON. NO.	PI/NOTES	STATUS
☐ De Havilland D.H.C.1 Chipmunk 22 (T.10)	G-BBMX	C1/0800	WP924	RAA
☐ Fairchild 24R46A Forwarder (UC-61A) (Argus III)	'314887'	R46-851	43-14887, HB614, G-AJPI	RAAX
☐ Stinson V-76 Sentinel (L-5)	'298248'	76-489	42-98248, N57797	RAAX

DUKE OF BRABANT AIR FORCE (NET12)

Address:	Luchthavenweg 29, 5657 EA Luchthaven Eindhoven.
Tel:	040-2525661
Fax:	040-2514850
Email:	info@dbaf.orgl
Admission:	By prior permission only.
Location:	The airport is about 6 km west of the city.

Founded on December 29th 1989 with the aim of establishing a collection of flyable historic aircraft this group is based at Eindhoven. The Mitchell arrived in Holland in May 1990 and is now painted in the colours of an aircraft flown by the Dutch 320 squadron when based at Dunsfold in Surrey in 1944. This twin engined bomber has been a regular performer at air shows around Europe over the last few years. The Beech 17 was used by the U.S Air Attaché in London between 1939 and 1941. This classic biplane was then impressed for Royal Air Force service. During this period it was based at Hendon with first the Allied Flight and later No 1316 (Dutch) Communications Flight and flown by Prince Bernhard. The Staggerwing went back to the U.S.A. at the end of the conflict. In 1950 it returned to England and then saw service in Southern Rhodesia and South Africa. In the late 1970s it was sold to the U.S.A. and restored to its original colours. The Mitchell and one of the Super Cubs have moved to Gilze-Rijen where they will be maintained and operated by the Stichting Koninklijke Luchtmacht Historische Vlucht. The Mustang divides its time between the Fighter Collection hangar at Duxford and Holland.

TYPE	REG/SER	CON. NO.	PI/NOTES	STATUS
☐ Beech D17S (YC-43)	N295BS	295	39-0139, DR628, 39-0139, NC91397, G-AMBY, VP-YIV, ZS-PWD	RAA
☐ Fokker S.11.1 Instructor (S.11)	PH-HTC	6209	E-18	RAA
☐ North American NA-108 Mitchell (B-25J) (CB-25J) (VB-25N)	'N5-149'	108-32782	44-29507, N3698G, N320SQ, PH-XXV, 'HD346' – based with KLHV at Gilze-Rijen	–
☐ North American NA-122 Mustang (P-51D)	'463864'	122-31590	44-63864, Fv26158, 2338 (Israel), 4X-AIM, SE-BKG, G-CBNM – spends some time here.	RAAX
☐ Piper PA-18-135 Super Cub (L-21B)	PH-APA	18-3814	54-2414, R-124 – based with KLHV at Gilze-Rijen.	–
☐ Piper PA-18-135 Super Cub (L-21B)	PH-KNG	18-3816	54-2416, R-126, (PH-KND)	RAA
☐ Piper PA-18-135 Super Cub (L-21B)	PH-ZCT	18-3859	54-2459, R-169	RAA

DUTCH DAKOTA ASSOCIATION (NET13)

Address:	Box 75090, 1117 ZP Schiphol.
Tel:	020-374-7700
Fax:	020-405-0221
Email:	dda@xs4all.nl
Admission:	By prior permission only.
Location:	At the airport which is about 12 km south west of Amsterdam off the E.10.

Two Transavia captains set up the association in March 1982 with the aim of preserving an example of the famous aircraft in flying condition. Two years later a former Finnish Air Force Dakota landed at Schiphol. Restored in a modified K.L.M. colour scheme of the 1950s the aircraft became a familiar sight at shows around Europe. On September 25th 1996 tragedy struck when the Dakota ditched in the Wadden See with the loss of six crew and twenty six passengers. A second DC-3 was bought in Malta in 1987. The original plan was to restore it to flying condition and then store it until 2010, the seventy fifth anniversary of the type. The association now has clearance to fly this Dakota which is painted in the colours of Martins Air Charter who flew the type on services and charter work in Holland. They have since acquired another example which is also in airworthy condition. This aircraft fitted, with a V.I.P. interior, was flown by Prince Bernhard for many years and also served as an official government transport. After retirement it was on show was on show at the old Aviodome for a long time. In 1988 a former Eastern Airlines DC-2 which had been used by the Royal Australian Air Force in World War II was brought to Schiphol after more the thirty years in store near Sydney. This airframe now rests at the Aviodrome who also have a flyable example of the classic type. In September 1995 a former South African Airways DC-4 was acquired. This airliner flew to Holland in the spring of 1996 and was joined by a second example of the four engined classic in June 1997. One is now on show at the Aviodrome and the other has been leased to a company in South Africa who operate it on charter flights.

TYPE	REG/SER	CON. NO.	PI/NOTES	STATUS
☐ Douglas DC-2-112	'PH-AJU'	1288	NC13738, A30-14, VH-CRH – on loan to Aviodrome.	–
☐ Douglas DC-3A-456 Skytrain (C-47A)	PH-PBA	19434	42-100971, PH-PBA, 'PH-TCB' – incorporates parts of C-47B c/n 9836 42-23974, FD938, 6867(South Africa), ZS-NJE, G-BVOL, 'KG391'	RAA
☐ Douglas DC-3A-456 Skytrain (C-47A)	PH-DDZ	19754	43-15288, N161, 60S-AAA, 60-AAA, N920, SU-BFY, (EI-BSJ)	RAA
☐ Douglas DC-4 Skymaster (C-54A)	PH-DDY	7488	42-107469, NC53103, PI-C102, HS-POE, 107469 (Thailand), VQ-ZEF, A2-ZEF, ZS-IPR, 6906 (South Africa), ZS-IPR – on loan to Aviodrome.	–
☐ Douglas DC-4-1009 Skymaster	ZS-AUA	42934	ZS-AUA, 6901, ZS-AUA, 6901, ZS-NUR, PH-DDS – operated on lease in South Africa until at least 2006.	RAA

DUTCH HISTORIC AIRCRAFT COMPANY (NET14)

Address:	Maraboeweg 24-26, Vliegveld Lelystad, 8218 PC Lelystad.
Tel:	0320-288333
Fax:	0320-288304
Admission:	By prior permission only.
Location:	The airfield is about 7 km south of the town off the N.302.

The group operates the Mustang from its Lelystad base. The aircraft served with the United States Army Air Force for a period and saw military use in Canada. The Mustang returned to the U.S.A. in the late 1950s and had a long civil career with many owners in several states. The flight acquired the aircraft and it arrived at Lelystad on April 6th 1994 was assembled and flew two days later. The Harvard is currently for sale and other types are being sought. The Kaydet is being rebuilt and has not yet joined the fleet.

TYPE	REG/SER	CON. NO.	PI/NOTES	STATUS
☐ Boeing-Stearman A75N1 Kaydet (PT-17)				RAC
☐ Noorduyn Harvard IIB [North American NA-77 (AT-16)]	PH-KLU	14A-1184	43-12885, FT144, B-59	RAA
☐ North American NA-122 Mustang (P-51D) (Mustang IV)	PH-SID	122-40965	44-74425, 9591 (RCAF), N6522D, (N51HB), N6522D, N11T, N11LT	RAA
☐ Piper PA-18-135 Super Cub (L-21B)	PH-TOK	18-3604	54-2404, R-114	RAA

DUTCH HISTORIC JET ASSOCIATION (NET15)

Address: Pelikaanweg 50,
8218 NT Lelystad Airport.
Tel: 035-623-2995
Admission: By prior permission only.
Location: The airfield is about7km south of the town off the N.302.

Four former French Air Force Fouga Magisters were acquired by the group. At the current time some of the aircraft are still in France being prepared for the ferry flight to the Netherlands. One has recently been sold.

TYPE	REG/SER	CON. NO.	PI/NOTES	STATUS
☐ Fouga CM.170R Magister	F-GSHG	45	45 (France), G-BSCT, G-FUGA	RAA
☐ Fouga CM.170R Magister	F-GPHU	374	374, (Chad), F-WIGZ	RAA
☐ Fouga CM.170R Magister	F-GLHF	406	406, F-WLHF	RAA

DUTCH NOSTALGIC WINGS (NET16)

Address: C/o Geert G. Smit,
Veenroede 22,
7881 XL Emmer-Compascium.
Tel: 059-135-7232
Fax: 059-135-7300
Admission: By prior permission only.
Location: At Hoogeveen Airfield which is the north eastern suburbs of the town.

Founded in February 1995 this organisation restores and flies a number of classic types. The initial base was at Lelystad and a move to Hoogeveen occurred in 1999. They were going to participate in a large flying museum but these plans did not survive. After parking their aircraft in the hangar of an overhaul company for three years they now have their own Romney Hut and clubhouse. The Spanish built Jungmann has been painted in period Dutch military markings. Some interesting aircraft are under restoration. The Sokol was clandestinely designed during the German occupation of Czechoslovakia and first flew in 1946. Two hundred and eighty seven were constructed in five versions. The former Swedish Air Force Klemm 35 has been based in Holland for many years with a number of different owners. The Ryan Recruit is resplendent in a World War II United States Army Air Corps markings. The Bestmann has recently arrived from Germany.

TYPE	REG/SER	CON. NO.	PI/NOTES	STATUS
☐ Bücker Bü 181C-1 Bestmann	F-BBMI	331396/FR-11	(Luftwaffe), VN174, F-BBMI, N9269Z	RA
☐ Construcciones A Aeronáuticas (CASA) 1.131E [Bücker Bü 131 Jüngmann]	'BI-005'	2092	E.3B-487, EC-333, G-BUVN – in false Dutch markings.	RAAX
☐ Fairchild M-62A-4 Cornell (PT-26)				RAC
☐ Klemm Kl 35D (Sk 15)	D-ECCI	1904	Fv5069, SE-BHX	RAA
☐ Mraz M-1C Sokol				RAC
☐ Piper J-3C-65 Cub (L-4H)	D-EGMG	12005	44-79709, OO-VVV, OO-VIL, G-CVIL	RAA
☐ Piper PA-18-95 Super Cub (L-18C)	D-EHCB	18-3219	53-4819, L-145 (Belgium), OL-L45 (Belgium)	RAA
☐ Ryan ST-3KR Recruit (PT-21)	'27'	1167	41-1942, N56792, G-AGYY	RAAX

F-27 FRIENDSHIP ASSOCIATION (NET17)

Address: Pelikaanweg 50,
8218 NT Lelystad Airport.
Tel: 075-6281798
Admission: By prior permission only.
Location: About 7 km south of the town off the N.302.

Formed in March 1987 the association acquired the oldest surviving Friendship in September 1995. The deal included a second example but this was later sold. The F.27 was built in late 1956 and served as a demonstrator making tours of the Middle East, India, Brazil and Africa between 1957 and 1959. The aircraft then spent over thirty years in service in Germany apart from lease periods in Luxembourg and the Netherlands. Now restored to the original Fokker prototype colours this historic airliner has been loaned to the Aviodrome. The group has now acquired the fifth example built, which was the first production aircraft, and this is kept in flying condition after a long ferry flight from Australia. An American built model is due to arrive soon.

TYPE	REG/SER	CON. NO.	PI/NOTES	STATUS
☐ Fairchild F.27	N235KT	16	N2705, N707WAN101FG	RAA
☐ Fokker F.27 Friendship 100	PH-NVF	10102	PH-NVF, D-BAKI – on loan to Aviodrome.	–
☐ Fokker F.27 Friendship 100	PH-FHF	10105	PH-FAA, EI-AKA, ZK-NAH, VH-NLS – operated by Fokker Heritage Flight.	PVA

FOKKER HERITAGE TRUST (NET18)

Address:	Harlingerweg 8, 8801 PA Fraaneker.
Admission:	By prior permission only.
Location:	With the Aviodrome at Leystad Airport which is about 7 km south of the town off the N.302.

The now defunct Fokker company owned the Spin which was on show at the old Aviodome and the D VII exhibited at the Militaire Luchtvaart Museum. The trust was set up to stop these historic machines being sold by the receivers. Now the group has moved to Lelystad and most of its aircraft are at the Aviodrome. Anthony Fokker flew his first aircraft in 1910 and developments were produced in small numbers. He moved to Germany where many outstanding fighters, including the D VII, were built by a number of companies. The D VII was used for film work in a long flying career in the U.S.A. Fokker returned to the Netherlands after the end of World War I and a new factory was completed at Schiphol in the mid-1920s. The plant produced many outstanding designs over the years. The Mach Trainer first flew in 1952 but only twenty were built. In 1955 the prototype Friendship took to the air and this achieved great success as did the later F.28 jet airliner. These were developed into the Fokker 50 and 100 and were the types in production when the company folded.

TYPE	REG/SER	CON. NO.	PI/NOTES	STATUS
☐ Fokker Spin III	PH-WEY		On loan to Aviodome.	–
☐ Fokker D VII	'266'		2528/18,N6268,N4729V – on loan to MLM.	–
☐ Fokker S.14.2 Mach Trainer (S.14.1)	PH-XIV	6289	(PH-NDY, K-1 – on loan to Aviodrome.	–
☐ Fokker F.27 Friendship 100	PH-NIV	10101	On loan to Aviodrome.	–
☐ Fokker F.28-1000 Fellowship	PH-MKH	11242	(PH-KRK), (PH-KLM) – fuselage only – on loan to Aviodrome.	–
☐ Fokker 50	PH-OSI	10688	On loan to Aviodrome.	–
☐ Fokker 100			Fuselage only – on loan to Aviodrome.	RA

GYROCOPTER AVIATION HISTORISCHE MUSEUM (NET19)

Address:	Calandseweg 2, 4341 RA Arnemuiden.
Tel:	0113-612610
Email:	information@gyrocopteraviation.nl
Admission:	Saturday-Sunday 1400-1730.
Location:	At Midden Zeeland Airport which is about 10 km east of Middelburg.

This museum of light aircraft was set up in the late 1990s. The company operates a gyrocopter training school and overhauls fixed wing types. The local branch of the homebuilt aircraft association also uses the premises to assemble completed projects. Slingsby built two Motor Tutors in the late 1940s. These comprised a new fuselage with a small engine in the nose and a fixed undercarriage married to Tutor wings and tail surfaces. The project was not developed due to certification problems. In the late 1960s a modern engine was fitted to a Slingsby Cadet. Other conversions from redundant former Air Training Corps gliders followed over the next two decades with a variety of engines. The McCulloch J-2 is a comparatively rare exhibit.

TYPE	REG/SER	CON. NO.	PI/NOTES	STATUS
☐ Construcciones Aeronáuticas (CASA) 1.131E [Bücker Bü 131 Jungmann]				PVA
☐ De Havilland D.H.82A Tiger Moth	G-ALBD	84130	T7748	PVC
☐ Fokker S.11.1 Instructor (S.11)	PH-UET	6198	(PH-BEB), OO-TIM, PH-UET, 'E-42'	RAC
☐ McCulloch J-2	N4321G	031		RA

TYPE	REG/SER	CON. NO.	PI/NOTES	STATUS
☐ Piper J-3C-65 Cub (L-4J)	PH-UCS	13228/NVAV50	45-4488	PV
☐ Piper PA-18-135 Super Cub (L-21B)		18-3821	54-2421, R-131,(PH-KND)	PV
☐ Piper PA-18-135 Super Cub (L-21B)	N83GR	18-3851	54-2451, R-161	PVA
☐ Piper PA-22-150 Tri-Pacer	G-APYW	22-4994	N7131D	RAC
☐ Slingsby T.31 Cadet III	G-BRTZ	PFA42-10545		PV

JUNCKERS COLLECTIE (NET20)

Address: Leeuwarden
Admission: By prior permission only.
Location: In the town.

This private collector has acquired seven former Polish Air Force MiG-21 front fuselages and the rear fuselage of the second Hunter F.4 used in the Netherlands. The first MiG-21PF was delivered to Poland in June 1961 and this variant was in service until late 1973. The PFM was operational in Poland from early 1966 until the mid-1990s. The MF version flew with the Air Force from December 1972 until withdrawn in January 2003.

TYPE	REG/SER	CON. NO.	PI/NOTES	STATUS
☐ Hawker P.1067 Hunter F.4	N-102		Rear fuselage only.	RA
☐ Mikoyan-Gurevich MiG-21MF	7399	967399	Front fuselage only – in Polish markings.	RA
☐ Mikoyan-Gurevich MiG-21MF-75	7555	967555	Front fuselage only – in Polish markings.	RA
☐ Mikoyan-Gurevich MiG-21PF	2411	762411	Front fuselage only – in Polish markings.	RA
☐ Mikoyan-Gurevich MiG-21PFM	5608	94A5608	Front fuselage only – in Polish markings.	RA
☐ Mikoyan-Gurevich MiG-21PFM	6603	94A6603	Front fuselage only – in Polish markings.	RA
☐ Mikoyan-Gurevich MiG-21PFM	6612	94A6612	Front fuselage only – in Polish markings.	RA
☐ Mikoyan-Gurevich MiG-21PFM	6909	94A6909	Front fuselage only – in Polish markings.	RA

KONINKLIJK NEDERLANDS LEGER EN WAPENMUSEUM (NET21)

Address: Korte Geer 1,
2611 CA Delft.
Tel: 015-215-0500
Fax: 015-215-0544
Email: info@legermuseum.nl
Admission: Monday-Friday 1000-1700; Saturday-Sunday 1200-1700.
Location: In the centre of the town.

This state war museum traces the military history of the country over the centuries. The collection includes many vehicles, uniforms, photographs and documents. The displays are informative and show many aspects of conflicts which have taken place in Holland and of those abroad which have involved Dutch forces. There is a section devoted to military aviation with the story of the various forces portrayed in detail. The V-1 was launched from a number of sites in Holland and also carried aloft under Heinkel He 111s from Gilze-Rijen and Venlo. The piloted version was designed in a short time by Otto Skorzeny and in two weeks the D.F.S. had built four variants. They were tested at Lärz in September 1944 again using a Heinkel He 111. A number of trials were carried out but problems emerged which resulted in several design changes.

TYPE	REG/SER	CON. NO.	PI/NOTES	STATUS
☐ Fieseler Fi 103A-1				PV
☐ Fieseler Fi 103A-1/Re4				PV

LUCHTOORLOGMUSEUM CRASH 1940-1945 (NET22)

Address: Gansoord 50,
2165 BD Lisserbroek.
Tel: 0297-530667
Fax: 0297-580795
Email: crash40-45@hetnet.nl
Admission: April-July Saturday 1100-1600.
Location: About 12 km south of Haarlem.

Since 1987 the Crash Research section of the Aviation Society Holland has been investigating the aerial battles over the country in World War II. Many crash sites were located and components recovered. A temporary exhibition was staged in 1991 and others followed. The museum opened in 1996 and has on view components, engines and instruments found at the digs. Photographs and documents tracing the history of each aircraft can be seen. The majority of the fuselage of a Fokker D.XXI has been reconstructed. The engine and propeller, complete with bullet holes, can be seen. Piloted by Koos Ross this fighter was shot down on May 11th 1940 when the Germans invaded the country. Large fuselage sections of a Wellington which took part in the first 'Thousand Bomber' raid have been found. There are also components from number of German types.

TYPE	REG/SER	CON. NO.	PI/NOTES	STATUS
☐ Fokker D.XXI	229	5502	Major fuselage parts.	PVD
☐ Short S.29 Stirling III	BK657		Major components.	PVD
☐ Supermarine 361 Spitfire LF.IXe	'EP947'		Contains many original parts.	PVX
☐ Vickers 406 Wellington II	W5361		Fuselage sections.	PVD

LUCHTVAART MUSEUM TEXEL (NET23)

Address:	Postweg 126, 1795 JS de Cocksdorp.
Tel:	0222-311689
Fax:	0222-311267
Email:	a.vandijk@texel.com
Admission:	Easter-September daily 1100-1700.
Location:	At Texel Airport which is about 6 km north of Den Burg.

Texel Airport was established in 1937 and the museum opened in the old motor glider hangar on May 17th 1996. The displays trace the history of aviation on the island covering four main themes – naval aviation at Texel since 1917, the history of the airport, the air war on and around the island and the story of the Georgian prisoners of war who fought against the occupying Germans in April 1945. On show are documents, photographs, uniforms, maps, models, components and engines. Hanging in the building is the homebuilt designed in 1965 by Cor Dijkman-Dulkes. The low wing aircraft was built by him and his brother incorporating parts from a Piper Cub and a glider. On September 13th 1969 the aircraft made its only flight from a beach near Wijk aan Zee to Rotterdam Airport. The unlicensed design was banned from flying by the authorities and spent almost twenty years in store before moving to Texel. Only one Fokker S.13 twin engined trainer was built in the late 1940s and the nose is on show. The type first flew at Schiphol on March 13th 1950 and did not enter production as the Dutch Air Force received a gift of twenty eight Beech 18s for the training of pilots, navigators and bomb-aimers. The aircraft was used in February 1953 to photograph the areas devastated by floods.

TYPE	REG/SER	CON. NO.	PI/NOTES	STATUS
☐ Dijkman Dulkes FB-25 Bravo	'PH-COR'			PV
☐ Ercoupe 415CD	PH-NCE	4765		PVA
☐ Fokker S.13 Universal Trainer	PH-NEI	6288	PH-NDW, D-101 – front fuselage only.	PV
☐ Lockheed 683-10-19 Starfighter (F-104G)	D-8266	683-8266	On loan from MLM.	PV

MILITAIRE LUCHTVAART MUSEUM (NET24)

Address:	P.O. Box 184, Kamp van Zeist, 3769 DL Soesterberg.
Tel:	0346-356000
Fax:	0346-356020
Email:	info@mlm.af.dnet.mindef.nl
Admission:	Tuesday- Friday 1000-1630 Sunday 1200-1630.
Location:	About 10 km north east of Utrecht just south of the A.28.

The Netherlands Air Force Museum opened in 1968 in a hangar at Soesterberg Air Force Base. Initially ten aircraft were on show and the displays traced the history and traditions of the service. Operational requirements forced the exhibition to close and in 1980 two large halls at a nearby army base were allocated to the museum which opened the following year. The present name 'The Military Aviation Museum' was adopted to cover the flying aspects of the Air Force, the Naval Air Service and operations in the former Dutch East Indies. The museum now has responsibility for most of the aircraft preserved on military bases in the country and in a number of technical schools. Military flying in the country started in 1913 at Soesterberg when an aviation division of the Army was established. Two aircraft built in Holland by Marinus van Meel and three Farman HF-22s purchased in France were used. The Farman replica on show was built as an HF-22 by Lips Autotron in 1978 and has now been modified to HF-20 configuration. The Fokker D VII was shipped to the U.S.A. after World War I, bought by the Fokker company in the 1980s and loaned to the museum. The replica D.XXI was built in 1988 and the G.1 constructed for use in a television programme. During World War II a Dutch flying School was set up in the U.S.A. and among the types used was the Lockheed 12. The museum obtained one of this fleet from the Egeskov Museum in Denmark. The Mitchell was operated by the Netherlands East Indies Air Force in 1945 and taken over by the Indonesian Air Force after the country gained its independence. Prince Bernhard obtained the bomber for the museum in 1970. At the end of World War II large numbers of British aircraft were supplied to re-establish the Dutch Air Force. On show are the first Spitfire delivered to Holland, a Tiger Moth and a Dragon Rapide. In the jet era Meteors and Hunters, some built under licence, were used before American fighters began to dominate. The naval aviation section has been expanded in recent years. The Dornier Do 24T-3, on loan from the Royal Air Force Museum, has been painted in the colours of a Do 24K which made many flights into the interior of New Guinea in 1943 to help local resistance fighters in their struggle against the Japanese occupiers. The Catalina has been restored at Valkenburg and is back in store. The Americans used Soesterberg for many years and an exhibition of types flown by the U.S.A.F. is being set up. In addition to the aircraft there are informative associated displays.

TYPE	REG/SER	CON. NO.	PI/NOTES	STATUS
☐ Agusta-Bell 204B	225	3023	With parts from 220.	PV
☐ Auster E AOP.3	'R-5'	350	MZ236, R-11, 8A-13, PH-NGH, 'R-55'	RA
☐ Beech D18S (B18S) (AT-7)	'G-10'	A-472	43-33270, PH-UDT	RAX
☐ Bölkow BO 105C	'B-00'	S-34	G-AZTI – part fuselage.	RAX
☐ Bölkow BO 105CB-4	B-37	S-237		PV
☐ Bölkow BO 105CB-4	B-42	S-242	At Gilze-Rijen AFB.	–
☐ Brewster B.239 Buffalo (F2A-1) (FSM)				RAC
☐ Canadair CL-226 Freedom Fighter (NF-5A) [Northrop N-156A]	'K-3066'	3003	K-3003 – at Gilze-Rijen AFB.	–
☐ Canadair CL-226 Freedom Fighter (NF-5A) [Northrop N-156A]	K-3011	3011		RA
☐ Canadair CL-226 Freedom Fighter (NF-5A) [Northrop N-156A]	K-3020	3020	On loan to NLC. Hoofddorp.	–
☐ Canadair CL-226 Freedom Fighter (NF-5A) [Northrop N-156A]	K-3029	3029	On loan to Twenthe AFB.	–
☐ Canadair CL-226 Freedom Fighter (NF-5A) [Northrop N-156A]	K-3034	3034	On loan to Gilze Rijen AFB.	–
☐ Canadair CL-226 Freedom Fighter (NF-5A) [Northrop N-156A]	K-3045	3045	At Haarlem HS.	RA
☐ Canadair CL-226 Freedom Fighter (NF-5A) [Northrop N-156A]	K-3068	3068	On loan to Eindhoven AFB.	–
☐ Canadair CL-226 Freedom Fighter (NF-5B) [Northrop N-156B]	K-4011	4011	Wings from c/n 4008 K-4008.	PV
☐ Canadair CL-226 Freedom Fighter (NF-5B) [Northrop N-156B]	K-4012	4012	At Zwolle.	RA
☐ Canadair CL-226 Freedom Fighter (NF-5B) [Northrop N-156B]	K-4028	4028		RA
☐ Consolidated 28-5A Catalina (PBY-5A)	16-212	1679	Bu48317, N1495V	RA
☐ Consolidated 28-5A Catalina (PBY-5A)	16-212	1679	Bu48317, N1495V – restored at Valkenburg	RAC
☐ Convair 8-10 Delta Dagger (F-102A)	'61032'		56-1052, 61052 (Greece)	PVX
☐ De Havilland D.H.82A Tiger Moth	A-10	86587	PG690, A-10, PH-UFC	RA
☐ De Havilland D.H.89A Dragon Rapide (D.H.89B Dominie I)	V-3	6740	NF869, PH-RAE, V-3, PH-VNC, V-3, PH-TGC, PH-OTA	PV
☐ De Havilland D.H.C.2 Beaver (L-20A)	S-6	959	55-4582	RA
☐ De Havilland D.H.C.2 Beaver (L-20A)	PH-DHC	965	55-4585, S-9, G-BUVF – on loan to SKHHV.	–
☐ Dornier Do 24T-3	'X-24'	5342	EC-DAF, 65-6 (Spain), HD.5-1 (Spain), HR.5-1 (Spain), N99225, HR.5-1 – on loan from R.A.F. Museum , England.	PVX
☐ Douglas DC-3A-456 Skytrain (C-47A)	'X-5'	20118	43-15652, T-AN (Norway), BW-N (Norway), BW-T (Norway), 68-688 (Denmark), K-688 (Denmark), 'ZU-5'	PVX
☐ Farman HF-20 (R)	'LA-2'		Was painted as HF-22 'LA-16' – on loan from Autotron.	PVX
☐ Fieseler Fi 103A-1			On loan from R.A.F. Museum, England.	PV
☐ Fokker C.X (FSM)				RAC
☐ Fokker C.11W				RAD
☐ Fokker D VII	'266'	2523	436/18, N6268, N4729V – on loan from FHT.	PVX
☐ Fokker D.XXI (FSM)	'221'			PVX
☐ Fokker T-4A				RAD
☐ Fokker T-5				RAC
☐ Fokker F.27 Troopship 300M	C-8	10158	PH-FBW, C-8, PH-FSC – on loan to Eindhoven AFB.	–
☐ Fokker F.27 Troopship 300M	C-10	10160	PH-FBY	PV
☐ Fokker G.1A (FSM)	'330'			PVX
☐ Fokker S.11.1 Instructor (S.11)	E-22	6213		PV
☐ Fokker S.11.1 Instructor (S.11)	PH-SII	6215	E-24 – on loan to SKLHV.	–
☐ Fokker S.14.1 Mach Trainer	L-11	7356		PV
☐ Fokker S.14.1 Mach Trainer	PH-SIY	7362	L-17 – on loan to SKLHV.	–
☐ Fouga CM.170R Magister			(Belgium) – due soon.	–
☐ General Dynamics 401 Fighting Falcon (F-16A)	J-213	6D-2	78-0213 – at Breda.	RA
☐ General Dynamics 401 Fighting Falcon (F-16A)	J-215	6D-4	78-0215	PV
☐ General Dynamics 401 Fighting Falcon (F-16A)	J-219	6D-8	78-0219 – on loan to Leeuwarden AFB.	–
☐ General Dynamics 401 Fighting Falcon (F-16A)	J-221	6D-10	78-0221- at Haarlem HS.	–
☐ General Dynamics 401 Fighting Falcon (F-16A)	J-222	6D-11	78-0222 – on loan to Volkel AFB.	–
☐ General Dynamics 401 Fighting Falcon (F-16A)	J-226	6D-15	78-0226 – at Delft Tech. Univ.	RA
☐ General Dynamics 401 Fighting Falcon (F-16A)	J-228	6D-17	78-0228 – on loan to Leeuwarden AFB.	–
☐ General Dynamics 401 Fighting Falcon (F-16A)	'80229'	6D-18	78-0229, J-229 – on loan to Volkel AFB.	–

Type	Reg	c/n	PI/Notes	Status
☐ General Dynamics 401 Fighting Falcon (F-16A)	J-230	6D-19	78-0230,	RA
☐ General Dynamics 401 Fighting Falcon (F-16A)	J-236	6D-25	78-0236 – On loan to NLC. Hoofddorp.	–
☐ General Dynamics 401 Fighting Falcon (F-16A)	J-238	6D-27	78-0238 – on loan Eindhoven AFB.	–
☐ General Dynamics 401 Fighting Falcon (F-16A)	J-240	6D-29	78-0240 – on loan to Volkel AFB.	–
☐ General Dynamics 401 Fighting Falcon (F-16A)	'J-315'	6D-30	78-0241, J-241 – At Tilburg.	–
☐ General Dynamics 401 Fighting Falcon (F-16A)	J-245	6D-34	78-0245 – on loan to Leeuwarden AFB.	–
☐ General Dynamics 401 Fighting Falcon (F-16A)	J-246	6D-35	78-0246 – on loan to Woensdrecht AFB.	–
☐ General Dynamics 401 Fighting Falcon (F-16A)	J-249	6D-38	78-0249 – At Maastricht.	–
☐ General Dynamics 401 Fighting Falcon (F-16A)	J-250	6D-39	78-0250 – on loan to Woensdrecht AFB.	–
☐ General Dynamics 401 Fighting Falcon (F-16B)	J-259	6E-1	78-0259 – on loan to Woensdrecht AFB.	–
☐ General Dynamics 401 Fighting Falcon (F-16B)	J-260	6E-2	78-0260 – on loan to Woensdrecht AFB.	–
☐ General Dynamics 401 Fighting Falcon (F-16B)	J-263	6E-5	78-0263	RA
☐ Gloster Meteor F.4	I-69		VZ409	PV
☐ Gloster Meteor T.7	I-19		WH233	RA
☐ Gloster Meteor T.7	I-320		VW417 – on loan to Leeuwarden AFB.	–
☐ Gloster Meteor F.8	'I-147'	6466	I-187	RA
☐ Gloster Meteor F.8	I-189	6468		RA
☐ Grumman G-89 Tracker (S2F-1) (S-2N) (US-2N)	160	721	Bu148282	PV
☐ Hawker Sea Fury FB.50	'G-18'		Front fuselage only.	RAX
☐ Hawker Sea Fury FB.50	6-43	6310	On loan from Aviodome.	PV
☐ Hawker P.1040 Sea Hawk FB.5 (FB.3)	'131'	6021	WM983, A2511 – with parts of XE489.	PVX
☐ Hawker P.1067 Hunter F.4	N-122	8622		RA
☐ Hawker P.1067 Hunter F.4	N-138	8638	On loan to Leeuwarden AFB.	–
☐ Hawker P.1067 Hunter F.4	N-144	8644		PV
☐ Hawker P.1099 Hunter F.6	N-226	8858	At Bosbad Hoeven.	PV
☐ Hawker P.1099 Hunter F.6	N-258	8934		RA
☐ Hawker P.1101 Hunter T.7	N-305	41H/693457		RA
☐ Hiller UH12C Raven (H-23C) (OH-23C)	O-36	937	57-6521	PV
☐ Koolhoven FK.51 (R)			Built by Koolhoven Foundation.	RAC
☐ Lockheed 12-26 Electra Junior	'L2-100'	1306	L2-38, PJ-AKD, BX238, T-2, SE-BXR, OH-ETA, LN-BFS, OY-AOV, L2-38	PVX
☐ Lockheed 580 (T-33A)	M-50	580-5679	51-4384 – on loan to NLC Hoofddorp.	–
☐ Lockheed 580 (T-33A)	M-5	580-6812	51-9028	RA
☐ Lockheed 580 (T-33A)	'M-51'	580-7150	51-17411, M-54 – on loan to Woensdrecht AFB.	–
☐ Lockheed 583-10-20 Starfighter (TF-104G)	D-5803	583E-5803		RA
☐ Lockheed 583-10-20 Starfighter (TF-104G)	D-5804	583E-5804	On loan to Motortechnica, GER.	–
☐ Lockheed 583-10-20 Starfighter (TF-104G)	D-5805	583E-5805	On loan to Bev V.	–
☐ Lockheed 583-10-20 Starfighter (TF-104G)	D-5806	583E-5806		RA
☐ Lockheed 583-10-20 Starfighter (TF-104G)	D-5810	583E-5810		RA
☐ Lockheed 683-10-19 Starfighter (F-104G)	D-8022	683-8022		PV
☐ Lockheed 683-10-19 Starfighter (F-104G)	D-8051	683-8051	On loan to Leeuwarden AFB.	–
☐ Lockheed 683-10-19 Starfighter (F-104G)	D-8053	683-8053	At Nieuw Milligan CRC.	RA
☐ Lockheed 683-10-19 Starfighter (F-104G)	D-8061	683-8061		RA
☐ Lockheed 683-10-19 Starfighter (F-104G)	D-8062	683-8062		RA
☐ Lockheed 683-10-19 Starfighter (F-104G)	D-8063	683-8063	On loan to Volkel AFB.	–
☐ Lockheed 683-10-19 Starfighter (F-104G)	D-8098	683-8098	On loan to Deelen AFB Museum.	–
☐ Lockheed 683-10-19 Starfighter (F-104G)	D-8114	683-8114	At Delft Tech. Univ.	RA
☐ Lockheed 683-10-19 Starfighter (F-104G)	D-8244	683-8244		RA
☐ Lockheed 683-10-19 Starfighter (F-104G)	D-8245	683-8245	At Soesterberg AFB.	PV
☐ Lockheed 683-10-19 Starfighter (F-104G)	D-8256	683-8256	On loan to Volkel AFB.	–
☐ Lockheed 683-10-19 Starfighter (F-104G)	D-8257	683-8257	Front fuselage only.	RA
☐ Lockheed 683-10-19 Starfighter (F-104G)	D-8259	683-8259	On loan to NLC Hoofddorp.	–
☐ Lockheed 683-10-19 Starfighter (F-104G)	D-8266	683-8266	On loan to LM Texel.	–
☐ Lockheed 683-10-19 Starfighter (F-104G)	D-8268	683-8268	At Zwolle.	RA
☐ Lockheed 683-10-19 Starfighter (F-104G)	D-8279	683-8279	On loan to Volkel AFB.	–
☐ Lockheed 683-10-19 Starfighter (F-104G)	D-8282	683-8282	On gate at Budel AFB.	RA
☐ Lockheed 683-10-19 Starfighter (F-104G)	D-8300	683-8300	At Uithuizen.	RA
☐ Lockheed 683-10-19 Starfighter (F-104G)	D-8312	683-8312	On loan to Volkel AFB.	–
☐ Lockheed 683-10-19 Starfighter (F-104G)	D-8318	683-8318		RA
☐ Lockheed 683-10-19 Starfighter (F-104G)	D-8338	683-8338	On loan to Twenthe AFB.	–
☐ Lockheed 726-45-18 Neptune (P2V-7B) (P2V-7S) (SP-2H)	218	726-7157	Bu146438 – front fuselage only.	RA
☐ Lockheed 726-45-18 Neptune (P2V-7B) (P2V-7S) (SP-2H)	201	726-7241		PV
☐ McDonnell M.199-1A Eagle (F-15A)	'77-0132'	A044	74-0083	PVX
☐ McDonnell M.98HO Phantom II (F-4E)			(USAF), (Greece) – due soon.	–
☐ Mikoyan-Gurevich MiG-21PFM	'47'	940MS13	21 (Soviet)	PVX
☐ Mikoyan-Gurevich MiG-21SPS (MiG-21PFM)	'804'	94A5511	919 (DDR), 22+40 – at De Peel.	RAX
☐ Noorduyn Harvard IIB [North American NA-77 (AT-16)]	PH-LSK	14-641	42-12394, FE907, B-64, 12-6, B-64, PH-FAR, '219'- with parts from c/n 14A-1161 43-12892, FT151, B-5 – on loan to SKLHV.	–

Type	Reg	c/n	Notes	Status
☐ Noorduyn Harvard IIB [North American NA-77 (AT-16)]	B-177	14-733	42-12486, FE999 – on loan to Woensdrecht AFB.	–
☐ Noorduyn Harvard IIB [North American NA-77 (AT-16)]	'A-50'	14-764	42-12517, FH130, 'PH-AFS' – on loan to NLC Hoofddorp.	–
☐ Noorduyn Harvard IIB [North American NA-77 (AT-16)]	B-175	14-765	42-12518, FH131 – bare fuselage only	RA
☐ Noorduyn Harvard IIB [North American NA-77 (AT-16)]	PH-TBR	14A-808	43-12509, FS668, B-182 – on loan to SKLHV.	–
☐ Noorduyn Harvard IIB [North American NA-77 (AT-16)]	PH-MLM	14A-1444	43-13145, FT404, B-71, '218', B-71 – on loan to SKLHV.	–
☐ Noorduyn Harvard IIB [North American NA-77 (AT-16)]	'099'	14A-1459	43-13160, FT419, B-103	PVX
☐ North American NA-108 Mitchell (B-25J)	M-464	108-37333	44-31258, N5-264	PV
☐ North American NA-111 Mustang (P-51K)	'H-307'	111-30258	44-12125 – composite with parts from a P-51D.	PVX
☐ North American NA-191 Sabre (F-86F)	'52-5385'	191-876	52-5180, 5307 (Portugal) – on loan from NASM, USA.	RAX
☐ North American NA-213 Sabre (F-86K)	Q-244	213-14	54-1244 – front fuselage only	RA
☐ North American NA-213 Sabre (F-86K)	Q-283	213-53	54-1283 – on loan to Twenthe AFB.	–
☐ North American NA-222 Sabre (F-86K)	'Q-305'	222-33	53-8305, MM53-8305	PVX
☐ North American NA-223 Super Sabre (F-100D)	'41871'	223-145	54-2265	PVX
☐ Piper PA-18-95 Super Cub (L-18C)	R-87	18-3185	53-4785, OL-111 (Belgium),	RA
☐ Raytheon Hawkraket Hang Glider				RA
☐ Republic F-84E Thunderjet	K-8		51-9591 – control systems only.	PV
☐ Republic F-84F Thunderstreak	P-109		52-7140 – front fuselage only.	PV
☐ Republic F-84F Thunderstreak	P-134		52-7185 – on loan to NLC Hoofddorp.	–
☐ Republic F-84F Thunderstreak	P-170		53-6673 – on loan to Woensdrecht AFB.	–
☐ Republic F-84F Thunderstreak	P-171		53-6687 – on loan to Twenthe AFB.	–
☐ Republic F-84F Thunderstreak	P-191		53-6916 – at Gilze-Rijen AFB.	–
☐ Republic F-84F Thunderstreak	P-230		Front fuselage only.	RA
☐ Republic F-84F Thunderstreak	P-226		53-6612	PV
☐ Republic F-84F Thunderstreak	P-231		53-6742 – on loan to Eindhoven AFB.	–
☐ Republic F-84F Thunderstreak	P-248		53-6584	RA
☐ Republic F-84F Thunderstreak	P-254		53-6600 – on loan to NLC Hoofddorp.	–
☐ Republic F-84F Thunderstreak	P-263		53-6780 – on loan to Autotron.	–
☐ Republic F-84F Thunderstreak	P-277		53-6924 – on loan to Volkel AFB.	
☐ Republic RF-84F Thunderflash	P-5		51-11253, P-5, 111253 (Greece)	RA
☐ Republic RF-84F Thunderflash	FR-31		53-7644, EA+311 – in Belgian markings.	RA
☐ Republic F-84G Thunderjet	K-85		51-10178 – on loan to Eindhoven AFB.	–
☐ Republic F-84G Thunderjet	'K-40'		51-10806, K-171 – may contain parts of 51-9722, K-40.	PVX
☐ Sikorsky S-58 Seahorse (HUS-1N) (UH-34J)	134	581597	Bu150729, N266	PV
☐ Sud-Est SE.3130 Alouette II	'H-4'	1753	A-29 (Belgium)	PVX
☐ Sud-Est SE.3160 Alouette III	A-293	1293	On loan to NLC Hoofddorp.	–
☐ Sud-Est SE.3160 Alouette III	A-319	1319		RA
☐ Sud-Est SE.3160 Alouette III	H-20	1320		PV
☐ Sud-Est SE.3160 Alouette III	A-343	1343	On loan to Woensdrecht AFB.	–
☐ Sud-Est SE.3160 Alouette III	A-391	1391	At base gate.	RA
☐ Sud-Est SE.3160 Alouette III	A-465	1465		RA
☐ Sukhoi Su-20R	'56'	72410	(Egypt), 98+62 – in false Soviet markings – on loan to Leeuwarden AFB.	–
☐ Supermarine 361 Spitfire LF.IXc	H-1	CBAF-IX-907	MJ143	PV
☐ Supermarine 361 Spitfire LF.IXc (FSM)	'H-27'		'PT987' – on loan to SKLHV.	–
☐ Supermarine 361 Spitfire LF.IXc (FSM)	'MJ964'		On loan to Leeuwarden AFB.	–
☐ Supermarine 361 Spitfire LF.IXc (FSM)	'MK???'			RAX
☐ Supermarine 361 Spitfire LF.IXc (FSM)	'H-15/MK959'		On loan to Eindhoven AFB.	–
☐ Supermarine 361 Spitfire LF.IXc (FSM)	'MJ881'			PVX
☐ Westland-Sikorsky WS-51 Dragonfly HR.3	'8-1'	WA/H/62	WG752 – on loan from Aviodrome.	PVX

MUSEUM VLIEGBASIS DEELEN (NET25)

Address:	Hoenderloseweg 10, Building 20, 6816 SW Arnhem/Deelen.
Tel:	026-334-1625
Fax:	06-2297-3911
Email:	info@museumvlbdeelen.nl
Admission:	Saturday-Sunday 1100-1700.
Location:	About 8 km north of Arnhem on N.304.

The airfield was constructed for the Germans during their occupation of the country. During the conflict a number of fighter and bomber squadrons were in residence. The site was handed over to the Dutch Air Force after the end of hostilities. 298 Squadron was formed at Soesterberg in March 1950 and was equipped with Auster IIIs. The unit moved to Deelen and their first helicopters, Hiller H-23s, arrived in 1955. Later Alouette IIIs were flown and the unit moved back to Soesterberg in 1968. For a period in the late 1950s 304 Squadron operating RF-84F Thunderflashes was based at the field. Deelen closed as an operational military site on January 1st 1996. This museum traces the history of the airfield as well as concentrating on crash sites of World War II. The remains of a Spitfire, which was downed in 1944, have been put on show.

TYPE	REG/SER	CON. NO.	PI/NOTES	STATUS
☐ Auster E AOP.3	PH-NIN		NX537, R-7	RAC
☐ Lockheed 683-10-19 Starfighter (F-104G)	D-8098	683-8098	On loan from MLM.	PV
☐ Lockheed 683-10-19 Starfighter (F-104G) (Scale R)				PVX
☐ Mikoyan-Gurevich MiG-21PF	0812	760812	Front fuselage only – in Czech markings	PV
☐ Short S.29 Stirling IV	LF545		Upper rear fuselage only.	PVD
☐ Sud-Est SE.3130 Alouette II (AH.2)	PH-NSW	1185	F-WIPG, XN132, G-BIUV	PV
☐ Supermarine 361 Spitfire LF.IXe	MJ874		Front fuselage only.	PVD

MUSEUM VOOR VLUCHTSIMULATIE (NET26)

Address:	Half Elfje, 5711 ES Someren.
Tel:	0493-493387
Email:	museum@voorvluchtsimulatie.nl
Admission:	Sunday 1000-1300.
Location:	In the north western part of the town which is about 16 km south east of Eindhoven.

This privately run museum aims to trace the development of flight simulators from World War II Link Trainers up to modern computer assisted models. The majority have been restored to working order. The history of each type is shown and this includes the commercial use of the model. There is also a display of photographs.

NATIONAAL AUTOMOBIEL MUSEUM (NET27)

Address:	Steurweg 8, 4941 VR Raamsdonksveer.
Tel:	0162-585400
Fax:	0162-585554
Email:	info@louwmancollection.nl
Admission:	April-September Tuesday-Saturday 1000-1700; Sunday 1100-1700.
Location:	About 14 km north of Breda off the A.27 just south of the River Maas.

The present owners bought the oldest car museum in the country in 1969 and thirteen years later moved the collection from Leidschendam near Den Haag. A superb range of cars, carriages and commercial vehicles may be seen. Twelve Koolhooven FK.43s were built in the 1930s and between 1946 and 1948 Fokker constructed a further eight. The sole survivor, which is on show in the museum, is from the post-war batch. This aircraft was active from 1947 until 1950 and has been part of the collection for many years. The Blériot, which contains some original parts, was obtained from England in 1986. One of the owners of the museum is an active balloonist and a special exhibition of gondolas used in trans-Atlantic flights can be seen.

TYPE	REG/SER	CON. NO.	PI/NOTES	STATUS
☐ Blériot XI (R)				PV
☐ Cameron A-210 Hot Air Balloon	PH-LEP	1272		RA
☐ Cameron DP-70 Hot Air Airship	PH-OHO	1683		RA
☐ Cameron N-90 Hot Air Balloon	PH-EVH	1385		RAA
☐ Cameron N-105 Hot Air Balloon	PH-OOH	1682		RA
☐ Cameron N-120 Hot Air Balloon	PH-EVE	3903		RAA
☐ Cameron R-225 Hot Air Balloon	PH-EIS	1230		RA
☐ Koolhoven FK.43	PH-NAK	6168		PV

NATIONAAL BEVRIJDINGSMUSEUM 1944-1945 (NET28)

Address:	Wylerbaan 4, 6560 AC Groesbeek.
Tel:	024-3974004
Fax:	024-3976694
Email:	info@bevrijdingsmuseum.nl
Admission:	Monday-Saturday 1000-1700; Sunday 1200-1700.
Location:	Just north east of the town which is about 8 km south east of Nijmejen.

The liberation of the country is commemorated in the displays at this museum. Operation 'Market Garden' features prominently in the exhibition. An original front fuselage of a Waco Hadrian glider can be seen along with many photographs, uniforms, documents and items of memorabilia.

TYPE	REG/SER	CON. NO.	PI/NOTES	STATUS
☐ Waco NZR Hadrian (CG-4A)			Front fuselage only.	PV

NATIONAAL LUCHTVAART COLLEGE COLLECTIE (NET29)

Address:	Opaallan 25, 2132 XV Hoofddorp.
Tel:	023-569-3691
Fax:	023-5693699
Email:	info@nlctraining.nl
Admission:	By prior permission only.
Location:	About 12 km south west of Amsterdam.

The college incorporates the former Anthony Fokker School, which closed in the early 1990s. The majority of the aircraft used at Den Haag moved to this new location. The Militaire Luchvaart Museum has recently taken on charge the military aircraft loaned to the school by the Air Force. The other airframes are also listed.

TYPE	REG/SER	CON. NO.	PI/NOTES	STATUS
☐ Canadair CL-226 Freedom Fighter (NF-5A) [Northrop N-156A]	K-3020	3020	On loan from MLM.	RA
☐ Cessna 150E	'PH-SKS'	15060797	N6097T, PH-ALB	RAX
☐ General Dynamics 401 Fighting Falcon (F-16A)	J-236	6D-25	On loan from MLM.	RA
☐ Grumman G-89 Tracker (S2F-1) (S-2N) (US-2N)	151	712	Bu147641	RA
☐ Handley Page H.P.137 Jetstream 1	TF-ODM	202	G-AWSE, N1039S, N14RJ, N114CP	RA
☐ Handley Page H.P.137 Jetstream 1	TF-ODI	210	G-AWYM, N62BS, N2MG, N2MQ – front fuselage only.	RA
☐ Handley Page H.P.137 Jetstream 1	PH-HAN	214	G-AXHB, N17RJ, TF-ODN	RA
☐ Lockheed 580 (T-33A)	M-50	580-5679	51-4384 – on loan from MLM.	RA
☐ Lockheed 683-10-19 Starfighter (F-104G)	D-8259	683-8259	On loan from MLM.	RA
☐ Noorduyn Harvard IIB [North American NA-77 (AT-16)]	'A-50'	14-764	42-12517, FH130, B-165, 'PH-AFS' – on loan from MLM.	RA
☐ Republic F-84F Thunderstreak	P-134		52-7185 – on loan from MLM.	RA
☐ Republic F-84F Thunderstreak	P-254		53-6600 – on loan from MLM.	RA
☐ Robin HR.200/100 Club	PH-DIS	47	D-EEAX, (PH-RLM)	RA
☐ Sud-Est SE.3160 Alouette III	A-293	1293	On loan from MLM.	RA
☐ Svenska Aeroplan Aktiebolaget (SAAB) 91D Safir	'PH-AFS'	91372	PH-RLE	RAX

NEDERLANDS NATIONAAL OORLOGS EN VERZETSMUSEUM (NET30)

Address:	Museumpark 1, 5825 AM Overloon.
Tel:	0478-641820
Email:	info@oorlogsmuseum.nl
Admission:	June-August daily 0930-1800; September-May daily 1000-1700.
Location:	In a large park about 30 km south of Nijmegen and 6 km north of Venray.

Overloon was the location of one of the largest tank battles in World War II and this took place in September/October 1944. The Dutch National War and Resistance Museum opened in 1946 with many remnants of the 1944 engagement still in place. New buildings have recently been constructed and one will portray this battle in detail. A replica of part of a concentration camp which was nearby has been assembled. A display tracing the liberation of Holland can now be seen. This shows in chronological order how the German forces were driven back. The museum occupies a thirty five acre wooded park with over eighty exhibits on view. The Marshall Museum, which contained many military vehicles, has combined with this museum and its collection has moved to Overloon. The Mitchell took part in over one hundred missions with 320 Squadron flying from Dunsfold in Surrey. The Spitfire was exchanged in 1987 for a PR.XI which had been on show for many years. The aircraft is painted in the colours of a 322 Squadron example. This unit operated Spitfires against the V-1 attacks on England during World War II so it is appropriate that an example of the German weapon can be seen in this delightful setting. The remains were found locally and restored to original condition. Over two hundred Harvards were used by the Dutch Air Force for advanced training between 1947 and 1968. The museum has recently acquired the collection from the International 1939-1945 Museum at Uithuizen which closed several years ago. The only complete aircraft there was the former East German MiG-21. A number of military vehicles and weapons from several countries have made the move south. At Uithuizen there was a superb display of radio equipment including that from the clandestine 'Radio Oranje'. The aviation section included models and many components from crashed aircraft. Among the engines was a Vulture from Scampton based 83 Squadron Avro Manchester R5779 which was shot down near Smilde on March 9th 1942 after a raid on Essen.

TYPE	REG/SER	CON. NO.	PI/NOTES	STATUS
☐ Fieseler Fi 103A-1				PV
☐ Mikoyan-Gurevich MiG-21SPS (MiG-21PFM)	22+39	94A5510	898 (DDR)	PV
☐ Noorduyn Harvard IIB [North American NA-77 (AT-16)]	'12964'	14-610	42-12363, FE876, B-199 composite with parts of c/n 14A-807 43-12508, FS667, B-179 and c/n 14A-1263 43-12964, FT223	PVX
☐ North American NA-87 Mitchell (B-25D)	FR193	87-8957	41-30792, FR193, A-17, M-6, B-6, 2-6	PV
☐ Supermarine 379 Spitfire F.XIVc	NH649	6S.672268	NH649, HS649, (India) – may be ex TP285.	PV

NOORDUYN FOUNDATION (NET31)

Address:	Pelikaanweg 50, 8218 NT Lelystad Airport.
Tel:	0320-289840 (Aviodrome)
Fax:	0320-289841 (Aviodrome)
Email:	info@aviodrome.nl
Admission:	Contact the Aviodrome.
Location:	About 7 km south of the town off the N.302.

The foundation obtained an example of the Norseman from the Salis Collection in France. The aircraft had not flown for some time and is now being restored at the Aviodrome. It is being be rebuilt to airworthy standards with the possibility it might take to the air again. Robert Noorduyn was born in Holland and he worked for Armstrong-Whitworth and Sopwith in England before emigrating to the U.S.A. in 1920. There he was employed by Anthony Fokker and later by the Bellanca company. In the early 1930s he moved to Canada and set up his own firm. The Norseman first flew in 1935 and was designed for bush flying. Over seven hundred and sixty were built for the United States military and another fifty were constructed for civilian use after World War II. The example in the collection has an interesting history. After its military days were over it saw civilian use in Italy, Yemen, Spain and Morocco before moving to La Ferté Alais. Another of the type was converted into a Latécoère replica but this one remained untouched.

TYPE	REG/SER	CON. NO.	PI/NOTES	STATUS
☐ Noorduyn Norseman VI (C-64A) (UC-64A)	F-AZBN	774	44-70509, I-AIAK, YE-AAD, I-AIAK, EC-ANO, CN-TEE – on loan to Aviodrome.	–

STEINADLER SEGELFLUG (NET32)

Address:	Randenbroekerweg 9, 3816 BD Amersfoort.
Tel:	033-4720431
Admission:	By prior permission only.
Location:	At a store in Zeewolde.

This collection contains several Austrian designed gliders constructed at the Oberlerchner factory. The two seat Mg 19 first flew in the mid-1950s and took part in the 1956 World Gliding championships at St Yan in France. The single seat high performance Mg 23 flew in prototype form in June 1955, entered production seven years later and around one hundred were built. The classic Bergfalke two seater was also acquired in Austria. The Ifjusag originates from Hungary and only a few were exported. Designed by Ferenc Zsebo the prototype flew in 1953 and the Z.03b version appeared four years later. About thirty of the latter type were built in the late 1950s at Dunarkeszi and served with gliding clubs in the country for many years. The Grasshopper primary gave many British military cadets their first experience of flying. The fuselage was based on the German SG-38 to which the wings and tail of a T.7 Cadet were fitted. The first one flew in the early 1950s. The Piper Cub was operated by the National Flying School at Ypenburg from 1947 until 1976.

TYPE	REG/SER	CON. NO.	PI/NOTES	STATUS
☐ Jacobs Olympia-Meise 51	OE-0477	17		RA
☐ Musger Mg 19 Steinadler	OE-0310	014		RA
☐ Musger Mg 19b Steinadler	OE-0345	017		RAA
☐ Musger Mg 23	OE-0407	006		RAC
☐ Musger Mg 23SL	OE-0752	24		RA
☐ Piper J-3C-65 Cub (L-4J)	PH-UCH	13248	45-4508	RAD
☐ Scheibe 138 Specht	OE-5328	64		RA
☐ Scheibe Bergfalke II	OE-0266	003		RA
☐ Scheibe Bergfalke II/55	OE-0520	305		RA
☐ Schneider ESG 31 Grunau Baby IIB	OE-5046	3366	OE-0092	RA
☐ Slingsby T.38 Grasshopper TX.1	XP462	1261		RA
☐ Szybowcowy Zaklad Doswiadczalny S.Z.D.9bis Bocian 1D	OE-0540	P-387		RA
☐ Szybowcowy Zaklad Doswiadczalny S.Z.D.22C Mucha Standard	OE-0532	F-598		RA
☐ Zsebo-Bohn Z.03b Ifjusag	OE-0372	103		RA

STICHTING HISTORISCHE VLIEGTUIGEN ZEELAND (NET33)

Address: Calandweg 2E,
4341 RA Arnemuden.
Tel: 0113-614370
Admission: By prior permission only.
Location: At Midden Zeeland airfield which is about 9 km west of Middelburg.

Built on reclaimed land, Midden Zeeland is home to a number of classic aircraft. Some of the owners of these machines have set up a foundation with the aim of forming a flying museum. At the present time the aircraft are housed in several hangars to the west of the control tower. The Auster Autocar was delivered to Holland in 1951 and in the following year was registered to the Technical University at Delft. The prototype of this four seat aircraft first flew in August 1949 and about one hundred were built at Rearsby with the majority being exported. After a long period in store and time as an instructional airframe the aircraft was moved to Midden Zeeland in 1984 and has been painstakingly restored to flying condition. One of the SAAB Safirs, the D model, was operated by Netherlands Government Flying School at Eelde near Groningen for many years. A de Havilland Beaver has been sold to the U.S.A. and replaced by a Cessna 195 bought in Germany.

TYPE	REG/SER	CON. NO.	PI/NOTES	STATUS
☐ Auster J/5B Autocar	PH-NEH	2932		RAA
☐ Cessna 195	PH-NEN	7496	N9817A,D-EVLA	RAA
☐ Construcciones Aeronáuticas (CASA) 1.131E [Bücker Bü 131 Jungmann]	D-EDWC		E.3B-419	RA
☐ Piper PA-18-135 Super Cub (L-21B)	PH-KNK	18-3848	54-2448, R-158, (PH-KNM)	RAA
☐ Piper PA-18-135 Super Cub (L-21B)	PH-LWD	18-3931	54-2531, MM54-2531, I-EIQF, EI-234, OO-LWD	RAA
☐ Svenska Aeroplan Aktiebolaget (SAAB) 91B Safir	PH-RJB	91309	SE-XAU, D-EBUC	RAC
☐ Svenska Aeroplan Aktiebolaget (SAAB) 91D Safir	PH-RLB	91368		RAA

STICHTING KONINKLIJKE LUCHTMACHT HISTORISCHE VLUCHT (NET34)

Address: Postbus 229,
5120 AE Gilze-Rijen.
Tel: 0161-296835
Email: office@skhv.nl
Admission: By prior permission only.
Location: The airfield is south of the N.283 between Breda to Tilburg.

Stitching Vliegsport Gilze-Rijen was set up in 1969 and over the years has built a clubhouse, several hangars and a workshop on the south side of the airfield. In 1910 Adriaan Mulder flew a Blériot XI at Gilze-Rijen and the site was later developed for military use. At the time of the German invasion in 1940 it was home to a group flying Fokker C.Vs and Koolhoven FK-51s. For many years the airfield was a fighter base and is now used by helicopter squadrons. There are a number of preserved aircraft on the military part of the airfield with three by the main gate. Members of the Harvard fleet have been modified to represent Thunderbolts, Fokker D.XXIs, Typhoons and Focke-Wulf Fw 190s in a number of films including 'A Bridge too Far' and 'Soldaat van Oranje'. The classic Beech 18, in Canadian Air Transport Command markings, was acquired from the Dutch Dakota Association. Over one hundred and fifty Super Cubs were operated by the Dutch military and six are flown by this group. The Fokker Instructor first flew in 1947 and forty eight were delivered for air force and navy use. One hundred and eighty were built in Italy as the Macchi M.416 and a further ninety five by Fabrica do Galeao in Brazil. One of the surviving Fokker S.14s is being restored. The prototype flew on May 19th 1952 and only twenty examples of this jet trainer were completed. They were in service between 1955 and 1965 and then many were used for fire practice. The Tiger Moth, which was imported into Holland in 1986, is painted in false Dutch Air Force colours. The present name was adopted in 1999 when the group joined forces with the Dutch Spitfire Flight. Formed on March 8th 1991 this organisation started work on the Spitfire which had been stored at Gilze-Rijen for many years. The aircraft first served with a New Zealand unit, 485 Squadron, and shot down one Fw 190 as well as sharing in the kill of a Ju 88. At the end of the conflict it joined the Netherlands Air Force and flew with 322 squadron at Twenthe. After decoy use at Eindhoven the aircraft was taken to Germany by the R.A.F. and spent nine years on show at Gütersloh. The Spitfire returned to the U.K. in 1969 and in 1983 Harry van der Meer, then working at the old Aviodome, persuaded the Air Board to return the airframe to 322 squadron. The rebuild was completed in England and the aircraft flew again on June 10th 1993. Recent arrivals from Eindhoven are the Duke of Brabant Air Force Mitchell and one of their Super Cubs on lease.

TYPE	REG/SER	CON. NO.	PI/NOTES	STATUS
☐ Auster E AOP.3	PH-NGK	344	MZ231, R-18, 8A-18, 'RT607'	RAC
☐ Beech D18S Expeditor 3NM	'G-29'	CA-254	2375 (RCAF), CF-AID, N7820, C-FAID, (PH-BBA), (PH-DDB), N5369X, PH-KHV	RAAX
☐ De Havilland D.H.82A Tiger Moth	PH-TYG	82535	N9508, G-APCU, (PH-TGR), G-APCU, (PH-TGR)	RAC
☐ De Havilland D.H.C.2 Beaver (L-20A)	S-9	965	55-4585 S-9, G-BUVF, PH-DHC – on loan from MLM.	RAA

☐ Fokker F.27 Friendship 100	C-3	10150	PH-FBP – currently stored at Woensdrecht.	RA
☐ Fokker S.11.1 Instructor (S.11)	PH-HOE	6195	E-6, (PH-HOT)	PV
☐ Fokker S.11.1 Instructor (S.11)	PH-GRB	6211	E-20, (PH-GRA)	RAA
☐ Fokker S.11.1 Instructor (S.11)	PH-SII	6215	E-24 – on loan from MLM.	RAA
☐ Fokker S.11.1 Instructor (S.11)	PH-HOI	6282	E-32, 175, (PH-DHF)	RAA
☐ Fokker S.14.1 Mach Trainer	PH-SIY	7362	L-17 – on loan from MLM.	RAC
☐ Noorduyn Harvard IIB [North American NA-77 (AT-16)]	PH-IBI	14-543	42-12296, FE809, B-181	RAA
☐ Noorduyn Harvard IIB [North American NA-77 (AT-16)]	PH-LSK	14-641	42-12394, FE907, B-64, 12-6, B-64, PH-FAR, '219' – with parts from c/n 14A-1161 43-12892, FT151, B-5 – on loan from MLM.	RAA
☐ Noorduyn Harvard IIB [North American NA-77 (AT-16)]	PH-???	14-765	42-12518, FH131, B-175	RAC
☐ Noorduyn Harvard IIB [North American NA-77 (AT-16)]	PH-TBR	14A-808	43-12509, FS668, B-182 – on loan from MLM.	RAA
☐ Noorduyn Harvard IIB [North American NA-77 (AT-16)]	PH-IBY	14A-1100	43-12901, FS960, B-184	RAC
☐ Noorduyn Harvard IIB [North American NA-77 (AT-16)]	PH-MLM	14A-1444	43-13145, FT404, B-71, '218', B-71 – on loan from MLM.	RAA
☐ Noorduyn Harvard IIB [North American NA-77 (AT-16)]	PH-IIB	14A-1467	43-13168, FT427, B-118, PH-TOO, '241', 'PH-320', '241'	RAA
☐ North American NA-108 Mitchell (B-25J) (CB-25J) (VB-25N)	'N5-149'	108-32782	44-29507, N3698G, N320SQ, PH-XXV, 'HD346' – Duke of Brabant AF aircraft.	RAAX
☐ Piper J-3C-90 Cub (J-3C-65) (L-4J)	PH-GEN	12893	44-80597, HB-OWN, D-EGUH, OO-SKY, PH-GEN, (PH-CUB),	RAA
☐ Piper PA-18-135 Super Cub (L-21B)	PH-GAZ	18-3537	54-2337, R-109	RAA
☐ Piper PA-18-135 Super Cub (L-21B)	PH-PPW	18-3812	54-2412, R-122, (PH-GAP), (PH-JZM)	RAA
☐ Piper PA-18-135 Super Cub (L-21B)	PH-APA	18-3814	54-2414, R-124 – leased from DBAF.	RAA
☐ Piper PA-18-135 Super Cub (L-21B)	PH-PSC	18-3827	54-2427, R-137	RAA
☐ Piper PA-18-135 Super Cub (L-21B)	PH-KNR	18-3867	54-2467, R-177, (PH-KNT)	RAA
☐ Piper PA-18-135 Super Cub (L-21B)	PH-GAU	18-3871	54-2471, R-181	RAA
☐ Ryan STM-2E	PH-STM	452	S-16, A50-47, VH-AGY, VR-HDL, LN-TVF, N9761	RAC
☐ Stinson V-76 Sentinel (L-5B)	PH-PBB	76-3401	44-17113, PH-PBB, OO-PBB	RAA
☐ Supermarine 361 Spitfire LF.IXc	PH-OUQ	CBAF-IX-1732	MK732, H-25 (Netherlands), MK732, 8633M	RAA
☐ Supermarine 361 Spitfire LF.IXc (FSM)	'H-27'		'PT987' – on loan from MLM.	PVX

STICHTING KOOLHOVEN VLIEGTUIGEN (NET35)

Address:	Pelikaanweg 50, 8218 NT Lelystad Airport.
Tel:	020-653-0357
Admission:	By prior permission only.
Location:	About 7 km south of the town off the N.302.

Frederick Koolhoven was chief designer for the Armstrong Whitworth company from 1913 to 1917. He then joined British Aerial Transport at Willesden. B.A.T. closed in 1921 and Koolhoven returned to the Netherlands and later set up his own company. Aircraft were produced until 1940 when the factory was bombed. A small number of his later designs were made by Fokker just after World War II. Nine single seat Bantam fighters were built and eight became civil machines. One two seat version appeared in 1919. Mainly used for racing the aircraft had short careers. One was flown to the Netherlands in 1921 and another was acquired by Koolhoven in 1924. The remains of at least two aircraft were stored by C.P.B. Ogilvie at Willesden and later Watford before being acquired by the Shuttleworth Collection in the early 1950s. The foundation has restored one example and this is on show in the Aviodome. The second will be rebuilt to airworthy standards for its owner Stitching Vroege Vogels at Lelystad. The Junior was a two seat side by side low wing cabin monoplane powered by' Walter Mikron engine. One was built in 1936 and another in 1938. Both aircraft disappeared during World War II. Under construction at Kamp van Zeist for the Militaire Luchtvaart Museum is a replica FK.51. This biplane trainer made its maiden flight in 1935 and about one hundred and sixty were built for the Dutch military. Work on this project started in 2002 and on August 30th 2005 it was unveiled to the public. The wings and tail surfaces have been completed and so has the basic fuselage frame and undercarriage. Fitting out of the fuselage is now under way.

TYPE	REG/SER	CON. NO.	PI/NOTES	STATUS
☐ British Aerial Transport FK.23 Bantam	K-123	FK.23/15	F1654, K-123, (G-EACN) – on loan to Aviodrome.	–
☐ British Aerial Transport FK.23 Bantam			For SVV.	RAC
☐ Koolhoven FK.41 (R)			Planned replica.	–
☐ Koolhoven FK.51 (R)			For MLM	RAC
☐ Koolhoven FK.53 Junior (R)	PH-ATG		Planned replica.	–
☐ Koolhoven FK.53 Junior (R)	PH-FKJ		Planned replica.	–

STICHTING NEDERLANDS LUCHTVAART MUSEUM (NET36)

Address:	H. Duin en Paalseweg 18, 2061 AG Bloemendaal.
Admission:	By prior permission only.
Location:	Believed to be in the Den Haag area.

Three gas balloons are owned by this long established group and often appear at meetings in the country. The van den Bemden was produced in Belgium in 1958 and is one of the oldest airworthy balloons in Holland.

TYPE	REG/SER	CON. NO.	PI/NOTES	STATUS
☐ Ballonfabrik See und Luftaufrustung K-630/1-RI Gas Balloon	PH-BVH	8619		RAA
☐ Ballonfabrik See und Luftaufrustung K-630/1-RI Gas Balloon	PH-HBC	9886	(PH-BAL)	RAA
☐ Van den Bemden K-460 Gas Balloon	PH-BOX	VDB-22	PH-BOX, G-BWCC	RAA

STICHTING NEPTUNE (NET37)

Address:	Postbus 590, 2220 AN Katwijk aan Zee.
Tel:	071-405-2531
Email:	info@neptune-association.nl
Admission:	By prior permission only.
Location:	At Lelystad Airfield which is 7 km south of the town off the N.302.

Acquired by the foundation in 1995 the Catalina is now a familiar sight at shows around Europe. Originally built for use by the U.S. Navy, the aircraft later served with the U.S. Coast Guard. For more than forty years it operated in Canada, the majority of this time as a fire tanker. In World War II the Dutch military flew a number of the type in the Dutch East Indies and when these islands were occupied they moved to Ceylon. The majority were written off on active service. At the end of the conflict the survivors returned to the East Indies and more examples were delivered. Under construction is a replica of the Van Berkel WA. The biplane, equipped with floats, was built for naval use and first flew in 1929. The Dutch Navy acquired twenty eight Trackers in the early 1960s and these were flown from Valkenburg and Hato in the Dutch Antilles. Also twelve ex-Canadian Navy machines were overhauled by Fairey Canada and delivered to Biak in the Dutch East Indies. The survivors returned to Holland a decade later and were either scrapped or used for instruction.

TYPE	REG/SER	CON. NO.	PI/NOTES	STATUS
☐ Consolidated 28-5A Catalina (PBY-5A)	PH-PBY	300	Bu2459, NC18446, N18446, CF-HHR, (PH-PBY), C-FHHR, N27311	RAA
☐ Grumman G-103 Tracker (CS2F-1) (CS-2A)	184	DHC-5	1506 (Canada)	RA
☐ Van Berkel WA (FSM)				RAC

STICHTING VLIEGSPORT SEAGULL FORMATION (NET38)

Address:	Ruinerweg 55, 7958 Koehangerveld.
Tel:	0522-452885
Email:	info@seagull-formation.nl
Admission:	By prior permission only.
Location:	At Hooegeveen airfield which is in the north eastern suburbs of the town.

Founded in the mid-1980s by former military pilots who had learned to fly on the type the organisation was originally based at Lelystad. A move has now been made to Hoogeveen where a hangar and clubhouse have been built. The aircraft appear regularly at shows as a formation team. The Luftwaffe operated one hundred and ninety Piaggio 149s built under licence by Focke Wulf and another seventy six supplied by the parent company in Italy. Several were flown by the Lufthansa Training School at Bremen which provided instruction for both civil and military pilots. The majority were sold on the civilian market in the early 1970s.

TYPE	REG/SER	CON. NO.	PI/NOTES	STATUS
☐ Piaggio FWP.149D	D-EFTU	091	AS+404, 90+73	RAA
☐ Piaggio FWP.149D	D-EIFE	129	KB+106, BF+417, 91+08	RAA
☐ Piaggio P.149D	D-EERP	259	AS+410, AC+410, 91+77	RAA
☐ Piaggio P.149D	D-EGIT	260	AS+411, AC+411, 91+78	RAA
☐ Piaggio P.149D	D-EEGD	315	AS+466, AC+466, CA+478, 92+18	RAA

The Autotron at Rosmalen is home to this replica Nieuport 11.

A Viggen from Sweden is shown after landing at Lelystad for display at the Aviodrome. (Klaas-Reinder Sluijs)

This Mitchell has been on show for many years in the impressive Dutch War and Resistance Museum at Overloon.

The Autotron at Rosmalen has loaned this replica Farman HF-20 to the Militaire Luchtvaart Museum at Kamp Van Zeist.

On show at the car museum at Raamsdonksveer is this Fokker built Koolhoven FK.43.

One of the Super Cubs operated by the Historic Flight at Gilze-Rijen is shown in front of a Fokker Instructor.

STICHTING VROEGE VOGELS (NET39)

Address:	Foundation Early Birds, Maraboeweg 20, 8218 PC Lelystad.
Tel:	0320-284101
Email:	J.grootnuelend@chello.nl
Admission:	By prior permission only.
Location:	At Lelystad airfield which is about 7 km south of the town off the N.302.

This collection was set up in the mid-1970s when some partly restored or restorable aircraft were obtained as payment for work carried out on the rebuild of rotary engines for Jean Salis. The foundation has its own hangar at Lelystad where most of the fleet can be seen. The Gipsy Moth which still carries its Australian registration, is one of thirty two built at Melbourne by the Larkin Supply Company in 1929. This biplane has been rebuilt after a recent crash. A rarity in Europe is the Fleet 2 although over six hundred examples of the radial engined biplane were built in the U.S.A. First flown in 1928 the Fleet 1 employed a similar airframe but was powered by a 100 Kinner radial. Other imports from America include the classic Monocoupe 110, the Luscombe Silvaire and the Pietenpol Aircamper. The first Monocoupe designed by Clayton Folkerts and Don Luscombe flew at Moline Illinois in April 1927. Over three hundred and fifty were built. The type was developed into the Monocoupe 90 and 110. About fifty 110s were delivered powered by a 125 h.p. Warner radial. In 1933 Luscombe left to form his own company and in 1937 the Model 8 appeared. This all metal high wing monoplane was built in large numbers both before and after World War II. Almost five thousand nine hundred left the production lines over this period. Bernard Pietenpol began selling plans of the two seater Aircamper in 1930 and well over two hundred were built in the U.S.A. with a few completed in other countries. One of the Fokker Dr I replicas was built in the 1950s in California by Harry Provolt and the other in Holland. Two other Fokker replicas are under construction. Other World War I replicas are being acquired so that 'dog-fights' between the Allied and German machines can be staged. The Stampe S.V.4 was obtained from America and its original identity has been lost. The Argus was flown in Switzerland for many years and this is now under rebuild.

TYPE	REG/SER	CON. NO.	PI/NOTES	STATUS
☐ Aeronca 7AC Champion	N1079E	7AC-4632		RAA
☐ Blériot XI (R)	PH-BLE	NVAV-78		RAA
☐ British Aerial Transport FK.23 Bantam			Under restoration by Koolhoven Foundation.	RAC
☐ Construcciones Aeronáuticas (CASA) 1.131E [Bücker Bü 131 Jungmann]	N131EB	'2012'	E.3B-478	PVA
☐ De Havilland D.H.60G Gipsy Moth	N168G		A7-44, VH-AFN	PVA
☐ De Havilland D.H.82A Tiger Moth	G-BWMS	82712	R4771, T-29 (Belgium), OO-EVJ	RAA
☐ De Havilland D.H.82A Tiger Moth	ZS-DLK	83912	T5902, 562 (South Africa), ZS-DLK, PH-DLK	RA
☐ De Havilland D.H.82A Tiger Moth	N82AM	86568	PG671, F-BDOS – with parts of c/n 85569, DE615, G-ANSG.	RAA
☐ Fairchild 24W41A Forwarder (C-61A) (UC-61A) (Argus II)	PH-FAI	W41A-418	43-14454, FS537, HB-EIM, N165EB	RAC
☐ Fleet 2	NC724V	290	NC724V,N724V	RAA
☐ Fokker Spin (R)				RAC
☐ Fokker D VII (R)	'LVA-256'		(PH-VII), PH-LVA	RAX
☐ Fokker Dr I (R)	PH-EBF	102/NVAV-91	N5505V, – On loan to Stampe Museum, Belgium.	–
☐ Fokker Dr I (R)	PH-DRI	152/17/NVAV-39		RAA
☐ Luscombe 8A Silvaire	N41902	1863		RA
☐ Mono Aircraft Monocoupe 110	N542W	5W90	NC542W	RA
☐ Morane-Saulnier MS.505 Criquet (MS.500) [Fieseler Fi 156 Storch]	N156EB	752	752, F-BAYE	RA
☐ Nieuport 28C.1 (R)	N6256	1		RAA
☐ Nord N.1101 Noralpha (Ramier I) [Messerschmitt Me 208]	F-BLLO	179	179	RA
☐ North American NA-122 Mustang (P-51D)		122-41463	44-74923, N5438V, 410 (El Salvador), N100DD, N345, N6395	RAA
☐ Pietenpol B4-A Aircamper	N1858	A7-1968		RAA
☐ Sopwith F.1 Camel (R)	N1917K	C-1		RA
☐ Sopwith Pup (R)	N1915K	3		RAA
☐ Stampe et Vertongen S.V.4C	N102JW	'T-67283'		RA

TRADITIEKAMER VAN DE MARINELUCHTVAARTDIENST (NET40)

Address:	NAS De Kooy, P.O. Box 10.000, 1780 CA Den Helder.
Tel:	0223-658777
Fax:	0223-658775
Email:	info@traditiekamer.com
Admission:	By prior permission only.
Location:	About 5 km south of Den Helder on the N.250.

In 1914 a naval air station was built at De Mok on the island of Texel. A second site at Schellingwoude near Amsterdam was completed the following year. Formed in August 1917 the Marine Luchvaart Dienst constructed the airfield at de Kooy in 1918. The service has set up the exhibition which traces the history of its units, aircraft and personnel. On show are models, photographs, documents, uniforms, engines and components. Three aircraft can be seen. The Seahawk is the only jet fighter used by the MLD and twenty two operated from the carrier 'Karel Doorman' and shore bases. The example on show is a former Royal Navy aircraft, on loan from the Aviodrome, painted to represent one of those used. A former Fleet Air Arm Wasp is also on show in Dutch colours. Nine Agusta Bell 204B were operated by the Navy from the early 1960s until replaced by the Westland Lynx in the late 1970s. Several were sold to Sweden and the one in the collection returned in December 2001 from Malmslatt. Twelve Neptunes were used on patrol duties mainly from at Valkenburg.

TYPE	REG/SER	CON. NO.	PI/NOTES	STATUS
☐ Agusta-Bell 204B	220	3010		RAC
☐ Hawker P.1040 Sea Hawk FGA.6 (FGA.4)	'118'	7474	WV828 – in false Dutch markings – on loan from Aviodrome.	PV
☐ Lockheed 726-45-18 Neptune (P2V-7B) (P2V-7S) (SP-2H)	207	726-7257	Front fuselage only.	PV
☐ Westland Wasp HAS.1	'235'	F9677	XT795	PVX

VLIEGBASIS EINDHOVEN 'LANE OF FAME' (NET41)

Address:	Siffertstrasse 25, 5657 AL Eindhoven.
Tel:	040-250-6911
Admission:	By prior permission only.
Location:	About 6 km west of the city.

The original airfield was constructed during the German occupation of the country. In the early 1950s a wing of Dutch Air Force Thunderjets took up residence and subsequently Thunderstreaks and NF-5Bs were operated from the site. A new runway was constructed for both military and civil use but parts of the Luftwaffe base can still be seen. The field now houses the transport wing of the Air Force. In service are two C-130 Hercules, three DC-10 tankers, two Fokker 50s, four Fokker 60s and a Gulfstream IV. From 1955 to 1987 a Spitfire was mounted on a pole outside the officers mess but this has now been replaced by a plastic replica. The Thunderjet and Thunderstreak are positioned just inside the base gate with the NF-5 a short distance along the main road inside the camp. These were joined in 2002 by a General Dynamics F-16.

TYPE	REG/SER	CON. NO.	PI/NOTES	STATUS
☐ Canadair CL-226 Freedom Fighter (NF-5A) [Northrop N-156A]	K-3068	3068	On loan from MLM.	RA
☐ Fokker F.27 Troopship 300M	'C-8'	10162	C-12 – on loan from MLM.	RAX
☐ General Dynamics 401 Fighting Falcon (F-16A)	J-238	6D-27	On loan from MLM.	RA
☐ Republic F-84F Thunderstreak	P-231		53-6742 – on loan from MLM.	PV
☐ Republic F-84G Thunderjet	'K-167'		51-10178, 'K-85' – on loan from MLM.	PVX
☐ Supermarine 361 Spitfire LF.IXc (FSM)	'H-15/MK959'		On loan from MLM.	PVX

VLIEGBASIS GILZE RIJEN COLLECTIE (NET42)

Address:	Rijksweg 121, 5121 RD Gilze.
Admission:	By prior permission only.
Location:	South of the N.283 between Breda to Tilburg.

The airfield was home to fighter squadrons for many years but now it is the main Air Force helicopter base. At the outbreak of World War II squadrons flying the Fokker C V and the Koolhoven FK.51 were in residence. Used by the Luftwaffe during the conflict the airfield was returned to Dutch control at the end of the hostilities. In 1950 the site was used by an advanced flying school using Fokker S.11 Instructors and Harvards. Later the basic school moved in. In May 1971 a squadron of Northrop NF-5s arrived from Eindhoven and a second unit was formed. Two combat types are displayed by the main gate and they have now been joined by a BO 105. A Starfighter which was on show for a long period has recently returned to the MLM storage hangar at Soesterburg. One of the NF-5A's also serves as an instructional airframe.

TYPE	REG/SER	CON. NO.	PI/NOTES	STATUS
☐ Bölkow BO 105CB-4	B-42	S-242	D-HDGM	PV
☐ Canadair CL-226 Freedom Fighter (NF-5A) [Northrop N-156A]	'K-3066'	3003	K-3003 – On loan from MLM.	PVX
☐ Canadair CL-226 Freedom Fighter (NF-5A) [Northrop N-156A]	K-3034	3034	On loan from MLM.	RA
☐ Republic F-84F Thunderstreak	P-191		53-6916 – On loan from MLM.	PV

VLIEGBASIS LEEUWARDEN COLLECTIE (NET43)

Address:	Keegsdijkie 4 8919 AK Leeuwarden. 4
Tel:	058-234-6911
Admission:	By prior permission only.
Location:	About 3 km north west of the town.

Holland's first jet squadron, No.323, was formed at Twenthe in November 1948 and moved its Meteor F.4s into Leeuwarden on January 23rd 1949. A second Squadron, No 324, formed at the base in April 1949. Since then the field has been home to fighter units. Over the years Meteor T.7s, Meteor F.8s, Hawker Hunters and Starfighters have been in use. Currently the F-16 is flown by the resident units. Examples of types operated have been preserved around the base. The replica Spitfire is painted in the colours of the World War II 322 squadron which contained many Dutch personnel. This unit has been based at the field since 1964.

TYPE	REG/SER	CON. NO.	PI/NOTES	STATUS
☐ General Dynamics 401 Fighting Falcon (F-16A)	J-219	6D-8	On loan from MLM.	RA
☐ General Dynamics 401 Fighting Falcon (F-16A)	J-228	6D-17	78-0228 – On loan from MLM.	RA
☐ General Dynamics 401 Fighting Falcon (F-16A)	J-245	6D-34	On loan from MLM.	RA
☐ Gloster Meteor T.7	I-320		VW417 – on loan from MLM.	RA
☐ Hawker P.1067 Hunter F.4	N-138	8638	On loan from MLM.	RA
☐ Lockheed 683-10-19 Starfighter (F-104G)	D-8051	683-8051	On loan from MLM.	RA
☐ Sukhoi Su-20R	'56'	72410	(Egypt), 98+62 – in false Soviet markings – on loan from MLM.	RA
☐ Supermarine 361 Spitfire LF.IXc (FSM)	'MJ964'		On loan from MLM.	RA

VLIEGBASIS TWENTHE COLLECTIE (NET44)

Address:	Weerseloseweg 1, 7522 PT Enschede.
Tel:	053-480-6911
Admission:	By prior permission only.
Location:	About 5 km north of Enschede.

Twenthe was built for the Luftwaffe use during World War II. In 1948 the site was used for advanced pilot training and a fleet of Meteor T.7s was operated. Fighter squadrons soon followed and over the years Spitfires, Sabres, Starfighters and NF-5Bs have been flown. With the run down of the F-16 fleet the base was closed in 2005 and its future as a military field is under discussion. The Luchtvaartmuseum Twenthe shut its doors in 2004 and its collection has been dispersed. Many interesting items tracing the history of the airfield and its units were on show and it is hoped that an exhibition can once again be staged. The replica Spitfire moved to Gilze Rijen. Three preserved aircraft on the base a Starfighter, a Thunderstreak and a Canadian built Freedom Fighter have been returned to storage at Soesterburg. The Sabre remains on show at the current time.

TYPE	REG/SER	CON. NO.	PI/NOTES	STATUS
☐ North American NA-213 Sabre (F-86K)	Q-283	213-53	54-1283 – on loan from MLM.	RA

VLIEGBASIS VOLKEL COLLECTIE (NET45)

Address:	Zeelandsedijk 10, 5408 SM Volkel.
Tel:	0413-276911
Admission:	By prior permission only.
Location:	About 2 km east of the town which is about 25 km north east of Eindhoven.

Volkel was constructed by the Germans during World War II and saw extensive use. The site suffered considerable damage during the conflict. The airfield was rebuilt in 1950 and since then has been home to fighter units. The first Thunderjet to be supplied to the Netherlands flew from the field in April 1951 after a journey across the Atlantic in a crate. The Thunderstreak arrived in 1955 and was operated until 1965.

TYPE	REG/SER	CON. NO.	PI/NOTES	STATUS
☐ General Dynamics 401 Fighting Falcon (F-16A)	J-222	6D-11	78-0222 – on loan from MLM.	RA
☐ General Dynamics 401 Fighting Falcon (F-16A)	'80229'	6D-18	78-0229, J-229 – On loan from MLM.	RAX
☐ General Dynamics 401 Fighting Falcon (F-16A)	J-240	6D-29	78-0240 – on loan from MLM.	RA
☐ Lockheed 683-10-19 Starfighter (F-104G)	D-8063	683-8063	On loan from MLM.	RA
☐ Lockheed 683-10-19 Starfighter (F-104G)	D-8256	683-8256	On loan from MLM.	RA
☐ Lockheed 683-10-19 Starfighter (F-104G)	D-8279	683-8279	On loan from MLM.	RA
☐ Lockheed 683-10-19 Starfighter (F-104G)	D-8312	683-8312	Tail from c/n 683-8084 D-8084 – on loan from MLM.	RA
☐ Republic F-84F Thunderstreak	P-277		53-6924 – on loan from MLM.	RA

VLIEGBASIS WOENSDRECHT COLLECTIE (NET46)

Address:	Kooiweg 40, 4631 SZ Hoogerheide.
Tel:	0164-692911
Admission:	By prior permission only.
Location:	About 6 km south of Bergen op Zoom off the N.289.

326 Squadron was established on April 1st 1950 and flew Meteor F.4s. These were soon replaced by F.8s and later Hunter F.4s. The unit moved to Soesterberg in August 1960. 328 Squadron equipped with Meteor F.4s formed at Woensdrecht in May 1951. Meteor F.8s soon replaced the earlier version and were flown until the unit disbanded in 1955. A joint system of flying instruction was set up by Belgium and Holland in 1962 and part of the school flew T-33s until the airfield was closed for operational flying in 1968. The preserved T-33 is a reminder of this period. The site is now used for aircraft storage and primary flying training. Some of the aircraft on MLM charge also serve as instructional airframes and others are stored for future display.

TYPE	REG/SER	CON. NO.	PI/NOTES	STATUS
☐ General Dynamics 401 Fighting Falcon (F-16A)	J-241	6D-30	On loan from MLM.	RA
☐ General Dynamics 401 Fighting Falcon (F-16A)	J-246	6D-35	78-0235 – on loan from MLM.	RA
☐ General Dynamics 401 Fighting Falcon (F-16A)	J-250	6D-39	78-0250 – On loan from MLM.	RA
☐ General Dynamics 401 Fighting Falcon (F-16B)	J-259	6E-1	78-0259 – On loan from MLM.	RA
☐ General Dynamics 401 Fighting Falcon (F-16B)	J-260	6E-2	78-0260 – on loan from MLM.	RA
☐ Lockheed 580 (T-33A)	'M-51'	580-7150	51-17411, M-54 – on loan from MLM.	PVX
☐ Noorduyn Harvard IIB [North American NA-77 (AT-16)]	B-177	14-733	43-12486, FE999 – on loan from MLM.	RA
☐ Republic F-84F Thunderstreak	P-170		53-6673 – on loan from MLM.	RA
☐ Sud-Est SE.3160 Alouette III	A-343	1343	On loan from MLM.	RA

VLIEGEND MUSEUM SEPPE (NET47)

Address:	Hogeslede 54, 7701 JH Rosendaal.
Tel:	0165-545842
Fax:	0165-548611
Email:	sander@museum.tmfweb.nl
Admission:	Wednesday 1300-1700; Saturday-Sunday 1100-1700.
Location:	Seppe Airfield is about 6 km north east of Rosendaal off the A.50.

The airfield was opened in 1949 and the museum established in 1990. A display of instruments, engines, propellers, photographs and models has been set up in the hangar. A British registered Tiger Moth is regularly flown and this has been joined by a Hornet Moth and an American built Gipsy Moth. A protracted rebuild of the Auster 5 has just been completed. This aircraft was imported into Holland in 1952 and withdrawn from use in 1970. After almost twenty years in store with the Military Aviation Museum the aircraft was sold as a restoration project. The Lancair arrived in the late 1990s to show an example of a modem homebuilt type and a second can now be seen. Likely join the collection is a replica of the 1930s Lambach HL-II. The original was operated by the Delft Technical University flying club. Students at the university started the construction of the replica in 1989 and it flew in the early 1990s. The Erla built Messerschmitt 109 was based at Schiphol and shot down by a P-47 over Moerkapelle on December 4th 1943. The wreck was recovered in the mid-1980s by a former Fokker engineer. He decided to build a frame on which he would put the original pieces. The Wright Flyer was built by members to commemorate the centenary of powered flight In 1992 the museum flew several of its fleet to the Popular Flying Association Rally at Wroughton in England and won a trophy for the 'Most Meritorious Flight'. There are plans to construct larger facilities on a site close to the control tower.

TYPE	REG/SER	CON. NO.	PI/NOTES	STATUS
☐ Auster J AOP.5	PH-NET	1416	TJ347, G-AIPE	PVA
☐ Bensen B-8M Gyrocopter	N2893	4457034		PV
☐ Bölkow BO 208C Junior	PH-END	515	D-ENDA, (VH-UES), D-ENDA	PVA
☐ Cessna T210M Turbo Centurion	PH-VDC	21062368	N761MR, (PH-AXZ)	PVA
☐ De Havilland D.H.60GMW Moth	G-AAMY	86	NC585M, N585M	PVA
☐ De Havilland D.H.82A Tiger Moth	G-AJHS	82121	N6866	PVA
☐ De Havilland D.H.87B Hornet Moth	G-ADLY	8020		PVA
☐ Europa Aviation Europa XS-TG	PH-JGW	206		PVA
☐ Lambach HL-II			Possibly due.	–
☐ Luscombe T-8F	N9945C	S-49		PVA
☐ Messerschmitt Bf 109G-5	11	15343		PVC
☐ Neibauer Lancair 360	PH-BPM	747		RAA
☐ Neibauer Lancair 360	PH-JPR	SFB2001-442		PVA
☐ Piaggio FWP.149D				PVA
☐ Piper PA-18-135 Super Cub (L-21B)	PH-VCY	18-3601	54-2401, R-111	PVA
☐ Ryan ST-3KR Recruit (PT-22)	N56028	2014	41-20805	PVA
☐ Svenska Aeroplan Aktiebolaget (SAAB) 91D Safir	PH-RLD	91370		PVA
☐ Wright Flyer (R)				RAC
☐ Yakovlev Yak-52	LY-AQC	877401		PVA

NORWAY

0 65 130 miles
0 65 130 km
Barents Sea
16
Tromso
RUSSIA
9 Narvik
Bodo
11
FINLAND
Norwegian Sea
unknown: 14
Namsos
Steinkjer
SWEDEN
Trondheim
Alesund
Gulf of Bothnia
6
Lillehammer
Bergen
3
Hamar
Sauda
Honefoss
8,17
Oslo
4,5,12
10
13,15
Stavanger
1
2
Gulf of Finland
Vanern
ESTONIA
7
Arendal
Mandal
Kristiansand
Vattern
Gulf of Riga
North Sea
LATVIA
DENMARK
Baltic Sea
LITHUANIA

DAKOTA NORWAY (NOR1)

Address:	Sandefjord Lufthavn, N-3233 Sandefjord.
Tel:	33 46 26 06
Email:	pettenge@online.no
Admission:	By prior permission only.
Location:	The airfield is about 5 km north of the town at Torp.

The group was formed in 1986 and now has over seven hundred members. The Dakota was acquired in July 1986 and has been restored to a polished metal finish. This aircraft served with the Eighth Air Force of the U.S.A.A.F. during World War II and in 1948 was sold to Finnair who operated it on their European services for twenty one years. Sixteen years military service in Finland followed. The aircraft was owned for a short period by Aces High and moved to their North Weald base in England.

TYPE	REG/SER	CON. NO.	PI/NOTES	STATUS
☐ Douglas DC-3A-457 Skytrooper (C-53D)	LN-WND	11750	42-68823, OH-LCG, DO-9 (Finland) , G-BLYA, N59NA	RAA

FLYHISTORISK MUSEUM SOLA (NOR2)

Address:	P.O. Box 512, N-4055 Stavanger-Lufthavn.
Tel:	51 65 56 57
Admission:	May-June August-November Sunday 1200-1600 ; mid-June – mid-August daily 1200-1600.
Location:	The airfield is about 14 km south-west of the city.

Run by volunteers, this museum was set up in 1984 with the aim of tracing the history of the military base at Sola and Stavanger Airport. The display is housed in the hangar of the former seaplane base. A wide range of civil and military aircraft has been acquired. Around thirty airframes and about a dozen engines are on show. The rooms at the rear of the hangar are being used for informative displays incorporating models, photographs, documents and uniforms. The history of the airfield is portrayed in great detail. The development of military and civil flying in Norway is also shown. The Catalina was acquired from Denmark in 1989 and is being restored to represent an aircraft which flew from Sola in the late 1950s. Over the last few years a number of wrecks of German World War II aircraft have been recovered. The Messerschmitt Bf 109 crashed in the sea off Egersund on November 11th 1943 and was lifted in December 1988. The restoration is proceeding well using parts from other crash sites. Also under rebuild is an Arado Ar 96 which made a forced landing in a lake near Bremnes on March 14th 1943 when on a flight from Herdla to Sola. The airframe was recovered in September 1992. Corroded remains of an Arado Ar 66 and an Ar 196 await their turn in the queue. Another long term project is the rebuild of a Fieseler Storch. The remains of a French built airframe were acquired along with parts from other examples of type. The aircraft will eventually emerge as a Fi 156C-3 model. The tail section of a Wellington which went missing on a minelaying mission in October 1942 can be seen. Not many Taylorcraft As found their way to Europe. The museum example arrived in Norway in 1938 and was put in storage at the outbreak of World War II. The airframe was discovered in 1971 by members of Norwegian Aviation Historical Society. The EoN Baby is an improved version of the famous Grunau Baby built in England by Elliott's of Newbury. The Heron has been painted in the colours of the first of those operated by Braathens in 1952. The Norwegian Airline used a fleet of these four engined airliners on its services from small airports around the country. The Convair 440 flew from Stavanger with Nor-Fly in the 1970s and when withdrawn was bought by a group at Sola. This aircraft flew with the Norsk Metropolitan Klubb until 1987 and joined the museum four years later. The former Swiss Force Hunter arrived in the late 1990s.

TYPE	REG/SER	CON. NO.	PI/NOTES	STATUS
☐ Aero Commander 680FL	LN-LMD	1401-56	CF-SHC, N8484A	PV
☐ Aero Jet Commander 1121		19		PV
☐ Aerodyne Vector 610	LN-YCK	1203-270		PV
☐ Aerodyne Vector 610	LN-YAC	1389		PV
☐ Antonov An-2R	LY-AEQ	1G 185-20	CCCP-54860	PV
☐ Arado Ar 66c			Fuselage frame only.	RA
☐ Arado Ar 96B-1	PI+OT	4246	On loan from FVM.	PVC
☐ Arado Ar 196A-2	6W+?N		On loan from FVM.	PVC
☐ Bell 204 Iroquois (HU-1B) (UH-1B)	580	226	60-3580	PV
☐ Bell 204 Iroquois (HU-1B) (UH-1B)	688	268	61-0688	RA
☐ Bensen B-8 Gyroglider				RAC
☐ Britten-Norman BN-2A-21 Islander	LN-MAF	441	G-BCZS	PV
☐ Canadair CL-90 Starfighter (CF-104) [Lockheed 683-04-12] (Canada) – on loan from FVM.	PV	104730	683A-1030	12730
☐ Caproni Ca.310			Fuselage frame only.	RAD
☐ Cessna FT337HP Super Skymaster	HB-LOU	FP3370023/02960	F-GCVP, OO-ADI	RA
☐ Consolidated 28-5A Catalina (PBY-5A)	'KK-A'	928	Bu08109, 82-857 (Denmark), L-857 (Denmark)	PVCX
☐ Convair 440-75	LN-KLK	357	SE-BSR	PV
☐ De Havilland D.H.114 Heron 1B	'LN-PSG'	14015	PK-GHB, G-AOXL, LN-BFY – contains parts of c/n 14020 PK-GHE, JA6156, LN-BFX	PVX
☐ De Havilland D.H.115 Vampire T.55	U-1217	977	In Swiss markings – part owned by Warbirds of Norway.	PV
☐ Dornier Do 28A-1	LN-LMZ	3003		RA

Type	Reg	C/n	History	Status
☐ Elliott AP.8 EoN Baby	LN-GBI	EoN/B/018		PV
☐ Fairchild M-62A-4 Cornell	LN-BIV	T41-975	161, L-BA – parts only.	RAD
☐ Fairchild M-62A-4 Cornell (PT-26) (Cornell I)	LN-BIO	T43-4646	44-19534, EW587, 243, L-DD – parts only.	RAD
☐ Fokker F.27 Friendship 100	LN-SUF	10298	PH-FIS, PH-SAN	PV
☐ Grumman G-44A Widgeon (J4F-2)	LN-HAL	1332	Bu32978, SE-ARZ – on loan from NTM.	PV
☐ Hawker P.1099 Hunter F.58A (P.1067 Hunter F.4)	J-4110	HABL 003079	XF318, G-9-328 – in Swiss markings.	PV
☐ Hiway Demon 175 Hang Glider	75-Y			PV
☐ Jacobs Meise (D.F.S. 108-70)	LN-GAR	527/1944	LZ+ET, LN-SCA – on loan from NTM.	RAC
☐ Lockheed 580 (T-33A)	'DP-X'	580-5903	51-6571, DT-571 (Denmark) – false Norwegian markings on loan from FVM.	PVX
☐ Messerschmitt Bf 109G-1/R2	DG+UF	14141	On loan from FVM.	PVC
☐ Messerschmitt Bf 110F-2	LN+DR		Wings, tail and fuselage parts	RAD
☐ Miles M.65 Gemini 1A	LN-TAH	6528	G-AKKA – on loan from NTM.	RA
☐ Morane-Saulnier MS.500 Criquet [Fieseler Fi 156 Storch]			With parts of MS.502 c/n 540 F-BDHZ and at least two other aircraft.	RAC
☐ Noorduyn Harvard IIB [North American NA-77 (AT-16)]	M-BE	14-355	42-818, FE621 – parts only.	RAD
☐ Noorduyn Norseman IV	LN-BDR	92	492 (Canada), R-AK (Norway), LN-BDR, '470384'	RAC
☐ North American NA-66 Harvard II	2605	66-2338	In Canadian markings.	PV
☐ North American NA-202 Sabre (F-86F)	31082	202-11	53-1082 – on loan from FVM.	PV
☐ North American NA-213 Sabre (F-86K)	41266	213-36	54-1266	PV
☐ Northrop N-156A Freedom Fighter (F-5A)	'14896'	N.7043	66-9220, 220 – on loan from FVM.	PVX
☐ Numan Raven Hang Glider				PV
☐ Piaggio FWP.149D	LN-BNR	088	AS+497, YA+004, D-EBDA, (90+70), D-EBDA	PV
☐ Piel CP.301C Emeraude	LN-FAD	L-355/67		PV
☐ Piper J-3C-65 Cub (L-4H)	LN-NAU	11673	43-30382 – on loan.	PV
☐ Republic RC-3 Seabee	LN-BDT	202	LN-MAF, SE-BXA – parts only.	RAD
☐ Republic RF-84F Thunderflash	117045		51-17045 – on loan from FVM.	PV
☐ Republic F-84G Thunderjet	28470		52-8470 – tail from 51-10161 – on loan from FVM.	PV
☐ Scheibe Bergfalke II/55	LN-GBH	202	D-1271	PV
☐ Svenska Aeroplan Aktiebolaget (SAAB) 35XD Draken (RF-35)	AR-114	351114	In Danish markings – on loan from FHS, Denmark.	PV
☐ Svenska Aeroplan Aktiebolaget (SAAB) 91B-2 Safir	336	91336	On loan from FVM.	PV
☐ Taylorcraft A	LN-FAG	416		RAD
☐ Teratorn Tierra 1	LN-YRH	860303003		PV
☐ Vickers 417 Wellington III	BK309		Tail section only.	PV
☐ Westland-Bell 47G-3B-1 Sioux AH.1	'LN-ORB'	WA.583	XT404, 404 (South Yemen), G-BBZL, SE-HME	PVX

FORSVARET FLYSAMLING GARDERMOEN (NOR3)

Address:	Postboks 0155, N-2261 Gardermoen.
Tel:	63 92 86 60
Fax:	63 92 86 61
Email:	office@flysamlingen.museum.no
Admission:	December-February Saturday-Sunday 1200-1600: March- mid June Tuesday, Thursday, Saturday, Sunday 1200-1600; Mid-June- mid August Tuesday-Thursday Saturday-Sunday 1100-1700. Mid-August-November Tuesday, Thursday, Saturday, Sunday 1200-1600.
Location:	Gardermoen is about 55 km north west of Oslo off the E.6.

The Norwegian Air Force collected and restored a number of historic aircraft at bases throughout the country in the 1960s and 1970s. Plans for a museum were put forward and on June 16th 1984 an exhibition opened in a former German hangar at Gardermoen. Aircraft arrived from other airfields and about thirty machines were put on show. The control of these aircraft and those on other bases was transferred to the Forvarsmuseet. In 1992 a proposal was made, with the support of some politicians, to construct a museum at Bodø and just over twenty aircraft made the long trip north. Gardermoen Airport has been completely rebuilt and the hangar was demolished in 1999. Plans for a new building were approved and construction started on a site close to the terminal area. The new exhibition opened in 2000 with about thirty aircraft on show and there are plans for further additions. The history of military flying in the country is featured in the exhibition. The Rumpler Taube was the first military aircraft in Norway. This machine was donated to the Navy in 1912 and damaged in 1915. Rebuilt in 1922 for the tenth anniversary of its first flight the Taube was then donated to the predecessor of the technical museum and stored in the open. Found derelict by Luftwaffe officers during the occupation the airframe was taken to its original base at Horten and rebuilt. The Taube hung in one of the halls until the 1950s when it was obtained by the museum in Oslo and finally put on display in 1973. This historic machine moved here soon after the new building opened. Ten B.E.2Es were acquired in 1917 and operated until 1925. The Farman F.46 is one of ten delivered to Norway in 1916/17. Along with many other vintage aircraft, including the B.E.2, it was restored by John Amundsen at Kjevik. A unique aircraft is the 1941 Northrop N-3PB, one of twenty four delivered to 'Little Norway' in Canada. These were operated by 330 Squadron in Iceland and the floatplane crashed in 1943 on a flight from Budareyi to Reykjavik where it was due to be scrapped. The wreck was recovered in 1979 and taken to California to be rebuilt by the makers. This restored aircraft was unveiled on November 10th 1980 to celebrate the eighty fifth birthday of the founder of the company, John K. Northrop. The N-3PB finally arrived in Norway in October 1981 forty years after it was ordered. The country has been scoured for wrecks from the World War II period and a number of German aircraft are in the collection. The first airframe to be recovered was the Heinkel He 111P which force landed near Lake Lesjaskog on April 25th 1940. The bomber arrived at Gardermoen in 1976 and has been superbly restored to original condition. Several Junkers Ju 52s were raised from Lake Hartvikannet in the rnid-1980s. Eleven aircraft were forced to land on the frozen surface in April 1940 and subsequently sunk. The Focke-Wulf Fw 190 was partially rebuilt by the Texas Air Museum in the U.S.A. in a deal involving several other Fw 190 airframes. The Norwegian Aviation Historical Society restored the Interstate Cadet which was one of a pair used at 'Little Norway'. The aircraft was taken to Norway after the war and crashed in 1952 while flying from a frozen river. The remains were found in a remote barn after a long search. The unique Kjølseth helicopter was built at Kjeller in the mid-1950s but after tests in 1957 the Bell 47 was ordered. Not many aircraft have been designed in Norway and the derelict fuselage of the Larsen Special is another. The true identity of the Auster is a problem as noted below. Most types used by the services in recent years have been preserved.

TYPE	REG/SER	CON. NO.	PI/NOTES	STATUS
☐ Auster J/1 Autocrat	'RT514'		Museum give c/n B.617 which is a conversion of Auster K T.7 WE548, which was rebuilt into Terrier G-ASCF SE-ELO but they also say fuselage from HB-EOT, D-EDAX, OY-DUY which is c/n 2181 wings from c/n 2332 G-AJIN, D-EJYN, OY-DTP – composite.	PVX
☐ Bell 47D-1	BE-D	642	KK-R, BE-D, LN-ORM – composite.	PV
☐ Bell 204 Iroquois (UH-1B)	966	1090	64-13966, JT-B	PV
☐ Canadair CL-90 Starfighter (CF-104) [Lockheed 683-04-12]	759	683A-1059	12759 (Canada), 104759 (Canada)	PV
☐ Canadair CL-90 Starfighter (CF-104) [Lockheed 683-04-12]	801	683A-1101	12801 (Canada), 104801 (Canada)	PV
☐ Cessna 305A Bird Dog (L-19A) (O-1A)	4953	21845	51-4953, CE-W – also reported as c/n 21838.	PV
☐ Cessna 305A Bird Dog (L-19A) (O-1A)	641	23096	51-12641	RAC
☐ Dassault Mirage IIIS	J-2315	1005	Front fuselage only.	PV
☐ De Havilland D.H.100 Vampire F.3	P42408	EEP42408	VT833(?), B-AE, PX-E, SI-D	PV
☐ De Havilland D.H.115 Vampire T.55 (DH.100 FB.50) (J 28) (Sk 28C-3)	Fv28456			PV
☐ De Havilland D.H.C.6 Twin Otter	7062	062		PV
☐ Douglas DC-3A-456 Skytrain (C-47A)	93797	13749	42-93797, T-AO, BW-D, BW-L	PV
☐ Fairchild M-62A Cornell	103	T40-208	103, L-AB	PV
☐ Farman F.46	25	25		PV
☐ Focke-Wulf Fw 190A-3		0122219		PVC
☐ Heinkel He 111P-2	5J+CN	1526	33+C25	PV
☐ Interstate S.1A Cadet	505	203	NC37360, 505, LN-DAV	PV
☐ Junkers Ju 52/3mg4e	CA+JY	6657		PVC
☐ Junkers Ju 88A-1	U4+TH	088119		RAC
☐ Junkers Ju 88A-5 (A-1)	CF+VP	0886146		RA
☐ Junkers Ju 88C-2	4D+FH	0881033		PVD
☐ Kjølseth P.K. X-1		1		PV
☐ Larsen Special			Fuselage only.	RAD
☐ Lockheed 18-56-23 Lodestar (C-60A)	'G-AGIH'	18-2444	42-55983, NC69898, N69898, N105G, N9223R, N283M, OH-MAP, OH-SIR, G-BMEW, N283M, OH-SIR	PVX
☐ Lockheed 580 (T-33A)	117546	580-7691	51-17546, DP-P, DP-K, 117546 (France)	PV
☐ Lockheed 583-10-20 Starfighter (TF-104G)	469	583D-5779	63-8469, KF+271, 27+70	PV
☐ Noorduyn Norseman IV	R-AV	64	2491 (Canada), R-AV, LN-BDP, SE-FUP, LN-BDP	PV
☐ North American NA-191 Sabre (F-86F)	25069	191-765	52-5069, HA-D	PV
☐ North American NA-213 Sabre (F-86K)	41274	213-44	54-1274, ZK-H, RI-T	PV
☐ North American NA-213 Sabre (F-86K)	41290	213-60	54-1290, ZK-Z, ZK-O, RI-Z, RI-D	PV
☐ Northrop N-3PB	20	320		PV
☐ Northrop N-156A Freedom Fighter (F-5A)	208	N.7031	66-9208	PV
☐ Northrop N-156A Freedom Fighter (RF-5A)	105	RFG.1006	68-9105, AZ-M	PV
☐ Northrop N-156B Freedom Fighter (F-5B)	594	N.9003	65-10594, AH-Z, AZ-Q	PV
☐ Piper PA-18-95 Super Cub (L-18C)	53-4845	18-3245	53-4845, F-AI, 845	PV
☐ Republic RF-84F Thunderflash	117053		51-17053, T3-G, AZ-G	PV
☐ Republic F-84G Thunderjet	111209		51-11209, FN-2, FN-G, MU-5	PV
☐ Royal Aircraft Factory B.E.2e	131		A1380, 59	PV
☐ Rumpler Taube				PV
☐ Schneider Grunau SG-38 (D.F.S. 108-14)	LN-GBM	209	On loan – possible identity	RA
☐ Sikorsky S-55D Chickasaw (H-19D) (UH-19D)	64279		56-4279, HA-B	PV
☐ Supermarine 365 Spitfire PR.XI	PL979	6S.583719	PL979, A-ZB	PV
☐ Svenska Aeroplan Aktiebolaget (SAAB) 91B-2 Safir	329	91329		PV

FORSVARSMUSEET (NOR4)

Address:	Festnung Akershus, N-0015 Oslo.
Tel:	23 09 35 70
Fax:	23 09 31 90
Email:	post.fmu@mil.no
Admission:	June-August Monday-Friday 1000-1800; Saturday-Sunday 1100-1600: September-May Monday-Friday 1000-1500; Saturday-Sunday 1100-1600.
Location:	In the city centre near the harbour.

Construction of this historic castle, located on the waterfront, began in the thirteenth century. One building houses the excellent Resistance Museum which traces the history of the country when it was under German control. The Armed Forces Museum opened in 1978 in an old arsenal dating from 1860. The military and political history of the country from the Viking times is portrayed in the informative displays. The Tiger Moth was built in Norway by Haerens Flyvemaskinfabric, who constructed seventeen D.H.82s and twenty D.H.82As, at Kjeller Brought back from Sweden by the Norwegian Aviation Historical Society, the biplane was restored to its original colours and then donated to the museum. For many years a Spitfire was on display but this has moved to Bodø and been replaced by a replica. A Vampire also made the long trek north. The Cornell, in period colours, has now joined the exhibition. This was once used at the 'Little Canada' training base in World War II.

TYPE	REG/SER	CON. NO.	PI/NOTES	STATUS
☐ De Havilland D.H.82 Tiger Moth	151	161	151, SE-ANL – identity doubtful	PV
☐ Fairchild M-62A-4 Cornell (PT-26B) (Cornell III)	205		43-36254, FZ204, 10757 (Canada), 205, L-CL, LN-OAU	PV
☐ Fieseler Fi 103A-1				PV
☐ Henschel Hs 293A-1		218160		PV
☐ Supermarine 349 Spitfire F.Vc (FSM)	'V-AH'			PVX

FORSVARSMUSEET FLYSAMLINGEN (NOR5)

Address:	Festnung Akershus, N-0015 Oslo.
Tel:	23 09 35 70
Fax:	23 09 31 90
Email:	post.fmu@mil.no
Admission:	Not applicable.
Location:	Office at the Forvarsmuseet.

The military museum owns many of the aircraft displayed at Bodø and Gardermoen and other museums. In addition some of the collection has been loaned out to military bases around the country. Some of these serve as display aircraft and others may be used as instructional airframes in military schools. The museum is actively searching for wrecks around the country. Over the years several have been located. Many airframes have been recovered and restored for display. More are waiting their turn in the rebuild queue and others are still in the mountains. Several German flying boats have been located around the coasts and the possibility of raising some of these is being investigated. A Dornier Do 26 has been found and this is in reasonable condition.

TYPE	REG/SER	CON. NO.	PI/NOTES	STATUS
☐ Arado Ar 66c			Fuselage only – on loan to NLM.	RAD
☐ Arado Ar 66c			Fuselage only – on loan to NLM.	RAD
☐ Arado Ar 66c			Fuselage only – on loan to NLM.	RAD
☐ Arado Ar 96B-1	PI+OT	4246	On loan to FMS.	–
☐ Arado Ar 196A-2	6W+?N		On loan to FMS.	–
☐ Avro 504K (504A)	103		B4505 (?) – on loan to NLM.	–
☐ Bell 204 Iroquois (HU-1B) (UH-1B)	591	237	60-3591 – at Bardufoss.	RA
☐ Bell 204 Iroquois (HU-1B) (UH-1B)	025	545	62-2025 – at Rygge.	RA
☐ Bell 204 Iroquois (UH-1B)	961	1085	64-13961 – at Rygge.	RA
☐ Bell 204 Iroquois (UH-1B)	079	1203	64-14079 – on loan to NLM.	–
☐ Canadair CL-90 Starfighter (CF-104) [Lockheed 683-04-12]	104730	683A-1030	12730 (Canada) – on loan to FMS.	PV
☐ Canadair CL-90 Starfighter (CF-104) [Lockheed 683-04-12]	'F-104'	683A-1066	12866 (Canada), 104766 (Canada) – at Kjeller.	PVX
☐ Canadair CL-90 Starfighter (CF-104) [Lockheed 683-04-12]	890	683A-1190	12890 (Canada), 104890 (Canada) – on loan to NLM.	RA
☐ Canadian Car & Foundry Harvard 4 [North American NA-186 (T-6J)]	'M-BS'	CCF4-491	52-8570, AA+696, AA+622 – in false Norwegian markings – on loan to NLM.	–
☐ Cessna 305A Bird Dog (L-19A) (O-1A)	712	21448	50-1712 – on loan to NLM.	–
☐ Cessna 318B Tweety Bird (318A) (T-37A) (T-37B)	57-2247	40180	On loan to NLM.	–
☐ Consolidated 28-6A Catalina (PBY-6A)	'FP535'	2009	Bu46645, N10013, CF-IZO, C-FIZO – on loan to NLM.	–
☐ Dassault Mirage IIIE	588	588	On loan to NLM.	–
☐ De Havilland D.H.82A Tiger Moth	'141'	82210	N6972, 6317M, N6972 – on loan to NLM.	–
☐ De Havilland D.H.98 Mosquito T.III	'TD753'		TW117, 'HR155', 7805M, TW117 – on loan to NLM.	–
☐ De Havilland D.H.100 Vampire FB.52	V0184	V0184	B-BI – on loan to NLM.	–

TYPE	REG/SER	CON. NO.	PI/NOTES	STATUS
☐ De Havilland D.H.C.3 Otter	'O-AM'	81	CF-IKT, C-FIKT – on loan to NLM.	–
☐ Fairchild M-62A-4 Cornell (PT-26B) (Cornell III)	'L-DM/163'		43-36487, FZ708, 261 – composite with parts from M-62A c/n T40-269 119, L-AI, LN-BIS – on loan to NLM.	–
☐ Fokker C.VD	349	133	349, SE-ALS – on loan to NLM.	–
☐ Gloster Gladiator II	N5641		On loan to NLM.	–
☐ Haerens Flyvemaskinfabrik FF.9 Kaie	33	76	On loan to NLM.	–
☐ Hawker P.1099 Hunter F.58	J-4027	41H/697393	In Swiss markings – on loan to NLM.	–
☐ Ilyushin Il-2m3	2	303560	On loan to Sör Varanger Museum.	–
☐ Junkers Ju 88A-4	4D+AM	0881478	On loan to NLM.	–
☐ Junkers Ju 88C-0				RAD
☐ Lockheed 580 (T-33A)	'DP-X'	580-5903	51-6571, DT-571 (Denmark) – in false Norwegian markings – on loan to FMS.	–
☐ Lockheed 583-04-15 Starfighter (CF-104D)	4637	583A-5307	12637 (Canada), 104637 (Canada) – on loan to NLM.	–
☐ McDonnell M.98HO Phantom II (F-4E)	67-0333	3168	On loan to NLM.	–
☐ Messerschmitt Bf 109G-1/R2	DG+UF	14141	On loan to FMS.	–
☐ Messerschmitt Bf 109G-2	13470	13470	In store at Bodø.	–
☐ Mikoyan-Gurevich MiG-21SPS (MiG-21PFM)	22+37	94A5210	891 (DDR) – on loan to NLM.	–
☐ North American NA-191 Sabre (F-86F)	25202	191-898	52-5202 – at Orland.	RA
☐ North American NA-202 Sabre (F-86F)	31082	202-11	53-1082 – on loan to FMS.	–
☐ North American NA-202 Sabre (F-86F)	31206	202-135	53-1206 – on loan to NLM.	–
☐ North American NA-213 Sabre (F-86K)	41245	213-15	54-1245 – on loan to NLM.	–
☐ North American NA-213 Sabre (F-86K)	41266	213-36	54-1266 – on loan to FMS.	–
☐ North American NA-213 Sabre (F-86K)	41313	213-83	54-1313 – with tail of c/n 213-94 54-1334 – at Bardufoss	RA
☐ Northrop N-156A Freedom Fighter (F-5A)	563	N.7011	65-1-563 – on loan to NLM.	–
☐ Northrop N-156A Freedom Fighter (F-5A)	215	N.7038	66-9215 – at Orland.	RA
☐ Northrop N-156A Freedom Fighter (F-5A)	220	N.7043	66-9220 – on loan to FMS.	–
☐ Northrop N-156A Freedom Fighter (F-5A)	895	N.7058	67-14895 – at Rygge.	RA
☐ Northrop N-156A Freedom Fighter (RF-5A)	102	RFG.1003	68-9102 – on loan to NLM.	–
☐ Northrop N-156A Freedom Fighter (RF-5A)	112	RFG.1013	68-9112	RA
☐ Petlyakov Pe-2FT		16/141	On loan to NLM.	–
☐ Petlyakov Pe-2FT	33	2/225	On loan to NLM.	RAC
☐ Piper PA-18-95 Super Cub (L-18C)	835	18-3235	53-4835 – on loan to NLM.	–
☐ Republic RF-84F Thunderflash	117045		51-17045 – on loan to FMS.	–
☐ Republic RF-84F Thunderflash	117055		51-17055 – at Kjevik.	RA
☐ Republic RF-84F Thunderflash	117047		51-17047 – front fuselage only – on loan to NLM.	–
☐ Republic RF-84F Thunderflash	52-8723			RA
☐ Republic F-84G Thunderjet	28465		52-8465 – on loan to NLM.	–
☐ Republic F-84G Thunderjet	28470		52-8470 – tail from 51-10161 – on loan to FMS.	–
☐ Republic F-84G Thunderjet	52-2912		At Orland.	RA
☐ Supermarine 361 Spitfire LF.IXe	MH350	CBAF-IX-490	MH350, A-BM, M-FM – on loan to NLM.	–
☐ Svenska Aeroplan Aktiebolaget (SAAB) 91B-2 Safir	336	91336	On loan to FMS.	–
☐ Svenska Aeroplan Aktiebolaget (SAAB) 91B-2 Safir	337	91337	On loan to NLM.	–
☐ Valtion Lentokonetehdas Saaski II (R)	'40'		On loan to NLM.	–

HERDLA MUSEUM (NOR6)

Address:	P.O. Box 323, N-5323 Kleppstø.
Tel:	056-145150
Fax:	056-158396
Email:	herdla.museum@askoy.kommune.no
Admission:	April and September-October Sunday 1200-1700; May-August daily 1200-1700.
Location:	About 35 km north of Bergen

The island of Herdla has been settled since Viking times and is home to over two hundred species of birds. During World War II a Luftwaffe fighter base was constructed and the remains of the runways, hangars and other buildings can still be seen. The local population was forced to move off the island whilst the Germans were in residence. The museum opened in 1995 to celebrate the fiftieth anniversary of the ending of the conflict. The history of the island over the last thousand years is portrayed in the exhibition. There are several dioramas showing the wildlife of the area. The settlement of the region is portrayed in detail and many every day items are on show. The development of the airfield is shown in a photographic display. On show are many models depicting the Luftwaffe types based at the field and the allied machines which attacked it. In May 2005 the wreck of a Focke-Wulf Fw 190 was located. The aircraft ditched in the sea in 1943 and is still in a reasonably good condition. Efforts are being made to raise it for display and hopefully this will soon occur.

TYPE	REG/SER	CON. NO.	PI/NOTES	STATUS
☐ Focke-Wulf Fw 190A-2	13	5425		RAD

Eight jet types are shown on the apron outside the hangar of the Flyhistorisk Museum Sola. (FMS)

The unique C.5 Polar can be seen in the Norsk Luftsfartsmuseum at Bodø. (Sven Scheiderbauer)

The Warbirds of Norway operated this former Swiss Air Force Vampire FB.6. (W of N.)

JENS RINO HAUGEN FLYSAMLINGEN (NOR7)

Address:	Vindveien 13, N-4885 Grimstad.
Tel:	417 32 02
Admission:	By prior permission only.
Location:	In the eastern part of the town.

This private collection of components and memorabilia is located at the owner's home. The aircraft are currently stored in the garden. A North American F-86K front fuselage was here but this has been sold to a collector in Belgium. The origins of the MiG-23 are not known at the present time.

TYPE	REG/SER	CON. NO.	PI/NOTES	STATUS
☐ McDonnell M.98 Phantom FGR.2			Front fuselage only.	RA
☐ Mikoyan-Gurevich MiG-23BN			Front fuselage only.	RA
☐ Northrop N-156A Freedom Fighter (RF-5A)	101	RFG.1002	68-9101	RA
☐ Republic RF-84F Thunderflash	117051		51-17051 – front fuselage only.	RA

KJELLER FLYHISTORISKE FORENING (NOR8)

Address:	Lufthavn, N-2007 Kjeller.
Tel:	33 37 00 01
Email:	kff@luftnet.com
Admission:	By prior permission only.
Location:	About 20 km east of Oslo off Road 22.

Kjeller airfield opened in 1916 with the move of the Army Aircraft factory from Oslo. Both original designs and licence built aircraft were constructed and the site is still a military establishment. The Canadian built Starfighter is mounted by the main gate to this facility. Members of the group based at the civilian part of the field are working to set up a museum tracing the history of the field. A Farman Shorthorn replica incorporating some original parts is complete. Work has started on two others. Now arrived from Australia is a Metal Moth which crashed in May 1930. The airframe was placed in store where it remained undisturbed until 1993. The Tiger Moth, which was built at Kjeller, spent over forty years in a barn south of Stockholm along with several other aircraft. After protracted negotiations the biplane was acquired and moved back to be restored in period markings. Some work was carried out before it was sold to the group.

TYPE	REG/SER	CON. NO.	PI/NOTES	STATUS
☐ Bell 204 Iroquois (UH-1B)				RA
☐ Canadair CL-90 Starfighter (CF-104) [Lockheed 683-04-12]	'F-104'	683A-1066	12766 (Canada), 10476 (Canada)	PVX
☐ De Havilland D.H.60M Moth	LN-KFM	711	G-AUKC, VH-UKC	RAC
☐ De Havilland D.H.82A Tiger Moth	'189'	183	185 (Norway), SE-ALP, LN-KFT	RAX
☐ De Havilland D.H.100 Vampire FB.6	LN-JET	665	J-1146 (Switzerland), LN-17 – Warbirds of Norway aircraft.	RAA
☐ Fairchild M-62A Cornell (PT-19A)	G-BVCV	T42-3418	42-33752, 621 (Uruguay), CX-BCU	RAD
☐ Farman MF-11 Shorthorn (R)				RA
☐ Farman F.40 (R)				RAC
☐ Haerens Flyvemaskinfabrik FF.1 [Farman Longhorn] (R)				RAC

KRIGSMINNEMUSEUM (NOR9)

Address:	P.O. Box 513, N-8507 Narvik.
Tel:	076-944426
Fax:	076-944560
Email:	post@warmuseum.no
Admission:	January-April mid-September -December Monday-Friday 1100-1500; May- mid June Monday-Saturday 1000-1600 Sunday 1200-1600; June-mid August Monday-Saturday 1000-2100 Sunday 1200-1800; mid August-mid September Monday-Saturday 1000-1600 Sunday 1200-1600.
Location:	In the centre of the town

This war museum run by the Norwegian Red Cross opened in 1964 and the building was enlarged twice in the 1980s. The displays trace the story of the area during the German occupation in World War II. The fierce battle for the town in 1940 is shown in detail. German troops landed from ships in April 1940s and over the next month British boats attacked but were repelled. On show are many relics, photographs and documents. Fighting on land, in the air and on sea are highlighted. The Junkers Ju 52 will be restored at Bjervik in the near future.

TYPE	REG/SER	CON. NO.	PI/NOTES	STATUS
☐ Junkers Ju 52/3mg4e	CO+EI	6791		RAD

MARINEMUSEET (NOR10)

Address:	P.O. Box 21, Karljohansvern, N-3191 Horten.
Tel:	33 03 35 46
Fax:	33 03 35 05
Email:	mar-mus@online.no
Admission:	Monday-Friday 1000-1500; Saturday-Sunday 1200-1600. (Closed Saturday in winter)
Location:	In the northern part of the town.

This museum was established in 1853 by Captain C.F. Clinck. The history and development of the Norwegian Navy is portrayed in a series of displays incorporating models, photographs, documents and artefacts. In 1914 the Marinens Flyvebatfabrik (Naval Flying Boat Factory) was set up at Horten. Over the next quarter of a century several indigenous designs appeared. Kjell Undbekken is building a replica Sopwith Baby at his home near Oslo. This aircraft will be flown by Warbirds of Norway for about five years and then go on show at Horten.

TYPE	REG/SER	CON. NO.	PI/NOTES	STATUS
☐ Sopwith Baby (R)				RAC

NORSK LUFTFARTSMUSEUM (NOR11)

Address:	Postboks 1124, N-8001 Bodø.
Tel:	75 50 85 50
Fax:	75 50 78 51
Email:	flymuseum@luftfart.museum.no
Admission:	May-September Monday-Friday 1000-2000; Saturday 1000-1700; Sunday 1000-2000.
Location:	In the southern suburbs of the town.

The Norwegian Aviation Centre was opened by King Harald V on May 15th 1994. Housed in a new building constructed in shape of a propeller the museum has impressive displays tracing the history of aviation in the country. Modern techniques have been used to enhance the exhibition which includes a flight simulator. Bodø airfield has been an important military and civil field for many years and an exhibition traces the story of the site. The entrance area is devoted to the pioneer years where models and photographs can be seen. The inter-war period includes several interesting machines. The Kaie was built at Kjeller in 1922 and used for training until the introduction of the Tiger Moth in the mid-1930s. The Gladiator from 263 Squadron of the Royal Air Force landed on the frozen Lake Lesjaskog in 1940 and was one of several left behind when the ice melted. Bought by a local resident it spent many years in a specially constructed shed. In 1977 it was taken to Rygge to be rebuilt. The Mosquito, used in the film '633 Squadron', was on show in the Royal Air Force Museum at Hendon from 1972 to 1991. The remains of a Blackburn Skua which crashed in World War II have recently been found. The Lockheed U-2 was donated by the U.S.A. in recognition of the assistance given by Norway in flights from their airfields. The unique Polar was built for the Widerøe company in 1948. The high wing monoplane carried a pilot and five passengers and was powered by a 350 hp Wright radial. This aircraft was withdrawn in 1972 and has recently been restored for the exhibition. The former Portuguese Air Force Junkers Ju 52/3m has been mounted on floats and is painted in the colours of one flown in the area prior to World War II.

TYPE	REG/SER	CON. NO.	PI/NOTES	STATUS
☐ Aero Jet Commander 1121	N16SK	1121-101		PV
☐ Arado Ar 66c			Fuselage only – on loan from FVM.	RAD
☐ Arado Ar 66c			Fuselage only – on loan from FVM.	RAD
☐ Arado Ar 66c			Fuselage only – on loan from FVM.	RAD
☐ Arado Ar 66c	8J+NL	850		RAC
☐ Avro 504K (504A)	103		B5405(?) – on loan from FVM.	PV
☐ Bell 26E Airacobra (P-39Q)	42		42-20442	RAD
☐ Bell 47G	LN-ORW	632	KK-P, BE-A, JT-O	PV
☐ Bell 204 Iroquois (UH-1B)	079	1203	64-14079 – on loan from FVM.	PV
☐ Blackburn B-24 Skua I	L2910			RAC
☐ Cameron O-84 Hot Air Balloon	LN-ASI	38	Basket only.	PV
☐ Canadair CL-90 Starfighter (CF-104) [Lockheed 683-04-12]	890	683A-1190	12890 (Canada), 104890 (Canada) – on loan from FVM.	RA
☐ Canadian Car & Foundry Harvard 4 [North American NA-186 (T-6J)]	'M-BS'	CCF4-491	52-8570, AA+696, AA+622 – in false Norwegian markings – on loan from FVM.	PVX
☐ Cessna 150	LN-FAF	17257	N5757E, OY-AEF, SE-CNN	PV
☐ Cessna 305A Bird Dog (L-19A) (O-1A)	712	21448	50-1712 – on loan from FVM.	PV
☐ Cessna 318B Tweety Bird (318A) (T-37A) (T-37B)	57-2247	40180	On loan from FVM.	PV
☐ Cessna 337D Super Skymaster	LN-TVY	33701084	N12500	PV
☐ Consolidated 28-6A Catalina (PBY-6A)	'FP535'	2009	Bu46645, N10013, CF-IZO, C-FIZO – on loan from FVM.	PVX
☐ Curtiss 87V Warhawk (P-40N)	26			RAD
☐ Dassault Mirage IIIE	588	588		RA
☐ De Havilland D.H.82A Tiger Moth	'141'	82210	N6972, 6317M, N6972 – on loan from FVM.	PVX

Type	Reg.	c/n	Notes	Status
☐ De Havilland D.H.98 Mosquito T.III	'TD753'		TW117, 'HR155', 7805M, TW117 – on loan from FVM.	PVX
☐ De Havilland D.H.100 Vampire FB.52	V0184	V0184	B-BI – on loan from FVM.	PV
☐ De Havilland D.H.C.3 Otter	'0-AM'	81	CF-IKT, C-FIKT – on loan from FVM.	PVX
☐ De Havilland D.H.C.6-300 Twin Otter	LN-LMN	127	LN-LMN, D-IORA, N25TC	PV
☐ English Electric EA.1 Canberra T.17A (B.2)	WD955	EEP71037		RA
☐ Fairchild M-62A-4 Cornell (PT-26B) (Cornell III)	'L-DM/163'		43-36487, FZ708, 261 – parts from M-62A c/n T40-269 119, L-AI, LN-BIS – on loan from FVM.	PVX
☐ Focke-Wulf Fw 58 Weihe		1017	Wreck to be recovered soon.	–
☐ Focke-Wulf Fw 190A-3	KI+GX	0122219	Fuselage only.	RA
☐ Fokker C.VD	349	133	349, SE-ALS – on loan from FVM.	PV
☐ Fokker F.28-1000 Fellowship	OB-1636	11109	LN-SUC	RA
☐ Gloster Gladiator II	N5641		On loan from FVM.	PV
☐ Haerens Flyvemaskinfabrik FF.9 Kaie	33	76	On loan from FVM.	PV
☐ Hawker Hurricane I	L1988		Crash remains.	RAD
☐ Hawker Hurricane IIB (FSM)	'BD734'			PVX
☐ Hawker P.1099 Hunter F.58	J-4027	41H/697393	On loan from FVM.	RA
☐ Junkers W 34	BV+GI		Wreck to be recovered soon.	–
☐ Junkers Ju 52/3mg3e	'LN-DAF'	5664	106 (Portugal), 6306 (Portugal)	PVX
☐ Junkers Ju 88A-4	4D+AM	0881478	On loan from FVM.	PVD
☐ Junkers Ju 88C-4	4D+HA	0880797		RAD
☐ Junkers Ju 88D-1	4N+EH	0881203		RAC
☐ Junkers Ju 88D-1	G2+HH	430813	Wings and tail only.	RAD
☐ Larsen Special I/II	LN-LMI	02		RAC
☐ Let L-13 Blanik	'LN-GGS'			PVX
☐ Lilienthal Normal-Segelapparat (R)				PV
☐ Lockheed 583-04-15 Starfighter (CF-104D)	4637	583A-5307	12637 (Canada), 104637 (Canada) – on loan from FVM.	PV
☐ Lockheed 683-10-19 Starfighter (F-104G)	'104'	683-9010	KH+110, JA+246, 25+64	PVX
☐ Lockheed U-2CT (U-2D) (WU-2D)	56-6953	393		PV
☐ McDonnell M.98HO Phantom II (F-4E)	67-0333	3168	On loan from FVM.	RA
☐ Messerschmitt Bf 109G-2/R1		13470		RAC
☐ Mikoyan-Gurevich MiG-15UTI	34	5771		RA
☐ Mikoyan-Gurevich MiG-21SPS (MiG-21PFM)	22+37	94A5210	891 (DDR) – on loan from FVM.	RA
☐ Noorduyn Norseman VI (C-64A) (UC-64A)	LN-PAB	811	44-70546	RAD
☐ Norsk Flyindustri C.5 Polar	LN-DBW	1/1948	LN-11, LN-DAW	PV
☐ North American NA-202 Sabre (F-86F)	31206	202-135	53-1206 – on loan from FVM.	PV
☐ North American NA-213 Sabre (F-86K)	41245	213-15	54-1245 – on loan from FVM.	RA
☐ Northrop N-156A Freedom Fighter (F-5A)	563	N.7011	65-10563 – on loan from FVM.	PV
☐ Northrop N-156A Freedom Fighter (RF-5A)	102	RFG.1003	68-9102 – on loan from FVM.	PV
☐ Petlyakov Pe-2FT	33	2/225	On loan from FVM	RA
☐ Petlyakov Pe-2FT		16/141	On loan from FVM.	RAC
☐ Piper PA-18-95 Super Cub (L-18C)	835	18-3235	53-4835 – on loan from FVM.	PV
☐ Piper PA-22-108 Colt	LN-BND	22-8947	N10F	PV
☐ Piper PA-23-250 Aztec C	LN-AEX	27-2538	SE-EMG	RA
☐ Piper PA-28-140 Cherokee	LN-DBI	28-7325219	Rear fuselage only.	PV
☐ Piper PA-28-140B Cherokee	LN-HAK	28-20733	SE-EOF	PV
☐ Reinfjell Special		1		PV
☐ Republic RF-84F Thunderflash	117047		51-17047 – front fuselage only. – on loan from FVM.	PV
☐ Republic F-84G Thunderjet	28465		52-8465 – on loan from FVM.	PV
☐ Schneider ESG 29 Grunau 9 (D.F.S. 108-10)	LN-GHT	01-EB	D-1161	S
☐ Schneider ESG 29 Grunau 9 (D.F.S. 108-10)	LN-GAH	Jeloy.2		PV
☐ Schneider Grunau SG-38 (D.F.S. 108-14)	LN-GBM			PV
☐ Solar Wings Typhoon S4 Hang Glider				PV
☐ Supermarine 361 Spitfire LF.IXe	MH350	CBAF-IX-490	MH350, A-BM, M-FM – on loan from FVM.	PV
☐ Svenska Aeroplan Aktiebolaget (SAAB) 32D Lansen (32B) (J 32B) (J 32D)	Fv32545	32545		RA
☐ Svenska Aeroplan Aktiebolaget (SAAB) 35XD Draken (RF-35)	AR-120	351120	On loan from FHS, Denmark.	PV
☐ Svenska Aeroplan Aktiebolaget (SAAB) 91B-2 Safir	337	91337	On loan from FVM.	PV
☐ Thunderwing Spitfire 9 (R)	LN-ANV	TW09K-BR87C		PV
☐ Valtion Lentokonetehdas Saaski II (R)	'N-40'		On loan from FVM.	PVX
☐ Volkseigener Betrieb Apparatebau Lommatzsch FES-530/II Lehrmeister	LN-GGV	0245	DM-3295	PV
☐ Wasp 220 Hang Glider				PV

NORSK TEKNISK MUSEUM (NOR12)

Address:	Kjelasveien 143, N-0491 Oslo
Tel:	22 79 60 00
Fax:	22 79 61 00
Email:	post@tekniskmuseum.no
Admission:	June-August Tuesday-Sunday 1000-1900; September-May Tuesday 1000-2100, Wednesday-Saturday 1000-1600; Sunday 1000-1700.
Location:	In the north eastern suburbs of the city.

There has been an exhibition of technical items in the city for many years. Just after World War II the current museum opened in premises close to the centre of the city. The exhibition closed in the early 1980s. A magnificent new building was constructed on the outskirts of the city and opened a few years later. An informative exhibition portraying many aspects of science, technology and industry can be viewed on four floors. The historical aspects are also covered in detail. An early aircraft, which played a significant part in the aviation history of the country, is a prized exhibit. The Blériot made the first crossing of the North Sea when Lieutenant Tryggve Gran flew from Cruden Bay in Scotland to Stavanger on July 30th 1914. The Loening Air Yacht was flown by Thor Solberg on an epic journey from New York to Oslo in the 1930s. S.A.S. operated a fleet of Caravelles on their European services from 1957 until the mid-1970s.

TYPE	REG/SER	CON. NO.	PI/NOTES	STATUS
☐ Aero Commander 680FL	LN-LMN	1202-106	N-78342 – Front fuselage only.	PV
☐ Bell 47J	LN-ORD	1562		PV
☐ Blériot XI				PV
☐ De Havilland D.H.100 Vampire F.3	P42459	EEP42459	B-AH – front fuselage only.	PV
☐ Deperdussin A				PV
☐ Farman MF-1 Longhorn	F.16/1			PV
☐ Grumman G-44A Widgeon (J4F-2)	LN-HAL	1332	Bu32978, SE-ARZ – on loan to FMS.	–
☐ Haerens Flyvemaskinfabrik FF.7 Hauk [Hannover CL V]			Front fuselage only	PV
☐ Jacobs Meise (D.F.S. 108-70)	LN-GAR	527/1944	LZ+ET, LN-SCA – on loan to FMS.	–
☐ Loening C-2 Air Yacht	LN-BAH	308	NR10239, NC10239	PV
☐ Miles M.65 Gemini 1A	LN-TAH	6528	G-AKKA – on loan to FMS.	–
☐ Norge C	LN-BWD	1	LN-14	PV
☐ Raab Doppelraab V	LN-GAT	548/54	D-1484	RA
☐ Sud-Est SE.210 Caravelle III (I)	LN-KLH	3		PV

SAMLINGEN LINDBERG (NOR13)

Address:	Edvard Munchsgt 10, N-1511 Moss.
Tel:	69 27 10 80
Email:	plinb@online.no
Admission:	By prior permission only.
Location:	At a number of locations in the Moss area.

Petter Lindberg who is one of the officials of the Seilflyhistorisk Forening, has a collection of vintage and classic sailplanes. Several were withdrawn from use many years ago and others have survived minor crashes. There are a number of interesting machines in the fleet. The three Schweizer brothers were pioneers in sailplane construction in America. They built their first primary in 1930. A few more advanced models followed in the 1930s. In 1937 they were asked to design a two-seat model for a club in New York state. Orders followed and a move was made to Elmira to set up a factory. With the entry of the U.S.A. into World War II there was a need for glider pilots and a production line was set up. When peace returned the company continued with new designs and when glider manufacture ceased over two thousand had left the factory.

TYPE	REG/SER	CON. NO.	PI/NOTES	STATUS
☐ Antonov A-15	LN-GPM	304		RA
☐ Elliott AP.5 EoN Olympia 2	LN-GPL	EoN/0/033		RA
☐ Osterreich Aero Club Standard Austria	LN-GBL	81		RA
☐ Scheibe Bergfalke II/55	LN-GBB	253		RA
☐ Scheibe Bergfalke IIa	LN-GAI	343		RA
☐ Schleicher K.7	LN-GAG	7266		RA
☐ Schleicher K.8B	LN-GGT	521		RA
☐ Schneider ESG 31 Grunau Baby IIB	LN-GGD			RA
☐ Schneider ESG 31 Grunau Baby IIB	LN-GBS	036/42	SE-???	RA
☐ Schneider ESG 31 Grunau Baby IIB	LN-GAG	124/1945	SE-SPT	RA
☐ Schneider ESG 31 Grunau Baby IIB	LN-GBE	2/1950		RA
☐ Schweizer SGU.1-19A	LN-GBR	51A	SE-SGX	RA
☐ Schweizer SGU.2-22	LN-GBP	21	SE-SGU	RA
☐ Slingsby T.21B Sedbergh TX.1	LN-GHR		WB987, BGA.3338	RA
☐ Slingsby T.30B Prefect	LN-GLV	1132	BGA.853	RA
☐ Szybowcowy Zaklad Doswiadczalny S.Z.D.24A Foka 4	LN-GPL	W-352		RA

SCANDINAVIAN HISTORIC FLIGHT (NOR14)

Address:	Ovre Ullern Terrasse 27, N-0380 Oslo.
Tel:	022-50 23 65
Fax:	022 52 14 89
Email:	aks.shf@online.no
Admission:	By prior permission only.
Location:	At a number of airfields in Denmark, Norway and Sweden.

The organisation was formed in the mid-1980s with the aim of preserving historic military aircraft in flying condition. The Mustang saw military service with the U.S.A.A.F. and the R.C.A.F. before embarking on a civil career. The Invader was flown to Norway in 1988 and wears the colours of a 72nd Bomb Squadron aircraft of the Korean War period. The group has led a nomadic existence over recent years.

TYPE	REG/SER	CON. NO.	PI/NOTES	STATUS
☐ De Havilland D.H.100 Vampire FB.6	LN-VMP	693	J-1184 (Switzerland), SE-DXY, (OY-VAM), SE-DXY	RAA
☐ Douglas A-26B Invader	LN-IVA	27881	44-34602, N8392H, N167B, N8392H, N26A, N167B	RAA
☐ Hawker P.1099 Hunter F.58	LN-HNT	41H/697456	J-4089 (Switzerland), (OY-SKB), SE-DXA	RAA
☐ Noorduyn Harvard IIB [North American NA-77]	LN-TEX	14A-2268	KF568, H-58 (Belgium), OO-AAR, D-FIBU, 1794 (Portugal)	RAA
☐ North American NA-122 Mustang (P-51D)	'473877'	122-40417	44-73877, 9279 (Canada), N6320T, CF-PCZ, N167F, LN-AKS	RAAX
☐ Piper J-3C-65 Cub (L-4J)	LN-LKT	12847	44-80551, HB-OAB, OE-ABO, LX-ABO, (D-EFBP), OY-ALP	RAA
☐ Svenska Aeroplan Aktiebolaget (SAAB) 35XD Draken (TF-35)	OY-SKA	351158	AT-158	RAA

SEILFLYHISTORISK FORENING (NOR15)

Address:	Edvard Munchsgt 10, N-1511 Moss.
Tel:	69 27 10 80
Email:	plind@online.no
Admission:	By prior permission only.
Location:	At Rygge airfield which is about 10 km south east of Moss off the E.6.

This group which is based at the military field at Rygge has three active sailplanes. The replica Grunau 9, fitted with a nacelle for the pilot, was built by members of the group and is painted in pre-war German civil colours.

TYPE	REG/SER	CON. NO.	PI/NOTES	STATUS
☐ Scheibe Bergfalke II/55	SE-SUI	217		RAA
☐ Scheibe 138 Specht	LN-GAD	410		RAA
☐ Schneider ESG 29 Grunau 9 (R)	'D-1911'		LN-GHT	RAA

SÖR VARANGER MUSEUM – GRENSELAND MUSEUM (NOR16)

Address:	Forstevannslia, N-9900 Kirkenes.
Tel:	78 99 48 80
Fax:	78 99 48 90
Email:	infomuseum@sor-varanger.kommune.no
Admission:	June-August daily 1000-1800; September- May daily 1000-1530.
Location:	Close to the entrance to the town.

The new main building housing the Grenseland Museum (Border Country Museum) presents the history, traditions and culture of the region in a number of innovative displays. Soviet forces liberated Kirkenes in 1944 but only stayed a short time before the border was closed. The Ilyushin Il-2 took part in the liberation of the area in 1944 was shot down on October 22nd 1944 and sank to the bottom of a lake. The pilot survived but the tail gunner perished. The wreck was raised in 1984 by a local group and the engine restored in the area. The Il-2 was taken to a factory in Revda and in December 1989 returned to Kirkenes in pristine condition.

TYPE	REG/SER	CON. NO.	PI/NOTES	STATUS
☐ Ilyushin Il-2m3	2	303560	3560 (Soviet) – on loan from FVM	PV

WARBIRDS OF NORWAY (NOR17)

Address:	Box 58, N-1411 Kolbotn.
Tel:	67 55 03 14
Email:	info@warbirds.no
Admission:	By prior permission only.
Location:	Kjeller is about 20 km north east of Oslo on Route 22.

Founded in 1985, with the aim of keeping warbirds in airworthy condition, the organisation now has about three hundred members. All the aircraft are either individually or group owned. The Vampire FB.6 is painted in the colour scheme worn by Norwegian examples of the type when they served in the 1950s. The Tiger Moth is resplendent in the markings worn by Norwegian built machines in the 1930s.

TYPE	REG/SER	CON. NO.	PI/NOTES	STATUS
☐ Aero L-29 Delfin	LN-ADA	294879	(Soviet), A-121 (Estonia), ES-YLA	RAA
☐ Cessna 305C Bird Dog (L-19E) (O-1E)	LN-WNO	24588	24588 (France),F-GEGB, (LN-AAN)	RAC
☐ Construcciones Aeronáuticas (CASA) 1.131E [Bücker Bü 131 Jungmann]	LN-ESS	2156	E.3B-540, F-AZGG, G-BRSH	RAA
☐ De Havilland D.H.82A Tiger Moth	LN-MAX	84167	T7794, G-ASPV – Built from frame of 84167 but registered as c/n 85738 DE840, G-ANSE, LN-BDO.	RAA
☐ De Havilland D.H.100 Vampire FB.6	LN-JET	655	J-1146 (Switzerland), (LN-JET), LN-17	RAA
☐ De Havilland D.H.115 Vampire T.55	U-1217	977	In Swiss markings – part owned by FMS at Sola.	–
☐ De Havilland D.H.115 Vampire T.55	'WZ589'	990	U-1230 (Switzerland), G-DHZZ	RAA
☐ De Havilland D.H.C.1 Chipmunk 22 (T.10)	LN-DHC	C1/0038	WB586	RAA
☐ Fairchild M-62A Cornell (PT-19)	LN-BIF	T43-7228	43-83641, N51324	RAA
☐ Max Holste MH.1521M Broussard	LN-WNB	16	16 (France), F-GHGH – at Kjeller.	RAA
☐ North American NA-88 Texan (AT-6D) (Harvard III)	LN-WNH	88-14552	41-33854, EX881, 7424 (South Africa), 1506 (Portugal), G-SUES, (LN-LFW	RAA
☐ Piper J-3C-65 Cub (L-4J)	LN-RAP	12583	44-80287	RAA
☐ Piper PA-18-95 Super Cub (L-18B)				RAA
☐ Svenska Aeroplan Aktiebolaget (SAAB) 91B Safir				RAA
☐ Yakovlev Yak-52				RAA
☐ Yakovlev Yak-52	LN-ACT	867014	(DOSAAF), LY-ANS	RAA

POLAND

KOLEKCJA AEROKLUBU WROCŁAWSKIEGO (POL1)

Address:	Lotniska Szymanów, 51-180 Wrocław.
Tel:	071-387-16
Admission:	By prior permission only.
Location:	About 10 km north of the town.

This long established club has an active gliding section with a large fleet of sailplanes. Three classic types have been preserved in their hangar and more will be saved as they are withdrawn from use. The prototype IS-2 Mucha flew in April 1948 and well over one hundred were built. The improved S.Z.D. 12 Mucha 100 appeared in 1953 and more than three hundred and fifty were produced with many being exported. The design was the basis for the Chinese Lie Fang 1. The powered section of the organisation has three interesting types in regular use.

TYPE	REG/SER	CON. NO.	PI/NOTES	STATUS
☐ Antonov An-2T				RAA
☐ Antonov An-2T				RAA
☐ Szybowcowy Zaklad Doswiadczalny S.Z.D.10bis Czapla	SP-8009	W-30	SP-1854	RAA
☐ Szybowcowy Zaklad Doswiadczalny S.Z.D.12 Mucha 100	SP-1492	Gd-043		RA
☐ Szybowcowy Zaklad Doswiadczalny S.Z.D.25A Lis	SP-2354	F-738		RA
☐ Yakovlev Yak12M				RAA

KOLEKCJA ART METAL (POL2)

Address:	Lapino Gorne 34, 83 331 Przyjazn.
Tel:	058-681-8078
Fax:	058-681-8064
Email:	biuro@artmetal.pl
Admission:	By prior permission only.
Location:	About 15 km south west of Gdansk.

The company produces reproductions of classic lanterns. They have acquired a number of former military aircraft which have been put on show near to their factory. One of the Iskras is from a batch returned to Poland from India. Thirty six MiG-23MFs were flown from 1979 to 1999 with the main base being along the coast at Słupsk. The ubiquitous Antonov An-2 has been in service with the Polish Air Force since 1951 and a few are still in use.

TYPE	REG/SER	CON. NO.	PI/NOTES	STATUS
☐ Antonov An-2T	8552	1G 85-52		PV
☐ Mikoyan-Gurevich MiG-23MF	005	0390221005		PV
☐ Panstwowe Zaklady Lotnicze (PZL) TS-11 Iskra 100bisB	813	1H 08-13	0813	PV
☐ Panstwowe Zaklady Lotnicze (PZL) TS-11 Iskra 200bisD	W1764	3H 15-04	In Indian markings.	PV

KOLEKCJA BAZY MARYNARKI WOJENNEJ GDYNIA BABIE DOLY (POL3)

Address:	Shwer Kosciuszki, 81-912 Gdynia. (Naval Public Relations Office)
Tel:	058-626-3919 058-626-3487
Admission:	By prior permission only.
Location:	About 3 km north of the town.

The Polish Navy flew fighter aircraft along the Baltic coastline for many years. The last MiG-21s were withdrawn in December 2003. The role has now been transferred to the Air Force. Currently flown from the field are Antonov An-28s, Mil Mi-2s, Mi-8s, and Mi-17s along with SM-2s and W-3 Sokol helicopters. This field is the main base of the service and three combat types previously operated have been preserved.

TYPE	REG/SER	CON. NO.	PI/NOTES	STATUS
☐ Mikoyan-Gurevich MiG-17PF	926	0926		RA
☐ Mikoyan-Gurevich MiG-21PF	'0716'	760901	0901	RAX
☐ Wytwornia Sprzetu Komunikacyjnego (WSK) Lim-1 [MiG-15]	'001'			RA

KOLEKCJA BAZY SIL POWIETRZNYCH RADOM-SADKÓW (POL4)

Address:	2 Osrodek Szkolenia Lotniczego, ul Lubelska 150 26-600 Radom.
Tel:	035-11500
Fax:	035-11300
Admission:	By prior permission only.
Location:	In the south eastern suburbs of the town.

The airfield opened in 1927 and also serves as the civil airport for the town. The military base is home to a pilot training school which is attached to the main Air Force Academy at Deblin. Currently in service are Mil-2 and W-3 Sokol helicopters plus PZL-130 Orliks. In the past MiG-15UTIs and TS-11 Iskras were operated.

TYPE	REG/SER	CON. NO.	PI/NOTES	STATUS
☐ Mikoyan-Gurevich MiG-21M	'04'	961808	1808	RAX
☐ Mikoyan-Gurevich MiG-23MF	'40'	0390217140	140	RAX
☐ Mil Mi-24D	4004	B4004	412 (DDR), 96+23	RA
☐ Panstwowe Zaklady Lotnicze (PZL) TS-11 Iskra 100bisB	721	1H 07-21		RA
☐ Sukhoi Su-22M4	'22'	28104	8001	RAX

KOLEKCJA BAZY SIL POWIETRZNYCH SŁUPSK (POL5)

Address:	JW 2848, 76-206 Słupsk 6.
Admission:	By prior permission only.
Location:	About 5 km east of the town on Route 6.

The base was home to a fighter wing for many years and the MiG-23 was operated up to the late 1990s. A collection of preserved types previously used by the unit has been put on display just inside the main gate to the field. They have all been given false codes relating to significant dates in their service life.

TYPE	REG/SER	CON. NO.	PI/NOTES	STATUS
☐ Mikoyan-Gurevich MiG-19PM	'1958'	650908	908	RAX
☐ Mikoyan-Gurevich MiG-21PF	'1974'	761815	1815	RAX
☐ Mikoyan-Gurevich MiG-23M	'1979'	0390224692	46 (Soviet)	RAX
☐ Wytwornia Sprzetu Komunikacyjnego (WSK) Lim-5 [MiG-17F]	'1952'	1C 03-01	301	RAX

KOLEKCJA BAZY SIL POWIETRZNYCH STRACHOWICE (POL6)

Address:	Skarzynskiego, 54-530 Wrocław.
Admission:	By prior permission only.
Location:	About 10 km west of the city.

The military side of the field houses a liaison and transport squadron operating a variety of types. Currently flying are Antonov An-2s, Antonov An-28s, Mil Mi-2s, Mill Mi-8s, PZL TS-11 Iskras and PZL W-3 Sokols. The Il-28 bears the same serial as one at Deblin. The airfield is also the civil airport for the town.

TYPE	REG/SER	CON. NO.	PI/NOTES	STATUS
☐ Ilyushin Il-28	65			RA
☐ Mikoyan-Gurevich MiG-21MF	8007	968007		RA
☐ Panstwowe Zaklady Lotnicze (PZL) TS-8 Bies	'1979'			RAX

KOLEKCJA BOGUCHWALA (POL7)

Address:	36-040 Boguchwala,
Admission:	On permanent view.
Location:	About 8km south of Rzeszów on Route 9.

Five aircraft are displayed at this restaurant which is located on the main road from Rzeszów to Svidnik in the Slovak Republic. The quintet are all in good condition. The Mi-2 has been painted in a yellow and blue scheme masking its identity. The German built Il-14 came from the museum at Łódz in the late 1990s. The aircraft entered service with LOT in October 1957 and flew on their services until 1969. Twenty years were then spent on calibration duties and the airliner was put into storage at Warsaw for a period.

TYPE	REG/SER	CON. NO.	PI/NOTES	STATUS
☐ Ilyushin Il-14P	SP-FNM	14803010	SP-LNG	PV
☐ Mil Mi-2		525520028	SP-SEU	PVX
☐ Panstwowe Zaklady Lotnicze (PZL) TS-8 Bies		1E 05-22	0522	PV
☐ Wytwornia Sprzetu Komunikacyjnego (WSK) SBLim-2 (Lim-1) (MiG-15) [MiG-15UTI]	002	1A 090-02		PV
☐ Wytwornia Sprzetu Komunikacyjnego (WSK) Lim-5 [MiG-17F]	517	1C 05-17		PV

KOLECKJA BUK (POL8)

Address:	64-320 Buk
Admission:	By prior permission only.
Location:	About 30 km south west of Poznan.

The owners of this business had a yard at Babimost airfield. They purchased former military aircraft and their airframes and components were often sold to other museums and collectors. Most of the collection are now stored at a house in Buk. No doubt some of these will appear at museums soon.

TYPE	REG/SER	CON. NO.	PI/NOTES	STATUS
☐ Antonov An-2T	7352	1G 73-52		RA
☐ Mikoyan-Gurevich MiG-21M	1814	961814		RA
☐ Mikoyan-Gurevich MiG-21M	1903	961903		RA
☐ Mikoyan-Gurevich MiG-21MF	7902	967902		RA
☐ Mikoyan-Gurevich MiG-21MF	9105	969105		RA
☐ Mikoyan-Gurevich MiG-21PF	'2002'	762048	2048 – Probable identity.	RAX
☐ Mikoyan-Gurevich MiG-21PFM	6910	94A6910		RA
☐ Mikoyan-Gurevich MiG-21PFM	6915	94A6915		RA
☐ Mikoyan-Gurevich MiG-21PFM	7102	94A7102		RA
☐ Mikoyan-Gurevich MiG-21R	2533	94R022533		RA
☐ Mikoyan-Gurevich MiG-21UM	7507	07695175		RA
☐ Mikoyan-Gurevich MiG-21UM	5709	09695157		RA
☐ Mikoyan-Gurevich MiG-21UM	5710	10695157		RA
☐ Mikoyan-Gurevich MiG-21UM	5016	516905016		RA
☐ Mikoyan-Gurevich MiG-21UM	9292	516999292		RA
☐ Mikoyan-Gurevich MiG-21UM	9354	516999354		RA
☐ Mikoyan-Gurevich MiG-23MF	149	0390217149		RA
☐ Mikoyan-Gurevich MiG-23MF	457	0390220457		RA
☐ Mil Mi-2RL	1046	561046059		RA
☐ Panstwowe Zaklady Lotnicze (PZL) TS-11 Iskra 100bisA	412	1H 04-12		RA
☐ Panstwowe Zaklady Lotnicze (PZL) TS-11 Iskra 200bisD	W1741	3H 14-16	In Indian markings.	RA
☐ Panstwowe Zaklady Lotnicze (PZL) TS-11 Iskra 200bisD	'W1758'	3H 14-23 (?)	W1748 – Identity doubtful.	RAX
☐ Wytwornia Sprzetu Komunikacyjnego (WSK) Lim-2 [MiG-15bis]	'1978'	1B 012-29	1229	RAX
☐ Wytwornia Sprzetu Komunikacyjnego (WSK) SBLim-2 (Lim-1) [MiG-15] [MiG-15UTI]	'301'	1A 08-005	805	RAX

KOLEKCJA FUNDACJI POLSKIE ORLY (POL9)

Address:	Ul Woloska 18, 02-675 Warszawa.
Tel:	022-640-2711
Fax:	022-848-9657
Email:	aviation@curtisgroup.pl
Admission:	By prior permission only.
Location:	At Goraszka airfield which is about 15 km east of Warsaw off Route 17.

At the current time this organisation is restoring aircraft for museums in the country although the eventual aim is to set up their own exhibition. The Messerschmitt was recovered from Lake Trzebun in 1999. The aircraft had crashed soon after take off from a field at Gebbert. The pilot Ernst Pleines was killed and is buried in the town. The wreck was raised in three sections plus the engine. A painstaking rebuild commenced and the aircraft is now able to taxy. The 109 has spent some time on display in the museum at Krakow. A Yak-18 from the museum store has moved in for rebuild. Two helicopters have arrived from the Muzeum im Orla Bialego at Skarzysko-Kamienna. The pair had been on show there for many years and it is hoped that both can be rebuilt to flying condition. A few Polish built Po-2s are still active and more are under rebuild.

TYPE	REG/SER	CON. NO.	PI/NOTES	STATUS
☐ Centralne Studium Samolotow (CSS) 13 [Polikarpov Po-2A]	SP-YZN	420-37	(Polish AF),SP-AHT,SP-FZN	RAA
☐ Messerschmitt Bf 109G-6	'3'	163306	RQ+DR.	RA
☐ Mikoyan-Gurevich MiG-21U-600	'2420'	662719	2719	RAX
☐ Mil Mi-4A	611	16114		RA
☐ Wytwornia Sprzetu Komunikacyjnego (WSK) Lim-2 [MiG-15bis]	602	1B 006-02		RA
☐ Wytwornia Sprzetu Komunikacyjnego (WSK) SBLim-2 (Lim-1) [MiG-15] [MiG-15UTI]	006	1A 06-006		RA
☐ Wytwornia Sprzetu Komunikacyjnego (WSK) SM-1/300 [Mil Mi-1]	6003	S116003		RA
☐ Wytwornia Sprzetu Komunikacyjnego (WSK) SM-2	3025	S203025		RA
☐ Yakovlev Yak-18	SP-YYY	EM005	SP-AOP, SP-FYY	RAA

KOLEKCJA LOTNICZYCH ZAKLADÓW NAUKOWYCH (POL10)

Address:	Ul Kielzczwska 43 Psie Pole, 51-315 Wrocław.
Admission:	By prior permission only.
Location:	About 8 km north east of Wrocław off Route 8.

This training school for airframe and engine fitters was established just after World War II. Over the years many engineers left this establishment to work at airfields throughout the country. Several of the aircraft are parked in the courtyard and are displayed on open days. There is also a collection of photographs and parts to be seen.

TYPE	REG/SER	CON. NO.	PI/NOTES	STATUS
☐ Antonov An-2R	SP-DNA	1G 62-58		RA
☐ Mikoyan-Gurevich MiG-21PFM	5609	94A5609	5609, '11'	RA
☐ Mikoyan-Gurevich MiG-21UM	7502	02695175		RA
☐ Mil Mi-2	SP-SCE	534521125		RA
☐ Panstwowe Zaklady Lotnicze (PZL) TS-11 Iskra 100bisB	706	1H 07-06	0706	RA
☐ Wytwornia Sprzetu Komunikacyjnego (WSK) Lim-1 [MiG-15]	'1'		151	RAX

KOLEKCJA OLCHOWA (POL11)

Address:	Olchowa.
Admission:	By prior permission only.
Location:	About 15 km west of Rzeszów on Route 4.

This private collection has been placed next to the main road from to Rzeszów to Tarnów. Several of the airframes are in need of restoration. The Mi-2 obtained from Russia has been painted in false Soviet markings.

TYPE	REG/SER	CON. NO.	PI/NOTES	STATUS
☐ Antonov An-2T	5706	1G 157-06	Fuselage only.	PVD
☐ Mikoyan-Gurevich MiG-21R	2503	94R022503		PV
☐ Mikoyan-Gurevich MiG-21UM	9296	516999296		PV
☐ Mikoyan-Gurevich MiG-23MF	455	0390220455		PVD
☐ Mikoyan-Gurevich MiG-23MF	012	0390221012		PV
☐ Mil Mi-2	'28'	544115045	CCCP-23688, RA-23688	PVX
☐ Mil Mi-2Sz	SP-FSI	542503072	2503	PV
☐ Panstwowe Zaklady Lotnicze (PZL) TS-11 Iskra 100	108	1H 01-08		PV
☐ Panstwowe Zaklady Lotnicze (PZL) TS-11 Iskra 100bisA	321	1H 03-21		PV

KOLEKCJA PAŃSTWOWEJ STRAZY POZARNEJ (POL12)

Address:	Ul Prosta 32, 87-100 Torun.
Tel:	056-658-0124
Admission:	By prior permission only.
Location:	On the east side of the town at the junctions of Route 10 and Route 52.

The local fire brigade has set up a museum at their station. On show are vehicles used by the service, fire fighting equipment and photographs. The only aircraft is the MiG-21. A Bies has now disappeared.

TYPE	REG/SER	CON. NO.	PI/NOTES	STATUS
☐ Mikoyan-Gurevich MiG-21MF	9015	969015		PV

KOLEKCJA PAŃSTWOWYCH ZAKLADÓW LOTNICZYCH-OKĘCIE (POL13)

Address:	Al. Krakowska 110/114, 02-256 Warszawa-Okecie.
Tel:	022-461173
Admission:	By prior permission only.
Location:	About 7 km south west of the city on Route 7.

The P.Z.L. factory moved to Okecie in the early 1930s and is still producing aircraft. Set up in 1928 the company produced many original designs until the outbreak of World War II. Three aircraft are near the main gate.

TYPE	REG/SER	CON. NO.	PI/NOTES	STATUS
☐ Panstwowe Zaklady Lotnicze (PZL) TS-8 Bies	'114'			PVX
☐ Panstwowe Zaklady Lotnicze (PZL) 104 Wilga 40	'SP-PZL'	PR59091	SP-PHC, 'SP-CNP'	PVX
☐ Panstwowe Zaklady Lotnicze (PZL) 106/I Kruk	SP-PBK	05005		RA

KOLEKCJA PAŃSTOWOWYCH ZAKLADÓW LOTNICZYCH-SWIDNIK (POL14)

Address:	Ajeja Lotników Polskich 1, 21-045 Swidnik.
Tel:	081-468091
Fax:	081-4680919
Email:	jan.mazur@pzl.swidnik.pl
Admission:	By prior permission only.
Location:	In the northern part of the town which is 8 km east of Lublin.

The first aircraft factory in the region opened in Lublin in 1920 and the initial contract was to produce under licence one hundred Ansaldo A-1s. Many types were constructed up to the outbreak of World War II. In the late 1940s the government decided to build a new factory at Swidnik. The wings for the Lim-1 (MiG-15) were made here before the factory turned its attention to the Mil Mi-1 helicopter. The first original design the SM-2 flew in 1959 and since then many have been built along with more modern designs and some advanced sailplanes.

TYPE	REG/SER	CON. NO.	PI/NOTES	STATUS
☐ Mil Mi-2M2	02	ZD 0102113	SP-PSK	PV
☐ Wytwornia Sprzetu Komunikacyjnego (WSK) Lim-2 [MiG-15bis]	'306'	1B 013-06	1306	RAX
☐ Wytwornia Sprzetu Komunikacyjnego (WSK) SM-1/300 [Mil Mi-1]	'SM-1'			RAX
☐ Wytwornia Sprzetu Komunikacyjnego (WSK) SM-2	'SM-2'			RAX

KOLEKCJA POLIGONU NADARZYCE (POL15)

Address:	Nadarzyce.
Admission:	By prior permission only.
Location:	North of Walcz.

The site is used as a gunnery and bombing range and several airframes are parked on the vast area. A collection of preserved aircraft has been assembled near the camp. These represent types which have used the base.

TYPE	REG/SER	CON. NO.	PI/NOTES	STATUS
☐ Mikoyan-Gurevich MiG-21M	1912	961912		RA
☐ Mikoyan-Gurevich MiG-23MF	117	0390224117		RA
☐ Mil Mi-2	0609	510609018	609	RA
☐ Panstwowe Zaklady Lotnicze (PZL) TS-11 Iskra 100bisB	614	1H 06-14		RA
☐ Wytwornia Sprzetu Komunikacyjnego (WSK) SBLim-2 [MiG-15UTI]	315	3315		RA

KOLEKCJA WYŻSZEJ SZKOŁY OFICERSKIEJ SIL POWIETRZNYCH (POL16)

Address:	3 Ul. Warszawska 08-521 Deblin.
Tel:	081-8830612
Fax:	081-8837103
Admission:	Some aircraft on permanent view.
Location:	In the eastern suburbs of the town off Route 822.

In 1927 the Officers Flying School moved to Deblin from Grudziadz. The site still houses the unit and a display of types operated over the last few years has been set up outside the main gate to the base. On view are three Polish designed machines. The Junak was the first indigenous design to be made in large numbers after World War II. The prototype flew in February 1948 and the production Junak 2 entered service in 1952. The tricycle undercarriage Junak 3 followed two years later. The Bies made its maiden flight in 1955 and the Air Force received its first examples in early 1958. More types have been put on show in front of the hangar of the official Air Force aerobatic team 'Bialo-Czerwone Iskry'. Since the 1950s the service has operated a display team and various versions of MiG were flown. The Iryda jet was designed as a replacement for the Iskra and it made its maiden flight in 1985. The type was bedevilled by problems and only just over twenty were produced. Service trials took place in the mid-1990s and in 2003 the Air Force abandoned the programme. The fourth prototype is in the collection. The piston engined Orlik took to the air in October 1984 and the turbo version followed in July 1986. Acceptance trials started in January 1990 and the first production aircraft were delivered in March 1994. The type is now in service with the pilot training school at Radom. The Traditions Room displays photographs, models, documents, uniforms etc. tracing the history of the base and its units.

TYPE	REG/SER	CON. NO.	PI/NOTES	STATUS
☐ Antonov An-2T	9866	1G 98-66		RA
☐ Dassault Mirage 5BA	BA-21	21	In Belgian markings.	RA
☐ Ilyushin Il-28E	65	2212		RA
☐ Lotnicze Warsztaty Doswiadczalne (L.W.D.) Junak 3	'12'		86	PVX
☐ Mikoyan-Gurevich MiG-17PF	948	0948		PV
☐ Mikoyan-Gurevich MiG-21MF	9113	969113		RA
☐ Mikoyan-Gurevich MiG-23MF	021	0390224121		RA
☐ Mil Mi-2TSz	'085'	541628100	1628	PVX
☐ Mil Mi-8T	414	0414		RA
☐ Mil Mi-24D	015	A1015		RA
☐ Mil Mi-24D	016	A1016		RA
☐ Panstwowe Zaklady Lotnicze (PZL) TS-8 Bies	910	1E 09-10	0910	PV
☐ Panstwowe Zaklady Lotnicze (PZL) TS-11 Iskra 100	7	1H 02-10	0210, 210	RA
☐ Panstwowe Zaklady Lotnicze (PZL) TS-11 Iskra 100bisB	801	1H 08-01	0801	PV
☐ Panstwowe Zaklady Lotnicze (PZL) 130TM Orlik	005	01870005		RA
☐ Panstwowe Zaklady Lotnicze (PZL) I-22 Iryda	'104'	1ANP 01-04	SP-PWC	RA
☐ Sukhoi Su-20R	6265	74415		RA
☐ Wytwornia Sprzetu Komunikacyjnego (WSK) Lim-2 [MiG-15bis]		1B 019-29	1929, '1980'	PV
☐ Wytwornia Sprzetu Komunikacyjnego (WSK) SBLim-2M [MiG-15UTI] (MiG-15bis)	197	142697		RA
☐ Wytwornia Sprzetu Komunikacyjnego (WSK) SM-1/300 [Mil Mi-1]	'1540'	S115005	5005	RAX
☐ Wytwornia Sprzetu Komunikacyjnego (WSK) SM-2	'405'	S204005	4005	PVX
☐ Yakovlev Yak-18A	'26'		25, SP-BMN	PVX
☐ Yakovlev Yak-23	087			PV

LUBUSKIE MUZEUM WOJSKOWE (POL17)

Address:	Drzonow 54, 66-014 Letnica.
Tel:	068-3211829
Admission:	Wednesday-Friday 0900-1530; Saturday-Sunday 1000-1500.
Location:	About 15 km south west of Zielona Gora. Off Road 275 to Swiecko – follow signs to Radomia then proceed for 2 km.

Opened as the Muzeum Braterstwa Broni on January 1st 1978 the museum changed its name a decade later. The indoor displays in a country house trace the development of military technology from early swords up to modern automatic guns. There is special emphasis on the moral and social aspects of warfare. The majority of the aircraft and military vehicles are located in parkland surrounding the mansion. A former workshop has been converted into an exhibition hall and three aircraft are on view here. The first aircraft to arrive was the Swidnik produced SM-2 helicopter which was delivered to Drzonow in July 1978. The display includes a wide range of types used by the Polish Air Force in recent years. A rarity is one of the few single seat versions of the locally designed Iskra trainer. A number of licence built MiG jets produced at Mielec are on show along with several built in Russia. Two transport types can be seen. The Lisunov Li-2 was delivered to LOT in June 1946 and flew on their routes for fifteen years. The pleasant grounds of the house provide an excellent setting for this ever improving display of aircraft, military vehicles and weapons.

TYPE	REG/SER	CON. NO.	PI/NOTES	STATUS
☐ Avia B-33 [Ilyushin Il-10]	'01'	B33-5339	11	PVX
☐ Ilyushin Il-14FG (Il-14P)	3069	14803069	3069, SP-LNR, 3069, SP-LNP, 3069, SP-LNU, 3069, SP-LNU	PV
☐ Ilyushin Il-28	50	56538		PV
☐ Lisunov Li-2P [Douglas DC-3 modified]	SP-LAS	18423203		PV
☐ Mikoyan-Gurevich MiG-17PF	307	58310307		PV
☐ Mikoyan-Gurevich MiG-21F-13	2307	742307		PV
☐ Mikoyan-Gurevich MiG-21PFMN	7815	94N7815		PV
☐ Mikoyan-Gurevich MiG-21R	1423	94R01423		PV
☐ Mikoyan-Gurevich MiG-21U-400	1318	661318		PV
☐ Mil Mi-2M2	01-04	ZD 0104054		PV
☐ Mil Mi-2Sz	1624	541624100		PV
☐ Mil Mi-4A	314	03141		PV
☐ Panstwowe Zaklady Lotnicze (PZL) TS-8 Bies	0310	1E 03-10		PV
☐ Panstwowe Zaklady Lotnicze (PZL) TS-11 Iskra 100bisB	0506	1H 05-06		PV
☐ Panstwowe Zaklady Lotnicze (PZL) TS-11 Iskra 200bisC	0530	2H 05-30		PV
☐ Panstwowe Zaklady Lotnicze (PZL) TS-11 Iskra 200BR	0823	4H 08-23		PV
☐ Sukhoi Su-7UM	905	2905		PV
☐ Sukhoi Su-20R	6138	74828		PV
☐ Wytwornia Sprzetu Komunikacyjnego (WSK) Lim-2R [MiG-15bis]	1809	1B 018-09		PV
☐ Wytwornia Sprzetu Komunikacyjnego (WSK) SBLim-2A (Lim-1) [MiG-15] [MiG-15UTI]	8020	1A 08-020		PV
☐ Wytwornia Sprzetu Komunikacyjnego (WSK) SBLim-2M (Lim-1) [MiG-15] [MiG-15UTI]	112	1A 10-012		PV
☐ Wytwornia Sprzetu Komunikacyjnego (WSK) Lim-5R (Lim-5) [MiG-17F]	1721	1C 17-21		PV
☐ Wytwornia Sprzetu Komunikacyjnego (WSK) Lim-6R [MiG-17F]	635	1J 06-35		PV
☐ Wytwornia Sprzetu Komunikacyjnego (WSK) SM-1Sz [Mil Mi-1U]	1105	1105		PV
☐ Wytwornia Sprzetu Komunikacyjnego (WSK) SM-2	1005	S201005		PV
☐ Yakovlev Yak-11	'08'	64233	17 (DDR)	PVX
☐ Yakovlev Yak-12A		12640	SP-BKK, SP-CXH – In false military markings.	PVX
☐ Yakovlev Yak-18	'08'	6131	DM-WDG, SP-BRN	PVX
☐ Yakovlev Yak-23	06	807		PV

MUZEUM AEROKLUB GLIWICE (POL18)

Address:	Lotnisko, PL 44-100 Gliwice.
Tel:	032-230-1592
Fax:	032-230-1592
Email:	mail@vgcpoland.aleja.info
Admission:	When the airfield is open.
Location:	About 3 km south of the town.

This active club has set up a glider museum in one of its hangars. On show are photographs and documents along with components. A number of withdrawn sailplanes have been exhibited. The active fleet includes more classic types and these are listed here. The International Vintage Glider Rally was held at the airfield in 2004 when participants arrived from many countries. Some of the gliders are privately owned.

TYPE	REG/SER	CON. NO.	PI/NOTES	STATUS
☐ Antonov An-2T				RAA
☐ Mikoyan-Gurevich MiG-21PFM	5615	94A5615		RA
☐ Panstwowe Zaklady Lotnicze (PZL) 101A Gawron	SP-CGC	96184		RAA
☐ Panstwowe Zaklady Lotnicze (PZL) 104 Wilga 35A	SP-FDA	62161		RAA
☐ Panstwowe Zaklady Lotnicze – Krosno KR-03A Puchatek	SP-3547			RA
☐ Szybowcowy Zaklad Doswiadczalny S.Z.D.8bis Jaskolka				RAC
☐ Szybowcowy Zaklad Doswiadczalny S.Z.D.9bis Bocian 1D	SP-2444	F-853		RAA
☐ Szybowcowy Zaklad Doswiadczalny S.Z.D.9bis Bocian 1E	SP-2687	P-643		RAA
☐ Szybowcowy Zaklad Doswiadczalny S.Z.D.9bis Bocian 1E	SP-2825	P-709		RA
☐ Szybowcowy Zaklad Doswiadczalny S.Z.D.9bis Bocian 1E	SP-3046	P-759		RAA
☐ Szybowcowy Zaklad Doswiadczalny S.Z.D.12A Mucha 100	SP-1999	F-460		RAA
☐ Szybowcowy Zaklad Doswiadczalny S.Z.D.21-2B Kobuz 3	SP-2473	W-261		RA

TYPE	REG/SER	CON. NO.	PI/NOTES	STATUS
☐ Szybowcowy Zaklad Doswiadczalny S.Z.D.21-2B Kobuz 3	SP-2480	W-268		RA
☐ Szybowcowy Zaklad Doswiadczalny S.Z.D.21-2B Kobuz 3	SP-2482	W-270		RAA
☐ Szybowcowy Zaklad Doswiadczalny S.Z.D.21-2B Kobuz 3	SP-2489	W-277		RA
☐ Szybowcowy Zaklad Doswiadczalny S.Z.D.21-2B Kobuz 3	SP-2500	W-287		RAA
☐ Szybowcowy Zaklad Doswiadczalny S.Z.D.22C Mucha Standard	SP-2288	F-603		RAA
☐ Szybowcowy Zaklad Doswiadczalny S.Z.D.22C Mucha Standard	SP-2118	F-780		RA
☐ Szybowcowy Zaklad Doswiadczalny S.Z.D.24 Foka	SP-2384	W-179		RAA
☐ Szybowcowy Zaklad Doswiadczalny S.Z.D.25A Lis	SP-3534	F-730	SP-2346	RAA
☐ Szybowcowy Zaklad Doswiadczalny S.Z.D.30 Pirat	SP-3652	B-363	DM-1759,DDR-1759,D-3759	RAA
☐ Szybowcowy Zaklad Doswiadczalny S.Z.D.30 Pirat	SP-2593	B-450		RAA
☐ Szybowcowy Zaklad Doswiadczalny S.Z.D.30 Pirat	SP-2877	S-05-48		RAA
☐ Szybowcowy Zaklad Doswiadczalny S.Z.D.30 Pirat	SP-3024	S-09.23		RAA
☐ Szybowcowy Zaklad Doswiadczalny S.Z.D.31 Zefir 4	SP-2519	293		RAA
☐ Szybowcowy Zaklad Doswiadczalny S.Z.D.35 Bekas	SP-2557	X-101		RAA
☐ Szybowcowy Zaklad Doswiadczalny S.Z.D.36A Cobra 15	SP-3088	W-819		RAA
☐ Szybowcowy Zaklad Doswiadczalny S.Z.D.38A Jantar 1	SP-2913	B-683		RAA
☐ Szybowcowy Zaklad Doswiadczalny S.Z.D.40X Halny	SP-2645	X-106		RAA
☐ Szybowcowy Zaklad Doswiadczalny S.Z.D.48-3 Jantar Standard 3	SP-3297	B-1432		RAA
☐ Szybowcowy Zaklad Doswiadczalny S.Z.D.50-3 Puchacz	SP-3319	B-1545		RAA
☐ Szybowcowy Zaklad Doswiadczalny S.Z.D.50-3 Puchacz	SP-3488	B-1868		RAA
☐ Szybowcowy Zaklad Doswiadczalny S.Z.D.51-1 Junior	SP-3430	B-1795		RAA
☐ Szybowcowy Zaklad Doswiadczalny S.Z.D.51-1 Junior	SP-3478	B-1839		RAA
☐ Szybowcowy Zaklad Doswiadczalny S.Z.D.51-1 Junior	SP-3310	W-932		RAA
☐ Wojskowe Warsztaty Szybowcowe W.W.S.1 Salamandra				RAC
☐ Yakovlev Yak-12M	SP-AWC	189776		RAA
☐ Zlin Z-42				RAA
☐ Zlin Z-526F Trener Master				RAA

MUZEUM BARWY I OREŻA 'ARSENAŁ' (POL19)

Address:	ul Zamkowa 2, 22-400 Zamosc
Tel:	084-6384076
Fax:	084-6384076
Admission:	Tuesday-Sunday 0900-1600. Outside weapons park – April October daily 0900-1800.
Location:	In the town which is about 70 km south east of Lublin.

The development of weapons from the early times is portrayed in this museum which was established in 1980. The exhibition, which also features uniforms, is housed in the armoury building erected in the 1580s. The Mil Mi-2 and Iskra arrived in 2001 from the local technical school which closed in the mid-1990s.

TYPE	REG/SER	CON. NO.	PI/NOTES	STATUS
☐ Mil Mi-2Sz	4601	544601016		PV
☐ Panstwowe Zaklady Lotnicze (PZL) TS-11 Iskra 100bisB	611	1H 06-11	0611	PV

MUZEUM CYTADELI POZNAŃSKIEJ (POL20)

Address:	Stary Rynek 9, 61-772 Poznan.
Tel:	061-852-6739
Email:	Mnoffice@man.poznzn.pl
Admission:	Summer Daily 0900-1700; Winter Daily 1000-1600.
Location:	In the citadel in the Park of Friendship which is in the northern part of the city off the road to Kosalin.

Built by the Prussians in the 1830s the massive citadel fortress overlooked the city. In 1945 the German forces held out for four weeks and the fortifications were almost completely destroyed in the battle. The museum opened in 1964 and at that time three aircraft, the Czech built Yak-11, the MiG-15 and the Bies were show. The display is laid out on a terrace around one of the few remaining parts of the fort. Also on show in this area are several guns and vehicles. An exhibition tracing the military history of the city is by the main gate to the park.

TYPE	REG/SER	CON. NO.	PI/NOTES	STATUS
☐ Antonov An-2T	9863	1G 98-63		PV
☐ Ilyushin Il-28R	4	1910		PV
☐ Let C-11 [Yakovlev Yak-11]	04	172105		PV
☐ Mikoyan-Gurevich MiG-15	01			PV
☐ Mikoyan-Gurevich MiG-21PFMA	4106	94A4106		PV
☐ Mil Mi-2R	3649	563649094		PV
☐ Panstwowe Zaklady Lotnicze (PZL) TS-8 Bies	0306	1E 03-06		PV
☐ Panstwowe Zaklady Lotnicze (PZL) TS-11 Iskra 100bisB	710	1H 07-10	0710	PV
☐ Sukhoi Su-20R	4245	6605	05	PV
☐ Wytwornia Sprzetu Komunikacyjnego (WSK) Lim-5 [MiG-17F]	1419	1C 14-19		PV
☐ Wytwornia Sprzetu Komunikacyjnego (WSK) SM-1Wszb (SM-1Wb) [Mil Mi-1M]	2018	402018	18	PV
☐ Yakovlev Yak-12M	998	210998		PV

MUZEUM IM ORLA BIALEGO (POL21)

Address:	ul. Sloneczna 90, 26-110 Skarzysko-Kamienna.
Tel:	041-2520231
Fax:	041-2520231
Email:	bialy@wp.pl
Admission:	Museum daily 0900-1700; Outside park daily dawn-dusk.
Location:	In the southern part of the town about 1 km. east of Route 7.

The museum opened about a quarter of a century ago as the Muzeum Zygmunt Berling and took up its present name (White Eagle Museum) in 1991. The outside park has an impressive range of military hardware, including missiles, on show. The indoor display traces the history of the Polish forces. There is a section devoted to the local resistance movement during World War II. The exhibits show vividly the bravery of members of the groups and the hardship and dangers they endured. On show are many photographs highlighting this. The aircraft outside have all been provided by the Air Force and include a comparatively rare Yak-23 fighter. The East German built Il-14 was delivered to the Polish Air Force in February 1959 and apart from a three month spell with LOT in 1962 it served until the military until retired in the late 1980s. Two helicopters a Mil Mi-4 and a WSK SM-1 left in 2005. Both these have gone to the Polish Eagles facility at Goraszka for rebuilds.

TYPE	REG/SER	CON. NO.	PI/NOTES	STATUS
☐ Ilyushin Il-14P	3054	14803054	DM-ZZL, 009 (Poland), SP-LNR, 009, 47 (Poland)	PV
☐ Mikoyan-Gurevich MiG-17PF	1001	1001		PV
☐ Mikoyan-Gurevich MiG-21PF	2401	762401		PV
☐ Panstwowe Zaklady Lotnicze (PZL) TS-8 Bies	'0401'	1E 02-07	0207, SP-CLC	PVX
☐ Sukhoi Su-7BKL	809	7809		PV
☐ Wytwornia Sprzetu Komunikacyjnego (WSK) Lim-2 [MiG-15bis]	1526	1B 015-26		PV
☐ Wytwornia Sprzetu Komunikacyjnego (WSK) Lim-6MR (Lim-5P) [MiG-17PF]	635	1D 06-35		PV
☐ Yakovlev Yak-23	21			PV

MUZEUM KATYNSKIE / MUZEUM POLSKIEJ TECHNIKI WOJSKOWEJ (POL22)

Address:	Fort Sadyba, ul. Powinska 13, 02-920 Warszaw.
Tel:	022-8582221
Admission:	Wednesday-Sunday 1000-1600.
Location:	In the south eastern suburbs of the city.

Located in a fort in the south eastern part of the city this museum is a branch of the main Polish Army Museum. The structure was part of the eastern defences of the city across the River Vistula from the main centre. The museum has staged a display of heavy armaments in the grounds. Military vehicles and guns can be seen parked near the main entrance. The display highlights the development of military technology. Behind the fortifications is the collection of aircraft. Examples of types used by the Air Force have been acquired and several await restoration. The events of 1940 when twenty thousand Polish officers were executed by their Russian captors is portrayed. Many personal items have been recovered from the site near Smolensk.

TYPE	REG/SER	CON. NO.	PI/NOTES	STATUS
☐ Ilyushin Il-28	'65'	56729	22, 41	PVX
☐ Mikoyan-Gurevich MiG-15	'365'	231873	625, 873, '1964'	PVX
☐ Mikoyan-Gurevich MiG-21MF-75	8113	968113		PV
☐ Mikoyan-Gurevich MiG-21PF	1802	761802		PV
☐ Mikoyan-Gurevich MiG-21PFM	6604	94A6604		PV
☐ Mikoyan-Gurevich MiG-21UM	6006	06695160		PV
☐ Mikoyan-Gurevich MiG-23MF	148	0390217148		PV
☐ Mil Mi-2R	5827	565827128		PV
☐ Mil Mi-2T	2215	542215012		PV
☐ Mil Mi-2URN	3101	563101093		PV
☐ Mil Mi-24D	013	A1013		PV
☐ Panstwowe Zaklady Lotnicze (PZL) TS-8 Bies		1E 04-09	0409, '1751'	PV
☐ Sukhoi Su-7BKL	13	6013		PV
☐ Sukhoi Su-7BKL	17	6017		PV
☐ Sukhoi Su-7BKL	815	7815		PV
☐ Sukhoi Su-7UM	331	3313		PV
☐ Sukhoi Su-20R	6131	76301		PV
☐ Wytwornia Sprzetu Komunikacyjnego (WSK) Lim-2 [MiG-15bis]	'1132'	1B 013-12	1312	PVX
☐ Wytwornia Sprzetu Komunikacyjnego (WSK) SBLim-2A (Lim-1) [MiG-15] [MiG-15UTI]	6010	1A 06-010		PV
☐ Wytwornia Sprzetu Komunikacyjnego (WSK) SBLim-2A [MiG-15UTI]	3303	3303		PV
☐ Wytwornia Sprzetu Komunikacyjnego (WSK) Lim-5 [MiG-17F]	1217	1C 12-17		PV
☐ Wytwornia Sprzetu Komunikacyjnego (WSK) Lim-5 [MiG-17F]	1604	1C 16-04		PV
☐ Wytwornia Sprzetu Komunikacyjnego (WSK) Lim-6bis (Lim-5M) [MiG-17F]	101	1F 01-01		PV
☐ Yakovlev Yak-23	17	1017	17, '12', '23'	PV

MUZEUM LOTNICTWA POLSKIEGO (POL23)

Address:	Al. Jana Pawla II 39, 30-969 Kraków.
Tel:	012-4129000
Fax:	012-4127855
Email:	muzlot@bci.krakow.pl
Admission:	May-October Tuesday-Friday 0900-1600; Saturday 1000-1500; Sunday 1000-1600.
Location:	At the disused airfield of Rakowice which is about 5 km east of the city off Route 777.

Traditionally Poland has been to the forefront in aviation. Gliding started in the country in the 1890s and several powered aircraft took to the air before the outbreak of World War I. The Polish aircraft industry was one of the most technically advanced in the inter-war period. After the end of the conflict factories produced Soviet types under licence along with their own products. The first aviation exhibitions were set up in the country in the early 1920s and in Poznan a museum had a number of World War I types on show. In 1968 a report was published of the survival of a number of aircraft from the famous Deutsche Luftfahrt Sammlung in Berlin destroyed by Allied bombing in November 1943. The damaged airframes and engines from Berlin were sent on a train to Czarnkow where they remained until 1945. The collection moved to Gadki near Poznan and in 1950 to Pilawa near Deblin. Polish built aircraft and engines were added. A further change of location to Wroclaw took place. In the early 1960s it was decided to set up an aviation museum at the disused airfield of Rakowice in the eastern suburbs of Krakow. The collection has grown steadily over the last thirty years and many important Polish prototypes and production models have been saved. I made my first visit to Krakow in the summer of 1968 when the exhibits were just stored in the hangar with the Berlin aircraft laid out on one side. Ten years on a display had been set up in the front of the hangar and a decade later this filled the whole building. A pavilion has now been built to house some of the Berlin collection and several restored aircraft and fuselages can be seen. The Messerschmitt Me 209 is the aircraft in which Fritz Wendel set the then World Air Speed Record for landplanes at Augsburg on April 26th 1939. A number of exchanges have taken place with a D.H.9 coming to England in return for a Spitfire, the Fokker Spin going to Holland and a Jeannin Stahltaube returning to Berlin. The main hangar presents an excellent display of the Polish post-war aviation industry along with some American and British aircraft. Gliding has always been important in Poland and examples of types spanning the last sixty years are suspended from the roof. The outside area has been reorganised and lines of military jets are on show along with some piston engined transports and helicopters. Almost all types used by the Polish Air Force in recent years have been acquired. Aircraft from other air forces are also joining the collection. The museum has an active restoration programme in its own workshops and the Polish aviation industry has rebuilt several other machines. There are plans for new buildings which will result in more aircraft being placed under cover.

TYPE	REG/SER	CON. NO.	PI/NOTES	STATUS
☐ Aachen FVA 10B Rheinland (D.F.S. 108-74)	SP-051	'B-1939'		RAD
☐ Aero Super 45S	SP-LXC	03-002		RA
☐ Aero 145	SP-LXH	172006		PV
☐ Aero 145	SP-TNA	172011	OK-NHH	RA
☐ Aero L-60 Brigadyr	SP-FXA	150723		PV
☐ Akaflieg München Mü 13d	SP-824	1535	(Germany)	RA
☐ Albatros B IIa (L 30)	'1302/17'	10019	D-690, D-EKDU, NG+UR	PVX
☐ Albatros C I (L 6)	C.197/15		C.197/15, D-142 – fuselage on show.	PV
☐ Albatros H I (Siemens-Schuckert D IV modified)	10114	10114		RAC

☐ Albatros L 101	D-EKYQ	245		RAD
☐ Allgemeine Elektrizitats A.E.G.-Wagner Eule		E2		RAD
☐ Antonov An-2T	5705	1G 157-05		PV
☐ Avia B-33 [Ilyushin Il-10]	4	B33-3061		PV
☐ Aviatik C III	C.12250/17	1996	Fuselage on show.	PV
☐ Bell 26E Airacobra (P-39Q)			Wings and tail only.	RAD
☐ Blériot XI (R)		Z2		PV
☐ Borzecki Altostratus				RA
☐ Bücker Bü 131B Jungmann	SP-AFO	'13113'	(German) – c/n possibly corruption of 131B.	PV
☐ Centralne Studium Samolotow (CSS) 12	SP-BAR	1	Cockpit only	RAD
☐ Centralne Studium Samolotow (CSS) 13 [Polikarpov Po-2A]	SP-API	420-64		RA
☐ Centralne Studium Samolotow (CSS) S-13 [Polikarpov Po-2S]	SP-AXT	9-3505	Ambulance Version	PV
☐ Cessna 318E Dragonfly (A-37B)	87916	43063	68-7916 – in South Vietnamese markings.	PV
☐ Cessna T-50 Bobcat (C-78) (UC-78)	SP-GLC	5765	43-31827, SP-LEM	PV
☐ Curtiss 35B Hawk II	D-IRIK	H.81	D-3165, D-1515	RAC
☐ De Havilland D.H.82A Tiger Moth	'T8209'	86514	NM206, F-BGCQ	PVC
☐ Deutsche Flugzeugwerke (D.F.W.) C Vc	17077/17	473		PV
☐ Farman HF-4 (R)		Z1		PV
☐ Friedrich Etrich Taube (R)	D-EFRI			RAD
☐ Geeste Moewe 4		4		RA
☐ Gotha Go 147			Wings only.	RAD
☐ Grigorovich M.15		R 11C.262		PV
☐ Halberstadt CL II	15459/17	1046 (or 1048)	CL.15459/1 – fuselage on show.	PV
☐ Harcerskie Warsztaty Lotnicze Pegaz	SP-590	1		RA
☐ Heinkel HE 5f	D-1		D-1, D-OMIP	RA
☐ Horten Ho II	D-Habicht	2	Major components	RAD
☐ Ilyushin Il-14S	3078	14803078		PV
☐ Ilyushin Il-28R	72	41909		PV
☐ Ilyushin Il-28U	S3	69216		PV
☐ Instytut Lotnictwa BZ-1 Gil	SP-GIL	1		PV
☐ Instytut Lotnictwa BZ-4 Zuk		2		RA
☐ Instytut Lotnictwa JK-1 Trzmiel		2		PV
☐ Instytut Lotnictwa TS-8 Bies	SP-GLF	P.1		RA
☐ Instytut Szybownictwa IS-1 Sep bis	SP-552	011		PV
☐ Instytut Szybownictwa IS-3 ABC-A	SP-1697	270		PV
☐ Instytut Szybownictwa IS-4 Jastrzab	SP-1383	009		PV
☐ Instytut Szybownictwa IS-4 Jastrzab	SP-1391	017		PV
☐ Instytut Szybownictwa IS-6X Nietoperz	SP-1220	069		PV
☐ Instytut Szybownictwa IS-A Salamandra	SP-322	003		PV
☐ Instytut Szybownictwa IS-B Komar 49	SP-985	144P		PV
☐ Instytut Szybownictwa IS-C Zuraw [Jacobs Kranich II]	SP-1213	GD-009		PV
☐ Instytut Szybownictwa IS-C Zuraw [Jacobs Kranich II]	SP-1295	GD-012		PV
☐ Jacobs Meise (D.F.S. 108-70)	SP-390	82	(Germany)	RAD
☐ Jacobs Rhönsperber (D.F.S. 108-51)	SP-148		(Germany)	PV
☐ Jacobs Weihe (D.F.S. 108-68)	SP-029	00316	(Germany)	PV/R
☐ Janowski J-3				RA
☐ Jeannin Stahltaube	A.180/14	76	On loan to DTM, Germany.	–
☐ Kazan Aviation Institute KAI-12 Primorec	SP-2062	2008		PV/R
☐ Let L-200A Morava	SP-NXA	170409	SP-NAA	PV
☐ Letov LF-107 Lunak	SP-1146	15		PV
☐ Levasseur Antoinette				RAD
☐ Lilienthal Normal-Segelapparat (R)				PV
☐ Lisunov Li-2T [Douglas DC-3 modified]	027	18439102	05, SP-LDA	PV
☐ Lotnicze Warsztaty Doswiadczalne (L.W.D.) Junak 1	SP-GLA	16		RA
☐ Lotnicze Warsztaty Doswiadczalne (L.W.D.) Junak 2	SP-ADM	732	(Polish A.F.)	RA
☐ Lotnicze Warsztaty Doswiadczalne (L.W.D.) Junak 3	SP-BPL	13-9578	(Polish A.F.)	PV
☐ Lotnicze Warsztaty Doswiadczalne (L.W.D.) Szpak 2	SP-AAA	01		RAC
☐ Lotnicze Warsztaty Doswiadczalne (L.W.D.) Szpak 3	SP-AAB	002		RAD
☐ Lotnicze Warsztaty Doswiadczalne (L.W.D.) Szpak 4T	SP-AAG	48-004		PV
☐ Lotnicze Warsztaty Doswiadczalne (L.W.D.) Zak 3	SP-AAX	10		RA
☐ Lotnicze Warsztaty Doswiadczalne (L.W.D.) Zuch 1	SP-BAD	17		RA
☐ Lotnicze Warsztaty Doswiadczalne (L.W.D.) Zuch 2	SP-BAM	22		RA
☐ Lotnicze Warsztaty Doswiadczalne (L.W.D.) Zuch 2	SP-BAO	24		RA
☐ Lotnicze Warsztaty Doswiadczalne (L.W.D.) Zuraw	SP-GLB	26		RA
☐ Luft-Verkehrs-Gesellschaft (L.V.G.) B IIa	B.350/17			PV
☐ Luftfahrzeug-Gesellschaft (L.F.G.) Roland D VIB	D 2225/18		Fuselage on show.	PV
☐ Marganski EM-10 Bielik (FSM)		P-19		PV
☐ Marganski S-1 Swift	SP-P600	P03/XP	SP-P600, (SP-3499)	PV
☐ Messerschmitt Me 209V1	D-INJR	1185	Fuselage only	RAC
☐ Mikoyan-Gurevich MiG-19PM	905	650905		PV
☐ Mikoyan-Gurevich MiG-21F-13	809	740809		PV

☐ Mikoyan-Gurevich MiG-21bis	9204	75089204		PV
☐ Mikoyan-Gurevich MiG-21MF	6504	966504		PV
☐ Mikoyan-Gurevich MiG-21PF	1901	761901		PV
☐ Mikoyan-Gurevich MiG-21PF	2004	762004		PV
☐ Mikoyan-Gurevich MiG-21PF	2009	762009		PV
☐ Mikoyan-Gurevich MiG-21PFM	6513	94A6513		PV
☐ Mikoyan-Gurevich MiG-21PFM	6614	94A6614		PV
☐ Mikoyan-Gurevich MiG-21PFM	01	94ML-01		PV
☐ Mikoyan-Gurevich MiG-21R	1125	94R021125		PV
☐ Mikoyan-Gurevich MiG-21U-400	1217	661217		PV
☐ Mikoyan-Gurevich MiG-21UM	9349	51699349		PV
☐ Mikoyan-Gurevich MiG-21US	4401	01685144		PV
☐ Mikoyan-Gurevich MiG-23MF	120	0390217120		PV
☐ Mil Mi-2Ch	6048	516048049		PV
☐ Mil Mi-2URP	4316	564316105		PV
☐ Mil Mi-4A	511	15114		PV
☐ Mil Mi-4ME	617	06175		PV
☐ Misztal-Duleba MD-12F	SP-PBL	0004		PV
☐ North American NA-182 Texan (T-6G)	'49-2983'	182-415	51-14728	PVX
☐ Northrop N-156E Tiger II (F-5E)	00852	R.1033	78-0852, 00852 (Vietnam)	PV
☐ Panstwowe Zaklady Lotnicze (PZL) P.11c	2	562	8.63	PV
☐ Panstwowe Zaklady Lotnicze (PZL) M-2		1/2	Static test airframe.	RA
☐ Panstwowe Zaklady Lotnicze (PZL) M-4P Tarpan	SP-PAK	1/3		PV
☐ Panstwowe Zaklady Lotnicze (PZL) S-4 Kania 3	SP-PBB	02		PV
☐ Panstwowe Zaklady Lotnicze (PZL) TS-8 Bies	0309	1E 03-09		PV
☐ Panstwowe Zaklady Lotnicze (PZL) TS-11 Iskra	04	111 PR04		RA
☐ Panstwowe Zaklady Lotnicze (PZL) TS-11 Iskra 100bisB	1007	1H 10-07		PV
☐ Panstwowe Zaklady Lotnicze (PZL) 104 Wilga 43	SP-PHE	PR59093		RA
☐ Panstwowe Zaklady Lotnicze (PZL) 105 Flamingo	SP-PRC	0089002		PV
☐ Panstwowe Zaklady Lotnicze (PZL) 106A Kruk	SP-KFB	07810131		PV
☐ Panstwowe Zaklady Lotnicze (PZL) 130 Orlik	SP-PCB	003		PV
☐ Panstwowe Zaklady Lotnicze (PZL) 130TC Orlik	SP-PCE	0930011		PV
☐ Piper J-3C-65 Cub (O-59A) (L-4A)	43-29233	10524	43-29233, SP-AFP	RA
☐ Podlaska Wytwornia Samolotow P.W.S.26	5	81.123	(Polish A.F.), (Germany), SP-AJB	PVX
☐ Polikarpov Po-2LNB	'4'	641-646	02	PVAX
☐ Polikarpov Po-2VS	SP-ADE	9725		RA
☐ Politechnika Warszawska PW-2 Gapa		U-01	Static test airframe.	RA
☐ Politechnika Warszawska PW-5 Smyk		K-02	Static test airframe.	RA
☐ Rogalski, Wigura, Drzewiecki R.W.D.13	SP-BNU	283	SP-BNU, 6 (Romania), YR-INS, SP-ARL	PV
☐ Rogalski, Wigura, Drzewiecki R.W.D.21	'SP-BPE'	331	SP-BRH, YR-AEZ, SP-AKG	PVX
☐ Schneider Grunau SG-38 (D.F.S. 108-14)				PV
☐ Schneider Motorbaby	SP-213	1028	(German)	PV/R
☐ Sopwith F.1 Camel	B7280			PVC
☐ Staaken R VI	R.35/17		Nacelle only	RAD
☐ Stelmasczyk S-1 Bozena (R)				RA
☐ Stinson V-76 Sentinel (L-5)	42-98643			RAD
☐ Sukhoi Su-7BKL	806	7806		PV
☐ Sukhoi Su-7BKL	807	7807		PV
☐ Sukhoi Su-7BM	01	5301		PV
☐ Sukhoi Su-7BM	06	5306		PV
☐ Sukhoi Su-7UM	116	2116		PV
☐ Sukhoi Su-20R	4242	6602		PV
☐ Supermarine 361 Spitfire LF.XVIe	'TB995'		SM411, 7242M, SM411	PVX
☐ Svenska Aeroplan Aktiebolaget (SAAB) 35J Draken (35F-2) (J 35F-2) (J 35J)	Fv35520	35520	On loan from FVM, SWE	PV
☐ Svenska Aeroplan Aktiebolaget (SAAB) 37 Viggen (SF 37) (AJSF 37)	Fv37954	37954	On loan from FVM, SWE.	PV
☐ Szybowcowy Zaklad Doswiadczalny S.Z.D.8bis Jaskolka	SP-1335	114		PV
☐ Szybowcowy Zaklad Doswiadczalny S.Z.D.9bis Bocian 1A	SP-1358	P-231		PV
☐ Szybowcowy Zaklad Doswiadczalny S.Z.D.10bis Czapla	SP-1477	124		PV
☐ Szybowcowy Zaklad Doswiadczalny S.Z.D.10bis Czapla A	SP-1907	W-72		PV/RA
☐ Szybowcowy Zaklad Doswiadczalny S.Z.D.12 Mucha 100	SP-1460	W-86		RA
☐ Szybowcowy Zaklad Doswiadczalny S.Z.D.12 Mucha 100	SP-1463	W-89		PV
☐ Szybowcowy Zaklad Doswiadczalny S.Z.D.12 Mucha 100	SP-1469	W-95		PV/RA
☐ Szybowcowy Zaklad Doswiadczalny S.Z.D.12A Mucha 100A	SP-1846	W-20		RA
☐ Szybowcowy Zaklad Doswiadczalny S.Z.D.15 Sroka	SP-1598	176		PV/RA
☐ Szybowcowy Zaklad Doswiadczalny S.Z.D.15 Sroka	SP-1726	299		PV
☐ Szybowcowy Zaklad Doswiadczalny S.Z.D.17X Jaskolka L	SP-1506	179		PV
☐ Szybowcowy Zaklad Doswiadczalny S.Z.D.18 Czajka	SP-1640	211		PV

Type	Reg/Ser	Con. No.	PI/Notes	Status
☐ Szybowcowy Zaklad Doswiadczalny S.Z.D.19-2B Zefir 2B	SP-2371	P-405		PV
☐ Szybowcowy Zaklad Doswiadczalny S.Z.D.19X Zefir 1	SP-1841	232		PV/R
☐ Szybowcowy Zaklad Doswiadczalny S.Z.D.21-2B Kobuz 3	SP-2499	W-286		PV
☐ Szybowcowy Zaklad Doswiadczalny S.Z.D.22C Mucha Standard	SP-2292	F-607		PV
☐ Szybowcowy Zaklad Doswiadczalny S.Z.D.25A Lis	SP-2356	F-740		PV
☐ Szybowcowy Zaklad Doswiadczalny S.Z.D.27 Kormoran	SP-2463	285		PV/R
☐ Szybowcowy Zaklad Doswiadczalny S.Z.D.31 Zefir 4	SP-2518	292		RA
☐ Szybowcowy Zaklad Doswiadczalny S.Z.D.43 Orion	SP-2635	X-103		PV
☐ Tupolev Tu-2S (modified)				PV
☐ Tupolev Tu-134A	SP-LHB	3351809	SP-LHB, 103	PV
☐ Warsztaty Szybowcowe Wrona bis	'SP-127'	127	SP-447	PVX
☐ Wojskowe Warsztaty Szybowcowe W.W.S.1 Salamandra	SP-139	41		RADX
☐ Wojskowe Warsztaty Szybowcowe W.W.S.2 Zaba	SP-167		SP-1265, SP-402	PVX
☐ Wytwornia Sprzetu Komunikacyjnego (WSK) Lim-1 [MiG-15]	712	1A 07-012		PV
☐ Wytwornia Sprzetu Komunikacyjnego (WSK) Lim-2 [MiG-15bis]	1230	1B 012-30		PV
☐ Wytwornia Sprzetu Komunikacyjnego (WSK) SBLim-2 (Lim-1) [MiG-15] [MiG-15UTI]	014	1A 06-014		PV
☐ Wytwornia Sprzetu Komunikacyjnego (WSK) SBLim-2 (Lim-1) [MiG-15] [MiG-15UTI]	018	1A 06-018		PV
☐ Wytwornia Sprzetu Komunikacyjnego (WSK) SBLim-2A (Lim-1) [MiG-15] [MiG-15UTI]	035	1A 06-035		PV
☐ Wytwornia Sprzetu Komunikacyjnego (WSK) SBLim-2A [MiG-15UTI]	304	3404		PV
☐ Wytwornia Sprzetu Komunikacyjnego (WSK) SBLim-2A {MiG-15UTI]	2004	27004		PV
☐ Wytwornia Sprzetu Komunikacyjnego (WSK) Lim-5 [MiG-17F]	415	1C 04-15		PV
☐ Wytwornia Sprzetu Komunikacyjnego (WSK) Lim-5 [MiG-17F]	601	1C 06-01		PV
☐ Wytwornia Sprzetu Komunikacyjnego (WSK) Lim-5 [MiG-17F]	1023	1C 10-23		PV
☐ Wytwornia Sprzetu Komunikacyjnego (WSK) Lim-5 [MiG-17F]	1508	1C 15-08		PV
☐ Wytwornia Sprzetu Komunikacyjnego (WSK) Lim-5 [MiG-17F]	1909	1C 19-09		RA
☐ Wytwornia Sprzetu Komunikacyjnego (WSK) Lim-5R (Lim-5) [MiG-17F]	506	1C 05-06		PV
☐ Wytwornia Sprzetu Komunikacyjnego (WSK) Lim-5R (Lim-5) [MiG-17F]	1414	1C 14-14		PV
☐ Wytwornia Sprzetu Komunikacyjnego (WSK) Lim-5R (Lim-5) [MiG-17F]	1910	1C 19-10		PV
☐ Wytwornia Sprzetu Komunikacyjnego (WSK) Lim-6bis (Lim-5M) [MiG-17F]	105	1F 01-05		PV
☐ Wytwornia Sprzetu Komunikacyjnego (WSK) Lim-6M (Lim-5P) [MiG-17PF]	606	1D 06-06		PV
☐ Wytwornia Sprzetu Komunikacyjnego (WSK) Lim-6MR (Lim-5P) [MiG-17PF]	618	1D 06-18		PV
☐ Wytwornia Sprzetu Komunikacyjnego (WSK) M-15-03 Belphegor		1S 006-03	Tail from c/n 1S 006-01	PV
☐ Wytwornia Sprzetu Komunikacyjnego (WSK) SM-1/300 [Mil Mi-1]	SP-SAD	S101003		PV
☐ Wytwornia Sprzetu Komunikacyjnego (WSK) SM-1/300 [Mil Mi-1]	23	S115007		RA
☐ Wytwornia Sprzetu Komunikacyjnego (WSK) SM-2	SP-SAP	S202016		PV
☐ Yakovlev Yak-11	36	64236		PV
☐ Yakovlev Yak-12	SP-ASZ	5013		PV
☐ Yakovlev Yak-17W	02	3120132	(Polish A.F.), SP-GLW	PV
☐ Yakovlev Yak-18	SP-BRI	9732	(Polish A.F.)	RA
☐ Yakovlev Yak-18	SP-AOU	EM016		RA
☐ Yakovlev Yak-23	16	1216	SP-GLK	PV
☐ Zlin Z-26 Trener	SP-ARM	640		PV

MUZEUM MARYNARKI WOJENNEJ (POL24)

Address:	ul Sedzickiego 3, Bulwar Nadmorski, 81-912 Gdynia.
Tel:	058-6263565
Admission:	Tuesday-Sunday 1000-1700.
Location:	In the town centre near the southern pier.

Established in 1953 the museum traces the history of the Polish maritime forces. On show in the nearby Basin 1 of the port is the destroyer Blyskawia which served with distinction in World War II and joined the museum in the mid-1970s. The Navy has operated aircraft for many years and a display of models tracing the types flown can be seen in the building. The Yak-9, put on show in 1956, took part in the campaign to liberate northern Poland in 1945. This Soviet design fighter first flew in 1942 and over sixteen thousand seven hundred were completed before production ended in 1948. The main naval aviation base is nearby at Gdynia Babie Doly and the history of this airfield is portrayed. Also on show in the terraced park overlooking the sea are small boats and weapons. Construction of a new building started in 2002 and this will house the local museum as well as the naval one.

TYPE	REG/SER	CON. NO.	PI/NOTES	STATUS
☐ Ilyushin Il-28R	69	41302		PV
☐ Mikoyan-Gurevich MiG-21bis	8905	75078905		PV
☐ Mil Mi-4ME	'1717'	02177	'021'	PVX
☐ Panstwowe Zaklady Lotnicze (PZL) TS-11 Iskra 100bisA	414	1H 04-14		PV
☐ Wytwornia Sprzetu Komunikacyjnego (WSK) Lim-6bis (Lim-5M) [MiG-17F]	316	1F 03-16		PV
☐ Wytwornia Sprzetu Komunikacyjnego (WSK) SM-1Wb [Mil Mi-1M]	4017	S402017		PV
☐ Yakovlev Yak-9P	2			PV

MUZEUM MOTORYZACJI I TECHNIKI (POL25)

Address: ul Warszawska 21,
05-800 Otrebusy.
Tel: 022-758500
Fax: 022-758067
Admission: Daily 1000-1700
Location: About 20 km south west of Warsaw off Road 719.

This car museum opened in 1995. In addition to the history of motoring the technical progress can be followed. Displays highlight the developments which have taken place in both body and mechanical design. Posters and brochures can be seen along with components. The oldest vehicle is an 1895 American Titan tractor. Lorries from 1910 and cars from the same period are on show. A ZIS convertible used by Joseph Stalin is a rare exhibit. Cars used by Elvis Presley and Marilyn Monroe can be seen. Several tanks have been acquired along with other military vehicles. The collection now numbers over three hundred and many have been restored in the museum's workshops. The one aircraft on show is a Bies trainer. The prototype first flew in 1952 and the type was in production between 1957 and 1963. Another example is stored nearby.

TYPE	REG/SER	CON. NO.	PI/NOTES	STATUS
☐ Panstwowe Zaklady Lotnicze (PZL) TS-8 Bies	'B-53'		'SP-1'	RAX
☐ Panstwowe Zaklady Lotnicze (PZL) TS-8 Bies	0929	1E 09-29		PV

MUZEUM OREŻA POLSKIEGO (POL26)

Address: Ul. Armii Krojoweg 13,
78-100 Kolobrzeg.
Tel: 094-3522091
Email: mopk@crs.pl
Admission: Monday-Wednesday 0900-1300 ; Thursday- Saturday 0900-1500; Sunday 0830-1430.
Location: In the centre of the town which is about 200 km west of Gdansk.

Kolobrzeg is one of the oldest towns in the country and was first settled in the seventh century. When it became part of Poland in 972 it was a fortified stronghold. Over the next centuries it was captured by the Swedes, the Russians, the French and the Germans. In March 1945 a two week battle left the town almost completely destroyed. The museum opened in 1963 in buildings which were once a collegiate church. The history of the Polish Army from its beginnings up to the present day is portrayed in vivid detail with photographs, documents, uniforms, maps and weapons. There are many personal items from the World War II period. Displays highlight the struggle for freedom in the area and modem military developments. The Po-2 is displayed in the building. The other aircraft are parked outside along with military vehicles, guns and a patrol boat.

TYPE	REG/SER	CON. NO.	PI/NOTES	STATUS
☐ Centralne Studium Samolotow (CSS) 13 [Polikarpov Po-2]		8-0511	SP-BFA	PVX
☐ Focke-Wulf Fw 190F-8/R1				PVD
☐ Ilyushin Il-28	'52'	2113	64	PVX
☐ Mikoyan-Gurevich MiG-19P	'723'	620728	728	PVX
☐ Panstwowe Zaklady Lotnicze (PZL) TS-8 Bies	0710	1E 07-10	0710, '315'	PV
☐ Wytwornia Sprzetu Komunikacyjnego (WSK) Lim-2 [MiG-15bis]	'1984'	1B 017-05	1705, '1978'	PVX
☐ Wytwornia Sprzetu Komunikacyjnego (WSK) SM-2	'417'	S203010	3010	PVX

On show at the White Eagles Museum at Skarzysko-Kamienna is this Bies painted in false markings. (Douglas Rough)

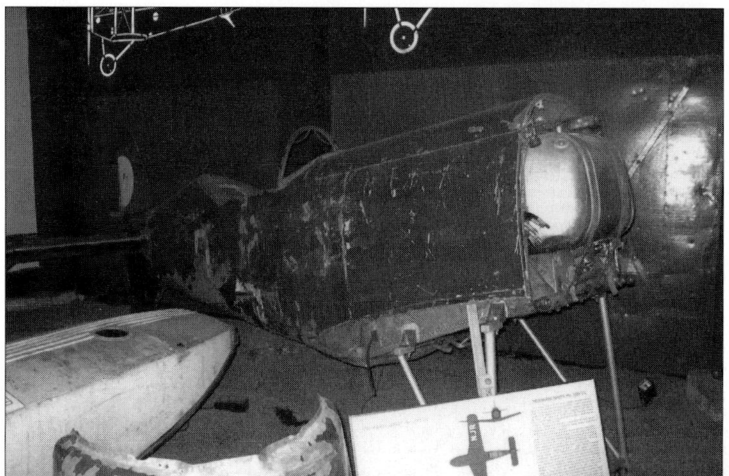

The fuselage of the record breaking Messerschmitt Me 209 resides in a building at the Muzeum Lotnictwa at Krakow. (Douglas Rough)

On show inside the main building in the Army Museum at Kolobrzeg is this Polish built Polikarpov Po-2.

MUZEUM SPRZETU BOJOWEGO (POL27)

Address:	ul Szubinska 105, 85-815 Bydgoszcz.
Tel:	052-3785399
Admission:	By prior permission only.
Location:	In the south western suburbs of the town.

The site is one of four main repair factories for military aircraft. Major work is currently carried out on MiG-29s, Su-22s and TS-11s. In addition minor repairs on P.Z.L. light civil types take place. The idea of the museum was put forward in 1992 when the last combat units left the field. The exhibition opened in 1993 and types previously used by the units were put on show on the airfield. In addition there are rockets and armaments to be seen The memorial rooms of the 2nd Air Defence Corps and the 2nd Airbase can also be visited.

TYPE	REG/SER	CON. NO.	PI/NOTES	STATUS
☐ Antonov An-2T	7448	1G 74-48		RA
☐ Centralne Studium Samolotow (CSS) 13 [Polikarpov Po-2]	4	0413	SP-BFP	RAC
☐ Mikoyan-Gurevich MiG-21M	2001	962001		RA
☐ Mikoyan-Gurevich MiG-21PF	0608	760608	At barracks near base.	RA
☐ Mikoyan-Gurevich MiG-23MF	139	0390217139		RA
☐ Mil Mi-2P	4710	534710036		RA
☐ Panstwowe Zaklady Lotnicze (PZL) TS-11 Iskra 100	209	1H 02-09	0209	RA
☐ Sukhoi Su-7BM	'3117'	5303	03	RAX
☐ Sukhoi Su-20R	7125	74105		RA
☐ Sukhoi Su-20R	6250	74210		RA
☐ Sukhoi Su-20R	6252	76302		RA
☐ Wytwornia Sprzetu Komunikacyjnego (WSK) Lim-5 [MiG-17F]	'1302'	1C 13-08	1308	RAX

MUZEUM TECHNIKI (POL28)

Address:	Palac Kultury i Nauki, 00-901 Warszawa.
Tel:	022-620-4710
Fax:	022-620-4710
Fax:	Mt@muzeum-techniki.waw.pl
Admission:	Wednesday, Friday, Saturday 0900-1600; Tuesday, Thursday 0900-1900; Sunday 1000-1700.
Location:	In the city centre.

The giant Palace of Culture, which dominates the Warsaw skyline, was constructed by the Soviet Union as a gift to the Polish people. The building is similar to four which were built in Moscow during the Stalin era. The complex opened in 1955 and the museum is housed in one corner of the ground floor. The displays trace the developments which have taken place in all fields of technology. Modern aspects of the subjects are being added to the innovative displays. The small aviation section houses an original 1894 Lilienthal glider which was stored by the Warsaw Polytechnic for many years. Pawel Zolotow constructed the two replicas and the Bensen. Czeslaw Tanski was one of the pioneers of Polish aviation. In the 1890s be built a number of flying models along with a man carrying hang glider. The Lotnia III made short flights in 1898 and these were the first by a Polish heavier than air machine. Also on show are engines, components, photographs and models.

TYPE	REG/SER	CON. NO.	PI/NOTES	STATUS
☐ Bensen B-8M Gyrocopter		5		PV
☐ Lilienthal Normal-Segelapparat				PV
☐ Lotnicze Warsztaty Doswiadczalne (L.W.D.) Junak 3		94036	(Polish A.F.)	PV
☐ Santos-Dumont XX Demoiselle (R)				PV
☐ Tanski Lotnia (R)				PV

MUZEUM WOJSKA POLSKIEGO (POL29)

Address:	Aleje Jerozolimskie 3, 00-495 Warszawa.
Tel:	022-6295271/2
Fax:	022-6295273
Email:	muzeumwp@wp.mil.pl
Admission:	Wednesday-Sunday 1000-1600.
Location:	In the city centre near the River Vistula.

Located in an impressive building overlooking the River Vistula this museum traces the military history of the country over many centuries. Displays of trophies, badges, uniforms and models can be seen along with several dioramas. The outside park contains the aircraft, military vehicles, tanks and heavy weapons. The aircraft have suffered from the harsh weather but efforts are being made to restore the older types. The Il-2, Yak-9P and Pe-2 have been in the park since 1950. The Il-2, of which over thirty five thousand were made, was one of the outstanding aircraft of World War II. The Tu-2 and Pe-2 were successful light bombers of the same period. The Yak-9 is one of the last piston engined fighters used in Poland. The licence built MiG fighters have been removed to the Muzeum Katynskie and been replaced by other types. By the main entrance is a propeller from Wellington 1C HX384 which crashed in 1942 and was found by members of a diving club.

TYPE	REG/SER	CON. NO.	PI/NOTES	STATUS
☐ Antonov An-2P	5928	1G 159-28		PV
☐ Avia B-33 [Ilyushin Il-10]		B33-5523	011	PVX
☐ Ilyushin Il-2m3			21, '23'	PVX
☐ Mikoyan-Gurevich MiG-21PF	0615	760615		PV
☐ Mil Mi-2P	1449	531449040		PV
☐ Mil Mi-8T	0614	10614	0204	PV
☐ Panstwowe Zaklady Lotnicze (PZL) TS-11 Iskra 100	101	1H 01-01	0101	PV
☐ Panstwowe Zaklady Lotnicze (PZL) I-22 Iryda	SP-PWG	1AN 02-04		
☐ Petlyakov Pe-2FT				PV
☐ Tupolev Tu-2S			'8'	PVX
☐ Yakovlev Yak-9P	'23'			PVX

MUZEUM ZIEMI SOCHACZEWSKIEJ I POLA BITWY NAD BZURA (POL30)

Address: pl Kosciuszki 2,
95-500 Sochaczew.
Tel: 0862-3309
Email: muzeum@e-sochaczew.pl
Admission: Tuesday,Thursday,Saturday-Sunday 1000-1600. Wednesday, Friday 1000-1500.
Location: In the town which is about 50 km west of Warsaw.

The main theme of the displays at this museum is the 'Battle of the Bzura River' which took place in September 1939 during the German invasion of the country. In the engagement over twenty thousand Polish troops were killed when they faced large numbers of attackers. A large model of the battlefield is the centre of the exhibition. Military vehicles and tanks are also in the collection.

TYPE	REG/SER	CON. NO.	PI/NOTES	STATUS
☐ Mikoyan-Gurevich MiG-21R	1706	94R01706		PV

TECHNIKI LOTNICZ MUSEUM AEROKLUB ZGORZELEC (POL31)

Address: Ul 3 go Maja 26,
59-900 Zarska Weis.
Tel: 0662-812691
Email: aeroklub@poczta.onet.pl
Admission: On permanent view.
Location: At an airfield south of the town.

The aero club has set up a display of former military jets at its airfield and named it an aviation technical museum. There are plans to put up a small exhibition building to display items relating to the history of aviation.

TYPE	REG/SER	CON. NO.	PI/NOTES	STATUS
☐ Mikoyan-Gurevich MiG-15bis	165			PV
☐ Mikoyan-Gurevich MiG-21PFM	6510	94A6510		PV
☐ Mikoyan-Gurevich MiG-21PFM	6606	94A6606		PV
☐ Mikoyan-Gurevich MiG-21PFM	6610	94A6610		PV
☐ Mikoyan-Gurevich MiG-23MF	461	0390224461		PV

WYSTAWA SPRZETU LOTNICZEGO I WOJSKOWEGO MUZEUM (POL32)

Address: Lotnisko Lublinek,
93-468 Łódz.
Tel: 042-847569
Admission: By prior permission only.
Location: About 6 km. south west of the city and about 1 km west of Route 14.

The collection was the first privately owned aviation museum in the country. The prototype Bies first flew in July 1955 and production machines entered service in 1958. Over three hundred were constructed and a few were exported to Indonesia. The museum has recovered several which served as monuments around the country. Amongst the many examples of the licence built MiG fighters are two LiM-2s which were flown by the air force aerobatic team in the 1950s. Two of the reserve aircraft are parked nearby. The MiG-17PF in the collection was the personal aircraft of Poland's astronaut when he was in the air force. One of the owners recently died and progress has stalled. Access to the storage areas is difficult and some of the aircraft listed may have left.

TYPE	REG/SER	CON. NO.	PI/NOTES	STATUS
☐ Antonov An-2PF	SP-TBA	1G 159-01		PVD
☐ Antonov An-2R	SP-WWE	1G 173-56	Fuselage only.	PV
☐ Antonov An-2R	SP-DNG	1G 86-09		RA
☐ Antonov An-2T	SP-FAR	1G 187-06	SP-DTA, SP-TTA, SP-TCF	RAD
☐ Dassault Mirage IIIC	36	36	In French markings.	PV
☐ Ilyushin Il-14P	0916	14600916	006 (Poland)	PV
☐ Ilyushin Il-28R		2402010		PV
☐ Mikoyan-Gurevich MiG-17PF	305	0305		PV
☐ Mikoyan-Gurevich MiG-21F-13	2015	742015		PV
☐ Mikoyan-Gurevich MiG-21MF	6510	966510		PV
☐ Mikoyan-Gurevich MiG-21PF	1702	761702		PV
☐ Mikoyan-Gurevich MiG-21PF	1703	761703	At Mercedes dealer.	RA
☐ Mikoyan-Gurevich MiG-21PF	1809	761809		RA
☐ Mikoyan-Gurevich MiG-21PFM	5705	94A5705		PV
☐ Mikoyan-Gurevich MiG-21PFM	6509	94A6509		PV
☐ Mikoyan-Gurevich MiG-21PFMA	06	94ML-06		PV
☐ Mikoyan-Gurevich MiG-21PFMA	09	94ML-09		PV
☐ Mikoyan-Gurevich MiG-21PFMA	10	94ML-10		PV
☐ Mikoyan-Gurevich MiG-21U-600	2720	662720		PV
☐ Mil Mi-2	SP-FHM	514520115	SP-SPE	RA
☐ Mil Mi-2	SP-TVA	533443044		PV
☐ Mil Mi-2R	5826	565826128		PV
☐ Mil Mi-6A	670	10670	SP-ITB	PV
☐ Panstwowe Zaklady Lotnicze (PZL) TS-8 Bies	0302	1E 03-02		RA
☐ Panstwowe Zaklady Lotnicze (PZL) TS-8 Bies	SP-FBB	1E 04-19	0419	RAD
☐ Panstwowe Zaklady Lotnicze (PZL) TS-8 Bies	SP-CNO	1E 07-24	0724	RAD
☐ Panstwowe Zaklady Lotnicze (PZL) TS-8 Bies	'SP-FNP'	1E 09-09	0909, SE-CNP	PVX
☐ Panstwowe Zaklady Lotnicze (PZL) TS-8 Bies	SP-CLZ	1E 09-25	0925	RA
☐ Panstwowe Zaklady Lotnicze (PZL) TS-11 Iskra 100	103	1H 01-03	0103	PV
☐ Panstwowe Zaklady Lotnicze (PZL) TS-11 Iskra 100bisA	309	1H 03-09	0309	RA
☐ Panstwowe Zaklady Lotnicze (PZL) 106BS Kruk (106)	SP-PBH	04003		RA
☐ Sukhoi Su-7BKL	12	6012		PV
☐ Sukhoi Su-7BKL	22	6022		PV
☐ Sukhoi Su-7UM	702	3702		PV
☐ Sukhoi Su-20R	6255	76305		PV
☐ Tupolev Tu-134A	SP-LHE	48405		PV
☐ Wytwornia Sprzetu Komunikacyjnego (WSK) Lim-2 [MiG-15bis]	109	1B 001-09		PV
☐ Wytwornia Sprzetu Komunikacyjnego (WSK) Lim-2 [MiG-15bis]	1612	1B 016-12		PV
☐ Wytwornia Sprzetu Komunikacyjnego (WSK) Lim-2R [MiG-15bis]	307	1B 003-07		PV
☐ Wytwornia Sprzetu Komunikacyjnego (WSK) Lim-2R [MiG-15bis]	311	1B 003-11		PV
☐ Wytwornia Sprzetu Komunikacyjnego (WSK) Lim-2R [MiG-15bis]	512	1B 005-12		PV
☐ Wytwornia Sprzetu Komunikacyjnego (WSK) SBLim-2 (Lim-1) [MiG-15] [MiG-15UTI]	905	1A 09-005		RA
☐ Wytwornia Sprzetu Komunikacyjnego (WSK) SBLim-2 [MiG-15UTI]	193	142693		PV
☐ Wytwornia Sprzetu Komunikacyjnego (WSK) SBLim-2 [MiG-15UTI]	776	712276		RA
☐ Wytwornia Sprzetu Komunikacyjnego (WSK) SBLim-2A (Lim-1) [MiG-15] [MiG-15UTI]	6008	1A 06-008		PV
☐ Wytwornia Sprzetu Komunikacyjnego (WSK) SBLim-2A (Lim-1) [MiG-15] [MiG-15UTI]	7039	1A 07-039		PV
☐ Wytwornia Sprzetu Komunikacyjnego (WSK) Lim-5 [MiG-17F]	408	1C 04-08		RA
☐ Wytwornia Sprzetu Komunikacyjnego (WSK) Lim-5R (Lim-5) [MiG-17F]	1730	1C 17-30		PV
☐ Wytwornia Sprzetu Komunikacyjnego (WSK) Lim-5R (Lim-5) [MiG-17F]	1913	1C 19-13		PV
☐ Wytwornia Sprzetu Komunikacyjnego (WSK) Lim-6bis [MiG-17F]	427	1J 04-27		PV
☐ Wytwornia Sprzetu Komunikacyjnego (WSK) Lim-6R [MiG-17F]	608	1J 06-08		PV
☐ Wytwornia Sprzetu Komunikacyjnego (WSK) Lim-6R [MiG-17F]	637	1J 06-37		PV
☐ Wytwornia Sprzetu Komunikacyjnego (WSK) SM-1W [Mil Mi-1M]	SP-SXD	W05019		PVD

PORTUGAL

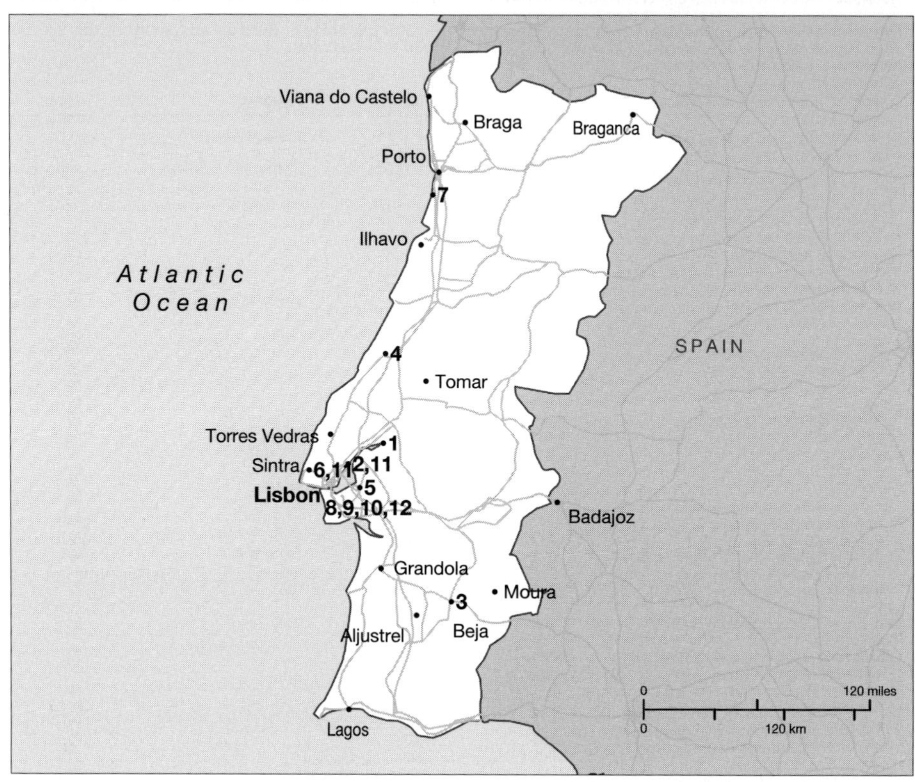

ASSOCIAÇAO DOS AMIGOS DO MUSEU AÉRO FÉNIX (POR1)

Address:	Aerodromo de Santarém, Quinta de S. Lino, 2000-478 Santarém.
Tel:	21 962 3947
Fax:	21 962 4919
Email:	aero.fenix@sapo.pt
Admission:	By prior permission only.
Location:	The airfield is just south of the town.

This group was formed in the 1990s with the aim of setting up a museum of airworthy historic types. The group now has headquarters at Santarém airfield and is repairing a hangar to house the fleet. The Texan has been undergoing a lengthy rebuild and is not too far from completion. The locally built Chipmunk is progressing well in its restoration. The Culver V first flew in 1946 and the type was never common in Europe. The flyable Cub is painted in the classic yellow Piper scheme and the second example is in the workshops.

TYPE	REG/SER	CON. NO.	PI/NOTES	STATUS
☐ Boeing-Stearman A75N1 Kaydet (N2S-1)	N62TS	75-971	Bu3194, N50087	RAA
☐ Culver V	CS-ACY	348		RA
☐ De Havilland D.H.C.1 Chipmunk T.20	CS-AZX	P.24	1334	RAC
☐ Max Holste MH.1521M Broussard	179	179		RA
☐ North American NA-188 Texan (T-6G)	1635	188-40	51-15177	RAC
☐ Piper J-3C-65 Cub (L-4H)				RAC
☐ Piper J-3C-65 Cub (L-4J)	CS-DIE	13950	45-55184, N2075N	RAA
☐ Schleicher Ka-4 Rhönlerche II	CS-PAS	802		RA
☐ Schleicher Ka-4 Rhönlerche II	CS-PBA	3087		RA

COLECÇAO DA OGMA (POR2)

Address:	Oficinas Gerais de Material Aeronáutico, 2615-173 Alverca.
Tel:	219581000
Fax:	219580401
Email:	geral@ogma.pt
Admission:	By prior permission only.
Location:	About 20 km north east of Lisboa off the A1.

The factory was set up in 1918 to provide overhaul and repair facilities for aircraft, engines and associated equipment and took up its current name ten years later. From 1922 types were built under licence for the Air Force. The first order, received in 1922, was for fifty Caudron G.3s and since then over three hundred and fifty aircraft have been constructed. The company preserved items of interest including engines, instruments, books, models etc. but with the opening of the Museu do Ar in July 1968 the collection was donated to the museum. The first of ninety one Tiger Moths built by OGMA and a Caudron G.3 replica built for the fiftieth anniversary of the company were included in the deal. In 1993 the old balloon hangar was restored and became home to a new collection of engines, components, avionics etc. Five years later a project to rebuild four aircraft to flying condition was initiated. These include the last Chipmunk built in the world (OGMA constructed sixty) and one of the hundred and forty eight Auster D.5s Huskies which left the Alverca factory. The T-37 is at the Air Force gate close to the main complex.

TYPE	REG/SER	CON. NO.	PI/NOTES	STATUS
☐ Auster D5/160 Husky	CS-AMX	P.81		RAC
☐ Cessna 318C Tweety Bird (T-37C)	02411	40735	62-5936, 2411 – on air force gate.	RAX
☐ De Havilland D.H.82A Tiger Moth	CS-AEL	P.55		RA
☐ De Havilland D.H.C.1 Chipmunk T.20	1376	P.66	1376, CS-DAR	RAA
☐ Piper J-3C-85 Cub (J-3C-65)	CS-AAP	21984	G-AKBT	RAC
☐ Sud-Est SE.3160 Alouette III	9258	1116	Composite with parts of c/n 1138 9265.	RA

COLECÇAO DE BASE AÉREA BEJA (POR3)

Address:	Base Aérea 11, 7800-958 Beja.
Tel:	284310500
Fax:	284323400
Admission:	By prior permission only.
Location:	About 8 km north west of the town off Road IP.2.

The base was opened in 1964 and for many years up to 1993 it was used by the Luftwaffe for weapons training. At the present time it is home two squadrons of Alpha Jets, one flying Epsilons and a fourth operating the Alouette III. In addition the official Air Force aerobatic team 'Asas de Portugal' is based here. The flight was first formed in 1977 by instructors at Sintra but was disbanded after a few years. In 1987 it reformed with Cessna T-37Cs but was stood down again in the early 1990s due to airframe corrosion. In 1999 it emerged again using up to seven Alpha Jets. Several aircraft of the Museu do Ar are stored in the hangars. The Luftwaffe put a Fiat G.91 on show near the Officer's Mess. The T-33 was placed close to the gate in the late 1980s.

TYPE	REG/SER	CON. NO.	PI/NOTES	STATUS
☐ Canadair CL-30 Silver Star 3 (CT-133) [Lockheed 580 (T-33AN)]	1951	T33-045	21045 (Canada)	PV
☐ Dornier-Breguet Alpha Jet A	15248	0146		RA
☐ Fiat G.91R/3		91-507	KD+497, EC+123, EC+103, MD+103, 32+38, '35+38'	RAX
☐ Lockheed 683-10-19 Starfighter (F-104G)	20+99	683-6620	KC+131, 20+99, '23+81'	PV
☐ Northrop N-156T Talon (T-38A)	2602	N.5219	661-0853	PV

COLECÇAO DE BASE AÉREA MONTE REAL (POR4)

Address:	Base Aérea 5, 2425-022 Monte Real.
Tel:	244618000
Fax:	244612550
Admission:	By prior permission only.
Location:	About 10 km north of Leiria.

The site has housed fighter units since it opened in October 1959. The two squadrons flew the F-86F Sabre until the early 1980s when A-7P Corsair arrived. This type is now being replaced by the F-16 Fighting Falcon. One F-86 is preserved by the gate and another, stored on the field, is used for exhibition purposes at special events. A Corsair should soon be displayed by the entrance.

TYPE	REG/SER	CON. NO.	PI/NOTES	STATUS
☐ General Dynamics 401 Fighting Falcon (F-16A)	'15100'	61-529	82-0936	RAX
☐ North American NA-191 Sabre (F-86F)	5301	191-864	52-5168	PV
☐ North American NA-191 Sabre (F-86F)	'5320'	191-900	52-5204, 5338	RAX
☐ North American NA-191 Sabre (F-86F)	5320	191-964	52-5268 – on loan from MA.	RA
☐ Vought A-7P Corsair II (A-7A)	15521	A-043	Bu153134, 5521	RA
☐ Vought A-7P Corsair II (A-7A)	15524	A-071	Bu153162.	PV
☐ Vought A-7P Corsair II (A-7A)	15531	A-121	Bu153212	RA

COLECÇAO DE BASE AÉREA MONTIJO (POR5)

Address:	Base Aérea 6, 2870-064 Montijo.
Tel:	212310901
Fax:	212328504
Admission:	By prior permission only.
Location:	About 2 km west of the town which is about 15 km east of Lisboa.

Montijo was originally a naval base with both land and seaplanes in residence. The site was then assigned to the Air Force and is now home to the transport fleet of the service. In use are small numbers of Lockheed C-130s and Dassault Falcon 20s and 50s. The maritime patrol squadron with Lockheed P-3P Orions is also in residence as is a SAR flight with Pumas. Three Fiat G.91s are preserved on the site. One is by the main gate, another by the control tower and the third is used for instructional and display duties.

TYPE	REG/SER	CON. NO.	PI/NOTES	STATUS
☐ Fiat G.91R/3	5447	91-387	KD+376, BD+414, 31+20	RA
☐ Fiat G.91R/3	'5463'	91-520	KD+510, EC+110, MD+110, 32+51, 5453, '5423'	PVX
☐ Fiat G.91R/4	5404	91-4-0117	BD+243, BR+243	RA

COLECÇAO DE BASE AÉREA SINTRA (POR6)

Address:	Base Aérea 1, Granja do Marquês, 2715-021 Sintra.
Tel:	219671046
Fax:	219678991
Admission:	By prior permission only.
Location:	Just north east of the town which is about 25 km west of Lisboa.

The airfield at Sintra was opened in February 1920 and was later named Base Aérea 1. The site is now home to the Air Force Academy which uses L-23 Super Blaniks and ASK-21 powered gliders for basic pilot training. A small number of re-engined Chipmunks have been returned to service. A squadron operating Cessna 337s is in residence along with another flying CASA 212s. The Museu do Ar has a facility at the field, which is now open on a regular basis, and there are plans to move the exhibition to a purpose built complex in the not too distant future. The four preserved aircraft are positioned around the base.

TYPE	REG/SER	CON. NO.	PI/NOTES	STATUS
☐ Cessna 318C Tweety Bird (T-37C)	2424	40749	62-5949	RA
☐ Cessna 318C Tweety Bird (T-37C)	2427	40781	62-12498 – Museo do Ar aircraft.	RA
☐ Cessna 318C Tweety Bird (T-37C)	2430	40784	62-12501	RA
☐ Fiat G.91R/3	5457	91-464	KD+454, BD+247, 31+96	RA

COLECÇAO DO AÉRODROMO DE MANOBRA DE MACEDA (POR7)

Address:	Aerodromo de Manobra No.2, Rua da Base Aerea, 3885-718 Maceda.
Tel:	256790900
Fax:	256790997
Admission:	By prior permission only.
Location:	About 8 km north of Ovar.

This military airfield has no based squadrons and has been regularly used by NATO aircraft. A single Alouette III resides here for local SAR duties. The A-7 is at the gate and the T-38 is the first of a planned detachment of the Museu do Ar. The museum wishes to establish a display in the north of the country.

TYPE	REG/SER	CON. NO.	PI/NOTES	STATUS
☐ Northrop N-156T Talon (T-38A)	2608	N.5203	61-0837	RA
☐ Vought A-7P Corsair II (A-7A)	15506	A-159	Bu153184	PV

COLECÇAO ESTADO MAIOR DA FORÇA AÉREA (POR8)

Address: Avenue Força Aérea Portuguesa, 2724-506 Alfragide.
Tel: 214713500
Fax: 214713583
Admission: By prior permission only.
Location: In the north western part of the city.

Two Fiat G.91s are mounted on pylons in the gardens around the Air Force Headquarters. Displayed in the building is an Avro Cadet which is part of the Museu do Ar collection. This biplane was acquired in 1934 and evaluated against the de Havilland Tiger Moth and the Caproni Ca.100 in a contest to find a primary trainer. Also to be seen are engines, uniforms, badges and photographs tracing the history of the service.

TYPE	REG/SER	CON. NO.	PI/NOTES	STATUS
☐ Avro 631 Cadet	501	727	On loan from Museu do Ar.	RA
☐ Fiat G.91R/3	5444	91-089	EC+234, ER+234, MC+244, 30+31	PV
☐ Fiat G.91R/3	5467	91-517	KD+507,EC+120, MD+120, 32+48	PV

MUSEU DA LIGO DOS COMBATENTES (POR9)

Address: Rua João Periera da Rosa 18, Lisboa 1249-632.
Tel: 213468245
Fax: 213463394
Email: info@liagcombatentes.org.pt
Admission: Tuesday-Sunday 1000-1200; 1300-1700.
Location: In the southern part of the city.

This organisation of ex-servicemen has set up a museum at the headquarters in the city. On show are photographs, documents, uniforms etc. There are also many personal items tracing the lives of soldiers, sailors and airmen.

TYPE	REG/SER	CON. NO.	PI/NOTES	STATUS
☐ Fiat G.91R/4	5420	91-4-0130	BD+362,BR+363 - front fuselage only – on loan from M. do Ar.	PV

MUSEU DE MARINHA (POR10)

Address: Praça do Império, 1400-206 Lisboa.
Tel: 213620019
Fax: 213631987
Email: gero@museumarinha.pt
Admission: Tuesday-Sunday 1000-1700. (Closes at 1800 in summer)
Location: In the Belem suburb of the city off the N.6 about 2 km west of Ponte Salazar.

This excellent museum was established in 1863 and first located at the former Naval School in Lisbon. A fire in 1916 destroyed a large proportion of the collection. The display moved in 1948 to the Conde de Ferrebo's Palace at Laranjeiras where it remained for fourteen years. On August 15th 1962 the museum was officially opened in the Hieronymite Monastery in Belém. The exhibition was located in the north and west wings of the building and a large new pavilion to house a magnificent display of restored galleys and other boats was soon erected. The voyages of the pioneer explorers are shown in detail. The Army Aviation School formed a naval section in 1916 and two Schreck flying boats, later joined by a third, were used for training and coastal reconnaissance. In 1922 a flight from Lisbon to Rio de Janiero was planned. The first Fairey IIID, fitted with long range tanks, left the Portuguese capital on March 30th. but was wrecked on April 18th. A second machine was shipped out to take over but this had engine failure. The aircraft on show, named 'Santa Cruz' completed the journey from St. Vincent to Brazil between June 5th and the 17th. The Widgeon is one of twelve supplied in 1940.

TYPE	REG/SER	CON. NO.	PI/NOTES	STATUS
☐ Fairey IIID	17	F402		PV
☐ Grumman G-44 Widgeon	'128'	1242	120, CS-AHG	PVX
☐ Schreck FBA	2	203		PV

MUSEU DO AR (POR11)

Address: Rua dos Pioneiros da Aviação
2615-174 Alverca.
Tel: 219582782
Fax: 219571931
Email: museudoar@mail.telepac.pt

Admission: Tuesday-Sunday 1000-1700. (closes at 1800 July-September)
Location: Alverca is 20 km north east of Lisboa off the N.10 / Autoroute A.1.
Sintra airfield is north east of the town which is about 25 km west of Lisboa.
Ota airfield is about 15 km north of Vila Franca off the N.1
Beja airfield is about 8 km north west of the town off Road IP.2.

Military flying in Portugal started in 1910 when an Army balloon company was formed. Five aircraft were presented to the government over the next two years and three were flown by the new unit. A military aviation school was established on May 14th 1914 but did not come into being until July 17th 1916. In June 1918 the Military Aviation Service was formed with two Caudron G.3s based at Vila Nova da Rainha. In the inter-war period the types flown by the service were all of British and French design with a number built under licence by OGMA at Alverca. This trend was broken in 1937 with an order for ten Junkers Ju 52/3ms, some of which are now in the museum collection. During World War II the first American aircraft joined the Air Force – eleven P-39s and two P-38 s – landed in error at Lisbon's unfinished airport and were impounded. Negotiations with the United States resulted in them being transferred to Portugal. A decree to set up a museum was issued on February 21st 1968 and it was officially set up as an air force unit on July 1st 1969. Work started on collecting material and aircraft and the exhibition opened in a former OGMA hangar on July 1st 1971. OGMA donated its collection and aircraft were rescued from around the country. The displays have steadily been improved and the story of both military and civil aviation is presented in detail. Space is restricted but a range of aircraft and artefacts can be seen. Replicas of three early types – a Caudron G.3, a Blériot XI and a Farman MF-4 – represent the pioneer period. During World War II over one hundred Hurricanes were flown and a few of the survivors returned to England in the 1950s to be used in the film 'Reach for the Sky'. Sadly all were scrapped on their return to Portugal and a replica has been constructed to honour this much loved fighter. The Spitfire on show was obtained from South Africa in the late 1980s with a Beaufighter travelling in the opposite direction. A number of homebuilts, including the Nikus Miniplane built as a design exercise at Coimbra University, can be seen. A recent development at Alverca has seen the construction of an outside exhibition area in front of the hangar where several modern jets are parked. The museum also has a large storage compound within the Air Force complex where several derelict airframes are to be found. For over a quarter of a century the museum used part of two hangars at Sintra for storage. This facility is now open to the public on a regular basis. Several aircraft are on show along with the fleet of airworthy machines maintained by the museum. There are long term plans to construct a new facility at this site. The operational units were withdrawn from BA 2 at Ota in the early 1990s. One large hangar is now used for storage and over twenty five aircraft are located here.

Location Codes : 1: Alverca; 2: Sintra; 3: Ota; 4: Beja.

TYPE	REG/SER	CON. NO.	PI/NOTES	STATUS
☐ Ateliers Aéronautiques de Colombes AAC.1 [Junkers Ju 52/3mg10e]	6315	005	F-BAJE, 5 (France)	RA.1
☐ Ateliers Aéronautiques de Colombes AAC.1 [Junkers Ju 52/3mg10e]	6311	205	205 (France)	RA.1
☐ Auster D5/160 Husky	3548	45		PVA.2
☐ Auster D5/160 Husky	3564	70		PV.1
☐ Avro 626			Major components.	RA.1
☐ Avro 631 Cadet	501	727	On loan to Air Force HQ	-
☐ Beagle A.109 Airedale	CS-AIB	B.527	G-ASCB	RA.3
☐ Beech C18S Kansan (AT-11)	2504	1431 (?)	41-27586 (?) , BC-4	RA.3
☐ Beech D18S Expeditor (C-45H)	2515		(USAF)	RA.3
☐ Beech D18S Expeditor (C-45H)	2516		(USAF)	RA.3
☐ Beech D18S Expeditor 3TM	2513	CA-76	2278 (Canada)	RA.3
☐ Beech D18S Expeditor 3TM	2517	CA-94	2296 (Canada) - parts only	RAD.1
☐ Blériot XI (R)				PV.1
☐ Canadair CL-30 Silver Star 3 (CT-133) [Lockheed 580 (T-33AN)]	1951	T33-045	21045	PV.4
☐ Canadair CL-90 Starfighter (CF-104) [Lockheed 683-04-12]	104750	683A-1050	12750 - with tail of c/n 583A-5318 12648, 104648	RA.3
☐ Canadian Car & Foundry Harvard 4 [North American NA-186 (T-6J)]	1769	CCF4-517	52-8596, AA+078, BF+078	PVC.2
☐ Canadian Car & Foundry Harvard 4 [North American NA-186 (T-6J)]	1737	CCF4-521	52-8600, AA+077, BF+077	RA.3
☐ Caudron G.3 (R)				PV.1
☐ Cessna 318C Tweety Bird (T-37C)	2412	40736	62-5937 - in Alverca village.	PV
☐ Cessna 318C Tweety Bird (T-37C)	2419	40744	62-5944	RA.4
☐ Cessna 318C Tweety Bird (T-37C)	2420	40745	62-5945	PV.1
☐ Cessna 318C Tweety Bird (T-37C)	2427	40781	62-12498 – on base at Sintra.	PV.2
☐ Cessna FTB337G Super Skymaster				RA.3
☐ Cessna FTB337G Super Skymaster	3707	FTB337008		RA.3
☐ Cessna FTB337G Super Skymaster	3719	FTB337020		RA.3
☐ Cid Varela Hydroplane				RAD.1
☐ Dassault Mirage IIIR	313	313	In French markings.	RA.3
☐ De Havilland D.H.82A Tiger Moth	111	P.1	111, CS-AAA	PV.1
☐ De Havilland D.H.82A Tiger Moth	102	3650	102, CS-AEF May be c/n DHTM.3A ex 111.	PVA.2
☐ De Havilland D.H.82A Tiger Moth	'119'	86371	NL928 may be c/n P.37 CS-AEO	PVAX.2
☐ De Havilland D.H.87B Hornet Moth	CR-AAC	8104		PV.2

☐ De Havilland D.H.89 Dragon Rapide (D.H.89B Dominie I)	'2307'	6430	G-AFMA, Z7255, G-AFMA, CS-LEB, CR-LCO	PVX.2
☐ De Havilland D.H.100 Vampire FB.9	'5801'		248 (South Africa)	PVX.1
☐ De Havilland D.H.104 Dove 1B (1)	CR-CAL	04157	CR-ACL	RA.3
☐ De Havilland D.H.C.1 Chipmunk T.10	1305	C1/0292		RA.3
☐ Dornier Do 27A-1	3487	141	PB+114, PB+104	RAD.3
☐ Dornier Do 27A-1	3489	251	PG+111, PA+105	RA.3
☐ Dornier Do 27A-3 (A-1)	'3357'	235	PB+224, QB+401, PZ+218, 55+85, 3358	PVAX.2
☐ Dornier Do 27A-3 (A-1)	'3480'	350	PL+427, QW+703, 3339, CS-AQI	PVAX.2
☐ Dornier Do 27H-2	'3422'	2013	V-606 (Switzerland), HB-HAC - may be K-2 c/n 2136	RAD.2
☐ Douglas A-26B Invader	7104	28005	44-34726, N3152G - major parts.	RA.1
☐ Douglas DC-3A-456 Skytrain (C-47A)	6157	19755	43-15289	PV.2
☐ Douglas DC-4 Skymaster (C-54A)	6606	3069	41-37279, N95441, PH-XBY, CS-TSC - major parts.	RA.1
☐ Douglas DC-6B-1225A	6706	44116	N6116C	RA.1
☐ Fairey IIID (R)	'17'		Real No.17 at Museu de Marinha	PVX.1
☐ Farman MF-4 (R)				PV.1
☐ Fiat G.91R/3	5441	91-064	BD+104, EC+104, MC+255, 30+11	PV.1
☐ Fiat G.91R/3	5445	91-091	BD+235, EC+235, ER+235, MC+245, 30+32	PV.2
☐ Fiat G.91R/3	5452	91-469	KD+459, BD+257, 32+01	RA.2
☐ Fiat G.91R/3	5454	91-532	KD+522, EC+235, MD+235, MC+258, 32+62	PV.2
☐ Fiat G.91R/3	5473	91-590	KD+580, MB+251, 33+19	RA.1
☐ Fiat G.91R/4	5436	91-4-0128	BD+254, BR+254	RA.3
☐ Fiat G.91R/4	5420	91-4-0130	BD+363, BR+363 – front fuselage only – on loan to M. do L. C.	–
☐ Fiat G.91R/4	5438	91-4-0143	BD+375, BR+375	PV.2
☐ Fiat G.91T/3 (T/1)	1806	91-2-0025	BD+124, 34+23	RA.3
☐ Grumman G-44 Widgeon	129	1251	(129), 121, 129, CS-AHF	PV.1
☐ Hawker Hurricane IIC (FSM)	'591'			PVX.1
☐ Jacobs Kranich IIC (D.F.S. 108-30)	CS-PAD	983		RA.4
☐ Jacobs Weihe A-3 (D.F.S. 108-68)	CS-PAF	244		RA.4
☐ Jodel D.9 Bébé	CS-AXA	436		PV.1
☐ Junkers Ju 52/3mg3e	6304	5661	104	RA
☐ Junkers Ju 52/3mg3e	6301	5893	101	RAD.1
☐ Junkers Ju 52/3mg8e	6300	501219		RA.1
☐ Junkers Ju 52/3mg8e	6310	501219	PR+WK, 7U+??, Y-AB (Norway), 110	RA.1
☐ Jurca MJ.2B Tempête	CS-AXB	9		PV.2
☐ Le Cerf Aeroplane J.V.				RA.1
☐ Lockheed 15-27-01 Harpoon (PV-2)	4620	15-1439	Bu37473 - major parts.	RA.1
☐ Lockheed 185 Orion (P-3B) (P-3P)	14806	185-5408	Bu155298, A9-298	PV.2
☐ Lockheed 426-42-16 Neptune (P2V-5)	4711	426-5283	Bu134722, 19-31 (Netherlands), 096 (Netherlands)	PV.2
☐ Lockheed 580 (T-33A)	1923	580-1189	56-6858	RA.2
☐ Lockheed 580 (T-33A)	1926	580-1343	57-0614	PV.2
☐ Lockheed 580 (T-33A)	1928	580-7573	51-17513, FT-21 (Belgium)	RA.4
☐ Lockheed 580 (T-33A)	1914	580-8444	53-5105 may be c/n 580-9626 55-3085.	RA.4
☐ Lockheed 580 (T-33A)	1929	580-9091	53-5662, FT-28 (Belgium)	RA.4
☐ Lockheed 580 (T-33A)	1930	580-9093	53-5754, FT-30 (Belgium)	RA.4
☐ Lockheed 580 (T-33A) (RT-33A)	1916	580-8813	53-5474	PV.2
☐ Max Holste MH.1521M Broussard	3301	51C	F-WJSO	RA.3
☐ Max Holste MH.1521M Broussard	3303	53C		RAD.3
☐ Max Holste MH.1521M Broussard	3304	54C	3304, CS-AQJ	PVA.2
☐ Nord N.2501D Noratlas	6420	032	GB+108, (GA+108), GB+102, GA+118, AS+568, 52+30	RA.1
☐ Nord N.2501D Noratlas	6417	059	GC+103, GA+118, GA+248, GC+248 - parts only.	RAD.1
☐ Nord N.2502A Noratlas	6403	6	F-BGZF - may be 6405 painted as 6403.	RA.1
☐ Nord N.2502F Noratlas	6412	006		RA.1
☐ North American NA-188 Texan (T-6G)	1645	188-38	51-15175	RA.3
☐ North American NA-191 Sabre (F-86F)	5333	191-880	52-5184	RA.1
☐ North American NA-191 Sabre (F-86F)	5337	191-895	52-5199	RA.3
☐ North American NA-191 Sabre (F-86F)	5319	191-958	52-5262	PV.1
☐ North American NA-191 Sabre (F-86F)	5320	191-964	52-5268 - at Monte Real.	-
☐ North American NA-202 Sabre (F-86F)	5347	202-12	53-1083	RA.4
☐ North American NA-202 Sabre (F-86F)	5360	202-119	53-1190	RA.1
☐ North American NA-202 Sabre (F-86F)	5361	202-133	53-1204	PV.2
☐ North American NA-88 Texan (AT-6D) (Harvard III)	1517	88-14544	41-33846, EX873, 7430 (South Africa)	PV.2
☐ Northrop N-156T Talon (T-38A)	2601	N.5209	61-0843	PV.1
☐ Northrop N-156T Talon (T-38A)	2605	N.5263	61-0897	PV.2
☐ Oliveira Nikus Miniplane				PV.1
☐ Piper J-3C-65 Cub	CS-ABY	17243		RA.4
☐ Piper PA-12 Super Cruiser	CS-ADW	12-1028	Major parts only.	RAD.4
☐ Piper PA-18-125 Super Cub	CS-ALQ	18-1290	3201, CS-207	RAD.1
☐ Piper PA-18-125 Super Cub	CS-ALN	18-1297	3208	RA.4

☐ Piper PA-18-135 Super Cub (L-21B)	3212	18-2534	52-6234	PV.1
☐ Piper PA-18-135 Super Cub (L-21B)	3218	18-2573	52-6273	PVA.2
☐ Republic F-84G Thunderjet	5176		51-9957, FZ-41 (Belgium)	RA.3
☐ Republic F-84G Thunderjet	5187		51-9928, 19928 (France)	RA.3
☐ Santos-Dumont XX Demoiselle (R)				PV.1
☐ Schneider ESG 31 Grunau Baby IIB	CS-PAA			PV.1
☐ Schneider ESG 31 Grunau Baby IIB	CS-PAE	3567		PV.1
☐ Schneider Grunau SG-38 (D.F.S. 108-14)	PE-1			PV.1
☐ Schneider Grunau SG-38 (D.F.S. 108-14)	PE-2			RA.4
☐ Sikorsky S-55B Chickasaw (H-19A) (UH-19A)	9101	55137	51-7139 – parts only.	RAD.4
☐ Sikorsky S-55D Chickasaw (H-19D) (UH-19D)	'9101'	551237	57-5979, MM57-5979	PVX.2
☐ Slingsby T.21	CS-PAI	551	BGA.619	RA.3
☐ Stamer-Lippisch Z-12 Zögling 35 (D.F.S. 108-11)				RA
☐ Sud-Est SE.3130 Alouette II	9218	1267	75+15	RA.4
☐ Sud-Est SE.3130 Alouette II	A-13	1566	In Belgian markings.	RA.3
☐ Sud-Est SE.3130 Alouette II	9216	1638	76+33	PV.1
☐ Sud-Est SE.3130 Alouette II	9217	1640	76+35	PV.2
☐ Supermarine 361 Spitfire HF.IXc	ML255	CBAF-8342	ML255, 5563 (South Africa)	PVX.1
☐ Vought A-7P Corsair II (A-7A)	15508	A-128	Bu153219	PV.1
☐ Vought A-7P Corsair II (A-7A)	15519	A-157	Bu153248	RA.3
☐ Vought A-7P Corsair II (A-7A)	15503	A-181	Bu153272,	PV.2

MUSEU DOS TRANSPORTES AÉREOS PORTUGUESES (POR12)

Address:	Aeroporto de Lisboa, Edificio19, Andar, 1700 Lisboa.
Tel:	218415779
Fax:	218415881
Email:	museutap@tap.pt
Admission:	By prior permission only.
Location:	At the International Airport which is in the northern suburbs of the city.

The company was formed in September 1944 and non-scheduled flights were operated for the next two years. The first scheduled service took place between Lisbon and Madrid using DC-3s. Three Super Constellations were delivered in the autumn of 1955. They were initially used on services to Portugal's African colonies which had been served by DC-4s since late 1946. The collection of historical material started in the mid-1980s and a large number of uniforms, documents, photographs, technical manuals have been gathered along with components and engineering machinery. The Dakota, which was operated by the Directorate of Civil Aviation from 1963 until the mid-1980s has been painted to represent the first one used by the airline. The cockpit section of the Super Constellation carries the markings of the first of the TAP fleet. A small display is being set up in a room in the company complex at the airport and there are plans to open it on a regular basis.

TYPE	REG/SER	CON. NO.	PI/NOTES	STATUS
☐ Douglas DC-3A-456 Skytrain (C-47A)	'CS-TDA'	19503	43-15037, EI-ACK, 4X-AOC, CS-DGA	RAX
☐ Lockheed 1049G-82-105 Super Constellation	'CS-TLA'	1049G-4640	(D-ACID), D-ALEC, '5T-TAK', 'N8025' – front fuselage only.	RAX
☐ Sud-Est SE.210 Caravelle VI-R			Front fuselage only.	RA

REPUBLICA SRPSKA

MILITARY MUSEUM (RS1)

Address:	Banja Luka.
Admission:	Possibly not yet open.
Location:	In the town

The Serbian population of Bosnia have set up their own enclave and a museum tracing their role in the recent conflicts is being established at Banja Luka. A collection of military vehicles and weapons has been assembled. Four former Yugoslav Air Force aircraft are currently at the site and more are expected.

TYPE	REG/SER	CON. NO.	PI/NOTES	STATUS
☐ Ikarus Kurir L				RA
☐ Jacobs D.F.S. 230C-1			Fuselage frame only.	PVD
☐ Soko J-21 Jastreb	24160			RA
☐ Vazduhoplovno Tehnicki Centar – Vrsac Trener				RA
☐ Vazduhoplovno Tehnicki Centar – Vrsac VTC-76 Jastreb Vuk-T				RA

Above: The collection of aircraft owned by OGMA is kept in this restored balloon hangar at Alverca. Parked outside are their Chipmunk and Cub. (Rui Ferreira)

Right: This Northrop T-38A is at the gate at Manobra de Maceda where the Museu do Ar hopes to establish an exhibition in the north of Portugal. (Rui Ferreira)

This Fairey IIIF replica is in the Museu do Ar at Alverca. The original is in the Museu de Marinha in Lisbon.

The museum at Otopeni is home to this Ilyushin Il-10. (Peter Foster)

This Yakovlev Yak-23 is on show in the Muzeul Aviatei at Otopeni. (Alex Trandafir)

This replica of the 1910 Coanda Monoplane is in the Central Military Museum in Bucharest. The type was the first jet aircraft in the world. (Alex Trandafir)

ROMANIA

AVIASTAR FACTORY COLLECTION (ROM1)

Address:	Condorilar Str. 9, 600302 Bacău.
Tel:	0234-575070
Fax:	0234-572259
Email:	aerostar@aerostar.ro
Admission:	By prior permission only.
Location:	Just south of the town off Route 2.

Before World War II the Regia Automna Industria Aeronautica Romana was controlled by the War Ministry. The factory was destroyed in 1944. Rebuilt for tractor manufacture it returned to aeronautical work with the production of the IAR.811 trainer. Since then it has undergone several name changes before taking up its present title in 1991. In the 1950s the factory was privatised and once again produced aircraft of its own design as well as carrying out maintenance work on civil and military types. The company has preserved a few aircraft and constructed a replica of Traian Vuia's 1906 monoplane which he flew in France. The two MiG-15s also serve as instructional airframes at the apprentice training school.

TYPE	REG/SER	CON. NO.	PI/NOTES	STATUS
☐ Antonov An-2R	YR-YAV	1G 124-47	YR-PAB, 47	RA
☐ Industria Aeronautica Romana IAR.813	YR-LIA			RA
☐ Mikoyan-Gurevich MiG-15	253			RA
☐ Mikoyan-Gurevich MiG-15UTI	2199			RA
☐ Mikoyan-Gurevich MiG-21bis (Lancer B)	165	7500101/0102		RA
☐ Vuia 1 (R)				RA

BACĂU BASE COLLECTION (ROM2)

Address:	Baza 95 Aeriana, 600304 Bacău.
Tel:	0744-386-402
Admission:	By prior permission only.
Location:	Just south of the town off Route 2.

Bacau has been a fighter base for many years and currently updated MiG-21 Lancers are in service along with locally produced Puma helicopters. A small collection of preserved aircraft is on the field.

TYPE	REG/SER	CON. NO.	PI/NOTES	STATUS
☐ Aero L-29 Delfin	35	893036		RA
☐ Mikoyan-Gurevich MiG-15UTI	134			RA
☐ Mikoyan-Gurevich MiG-21F-13	23			RA

BOBOC BASE COLLECTION (ROM3)

Address: Institutelui de Aplicatie 'Aurel Vlaicu', 127190 Boboc.
Tel: 0724-212-673
Admission: By prior permission only.
Location: About 15 km north east of Buzau.

This site is home to the Institute for Aviation which runs air and ground crew courses for the Air Force. A collection of preserved aircraft has been acquired to show students the history and traditions of the service.

TYPE	REG/SER	CON. NO.	PI/NOTES	STATUS
☐ Aero L-29 Delfin	37	893038		RA
☐ Ilyushin Il-14P	2002	148002002	YR-ILW	RA
☐ Mikoyan-Gurevich MiG-15UTI	3020	3020		RA
☐ Mikoyan-Gurevich MiG-21PFMA	8005	94A8005		RA

CLUBUL COPIILOR (ROM4)

Address: Olanescu 19, 0275 Pucioasa.
Tel: 045-760803
Admission: By prior permission only.
Location: About 15 km north of Tirgoviste on Route 71.

Three aircraft are preserved at this children's club with the aim of interesting young people in aviation. The Aero 45 twin was built in large numbers in Czechoslovakia and served in many countries. The first Zlin Z-26 Trener flew in 1949 and the type has been developed in both single and two seat versions.

TYPE	REG/SER	CON. NO.	PI/NOTES	STATUS
☐ Aero 45				PV
☐ Mikoyan-Gurevich MiG-15				PV
☐ Zlin Z-526F Trener Master				PV

CRAIOVA BALTA VERDE BASE COLLECTION (ROM5)

Address: Baza 67 Aeriana, Craiova.
Admission: By prior permission only.
Location: About 7 km east of the town off Route 65.

A combat regiment moved out of this field a few years ago. Now the site is used for aircraft storage and many of the airframes will ultimately be scrapped. Two of the preserved aircraft moved to the museum at Otopeni.

TYPE	REG/SER	CON. NO.	PI/NOTES	STATUS
☐ Mikoyan-Gurevich MiG-15	415	??415		RA
☐ Mikoyan-Gurevich MiG-19PM	0906	960906		RA
☐ Mikoyan-Gurevich MiG-21F-13	16	742216		RA

HENRI COANDA ACADEMY COLLECTION (ROM6)

Address: Str Mihai Viteazul, 500183 Brasov.
Tel: 0721-356-436
Email: amhe@unitbv.ro
Admission: By prior permission only.
Location: The airfield is about 4 km east of the town.

Officers for the Air Force are trained at this school. There is a traditions room in the buildings where uniforms, models, photographs and documents can be seen. The collection of preserved types includes three indigenous designs. The IAR.823 first flew in 1973 and about ninety were built for both civil and military use. The IAR.93 was a joint venture with the former Yugoslavia.

TYPE	REG/SER	CON. NO.	PI/NOTES	STATUS
☐ Aero L-39ZA Albatros	139	432836		RA
☐ Industria Aeronautica Romana IAR.28MA	102	04		RA
☐ Industria Aeronautica Romana IAR.823	51			RA
☐ Industria Aeronautica Romana IAR.93DC	600	93287600		RA
☐ Mikoyan-Gurevich MiG-15bis	596	??596		RA
☐ Sud-Est SE.3160 Alouette III	152	1822		RA

MUZEUL ACADEMIE TEHNICE MILITAIRE (ROM7)

Address:	Bul George Cosbuc 81-83, 75275 Bucuresti.
Tel:	021-335-4660
Fax:	021-335-8763
Email:	atm@mta.ro
Admission:	By prior permission only.
Location:	In the northern part of the city.

This college trains Air Force personnel in many technical subjects. A small museum in the buildings traces the history of the service with photographs, models and documents to be seen. On show in the grounds is an IAR.93 and there may be other aircraft in the collection.

TYPE	REG/SER	CON. NO.	PI/NOTES	STATUS
☐ Industria Aeronautica Romana IAR.93B	232	93184232		RA

MUZEUL AVIATIEI (ROM8)

Address:	Strada Zborului 1, Otopeni, 71950 Bucuresti.
Tel:	0723-237600
Email:	proff@roaf.ro
Admission:	Winter daily 0800-1600; Summer daily 0900-1700.
Location:	About 16 km north of the city off Route 1.

The airfield was built in 1939 and has been home to fighter units for many years. The first MiG-15s were supplied to Romania in the early 1950s and one example has been preserved with other types which were flown from the base. The museum opened a display in the late 1990s at the historic airfield of Baneasa which was first used in 1909. The collection was set up a few years ago and has already acquired a sizeable collection of aircraft. A move to its current location took place in 2000. The Ilyushin Il-10 was on show for many years in the Central Military Museum. The Il-10 ground attack aircraft first flew in 1944 and replaced the famous Il-2 'Shturmovik' on the production lines at Rostov. Over twelve hundred were later built in Czechoslovakia as the Avia B-33. From a slightly later era is the Yakovlev Yak-23 which took to the air in June 1947. Only just over three hundred were built owing to the success of the MiG-15. After Soviet service a small number were transferred to Romania in the late 1950s and flown for a few years. The Soviet influence over the years is represented by the range of MiG jets and the Mil helicopters. The collection includes several indigenous designs by IAR. The first post-war Romanian aircraft was the IAR.811 which made its maiden flight in 1949. The design was developed into the IAR.813 which was produced in large numbers. The company also built Alouettes and Pumas. The first Britten-Norman Islander built under licence in Romania flew from Baneasa on August 4th 1969 and since then well over five hundred have been completed in the country. The museum is developing its displays which will highlight the rich aeronautical heritage of the country over the last century.

TYPE	REG/SER	CON. NO.	PI/NOTES	STATUS
☐ Aero 45	YR-ACH			RA
☐ Aero 45	YR-ACR			PV
☐ Aero L-29 Delfin	50	395059		RA
☐ Aero L-29 Delfin	15	993150		RA
☐ Britten-Norman BN-2A Islander	130	130	N863JA, YR-BND	PV
☐ Harbin H-5C [Ilyushin Il-28R]	402			RA
☐ Harbin H-5C [Ilyushin Il-28R]	405			PV
☐ Ilyushin Il-10M	817			PV
☐ Ilyushin Il-18V	YR-IME	183006205	YR-IME, B-232, YR-IME, 3D-AHO, EL-AHO	PV
☐ Industria Aeronautica Romana IAR.28MA	103			PV
☐ Industria Aeronautica Romana IAR.80 (FSM)	'1'			PVX
☐ Industria Aeronautica Romana IAR.93A	114	93180114		PV

TYPE	REG/SER	CON. NO.	PI/NOTES	STATUS
☐ Industria Aeronautica Romana IAR.93DC	002	RO-002		PV
☐ Industria Aeronautica Romana IAR.316B Alouette III [Sud SA.316B]	45	162		PV
☐ Industria Aeronautica Romana IAR.316B Alouette III [Sud SA.316B]	86	171		PV
☐ Industria Aeronautica Romana IAR.330H Puma [Sud SA.330H]	47	053/RO-67		PV
☐ Industria Aeronautica Romana IAR.813	YR-ICE		74	PV
☐ Industria Aeronautica Romana IAR.823	19			RA
☐ Industria Aeronautica Romana IAR.823	15			RA
☐ Industria Aeronautica Romana IAR.828	01	01		PV
☐ Lavochkin La-9	66			PV
☐ Mikoyan-Gurevich MiG-15	727			RA
☐ Mikoyan-Gurevich MiG-15bis	246			RA
☐ Mikoyan-Gurevich MiG-15bis	2713			PV
☐ Mikoyan-Gurevich MiG-15UTI	2543			PV
☐ Mikoyan-Gurevich MiG-15UTI	2579			RA
☐ Mikoyan-Gurevich MiG-17F	444			RA
☐ Mikoyan-Gurevich MiG-17F	442			PV
☐ Mikoyan-Gurevich MiG-17PF	502	0502		RA
☐ Mikoyan-Gurevich MiG-17PF	0904	0904		PV
☐ Mikoyan-Gurevich MiG-19PM	750			PV
☐ Mikoyan-Gurevich MiG-19PM	018	1018	718, 818	PV
☐ Mikoyan-Gurevich MiG-21F-13	10			PV
☐ Mikoyan-Gurevich MiG-21F-13	711	740711		PV
☐ Mikoyan-Gurevich MiG-21F-13	714	740714		PV
☐ Mil Mi-8PS	709	10709	09	PV
☐ Mil Mi-8SPS (Mi-8PS)	03	0326	03, YR-EVJ, 703	PV
☐ Mil Mi-8T	05	0526		PV
☐ Piper PA-25-235 Pawnee B				RA
☐ Silimon IS 30	YR-915			RA
☐ Sud SA.318C Alouette Astazou	76	2176	YR-ALB	RA
☐ Wytwornia Sprzetu Komunikacyjnego (WSK) SM-1/300 [Mil Mi-1]	01			RA
☐ Wytwornia Sprzetu Komunikacyjnego (WSK) SM-1/300 [Mil Mi-1]	04			RA
☐ Vuia 1 (R)				PV
☐ Yakovlev Yak-11	1			RA
☐ Yakovlev Yak-18	38			RA
☐ Yakovlev Yak-23	14			RA
☐ Yakovlev Yak-23	52	14/139		PV
☐ Zlin Z-526 Trener Master	15	1183		PV
☐ Zlin Z-526F Trener Master				RA
☐ Zlin Z-526F Trener Master				PV

MUZEUL GRUPUL SCOLAR DE AERONAUTICA 'HENRI COANDA' (ROM9)

Address:	Bul. Dul Ficusulu 44 Bucuresti.
Tel:	0232-3616
Admission:	By prior permission only.
Location:	At Baneasa Airport which is about 8 km north of the city off Route 1.

A small display of aircraft has been set up in the grounds of this college. The Antonov An-24 was delivered to TAROM in 1971 but was withdrawn after six years service following a landing accident. The An-2 was built at Kiev in the early 1960s and has been at the college for many years. The first MiG-15s were delivered to the Air Force in 1952 and the last were withdrawn after forty years service. The aircraft are also used for instruction.

TYPE	REG/SER	CON. NO.	PI/NOTES	STATUS
☐ Antonov An-2	YR-ANN	116473315		RA
☐ Antonov An-24RV	YR-AMC	17306906		RA
☐ Mikoyan-Gurevich MiG-15	735			RA
☐ Mikoyan-Gurevich MiG-15	744			RA
☐ Mikoyan-Gurevich MiG-15UTI	1526			RA
☐ Mikoyan-Gurevich MiG-21F-13	18			RA

MUZEUL MILITAR CENTRAL (ROM10)

Address:	Strada Stefan Furtuna 125, 010899 Bucuresti.
Tel:	021-637-3830
Admission:	Tuesday-Sunday 0900-1700.
Location:	Near the Gara de Nord in the city.

Founded in 1923 the museum traces the history and development of all forces in the country. The aviation section contains a number of interesting aircraft along with many engines, photographs and models. A large outside display park houses military vehicles and guns. Louis Blériot made the first flight in the country when he took off from the horserace course at Baneasa on October 18th 1909. Three replicas of early machines designed by Romanians are on show. Traian Vuia built his aircraft in France and it flew at Montesson on March 18th 1906. (The Vuia survived and is now on show in the Musée de l'Air at Le Bourget). Also built in France was Henri Coanda's 1910 biplane powered by an engine driving a ducted fan. Henri was the son of the Romanian War Minister and be later designed aircraft for the British and Colonial Aeroplane Company at Filton. Aurel Vlaicu built the first aeroplane in Romania and it won several prizes at a meeting in Vienna in 1912. Two rarities from the inter-war period are the Fleet and Nardi trainers. Over three hundred Fleet 10 biplanes were built in the country and gave excellent service. The low wing Nardi FN.305 first flew in 1935 and was successful in both military and sporting roles. The IAR.80 fighter was the pride of the Romanian Air Force during World War II and the last examples were withdrawn in 1949. Sadly none were saved and a replica has been built for the exhibition. Post-war designs from the IAR factory can also be seen.

TYPE	REG/SER	CON. NO.	PI/NOTES	STATUS
☐ Coanda Monoplane (R)				PV
☐ Fleet 10G	51	351		PV
☐ Industria Aeronautica Romana IAR.80 (FSM)	'42'			PVX
☐ Industria Aeronautica Romana IAR.316B Alouette III [Sud SA.316B]	23	37		PV
☐ Industria Aeronautica Romana IAR.330H Puma [Sud SA.330H]	20	009		PV
☐ Industria Aeronautica Romana IAR.813	01			PV
☐ Industria Aeronautica Romana IAR.823	01			PV
☐ Industria Aeronautica Romana IAR.93A	153	93181153		PV
☐ Mikoyan-Gurevich MiG-15bis	244	???244		PV
☐ Mikoyan-Gurevich MiG-19P	802		002, 702 – sectioned airframe.	PV
☐ Nardi FN.305	87	87		PV
☐ Silimon IS 28M-2	YR-808	46		RA
☐ Vlaicu II (R)				PV
☐ Vuia 1 (R)	1			PV
☐ Yakovlev Yak-11	47			PV

MUZEUL STIINTEI SI TEHNICII "STEFAN PROCOPIU" (ROM11)

Address:	Piata Stefan cel Mare, Sfant 1, 6600 Iasi.
Tel:	032-147402
Email:	palatis@mail.dntis.ro
Admission:	Tuesday-Sunday 1000-1700.
Location:	In the centre of the city.

The town was once the capital of Moldavia and contains many historic buildings. The museum is one of four in the Palace of Culture complex. Many aspects of science and technology are covered. The Yakovlev Yak-17 jet, developed from the Yak-15, first flew in the summer of 1947 and over four hundred of the single and two seat versions were produced. The engine is on display inside the building and the airframe is in the yard.

TYPE	REG/SER	CON. NO.	PI/NOTES	STATUS
☐ Yakovlev Yak-17UTI	7			PV

MUZEUL TECHNIC 'PROFESSOR INGINER DIMITRIE LEONIDA' (ROM12)

Address:	Str. Candiano Popescu 2, Sectorul 5, 75206 Bucuresti.
Tel:	01-336-7777
Admission:	Tuesday-Sunday 1000-1700.
Location:	In Libert Park in the southern part of the city.

This technical museum was founded in 1909 by Dimitrie Leionida who gathered historical items to show to his students of electrical engineering. There was a small aeronautical section with about six aircraft, including a Bücker Jungmeister, on show but these were destroyed in the 1980s when the roof of the building collapsed. Some of the models and components in this area were saved. The only aircraft to survive was the high wing IAR.817 which is parked outside the building but this is now in poor condition.

TYPE	REG/SER	CON. NO.	PI/NOTES	STATUS
☐ Industria Aeronautica Romana IAR.817	YR-ASB			PVD

RUSSIA (EUROPEAN)

610 COMBAT AND CONVERSION TRAINING CENTRE MUSEUM (RU1)

Address:	Novyi But, Ivanovo North
Admission:	By prior permission only.
Location:	Just north of the town which is about 300 km north east of Moscow off Road A113.

The base has been home to transport units for many years and currently houses squadrons flying the Antonov An-12 and Ilyushin Il-76. The museum traces the history of the site, its squadrons and the personnel who have served at Ivanovo. A range of types flown from the field has been preserved around the site.

TYPE	REG/SER	CON. NO.	PI/NOTES	STATUS
☐ Antonov An-2T	20	1G 199-44		RAA
☐ Antonov An-2T	11	1G 63-34		RA
☐ Antonov An-12BK	RA-11666		CCCP-11666	RA
☐ Antonov An-12BK-PPS	06	01347904		RA
☐ Antonov An-22A	RA-08830	053483308	CCCP-08830	RA
☐ Antonov An-26	CCCP-47403			RA
☐ Ilyushin Il-14T	15	147001621		RA
☐ Ilyushin Il-76MD	CCCP-86913	0023438108		RA
☐ Lisunov Li-2 [Douglas DC-3 modified]	55	23440706		RA

AEROFLOT ENGINEERING TRAINING SCHOOL (RU2)

Address:	Egor'evsk.
Admission:	By prior permission only.
Location:	About 100km south east of Moscow off Road P105.

The aircraft at this school serve a dual role. The airframes are used for training and also serve as a display. The Po-2 is marked '57' as this was the age of the engineer when he started to build it.

TYPE	REG/SER	CON. NO.	PI/NOTES	STATUS
☐ Antonov An-2P	CCCP-01759	1G 107-06		RA
☐ Antonov An-2P	CCCP-01760	1G 107-07		RA
☐ Antonov An-24	CCCP-46745	47300902		RA
☐ Antonov An-24B	RA-46409	77304004	CCCP-46409	RA
☐ Antonov An-24V	TZ-ACK	87304202		RA
☐ Polikarpov Po-2 (R)	'57'			RAAX
☐ Tupolev Tu-154	CCCP-85010	70M010		RA
☐ Tupolev Tu-154	CCCP-85011	71A-011		RA
☐ Yakovlev Yak-42	CCCP-42311	0103		RA

AEROFLOT MUSEUM (RU3)

Address:	Arrival Lounge, Sheremet'yevo-1, Moscow.
Tel:	095- 78-65-75
Admission:	Monday-Friday 0900-1800.
Location:	About 20 km. north of the city off Road M10.

Aeroflot was formed in 1930 replacing Dobrolet as the state airline. The company grew and at the downfall of the Soviet Union in 1991 it was the largest in the world. At this time about eleven thousand aircraft were operated. Since then numbers have decreased greatly and many independent airlines have taken over routes. This museum has been set up in Moscow with models, photos uniforms etc. tracing the history of the organisation. The routes flown are also highlighted. Over the years it has operated a wide variety of aircraft on many tasks.

AIR DEFENCE FORCES MUSEUM – NEMCHINOVKA (RU4)

Address:	Nemchinovka.
Admission:	By prior permission only.
Location:	Off the Smolensk/Tver road just outside the Moscow Ring Road west of the city.

The Air Defence Force became a separate part of the Armed Forces in 1948. Over the years a range of fighter aircraft and missiles have been employed. The history of the force, with special emphasis on the Moscow area, is portrayed in the indoor exhibition. In addition to the aircraft there are missiles, rockets and weapons on show.

TYPE	REG/SER	CON. NO.	PI/NOTES	STATUS
☐ Mikoyan-Gurevich MiG-9				RA
☐ Mikoyan-Gurevich MiG-17				RA
☐ Mikoyan-Gurevich MiG-19				RA
☐ Mikoyan-Gurevich MiG-23P				RA
☐ Mikoyan-Gurevich MiG-25P				RA
☐ Sukhoi Su-11				RA
☐ Sukhoi Su-15				RA

ANTI AIRCRAFT DEFENCE FORCE MUSEUM – RZHEV (RU5)

Address:	Pushskunskaya nab. 17, Rzhev-3, 172350 Tver Oblast.
Tel:	08232-239-86
Fax:	08232-239-86
Admission:	By prior permission only.
Location:	About 240 km north west of Moscow off Road M9.

This museum traces the history of the airfield and its units as well as the story of the force. On show are many models, uniforms, documents and components. A range of aircraft flown from the base has been preserved.

TYPE	REG/SER	CON. NO.	PI/NOTES	STATUS
☐ Mikoyan-Gurevich MiG-21bis	45			RA
☐ Mikoyan-Gurevich MiG-23P	20			RA
☐ Mikoyan-Gurevich MiG-25PD	46			RA
☐ Mikoyan-Gurevich MiG-29UB	80			RA
☐ Mikoyan-Gurevich MiG-31	24			RA
☐ Sukhoi Su-9	05			RA
☐ Sukhoi Su-15UM	46			RA
☐ Tupolev Tu-128	72			RA
☐ Tupolev Tu-128UT	15			RA

ANTI AIRCRAFT DEFENCE FORCE MUSEUM – SAVASLEIKA (RU6)

Address:	148th Combat and Training Division, Savasleika.
Admission:	By prior permission only.
Location:	About 10 km south east of the town which is about 200 km south east of Moscow.

An excellent display of types used by the force has been set up at this base which trains aircrew. The inside display has many models, components, photographs and uniforms on show. The history of the base and its units is portrayed. Over the years a variety of aircraft have been used by the unit and many have been preserved.

TYPE	REG/SER	CON. NO.	PI/NOTES	STATUS
☐ Aero L-29 Delfin	27			RA
☐ Aero L-39C Albatros	82			RA
☐ Mikoyan-Gurevich MiG-15UTI	02			RA
☐ Mikoyan-Gurevich MiG-17	01			RA
☐ Mikoyan-Gurevich MiG-17F	01		At base gate.	RA
☐ Mikoyan-Gurevich MiG-19PT	04			RA
☐ Mikoyan-Gurevich MiG-19S	03			RA
☐ Mikoyan-Gurevich MiG-21bis	09			RA
☐ Mikoyan-Gurevich MiG-21PFM	15			RA
☐ Mikoyan-Gurevich MiG-21UM	04			RA
☐ Mikoyan-Gurevich MiG-23M	05			RA
☐ Mikoyan-Gurevich MiG-23M	15			RA
☐ Mikoyan-Gurevich MiG-23P	67			RA
☐ Mikoyan-Gurevich MiG-23UB	70			RA
☐ Mikoyan-Gurevich MiG-25P	58			RA
☐ Mikoyan-Gurevich MiG-25PU	53			RA
☐ Mikoyan-Gurevich MiG-31	32			RA
☐ Sukhoi Su-9	07	100000510		RA
☐ Sukhoi Su-15	71			RA
☐ Sukhoi Su-15TM	34			RA

TYPE	REG/SER	CON. NO.	PI/NOTES	STATUS
☐ Sukhoi Su-15UM	30			RA
☐ Sukhoi Su-27UB	40			RA
☐ Tupolev Tu-128	71	501101		RA
☐ Yakovlev Yak-25	05			RA
☐ Yakovlev Yak-28R	06			RA

ARCTIC AND ANTARCTIC MUSEUM (RU7)

Address:	24 Marat Street. 191040 St. Petersburg.
Tel:	812 113 19 98
Fax:	812 164 68 18
Email:	vicaar@mail.wplus.net
Admission:	Wednesday-Sunday 1000-1700.
Location:	In the city centre.

Originally the museum displays covered many aspects of the Arctic region including natural history, exploration, art and the influence of Soviet policies. The exhibition has now been expanded to show the work carried out at the other end of the globe. Vadim Shavrov built his Sh-l as a private venture in the late 1920s. The aircraft was the first amphibian in the Soviet Union and it crashed at Leningrad in February 1930 when piloted by Chkalov. The improved Sh-2 appeared at the end of 1930 and two hundred and seventy were built in 1932/4. The Sh-2 was a success and some were still in use in the mid-1960s. The example on show was flown by Babushkin on several of his pioneering flights into the previously uncharted wastelands.

TYPE	REG/SER	CON. NO.	PI/NOTES	STATUS
☐ Shavrov Sh-2				PV

ARMY AVIATION CONVERSION TRAINING CENTRE MUSEUM (RU8)

Address:	Torzhok.
Admission:	By prior permission only.
Location:	About 220 km north west of Moscow off Road M10.

Many Army helicopters crews have trained at this base. A collection of types has been preserved to show what was formerly in service. The comprehensive range of Mil types is impressive and shows the versatility of this design bureau. Only about eighty Mil-10 flying cranes were constructed in the 1960s.

TYPE	REG/SER	CON. NO.	PI/NOTES	STATUS
☐ Kamov Ka-25PL	25			RA
☐ Kamov Ka-26				RA
☐ Kamov Ka-27PL	14			RA
☐ Mil Mi-1	01			RA
☐ Mil Mi-2	02	510925		RA
☐ Mil Mi-4	03			RA
☐ Mil Mi-6	09			RA
☐ Mil Mi-8	55	93114		RA
☐ Mil Mi-8TB	04			RA
☐ Mil Mi-10	10			RA
☐ Mil Mi-18	08			RA
☐ Mil Mi-24A	05			RA
☐ Mil Mi-24D	06			RA
☐ Mil Mi-24V	99			RA
☐ Mil Mi-26T	55	34001212093		RA

BERIEV TAGANROG AVIATION PARK (RU9)

Address:	1 Aviatorov Square, 347923 Taganrog
Tel:	07-86344-49901
Fax:	07-86344-41454
Admission:	By prior permission only.
Location:	About 70 km west of Rostov-on-Don off Road M23.

This factory was one of the first two set up in the Soviet Union. Polikarpov and Tupolev designs were constructed. Georgii Beriev was born in Georgia in 1902 and in the early 1920s worked with the French engineer Paul Richard who was building floatplanes near Moscow. He set up his own design bureau at Taganrog in 1932 and at the current time amphibious aircraft are still being produced. The company is setting up a display at the site. It is believed that more aircraft than those listed are on show and also there is a museum at a nearby air base. The Be-6 first flew in 1949 and over two hundred were built; some survive with marine aviation units.

TYPE	REG/SER	CON. NO	PI/NOTES	STATUS
☐ Beriev Be-6				RA
☐ Mikoyan-Gurevich MiG-25				RA

CENTRAL HOUSE OF AVIATION AND COSMONAUTICS (RU10)

Address:	4 Krasnoarmeiskaya Street, Moscow 125167.
Tel:	095-212-7301
Fax:	095-212-7301
Admission:	Tuesday-Sunday 1000-1800.
Location:	Near Khodinka Airfield.

The museum was founded in 1924 and traces the development of aviation in the country from the early days up to the present time. The collection was closed for refurbishment in the 1990s. In the past there have been aircraft on display but space is limited and these have long gone. There is an excellent collection of models, documents, photographs, clothing and components to be seen. A library houses many books and records.

CENTRAL MUSEUM OF THE ARMED FORCES (RU11)

Address:	Sovetskoi Armii Street, Moscow 2.
Tel:	095-281-1880
Email:	Army@nm.ru
Admission:	Wednesday-Sunday 1000-1630.
Location:	In the northern part of the city.

The museum was founded in 1919 in a building next to the present site. The current exhibition opened in 1965 and the displays mainly trace the development of the Soviet Air Force, Army and Navy since the Revolution. The building contains twenty five halls with uniforms, documents, memorabilia, weapons and paintings on show. There are sections devoted to the early military history of the country with the fighting skills of the Cossacks portrayed. The story of the White Army which was helped by the Americans, British and Japanese at the time of the Revolution and the founding of the Red Army are shown. The original documents setting up the communist run military forces are prized possessions. Captured German standards which were paraded through Red Square in 1945 feature prominently. In one of the rooms highlighting World War II, parts of a Heinkel He 111 can be seen. There are also small pieces from one of the many Hurricanes flown by the Russian forces. Almost three thousand examples of the classic Hawker fighter were delivered from 1941. The majority were shipped to the country on the North Cape convoy route. Due to lack of spares many were cannibalised or simply left to rot. The bitter battle for Stalingrad is portrayed in vivid detail. Close by, in the Cold War section, are the remains of Gary Powers' Lockheed U-2 shot down on May 1st 1960 near Sverdlovsk whilst on a flight from Peshawar in Pakistan to Bodø in Norway (parts of his aircraft are also reported to be on show at the Museum of Military Technology in Ekaterineburg). Also here are examples of spy satellites used by both sides. At the rear of the building are rows of tanks and artillery with most types used since World War II on show. Dispersed around this park are the aircraft. The types represent those which have made significant contributions to Soviet military aviation. New models are joining this impressive exhibition and over the years some have also left.

TYPE	REG/SER	CON. NO.	PI/NOTES	STATUS
☐ Aero L-29 Delfin	01	491282	43	PV
☐ Heinkel He 111H	??+XX		Rear fuselage only.	PVD
☐ Ilyushin Il-28	10	65010809	10, 16	PV
☐ Kamov Ka-25	101			PV
☐ Lockheed U-2C (U-2A)	56-6693(?)	360	Parts only - see also Museum of Military Technology Ekaterineburg.	PVD
☐ Mikoyan-Gurevich MiG-17	25	0515347	25, 20	PV
☐ Mikoyan-Gurevich MiG-21F	01			PV
☐ Mikoyan-Gurevich MiG-21S		95-01???	Front fuselage only.	PV
☐ Mikoyan-Gurevich MiG-21SM	70			PV
☐ Mikoyan-Gurevich MiG-23S	71	220008895		PV
☐ Mikoyan-Gurevich MiG-25PD	49	08895		PV
☐ Mikoyan-Gurevich MiG-29	02	545005106		PV
☐ Mil Mi-2	51			PV
☐ Mil Mi-4	05	3202109	64	PV
☐ Mil Mi-24A	07	3202109		PV
☐ Sukhoi Su-7B	65			PV
☐ Sukhoi Su-15TM	39	1209		PV
☐ Sukhoi Su-24	71		Front fuselage only.	PV
☐ Sukhoi Su-24MR	26	0115305 (?)		PV
☐ Sukhoi Su-25	22	07080		PV
☐ Sukhoi Su-27	27			PV
☐ Yakovlev Yak-50			01	PV

Parked behind the Central Army Museum in Moscow is this MiG-21F. (Keith Dexter)

Mounted outside the museum at the Ilyushin Design Bureau is this Il-2.

The Kamov OKB at Lubertsky has three of its products, including this Ka-25PL, on show. (Keith Dexter)

Several versions of the Tu-22 are on show at Ryazan. This PD version is part of the collection. (Keith Dexter)

Valery Chkalov's record breaking Tupolev ANT-25 is on show in the museum honouring his achievements in Chkalovsk. (Bob Ruffle)

The only aircraft on display in the Zhukovskii Memorial Museum in Moscow is this original Lilienthal glider.

CENTRAL MUSEUM OF THE GREAT PATRIOTIC WAR (RU12)

Address:	Kutuzovskiy Prospekt, Moscow.
Tel:	095-420-8441
Email:	oalexandrov@mtu-net.ru
Admission:	Wednesday-Sunday 1000-1800.
Location:	In the western suburbs of the city off Road M1.

This vast new museum opened in 1994 and has on view a superb collection of aircraft. A tall monument to the war has been erected on the large site known as Victory Park. The indoor displays trace the history of the Soviet forces in their struggle to repel Hitler's invasion. The rarest machine is the biplane Kochyerigin DI-6 two seat fighter. First flown in 1935 two hundred and twenty two were built from 1936 to 1938 but only a few saw service in the Great Patriotic War. None were known to have survived until the appearance of the example on show. Other famous types from this period include a Yakovlev Yak 3 which is believed to be the one formerly on view at the Central Army Museum in Sofia, Bulgaria. Two of Nikolai Polikarpov's classic fighters can be seen. The biplane I-15 and the low wing I-16 won their spurs in the Spanish Civil War. Components from a number of crash sites can be seen. A number of modem military jets are also on view

TYPE	REG/SER	CON. NO.	PI/NOTES	STATUS
☐ Bell 33 Kingcobra (P-63C) (FSM)	'08'		'44-44011'	PVX
☐ Hawker Hurricane I			Crash remains.	PVD
☐ Ilyushin Il-2 (FSM)	'21'		'15'	PVX
☐ Ilyushin Il-4		17403 or 17404		PV
☐ Junkers Ju 88			Crash remains.	PVD
☐ Kamov Ka-25PLO	77	2912205		PV
☐ Kochyerigin DI-6 (FSM)	'3'			PVX
☐ Lavochkin LaGG-3 (FSM)	'24'			PVX
☐ Lavochkin La-5FN (FSM)	'15'			PVX
☐ Lisunov Li-2 [Douglas DC-3 modified]	'17'	18438101	CCCP-48986, 01	PVX
☐ Messerschmitt Bf 109F-4 (FSM)		'13407 '		PVX
☐ Messerschmitt Bf 110F-2/trop	LN+AR	5020	Fuselage and wing parts.	PVD
☐ Mikoyan-Gurevich MiG-15UTI	06	922272		PV
☐ Mikoyan-Gurevich MiG-17	'39'	54211399	139, '66'	PVX
☐ Mikoyan-Gurevich MiG-21PFS	09	94210425		PV
☐ Mikoyan-Gurevich MiG-23ML	14	0390310225		PV
☐ Mikoyan-Gurevich MiG-29	26	2960505560		PV
☐ Mil Mi-8T	68	9710819		PV
☐ Mil Mi-24D	'15'	04274	115	PVX
☐ Nakajima Ki-43 Hayabusha			Wings and engine only.	PVD
☐ North American NA-108 Mitchell (B-25J)			Crash remains.	PVD
☐ Polikarpov I-15bis (FSM)	'3'		'14'	PVX
☐ Polikarpov I-16 tip 17 (FSM)	'91'			PVX
☐ Polikarpov Po-2 (FSM)	'4'			PVX
☐ Sukhoi Su-2 (FSM)	'27'			PVX
☐ Sukhoi Su-17UM3	81	17532372510		PV
☐ Sukhoi Su-25	12	25508103012		PV
☐ Yakovlev Yak-3 (FSM)	'7'			PV

CENTRAL RUSSIAN AIR FORCE MUSEUM (RU13)

Address:	141170 Monino.
Tel:	095-526-3327
Fax:	095-526-3351
Admission:	Tuesday-Wednesday Friday-Saturday 0930-1300 1415-1700; Saturday 0930-1400.
Location:	About 30 km east of Moscow at the Air War Academy off Road M7.

Monino houses the Air Force Academy which had for many years collected equipment and aircraft. The decision to set up a formal museum came about on November 23rd 1958 by the decree of the Commander of the Soviet Air Force, Marshal K.A. Vershinin. For years access was restricted, as the museum was part of the military establishment. In the last few years a separate entrance has been constructed enabling foreigners to visit the impressive collection without months of often difficult negotiations. The display of engines, models, armaments, photographs and uniforms was housed in 1930s buildings where the story of Soviet military aviation was portrayed in detail. Alongside was a hangar with the early aircraft on show. Sadly these were recently burned down but the aircraft there had been moved out. However a great deal of archive material was lost. Licence built examples of a Farman HF-4 and a Voisin L show the French influence of this period. The Sopwith Triplane could have been built at the Duks factory or may be one purchased in Britain in 1917. Two light aircraft on show here are the Tupolev ANT-2 of 1924 and the 1926 Buryvestnik S-2. Andrei Tupolev built his ANT-1 in 1922 and the ANT-2 was the first all metal aircraft produced in the country. Many examples of the famous designer's work can be seen in the outside park. The S-2, powered by a Harley-Davidson motor cycle engine, was reluctant to fly. Replicas of a Polikarpov I-16, a MiG-3 and a Bereznyak-Isayev BI, the first rocket powered fighter in the world, are on show. Significant fighters are a Lavochkin La-7 flown by three times Hero of the Soviet Union Ivan Kozhedub and a Yak-9U obtained from

Bulgaria and restored by the Yakovlev design bureau. The famous Il-2 is represented by an example recovered from a crash site in 1977 and rebuilt by the Ilyushin bureau. A fairly recent arrival is a Bell Kingcobra. Just after the end of hostilities a display of World War II aircraft was staged in Moscow and rumours abounded about the fate of the machines. Some people believed that they were placed in store and the emergence of the P-63 and the Douglas A-20G Havoc lend credence to this. An American warbird collector told me that over one hundred aircraft from World War II are stored in a military establishment near Moscow. If this is true then hopefully more will appear at museums in Russia. Three old hangars are used by the museum, two for display purposes and one for storage. Replicas of two famous aircraft are on show in these buildings. These are a Sikorsky Ilya Muromets built for a film and a Tupolev ANT-25. A number of unique experimental light aircraft are on view in this area. The outside aircraft park contains examples of most of the types which the Air Force has used in recent years along with several prototypes. The Tupolev Tu-4, which is a copy of the Boeing B-29 Superfortress, contrasts with the Tu-22M which formed the backbone of the long range bombing force in recent years. A range of fighters from MiG and Sukhoi is complemented by helicopters from Mil and Kamov. The Antonov, Ilyushin and Yakovlev design bureaux are also well represented. The museum has managed to acquire the remains of a number of missing types from crash sites. Some have been restored and placed on show and hopefully others will follow. Several airliners used by Aeroflot can also he seen in this impressive display and more are expected.

TYPE	REG/SER	CON. NO.	PI/NOTES	STATUS
☐ A-1-83 Primary Glider				PV
☐ Aero L-29 Delfin	69	390418		RA
☐ Antonov An-2	CCCP-70992	111847301		RA
☐ Antonov An-8	10	9340504		PV
☐ Antonov An-10A Ukrania	CCCP-11213	0402406		PV
☐ Antonov A-11				PV
☐ Antonov A-13M				PV
☐ Antonov An-12BP	04	8900203		PV
☐ Antonov An-14A	01	500303		PV
☐ Antonov A-15T				PV
☐ Antonov An-22	CCCP-09334	00340209		PV
☐ Antonov An-24V	CCCP-46746	47300903		PV
☐ Bartini VVA-14	'CCCP-10687'		CCCP-19172	PVDX
☐ Bell 26C Airacobra (P-39N) (Scale R)	01		'42-9033'	RA
☐ Bell 33 Kingcobra (P-63A)	91		42-69775	PV
☐ Beriev Be-12	25	4600302		PV
☐ Beriev Be-32	CCCP-67209	05		PV
☐ Buryevestnik S-3				PV
☐ Douglas A-20G Havoc	310052		43-10052	PV
☐ Farman HF-4 (R)				PV
☐ Gulaikin and Stoiko Albatross 20				PV
☐ Ilyushin DB-3A	12	891311		PV
☐ Ilyushin Il-2m3	19	301060	c/n also reported as 302060	PV
☐ Ilyushin Il-10M				PV
☐ Ilyushin Il-12T	10	30218		PV
☐ Ilyushin Il-18V	CCCP-75737	181002702		PV
☐ Ilyushin Il-28	04	53005771	04, 10	PV
☐ Ilyushin Il-62	CCCP-86670	70205		PV
☐ Ivensen Sailplane				PV
☐ Kamov Ka-15				RA
☐ Kamov Ka-18		180608	CCCP-68627	PV
☐ Kamov Ka-25PL	17	5910203		PV
☐ Kamov Ka-26	CCCP-26803	6900803	YR-EKC	PV
☐ Kamov Ka-26	CCCP-19364	7202405	Probably a composite.	RA
☐ Karvelius LAK-9M Lietuva	CCCP-408			PV
☐ Kashuk Glider				PV
☐ Kazan Aviation Institute KAI-19				PV
☐ Lavochkin La-7	27			PV
☐ Lavochkin La-11				RA
☐ Lavochkin La-15	01			PV
☐ Lavochkin La-250A	'04'	12500	03	PVX
☐ Let C-11 [Yakovlev Yak-11]	OK-KIO	172428		RA
☐ Let L-200D Morava	CCCP-26596	171103		RA
☐ Lilienthal Normal-Segelapparat (R)				PV
☐ Lisunov Li-2T [Douglas DC-3 modified]	CCCP-93914	23440808		PV
☐ Lisunov Li-2VP [Douglas DC-3 modified]	39	18418809	CCCP-84614 – 'CCCP-15010' on one side.	PV
☐ Mikoyan-Gurevich MiG-3 (FSM)				PV
☐ Mikoyan-Gurevich MiG-9	01	114010		PV
☐ Mikoyan-Gurevich MiG-15bisISh	27	2115368	2168	PV
☐ Mikoyan-Gurevich MiG-15UTI	03	22013		PV
☐ Mikoyan-Gurevich MiG-17	01	1402001	201	PV
☐ Mikoyan-Gurevich MiG-19PM	11	65210104		PV
☐ Mikoyan-Gurevich MiG-21bis	48	75021148		PV
☐ Mikoyan-Gurevich MiG-21I/2		010103	MiG-21 with scaled down Tu-144 wing	PV
☐ Mikoyan-Gurevich MiG-21S	'92'	952101102	92	PVX
☐ Mikoyan-Gurevich MiG-23	231			PV
☐ Mikoyan-Gurevich MiG-23	'231'	0393202201	233	PVX
☐ Mikoyan-Gurevich MiG-23ML	125	0390306625		PVD
☐ Mikoyan-Gurevich MiG-23ML	19	0390325365		PV
☐ Mikoyan-Gurevich MiG-25PD	04	0200001		PV
☐ Mikoyan-Gurevich MiG-25RB	02	020SL02		PV

☐ Mikoyan-Gurevich MiG-25RB (Ye-155R3)	25	6-01?		PV
☐ Mikoyan-Gurevich MiG-27	01	61912511018		PV
☐ Mikoyan-Gurevich MiG-29	03	03905502020		PV
☐ Mikoyan-Gurevich MiG-29	01	9-01		PV
☐ Mikoyan-Gurevich MiG-29KVP	18	9-18		PV
☐ Mikoyan-Gurevich MiG-31	202	69700102176		PV
☐ Mikoyan-Gurevich MiG-31	96	69700106125		PV
☐ Mikoyan-Gurevich 105/11		7510511101		PV
☐ Mikoyan-Gurevich E-152A (E-166)				PV
☐ Mil Mi-2	RA-20869	528230063	CCCP-20869	PV
☐ Mil Mi-2V2V	78	510309037		PV
☐ Mil Mi-4M	34	1104		PV
☐ Mil Mi-6	02			PV
☐ Mil Mi-6PZh-2	41	9683901		PV
☐ Mil Mi-6VKP	39	0454		PV
☐ Mil V-7				RA
☐ Mil Mi-8T	05			PV
☐ Mil Mi-8T	25	9744001	61 – also carries c/n 3470 on boom.	PV
☐ Mil Mi-10	44	8680604K		PV
☐ Mil V-12			CCCP-21142	PV
☐ Mil Mi-24A	50	2201201		PV
☐ Mil Mi-24P	37	3532431622374		PV
☐ Mil Mi-24V	44	3532424015897	54	PV
☐ Mil Mi-26		34001212102		PV
☐ Myasishchev 3MD	30	0301804		PV
☐ Myasishchev M-17	CCCP-17103	M-17-3		PV
☐ Myasishchev M-17	CCCP-17401	M-17-4		PVD
☐ Myasishchev M-50	12			PV
☐ North American NA-100 Mitchell (B-25D)	50	100-23681	43-3855	PV
☐ Petlyakov Pe-2FT				PV
☐ Petlyakov Pe-8	CCCP-H395			RAD
☐ Polikarpov U-2				RA
☐ Polikarpov Po-2LNB				PV
☐ Polikarpov R-5	'3316'			PVX
☐ Polikarpov I-15 (FSM)	'50'			PVDX
☐ Polikarpov I-15bis (FSM)	'50'			PVX
☐ Polikarpov I-16 tip 6 (FSM)				PV
☐ Rafaelyants Turbolet				RA
☐ Sikorsky S-6 Ilya Muromets (FSM)				PV
☐ Sopwith Triplane	N5486		May be an ex-RFC aircraft or a Duks built version	PV
☐ Sukhanov Diskoplan				RA
☐ Sukhanov Diskoplan 2				PV
☐ Sukhanov Diskoplan 3				PV
☐ Sukhoi Su-2 (FSM)	'38'			PVX
☐ Sukhoi Su-7B	25	1707	Also carries c/n 1708.	PV
☐ Sukhoi Su-7BKL	15	5733		PV
☐ Sukhoi Su-7BKL		6609		RA
☐ Sukhoi Su-7BM	51	3610		RA
☐ Sukhoi Su-7L (Su-7B)				RA
☐ Sukhoi Su-7L (Su-7B)		3608	Also carries c/n 2707.	PV
☐ Sukhoi Su-9	68	0615308		PV
☐ Sukhoi Su-11	14	0115307		PV
☐ Sukhoi Su-17	24	9024		PV
☐ Sukhoi Su-17M3	93	22301		PV
☐ Sukhoi Su-24	54	0515034		PV
☐ Sukhoi Su-25K	66	25503101056		PV
☐ Sukhoi Su-26	02			RA
☐ Sukhoi Su-35 (Su-27M) (Su T10M-1)	701	369110116202		PV
☐ Sukhoi T-4	101	6903048		PV
☐ Sukhoi T-6-1 (Su-24)	61			PV
☐ Sukhoi T-10-1	10			PV
☐ Sukhoi T-58L (T-58D-2) (Su-15)		T58-2	c/n also reported as 758.	PV
☐ Tatlin Letatlin				PV
☐ Tupolev Glider (R)				PV
☐ Tupolev ANT-2				PV
☐ Tupolev ANT-4 (TB-1)				PVD
☐ Tupolev ANT-6 (TB-3)				RAC
☐ Tupolev ANT-7 (R-6) (R)				RAC
☐ Tupolev ANT-25 (R)	'URSS-N-025'			PVX
☐ Tupolev ANT-40 (SB-2M-100)			Partial replica.	PV
☐ Tupolev Tu-2S				PV
☐ Tupolev Tu-4	01	2805103		PV
☐ Tupolev Tu-16K-26 (Tu-16A)	53	4201004		PV
☐ Tupolev Tu-16R-2 (Tu-16) (Tu-16R-1)	50	1880302		PV
☐ Tupolev Tu-22A	32	5050051		PV
☐ Tupolev Tu-22M0	33	5019029		PV
☐ Tupolev Tu-95N		4807		PV
☐ Tupolev Tu-104AK (Tu-104A)	46	8350705	CCCP-42390	PV
☐ Tupolev Tu-114	CCCP-L5611			PV
☐ Tupolev Tu-124	CCCP-45025	2350705		PV
☐ Tupolev Tu-128A	'0'	71281		PV

TYPE	REG/SER	CON. NO.	PI/NOTES	STATUS
☐ Tupolev Tu-144	CCCP-77106	10041		PV
☐ Turbolyot				PV
☐ Vertol V.44	N74056	146-13		PV
☐ Voisin L				PV
☐ Vyugov Aist 2	CCCP-06			PV
☐ Wytwornia Sprzetu Komunikacyjnego (WSK) M-15-01 Belphegor	CCCP-15105	1S 013-01		PV
☐ Wytwornia Sprzetu Komunikacyjnego (WSK) SM-1/300 [Mil Mi-1]	09	020309		PV
☐ Yakovlev UT-2 (R)				PV
☐ Yakovlev Yak-9				RAD
☐ Yakovlev Yak-9U		1257		PV
☐ Yakovlev Yak-11	06			RA
☐ Yakovlev Yak-12R	07			RA
☐ Yakovlev Yak-17	02			PV
☐ Yakovlev Yak-18				RA
☐ Yakovlev Yak-18P				RA
☐ Yakovlev Yak-18PM	10			RA
☐ Yakovlev Yak-18T				RA
☐ Yakovlev Yak-18U				RA
☐ Yakovlev Yak-23	15	31231015		PV
☐ Yakovlev Yak-24U	51	27203310	79	RA
☐ Yakovlev Yak-25M	03	0718		PV
☐ Yakovlev Yak-25RV-II		25992004		PV
☐ Yakovlev Yak-27R	14	0703		PV
☐ Yakovlev Yak-28L	44	2920903		PV
☐ Yakovlev Yak-28PP	45	0970603		PV
☐ Yakovlev Yak-28PP	43	1971002		PV
☐ Yakovlev Yak-28PP	53	1971105		PV
☐ Yakovlev Yak-28U	63	2930105		PV
☐ Yakovlev Yak-30				RA
☐ Yakovlev Yak-36	36			PV
☐ Yakovlev Yak-38	14	7977864401137	37	PV
☐ Yakovlev Yak-40K	CCCP-87490	9110117	CCCP-87597	PV
☐ Yakovlev Yak-41M	77	48-3		PV
☐ Yakovlev Yak-42	CCCP-42302	427401004		PV
☐ Yakovlev Yak-52B (Yak-54)	07		Armed Yak-18. Yak-54 is now an aerobatic type.	PV
☐ Yakovlev Yak-141	141			PV

CIVIL AVIATION BOARD MUSEUM (RU14)

Address: Ulyanovsk Airport,
432040 Ulyanovsk.
Tel: 08422-365163
Admission: ?
Location: Off Road A151 about 10 km south west of the town which is about 180km south of Kazan'.

Ulyanovsk housed one of three pilot training and conversion schools for Aeroflot. A factory which has produced a number of types including the giant Antonov An-124 is also located in the town. Aircraft collecting started in the late 1980s with the aim of setting up a museum tracing the work of the school and the history of civil aviation in the country. A great deal of effort has been put into locating wrecks of transport aircraft of the inter-war period. Several sites have been inspected and the damaged airframes transported to factories and aviation technical schools for restoration. Completed and on show is a Tupolev ANT-4. First flown in November 1925 at Moscow Central Aerodrome the ANT-4 served as a bomber and also carried out a number of survey and long distance flights including one from Moscow to New York. The trip started on August 23rd 1929 and was completed on November 1st of the same year. The example on view was found near Igarka in the early 1980s and restored at the Aeroflot School at Wyborg. Further examples of Tupolev's all metal monoplanes should soon join the exhibition. A replica of the AK-l, the first successful Soviet transport aircraft, has been built. Aircraft types used by the school and the airline in recent years can be seen along with a few military machines. A small number of Il-28 bombers were used by Aeroflot in the 1950s as crew trainers for the jet airliners joining the fleet and for the high speed transport of print matrices across the country.

TYPE	REG/SER	CON. NO.	PI/NOTES	STATUS
☐ Aero L-29 Delfin	125	190890	C/N also reported as 490890	PV
☐ Alexandrov-Kalinin AK-1 (FSM)				PV
☐ Antonov An-2TP	CCCP-41298	1G 64-13	Fuselage only.	PV
☐ Antonov An-2TP	RA-96235	1G 72-19	CCCP-96235	PV
☐ Antonov An-2TP	RA-40561	1G 84-14	CCCP-40561	PV
☐ Antonov An-14AQ	CCCP-48104	03307		PV
☐ Antonov An-24	CCCP-46761	47301201		PV
☐ Avia 14/32 [Ilyushin Il-14M]	CCCP-91588			PV
☐ Ilyushin Il-14P	CCCP-06132	146000709		PV
☐ Ilyushin Il-18D	CCCP-74250	187010504		PV
☐ Ilyushin Il-28	33	56605702		PV
☐ Ilyushin Il-62	CCCP-86650	00705	CCCP-86650, SU-ARO	PV
☐ Let L-410A Turbolet	CCCP-67252	720104		PV
☐ Mikoyan-Gurevich MiG-25PDS	04			PV
☐ Mil Mi-2SKh	CCCP-23855	521308119		PV

TYPE	REG/SER	CON. NO.	PI/NOTES	STATUS
☐ Mil Mi-4P	CCCP-35277	12145		PV
☐ Mil Mi-6	CCCP-21868	3681404		PV
☐ Mil Mi-8T	CCCP-25564	3014		PV
☐ Polikarpov Po-2				PV
☐ Polikarpov R-5				PV
☐ Shavrov Sh-2				RA
☐ Tupolev ANT-4 (TB-1)	CCCP-N291			RAC
☐ Tupolev ANT-4 (TB-1)	CCCP-H317	2955		PV
☐ Tupolev ANT-6 (TB-3)				RAC
☐ Tupolev ANT-7 (R-6)				RAC
☐ Tupolev ANT-7 (R-6)				RAD
☐ Tupolev ANT-40 (PS-40)				RA
☐ Tupolev Tu-104A	CCCP-42322	6350103	CCCP-L5416	PV
☐ Tupolev Tu-114D	CCCP-76490	64M471		PV
☐ Tupolev Tu-116	CCCP-76462	6800402	7801	PV
☐ Tupolev Tu-124Sh	'CCCP-45017'	7350610	22	PVX
☐ Tupolev Tu-144S	CCCP-77110	06-1		PV
☐ Wytwornia Sprzetu Komunikacyjnego (WSK) M-15-01 Belphegor	CCCP-15154	1S 014-17		PV
☐ Wytwornia Sprzetu Komunikacyjnego (WSK) SM-1Wb [Mil Mi-1M]	CCCP-17411	507017		PV
☐ Yakovlev Yak-12M	07			RA
☐ Yakovlev Yak-18T	CCCP-44422	22202023918		PV
☐ Yakovlev Yak-40				RA

CIVIL AVIATION MUSEUM (RU15)

Address:	Ul. Pilotov 38, 196210 St. Petersburg.
Tel:	812-104-33-02
Fax:	812-104-37-02
Email:	m212@mail.museum.ru
Admission:	By prior permission only
Location:	Near Pulkova Airport.

This museum is located at a school. The MiG-31 is outside and the two front fuselages inside. The displays of photographs, memorabilia trace the history of civil aviation with particular reference to the city. On show are engines and components along with a number of items relating to Aeroflot.

TYPE	REG/SER	CON. NO.	PI/NOTES	STATUS
☐ Ilyushin Il-14M			Front fuselage only.	RA
☐ Mikoyan-Gurevich MiG-31	31			RA
☐ Yakovlev Yak-18A			Front fuselage only.	RA

COMBAT GLORY MUSEUM – VICTORY PARK – SARATOV (RU16)

Address:	Sokolov Hill, Saratov.
Admission:	Daily 0900-1600.
Location:	In the north eastern part of the town.

This large hill overlooking the city houses the park which commemorates the one hundred and seventy seven thousand local people who lost their lives in the Great Patriotic War. There is a large monument and the names of all who died are inscribed on tablets. The open air museum has on show boats, trains, tanks and weapons. The aircraft collection includes several types recently in military use.

TYPE	REG/SER	CON. NO.	PI/NOTES	STATUS
☐ Aero L-29 Delfin	74	294844		PV
☐ Aero L-39C Albatros	110	132022		PV
☐ Antonov An-2T	02	1G 160-50		PV
☐ Mikoyan-Gurevich MiG-17	25	26452		PV
☐ Mikoyan-Gurevich MiG-21SMT	11	19005		PV
☐ Mikoyan-Gurevich MiG-23MLD	40	0390316421		PV
☐ Mikoyan-Gurevich MiG-27	27			PV
☐ Mikoyan-Gurevich MiG-31	17	69700112811		PV
☐ Mil Mi-2	RA-23309	529130035	CCCP-23309	PV
☐ Mil Mi-24V	10		05	PV
☐ Sukhoi Su-25	14		25	PV
☐ Tupolev Tu-22KD	20			PV
☐ Tupolev Tu-134UBL	34	64182	CCCP-64182, RA-64182	PV
☐ Yakovlev Yak-18A	01			PV
☐ Yakovlev Yak-38	71			PV

COSMONAUT TRAINING CENTRE COLLECTION (RU17)

Address:	Chkalovskaya Baza. Shchelkovo.
Admission:	By prior permission only.
Location:	About 50 km north east of Moscow.

The museum, founded in 1967, at the centre traces the history of Soviet space flight from the days of the unmanned Sputniks. Small numbers of Tu-104 airliners were used in the weightless flight training of astronauts There is a special section devoted to the first man in space, Yuri Gagarin. Several personal items are on show and his career both in the Air Force and as an astronaut are highlighted. The modified Tu-16 was used for meteorological research duties and also for calibration work.

TYPE	REG/SER	CON. NO.	PI/NOTES	STATUS
☐ Mikoyan-Gurevich MiG-15UTI	19			RA
☐ Sukhoi Su-7BM	21			RA
☐ Tupolev Tu-16 Tsiklon NM (Tu-16A) (Tu-16KSR-2-5)	CCCP-42355	6203203		RA
☐ Tupolev Tu-104A-Ts (Tu-104A)	48	86601302	1302 (Czechoslovakia)	RA

DISTRICT STUDY MUSEUM (RU18)

Address:	Saratov.
Location:	In the town which is about 700 km south east of Moscow.

Yuri Gagarin became the first man in space on April 12th 1961 when he orbited the Earth in Vostok 1. The museum has displays commemorating his life. The Yak-18 is the aircraft in which he made his first solo flight in 1959. The Yak-1M was a lightened and improved version of the Yak-1 fighter.

TYPE	REG/SER	CON. NO.	PI/NOTES	STATUS
☐ Yakovlev Yak-1M				PV
☐ Yakovlev Yak-18	06			PV

EXHIBITION OF ECONOMIC ACHIEVEMENTS (RU19)

Address:	Prospekt Mira, Moscow.
Admission:	Monday-Friday 0930-2200; Saturday-Sunday 0930-2300. All the pavilions may not be open for these quoted hours.
Location:	In the northern part of the city centre.

Many pavilions are located on the vast site and all aspects of industry and commerce are featured in the displays. Two aircraft are currently on view but others have appeared temporarily over the years. The Tupolev Tu-154 first flew in October 1968 and the type entered service with Aeroflot on February 9th 1972. Well over one thousand have been built and used by airlines in more than a dozen countries. The Yakovlev Yak-42 made its maiden flight in March 1975 but it was over five years before Aeroflot used the three engined jet.

TYPE	REG/SER	CON. NO.	PI/NOTES	STATUS
☐ Tupolev Tu-154	CCCP-85005	M005		PV
☐ Yakovlev Yak-42	CCCP-42304	11820201		PV

FEDERATION OF AMATEUR AVIATORS OF RUSSIA (RU20)

Address:	Tushino Airport.
Admission:	By prior permission only.
Location:	At Tushino Airport and other airfields in the area.

Formed by a group of private pilots and mechanics this organisation aims to maintain a fleet of airworthy aircraft. A Lisunov Li-2 was restored to flying condition and visited some shows in Europe. Sadly this crashed and was destroyed. The Il-14 first flew in 1953 and substantial numbers were built for both civil and military use.

TYPE	REG/SER	CON. NO	PI/NOTES	STATUS
☐ Ilyushin Il-14M	RA-01301	146001042	01	RAA
☐ Let L-200D Morava	FLARF-01671	171212	CCCP-77115, RA-77115	RAA
☐ Polikarpov Po-2				RAA
☐ Technoavia SM-94 [Yakovlev Yak-18T modified]	RA-09101			RAA
☐ Victoria 326 (Zlin Z-326 Trener Master modified)	RA-02509			RAA
☐ Yakovlev Yak-12M	RA-02119			RAA
☐ Yakovlev Yak-18A	FLARF-01595		RA-01595	
☐ Yakovlev Yak-18T	FLARF-02015		CCCP--02015	RAA
☐ Yakovlev Yak-50	FLARF-02120		FLA-CCCP-39008	RAA
☐ Yakovlev Yak-52	FLARF-02121	790401	FLA-CCCP-39007	RAA

GREAT PATRIOTIC WAR MEMORIAL MUSEUM (RU21)

Address: Neftekumsk,
Stavropol Oblast.
Admission: Tuesday-Sunday 1100-1600.
Location: In the centre of the town which is about 200km. east of Stavropol.

Many museums honouring the Soviet contribution to World War II (The Great Patriotic War) have been set up around the country. Exhibits trace the history of the conflict on Russian soil with particular reference to the local battles. Almost five thousand examples of the Li-2, based on the famous Douglas DC-3, were built in Moscow and Tashkent. The type served with distinction in many roles during the campaign.

TYPE	REG/SER	CON. NO.	PI/NOTES	STATUS
☐ Lisunov Li-2 [Douglas DC-3 modified]				PV
☐ Sheremetev Kashuk				PV

ILYUSHIN OKB MUSEUM (RU22)

Address: 45G Leningradsky Prospekt,
125190 Moscow.
Tel: 095-943-8441
Fax: 095-212-2132
Admission: Monday-Friday 1000-1700 by appointment.
Location: In the north western suburbs of the city close to Khodinka Airport.

Sergei Ilyushin was born in 1894 and in 1922 became a student at the Zhukovskii Academy. He initially designed several gliders and from the mid-1930s aircraft bearing his name appeared. He remained in control of his design bureau until the 1970s and died in February 1977. He will always be associated with the ground attack aircraft and bombers of World War II and a successful range of transports in the post-war years. The museum at the bureau was set up in 1979 and traces the history of his work with a superb display of models, photographs, documents and memorabilia. Details of other preserved Ilyushin aircraft can be seen in a series of photographs in one of the rooms. Outside is mounted an example of his famous Il-2 Shturmovik.

TYPE	REG/SER	CON. NO.	PI/NOTES	STATUS
☐ Ilyushin Il-2				RA

KAMOV MUSEUM (RU23)

Address: Ul. 8,
Marta 8,
140007 Lubertsy.
Tel: 095-700-3204
Fax: 095-700-3071
Admission: By prior permission only.
Location: About 15 km south east of Moscow just outside the ring road.

Nikolai Kamov had been involved in autogyro work in the 1930s. A design bureau bearing his name was established in 1945. His first helicopter the Ka-8 appeared in 1947 and other experimental models followed. The first type to be put into production was the Ka-15 which made its maiden flight in 1952. Over the last half century many successful helicopters have been produced. A small museum with three types on show has been set up at the factory. There are photographs and models on show in addition to the helicopters.

TYPE	REG/SER	CON. NO.	PI/NOTES	STATUS
☐ Kamov Ka-15M	CCCP-30099	1520-20		RA
☐ Kamov Ka-25PL	19	1021907		RA
☐ Kamov Ka-26	CCCP-26002			RA

KAZAN' AIRCRAFT PRODUCTION ORGANISATION FACTORY DISPLAY (RU24)

Address:	10 Karl Marx Ul, 420111 Kazan'.
Tel:	08432-544552
Fax:	08432-545252
Admission:	By prior permission only.
Location:	Just east of the town off Road M7.

This vast plant was started in the late 1930s and produced the only Soviet four engined bomber of World War II, the Petlyakov Pe-8. In recent years the factory has constructed Tupolev Tu-22s and now Tu-204s and Tu-330s. The associated helicopter complex has turned out Mil helicopters since the 1950s. The Mil Mi-14 was a naval development of the Mi-8 and both search and rescue and anti submarine versions were produced. One of the withdrawn Tupolev Tu-144 supersonic airliners is in the collection. This aircraft spent some time at the nearby aviation institute before moving to the plant. A museum has been set up with models, photographs and documents on show. At one time the site was the largest aviation factory in the world.

TYPE	REG/SER	CON. NO.	PI/NOTES	STATUS
☐ Mikoyan-Gurevich MiG-23	16	3016		RA
☐ Mikoyan-Gurevich MiG-25	94	84037011		RA
☐ Mil Mi-1	CCCP-07125			RA
☐ Mil Mi-4	CCCP-21741			RA
☐ Mil Mi-14				RA
☐ Tupolev Tu-144S	CCCP-77107	05-1		RA
☐ Yakovlev Yak-28R	04	5941110		RA

KURSK BATTLE MEMORIAL MUSEUM (RU25)

Address:	ul Sovietskaya, 300650 Kursk.
Tel:	0251-417351
Admission:	Tuesday-Sunday 1100-1600.
Location:	The museum is in the town. The Yak is south of the town on the E95 to Belgorod.

The battle for Kursk was one of the major conflicts of the German invasion during the Great Patriotic War. A number of impressive memorials have been built in the area, several have tanks and weapons. The one incorporating the Yakovlev Yak-9 fighter is a vast marble plinth on which the names of the Soviet dead are recorded. The Yak-9 was used by the Air Force during the fighting against the large number of German attackers. The museum displays trace the story of the conflict in detail.

TYPE	REG/SER	CON. NO.	PI/NOTES	STATUS
☐ Yakovlev Yak-9				PV

LONG RANGE AVIATION FORCE MUSEUM – ENGELS (RU26)

Address:	Engels Air Force Base, Saratov.
Tel:	2-14-80
Admission:	Monday-Friday 0900-1700 by appointment.
Location:	Just south east of the town off Road P236.

The airfield opened in 1932 when a Higher Military Aviation School was formed. During World War II three all-female units were established at Engels. The site was used for training from 1944 until 1954 when the 22nd Guards Heavy Bomber Air Division moved in. Myasishchev M-4s and Tupolev Tu-16s were flown from the field. The Myasishchev 3MS and Tupolev Tu-22 replaced the earlier types. At the current time Tupolev Tu-95s and Tu-160s are in use. There is also a unit which scraps redundant bombers on the field. The base museum opened on September 6th 2000. The indoor displays trace the history of the site and the regiment with instruments, photographs, memorabilia and components on show. The aircraft are parked nearby.

TYPE	REG/SER	CON. NO.	PI/NOTES	STATUS
☐ Aero L-29 Delfin	91	294752		RA
☐ Aero L-39C Albatros	114	131927		RA
☐ Antonov An-2	03	113147308		RA
☐ Antonov An-12BP	15	402512		RA
☐ Antonov An-24	01			RA
☐ Antonov An-24T (An-24RT)	57			RA
☐ Ilyushin Il-62	RA-86556	31401	SP-LAC, CCCP-86556	RA

TYPE	REG/SER	CON. NO.	PI/NOTES	STATUS
☐ Myasishchev 3MS-2	14	7300805		RA
☐ Tupolev Tu-16K-26	11	5205605	Outside base.	PV
☐ Tupolev Tu-22KD	74		80 – outside base.	PV
☐ Tupolev Tu-22KD	77	5558053		RA
☐ Tupolev Tu-22PD	46			RA
☐ Tupolev Tu-22RDM	18			RA
☐ Tupolev Tu-22U			Front fuselage only.	RA
☐ Tupolev Tu-22UD	20	2497023		RA
☐ Tupolev Tu-95K-22	53			PV
☐ Tupolev Tu-134Sh-2	76	3350302		RA
☐ Tupolev Tu-134UBL	45			RA

LONG RANGE AVIATION FORCE MUSEUM – RYAZAN (RU27)

Address: Dyagilevo Air Base,
Ryazan.
Admission: By prior permission only.
Location: Just west of the town which is about 200 km south east of Moscow off Road M6.

The base has been home to the operational conversion unit for the long-range bomber force since the 1950s. Displays in the museum portray the history of aviation in the country with special emphasis on the work of the base and its unit. Over the years versions of every major bomber type flown by the force have served here.

TYPE	REG/SER	CON. NO.	PI/NOTES	STATUS
☐ Myasishchev M-4-2 (M-4)	60	6302831	01	RA
☐ Tupolev Tu-16E	50	1883108	On base gate.	PV
☐ Tupolev Tu-16R(ZA)	04	1883511	29	RA
☐ Tupolev Tu-22M2	42	2723321		RA
☐ Tupolev Tu-22M3	4504	2145345		RA
☐ Tupolev Tu-22PD	51	3603		RA
☐ Tupolev Tu-95K	35	6082307		RA

LUKHOVITSY FACTORY COLLECTION (RU28)

Address: 140500 Lukhovitsy.
Admission: By prior permission only.
Location: In the southern suburbs of the town which is about 120 km. south east of Moscow off Road M5.

This factory which has produced a number of types over the years has two aircraft preserved in its grounds and another nearby. All three types have been constructed in large numbers and given excellent service.

TYPE	REG/SER	CON. NO.	PI/NOTES	STATUS
☐ Ilyushin Il-28	30			RA
☐ Mikoyan-Gurevich MiG-15bis	01			RA
☐ Mikoyan-Gurevich MiG-23ML	96		In nearby park.	RA

MIKOYAN-GUREVICH OKB MUSEUM (RU29)

Address: 1 Botsinski Street,
125040 Moscow.
Tel: 095-250-1948
Fax: 095-250-1948
Admission: Monday-Friday 0900-1600 by appointment.
Location: In the north western suburbs of the city close to Khodinka Airport.

This famous bureau has produced almost exclusively fighter aircraft. Artyem Mikoyan was born in 1905 and in the early 1920s was a student at the Frunze Military Academy. He designed a light aircraft in 1936 and joined the Polikarpov team a year later. Mikhail Gurevich was born in 1893 and studied in Kharkov and Paris. He joined the Richard bureau in 1928 and later went to the U.S.A. with Lisunov to work on the DC-3 licence programme. The two joined forces after working together at Polikarpov. During World War II successful piston engined fighters were designed and the pair were later to the forefront in the development of jet interceptors. The museum traces the history of the bureau and its products. In the display rooms are many models, photographs and documents showing the range of types produced over the years. The MiG-15 flew in prototype form in and took to the air for the first time at Zhukovskii on December 30th 1947.

TYPE	REG/SER	CON. NO.	PI/NOTES	STATUS
☐ Mikoyan-Gurevich MiG-15	15			PV
☐ Mikoyan-Gurevich MiG-21MF			In nearby park.	PV

MILITARY MUSEUM (RU30)

Address:	Chaltyr, Rostov-on-Don.
Location:	About 15 km. west of Rostov-on-Don off Road M23.

A report has been received of this museum which traces the military history of the region. In addition to the four aircraft there are military vehicles, tanks, weapons, rocket launchers and radar equipment on show.

TYPE	REG/SER	CON. NO.	PI/NOTES	STATUS
☐ Ilyushin Il-14	10			PV
☐ Mikoyan-Gurevich MiG-15UTI	64			PV
☐ Mil Mi-1				PV
☐ Yakovlev Yak-28P	06			PV

MILITARY STAFF COLLEGE COLLECTION (RU31)

Address:	Moscow.
Admission:	By prior permission only.
Location:	About 10 km west of Moscow off Road A104/M4 before the ring road.

This college offers courses for serving officers and is believed to be equivalent to a number of similar institutions around the country. Four aircraft are preserved in the grounds.

TYPE	REG/SER	CON. NO.	PI/NOTES	STATUS
☐ Mikoyan-Gurevich MiG-23ML	51			RA
☐ Mikoyan-Gurevich MiG-27	49			RA
☐ Mikoyan-Gurevich MiG-29	51			RA
☐ Sukhoi Su-17M	60			RA

MONCHEGORSK MUSEUM (RU32)

Address:	Monchegorsk.
Admission:	By prior permission only.
Location:	About 80 km south of Murmansk.

A section of this local history museum is devoted to crashed World War II aircraft. Many sites have been investigated and on show are components, documents and photographs and maps.

MOSCOW AVIATION INSTITUTE MUSEUM (RU33)

Address:	Petrovka 27, 103767 Moscow.
Tel:	095-200-6883
Email:	aet@lh.mainet.msh.su
Admission:	By prior permission only.
Location:	In the north western part of the city.

The institute houses one of the largest aviation schools in the country. Over the years a number of aircraft have been designed by students and staff. In 1934 the EMAI was built to test the use of magnesium in aircraft structures. A small museum has been set up on the campus. The displays trace the history of aviation in the country and the work of the institute. The low wing Kvant aerobatic monoplane was designed by students in the late 1960s. There are small components from several types and a number of engines.

TYPE	REG/SER	CON. NO.	PI/NOTES	STATUS
☐ Aviatika MAI-890				RA
☐ General Dynamics F-111A			Cockpit section only.	RA
☐ Mikoyan-Gurevich MiG-23	234			RA
☐ Mikoyan-Gurevich MiG-25R	992	990002	Front fuselage only.	RA
☐ Mikoyan-Gurevich MiG-29	25			RA
☐ Mil Mi-2	CCCP-06180	0102		RA
☐ Mil Mi-24B		241-0202-12		RA
☐ Moscow Aviation Institute Kvant	02			RA
☐ Northrop N-156E Tiger II (F-5E)			Front fuselage only.	RA

TYPE	REG/SER	CON. NO.	PI/NOTES	STATUS
☐ Sukhoi Su-25	84			RA
☐ Sukhoi Su-27	31	36911012101		RA
☐ Yakovlev Yak-38	45	04		RA
☐ Yakovlev Yak-40	CCCP-19661	019		RA

MOSCOW REGION AIR FORCE MUSEUM (RU34)

Address:	Kubinka Air Force Base 143070.
Admission:	By prior permission only.
Location:	Just north west of the town which is about 80 km west of Moscow off Road M1.

It is known that many commands in the Air Force have their own museums and some have aircraft on show. The history of the force is portrayed in the displays. The headquarters responsible for operating fighters in the Moscow region has preserved six jets. MiG jet fighters have served with distinction for almost fifty years. The prototype Sukhoi Su-7 first flew in late 1955 and later versions are still in service in a few countries.

TYPE	REG/SER	CON. NO.	PI/NOTES	STATUS
☐ Mikoyan-Gurevich MiG-17F	55			RA
☐ Mikoyan-Gurevich MiG-19P	100			RA
☐ Mikoyan-Gurevich MiG-21PFM	01			RA
☐ Mikoyan-Gurevich MiG-21PFM	80			RA
☐ Mikoyan-Gurevich MiG-23S	59			RA
☐ Sukhoi Su-7B	42			RA

MUSEUM OF THE EXPERIMENTAL MACHINE BUILDING PLANT NAMED AFTER V.M. MYASISCHEV (RU35)

Address:	Zhukovskii 5, 140160 Moscow Region.
Tel:	095-556-7776
Fax:	095-556-5583
Email:	mdb@mastak.msk.su
Admission:	By appointment only.
Location:	About 30 km south east of Moscow off Road M5.

V.M. Myasischev was born in 1902 and was a pupil of Zhukovskii between 1918 and 1921. At the Central Aerodynamics and Hydrodynamics Institute he carried out work on Tupolev designs. He went to the U.S.A. in 1937 to work on the Douglas drawings for the Li-2. After a spell in prison he set up his own bureau in 1939/40. His name is best known for his large jet bombers and high altitude research machines. On show are models, photographs, documents, books and memorabilia tracing his life.

N.E. ZHUKOVSKII MEMORIAL MUSEUM (RU36)

Address:	17 Radio Street. 107005 Moscow.
Tel:	095-263-4185
Admission:	Monday-Friday 1000-1800;
Location:	In the north eastern part of the city.

Nikolai Zhukovskii was born in 1847 and graduated from Moscow University at the age of twenty one. He taught at the Higher Technical School and at the University. He built his first wind tunnel in 1902 and two years later set up the first aerodynamic institute in Europe. He researched many aspects of aerodynamics and published his results widely. In 1918 he was selected to lead the Central Aero-Hydrodynamics Institute. In 1920 Lenin bestowed upon him the title of 'The Father of Russian Aviation'. In 1919 he formed the Moscow Technical Aviation College which later became the Institute of Engineers of the Red Air Force and is now colloquially known as the Zhukovskii Academy. He died in 1921 and the museum, housed in the building in which he worked from 1915 until his death, traces the work of the pioneer and highlights research studies he carried out.

TYPE	REG/SER	CON. NO.	PI/NOTES	STATUS
☐ Lilienthal Normal-Segelapparat				PV

NATIONAL AIR AND SPACE MUSEUM (RU37)

Address:	Khodinka Airfield, 37 Leningradsky Prospekt, Moscow 125040.
Tel:	095-212-0351
Fax:	095-214-5680
Admission:	Currently closed
Location:	In the north western part of the city.

Khodinka Fields was the scene of a famous stampede in 1896 when at the coronation of Nicholas II over fourteen hundred people were killed trying to get free beer. They were all trampled to death and many more were injured in the rush. The first aeronautical activity was a flight by a Blériot in 1910 when Rossinsky became the first Russian to fly an aeroplane. The following year it saw the arrival of Alexander Vasilev also in a Blériot. He was the only one of eleven starters to complete the four hundred and fifty mile race from St. Petersburg to Moscow. Plans were later made for a purpose built airfield and the site was soon ready. The Duks factory, which manufactured over fifteen hundred aircraft during World War I, was located at the field which also housed the Moscow Aviation School. For many years it was the main airport for the city. The terminal is still in use for bus services. The Ilyushin and Sukhoi design bureaux are sited on the airfield boundary and Yakovlev is located just up the road. Many prototypes made their first flights from this historic field and in recent years it was home to light aircraft. The museum opened in 1991 with an impressive display of fairly modern military hardware. For the first few weeks after the opening a number of active machines flew in to supplement the exhibition but these have now left. Also the local bureaux lent aircraft from their collections. For example the Yak-32 and Yak-141 made the short trip down the main road. The museum closed a few years ago due to development of the site and a number of aircraft were scrapped. These included several Yak twin engined jets all of which had advanced corrosion. Only the Yak-25M survived the cull. A range of Sukhoi combat jets is one of the highlights of the display. The only transport design is the Ilyushin Il-14 and plans to acquire more airliners were put on hold. The remaining airframes have now been moved to a different area of the field and are currently stored while new plans are being discussed. A large housing and recreational complex will be built on the site of most of the historic airfield. The aircraft listed were seen in the summer of 2005 and it is hoped the exhibition will re-open in the not too distant future with some permanent buildings. The owners of the aircraft have also amassed a large archive of photographs and documents plus several uniforms and badges.

TYPE	REG/SER	CON. NO.	PI/NOTES	STATUS
☐ Aero L-29 Delfin	74	295106	Also reported as c/n 395406	RA
☐ Ilyushin Il-14T	08	148001908		RA
☐ Ilyushin Il-28	01	36603807		RA
☐ Ilyushin Il-76TD	RA-76751	0083487610	CCCP-76751	RA
☐ Mikoyan-Gurevich MiG-17	17	1215391		RA
☐ Mikoyan-Gurevich MiG-17	111	54211768		RA
☐ Mikoyan-Gurevich MiG-17	61	54211860		RA
☐ Mikoyan-Gurevich MiG-19SF	171	0615337		RA
☐ Mikoyan-Gurevich MiG-21PF	98	76212122		RA
☐ Mikoyan-Gurevich MiG-21PF	16	76212318		RA
☐ Mikoyan-Gurevich MiG-21R	30	030AT22		RA
☐ Mikoyan-Gurevich MiG-21SMT	59	501621		RA
☐ Mikoyan-Gurevich MiG-23B	321	0390217055		RA
☐ Mikoyan-Gurevich MiG-23M	21	0390206759		RA
☐ Mikoyan-Gurevich MiG-23M	11	0390209445		RA
☐ Mikoyan-Gurevich MiG-25MLDG	37	0390310645		RA
☐ Mikoyan-Gurevich MiG-25P	38	84028605		RA
☐ Mikoyan-Gurevich MiG-25PDS (MiG-25P)	08	84018081		RA
☐ Mikoyan-Gurevich MiG-25PU	90	22040416		RA
☐ Mikoyan-Gurevich MiG-25RBV	55	02007033		RA
☐ Mikoyan-Gurevich MiG-27	51	61912538152		RA
☐ Mikoyan-Gurevich MiG-29	04	9-04		RA
☐ Mikoyan-Gurevich Ye-266M (MiG-25M) (Ye-155M)	710	84019175		RA
☐ Mil Mi-2	03	511835031		RA
☐ Mil Mi-4A				RA
☐ Mil Mi-6	29	7683209		RA
☐ Mil Mi-8T	38	9732810	CCCP-11052	RA
☐ Mil Mi-24A	33	3201902		RA
☐ Mil Mi-24D	60	03035		RA
☐ Sukhoi Su-7B	12	1228		RA
☐ Sukhoi Su-7BKL			In false North Korean markings.	RAX
☐ Sukhoi Su-7BKL	07	5717		RA
☐ Sukhoi Su-7UM	16	2502		RA
☐ Sukhoi Su-9	10	0848		RA
☐ Sukhoi Su-15	01	0015301		RA
☐ Sukhoi Su-15	85	0844		RA
☐ Sukhoi Su-15TM	42	0615342		RA
☐ Sukhoi Su-15UT	50	1010		RA
☐ Sukhoi Su-17M3	95	26918		RA
☐ Sukhoi Su-17M4	71	50820		RA
☐ Sukhoi Su-17UMK	99	17532389606		RA
☐ Sukhoi T-10-20	20	3691101210151	31	RA
☐ Wytwornia Sprzetu Komunikacyjnego (WSK) SM-1Wb [Mil Mi-1M]	14	505005		RA
☐ Yakovlev Yak-25M	57	1314		RA
☐ Yakovlev Yak-38	60	797786406069		RA

NAVAL MUSEUM (RU38)

Address:	Vasilyevski Ostrov. Pushinskaya Square 4. 199034 St. Petersburg.
Tel:	0812-328-2701
Email:	museum@admiral.ru
Admission:	Wednesday-Sunday 1030-1730.
Location:	In the city centre close to the junction of the Malaya and Bolsbaja rivers.

Peter the Great founded the museum when he ordered that models of all ships then under construction should be kept. The collection covers four main topics, the Imperial Russian Fleet, shipping from the October Revolution until 1941, World War II and from 1945 to the present time. On show are paintings, uniforms, documents, medals and memorabilia in addition to the superb display of model ships. The only aircraft on view is the Polikarpov I-16. This low wing fighter first flew on December 31st 1933 with Chkalov at the controls.

TYPE	REG/SER	CON. NO.	PI/NOTES	STATUS
☐ Polikarpov I-16 tip 24	51			PV

NIZHNII NOVGOROD MILITARY MUSEUM (RU39)

Address:	Nizhnii Novgorod.
Admission:	?
Location:	In the town which is about 240 km east of Moscow.

Nizhnii Novgorod was the birthplace of novelist Maxim Gorky and was known as Gorky from 1932 to 1990. For many years after World War II the town was a restricted region and few visitors were allowed. Some years ago a report of a military museum, which has a Lavochkin La-9 replica on show, appeared in a Soviet magazine.

TYPE	REG/SER	CON. NO.	PI/NOTES	STATUS
☐ Lavochkin La-9 (FSM)	'30'			PVX

NORTHERN AVIATION MUSEUM (RU40)

Address:	Tagala, Archangelsk
Admission:	On permanent view.
Location:	At the airport which is about 10 km north east of the town.

The Ilyushin Il-14 was derelict at the airfield for many years but has now been restored and placed on show near the terminal building along with the MiG-25. The remains of the Junkers 88 were recovered from the area.

TYPE	REG/SER	CON. NO.	PI/NOTES	STATUS
☐ Ilyushin Il-14	CCCP-41835	147001824		PV
☐ Junkers Ju 88A-4	5K+AC	4588	Rear fuselage only.	PVD
☐ Mikoyan-Gurevich MiG-25	12			PV

NORTHERN FLEET AVIATION MUSEUM (RU41)

Address:	Safonovo, Severomorsk, Kola Peninsula.
Admission:	By prior permission only.
Location:	About 20 km. north east of Murmansk off Road M18.

The Kola Peninsula is the location for a number of airfields used by the Northern Fleet. At Safonovo an interesting collection has been assembled. The exhibition includes several aircraft from the World War II period. Almost three thousand Hurricanes were sent to the Soviet Union but many were lost on ships sunk on the hazardous North Cape convoys. The example on show is painted in Soviet colours. Three Beriev designs are in the collection. Dating from 1932 the MBR-2 flying boat remained in production for a decade and about thirteen hundred were built. The Be-12 amphibian flew for the first time in 1960 and approximately two hundred were made and served with all coastal fleets. Very few of the more than five thousand Ilyushin Il-4 twin engined bombers constructed seem to have survived. Among the modern types are a Myasishchev M-4 jet bomber and a Yakovlev Yak-38 VTOL naval fighter. Hopefully this excellent collection will be made more available to visitors.

TYPE	REG/SER	CON. NO	PI/NOTES	STATUS
☐ Antonov An-2				PV
☐ Bell 26E Airacobra (P-39Q)				PV
☐ Beriev MBR-2	08			PV
☐ Beriev Be-6				PV
☐ Beriev Be-12	33 (?)	7600902 (?)		PV
☐ Curtiss 87V Warhawk (P-40N)				PV
☐ Hawker Hurricane IIC				PVD
☐ Hawker Hurricane IIC	24			PV
☐ Ilyushin Il-2m3	13 (?)			PV
☐ Ilyushin Il-4 (DB-3EF)				PV
☐ Ilyushin Il-28	07			PV
☐ Lavochkin La-17				PV
☐ Lisunov Li-2 [Douglas DC-3 modified]	25			PV
☐ Messerschmitt Bf 109G-2	2	14658	KG+WF – front fuselage only ?	PV
☐ Mikoyan-Gurevich MiG-17F (mod)	43			PV
☐ Mil Mi-GVM	07			PV
☐ Myasishchev M-4VM				PV
☐ Petlyakov Pe-3				PVC
☐ Polikarpov I-153 (FSM)	10			PV
☐ Polikarpov I-16 (R)	10		Replica containing some original parts.	PV
☐ Sukhoi Su-9	03			PV
☐ Tupolev ANT-40 (SB-2M-100)			Partial replica.	PV
☐ Yakovlev Yak-7B	62			PV
☐ Yakovlev Yak-9				PV
☐ Yakovlev Yak-38	25			PV

NUMBER 275 AIRCRAFT REPAIR FACTORY MUSEUM (RU42)

Address:	Aviagorodok 5, 350005 Krasnodar.
Admission:	By prior permission only.
Location:	Just north of the town which is about 270 km south of Rostov-on-Don off Road A.146.

This factory has five aircraft exhibited in its grounds. The BI-1 was the first rocket powered fighter in the world and flew in powered form in early 1943. Prior to this a number of towed flight were made. Only seven were completed and production plans for fifty were abandoned. The prototypes continued to serve testing engines for some time although the acidic nature of the fuel caused problems with corrosion. The Antonov An-8 made its maiden flight at the company airfield near Kiev in February 1956. One hundred and fifty were built at Tashkent and the type was repaired at this plant. The Czech Aero L-29 Delfin was used throughout the Soviet Union for pilot training. Two MiG fighters complete this interesting display.

TYPE	REG/SER	CON. NO.	PI/NOTES	STATUS
☐ Aero L-29 Delfin	20			RA
☐ Antonov An-8				RA
☐ Bereznyak-Isayey BI-1 (FSM)				RA
☐ Mikoyan-Gurevich MiG-21F-13				RA
☐ Mikoyan-Gurevich MiG-29	01			RA

NUMBER 400 AIRCRAFT REPAIR FACTORY COLLECTION (RU43)

Address:	VARZ, Vnukovo, 103017 Moscow.
Admission:	By prior permission only
Location:	About 30 km south west of Moscow off Road M3.

This repair plant located on one of Moscow's main airports has a Tu-104 and a Tu-114 preserved in its grounds. Both types were serviced here whilst they were in regular use. The other Tu-104 is located near the main terminal building. The giant Tu-114, derived from the military Tu-95, made its first flight in November 1957. The type entered Aeroflot service in April 1961 on the Moscow-Khabarovsk route. Services to Havana and Delhi were introduced two years later. Thirty three were built and the Tu-114 was withdrawn in the mid-1970s. The Tu-104 was the first jet airliner in the world in regular service and the prototype was built at Vnukovo.

TYPE	REG/SER	CON. NO.	PI/NOTES	STATUS
☐ Tupolev Tu-104B	CCCP-42416	920403		RA
☐ Tupolev Tu-104B	'CCCP-L5412'	921102	CCCP-42450 – At nearby civil airport.	PVX
☐ Tupolev Tu-114	CCCP-76470	608431		RA

NUMBER 411 AIRCRAFT REPAIR FACTORY COLLECTION (RU44)

Address:	Aviagorodok 2, Stavropol', 357310 Mineralnye-Vody.
Admission:	By prior permission only.
Location:	South east of Rostov-on-Don off Road M29.

The Soviet Union set up a large number of airframe and engine repair plants around the country. A display has been staged at the factory at Mineralyne-Vody. Three types overhauled at the site are on display.

TYPE	REG/SER	CON. NO.	PI/NOTES	STATUS
☐ Lisunov Li-2 [Douglas DC-3 modified]	CCCP-13373	23441407		RA
☐ Mil Mi-2	CCCP-15724	522328032		RA
☐ Wytwornia Sprzetu Komunikacyjnego (WSK) SM-1W [Mil Mi-1M]	CCCP-17762	04020		RA

NUMBER 712 AIRCRAFT REPAIR FACTORY MUSEUM (RU45)

Address:	Gorodok 11, 454015 Chelyabinsk 15.
Tel:	03512-288-688
Fax:	03512-288-681
Email:	712-arp@chel.surnet.ru
Admission:	By prior permission only.
Location:	In the northern part of the town which is about 230 km south east of Ekaterineberg off Road M36.

Aircraft components and engines are overhauled at the plant. A small display has been set up in the building tracing the work carried out over the years. The Ilyushin Il-28 is mounted in the grounds.

TYPE	REG/SER	CON. NO.	PI/NOTES	STATUS
☐ Ilyushin Il-28	30			RA

ORENBURG MILITARY AVIATION SCHOOL MUSEUM (RU46)

Address:	Orenburg.
Admission:	By prior permission only.
Location:	About 10 km south west of the town.

The college has trained pilots for many years and many famous aviators are among its graduates. A museum has been set up in the building honouring these people which include Yuri Gagarin. The MiG-15 is mounted in the grounds and there are believed to be other aircraft displayed.

TYPE	REG/SER	CON. NO.	PI/NOTES	STATUS
☐ Mikoyan-Gurevich MiG-15bis	01			RA

PUSHKIN AIRFIELD MUSEUM (RU47)

Address:	St. Petersburg Regional Centre of Aviation Fans, Glinka Street, Pushkin, 189620 St. Petersburg.
Tel:	0812-470-7226
Admission:	By prior permission only.
Location:	About 3 km south of the town which is about 15 km south of St. Petersburg.

Local enthusiasts are trying to set up a museum at this historic airfield. The site is still used by the military and a number of their unairworthy machines are looked after by the group. The Tu-134UB-L was used as a conversion trainer for the Tu-160 when it was being introduced into service. The airframe of the Ilyushin Il-38 maritime patrol aircraft is based on the successful Il-18 airliner. A number of airworthy types are owned by the organisation. Progress is being made and hopefully a display will be staged in the not too distant future.

TYPE	REG/SER	CON. NO	PI/NOTES	STATUS
☐ Antonov An-2	FLARF-51740	113147320		RAA
☐ Antonov An-2	FLARF-02517	1G 209-48		RAA
☐ Antonov An-2R	FLARF-02517	1G 209-48	CCCP-17964, RA-17964	RAA
☐ Antonov An-12BP	16			RA
☐ Ilyushin Il-14TG	FLARF-02299	8344001	CCCP-48106, RA-02299	RAA
☐ Ilyushin Il-18V	RA-75786	181003905	CCCP-75786, RA-75786, 75786	RA
☐ Ilyushin Il-18V	RA-75423	182005601	CCCP-06160, CCCP-75423	RA
☐ Ilyushin Il-38	71	082011207		RA
☐ Mil Mi-14PS				RA
☐ Sukhoi Su-17UM3	44			RA
☐ Tupolev Tu-134UBL				RA
☐ Yakovlev Yak-28PP	50			RA
☐ Yakovlev Yak-28PP	54	9970501		RA
☐ Yakovlev Yak-28R	22			RA
☐ Yakovlev Yak-28R	34			RA
☐ Yakovlev Yak-28U	03			RA
☐ Yakovlev Yak-28U	07			RA

R.O.S.T.O. FACTORY COLLECTION (RU48)

Address: Balashikha,
Aviarembaza 7,
143991 Chernoe.
Admission: By prior permission only.
Location: About 30 km east of Moscow.

Three helicopters have been preserved with the Mi-2 on the gate and the other two inside. The factory has produced and overhauled several Mil types over the years. The first prototype Mil Mi-1 made its maiden flight on September 30th 1948 and eventually over one thousand were built at factories at Kazan', Orenburg and Rostov-on-Don. Licence production took place at the P.Z.L. factory at Swidnik in Poland. The Mi-2 first flew in 1961 and production was also transferred to Swidnik where their first example took to the air in November 1965. Large numbers were built up to the early 1990s and many are still in use. The Mi-4 was the first transport helicopter in the Soviet Union to be produced in quantity. Constructed at Kazan' and Saratov between 1952 and 1968 almost three and a half thousand were built with many being exported.

TYPE	REG/SER	CON. NO.	PI/NOTES	STATUS
☐ Mil Mi-1M	01			RA
☐ Mil Mi-2	RF-0600		On gate.	PV
☐ Mil Mi-4	87			RA

REVDA MUSEUM (RU49)

Address: Revda.
Admission: On permanent view.
Location: About 10 km west of of Ekaterineburg.

There are many aircraft wrecks in the tundra and the villagers of Revda retrieved a Hurricane in the mid-1980s. The basic framework had survived but all the wooden parts had to be replaced. This was restored and mounted on a plinth. The memorial was dedicated on September 3rd 1989 to commemorate the fiftieth anniversary of the outbreak of World War II. The story of the restoration can be seen in the local history museum which traces life over the centuries in the harsh climate. The aircraft bears a serial of one delivered to the Soviet Union during the early days of World War II but it is not known if this is the genuine identity of the aircraft.

TYPE	REG/SER	CON. NO.	PI/NOTES	STATUS
☐ Hawker Hurricane IIC	'BM959'			PVX

ROAD OF LIFE MUSEUM (RU50)

Address: Osinovets.
Admission: Tuesday-Saturday 1100-1600.
Location: About 30 km north east of the city on the shores of Lake Lagoda.

This museum is a branch of the Naval Museum in St. Petersburg. On show are two derelict boats and a number of guns taken from warships. Inside are scenes depicting life in St. Petersburg during World War II. There are many photographs, maps and flags showing how the city was defended. The Li-2 operated in the area during the conflict flying in food and ammunition and taking out people. The 'Road of Life' was the name given to the supply route from Lake Lagoda to the city during the German attack.

TYPE	REG/SER	CON. NO.	PI/NOTES	STATUS
☐ Lisunov Li-2 [Douglas DC-3 modified]	4681			PV

S.O.K.O.L. AIRCRAFT FACTORY MUSEUM (RU51)

Address:	Chaadajeva Street 1, 603035 Nizhnii Novgorod.
Tel:	08312-467103
Fax:	08312-247966
Admission:	By prior permission only.
Location:	In the town.

A small museum has been set up in this factory where almost eight thousand five hundred I-16s were manufactured between 1935 and 1941. A replica has been built for the display.

TYPE	REG/SER	CON. NO.	PI/NOTES	STATUS
☐ Polikarpov I-16 (FSM)				RA

S.P.A.R.C. AIRCRAFT FACTORY MUSEUM (RU52)

Address:	9 Pilotov, Pulkova, 196210 St. Petersburg.
Admission:	By prior permission only.
Location:	West of the town.

This factory overhauls helicopters at the present time. A display tracing the history of the plant has been set up with photographs, models and documents. The Mil-4 is on show outside the building.

TYPE	REG/SER	CON. NO.	PI/NOTES	STATUS
☐ Mil Mi-4A	CCCP-29027	15118		PV

SAMARA AEROSPACE COMPLEX MUSEUM (RU53)

Address:	Pskovskaya Street 32, 443052 Samara.
Tel:	08462-294278
Fax:	08462-270477
Admission:	By prior permission only.
Location:	In the city.

Two aircraft have been reported at the museum at this factory which has produced aircraft and space products over the years. The displays trace the history of the site with many models, photographs and documents to be seen. There are also engines and components on view. During World War II aircraft production was transferred here from Voronezh and Ilyushin Il-2s were among the types constructed. A civilian version of the ANT-4 bomber has been recovered from a crash site and the Il-2 is believed to have a similar history. The Il-2 is mounted on a plinth in front of the main building and the ANT-4 is inside the grounds.

TYPE	REG/SER	CON. NO.	PI/NOTES	STATUS
☐ Ilyushin Il-2				PV
☐ Tupolev ANT-4 (TB-1)	CCCP-401			RA

SAMARA STATE AEROSPACE UNIVERSITY MUSEUM (RU54)

Address:	Moskovskyve Shosse 34, 443086 Samara.
Tel:	08462-357288
Fax:	08462-358767
Email:	skb1@ssau.ru
Admission:	By prior permission only.
Location:	About 8 km north east of the town.

Displays at the museum trace the development of Russian aviation from the early days up to the current time. Models, documents, photographs and components are on show. Preserved at the site are a number of aircraft which also serve as instructional airframes. The Il-14 was once the personal transport of Korolev who pioneered the Soviet space programme. Many more aircraft used by the students are housed at the Smyshlyaevka airfield.

TYPE	REG/SER	CON. NO.	PI/NOTES	STATUS
☐ Antonov An-2P	CCCP-70774	1G 132-29		RA
☐ Antonov An-2R	CCCP-06258	1G 127-14		RA
☐ Antonov An-2R	CCCP-70510	1G 144-21		RA
☐ Antonov An-2R	CCCP-33619	1G 232-53		RA
☐ Antonov An-2T	CCCP-28853	1G 05-07		RA
☐ Antonov An-2TP	CCCP-41301	1G 64-16		RA
☐ Antonov An-2TP	CCCP-41361	1G 65-36		RA
☐ Antonov An-2TP	CCCP-96218	1G 72-02		RA
☐ Antonov An-2TP	CCCP-50517	1G 88-44		PV
☐ Antonov An-12BP	CCCP-11339	2400505		RA
☐ Antonov An-14A	CCCP-81556	600704		RA
☐ Ilyushin Il-14	CCCP-06150			RA
☐ Ilyushin Il-28	01	56606201	85	PV
☐ Let L-410UVP Turbolet	CCCP-67131	800327		RA
☐ Lisunov Li-2 [Douglas DC-3 modified]	CCCP-503??	'1230305'		RA
☐ Mikoyan-Gurevich MiG-15			Major components.	PV
☐ Mikoyan-Gurevich MiG-17	21			PV
☐ Mikoyan-Gurevich MiG-21M	71	961804		PV
☐ Mil Mi-2	CCCP-23481	526240089		RA
☐ Mil Mi-2	22	544446105	60	RA
☐ Mil Mi-24A	48	1200705		RA
☐ Mil Mi-6	RA-21856	4681603	CCCP-21856	RA
☐ Mil Mi-8	CCCP-72786			RA
☐ Mil Mi-8	CCCP-25570	3023		RA
☐ Mil Mi-8	CCCP-25687	3772		RA
☐ Mil Mi-8	CCCP-25696	4065		RA
☐ Mil Mi-8	CCCP-25730	4234		RA
☐ Mil Mi-8	CCCP-25736	4433		RA
☐ Mil Mi-8	CCCP-25816	4551		RA
☐ Mil Mi-8	CCCP-25822	4557		RA
☐ Mil Mi-8	CCCP-22374	7253		RA
☐ Mil Mi-8T	CCCP-25559	3007		RA
☐ Mil Mi-8T	CCCP-22963	99457734		RA
☐ Sukhoi Su-7U	50			PV
☐ Sukhoi Su-9	27			PV
☐ Sukhoi Su-15	51			PV
☐ Sukhoi Su-15	45	0103		RA
☐ Tupolev Tu-104E	CCCP-42441	920903		RA
☐ Tupolev Tu-144S	CCCP-77108	04-2		RA
☐ Tupolev Tu-154	CCCP-85703	M003		RA
☐ Tupolev Tu-154B1 (Tu-154)	CCCP-85038	73A-038	Wing only.	RA
☐ Wytwornia Sprzetu Komunikacyjnego (WSK) M-15-01 Belphegor	CCCP-15183	1S 019-06		PV
☐ Yakovlev Yak-25M	84		Major components.	RA
☐ Yakovlev Yak-42	CCCP-42309	01005		RA
☐ Yakovlev Yak-50	41	852903		PV

SARATOV AIRCRAFT FACTORY MUSEUM (RU55)

Address:	Orzhonikidze 1, 410015 Saratov.
Admission:	By prior permission only.
Location:	In the southern suburbs of the town.

The Yak-1 fighter first flew in early 1940 and was rapidly put into production at the factory at Saratov. Over the next three years this plant delivered almost seven and a half thousand examples. A small museum tracing the history of the site has been set up with many photographs, documents and models on show.

TYPE	REG/SER	CON. NO.	PI/NOTES	STATUS
☐ Yakovlev Yak-1		08110		RA

SOCHI-ADLER MUSEUM (RU56)

Address:	Adler Airport.
Location:	About 30km. south east of the town off Road M27.

On September 20th 1959 the Ilyushin Il-18 first flew scheduled passenger services. Two routes Moscow – Adler and Moscow – Alma Ata were inaugurated. A museum has been set up with an Il-18 on show.

TYPE	REG/SER	CON. NO.	PI/NOTES	STATUS
☐ Ilyushin Il-18V	CCCP-75784	181003903	Also reported as CCCP-75751	PV

ST. PETERSBURG MILITARY AVIATION TECHNICAL COLLEGE MEMORIAL MUSEUM (RU57)

Address: Lebyazh'e,
St. Petersburg.
Admission: By prior permission only.
Location: In the city.

Many aviation colleges in the country have museums depicting the history of aviation. The Ilyushin Il-2 was recovered from a crash site and rebuilt as a student project.

TYPE	REG/SER	CON. NO.	PI/NOTES	STATUS
☐ Ilyushin Il-2m3				PV

SUKHOI OKB MUSEUM (RU58)

Address: 23A Polikarpov Street,
124284 Moscow.
Tel: 095-945-6525
Admission: By prior permission only.
Location: In the north western part of the city on the south side of Khodinka Airport.

Pavel Sukhoi was born in 1895 and studied at Moscow Higher Technical School before serving in World War I. In the early 1920s he joined the design team of Tupolev. He formed his own bureau in 1939 and ten years later Stalin closed the organisation. Sukhoi served as deputy to Tupolev until Stalin's death in 1953 when be reopened his own bureau. He died in 1975 but the work of the team continued under the leadership of Ivanov and from 1983 Mikhail Simonov. Since the 1950s Sukhoi jet fighters and ground attack aircraft have served in large numbers with the Air Force. The displays at the museum trace the history of the bureau and its aircraft.

TYPE	REG/SER	CON. NO.	PI/NOTES	STATUS
☐ Polikarpov I-153 (FSM)	'42'			RAX
☐ Sukhoi Su-2 (FSM)				RAX
☐ Sukhoi S-32 (Su-17M2D)	01			RA
☐ Sukhoi Su-27	42	36911024307		RA

SYZRAN AVIATION MUSEUM (RU59)

Address: Syzran.
Admission: By prior permission only.
Location: About 200 km west of Samara on Road M.5.

A report in a magazine stated that two aircraft were preserved at a museum in the town. There is an aircraft factory and a military base in the area so I would welcome information on the exact location.

TYPE	REG/SER	CON. NO.	PI/NOTES	STATUS
☐ Antonov An-24				PV
☐ Mil Mi-4				PV

TAMBOV MILITARY PILOT SCHOOL MUSEUM (RU60)

Address: Tambov.
Admission: By prior permission only.
Location: About 220 km south east of Moscow off Road M6.

An outside display of aircraft has been set up at this airfield which trains pilots. There are many more aircraft on show than those listed here and attempts are being made to obtain details.

TYPE	REG/SER	CON. NO.	PI/NOTES	STATUS
☐ Ilyushin Il-28				RA
☐ Mikoyan-Gurevich MiG-23B	06			RA
☐ Mikoyan-Gurevich MiG-23ML	11			RA
☐ Mikoyan-Gurevich MiG-27	02			RA
☐ Sukhoi Su-17M2	01			RA

THIRD AIRBORNE GUARDS REGIMENT MEMORIAL (RU61)

Address: Kirshach.
Admission: On permanent view.
Location: In the town which is about 85 km north east of Moscow.

The regiment served with distinction during World War II and undertook several missions behind German lines. Over four hundred examples of the Antonov A-7 troop-carrying glider were produced. One has been preserved as the centrepiece of the memorial to the heroic deeds of the airborne forces.

TYPE	REG/SER	CON. NO.	PI/NOTES	STATUS
☐ Antonov A-7				PV

VALERY P. CHKALOV MUSEUM (RU62)

Address: Ul. Chklova 5,
Chkalovsk,
Nizhny Novororod Oblast.
Admission: Tuesday-Sunday 1000-1700.
Location: In the town which is about 70 km north west of Nizhny Novogorod.

Andrei Tupolev obtained permission from the Revolutionary War Council in December 1931 to produce a monoplane specifically designed for long distance flights. The ANT-25 first flew in the hands of Mikhail Gromov on June 22nd 1933. The type set a closed circuit record the following year. Preparations were made for a transpolar flight but the plans were altered. On July 20th 1936 Valery Chkalov and his crew took off from Moscow for the Soviet far east but were forced to land on the island of Udd after over fifty six hours aloft. Between June 18th and 20th 1937 the same crew flew from Moscow over the North Pole to Pearson Field in Washington State in the U.S.A. in a sixty three hour journey. The ANT-25 is the centrepiece of the display. Chkalov made the first test flights of the Polikarpov I-16 and I-17 fighters and examples of these are on show.

TYPE	REG/SER	CON. NO.	PI/NOTES	STATUS
☐ Mikoyan-Gurevich MiG-15bis	01	2415372		PV
☐ Mikoyan-Gurevich MiG-21PFS	14	94210810		PV
☐ Polikarpov I-16 tip 10				PV
☐ Polikarpov I-17				PV
☐ Polikarpov Po-2				PV
☐ Tupolev ANT-25	URSS-N025			PV

VICTORY PARK – KAZAN (RU63)

Address: Kazan'.
Admission: Daily 1000-1700.
Location: In the town

The town which was established many years ago is the capital of the Tatarstan Republic. The park has been set up to honour all those who fought in conflicts both in the area and in the former Soviet Union. On show are military vehicles and tanks as well as an impressive memorial. The town is home to a large aircraft factory which is currently producing Tupolev airliners and Mil helicopters.

TYPE	REG/SER	CON. NO.	PI/NOTES	STATUS
☐ Aero L-29 Delfin	36	491034		PV
☐ Mikoyan-Gurevich MiG-17	01			PV
☐ Mikoyan-Gurevich MiG-27K	41	76802635272		PV
☐ Mil Mi-8T		0203		PV
☐ Polikarpov Po-2 (FSM?)				PV
☐ Sukhoi Su-7U	53	2009		PV
☐ Tupolev Tu-2S (FSM ?)	36			PV

VOLOGDA MUSEUM (RU64)

Address:	160000 Vologda.
Admission:	On permanent view.
Location:	The town is about 450 km. north east of Moscow on the M8.

Aeroflot set up museums at many of its regional headquarters and at a number of airports. Most of these collections consisted of photographs, models, uniforms and memorabilia tracing the development of civil aviation in the area. An Ilyushin Il-18 and a Mill Mi-4 reported at the airport are probably at one of these.

TYPE	REG/SER	CON. NO.	PI/NOTES	STATUS
☐ Ilyushin Il-18V	CCCP-75518	183006701		PV
☐ Mil Mi-4A	CCCP-14295	08181		PV

VOLVOGRAD STATE PANORAMIC MUSEUM 'STALINGRAD BATTLE' (RU65)

Address:	47 Chuikova Street, 4000053 Volvograd.
Tel:	08442-34-72-72
Admission:	Summer Tuesday-Sunday 1000-1800; Winter Tuesday-Sunday 1000-1700.
Location:	In the centre of the town.

The original military museum in the town, then named Stalingrad, opened in 1937. In 1948 it took up the name 'Museum of the Defence of Tsaritsyn Stalingrad' and in 1963 the title changed to 'Volgograd State Defence Museum'. The current name was adopted in 1982 when new facilities were built. The largest painting in Russia depicts the defeat of the German Army at the famous battle. There are four dioramas to be seen and eight halls containing exhibitions of memorabilia, flags, trophies, maps, documents, uniforms and photographs. The three replica aircraft, representing types used at the time, are positioned on the ramp leading up to the entrance to the building. The Sukhoi Su-2 short range bomber first flew in prototype form in 1940 and eight hundred were completed but many were lost in repelling the German forces. The famous Il-2 dive bomber served with distinction in many conflicts and well over thirty six thousand were completed. The Yak-9 was in production from the early 1940s and saw its first combat duties at the Stalingrad battle.

TYPE	REG/SER	CON. NO.	PI/NOTES	STATUS
☐ Ilyushin Il-2 (FSM)				PV
☐ Sukhoi Su-2 (FSM)				PV
☐ Yakovlev Yak-9 (FSM)				PV

VORONEZH AIRCRAFT FACTORY DISPLAY (RU66)

Address:	Tsiolkovskogo Street 27, 394029 Voronezh.
Tel:	0732-499017
Fax:	0732-448666
Admission:	By prior permission only.
Location:	In the southern suburbs of the town.

This large factory opened in 1934 and among the types produced in World War II was the Ilyushin Il-2. In recent times Tupolev airliners have left the production lines. Parts for the supersonic Tu-144 were built here. The Il-2 was recovered from a crash site and rebuilt by volunteers. The Tu-144 is in a hangar on the airfield.

TYPE	REG/SER	CON. NO.	PI/NOTES	STATUS
☐ Ilyushin Il-2		1872932		RA
☐ Tupolev Tu-144	CCCP-77109	05-2		RA

VORONEZH-BALTIMOR AIRFIELD COLLECTION (RU67)

Address:	Baltimor Air Base, Voronezh.
Admission:	By prior permission only.
Location:	About 3 km south of the town.

A unit flying Antonov An-30s on long range reconnaissance missions is in residence alongside squadrons operating the Mil Mi-8 and the Sukhoi Su-24. There are also transport types based at the airfield. Photographs show a collection of preserved aircraft at the field. The list below is not complete as parts of other aircraft which cannot be identified can be seen in the background.

TYPE	REG/SER	CON. NO.	PI/NOTES	STATUS
☐ Mikoyan-Gurevich MiG-21SM				RA
☐ Mil Mi-2				RA
☐ Sukhoi Su-7	51			RA
☐ Sukhoi Su-24	55			RA

WAR MUSEUM (RU68)

Address:	Zarya, 143922 Moscow Oblast.
Admission:	Daily 1000-1300 1400-1800
Tel:	525-91-28
Location:	About 150 km north east of Moscow.

Displays at this museum trace the history of conflicts which have taken place in the region from early times. On show are weapons, vehicles, photographs, documents etc. The MiG is mounted on a pylon outside the building and nearby are several missiles, mobile radar equipment lorries and some tanks.

TYPE	REG/SER	CON. NO.	PI/NOTES	STATUS
☐ Mikoyan-Gurevich MiG-19	41			PV

YAKOVLEV OKB MUSEUM (RU69)

Address:	68 Leningradsky Prospekt, 125315 Moscow.
Tel:	095-158-3432
Fax:	095-787-2844
Email:	yakokb@cityline.ru
Admission:	Monday-Friday 1000-1700 by appointment.
Location:	In the north western suburbs of the city.

Aleksandr Yakovlev was born in 1906 and in 1923 he assisted Anoshchyenko in the building of a glider for the meeting at Koktobel. The following year he built his own sailplane with assistance from Sergei Ilyushin. In 1927 he designed a biplane which was later designated AIR-1 and this machine set records in its class. The AIR-1 is preserved in the museum. Another early aircraft on show is the AIR-14 prototype of 1936 which led to the successful UT-1 trainer of which over twelve hundred were produced. Yakovlev set up his own design bureau in 1934 in a derelict bed factory and the site is still home to the organisation. The museum, established in 1974, traces the history of the bureau with an excellent collection of photographs and documents on show. A range of models showing virtually every type produced and those which did not get beyond the drawing board can be seen. One area lists Yakovlev aircraft displayed at other museums throughout the world. All the aircraft have been immaculately restored. The UT-2 was the standard primary trainer of World War II with over seven thousand being constructed. During the conflict a series of successful fighters was designed and a Yak-3 and a Yak-9 have been preserved. Examples of the range of light aircraft produced since the war can be seen along with an example of the one of the first jets in the Soviet Union, the Yak-15. The Yak-30 competed unsuccessfully against the Czech L-29 Delfin and the Polish TS-11 Iskra in a 1961 contest to find a standard Warsaw Pact trainer. The single seat Yak-32 followed but only two were built. The Yak-38 S/VTOL aircraft joined the collection in the late 1990s. Designed in the 1980s as a multi-role type for carrier operations the Yak-44 did not progress beyond a full scale mock up which is now in store in the factory. Models of the some of the unmanned remote controlled aircraft can also be seen. Not all the aircraft held by the museum are on display at any one time and hopefully examples of other types produced will enhance the exhibition.

TYPE	REG/SER	CON. NO.	PI/NOTES	STATUS
☐ Yakovlev AIR-1 (VVA-3) (R)				PV
☐ Yakovlev UT-1 (AIR-14)				PV
☐ Yakovlev UT-2	3	20		PV
☐ Yakovlev Yak-3				RA
☐ Yakovlev Yak-9				RA
☐ Yakovlev Yak-11	25			PV
☐ Yakovlev Yak-12A	CCCP-^5275			RA
☐ Yakovlev Yak-15	37	31007 (?)		PV
☐ Yakovlev Yak-18A	DOSAAF03			PV
☐ Yakovlev Yak-18T	CCCP-81434	5201707 (?)		RA
☐ Yakovlev Yak-23UTI		115001	50	RA
☐ Yakovlev Yak-28PM	52	0921		RA
☐ Yakovlev Yak-30	90			RA
☐ Yakovlev Yak-32	70			RA
☐ Yakovlev Yak-38				PV
☐ Yakovlev Yak-44E (FSM)				RA
☐ Yakovlev Yak-141	141			PV

ZHUKOVSKII FLIGHT TEST INSTITUTE AIRFIELD COLLECTION (RU70)

Address:	140160 Moscow.
Admission:	By prior permission.
Location:	About 30 km. south east of Moscow.

Many companies have test facilities at this airfield which houses the Flight Research Institute and there are a number of derelict airframes around the site. Four types have been preserved near the main gate to the complex with another in the housing area of the base. The Ilyushin Il-102 close support attack jet first flew in September 1982. After five years of testing the sole example completed was withdrawn. The airfield holds a major airshow each summer when in addition to the display aircraft the others stored can be viewed. Some of these will undoubtedly put on display by their manufacturers in the future.

TYPE	REG/SER	CON. NO.	PI/NOTES	STATUS
☐ Ilyushin Il-102	10201			RA
☐ Mikoyan-Gurevich MiG-21UM	68		In Housing area.	RA
☐ Mikoyan-Gurevich MiG-23UB	09			RA
☐ Sukhoi Su-17UM3	09			RA
☐ Yakovlev Yak-38U	24			RA

SERBIA AND MONTENEGRO

MILITARY BARRACKS COLLECTION (SER1)

Address:	–
Admission:	By prior permission only.
Location:	South of Beograd on Road 251 to Vinca.

Three aircraft have been seen preserved in the camp south of the city. Yugoslavia bought a small number of Whirlwinds in the late 1950's. Some were supplied directly and others were assembled and produced in the country. The U.S.A. delivered many examples of the Sabre and Thunderjet to the country when it could not obtain Soviet aircraft. These two fighter types gave excellent service for many years

TYPE	REG/SER	CON. NO.	PI/NOTES	STATUS
☐ North American NA-190 Sabre (F-86D)				RA
☐ Republic F-84G Thunderjet				RA
☐ Westland-Sikorsky WS-55 Whirlwind HAR.5	11905			RA

MUZEJ JUGOSLOVENSKOG VAZDUHOPLOVSTVA (SER2)

Address:	P.O. Box 16, 11180 Aerodrom Beograd.
Tel:	011-698-209
Email:	airmuseum@beogrid.net
Fax:	011-670-992
Admission:	May-October Monday-Friday 0900-1730; Saturday-Sunday 1000-1730;November-April Monday-Friday 0900-1430; S/S 1000-1330.
Location:	At Surcin Airport which is about 14 km west of the city off the E.94.

The Yugoslav Aeronautical Museum was established in 1957 with the aim of collecting aircraft and material to show the development of aviation in the country. Temporary exhibitions were staged in Belgrade and at the former Zemun airfield on the outskirts of the city. As the collection grew the aircraft were stored around the country and a site was allocated at Surcin Airport. Ivan Straus designed the futuristic geodetic building which opened on May 21st. 1989 after a long period of construction. Well over two hundred aircraft are owned by the museum and about a quarter of them are on show. The museum also contains a large library and archive section. The basement of the building houses the workshops and many airframes are stored here. The first Yugoslav aircraft was made by Edvard Rusjan and flew on November 25th. 1909. In the following month Ivan Saric finished a low wing monoplane powered by a Delfosse engine. Parts of this aircraft survived and a partial replica was built in 1959 with the assistance of the constructor. The first Air Force unit was set up in Serbia in 1912 and the next year aircraft took part in operations in the Balkan War. France provided many aircraft during World War I including Nieuport fighters. The replica on show was built in France by Jean Salis and obtained in 1982 by the museum in an exchange deal. The World War II period is well represented with examples of the Messerschmitt Bf 109, the Hawker Hurricane, the Supermarine Spitfire, the Ilyushin Il-2 and the Yakovlev Yak-3 on view. Other fighters from this period are in store and some should be rebuilt in the future. The post-war Yugoslav aviation industry is featured prominently and many unique prototypes have been saved as well as production aircraft. Each company is well documented in the display with photographs of their products and production records. The Ikarus 451M, developed from the piston engined 451, was Yugoslavia's first jet aircraft. The country produced many successful glider designs and examples of these have been preserved. In the 1950's the Air Force obtained a number of American types and examples of these have been preserved. Some British aircraft were also obtained and one of the pair of Folland Gnats evaluated has been saved. The two were delivered by rail in 1958. Several redundant combat types have joined the collection for possible exchange deals. Parts from aircraft shot down in the recent conflicts have also been put on show. Also on show are many engines, models, documents, uniforms, photographs and memorabilia all of which help to present an excellent record of aviation in the region.

TYPE	REG/SER	CON. NO.	PI/NOTES	STATUS
☐ Antonov An-2M	YU-BCE	600404	CCCP-1662	RA
☐ Antonov An-12BP	LZ-SFA	02348007	73311, YU-AIC, LZ-SGA – leased to Bulgaria.	RAA
☐ Ateliers Aéronautiques de Colombes AAC.1 [Junkers Ju 52/3mg10e]	7208	222	F-BBYB	PV
☐ Boeing-Stearman A75N1 Kaydet (N2S-3)	YU-BAD	75-7614	Bu37993, N5115N	RA
☐ Boeing-Stearman A75N1 Kaydet (PT-17)	YU-BAI	75-3047	41-25440, N55360 – if c/n is as quoted.	RA
☐ Bücker Bü 133D-1 Jungmeister	9102	1069	7706 (Croatia) c/n doubtful.	PV
☐ Canadair CL-13 Sabre 4 [North American F-86E]	11054	439	19539, XB636	RA
☐ Canadair CL-13 Sabre 4 [North American F-86E]	11088	638	19738, XB875	RA
☐ Canadair CL-13 Sabre 4 [North American F-86E]	11025	756	19856, XB955	RA
☐ Cijan-Obad Orao IIC	YU-4096	185		PV
☐ Convair 440-0	YU-ADO	470	D-ADIL, D-ACEK	RA
☐ Cubrilo-Mirko BS-1 Student	YU-CKK	01		RA
☐ Cvjetkovic CA-51	YU-CMH			PV
☐ Cvjetkovic CA-51	YU-CMK			RA
☐ De Havilland D.H.82A Tiger Moth	NM150	86470	NM150, 0902, YU-CHX	PV
☐ De Havilland D.H.104 Dove 6 (2B)	72201	04432	YU-ABN, 9751	RA
☐ De Havilland D.H.C.2 Beaver	70101	587	0672, 672	PV
☐ Douglas DC-3A-456 Skytrain (C-47A)	YU-ABB	13713	42-93765	PV
☐ Douglas DC-3A-456 Skytrain (C-47A) (Dakota III)	YU-ABG	14035/25480	43-48219, KG803, G-AHLX	PV
☐ Douglas DC-3A-467 Skytrain (C-47B) (Dakota IV)	71214	16472/33220	44-76888, KN586, 7323	PV
☐ Fiat G.50bis	8	249	MM6197, 3505 (Croatia)	RA
☐ Focke-Wulf Fw 190F-8/R1	3	930838	930838	RA
☐ Folland Fo.141 Gnat F.1	11601	FL-14	G-39-8	PV
☐ General Dynamics 401 Fighting Falcon (F-16C)	88-0550	1C-52	Crash remains.	PVD
☐ Grumman G-164A Ag-Cat	YU-BEU	498	N984X	PV
☐ Hawker Hurricane IV	LD975	41H/368368	LD975, 9539	PV
☐ Henschel Hs 293A-1				RA
☐ Hiller UH12A	YU-HAB	143	N8143H- incomplete.	RA
☐ Ikarus 214-P	61019	19	YU-ABP	PV
☐ Ikarus 451 Pionyr		2		PV
☐ Ikarus 451-M Zolja	YU-COH			PV
☐ Ikarus Aero 2DE	YU-CVB		0875	PV
☐ Ikarus Kosava 60	YU-5022	1		PV
☐ Ikarus Kurir L	YU-CBD	100	50200	RAC
☐ Ikarus Kurir W	YU-CCB	57	50157	RA
☐ Ikarus Meteor 60	YU-4103			RAC
☐ Ikarus S-49A	2319	0301118		RA
☐ Ikarus S-49C	2400	50		PV
☐ Ikarus S 451-MM Matica	20001			RA
☐ Ikarus T 451-MM Strsljen II	21002			PV
☐ Ilic Ilindenka 1T	YU-4108	3005		RA
☐ Ilic Ilindenka 1T	YU-4109	3006		RA
☐ Ilyushin Il-2m3	4154	308331	14337 (Bulgaria)	PV
☐ Ilyushin Il-14S	71301	146001121	YU-ADE, 7401	PV
☐ Jacobs Kranich II (D.F.S. 108-30)	YU-5014	161		RA
☐ Jacobs Meise (D.F.S. 108-70)	YU-4106	33		RA
☐ Jacobs Weihe (D.F.S. 108-68)	YU-4073	443		RA
☐ Jacobs Weihe (D.F.S. 108-68)	YU-4093	491		RA
☐ Jacobs Weihe (D.F.S. 108-68)	YU-4089	492		RA
☐ Junkers Ju 87B-2	9801	0870406	VE+KU, S2+??, H4+??, 5B+?? – incomplete.	RA
☐ Kamov Ka-25PL (Ka-25BSh)	11323	4912519	1130	RA
☐ Kamov Ka-28PL	11401	5235003720222		PV
☐ Kamov Ka-28PL	11402	5235003720223		RA
☐ Koser-Hrovat KB-5 Jadran	YU-6001	104		RA
☐ Letalski Institut Branko Ivanus Slovenija (LIBIS) 17	YU-5069	319		RA
☐ Letalski Institut Branko Ivanus Slovenija (LIBIS) KB-6 Matajur	YU-CFD	177		PV
☐ Letov 22	YU-5038	263		RA
☐ Lisunov Li-3 [Douglas DC-3 modified]	7011	18422308		RA
☐ Lockheed 422-87-23 Lightning (P-38L)	9751	422-6790	44-25786 - incomplete.	RAD
☐ Lockheed 580 (T-33A)	10024	580-8189	52-9958	PV
☐ Lockheed 580 (T-33A) (TV-2) (T-33B)	10242			RA
☐ Lockheed F-117A	82-0806	A.4031	Crash remains.	PVD
☐ Messerschmitt Bf 109G-2/R3	9663	14792	GJ+QJ, 14792 (Bulgaria)	PV
☐ Mikoyan-Gurevich MiG-21F-13	22532	741702		PV
☐ Mikoyan-Gurevich MiG-21bis-K	17402	75095222		RA
☐ Mikoyan-Gurevich MiG-21bis-K	17405	75095251		RA

☐ Mikoyan-Gurevich MiG-21bis-K	17409	75095293		RA
☐ Mikoyan-Gurevich MiG-21M	22805	963007		RA
☐ Mikoyan-Gurevich MiG-21M	22818	963115		RA
☐ Mikoyan-Gurevich MiG-21PFM	22735	8407		RA
☐ Mikoyan-Gurevich MiG-21R	26105	94R1709		PV
☐ Mikoyan-Gurevich MiG-21U	22909	3416		RA
☐ Mikoyan-Gurevich MiG-21UM	22953	03685149		RA
☐ Mikoyan-Gurevich MiG-21US	16152	516909071		RA
☐ Mikoyan-Gurevich MiG-21US	16158	516995091		RA
☐ Mikoyan-Gurevich MiG-23ML	23269	0390325056	(Iraq)	PV
☐ Mil Mi-2	12506	511103059		PV
☐ Mil Mi-2	12512	511110059		RA
☐ Mil Mi-2	12513	541307129		PV
☐ Mil Mi-2	12515	541309129		RA
☐ Mil Mi-2	12514	541327129		RA
☐ Mil Mi-4	12013	06103		PV
☐ Mil Mi-8T	12208	0915		PV
☐ Mraz K-65 Cap [Fieseler Fi 156C-3 Storch]	YU-COE	91	9393	PV
☐ Nieuport 11 (R)	'12'	27	F-WZBC	PVX
☐ North American NA-109 Mustang (P-51D)	44-13278	109-26911	Parts only.	RAD
☐ North American NA-168 Texan (T-6G)	FT-152	168-503	50-1289	PV
☐ North American NA-190 Sabre (F-86D)	14102	190-748	52-10023	PV
☐ Panstwowe Zaklady Lotnicze (PZL) M-18 Dromader	YU-BDU			RA
☐ Panstwowe Zaklady Lotnicze (PZL) M-18 Dromader	YU-BMX	1Z 010-01		RA
☐ Petlyakov Pe-2FT	6054	18/246		RA
☐ Polikarpov Po-2	YU-CNT	01021	0089	PV
☐ Polikarpov Po-2W	YU-CNP	01096	0105	RA
☐ Republic P-47D Thunderbolt	13056	'5609'	44-90464	PV
☐ Republic F-84G Thunderjet	10501		52-2936	RA
☐ Republic F-84G Thunderjet	10530		52-8435	RA
☐ Republic RF-84G Thunderjet (F-84G)	10525		52-2939	PV
☐ Rogozarski R-100 Srs.2	9251	23	723 (Royal Yugoslav AF), 6511 (Croatia), 723 – parts on show.	PV/RA
☐ Saric 1 (R)				PV
☐ Schneider Grunau Baby III (D.F.S. 108-66)	YU-2113	151		RA
☐ Short SA.6 Sealand 1	0662	SH.1567	G-AKLS, YU-CFK	PV
☐ Sikorsky S-55B	11714	WA9-10-2319		PV
☐ Soko 522	60132	32		PV
☐ Soko 522	60157	57		RA
☐ Soko 522	60204	104		RA
☐ Soko J-2 Kraguj	30002			RA
☐ Soko J-20 Kraguj	30101	001		RA
☐ Soko J-20 Kraguj	30103	003		RA
☐ Soko J-20 Kraguj	30104	004		PV
☐ Soko J-20 Kraguj	30106	006		RA
☐ Soko J-20 Kraguj	30107	007		RA
☐ Soko J-20 Kraguj	30108	008		RA
☐ Soko J-20 Kraguj	30109	009		RA
☐ Soko J-20 Kraguj	30114	014		RA
☐ Soko J-20 Kraguj	30135	019		RA
☐ Soko J-20 Kraguj	30144	028		RA
☐ Soko J-20 Kraguj	30145	029		PV
☐ Soko J-20 Kraguj	30147	031		PV
☐ Soko J-20 Kraguj	30148	032		PV
☐ Soko J-20 Kraguj	30152	036		PV
☐ Soko J-20 Kraguj	30155	039		RA
☐ Soko J-20 Kraguj	30157	041		PV
☐ Soko J-1 Jastreb	24002			RA
☐ Soko J-21 Jastreb	24115	015		PV
☐ Soko J-21 Jastreb	24122	024		RA
☐ Soko J-21 Jastreb	24126	028		RA
☐ Soko J-21 Jastreb	24128	030		RA
☐ Soko J-21 Jastreb	24130	032		RA
☐ Soko J-21 Jastreb	24142	044		RA
☐ Soko J-21 Jastreb	24145	047		RA
☐ Soko J-21 Jastreb	24155	061		RA
☐ Soko J-21 Jastreb	24156	063		RA
☐ Soko J-21 Jastreb	24159	065		RA
☐ Soko J-21 Jastreb	24208	074		RA
☐ Soko J-21 Jastreb	24210	076		RA
☐ Soko J-21 Jastreb	24213	079		RA
☐ Soko J-21 Jastreb	24214	080		RA
☐ Soko IJ-21 Jastreb	24401	001		RA
☐ Soko IJ-21 Jastreb	24404	004		RA
☐ Soko IJ-21 Jastreb	24405	005		RA
☐ Soko IJ-21 Jastreb	24410	010		RA
☐ Soko IJ-21 Jastreb	24415	015		RA
☐ Soko IJ-21 Jastreb	24418	018		RA
☐ Soko IJ-21 Jastreb	24421	021		RA
☐ Soko IJ-21 Jastreb	24454	034		RA

☐ Soko IJ-21 Jastreb	24456	036		RA
☐ Soko IJ-21 Jastreb	24457	037		RA
☐ Soko NJ-21 Jastreb	23502	005		RA
☐ Soko NJ-21 Jastreb	23505	008		RA
☐ Soko NJ-21 Jastreb	23506	009		RA
☐ Soko NJ-21 Jastreb	23507	010		RA
☐ Soko NJ-21 Jastreb	23511	012		RA
☐ Soko NJ-21 Jastreb	23512	014		RA
☐ Soko NJ-21 Jastreb	23513	015		RA
☐ Soko J-22 Orao	25001			PV
☐ Soko J-22 Orao	25107	007		RA
☐ Soko J-22 Orao	25118	043		RA
☐ Soko J-22 Orao	25120	045		RA
☐ Soko IJ-22 Orao	25719	019		RA
☐ Soko IJ-22 Orao	25721	021		RA
☐ Soko IJ-22 Orao	25723	023		RA
☐ Soko IJ-22 Orao	25724	024		RA
☐ Soko INJ-22 Orao	25606	006		RA
☐ Soko NJ-22 Orao	25505	015		RA
☐ Soko NJ-22 Orao	25506	016		RA
☐ Soko NJ-22 Orao	25509	018		RA
☐ Soko NJ-22 Orao	25511	020		RA
☐ Soko N-60 Galeb G-2	23001			RA
☐ Soko N-60 Galeb G-2A	23108	108		PV
☐ Soko N-60 Galeb G-2A	23154	154		RA
☐ Soko N-60 Galeb G-2A	23156	156		RA
☐ Soko Super Galeb G-4	23629	009		RA
☐ Soko Super Galeb G-4	23636	016		RA
☐ Soko Super Galeb G-4	23686	042		RA
☐ Soko Super Galeb G-4	23733	065	Rear fuselage only.	PV
☐ Sostaric Cavka	YU-2127			RA
☐ Sostaric Cavka	YU-2227			RA
☐ Sostaric Jastreb 54	YU-3029	195		PV
☐ Sostaric Jastreb 54	YU-3056	251		PV
☐ Sostaric Kasava 2				RA
☐ Sostaric Macka	YU-4107	03		PV
☐ Sostaric Roda	YU-5210	24		PV
☐ Sostaric Vrabac A				PV
☐ Sud-Est SE.210 Caravelle VI-N	YU-AHB	135	F-WJAK	PV
☐ Supermarine 349 Spitfire LF.Vc	JK808	CBAF-4690	JK808, 9489 - may be MH592, 9486.	PV
☐ Utva Fabrica Aviona 213/3	1352	92		PV
☐ Utva Fabrica Aviona N-63 Lasti	54153			RA
☐ Utva Fabrica Aviona 65-S Privrednik	YU-BKI	736	0736	PV
☐ Utva Fabrica Aviona 66	51001			RA
☐ Utva Fabrica Aviona 66	51002			RA
☐ Utva Fabrica Aviona 66	51121			RA
☐ Utva Fabrica Aviona 66	51145			RA
☐ Utva Fabrica Aviona 66H	52101	0822		RA
☐ Utva Fabrica Aviona 66H	52102	0823		PV
☐ Utva Fabrica Aviona 66H	52104	0831		RA
☐ Utva Fabrica Aviona Aero 3				RA
☐ Utva Fabrica Aviona Aero 3				RA
☐ Utva Fabrica Aviona Aero 3-2	YU-CZA	86	40186	RA
☐ Utva Fabrica Aviona M/J1	YU-UTVA		Incomplete.	RA
☐ Vajic V-55	YU-CMR			RA
☐ Vazduhoplovno Tehnicki Centar - Vrsac Cirrus HS-64D	YU-5341	118		RA
☐ Vazduhoplovno Tehnicki Centar - Vrsac Delfin M-2	YU-4138	045		PV
☐ Vazduhoplovno Tehnicki Centar - Vrsac Trener	YU-4169	079		RA
☐ Vazduhoplovno Tehnicki Centar - Vrsac VTC-76 Jastreb Vuk-T	YU-4422	346		RA
☐ Westland-Sikorsky WS-51 Dragonfly 1B	11503	WA/H/97		PV
☐ Yakovlev Yak-3	2252	8543		PV
☐ Yakovlev Yak-9P	2826	04-36		RA
☐ Zlin XII	F-AQII	194		RA
☐ Zlin Z-37A Cmelak	YU-BGL	08-19		RA
☐ Zlin Z-526M Trener Master	YU-DIO	1024	41104	RA
☐ Zmaj Fizir FN	9009	9	YU-CAY	PV
☐ Zmaj Fizir FP-2		15	9308- incomplete.	RAD

VAZDUHOPLOVNI OPITNI CENTAR (SER3)

Address:	11273 Batajnica.
Tel:	011-614-756
Fax:	011-108-464
Email:	gsvjvoc@tehnicom.net
Admission:	By prior permission only
Location:	About 20 km north west of Belgrade off Route 11.

The Flight Test Squadron was originally established in December 1933. The Flight Test Centre was set up at Zemun in August 1945. When the site closed due to expansion of the city the organisation moved to Batajnica. Over the years almost one hundred indigenous designs, sixty foreign types and thirty five sailplanes have been evaluated In addition work is carried out on weapons, parachutes and avionics. There are also combat units in residence. Three preserved aircraft have been put on show.

TYPE	REG/SER	CON. NO.	PI/NOTES	STATUS
☐ Mikoyan-Gurevich MiG-21bis	17409			PV
☐ Soko N-60 Galeb G-2A				RA
☐ Soko Super Galeb G-4	23686			PV

VOJNI MUZEJ (SER4)

Address:	Kalemegdan B.B., 11000 Beograd.
Tel:	011-3343-441
Admission:	Tuesday-Sunday 100-1700.
Location:	At the citadel in the northern part of the city centre.

Housed in the impressive citadel the museum traces the military history of the region from early times. Uniforms, weapons, medals and dioramas of battles feature prominently. The fuselage frame of a D.F.S. 230 troop carrying glider is on show. The type was used in the area during World War II.

TYPE	REG/SER	CON. NO.	PI/NOTES	STATUS
☐ Jacobs D.F.S. 230C-1			Fuselage frame only.	PV

SLOVAK REPUBLIC

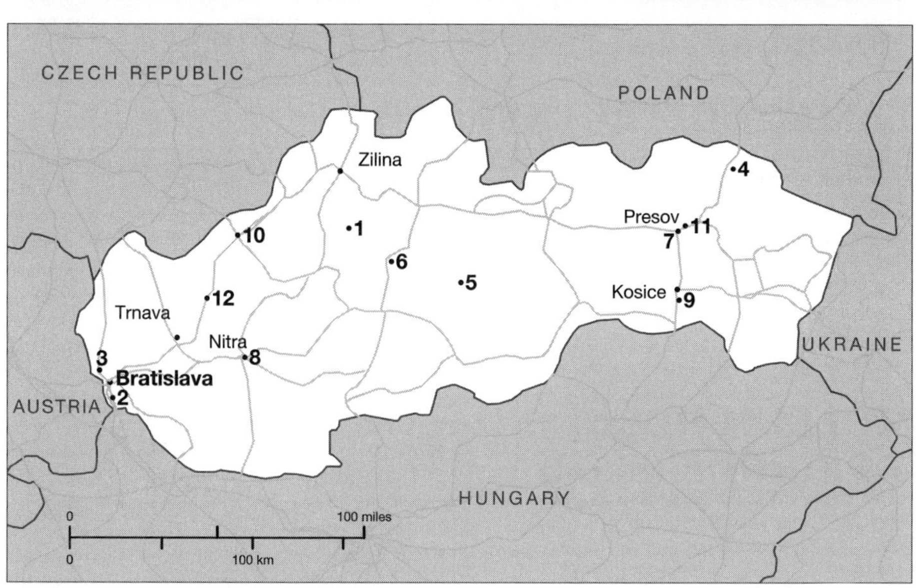

AERO MÚZEUM (SLO1)

Address:	S. Furdeka 24, 036 01 Martin.
Tel:	043-424-6213
Fax:	043-423-7077
Email:	pmazak@lombardini.it
Admission:	By prior permission only.
Location:	The airfield is about 2 km east of the town.

This thriving gliding club is setting up a museum at its airfield. Airshows are often held at the field which is located below a mountain range. The first preserved aircraft arrived at the site more than a decade ago but the collection has grown recently. All the types on show have served in the region over the years. A display is being set up which will trace the history of soaring flight from the field.

TYPE	REG/SER	CON. NO.	PI/NOTES	STATUS
☐ Aero L-29RS Delfin	2609	792609		PV
☐ Antonov An-2	OM-RIQ	117447314	7144 (Czechoslovakia), OK-RIQ	PV
☐ Let L-410A Turbolet	OK-ADN	710004		PV
☐ Mikoyan-Gurevich MiG-15bisR	3024	713204		PV
☐ Mikoyan-Gurevich MiG-19S	0302	150302		PV
☐ Mikoyan-Gurevich MiG-21F-13	0710	760710		PV
☐ Mikoyan-Gurevich MiG-21PFM	7913	94N7913		PV
☐ Mikoyan-Gurevich MiG-21U-600	2916	662916		RA
☐ Mil Mi-2	OM-NIN	528348103	OK-MIN	PV
☐ Sukhoi Su-7BKL	6506	6506		PV

HISTORICKE MÚZEUM (SLO2)

Address:	P.O. Box 13, Bratislavsky Hrad, 81006 Bratlislava 16.
Tel:	02-544-11444
Fax:	02-544-14981
Email:	komon@snm-hm-sk
Admission:	Tuesday-Saturday 0900-1700.
Location:	In the centre of the city on the north bank of the River Danube.

This site is one of many run by the national museum. The exhibition is located in the historic Bratislava Castle first built over one thousand years ago. The building was burned down in 1811 and remained derelict until after World War II. The site now houses museums and government offices. The replica Caproni bomber was started at Trencin in the 1990s and has been loaned to the museum for a period.

TYPE	REG/SER	CON. NO.	PI/NOTES	STATUS
☐ Caproni Ca.36 (R)	'11495'		On loan from VHM.	PVC

LAMAC COLLECTION (SLO3)

Address:	Lamac.
Admission:	By prior permission only.
Location:	About 10 km north west of Bratislava on the E.65.

The three aircraft are preserved at a garage on the main road between Bratislava and Brno. Well over one thousand examples of the L-410 were built at Kunovice in what is now the Czech Republic.

TYPE	REG/SER	CON. NO.	PI/NOTES	STATUS
☐ Let L-410UVP Turbolet	CCCP-67365	820921	CCCP-67365, OK-NDN, OM-NDN	PV
☐ Mil Mi-2				PV
☐ Mil Mi-2	OM-NIO	528523014	OK-NIO	PV

MÚZEUM DUKELSKO-KARPATSKÉ V PRÍRODĚ (SLO4)

Address:	089 01 Svidnik.
Tel:	0937-21398
Admission:	Mid April-mid October Tuesday-Friday 0800-1600 Saturday-Sunday 1000-1400.
Location:	In the centre of the town off Route 18. The Il-10 is on the road to Dukla.

The activities of the Czechoslovak forces in World War II are highlighted in this museum which opened in 1955. World War I also features in the display. On show are military vehicles, documents, uniforms and memorabilia. The Avia built Ilyushin Il-10 dates from the 1950s and is displayed in the Dukla pass north east of the town. Its predecessor the Il-2 was used by the Soviet backed Air Force in exile.

TYPE	REG/SER	CON. NO.	PI/NOTES	STATUS
☐ Avia B-33 [Ilyushin Il-10]	'40'	B33-5514 (?)	5514 (?)	PVX
☐ Lisunov Li-2P [Douglas DC-3 modified]	'50'	23442107	D-33, 2107, '40' – possible identity.	PVX

MÚZEUM LESNÍCKY SKANZEN (SLO5)

Address:	Vidrovo, 976 52 Cierny Balog.
Tel:	048-917662
Email:	lesycb@lesy.sk
Admission:	April-October daily 1030-1630.
Location:	In Vidrovo near to Cierny Balog which is about 8 km south of Brezno.

This open air museum in picturesque woodland contains many historic buildings from the area. These have been moved to the site and restored. A recently withdrawn Mi-2 has joined the exhibition.

TYPE	REG/SER	CON. NO.	PI/NOTES	STATUS
☐ Mil Mi-2	OM-KIX	526643050	OK-KIX	PV

MÚZEUM SLOVENSKÉHO NÁRODNÉHO POVSTANIA (SLO6)

Address:	Kapitulska 25, 974 01 Banska Bystrica.
Tel:	048-412-2358
Fax:	048-412-3716
Email:	Muzeumsnp@islenet.sk
Admission:	October-April Tuesday-Sunday 0900-1600; April-October Tuesday-Sunday 0800-1800.
Location:	In the centre of the town which is about 250 km north east of Bratislava.

In late 1944 the Slovakian National Uprising against the German 'puppet' state of Slovakia took place. Banska Bystrica was the centre of the revolt which was assisted by the Soviet forces who landed supplies and personnel. The displays in the building trace the history of the campaign. The Li-2 is painted in the markings of one of the Soviet aircraft which operated in the conflict. The aircraft was built at Khimki in 1952 and delivered to Prague as a gift to the Czechoslovakian government. A damaged centre section from a Lavochkin La-5 is in one of the halls along with small aircraft components and many photographs.

TYPE	REG/SER	CON. NO.	PI/NOTES	STATUS
☐ Lavochkin La-5FN			Centre section only	PV
☐ Lisunov Li-2P [Douglas DC-3 modified]	'20'	23442105	D-26, OK-GAA, OK-BYO, 2105 – in false Soviet markings.	PVX

PRESOV BASE COLLECTION (SLO7)

Address:	VU 6335, 080 01 Presov.
Tel:	0960-527180
Admission:	By prior permission only.
Location:	In the north eastern suburbs of the town off Route 18.

A helicopter wing of the Air Force is in residence at the field. Currently operational are Mil Mi-2s, Mi-17s and Mi-24s. A number of preserved aircraft are parked around the site. Several types which were stored here have moved to the museum at Kosice and others have been scrapped.

TYPE	REG/SER	CON. NO.	PI/NOTES	STATUS
☐ Aero L-29 Delfin	0007	190007		RA
☐ Mil Mi-4	'1992'	11114	1514	RAX
☐ Sukhoi Su-7BM	5617	5617		RA

SLOVENSKE POLNOHOSPODARSKE MÚZEUM (SLO8)

Address:	Dlhá 94, 949 01 Nitra.
Tel:	037-657-2553
Fax:	037-652-3359
Email:	muzeum@agrokomplex.sk
Admission:	November-March Tuesday-Saturday 0900-1600; Sunday 1000-1600. April-October Tuesday-Saturday 1000-1500; Sunday 1300-1600.
Location:	In the eastern suburbs of the town on the road to Jankovice.

The development of agricultural techniques and equipment is portrayed at this large site which houses many pavilions and outside displays. The aviation section includes several photographs showing crop-spraying aircraft in action. Also on display are a number of engines and components.

TYPE	REG/SER	CON. NO.	PI/NOTES	STATUS
☐ Antonov An-2R	OM-JIE	1G 186-19	OK-JIE	PV
☐ Mil Mi-2	OK-EIT	533501054	B-2401	PV

SLOVENSKE TECHNICKÉ MÚZEUM – LETECKE MÚZEUM (SLO9)

Address:	Hlavna 88, 043 82 Kosice.
Tel:	055-622-4035-7
Fax:	055-622-5965
Email:	stmke@stm-ke.sk
Admission:	Summer months Wednesday-Friday 1000-1500. Saturday-Sunday 1000-1600.
Location:	At the International Airport which is about 6 km south of city.

The Technical Museum in the town was set up in 1947 and in the main building all aspects of the subjects are covered. In addition a number of sites in the country are under its jurisdiction. These include a railway and transport museum in Bratislava and some historic mills and forges in the countryside. The second airfield in the country opened at Kosice in 1924 and the area has a strong aeronautical heritage. Some of the first ballooning flights in the region took place here. For many years the airfield housed a military academy but this closed in 2002. The idea of setting up an aeronautical museum was put forward and the collection opened on August 24th 2002. Over the winter of 2005/6 a new hangar was constructed. The Lubiscak Ultralight mock up is in the exhibition. This was built as a design exercise before deciding whether to go ahead with a flyable machine. A local university student started the replica of the Avia Bk-11 and this is now almost complete. Featured in the exhibition are ballooning, construction techniques, pioneer aviators and the development of the aero engine.

TYPE	REG/SER	CON. NO.	PI/NOTES	STATUS
☐ Aero L-29 Delfin				PV
☐ Aero L-29 Delfin	2846	892846		PV
☐ Aero L-29 Delfin	3232	993232		PV
☐ Aero L-29 Delfin	3246	993246		PV
☐ Aero L-29 Delfin	3407	993408		PV
☐ Aero L-39ZA Albatros	OK-188	X10		PV
☐ Avia Bk-11 (R)				PVC
☐ Bell 204 Iroquois (UH-1C) (UH-1M)	66-15084	1812		PV
☐ Canadair CL-226 Freedom Fighter (NF-5A) [Northrop N-156A]	3014	3014	K-3014 (Netherlands)	PV
☐ Dassault Mirage IIIE	506	506		PV
☐ Dassault Mirage IIIRS	R-2108	1033	In Swiss markings.	PV
☐ Lockheed 683-10-19 Starfighter (F-104S) (F-104S/ASA) (F-104S/ASAM)	MM6870	683-6870		PV
☐ Lubiscak Ultralight (Mock up)				PV
☐ McDonnell M.98NQ Phantom II (F-4F)	37+36	4436	72-1146	PV
☐ Mikoyan-Gurevich MiG-15bis	3305	613305		PVX
☐ Mikoyan-Gurevich MiG-19PM	1113	651113		PV
☐ Mikoyan-Gurevich MiG-21F-13	9904	269904		PV
☐ Mikoyan-Gurevich MiG-21F-13	0515	660515		PV
☐ Mikoyan-Gurevich MiG-21MA	1209	961209		PV
☐ Mikoyan-Gurevich MiG-21MA	1210	961210		PV
☐ Mikoyan-Gurevich MiG-21MA	2707	962707		PV
☐ Mikoyan-Gurevich MiG-21MF	7714	967714		PV
☐ Mikoyan-Gurevich MiG-21MF	7801	967801		PV
☐ Mikoyan-Gurevich MiG-21MF	8205	968205		RA
☐ Mikoyan-Gurevich MiG-21MF	8209	968209		PV
☐ Mikoyan-Gurevich MiG-21MF	9502	969502		PV
☐ Mikoyan-Gurevich MiG-21R	1703	94R1703		PV
☐ Mikoyan-Gurevich MiG-21R	1923	94R1923		PV
☐ Mikoyan-Gurevich MiG-21UM	0268	02695168		PV
☐ Mikoyan-Gurevich MiG-21UM	0475	04695175		PV
☐ Mikoyan-Gurevich MiG-23UB	8109	A1038109		PV
☐ Mil Mi-2	7738	517738072	With boom from 7739.	PV
☐ Mil Mi-2	7739	517739072	With boom from 7738.	PV
☐ Mil Mi-2	8213	518213053		PV
☐ Mil Mi-4	5153	05153		PV
☐ Mil Mi-24D				PV
☐ Mitchell Wing B-10				PV
☐ Nanchang Q-5	30521			RA
☐ Northrop N-156T Talon (T-38A) (AT-38B)	65-10456	N.5875	On loan from VHM.	PV
☐ Orlican VT-116 Orlik II	OK-2713			PV
☐ Panstwowe Zaklady Lotnicze (PZL) TS-11 Iskra 200bisD	1211	3H 12-11	In Polish markings.	PV
☐ Polikarpov Po-2	7		In Russian markings.	PV

TYPE	REG/SER	CON. NO.	PI/NOTES	STATUS
☐ Rubik R-26S Gobé	HA-5392	E-1261		PV
☐ Sud-Est SE.3130 Alouette II	A-75	2095	In Belgian markings.	PV
☐ Sukhoi Su-7BM	5608	5608		PV
☐ Sukhoi Su-15TM	15		In Ukranian markings.	PV
☐ Sukhoi Su-22M4	2702	27002		PV
☐ Sukhoi Su-22M4	4012	40512		PV
☐ Sukhoi Su-25K	5033	25508105033		PV
☐ Svenska Aeroplan Aktiebolaget (SAAB) 37 Viggen (SF 37) (AJSF 37)	Fv37951	37951		RA
☐ Zlin HC-102 Heli Baby	OK-RVY	0434		PV
☐ Zlin Z-37 Cmelak				PV

STEKLY MÚZEUM (SLO10)

Address: Opatovska 187,
911 00 Trencin.
Admission: By prior permission only.
Location: About 4 km north of the town off Route 61.

Karol Stekly has set up a museum at his home. He has collected components from crash sites in the area along with memorabilia and photographs. The only complete aircraft on show is the Mil Mi-1 helicopter.

TYPE	REG/SER	CON. NO.	PI/NOTES	STATUS
☐ Mikoyan-Gurevich MiG-15bis			Front fuselage only.	PV
☐ Wytwornia Sprzetu Komunikacyjnego (WSK) SM-1Wb [Mil Mi-1MU]	6007	506007		PV

SÚKROMNÉ SLOVENSKE DOPRAVNE MÚZEUM (SLO11)

Address: Bardejovska 35,
080 06 Presov.
Tel: 091-764423
Admission: By prior permission only.
Location: About 3 km north east of the town on Route 18.

The museum was established in 1989 with the aim of setting up a collection of aircraft, rockets and vehicles. Problems with the local authority have hindered the development of the collection but there is hope that these may soon be resolved. In addition to the aircraft there are several engines, a complete collection of Sonda probe rockets, flying targets and components recovered from crash sites. A great deal of archive material has been gathered tracing the history of aviation in the country. The collection includes several cars.

TYPE	REG/SER	CON. NO.	PI/NOTES	STATUS
☐ Aero L-29 Delfin	0115	290115		PV
☐ Aero L-29 Delfin	1417	591417	Front fuselage only.	PV
☐ Aero L-29RS Delfin	2802	892802		PV
☐ Antonov An-2	OM-RIO	117047303	7003 (Czechoslovakia), OK-RIO	PV
☐ Avia 14T [Ilyushin Il-14T]	3153	913153		PV
☐ Ilyushin Il-10	4369		Front fuselage only.	PVD
☐ Mikoyan-Gurevich MiG-15bis			Front fuselage only.	PV
☐ Mikoyan-Gurevich MiG-21F-13	0714	760714		PV
☐ Mikoyan-Gurevich MiG-21MF	9404	969404		PV
☐ Mikoyan-Gurevich MiG-21MF	9814	969814		PV
☐ Mikoyan-Gurevich MiG-21PF	1307	761307		PV
☐ Orlican VT-100 Demant	OK-5452			RA
☐ Sukhoi Su-7BMK	5315	5315	Front fuselage only.	PV
☐ Wytwornia Sprzetu Komunikacyjnego (WSK) Lim-6R [MiG-17F]	404	1J 04-04		PV
☐ Zlin VT-425 Sohaj 3	OK-5313			PV

VOJENSKÉ HISTORICKE MÚZEUM (SLO12)

Address: Zilinska 6545,
921 01 Piestany.
Tel: 033-771-8944
Fax: 033-771-8945
Email: vhm@stonline.sk
Admission: June-October Thursday-Sunday 0900-1500.
Location: About 3 km north of the town.

When the country left Czechoslovakia the idea was to set up a museum at Trencin where an aircraft plant was established in 1937. During World War II the Germans took over the site and at the end of hostilities many Czechoslovakian designs were maintained and modified. Since the 1960s a group of volunteers at the factory rebuilt airframes for the museum at Kbely (now in the Czech Republic) and constructed several replicas. In all over fifty aircraft were worked on for the Prague museum. In the 1990s aircraft and military vehicles were moved to Trencin for the new museum. Volunteers built the Caproni Ca 36 in a workshop in the factory. The type was one of the first operated when Czechoslovakia was former after World War I. This aircraft is currently on show at Bratislava Castle. Piestany closed as a transport air base in 2001 and a decision was made to establish the military museum at this location. The exhibition opened on September 25th 2004 and has several aircraft on show with numbers of tanks, armoured personnel carriers, weapons and lorries. The display concentrates on items used after World War II. The story of the forces under Soviet influences and after independence is portrayed. Several airframes are still at Trencin and other locations and some are being restored to join the exhibition. Five Yak-40s were flown by the Czechoslovakian Air Force and when the country split one was allocated to Slovakia. Large numbers of a number of variants of the MiG-21 are in the collection and hopefully examples of all will be moved to Piestany. The one indigenous design is the VZLU HC-3 helicopter. Three prototypes of this four seater were built but the type was not put into production. At the present time only a few aircraft are on show but as the buildings are modified for the museum more will move in.

TYPE	REG/SER	CON. NO.	PI/NOTES	STATUS
☐ Aero 45	OK-FHJ	51172		RA
☐ Aero L-29 Delfin	0306	290306		RA
☐ Aero L-29 Delfin	OM-JET	691901	1901	RA
☐ Aero L-29 Delfin	2845	892845		PV
☐ Aero L-29 Delfin	3228	993228		RA
☐ Aero L-29 Delfin	3229	993229		RA
☐ Aero L-29 Delfin	3250	993250		RA
☐ Aero L-29 Delfin	3405	993405		RA
☐ Aero L-29 Delfin	3408	993408		PV
☐ Aero L-29R Delfin	2823	892823		RA
☐ Aero L-29RS Delfin	2615	792615		RA
☐ Aero L-39C Albatros	0004	130004		PV
☐ Antonov An-2R	OK-KIC	1G 186-34		RA
☐ Avia 14S (14) [Ilyushin Il-14]	5101	015101	OK-OZB, 3X-PRG, 3X-GPA	RA
☐ Caproni Ca.36 (R)	'11495'		On loan to Historicke Muzeum.	–
☐ Mikoyan-Gurevich MiG-15SB (MiG-15)	3014	713014		PV
☐ Mikoyan-Gurevich MiG-19S	0409	150409		RA
☐ Mikoyan-Gurevich MiG-21F-13	0104	460104		RA
☐ Mikoyan-Gurevich MiG-21F-13	0109	460109		RA
☐ Mikoyan-Gurevich MiG-21F-13	0412	660412		RA
☐ Mikoyan-Gurevich MiG-21F-13	0712	760712		RA
☐ Mikoyan-Gurevich MiG-21F-13	0903	960903		RA
☐ Mikoyan-Gurevich MiG-21MA	1112	961112		RA
☐ Mikoyan-Gurevich MiG-21MA	1113	961113		RA
☐ Mikoyan-Gurevich MiG-21MF	7707	967707		PV
☐ Mikoyan-Gurevich MiG-21MF	9712	969712		RA
☐ Mikoyan-Gurevich MiG-21MF	9713	969713		RA
☐ Mikoyan-Gurevich MiG-21PF	0306	760306		RA
☐ Mikoyan-Gurevich MiG-21PF	1215	761215		RA
☐ Mikoyan-Gurevich MiG-21PFM	4415	94A4415		PV
☐ Mikoyan-Gurevich MiG-21PFM	7908	94N7908		RA
☐ Mikoyan-Gurevich MiG-21R	1918	94R01918		RA
☐ Mikoyan-Gurevich MiG-21R	1922	94R01922		RA
☐ Mikoyan-Gurevich MiG-21R	1924	94R01924		RA
☐ Mikoyan-Gurevich MiG-21R	1502	94R1502		RA
☐ Mikoyan-Gurevich MiG-21R	1702	94R1702		RA
☐ Mikoyan-Gurevich MiG-21U-600	2419	662419		RA
☐ Mikoyan-Gurevich MiG-21UM	5026	516905026		RA
☐ Mikoyan-Gurevich MiG-21UM	3041	516913041		RA
☐ Mikoyan-Gurevich MiG-21UM	5166	516921066		RA
☐ Mikoyan-Gurevich MiG-21UM	3156	516931056		RA
☐ Mikoyan-Gurevich MiG-21UM	3741	516937041		RA
☐ Mikoyan-Gurevich MiG-21US	0441	04685141		RA
☐ Mikoyan-Gurevich MiG-21US	0646	06685146		RA
☐ Mikoyan-Gurevich MiG-23ML	2402	0390322402		RA
☐ Mil Mi-2	0716	5110716098		RA
☐ Mil Mi-2	7737	517737072		PV
☐ Mil Mi-2Ch	9426	519426105		RA
☐ Mil Mi-2P	5434	535434127		RA
☐ Mil Mi-8P	0837	10837		RA
☐ Mil Mi-8T	2832	020832		RA
☐ Mil Mi-8T	1932	10812		RA
☐ Mil Mi-8T	2032	10813		PV
☐ Northrop N-156T Talon (T-38A) (AT-38B)	65-10456	N.5875	On loan to STM.	–
☐ Sukhoi Su-7BKL	6504	6504		RA
☐ Sukhoi Su-7BM	5021	5021	May be 5321.	PV
☐ Sukhoi Su-7BM	5316	5316		RA
☐ Sukhoi Su-22M4	2219	22719		PV
☐ Sukhoi Su-22UM3K	7208	17532372308		RA
☐ Sukhoi Su-25K	1007	25508110007		PV
☐ Vykumny a Zkusebni Letecky Ustav (VZLU) HC-3	OK-06	3	OK-17, OK-VZB	RA
☐ Wytwornia Sprzetu Komunikacyjnego (WSK) SM-1Wb [Mil Mi-1M]	1043	401043		RA
☐ Yakovlev Yak-40	0823	9230823		PV

SLOVENIA

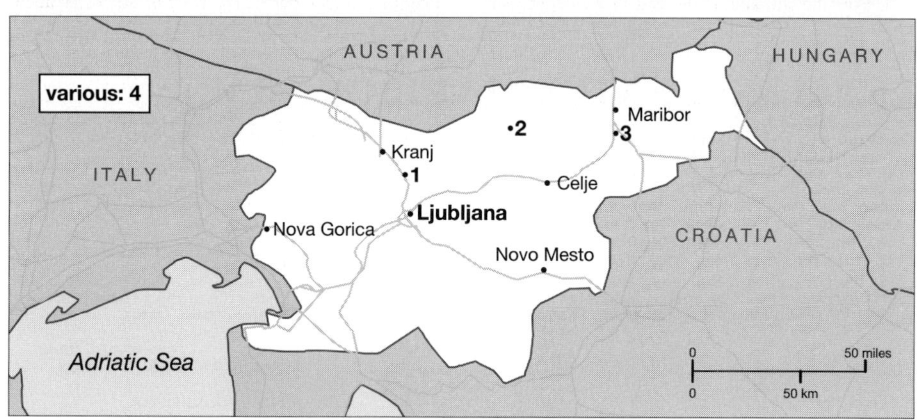

AERODROM LJUBLJANA (SLV1)

Address:	Zgornji Brnik 130a, SI-4210 Brnik.
Tel:	04-206-1000
Fax:	04-202-1220
Email:	info@lju-airport.si.
Admission:	On permanent view in terminal.
Location:	About 25 km north of Ljubljana.

Four aircraft are on show in the main terminal. The state technical museum was at one time responsible for setting up an aviation section but this has now been passed on to a new organisation. The quartet hanging above the main hall are part of these plans. A number of semi-derelict ex-Yugoslavian military machines are parked on the airport. In 1909/10 Edvard Rusjan of Gorica, with the help of his brother and friends, built seven powered aircraft. His first flew for about two hundred yards at a height of six feet on November 25th 1909. The Eda-I was a biplane, the II a triplane whilst the III and IV were improved versions of the I. The V was a replica of the Santos-Dumont Demoiselle and the VI a copy of the Blériot XI. Rusjan was killed in a crash at Belgrade on January 9th1911. In 1990 Albin Novak and Vlado Kikelj built a replica of the V which was flown by Novak on June 5th 1992. Ivo Sostaric designed many gliders in the post World War II period and two of these are on show.

TYPE	REG/SER	CON. NO.	PI/NOTES	STATUS
☐ Douglas DC-6B-1225A	YU-AFF	43553	PH-TFL, PH-DFL	PV
☐ Lilienthal Normal-Segelapparat (R)				PV
☐ North American NA-173 Sabre (F-86D)	146		(USAF), 14325	RA
☐ North American NA-173 Sabre (F-86D)	147		(USAF), 14307	RA
☐ Republic F-84G Thunderjet	914		51-10914	RA
☐ Rusjan Eda-V (R)				PV
☐ Soko 522	60162	62		RA
☐ Sostaric Jastreb 54	S5-1053	248	YU-3053	PV
☐ Sostaric Vrabec (R)				PV
☐ Sud SA.341L Gazelle	S5-HAA	028	12660 (Yugoslavia), T0-001, SL-HAA	PV

KOROSKI AEROKLUB (SLV2)

Address:	Mislinska Dobrava 10, SI-2303 Smartno.
Tel:	02-885-0500
Fax:	02-885-0510
Email:	info@aerodrom-sg.si
Admission:	By prior permission only.
Location:	About 12 km north of Sostanj.

An aero club was formed in the region in 1937 and flew a Zögling primary glider. After World War II a number of Sostaric designs were in use. At the current time two aircraft and eight sailplanes are used. A group of members has recently restored a Polikarpov Po-2. Last flown in 1968 the classic biplane took to the air again on June 18th 2005. Very few examples of the type are active and this one has visited a number of air shows. The three older sailplanes in the fleet are listed. A small display of photographs can be seen in the clubhouse.

TYPE	REG/SER	CON. NO.	PI/NOTES	STATUS
☐ Let L-13 Blanik	S5-7122	174425	YU-5311, SL-7122	RAA
☐ Let L-13 Blanik	S5-7123	174829	YU-5323, SL-7123	RAA
☐ Polikarpov Po-2	S5-MAY	0076	YU-CMJ	RAA
☐ Scheibe L-Spatz 55	S5-2000	537/2	D-5634	RAA

LETALSKI CENTER MARIBOR (SLV3)

Address: Letalski Cesta 30,
2204 Skoke.
Tel: 02-629-6206
Fax: 02-629-6207
Email: lcmaribor@siol.net
Admission: By prior permission only.
Location: About 10 km south of the town.

There has been an aero club in the area for many years. At the current time they operate a number of classic designs. The Thunderjet painted in a 'Thunderbirds' scheme is displayed near the terminal building. There are plans to set up a museum at the airfield which will trace the history of aviation in the region.

TYPE	REG/SER	CON. NO.	PI/NOTES	STATUS
☐ Piper PA-18-150 Super Cub	S5-DBV	18-7809161	N82096, YU-DCD, SL-DBV	RAA
☐ Republic F-84G Thunderjet	10660			PV
☐ Utva Fabrica Aviona 66	S5-DCP		51114 (Yugoslavia), YU-DLK, SL-DCP	RAA
☐ Utva Fabrica Aviona 75	S5-DCI		53171 (Yugoslavia), YU-DGF, SL-DCI	RAA
☐ Utva Fabrica Aviona Aero 3	S5-MBB		40199 (Yugoslavia), YU-CPX	RAA

VINTAGE/CLASSIC AIRCRAFT DESIGNATED FOR PRESERVATION (SLV4)

Admission: By prior permission only.
Location: At a number of airfields around the country.

There are plans for a museum at Maribor and a number of active powered aircraft and gliders owned by clubs and individuals have been designated as worthy of preservation. Those listed below are what I have been able to find out from contacts in the country. There are probably others to be considered.

TYPE	REG/SER	CON. NO.	PI/NOTES	STATUS
☐ Aero 145	S5-DAJ	19-11	YU-BBL	RAA
☐ Ikarus Kurir L	S5-MJT		50174 (Yugoslavia), YU-DAM	RAA
☐ Jacobs Kranich II (D.F.S. 108-30)	YU-5043	211		RA
☐ Jacobs Weihe (D.F.S. 108-68)	S5-1003			RAA
☐ Jacobs Weihe (D.F.S. 108-68)	S5-1008		YU-4115 (?)	RA
☐ Kunaver Autogyro				RA
☐ Letalski Institut Branko Ivanus Slovenija (LIBIS) 17				RA
☐ Letalski Institut Branko Ivanus Slovenija (LIBIS) 180	YU-CVR	291-11		RA
☐ Letalski Institut Branko Ivanus Slovenija (LIBIS) KB-14	S5-1112	252	YU-4112	RAA
☐ Letalski Institut Branko Ivanus Slovenija (LIBIS) Trener	YU-4161			RA
☐ Letalski Institut Branko Ivanus Slovenija (LIBIS) Trener	YU-4174			RA
☐ Letalski Institut Branko Ivanus Slovenija (LIBIS) Trener	YU-4188			RA
☐ Letalski Institut Branko Ivanus Slovenija (LIBIS) Trener	YU-4189			RA
☐ Letalski Institut Branko Ivanus Slovenija (LIBIS) Trener	YU-4190			RA
☐ Rusjan Eda-V (R)	S5-NBH			RAA
☐ Schneider Grunau Baby III (D.F.S. 108-66)	S5-1124		YU-2124	RAA
☐ Sostaric Cavka	S5-1183		YU-2183	RAA
☐ Sostaric Cavka	YU-2236			RA
☐ Sostaric Jastreb VUK-T	YU-4391			RA
☐ Sostaric Jastreb VUK-T	YU-4406			RA
☐ Sostaric Roda	YU-5220			RA
☐ Szybowcowy Zaklad Doswiadczalny S.Z.D.12 Mucha 100	S5-1000		YU-4147	RAA
☐ Vazduhoplovno Tehnicki Centar – Vrsac Delfin 3	YU-4145			RA
☐ Vazduhoplovno Tehnicki Centar – Vrsac Delfin 3	YU-4146			RA
☐ Vazduhoplovno Tehnicki Centar – Vrsac Delfin 3	S5-1135	F.BR.042	YU-4135	RAA

Only three Short Sealands survive and one is in the Belgrade museum.

Mounted in the Dukla Pass, this Czech built Il-10 is owned by the military museum in Svidnik.

This replica Rusjan Eda V will join a museum when its flying days are over. (Tomas Meze)

The Letalski Center at Maribor operate this Aero 3. (Tomas Meze)

This Spanish built Jungmann is on show at the Maestranza at Albacete.

Above: Talavera La Real is an important fighter base. This F-86F Sabre is parked near the headquarters building.

Two Aerotécnica AC-12's are in the Museo del Aire collection. One is on show at Cuatro Vientos.

SPAIN

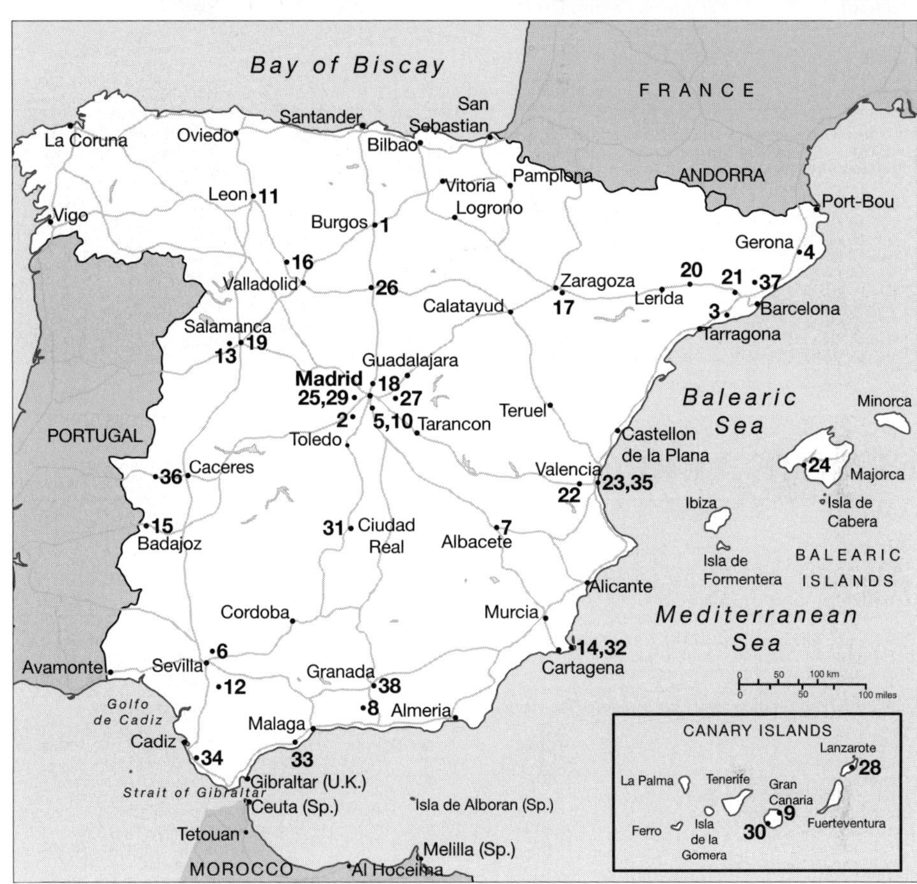

ASOCIACIÓN AEROCLASICA (SP1)

Address:	Aptdo.3025, 09080 Burgos.
Tel:	0947 222806
Admission:	By prior permission only.
Location:	At Villafria airport which is on the eastern outskirts of the town on the N.1.

This organisation is based at the former military field of Vilafria which now serves as the civil airport for Burgos. Under rebuild is the rare Piper L-14. Five prototypes were flown in early 1945 and production of the type started the following August. Only nine were completed with eight sold on the civilian market. The aircraft in the collection spent a period in Cuba before arriving in Spain in 1952. One of the trio of Autocrats is in flying condition and the other two require complete rebuilds. Two were exported from England in 1948 and the other in 1954. The Piper Cub was delivered new to Morocco and flew to Spain in 1962.

TYPE	REG/SER	CON. NO.	PI/NOTES	STATUS
☐ Auster J/1 Autocrat	EC-ACJ	1960	G-AHCF, EC-DAZ	RAC
☐ Auster J/1 Autocrat	EC-AIS	2190	G-AIGH	RAA
☐ Auster J/1 Autocrat	EC-ADG	2216	G-AJAL	RAC
☐ Piper J-5C Army Cruiser (L-14)	EC-AAP	5-3007	(45-55531), NC41594, CU-P18	RAC
☐ Piper PA-18A-150 Super Cub	EC-ASV	18-5408	F-DAFC, CN-TEC	RAA

ASOCIACIÓN DEPORTIVA JACOB 52 (SP2)

Address: Aerodromo Casarrubios 11, P.O. Box 152, 28600 Navalcarnero.
Email: jacob52@telefonua.net
Admission: By prior permission only.
Location: About 35 km south of Madrid off the A.5.

This group maintains a fleet of Yak-52s in airworthy condition. All of the aircraft were obtained from Lithuania and they regularly appear at shows around the country. The Yaks are painted in a variety of Soviet colour schemes to represent examples operated by DOSAAF in the former Soviet Union.

TYPE	REG/SER	CON. NO.	PI/NOTES	STATUS
☐ Yakovlev Yak-52	EC-HZQ	822102	(DOSAAF), LY-ROS	RAA
☐ Yakovlev Yak-52	EC-HYX	822105	(DOSAAF), LY-JDJ	RAA
☐ Yakovlev Yak-52	LY-IAP	822109	DOSAAF 36, LY-EDU	RAA
☐ Yakovlev Yak-52	EC-IAO	822808	DOSAAF 140, LY-NCE	RAA
☐ Yakovlev Yak-52	EC-IAI	833006	DOSAAF 16, LY-CRI	RAA
☐ Yakovlev Yak-52	EC-IAS	833312	DOSAAF 66, LY-CEO	RAA
☐ Yakovlev Yak-52	EC-IAL	833903	DOSAAF 147, LY-RON	RAA
☐ Yakovlev Yak-52	EC-IAN	844310	DOSAAF 55, LY-IBL	RAA
☐ Yakovlev Yak-52	EC-IAM	844504	DOSAAF 79, LY-TRO	RAA
☐ Yakovlev Yak-52	EC-IAJ	855705	DOSAAF 55, LY-KGB	RAA
☐ Yakovlev Yak-52	EC-IAK	880510	DOSAAF 43, LY-DER	RAA

CENTRE AERI (SP3)

Address: Avinguda de l'Aragui, 08800 Vilanova la Geltró.
Tel: 093 815 4481
Fax: 093 815 0475
Admission: By prior permission only.
Location: About 2 km west of the town off the old C.246 Barcelona to Valls road.

This group, which started as the Catalonian branch of the Museo del Aire, was established in 1981. Premises were acquired and workshops and a display area were set up. Civil and military aircraft are on show with a number parked on the roof of the building. The story of aviation in the region is told with photographs, documents and models. Some of the aircraft will eventually go to the new museum planned by the Parc Aéronautic de Catalunya. The site also serves as a training centre for airframe and engine fitters.

TYPE	REG/SER	CON. NO.	PI/NOTES	STATUS
☐ Aerotécnica AC-12	Z.2-11	11	On loan from M.A.	PV
☐ Beech A23-24 Musketeer Super	EC-BJG	MA-74	D-EMNY	PV
☐ Construcciones Aeronáuticas (CASA) 1.131E [Bücker Bü 131 Jungmann]				PV
☐ Hispano HA.200D Saeta	A.10B-45	20/51	E.14B-45, C.10B-45	PV
☐ Let L-13 Blanik	EC-CYT	026646		PV
☐ North American NA-168 Texan (T-6G)	E.16-97	168-478	49-3364 – on loan from MA.	PV
☐ North American NA-191 Sabre (F-86F)	C.5-71	191-414	52-4718 – on loan from MA.	PV

COL-LECCIÓ D'AUTOMÒBILS DE SALVADOR CLARET (SP4)

Address: Ctra. Nacional II, Km.698, 17410-Sils-Girona.
Tel: 0972 853036
Fax: 0972 853502
Email: casc@museoautomobilsclaret.com
Admission: Daily 1000-1300 1600-1900.
Location: About 85 km north west of Barcelona off the A.7.

The origins of this collection go back to 1950 when Salvador Claret acquired a 1923 Ford Model T. As he bought more cars he decided to open a museum and a large exhibition hall was built. Now there are more than one hundred and seventy vehicles on show from an 1883 Merry Weather up to cars from the 1980s. A number of engines and gearboxes are displayed to show technical developments in these areas. There are also motorcycles and components to be seen along with trophies and posters. The small aeronautical section has a 750 hp Hispano-Suiza engine. The Rearsby built Autocrat was sold to Spain in the summer of 1955.

TYPE	REG/SER	CON. NO.	PI/NOTES	STATUS
☐ Auster J/1 Autocrat	EC-ALD	1967	G-AGXS	PV

COLECCIÓN CONSTRUCCIONES AERONÁUTICAS – MADRID (SP5)

Address:	Avda. De John Lennon, Getafe, 28906 Madrid.
Tel:	091 624 2642
Fax:	091 624 2642
Email:	Cgt.de@airbus.com
Admission:	By prior permission only.
Location:	At the Getafe factory which is about 15 km south of Madrid west of the N IV.

The company was formed in 1923 and over the years has produced many types under licence as well as a variety of original designs. Five aircraft are displayed around the grounds of the Getafe factory. The Azor twin engined transport first flew in September 1955 and two prototypes and twenty production examples were built. The last were retired in the early 1980s. The Aviojet trainer made its maiden flight in June 1977 and now over one hundred and fifty have been delivered to several countries. The type replaced the Saeta in Spanish service. Two variants are in the collection. The Hispano company was taken over in 1972. C.A.S.A. partly built sixty two Northrop F-5s for the Air Force and the type has recently been withdrawn from service in Spain.

TYPE	REG/SER	CON. NO.	PI/NOTES	STATUS
☐ Construcciones Aeronáuticas (CASA) C-101CC Aviojet	EC-DVQ	107		RA
☐ Construcciones Aeronáuticas (CASA) C-101DD Aviojet	EC-DUJ	98		RA
☐ Construcciones Aeronáuticas (CASA) C-207C Azor	T.7-19	19		RA
☐ Hispano HA.200D Saeta	A.10B-49	20/55	E.10B-49, C.10B-49	RA
☐ Northrop N-156A Freedom Fighter (SF-5A)	A.9-042	2042	C.9-042	RA

COLECCIÓN CONSTRUCCIONES AERONÁUTICAS – SEVILLA (SP6)

Address:	Aeropuerto Nacional San Pablo, 41007 Sevilla.
Tel:	095 444 9080
Email:	sevilla@aerotec.es
Admission:	By prior permission only.
Location:	About 10 km north east of the city on the N.IV.

The company was originally set up in the city in 1925. Both indigenous designs and types built under licence were produced. Three aircraft are preserved at this factory which has serviced and modified many types in recent years. They have been restored and are maintained by a group of volunteers. The T-33 was moved from nearby Tablada and many Phantoms were overhauled at the site.

TYPE	REG/SER	CON. NO.	PI/NOTES	STATUS
☐ Hispano HA.220D Super Saeta	A.10C-112	22/117	C.10C-112	RA
☐ Lockheed 580 (T-33A)	E.15-54	580-8392	53-5033	RA
☐ McDonnell M.98DF Phantom II (RF-4C)	CR.12-51	1352	65-0851	RA

COLECCIÓN DE LA BASE AÉREA ALBACETE (SP7)

Address:	Base Aérea de Albacete, 02071 Albacete.
Tel:	0967 223 450
Fax:	06722 38 28
Admission:	By prior permission only.
Location:	About 6 km south of the town off the N 301.

A civilian flying school was set up at Albacete in 1928 to train pilots for airline service. Avro 504s and Bristol Fighters were used until the site closed in 1932. The installations were maintained and in June 1936 Republican forces took over the field. A variety of units were in residence over the next thirty years. Transport squadrons flew the DC-3 from 1962 until the early 1970s when they transferred to Villanubla. Ala 14 was set up to operate the F.1 Mirage and the first aircraft arrived in May 1975. With the closure of Manises in 1999 all the Mirages are now based here. Two have been put on show and both carry false markings. The field will be home to squadrons flying the Eurofighter Typhoon when it enters Spanish service in 2008/9. Also on the site is the Albacete Maestranza which services the Canadair CL-215, the CASA 101 and the Mirage. A volunteer team built the flyable replica of the Cierva C.30A which is now at the Museo del Aire.

TYPE	REG/SER	CON. NO.	PI/NOTES	STATUS
☐ Construcciones Aeronáuticas (CASA) 1.131E [Bücker Bü 131 Jungmann]	'E.3B-521'		E.3B-174	RAX
☐ Construcciones Aeronáuticas (CASA) C-101EB Aviojet	'E.25-22'	04-004	E.25-04	RAX
☐ Dassault Mirage F.1EDA	'C.14-01'	588	QA80 (Qatar), C.14C-82	PVX
☐ Dassault Mirage F.1M (F.1CE)	'C.14C-91'		C.14-33	RAX
☐ Lockheed 580 (T-33A)	E.15-30	580-9177	54-1546	PV

COLECCIÓN DE LA BASE AÉREA ARMILLA (SP8)

Address:	Base Aérea de Armilla, 18100 Armilla.
Tel:	05857 14 61
Fax:	05857 14 86
Admission:	By prior permission only.
Location:	About 5 km south west of Granada on the A 338.

This helicopter base has three rotary wing types on display. A Spanish built Jungmann was rebuilt a few years ago and placed on show. Inside the main building is an interesting display of memorabilia, photographs and models tracing significant events in Spanish military aviation.

TYPE	REG/SER	CON. NO.	PI/NOTES	STATUS
☐ Bell 205 Iroquois (UH-1H)	HE.10B-53	13553	73-22070, EC-STM, Z.10B-53	RA
☐ Bell 47G-2 Sioux (H-13H) (OH-13H)	'HE.7B-14'	2152	57-6223, HE.7A-48	RAX
☐ Construcciones Aeronáuticas (CASA) 1.131E [Bücker Bü 131 Jungmann]	'E3B-001'			RAX
☐ Hughes 269A-1	HE.20-15	1280754		RA

COLECCIÓN DE LA BASE AÉREA GANDO (SP9)

Address:	Jede del Ala 46, Base Aérea de Gando, 35230 Las Palmas.
Tel:	028 57 43 80
Fax:	028 57 40 08
Admission:	By prior permission only.
Location:	In the northern part of Gran Canaria.

In 1924 three Breguet 19s and a Dornier Wal flew from Morocco to Gando to show the gratitude of the military to the residents of the Canary Isles who had raised funds to purchase aircraft. The site was developed and has been used by a variety of types over the years. Currently in residence is a fighter squadron operating F-18s and a transport unit flying the Fokker F.27 Troopships and AS.332B Super Pumas.

TYPE	REG/SER	CON. NO.	PI/NOTES	STATUS
☐ Hispano HA.220D Super Saeta	A.10B-79	20/85		RA
☐ North American NA-168 Texan (T-6G)	'C.6.107'	168-604	49-3470, E.16-107	RAX
☐ Northrop N-156A Freedom Fighter (SF-5A)	C.9-048	2048		RA

COLECCIÓN DE LA BASE AÉREA GETAFE (SP10)

Address:	Ala 35/ Plana Mayor, Plaza Coronel Polanco, 28902 Getafe.
Tel:	091 681 9161 ext 3444
Email:	jcorrochano@eamde.es
Admission:	By prior permission only.
Location:	About 15 km south of Madrid west of the N IV.

Getafe airfield was opened in the early 1920s with the founding of the CASA company. The air force set up base on the field and it was headquarters to fighter and reconnaissance wings. In recent years transport units have operated from the site. Three preserved aircraft are parked around the camp which still has many early buildings. The prototype Azor is close to the main gate and is surrounded by a number of tails from other types. The Skymaster is currently parked on the ramp and the Super Saeta trainer has recently been put on show.

TYPE	REG/SER	CON. NO.	PI/NOTES	STATUS
☐ Construcciones Aeronáuticas (CASA) C-207A Azor	T.7-1	1		RA
☐ Douglas DC-4 Skymaster (C-54E)	T.4-8	27313	44-9087, N88884	RA
☐ Hispano HA.220D Super Saeta	A.10C-110	22/115	C.10C-110 – outside base.	PV

COLECCIÓN DE LA BASE AÉREA LEÓN (SP11)

Address:	Aeródromo Militar de León, 24071 Virgen del Camino.
Tel:	087 30 20 84
Fax:	087 30 04 35
Admission:	By prior permission only.
Location:	About 6 km south west of the town off the N 120.

Opened in 1929 this base housed Breguet XIXs during the 1930s. There was also an aircraft repair workshop on the field. During the civil war it became the centre of operations for the northern front after its capture by the Nationalists. Assembly of German aircraft was carried out in the hangars. The Air Academy was established in 1939 and four years later it moved to San Javier. From 1950 to the early 1990s the Specialists School of the Air Force was housed at the site. Currently in residence is the Basic Academy of the Air Force which trains personnel in a variety of trades including engines, airframes and avionics. The preserved aircraft are displayed around the site and there is an interesting collection of engines in one of the workshops.

TYPE	REG/SER	CON. NO.	PI/NOTES	STATUS
☐ Hispano HA.200D Saeta	C.10B-70	20/76	E.14B-70, C.10B-70, A.10B-70	PV
☐ Lockheed 580 (T-33A)	E.15-36	580-1379	57-0650	RA
☐ Lockheed 580 (T-33A)	E.15-49	580-7004	51-9220	RA
☐ Lockheed 580 (T-33A)	E.15-22	580-9079	53-5740	PV
☐ McDonnell M.98DJ Phantom II (F-4C)	C.12-01	1289	64-0884	RA
☐ North American NA-168 Texan (T-6G)	E.16-89	168-457	49-3343	RA
☐ North American NA-176 Sabre (F-86F)	C.5-1	176-125	51-13194	RA
☐ North American NA-227 Sabre (F-86F)	C.5-107	227-166	55-3981	RA

COLECCIÓN DE LA BASE AÉREA MORÓN (SP12)

Address:	Base Aérea de Morón, Ctra. Morón-Sevilla, 41530 Morón de la Frontera.
Tel:	05485 10 50
Fax:	05484 12 20
Admission:	By prior permission only.
Location:	About 45 km south east of Sevilla on the A 360.

Construction of the first airfield at Morón started in 1940 and the site was home to a fighter training school using Fiat CR.32s. During the 1950s a bomber wing flying Heinkel 111s was in residence and in 1959 this was replaced by a fighter unit with Sabres. A squadron of Northrop F-5s arrived in 1970. Ala 11 is now in residence and this serves as the OCU for the Typhoon. In the early 1990s a new field was built by the Americans. The original hangars and other buildings can be seen just to the east of the present base.

TYPE	REG/SER	CON. NO.	PI/NOTES	STATUS
☐ Grumman G-64 Albatross (SA-16A) (HU-16A)	AN.1B-13	G-237	51-7184	RA
☐ Hispano HA.200D Saeta	A.10B-52	20/58	E.14B-52, C.10B-52	RA
☐ North American NA-193 Sabre (F-86F)	C.5-231	193-36	52-5307	RA
☐ Northrop N-156A Freedom Fighter (SRF-5A)	AR.9-060	2060	CR.9-060	RA

COLECCIÓN DE LA BASE AÉREA SALAMANCA-MATACAN (SP13)

Address:	Grupo Escuelas Matacán 74, 378983 Matacán .
Tel:	0923 306 373
Admission:	By prior permission only.
Location:	About 15 km east of the town off the N.501.

After pilots have been trained at the academy at San Javier they move on to specialist units for their fifth year. The unit at Matacán is for those selected for multi-engine conversion. A squadron flying the Aviojet is also part of the wing. Two trainers are parked by the gate. They have recently been joined by the C-47, a type flown from the base for many years. This aircraft was sold by the Air Force in the 1970s and has been bought back.

TYPE	REG/SER	CON. NO.	PI/NOTES	STATUS
☐ Douglas DC-3A-467 Skytrain (TC-47B) (C-47D)	T.3-47	15986/32734	44-76402, N86441, T.3-47, EC-BUG	RA
☐ Lockheed 580 (T-33A)	E.15-25	580-9099	53-5760 – may be c/n 580-8826 53-5487.	RA
☐ North American NA-88 Texan (AT-6D) (SNJ-5)	E.16-122	88-16754	42-84973, Bu84893	RA

COLECCIÓN DE LA BASE AÉREA SAN JAVIER (SP14)

Address:	Base Aérea de San Javier, 30730 San Javier.
Tel:	0968 570 100
Fax:	06857 04 90
Admission:	By prior permission only.
Location:	About 5 km south east of the town which is about 45 km south east of Murcia.

A new base for both floatplanes and landplanes was set up by the Naval Air Service in 1928. At the end of the Civil War the newly formed Air Force took over all naval aerodromes. In 1943 it was proposed that the Air Force Academy should move to the field and the transfer from León was completed in 1945. The preserved aircraft are located along the drive from the main gate to the headquarters building.

TYPE	REG/SER	CON. NO.	PI/NOTES	STATUS
☐ Beech A45 Mentor (T-34A)	E.17-25	X.107		RA
☐ Construcciones Aeronáuticas (CASA) 1.131E [Bücker Bü 131 Jungmann]	E.3B-75			RA
☐ Hispano HA.200A Saeta (HA.200R1)	'E.14-12'	20/20	A.10A-12	RAX
☐ Lockheed 580 (T-33A)	E.15-27	580-9175	54-1544 – tail from c/n 580-8504 53-5165, E.15-27.	RA
☐ North American NA-182 Texan (T-6G)	E.16-199	182-778	51-15091	RA
☐ North American NA-191 Sabre (F-86F)	C.5-62			RA

COLECCIÓN DE LA BASE AÉREA TALAVERA (SP15)

Address:	Base Aérea Talavera La Real, 06050 Talavera la Real.
Tel:	024 25 11 11
Fax:	024 44 16 69
Admission:	By prior permission only.
Location:	About 10 km east of Badajoz north of the N.V.

Three aircraft are preserved at this important fighter base. The resident unit flew the Sabre for many years and used the T-33 for training and communications duties. Upgraded versions of the SRF-5B are still in service.

TYPE	REG/SER	CON. NO.	PI/NOTES	STATUS
☐ Lockheed 580 (T-33A)	'E.15-1/E.73-1'	580-8764	53-5425, E.15-60	RAX
☐ North American NA-176 Sabre (F-86F)	'C.5-199'	176-170	51-13239, C.5-2	RAX
☐ Northrop N-156A Freedom Fighter (SF-5A)	A.9-041	1007		RA

COLECCIÓN DE LA BASE AÉREA VILLANUBLA (SP16)

Address:	Base Aérea de Villanubla, 47620 Villanubla.
Tel:	0983-560-345
Fax:	0983-560-379
Admission:	By prior permission only.
Location:	About 10 km north west of Valladolid on the N 601.

Construction of this airfield started in the spring of 1938 and it was officially opened later in the year. The first aircraft to land was a Breguet XIX and for a period a scheduled service from Seville to Majorca was flown using Junkers Ju 52/3ms. A fighter pilot's school, operating Fiat CR-32s and Romeo Ro 41s, arrived in December 1938. Civil flights were allowed again in 1946 and over the next few years the Air Force flew Heinkel He 111Es, North American T-6s, Lockheed T-33s and Hispano HA-200 Saetas. The runway was extended in this period. In 1974 a transport wing (Ala 37) moved in from Albacete. The de Havilland Caribou was used until the CASA Aviocar arrived in the early 1990s. The three preserved aircraft are located on the parade ground.

TYPE	REG/SER	CON. NO.	PI/NOTES	STATUS
☐ De Havilland D.H.C.4A Caribou (AC-1) (CV-2A) (C-7A)	T.9-23	14	60-3763	RA
☐ Hispano HA.200D Saeta	A.10B-53	20/59	E.14B-53, C.10B-53	RA
☐ North American NA-121 Texan (AT-6D) (SNJ-5)	C.6-152	121-41843	44-81086, Bu90992	RA

COLECCIÓN DE LA BASE AÉREA ZARAGOZA (SP17)

Address:	Jefe del Ala 31, Base Aérea de Zaragoza, 50071 Zaragoza.
Tel:	0976 710 970
Fax:	0976 780 697
Admission:	By prior permission only.
Location:	About 5 km west of the city on the N 125.

In 1937 the first flights took place from an airfield at Garranpillos which is just north of the present site. This was used by civilian traffic and became a military base during the Civil War. After World War II plans for a new base were put forward for use by civil and military aircraft. Some of the original buildings were incorporated into the new site. The United States Air Force occupied the south side of this vast field from 1953 until 1992 and one of the preserved Sabres is mounted in this area. The Spanish Air Force operated Sabres from 1956 until the early 1970s. At the present time a fighter unit flying F-18s is in residence along with a transport squadron operating a number of C-130 Hercules. There is also a civil terminal on the airfield.

TYPE	REG/SER	CON. NO.	PI/NOTES	STATUS
☐ Lockheed 580 (T-33A)	E.15-50	580-8177	52-9871	RA
☐ North American NA-191 Sabre (F-86F)	C.5-70	191-379	52-4683	RA
☐ North American NA-227 Sabre (F-86F)	'FU-406'	227-156	55-3971, C.5-143	RAX

COLECCIÓN DE LA BASE EJÉRCITO DE TIERRA COLMENAR VIEJO (SP18)

Address:	Fuerzas Aeromoviles del Ejército de Tierra, 28770 Colmenar Viejo.
Tel:	091 845 2750
Fax:	091 845 0340
Admission:	By prior permission only.
Location:	On the M 325 about 3 km north east of the town which is 35 km north of Madrid.

This base houses the headquarters of the Spanish Army's Aviation section, a major helicopter overhaul facility and active units. The service was set up in 1965 and its initial equipment was nine Bell OH-13s and six UH-1s. Two of these types are preserved just inside the main gate along with an Agusta built Jet Ranger. The Bölkow 105 entered service with Army in late 1979. The GSH is a cannon equipped version designed for Spanish use.

TYPE	REG/SER	CON. NO.	PI/NOTES	STATUS
☐ Agusta-Bell 206A-1 Jet Ranger	'HR.12B-15'	8197	Z.12-1, HR.12A-1	RAX
☐ Bell 47G-3B Sioux (OH-13S)	'HE.7B-20'	3902	65-13006, HE.7B-26	RAX
☐ Bell 204 Iroquois (UH-1C)	HU.8B-10	3110	65-12764	RA
☐ Bölkow BO 105C	HE.15-6	S.2		RA
☐ Bölkow BO 105GSH	HR.15-18	S.452		RA

COLECCIÓN MONTERO (SP19)

Address:	Salamanca.
Admission:	By prior permission only.
Location:	In the town near the football stadium.

This large scrapyard which has handled aircraft for many years has put three on display. The Dakota was sold to Warbirds of Great Britain in the early 1980s but never made it to the United Kingdom. The Sioux was one of many operated by both the Air Force and the Army from the early 1960s up to 1990.

TYPE	REG/SER	CON. NO.	PI/NOTES	STATUS
☐ Bell 47G-2 Sioux (H-13H) (OH-13H)	HE.7A-39	2350	58-5327	PV
☐ Cessna 180E	EC-AXF	18051129	N2629Y	PV
☐ Douglas DC-3A-456 Skytrain (C-47A)	T.3-28	9914	42, 24052, NC65282, N44V, T.3-28, (G-BHUA)	PV

COLECCIÓN SANT PERE DELS ARQUELLS (SP20)

Address: 25215 Sant Pere dels Arquells
Admission: By prior permission only.
Location: About 12 km east of Tarrega on Route 50.

Reports have been received of three jets with a private collector. The MiG-23 arrived from Czechoslovakia and the pair of MiG-15s from the Ogivetar Museum at Alsónémedi in Hungary.

TYPE	REG/SER	CON. NO.	PI/NOTES	STATUS
☐ Mikoyan-Gurevich MiG-15bis	'1977'		(Hungary)	RAX
☐ Mikoyan-Gurevich MiG-21F-13	'1981'		(Hungary)	RAX
☐ Mikoyan-Gurevich MiG-23ML	4855	0390324855	In Czech markings.	RA

FUNDACIÓ PARC AERONÁUTIC DE CATALUNYA (SP21)

Address: Aeroport de Sabadell,
08205 Sabadell.
Tel: 093-712-4273
Fax: 093-720-6018
Email: fpac@fpac.com
Admission: By prior permission only.
Location: About 15 km north of Barcelona off the A 18.

This organisation has been formed by the local clubs and private owners with the aim of establishing a collection of flyable vintage and classic aircraft. The Ranger powered Argus is one of the few still airworthy in Europe. Another type with not many in flying condition is the Macchi MB.308. The Kaydet has recently been acquired from a group in Sweden. Aircraft are joining the collection in numbers so there is scope for an excellent display. There are plans to construct an exhibition building which will trace the history of aviation in Catalunya. At the present time the group has mounted a display at the Centri Aerei and two aircraft are on show in the terminal at Barcelona El Prat Airport. One of these is a replica of the Hedilla monoplane which made its first flight at Barcelona-Palma on July 2nd 1916. This reproduction was built by members of the organisation and features a monocoque fuselage. The Mignet Pou-du-Ciel was constructed by former students of a local school in 1935. The aircraft was in store in the area for over fifty years and is fitted with an Aubier et Dunne engine. A Blériot XI replica is currently in the workshops. A French built Jodel D.112 is airworthy and the airframe of one of the sixty eight D.1190.S models built by Aerodifusion is in store awaiting restoration. The Phantom has recently joined the collection and other military types have been promised. Exhibitions of memorabilia are regularly staged in the region to raise awareness of the foundation.

TYPE	REG/SER	CON. NO.	PI/NOTES	STATUS
☐ Aerodiffusion Jodel D.1190-S				RA
☐ Aeronáutica Industrial (AISA) I-115	EC-CQO	7	E.9-7	RAA
☐ Aeronáutica Industrial (AISA) I-115	EC-DEI	53	E.9-53	RAA
☐ Aeronáutica Industrial (AISA) I-11B Peque	EC-BPT	214	L.8C-129	RAA
☐ Aeronáutica Industrial (AISA) P.E.38 [Schneider Grunau SG-38]				RA
☐ Beech A45 Mentor (T-34A)	EC-JKM	X-104	E.17-24, EC-750, EC-GXQ	RAA
☐ Bell 47G-2 Sioux (H-13H) (OH-13H)	HE.7A-56	1943	56-2231, EC-BZH – on loan from M.A.	RA
☐ Blériot XI (R)				RAC
☐ Boeing-Stearman A75N1 Kaydet (PT-17)	SE-BOF	75-862	41-802, N56561	RAA
☐ Cessna 170A	EC-AFB	19169	N9708A, N11B, F-OAGF	RA
☐ Construcciones Aeronáuticas (CASA) 1.131E [Bücker Bü 131 Jungmann]	EC-DAU	2103	E.3B-608	RAA
☐ Construcciones Aeronáuticas (CASA) 1.131E [Bücker Bü 131 Jungmann]	EC-FUU	2167	E.3B-554	RA
☐ Construcciones Aeronáuticas (CASA) 1.131E [Bücker Bü 131 Jungmann]	EC-FTZ	2170	E.3B-556	RAA
☐ Construcciones Aeronáuticas (CASA) C-127 [Dornier Do 27]	U.9-22	22		RA
☐ De Havilland D.H.82A Tiger Moth	T7328	83839	T7238,G-APPN	RAA
☐ Dornier Do 27A-5 (A-3)	EC-CHQ	445	PC+106, PC+221, 57+17, L.9-71, U.9-71	RAA
☐ Dornier Do 27B-1	'EC-PAC'	149	PC+106, PL+112, SA+721, SA+114, 55+30, U.9-61, EC-CFO	PVX
☐ Fairchild 24R9 Forwarder (UC-61K) (Argus III)	EC-GXP	R9-946	43-14982, HB708, OO-PET, EC-AEN	RAA
☐ Fairchild 24W41A Forwarder (C-61A) (UC-61A) (Argus II)	EC-AJZ	W41A-663	43-14697, FZ723, HB-EAP	RAC
☐ Hedilla Monocoque II (R)			At Barcelona Airport.	PV

TYPE	REG/SER	CON. NO.	PI/NOTES	STATUS
☐ Hispano HA.220D Super Saeta	EC-GZN	22/103	A.10C-98, C.10C-98	RAA
☐ Hispano HA.220D Super Saeta	A.10C.111	22/116	C.10C.111	PV
☐ Jodel D.112 Club				RAA
☐ Lockheed 580 (T-33A)	E.15-48	580-1491	57-0662 – tail from E.15-19 – on loan from MA.	PV
☐ Macchi MB.308	EC-AGM	5807/34	I-MACC	RA
☐ McDonnell M.98DE Phantom II (F-4C)	C.12-26	1233	64-0861	RA
☐ Mignet HM-14 Pou-du-Ciel			At Barcelona Airport.	PV
☐ North American NA-88 Texan (AT-6D) (Harvard III)	F-AZDU	88-14948	41-33931, EX959, 7509 (South Africa), H-9 (Belgium), F-BJBF, G-AZJD, F-WZDU	RAA
☐ Piper J-3C-65 Cub (L-4H)	EC-AKQ	11190	43-29899, HB-ONR	RAA
☐ Polikarpov I-15 (Scale R)				RAC
☐ Scheibe Bergfalke II				RAA
☐ Siebelwerke ATG (SIAT) 223K-1 Flamingo	EC-CGL	058		RAA
☐ Tipsy T.66 Nipper II	EC-AVH	63	OO-FOL	RAA
☐ Zlin Z-326A Akrobat	EC-AXA	861	EC-WXA	RAC
☐ Zlin Z-526A Akrobat	EC-BDS	1001	EC-WDS	RAA

FUNDACIÓN AERONÁUTICA DE LA COMUNIDAD VALENCIANA (SP22)

Address: Poligono Industrial La Cova,
Calle Maestrat 71,
46940 Manises.
Tel: 961 53 44 50
Fax: 961 52 56 97
Email: info@funaereacv.es
Admission: By prior permission only.
Location: About 8 km west of the city.

Founded in 2003 the foundation aims to preserve the history of local aviation and also to educate people in all aspects of the subject. Visits to air shows, military bases and factories have taken place. The fleet of active aircraft is growing and a restoration workshop has been established. One of the Peques is in flying condition and two more airframes are in store. The Spanish built Jungmeister is currently undergoing a major rebuild in the workshops. CASA completed around twenty five of the type and they were initially powered by the 160 h.p. Hirth in-line engine. The majority of those which survived the civil war were then re-engined with the Siemens radial. One of the group's aims is to establish an aviation museum in Valencia.

TYPE	REG/SER	CON. NO.	PI/NOTES	STATUS
☐ Aerodiffusion Jodel D.1190-S	EC-BEK	E-103		RAC
☐ Aeronáutica Industrial (AISA) I-11B Peque				RAC
☐ Aeronáutica Industrial (AISA) I-11B Peque				RAC
☐ Aeronáutica Industrial (AISA) I-11B Peque	EC-BUB		L.8C-77	RAA
☐ Construcciones Aeronáuticas (CASA) 1.131E [Bücker Bü 131 Jungmann]	EC-GIS	2229	E.3B-610	RAA
☐ Construcciones Aeronáuticas (CASA) 1.133C [Bücker Bü 133C Jungmeister]				RAC
☐ Dornier Do 27A-5 (A-3)	EC-CHN	408	PB+221, 56+94, L.9-68	RAA
☐ Hispano HA.200D Saeta	EC-IFJ	22/107	A.10C-102	RAA
☐ Let L-13 Blanik	EC-CGD	025522		RAC
☐ McDonnell M.98DE Phantom II (F-4C)				RA
☐ North American NA-182 Texan (T-6G)	EC-HYY	182-736	51-15049, F-BMJP, F-AZAS, F-WZBN, F-AZAS	RAA

FUNDACIÓN AERONÁUTICA GUADALQUIVIR (SP23)

Address: P.I. Malpesa,
Calle Industrial 66,
Salteras,
41909 Valencia
Tel: 955-708-233
Admission: By prior permission only.
Location: In the city.

This group has been formed with the aim of setting up an aeronautical museum in the area. Two Saetas arrived at their premises in the summer of 2005 to coincide with the fiftieth anniversary of the maiden flight of the type. The Spanish built Dornier Do 27 is under rebuild and the German airframe is being used for spares. The workshop is in an industrial estate and premises are being sought so that a display can be staged. The group has collected many items of memorabilia along with photographs, documents and models. For many years the Air Force had a base at nearby Manises when it closed the Mirage F.1s moved to Albacete.

TYPE	REG/SER	CON. NO.	PI/NOTES	STATUS
☐ Construcciones Aeronáuticas (CASA) C-127 [Dornier Do 27]	U.9-7	7		RAC
☐ Dornier Do 27B-1	D-EDRL	228	PF+110, PD+112, PK+104, PY+218, 55+81	RA
☐ Hispano HA.200D Saeta	A.10B-60	20/66	C.10B-60	RA
☐ Hispano HA.200D Saeta	A.10B-75	20/81	C.10B-75	RA

FUNDACIÓN AERONÁUTICA MALLORQUINA (SP24)

Address:	Aéropuerto San Bonet, 09009 Mallorca.
Tel:	097160-732297
Email:	informacion@fam-ib.org
Admission:	By prior permission only.
Location:	About 6 km north east of Palma de Mallorca on the C.713.

The group has been set up to promote all aspects of aviation in the islands. Visits to factories, air bases and shows on the mainland have taken place. The Peque is airworthy and visits a number of locations to generate interest. Just over two hundred examples were built with one hundred and twenty five supplied to the Air Force.

TYPE	REG/SER	CON. NO.	PI/NOTES	STATUS
☐ Aeronáutica Industrial (AISA) I-11B Peque	EC-BTM	106	L.8C-31	RAA

FUNDACIÓN INFANTE DE ORLEANS (SP25)

Address:	Apartado de Correos 116091, 28080 Madrid.
Tel:	91-321-1657
Fax:	91-321-1659
Email:	fio@ctv.es
Admission:	September-June Tuesday-Saturday 1100-1400.
Location:	At the civil airport of Cuatro Vientos which is about 12 km south west of Madrid. About 15 km south of Madrid west of the N IV.

In 1984 a historical section of the Aeroclub J.L. Aresti was set up at Cuatro Vientos. This led, in 1989, to the establishment of the foundation with the aim of preserving vintage and classic aircraft in flying condition. The name honours Don Alfonso de Orleans y Borbón who was one of the pioneers of military aviation in Spain. A museum hangar was opened in 1990 and at the current time another is in use as a workshop and members of the fleet are also parked in adjacent hangars. Flying days now take place on the first Sunday of each month. The oldest aircraft is the 1928 Fleet 2 which was imported from Argentina where it had been used for training and glider towing since the mid-1930s. A fairly recent arrival is the Comper Swift which was active in England for almost seventy years. Permission has been obtained to paint the aircraft in the colours of the one flown by Fernando Loring on an epic flight from Madrid to Manila and back in 1933. The original Swift was probably destroyed in a bombing raid on Barajas Airport in October 1936. During restoration in England the Miles Falcon revealed what is thought to be its true identity. The aircraft was operated by the Basque air arm and inadvertently flew into a dogfight between Basque and Condor Legion aircraft. The German pilots thought they had encountered a new type of fighter and withdrew. Prior to the civil war there were at least four Klemm L.25s flying in civil hands. The group acquired the Swallow in 2001 to represent the German type. British Aircraft at Hanworth constructed just over one hundred examples of the low wing two seater in the late 1930s. The aircraft in the collection was rescued by the Northern Aircraft Preservation Society in the 1960s and then spent a period on show at East Fortune in Scotland. It was later restored to flying condition at Hamble. The Jungmeister was the mount of aerobatic pilot Jose Luis Aresti in the 1950s and 1960s and was regularly seen at airshows and competitions around Europe. The first jet is the Saeta which arrived in 1998. Several are now in flying condition with collections around the country. An exciting addition is the Polikarpov I-16. In order to help the Republican cause Russia supplied over one hundred and fifty of the stubby low wing fighter. At the end of the conflict the Nationalists continued production of the type. The last active example was withdrawn at Morón in 1953. Six I-16s were recovered from crash sites in Russia and restored in the country for the Alpine Fighter Collection in New Zealand. Now one has returned to Spain where the fighter first saw combat. Plans for a transfer to a new purpose built facility at Getafe have been approved and the short move should occur in 2007. The complex will include exhibition hangars, workshops and a museum. Development around Cuatro Vientos has cast doubts upon the future of the airfield which is slowly being absorbed into the city.

TYPE	REG/SER	CON. NO.	PI/NOTES	STATUS
☐ Aerodiffusion Jodel D.1190.S	EC-BSS	E.121		PVA
☐ Aeronáutica Industrial (AISA) I-11B Peque	EC-BKF	99	L.8C-14	S
☐ Aeronáutica Industrial (AISA) I-11B Peque	EC-BKH	101	L.8C-16	PVA
☐ Aeronáutica Industrial (AISA) I-115	EC-DDN	196	E.9-196	PVA
☐ Aeronáutica Industrial (AISA) P.E.38 [Schneider Grunau SG-38]				PV
☐ Beech D18S Expeditor (C-45H)	EC-ASJ	AF-752	52-10822, N9962Z - built as C18S (AT-7) c/n 4191 42-43462	PVA

☐ Beech A45 Mentor (T-34A)	EC-GMD	X.100	(USAF).E.17-20	RAC
☐ Boeing-Stearman E75 Kaydet (PT-13D) (N2S-5)	EC-FNM	75-8089	42-109056, Bu38468, 0325 (Argentina), LV-HDT, EC-973	PVA
☐ British Aircraft L.25c Swallow II	EC-IMP	475	G-AEVZ	PVA
☐ British Aircraft Eagle 2	G-AFAX	138	G-AFAX, VH-ACN	PVA
☐ Bücker Bü 133C Jungmeister	EC-ALP	1023	35-17, ES.1-17	PVA
☐ Comper C.L.A.7 Swift	'EC-AAT'	S.32/5	G-ABUU, EC-HAM	PVAX
☐ Construcciones Aeronáuticas (CASA) 1.131E [Bücker Bü 131 Jungmann]	EC-AHL		EE.3-205	PVA
☐ Construcciones Aeronáuticas (CASA) 1.131E [Bücker Bü 131 Jungmann]	EC-YTC		Built from spares – in false Luftwaffe colours as 'SB+BZ'	PVA
☐ Construcciones Aeronáuticas (CASA) 1.131E [Bücker Bü 131 Jungmann]	EC-ETT	1010/2123	E.3B-397	PVA
☐ Construcciones Aeronáuticas (CASA) 1.131E [Bücker Bü 131 Jungmann]	EC-ERP	1027	E.3B-321	PVA
☐ Construcciones Aeronáuticas (CASA) 1.131E [Bücker Bü 131 Jungmann]	EC-ERO	2012	E.3B-408	PVA
☐ Construcciones Aeronáuticas (CASA) 1.131E [Bücker Bü 131 Jungmann]	EC-DID	2119	E.3B-119	PVA
☐ Construcciones Aeronáuticas (CASA) 1.131E [Bücker Bü 131 Jungmann]	EC-GIN	2208	E.3B-591	PVA
☐ Construcciones Aeronáuticas (CASA) 1.131E [Bücker Bü 131 Jungmann]	EC-EFT	2226	E.3B-607	PVA
☐ De Havilland D.H.60X Moth	G-EBXU	627		PVA
☐ De Havilland D.H.60GIII Moth Major	EC-INK	5095	G-ACXK	PVA
☐ De Havilland D.H.C.1 Chipmunk 22A (T.10)	G-TRIC	C1/0080	WB635, G-AOSZ	PVA
☐ Dornier Do 27B-1	'L.9-60'	129	PB+105, PB+108, DE+391, MA+391, 55+21, EC-CFN	PVAX
☐ Fleet 2	EC-EYD	324	LV-PBC, LV-ZCD, EC-500	PVA
☐ Focke-Wulf Fw 44J Stieglitz	LV-YZP	143		PVA
☐ Hispano HA.200D Saeta	EC-DXR	20/56	E.14B-50, C.10B-50, A.10B-50	PVA
☐ Miles M.3C Falcon Six	EC-ACB	231	G-ADLS Probable identity but could be M.3A c/n 197 EC-W48, EC-BDD, EC-CAO, EC-ACB. The aircraft was delivered to F.I.O. as EC-ACB but examination during rebuild in England points to c/n 231.	PVA
☐ North American NA-182 Texan (T-6G)	EC-DUM	182-591	51-14904, 114904 (France), E.16-198	PVA
☐ North American NA-197 Texan (T-6G) [Built as NA-88 (AT-6D)]	EC-DUN	197-20	42-85931, 52-8216, 28216 (France), E.16-201	PVA
☐ Noorduyn Norseman VI (C-64A) (UC-64A)			Due from Argentina	RAC
☐ Piper J-3C-65 Cub (L-4H)	EC-GQE	10780	43-29489, G-AKAA	RAA
☐ Piper J-3C-65 Cub (L-4J)	EC-AJY	12965	44-80669, HB-OCM	PVA
☐ Piper PA-20-125 Pacer	EC-AGH	20-648		PVA
☐ Piper PA-24-260 Comanche			Possibly 24-4071 E.30-1 or 24-4075 E.30-2.	RAC
☐ Pitts S-2A Special	EC-DHU	2181		RAA
☐ Polikarpov I-16 (FSM)	'C.8-25'/'CM-260'			PVX
☐ Polikarpov I-16 tip 24 (tip 5)	'CM-249'	2421039	239, ZK-JJC	PVAX
☐ Stinson V-76 Sentinel (L-5)			Due from Argentina.	RAC
☐ Stinson 108-3 Voyager	EC-BTK	108-4226	N6226M	PVA
☐ Stinson 108-3 Voyager	EC-ADY	108-4344	N6344M	S
☐ Thunder Ax.6-56 Hot Air Balloon	EC-CPY	008		PV
☐ Zlin Z-326 Trener Master (Z-526F)	EC-BVJ	1122		S

FUNDACIÓN VARA DE REY (SP26)

Address:	Aerodromo Nava, 40529 Corral de Ayllón.
Tel:	016 616041
Admission:	By prior permission only.
Location:	About 5 km west of the town which is off the N.110 about 100 km north of Madrid.

The airfield was used extensively in the Civil War. The foundation is named after Colonel Carlos Martinez Vara de Rey, a famous monarchist pilot of the time. In 1936 he immobilised a Douglas DC-2 at Tablada by firing a shotgun into one of the engines. The local manager for the airline LAPE had been ordered to fill two DC-2s with bombs and attack Tetuán. He later flew Heinkel He 46s from León. The Slingsby Swallow first took to the air in 1957 and one hundred and six were completed before the 1968 factory fire which destroyed several more. Several aircraft in the fleet are in store and will be restored when time permits.

TYPE	REG/SER	CON. NO.	PI/NOTES	STATUS
☐ Construcciones Aeronáuticas (CASA) 1.131E [Bücker Bü 131 Jungmann]	EC-DAH	2041	E.3B-273	RA
☐ Construcciones Aeronáuticas (CASA) 1.131E [Bücker Bü 131 Jungmann]	EC-GIP	2171	E.3B-557	RA
☐ Construcciones Aeronáuticas (CASA) 1.131E [Bücker Bü 131 Jungmann]	EC-DAQ	2183	E.3B-578	RA

☐ Construcciones Aeronáuticas (CASA) 1.131E [Bücker Bü 131 Jungmann]	EC-DAS	2186	E.3B-583	RA
☐ Construcciones Aeronáuticas (CASA) 1.131E [Bücker Bü 131 Jungmann]	EC-GIR	2239	E.3B-620	RA
☐ Construcciones Aeronáuticas (CASA) C-127 [Dornier Do 27]	U.9-45	45		RA
☐ Dornier Do 27A-1	EC-CFM	122	PA+114, AS+916, AC+916, 55+15, L.9-59	RAA
☐ Dornier Do 27A-1	EC-CFU	324	JA+381, 56+43, L.9-66	RA
☐ Dornier Do 27A-5 (A-3)	EC-CHO	428	PK+220, 57+02, L.9-69	RA
☐ Dornier Do 27B-1	EC-CFQ	244	PG+106, GB+387, 55+86, L.9-63	RA
☐ Let L-13 Blanik	EC-CPJ	026033		RA
☐ Let L-13 Blanik	EC-CPK	026045		RAA
☐ Let L-13 Blanik	EC-CNM	026108		RA
☐ Let L-13 Blanik	EC-CYP	0266245		RAA
☐ Let L-13 Blanik	EC-BZC	174825		RA
☐ Let L-13 Blanik	EC-CCB	175225		RAA
☐ Scheibe L-Spatz 55	EC-BFD	808		RAA
☐ Slingsby T.45 Swallow	EC-BHN	1549		RA
☐ Slingsby T.45 Swallow	EC-BHR	1552		RAA
☐ Slingsby T.45 Swallow	EC-BHV	1556		RA
☐ Slingsby T.45 Swallow	EC-AGZ	1614		RAA
☐ Slingsby T.45 Swallow	EC-AIA	1656		RA
☐ Société de Construcions D'Avions de Tourisme et D'Affaires (SOCATA) Rallye 180T	EC-DPI	3349	F-OGLA	RAD
☐ Szybowcowy Zaklad Doswiadczalny S.Z.D.30 Pirat	EC-CQE	S-03.39		RAA
☐ Szybowcowy Zaklad Doswiadczalny S.Z.D.30 Pirat	EC-CYX	S-07.24		RAA

MUSEO BASE AÉREA TORREJÓN (SP27)

Address:	Base Aérea de Torrejón, N- II Km.25, 28850 Torrejón de Ardoz.
Tel:	01660 37 10
Fax:	01660 37 20
Admission:	By prior permission only.
Location:	About 25 km east of Madrid just north of N II.

This large base opened on June 1st. 1957 and units of the United States Air Force were in residence until May 1993. The Ejercito del Aire also flew from the field using F-86F Sabres from 1959 until 1965 when they were replaced by the F-104G Starfighter. The F-4C Phantom entered service in March 1971 and these served until the early 1990s. The fighter squadrons now operate the McDonnell EF/A-18A Hornet. The first of these arrived in the late 1980s and several are undergoing upgrades to prolong their service life. Also on the field are the Canadair CL-215s used in countering forest fires, a transport unit for VIP flights and a squadron operating Electronic Counter Measures types. A small museum has been set up and the displays trace the history of the base and its units. On show are models, uniforms, components, engines, photographs and documents.

TYPE	REG/SER	CON. NO.	PI/NOTES	STATUS
☐ Construcciones Aeronáuticas (CASA) 352L [Junkers Ju 52/3m]	T.2B-246	137		RA
☐ Lockheed 580 (T-33A)	E.15-13	580-8419	53-5080 - tail from c/n 580-1490 57-0661, E.15-47.	RA
☐ McDonnell M.98DJ Phantom II (F-4C)	C.12-31	1229	64-0859 - By base golf course.	RA
☐ McDonnell M.98DJ Phantom II (F-4C)	C.12-36	1240	64-0864	RA
☐ McDonnell M.98DJ Phantom II (F-4C)	C.12-19	1257	64-0872	RA
☐ McDonnell M.98DJ Phantom II (F-4C)	C.12-02	1331	64-0900	RA
☐ North American NA-227 Sabre (F-86F)	'C.5-82'	227-167	55-3982, C.5-98	RAX

MUSEO DE AVIACION EN LANZAROTE (SP28)

Address:	Aeropuerto Guacimeta, 35510 Lanzarote.
Tel:	0928-846001 (Airport)
Admission:	Tuesday-Sunday 1000-1400.
Location:	Between Arrecife and Puerto del Carmen.

The airport on the island also serves as a military base. Construction of an airfield was approved in 1940 and it was completed in 1946. The first civil terminal has been restored as nearly as possible to original condition to house the museum. The exhibition opened in December 2005 and the displays are still being set up. Eleven rooms display artefacts which trace the aeronautical history of the Canary Islands. Parts of the control tower have the instruments and radios from the 1940s. Models, uniforms, photographs can be seen showing the development of the site. The Mirage has been put on display at the nearby Air Force camp.

TYPE	REG/SER	CON. NO.	PI/NOTES	STATUS
☐ Dassault Mirage F.1EDA	C.14C-75	553	(Qatar) – at Air Force Base.	RA

MUSEO DEL AIRE (SP29)

Address:	Carretera N-V Km 10.500, Cuatro Vientos, 28024 Madrid.
Tel:	91-509-1690
Fax:	91-710-6847
Admission:	Tuesday-Sunday 1000-1400.
Location:	On the N.V road about 10 km south west of Madrid.

Cuatro Vientos was the location of the first flying school of the Military Aviation Service. The site opened in 1911 and two Henri Farmans and a pair of Maurice Farman Longhorns were operated. The airfield has been in continuous use since then and is the appropriate location for the museum. During General Franco's rule rumours persisted about a collection of preserved aircraft inside the military base and in 1978 I was fortunate to get permission to view them. Around twenty machines were parked in a large hangar and several gliders were stored dismantled in an adjoining building. After Franco's death the decision was made to open on a regular basis and the museum was officially inaugurated on March 14th 1982. Since then progress has been rapid. The original museum hangar was refurbished and the area landscaped. Two new exhibition halls are now in use and workshops and storage buildings have also been constructed. Future plans envisage more hangars located on what is now the outside display area. With almost one hundred and eighty aircraft in the collection the museum is now one of the largest in Europe. The earliest aircraft on show is the Vilanova Acedo which is in essence a Spanish version of a Blériot XI. The pioneer of the autogyro, Juan de la Cierva, was part of the team which produced in 1912 at Cuatro Vientos the first Spanish designed aircraft, the BCD.1. He later turned his attention to rotary wing machines and carried out his experiments at nearby Getafe. In 1924 he made the first cross-country flight by an autogyro when he flew the twelve kilometres between the two fields. A replica of his of 1925 C.6bis has been constructed. The original featured an Avro 504 fuselage. Nearby is a C.19 built by Avro. This aircraft spent a short time in England before leaving for Spain in December 1932. Impressed by the Nationalists in the Civil War it survived and was flown until the early 1960s. A fairly new arrival is a C.30 built to original specifications by the Air Force workshops at Albacete. The only major change is the fitting of a Siemens-Halske radial from a Jungmeister instead of the Genet. A highlight from the Civil War period is the rare Heinkel He 111E-1 which was restored to period markings in the early 1980s. Replicas of types which served in the conflict include the Polikarpov I-15 and I-16. An aircraft which helped shape the destiny of Spain is a Dragon Rapide which was chartered from Olley Air Services of Croydon.to fly General Franco from Las Palmas to Tetuán in Morocco to take charge of the Nationalist forces after the death of their leader. The aircraft carried on to Seville to land Franco on the Spanish mainland. After this the Rapide returned to England and after being withdrawn in 1953 it was presented to Franco The biplane now has a commemorative plaque on its nose. Six Miles Hawk Majors flew in the Civil War and two survived to fly again. One rotted away at Valencia in the 1970s. On show is a modified Hawk Trainer. This has Nationalist colours on one side and Republican markings on the other. After years of service in Switzerland it ended up with Jean Salis at La Ferte Alais before travelling south. Also from the same source is the Farman F.404 which was restored in France in 2000. The high wing monoplane was withdrawn in 1968 and spent almost three decades in store. Five similar aircraft were involved in the Civil War. Nationalist success in the conflict resulted in German designs being put into production by C.A.S.A. and Hispano. Examples of their work can be seen in the displays. An artificial lake has been constructed and floating on this is the Dornier Do 24. The three engined flying boat gave excellent service for many years. Twelve were purchased during World War II and they flew on maritime patrol duties until 1970 with the last being based in Majorca. The Aerotecnica AC-12 helicopter was derived from the French Cantinieau C.101. Two prototypes and twelve production models for the Air Force followed. Ten of the larger AC.14 were also produced. The only two surviving Huarte Mendicoa HM-1 trainers built in the 1950s are rarities. The Dornier Do 27 was developed in Spain before Germany was allowed to produce aircraft after World War II. Many products of Spanish factories are also on show along with types recently withdrawn from service. Replicas of designs which have made significant contributions to aviation in the country are also being built. Early types on show include an Avro 504 and a Bristol Fighter along with two Fokkers and a Nieuport IVG. There are plans to construct more to show the significant pioneer era of Spanish aviation. In 1926 Major Ramon Franco and his crew made the first flight across the South Atlantic in the Wal 'Plus Ultra'. This aircraft is preserved in Argentina and a few years ago it returned to the C.A.S.A. factory in Cadiz where several were built. The original was restored and an accurate replica was built for the museum. This can be compared with the later Do 24T-3. In 1935 a B.A. Eagle was bought by Juan Pombo for an attempt on the South Atlantic record. The aircraft crashed in Gambia but he was not deterred and he acquired a second Eagle in which he flew from Santander to Mexico City in twenty stages. A replica of this famous aircraft can be seen. A genuine record breaker is the C.A.S.A. built Breguet 19 which made a number of long distance flights, including a tour of South America. This is parked by a replica of a later variant of the type. After the end of the Civil War the country flew a variety of mainly obsolete types. A Defence Treaty was signed with the U.S.A. in 1953 and this resulted in the supply of modern designs. Also new bases were constructed, others upgraded and American aircraft could use the fields. Thus there are many American aircraft on show and as types are withdrawn they are flown in for display. The increasing use of helicopters by the services over the last half century is shown with a special area devoted to rotary wing flight. There is a large collection of models, photographs, memorabilia, components, maps, documents, uniforms and trophies. More than ninety engines are on view. The history of Spanish aviation is portrayed in the galleries above the original hangar. Several aircraft are being sought to enhance the exhibition.

TYPE	REG/SER	CON. NO.	PI/NOTES	STATUS
☐ Aeronáutica Industrial (AISA) I-11B Peque	EC-AKL	006		PV
☐ Aeronáutica Industrial (AISA) I-11B Peque	'L.8C-44'	159	L.8C-74, EC-BLD	PVX
☐ Aeronáutica Industrial (AISA) I-115	E.9-119	119		PV
☐ Aeronáutica Industrial (AISA) P.E.38 [Schneider Grunau SG-38]				RA
☐ Aeronáutica Industrial (AISA) P.E.38 [Schneider Grunau SG-38]	PE-37			PV
☐ Aerotécnica AC-12	Z.2-6	6		PV
☐ Aerotécnica AC-12	Z.2-7	7		PV
☐ Aerotécnica AC-12	Z.2-11	11	On loan to Centri Aeri.	–

Aircraft	Reg	c/n	Notes	Status
☐ Aerotécnica AC-14	Z.4-06	6		PV
☐ Agusta-Bell 47G-2	HE.7A-11	276	Z.7-11 – On military gate.	PV
☐ Agusta-Bell 47G-2	HE.7-13	278	Z.7-13	PV
☐ Agusta-Bell 47G-3B-1	HE.7B-16	1507		RA
☐ Agusta-Bell 47G-3B-1	HE.7B-21	1512	Z.7B-21	PV
☐ Agusta-Bell 47J-3B	HD.11-1	2094	MM80413, EC-AYN, EC-SSA, Z.11-1	PV
☐ Agusta-Bell 47J-3B-1	EC-AXE	2077		PV
☐ Agusta-Bell 204AS	HA.8A-2	3133	Z.8-1	RA
☐ Agusta-Bell 204AS	HA.8A-4	3151	Z.8-4	RA
☐ Agusta-Bell 205A	HE.10A-6	4011		RA
☐ Agusta-Bell 206A-1 Jet Ranger	HD.12-3	8136	EC-SSQ, HR.12-3	PV
☐ Agusta-Bell 206A-1 Jet Ranger	HR.12A-4	8140		RA
☐ Agusta-Bell 206A-1 Jet Ranger	HR.12A-5	8144		RA
☐ Agusta-Bell 212				RA
☐ Avro 504K (R)	'M-MABE'		Also carries 'A-28'	PVX
☐ Beech F33A Bonanza	E.24A-30	CJ-128	EC-CLG	PV
☐ Beech A45 Mentor (T-34A)	E.17-16	G-786	55-0229	PV
☐ Beech 95-B55 Baron	E.20-1	TC-1451		PV
☐ Bell 47G-2 Sioux (H-13H) (OH-13H)	Z.7A-60	1929	56-2217, HE.7A-60	PV
☐ Bell 47G-2 Sioux (H-13H) (OH-13H)	HE.7A-55	1934	56-2240 – fuselage only.	RAD
☐ Bell 47G-2 Sioux (H-13H) (OH-13H)	HE.7A-56	1943	56-2231, EC-BZH – on loan to FPAC.	–
☐ Bell 47G-2 Sioux (H-13H) (OH-13H)	HE.7A-62	2152	57-6217	RA
☐ Bell 47G-2 Sioux (H-13H) (OH-13H)	HE.7A-41	2386	58-5373, Z.7A-41	PV
☐ Bell 47G-2 Sioux (H-13H) (OH-13H)	HE.7A-52	2536	59-4953, Z.7A-52 – composite with parts from c/n 2541 59-4958, Z.7A-53	PV
☐ Bell 47G-3B Sioux (OH-13S)	HE.7B-30	3906	65-13010 – at Officers Club on base.	RA
☐ Bell 47G-3B-2 Sioux (TH-13T)	HE.7B-20	3760	67-17078	RA
☐ Bell 204 Iroquois (HU-1B) (UH-1B)	60-3558	204		RAD
☐ Bell 204 Iroquois (UH-1C)	HU.8B-9	3109		RA
☐ Bell 205 Iroquois (UH-1H)	HE.10B-39	13276	72-21577	PV
☐ Bell 205 Iroquois (UH-1H)	HE.10B-52	13552	73-22069	PV
☐ Boeing 367-76-66 Stratofreighter (KC-97G) (KC-97L)	TK.1-03	16971	53-0189	PV
☐ Boeing 727-256	EC-CFG	20817	Front fuselage only.	RA
☐ Boeing-Stearman E75 Kaydet (PT-13D)	EC-AIF	75-5513	42-17350, N4675V	PVA
☐ Bölkow BO 105LOH	HR.15-21	S-460		PV
☐ Bölkow BO 105LOH	HR.15-25	S-465		RAD
☐ Breguet 14A2 (R)			In France.	RAC
☐ Breguet 19 Super TR (R)		'195'		PVX
☐ Breguet 19GR Grand Raid	12-72	42		PV
☐ Bristol 14 F.2B Fighter (R)	'B21'			PVX
☐ British Aircraft Eagle 2 (FSM)	'EC-CBB'			RACX
☐ Bücker Bü 133C Jungmeister	E.1-14	9	35-14 (?), ES.1-14	PV
☐ Canadair CL-215-I	UD.13-1	1010	CF-TXD, EC-BXM	PV
☐ Cantieri Riuniti dell'Adriatico (CANT) Z.506 Airone	1.E-73		Fin and rear fuselage only	PV
☐ Caudron C.272 Luciole	'EL-007'			PVX
☐ Caudron G.3 (R)	'bC-6'			PVX
☐ Cessna 305A Bird Dog (L-19A) (O-1A)	L.12-2	22426	51-12112	PV
☐ Cierva C.6bis (R)	'C.6-B'			PVX
☐ Cierva C.19IVP (Avro 620)	EC-AIM	5158	G-ABXH, EC-W13, EC-ATT, 30-62, EC-CAB	PV
☐ Cierva C.30A (R)	XVU.1-1			PV
☐ Consolidated 28-5A Catalina (PBY-5A)	'DR.1/74-21'	1960	Bu46596, N6070C, N45998, CF-FFW, C-FFFW, EC-314, EC-693	PVX
☐ Construcciones Aeronáuticas (CASA) / SIAT 223A-1 Flamingo	EC-CGM	059		RA
☐ Construcciones Aeronáuticas (CASA) 1.131E [Bücker Bü 131 Jungmann]	E.3B-533			RA
☐ Construcciones Aeronáuticas (CASA) 1.131E [Bücker Bü 131 Jungmann]	E.3-198	0203	E.3-198, E.3B-198	PV
☐ Construcciones Aeronáuticas (CASA) 1.131E [Bücker Bü 131 Jungmann]	E.3B-565	2182		PV
☐ Construcciones Aeronáuticas (CASA) 1.131E [Bücker Bü 131 Jungmann]	E.3B-605	2224		RA
☐ Construcciones Aeronáuticas (CASA) 2.111F (2.111E) [Heinkel He 111H-16]	T.8B-97	108	T.8-97	PV
☐ Construcciones Aeronáuticas (CASA) 352L [Junkers Ju 52/3m]	T.2B-211	102		PV
☐ Construcciones Aeronáuticas (CASA) 352L [Junkers Ju 52/3m]	'D-2521'	145	T.2B-254, 'Wn4025'	PVX
☐ Construcciones Aeronáuticas (CASA) C-101 Aviojet	XE.25-01	P1/991	EC-ZDF, EC-ZDF, EC-ZDZ, EC-ZZZ	PV
☐ Construcciones Aeronáuticas (CASA) C-101EB Aviojet			Front fuselage only.	RA
☐ Construcciones Aeronáuticas (CASA) C-127 [Dornier Do 27]	U.9-01	01	L.9-01 – fuselage only.	RA
☐ Construcciones Aeronáuticas (CASA) C-127 [Dornier Do 27]	U.9-10	10	L.9-10	PV

☐ Construcciones Aeronáuticas (CASA) C-127 [Dornier Do 27]	U.9-14	14	L.9-14 – fuselage only.	RA
☐ Construcciones Aeronáuticas (CASA) C-127 [Dornier Do 27]	U.9-33	33	L.9-33	PV
☐ Construcciones Aeronáuticas (CASA) C-127 [Dornier Do 27]	U.9-49	49	L.9-49 – on loan to Museo Municipal de San Javier.	–
☐ Construcciones Aeronáuticas (CASA) C-207A Azor	T.7-6	6		PV
☐ Construcciones Aeronáuticas (CASA) C-207C Azor	T.7-17	17		PV
☐ Construcciones Aeronáuticas (CASA) C-212-10 Aviocar	XT.12-1	01		PV
☐ Construcciones Aeronáuticas (CASA) C-212AA Aviocar	T.12B-50	102		PV
☐ Construcciones Aeronáuticas (CASA) C-212B Aviocar	TR.12A-3	1-1		PV
☐ Construcciones Aeronáuticas (CASA) C-212B Aviocar	TR.12A-7	5-5		PV
☐ Convair 30A-5 Coronado 990	EC-BZO	30-10-30	In Palma.	RA
☐ Dassault Mirage F.1EDA	C.14C-77	560	QA75 (Qatar)	PV
☐ Dassault Mirage F.1EDA	C.14C-78	567	QA76 (Qatar)	PV
☐ Dassault Mirage IIIEE	C.11-9	596		PV
☐ Dassault Mirage IIIEE	C.11-13	600	Fuselage only.	RA
☐ De Havilland D.H.4 (R)	'M-MHEI'			PV
☐ De Havilland D.H.60GIII Moth Major	30-89		30-89, EE.1-89, EC-AFQ – composite of several aircraft – also carries 'EM-016'	PVX
☐ De Havilland D.H.82A Tiger Moth	'30-103'/'EP-003'			PVX
☐ De Havilland D.H.87A Hornet Moth	EC-ACA	8039		RA
☐ De Havilland D.H.89 Dragon Rapide	G-ACYR	6261		PV
☐ De Havilland D.H.89A Dragon Rapide	'40-1'	6345	G-AERN, EC-AKO	PVX
☐ De Havilland D.H.C.4A Caribou (AC-1) (CV-2A) (C-7A)	T.9-25	53	61-2394	PV
☐ De Havilland D.H.C.4A Caribou (AC-1) (CV-2A) (C-7A)	T.9-29	70	61-2592 – On military base.	RA
☐ Dornier J Wal (R)	'M-MWAL'			PVX
☐ Dornier Do 24T-3	HD.5-2	5341	EC-DA?, 65-2, HR.5-2	PV
☐ Dornier Do 27B-5 (B-3)	U.9-76	400	(PD+224), QK+503, QA+1-4, L.9-76	PV
☐ Dornier Do 28A-1	U.14-1	3014	EC-WQD, EC-AQD	PV
☐ Douglas DC-3A-467 Skytrain (C-47B)	T.3-36	20600	43-16134, N86444	PV
☐ Douglas DC-4 Skymaster (C-54A)	T.4-10	10366	42-72261, Bu50844, NC88934, N88934	PV
☐ Douglas DC-4 Skymaster (C-54D)	T.4-5	10824	42-72719 – nose only	PV
☐ Douglas DC-9-32	EC-BYE	47504	Front fuselage only.	RA
☐ Farman F.404 (F.400)	'SF-002'	7358/1	F-AMGY, F-BBAY, F-PBAY	PVX
☐ Fieseler Fi 156C-3 Storch	'L.16-23'	2027/2	Composite.	PVAX
☐ Fleet 2	LV-ZBR	177		PV
☐ Fokker C III (R)	'M-MOAB'			PVX
☐ Fokker Dr I (R)	D-EAWI	425/17		PVX
☐ Grumman G-111 Albatross (G-64) (SA-16A) (SA-16B) (HU-16B)	AD.1B-8	G-187	51-5304	PV
☐ Gurripato II				RA
☐ Gurripato II				PV
☐ Heinkel He 111E-3 (E-1)	B.2-82	2940	25-82, 14-16	PV
☐ Hirth Hi.27 Akrostar II	EC-CBS	4008	D-EMBD	RA
☐ Hispano HA-1112K1L [Messerschmitt Bf 109G]	C.4J-10	46		PV
☐ Hispano HA-1112M1L [Messerschmitt Bf 109G]	C.4K-158	211		PV
☐ Hispano HA.132L [Fiat CR.32]	'3-52'	'262'	Composite of a Fiat CR.32 and a HA.132L3-51	PVX
☐ Hispano HA.200R1 Saeta	XE.14-2	20/II	EC-AMN, EC-ANN, X.2.14-2	PV
☐ Hispano HA.200A Saeta (HA.200R1)	A.10A-12	20/20	E.14-12, E.14A-12,	PV
☐ Hispano HA.200D Saeta	A.10B-64	20/70	E.14B-64, C.10B-64	RA
☐ Hispano HA.220D Super Saeta	A.10C-104	22/109	C.10C-104	PV
☐ Hispano HA.220D Super Saeta	A.10C-106	22/111	C.10C-106	PV
☐ Hispano HA.220D Super Saeta (HA.200E)	A.10C-91	20/41	XC.10C-01, EC-BBA, C.10C-91	PV
☐ Hispano-Suiza HS.34 (Hispano E.34)	EC-AFJ	1		PV
☐ Huarte-Mendicoa HM-1B	E.4-161	161		PV
☐ Huarte-Mendicoa HM-1B	E.4-174	174		RA
☐ Hughes 269A-1	HE.20-3	880707		RAD
☐ Hughes 269A-1	HE.20-12	880746		RAC
☐ Hughes 269A-1	HE.20-13	1280747		RA
☐ Jacobs Kranich III	EC-ODK			PV
☐ Jacobs Weihe (D.F.S. 108-68)	EC-RAB			PV
☐ Jacobs Weihe (D.F.S. 108-68)	EC-RAQ			RA
☐ Klemm L 25 b I	'30-22'	277	CH-272, HB-EFU, D-ENAF, D-ENAE	PVX
☐ Let L-13 Blanik				RA
☐ Lilienthal Normal-Segelapparat (R)				PV
☐ Lockheed 185 Orion (P3V-1) (P-3A)	P.3-7	185-5042	Bu150516	PV
☐ Lockheed 414-56-11 Hudson IIIA (A-29A)	FH426	414-6716	41-37227	RAD
☐ Lockheed 580 (T-33A)	E.15-38	580-1381	57-0652 – Tail from c/n 580-8093 52-9947, E.15-12	RA
☐ Lockheed 580 (T-33A)	E.15-48	580-1491	57-0662 – tail from E.15-19 – on loan to FPAC.	–

Type	Reg/Ser	C/n	PI/Notes	Status
☐ Lockheed 580 (T-33A)	E.15-06	580-7699	51-17554	RA
☐ Lockheed 580 (T-33A)	E.15-51	580-8260	53-4921	PV
☐ Lockheed 580 (T-33A)	E.15-53	580-8389	53-5050 – tail from c/n 580-8396, 53-5057, E.15-56	RA
☐ Lockheed 580 (T-33A)	E.15-21	580-8894	53-5555 – fuselage only.	PV
☐ Lockheed 683-10-19 Starfighter (F-104G)	26+23	683-9174	Carries C.8-15 and 32733 on starboard side.	PV
☐ McDonnell M.98DF Phantom II (RF-4C)	CR.12-55	1217	65-0823	PV
☐ McDonnell M.98DF Phantom II (RF-4C)	CR.12-42	1726	65-0937	PV
☐ McDonnell M.98DJ Phantom II (F-4C)	C.12-37	1151	64-0820	PV
☐ McDonnell M.98DJ Phantom II (F-4C)	C.12-39	1308	64-0892	RA
☐ Mikoyan-Gurevich MiG-17F	'42'		(Bulgaria) – in false Soviet markings.	PVX
☐ Mikoyan-Gurevich MiG-21SPS (MiG-21PFM)	22+26	94A4302	740 (DDR)	PV
☐ Mikoyan-Gurevich MiG-23ML	20+12	0390324621	331 (DDR)	PV
☐ Mil Mi-2	CCCP-23760	544140055	34 (Soviet)	PV
☐ Miles M.2H Hawk Major	'30-145'/'EN-002'		Modified from M.14A Hawk Trainer 3 (Magister) c/n 429 L5997, HB-EEB	PVX
☐ Morane-Saulnier G (R)	A.No.1			PVX
☐ Morane-Saulnier MS.181	E-004	SM.1	F-PALY	PV
☐ Morane-Saulnier MS.230	'005'		F-	PVX
☐ Morane-Saulnier MS.733 Alcyon	F-BMMS	105	105 (France)	PV
☐ Nieuport IVG (R)	'm.N.n.5'			PVX
☐ Nord N.1002 Pingouin II [Messerschmitt Bf 108B]	'L.15-2'	97	97, F-BFUE, F-AZET	PVX
☐ North American NA-88 Texan (AT-6D) (SNJ-5)	C.6-128	88-16031	42-84250, Bu43859	RA
☐ North American NA-88 Texan (SNJ-4)	'C.6-35'	88-13578	Bu27842, C6-159	PVX
☐ North American NA-108 Mitchell (B-25J) (TB-25J) (TB-25N)	'41-30338'	108-32396	44-29121, N86427, '151724', '151451'	PVX
☐ North American NA-121 Texan (AT-6D) (SNJ-5)	C.6-124	121-41825	44-81103, Bu90974	RA
☐ North American NA-121 Texan (AT-6D) (SNJ-5)	C.6-155	121-41833	44-81111, Bu90982	PV
☐ North American NA-168 Texan (T-6G)	E.16-90	168-462	49-3348	PV
☐ North American NA-168 Texan (T-6G)	E.16-97	168-478	49-3364 – on loan to Centri Aeri.	–
☐ North American NA-168 Texan (T-6G)	E.16-118	168-584	49-3450	RA
☐ North American NA-176 Sabre (F-86F)	'C.5-175'	176-381	51-13450, C.5-223, 'C.5-104'	PVX
☐ North American NA-191 Sabre (F-86F)	C.5-58	191-290	52-4594	PV
☐ North American NA-191 Sabre (F-86F)	C.5-71	191-414	52-4718 – on loan Centri Aeri.	–
☐ North American NA-203 Sabre (F-86H)		203-125	55-1353 – Front fuselage only.	PV
☐ Northrop N-156A Freedom Fighter (SF-5A)	A.9-044	2044		RA
☐ Northrop N-156A Freedom Fighter (SF-5A)	A.9-050	2050	C.9-050	PV
☐ Northrop N-156A Freedom Fighter (SF-5A)	A.9-051	2051	c/n also given as 1017.	PV
☐ Northrop N-156A Freedom Fighter (SF-5A)	A.9-052	2052		RA
☐ Northrop N-156A Freedom Fighter (SRF-5A)	AR.9-062	2062	C.9-062	PV
☐ Piper PA-23-250 Aztec E	E.19-3	27-4809	N14239	PV
☐ Piper PA-24-260 Comanche	'E.30-2'	24-4071	E.30-1	PVX
☐ Piper PA-30-160 Twin Comanche	E.31-1	30-599		RA
☐ Piper PA-30-160 Twin Comanche	E.31-2	30-653	EC-AYC	PV
☐ Polikarpov I-15 (FSM)	'CA-125'/'A10-103'			PVX
☐ Polikarpov I-16 (FSM)				RA
☐ Potez 54			Part fuselage.	RAD
☐ Scheibe Bergfalke III	EC-BFA	5560		RA
☐ Scheibe L-Spatz 55	EC-BFF	810		PV
☐ Schleicher Ka-6CR Rhönsegler	EC-APS	727		RA
☐ Schleicher Ka-6CR Rhönsegler	EC-APR	784		PV
☐ Schneider ESG 31 Grunau Baby II (D.F.S. 108-49)	'EC-MCQ'		EC-MFG	PVX
☐ Schneider Grunau SG-38 (D.F.S. 108-14)				RA
☐ Slingsby HP.14C	EC-BOL	1637	BGA.1402	RA
☐ Slingsby T.34A Sky 1	EC-OBN			PV
☐ Slingsby T.34A Sky 1	EC-RAT			PV
☐ Slingsby T.45 Swallow	EC-BHG	1541		RA
☐ Slingsby T.45 Swallow	EC-BHI	1544		RA
☐ Slingsby T.45 Swallow	EC-BHO	1548		PV
☐ Société Pour l'Aviation et ses Dérivés (SPAD) XIII (R)			To be built.	–
☐ Solar Wings Typhoon S4 Hang Glider				PV
☐ Stampe & Vertongen S.V.4C	F-BFZJ	46	46	PVA
☐ Stinson 108-3 Voyager	EC-AZD	108-4338	N6338M, EC-AZD (?) – uncovered airframe.	PV
☐ Stinson 108-3 Voyager	L.2-21	108-5162		PV
☐ Sud SA.316B Alouette III	HD.16-1	1952	EC-STE	PV
☐ Sud SA.318C Alouette Astazou	EC-CLV	2373		PV
☐ Sud SA.319B Alouette III	EC-CBY	2021		PV
☐ Sukhoi Su-22M4	25+18	26205	686 (DDR)	PV
☐ Svenska Aeroplan Aktiebolaget (SAAB) 32E Lansen (32B) (J 32B) (J 32E)	Fv32543	32543		PV
☐ Svenska Aeroplan Aktiebolaget (SAAB) 37 Viggen (AJ 37) (AJS 37)	Fv37074	37074	On loan from FVM,SWE	PV
☐ Szybowcowy Zaklad Doswiadczalny S.Z.D.24A Foka 4	EC-BOM	W-366		RA
☐ Szybowcowy Zaklad Doswiadczalny S.Z.D.24A Foka 4	EC-BON	W-367		PV
☐ Transavia PL-12T-320 Turbo Airfarmer	VH-TRQ	G.783		PV

Two helicopters, including this Bell 47, can be seen at the Museo Naval at San Fernando.

The unusual roof of the Catalan Technical Museum near Barcelona can be seen above this Fairchild 24.

This Agusta-Bell 205 is parked outside the science museum in Granada.

TYPE	REG/SER	CON. NO.	PI/NOTES	STATUS
☐ Tupolev SB-2			Crash remains.	PVD
☐ Ultralight Soaring T-3 Wizard				PV
☐ Vilanova Acedo				PV
☐ Vögt Lo 100 Zwergreiher	EC-OCI			PV
☐ Vögt Lo 100 Zwergreiher	EC-ODK			PV
☐ Westland-Sikorsky WS-55 Whirlwind Series 2	ZD.1B-19	WA.394		RA
☐ Westland-Sikorsky WS-55 Whirlwind Series 2	ZD.1B-22	WA.396		PV
☐ Zlin Z-326A Akrobat	EC-AXD	898	EC-WXD	PV
☐ Zlin Z-326A Akrobat	EC-AXL	899	EC-WXL	PV
☐ Zlin Z-526A Akrobat	EC-BDV	1004		PV
☐ Zlin Z-526F Trener Master	EC-BVK	1123		RA

MUSEO ELDER DE LA CIENCIA Y LA TECNOLOGIA (SP30)

Address:	Parque de Santa Catalina 35007 Las Palmas.
Tel:	0828 011 828
Fax:	0828 011 001
Email:	museo.elder@museoelder.canariastelecom.com
Admission:	Tuesday-Sunday 1000-2000.
Location:	In the centre of the city.

All aspects of science and technology are covered in this modern museum which occupies a prominent postion by the main harbour. Many computer-assisted displays have been installed. The aviation section contains two aircraft along with models, engines and components. The SRF-5A once served with units based at Gando. The DC-9 was delivered to Aviaco in October 1979 and became a regular visitor to the island.

TYPE	REG/SER	CON. NO.	PI/NOTES	STATUS
☐ Douglas DC-9-34	EC-DGB	48103		PV
☐ Northrop N-156A Freedom Fighter (SRF-5A)	AR.9-053	1019		PV

MUSEO MUNICIPAL (SP31)

Address:	Calle Prada 4, 13001 Ciudad Real.
Tel:	0926-255304
Fax:	0926-255304
Admission:	Tuesday-Sunday 1000-1400 1700-2000.
Location:	In the centre of the town.

The history and culture of the region can be seen in the displays at this museum. The development of the area from the early times is shown in detail. There has been a settlement on the site since at least the Bronze Age. The archaeological section includes many items recovered from digs. There are many interesting items to be seen including paintings, sculptures and costumes. Local artists feature prominently. The aircraft are part of the transport section which also includes cars, motor cycles and commercial vehicles.

TYPE	REG/SER	CON. NO.	PI/NOTES	STATUS
☐ Cessna F150H	F-BPED	F1500261		PV
☐ Douglas DC-9-32	EC-BYI	47452	Front fuselage only.	PV
☐ Piper PA-23-250 Aztec E	EC-ESZ	27-7305201		PV
☐ Sud-Est SE.3130 Alouette II				PV

MUSEO MUNICIPAL DE SAN JAVIER (SP32)

Address:	Carretera de Cartegena, 30730 San Javier.
Tel:	0968 19 25 26
Fax:	0968 57 09 51
Location:	In the centre of the town which is about 45 km south east of Murcia.

This local museum, which portrays the history of the area, has recently acquired from the Museo del Aire a C.A.S.A. built Dornier Do 27. The type was developed in Spain and fifty were built under licence. The nearby airfield houses the Air Force Academy and the work of this unit is highlighted in the displays. Also to be seen are displays devoted to cultural life in the town and its environs.

TYPE	REG/SER	CON. NO.	PI/NOTES	STATUS
☐ Construcciones Aeronáuticas (CASA) C-127 [Dornier Do 27]	U.9-49	49	L.9-49 – on loan from M.A.	PV

MUSEO NACIONAL DE AÉROPUERTOS Y TRANSPORTE AÉREO (SP33)

Address:	Trapiche-Buzon 20, 29179 Malaga.
Tel:	0952-507377
Email:	agpmuseo@aena.es
Admission:	Tuesday 1000-1400 1700-2000; Sunday 1700-2000.
Location:	About 8 km south west of the town.

The museum is being set up in the former 1938 terminal building. The structure is being restored to original condition. Several display rooms are now ready and these trace the history of the airport and commercial flying. On show are engines, components, models, photographs, uniforms, instruments and documents. The collection of aircraft is being expanded and the highlight is the DC-3 which flew from the field for several years. This has now been painted in the colours of an Iberia aircraft which crashed in 1957. The Dove was one of a pair delivered to the Moroccan Ministry of Defence in May 1964. The Aero 45 came from Zaragoza and the Belgian Wassmer WA-40 is being rebuilt following an accident at the airport. This airframe was abandoned after the crash.

TYPE	REG/SER	CON. NO.	PI/NOTES	STATUS
☐ Aero Super 45S	EC-APH	04-005		PV
☐ Beech E18S	'EC-ASJ'	BA-6	N3600B, PH-LPS, N9886A	PVX
☐ De Havilland D.H.104 Dove 7	'PH-VLA'	04534	CN-MBA, N9888A	PVX
☐ Dornier Do 27B-1	EC-CFS	193	QB+403, EC+386, MD+386, 55+60, L.9-65	PV
☐ Douglas DC-3A-467 Skytrain (C-47B) (SC-47D)	'EC-ABC'	17094/34361	45-1091, N86442, T.3-50, EC-APO	PVX
☐ Douglas DC-9-32	EC-CGO	47640	Forward fuselage only.	PV
☐ McDonnell M.98DJ Phantom II (F-4C)				RA
☐ Wassmer WA.40 Super IV	OO-GRH	102		RAC

MUSEO NAVAL DE SAN FERNANDO (SP34)

Address:	San Fernando, 11100 Cadiz.
Tel:	0956-599052
Fax:	0956-599052
Email:	museonaval@laisladelsur.com
Admission:	Saturday-Sunday 1030-1330.
Location:	On the north side of the town which is about 12 km south east of Cadiz.

This excellent museum, located in historic buildings, traces the maritime history of the nation. On show are models, documents, photographs, uniforms, medals and personal items. The Spanish Naval Air Service was reformed in 1954 and has mainly operated helicopters. The Harrier was ordered in 1976 and a room at the museum has been prepared to portray Spanish use of the versatile jet. Two helicopters are preserved in the grounds of the complex. The first type flown by the Navy was the Bell 47 which served until 1987.

TYPE	REG/SER	CON. NO.	PI/NOTES	STATUS
☐ Bell 47G-5	HE.7B-31	7884		PV
☐ Bell 209 Huey Cobra (AH-1G)	HA.14A-8	21127	72-21464	PV

MUSEO PARQUE DE LAS CIENCIAS (SP35)

Address:	c/o Cuidad de las Artes y las Ciencias, C/ Arzobispo Mayoral 14-2, 46002 Valencia.
Tel:	96-352-55-07
Fax:	96-352-60-23
Email:	prensa@cac.es
Admission:	March – mid June and mid September-December Tuesday-Sunday 1000-1800. Mid June - mid September Tuesday-Sunday 1000-2000.
Location:	In the centre of the city.

This new science museum was constructed in the late 1990s. Two aircraft which were formerly on show at the now closed Air Force base at Manises have been donated. The Sabre is on show at Oeste Park, a former military barracks, in the city and the Mirage is displayed in the museum complex. Both fighter types served at the base The Brunet biplane was built in 1909 and a replica has been constructed for the display.

TYPE	REG/SER	CON. NO.	PI/NOTES	STATUS
☐ Brunet (FSM)				PV
☐ Dassault Mirage IIIEE	C.11-7	594	In Parque del Oeste.	PV
☐ North American NA-227 Sabre (F-86F)	'C.5-5'	227-185	55-4000, C.5-101	PVX

MUSEO VOSTELL MALPARTIDA(SP36)

Address:	Cntra del Barrueos, 10910 Malpardita de Cáceres.
Tel:	0927 010812
Fax:	0927 010814
Email:	museo@museovostell.org.
Admission:	Mid-March-Mid June Mid September-Mid MarchTuesday-Saturday 1000-1330 1600-1830 Sunday 1000-1430: April-August Tuesday: Mid June-Mid September Tuesday-Saturday 1030-1330 1700-2000. Sunday 1000-1430.
Location:	About 3 km south of Malpardita which is about 15 km west of Cáceres.

This modern art collection was founded by the German artist Wolf Vostell in 1976. In the large landscaped grounds there are many sculptures involving rocks and everyday objects. The MiG-21, of unknown origin and sub type, is part of one which has two cars and three pianos inter-twined. The fuselage is mounted vertically with its nose pointing towards the sky. There is also an exhibition of Mercedes cars which were once owned by the artist. In addition there are many paintings in the indoor galleries.

TYPE	REG/SER	CON. NO.	PI/NOTES	STATUS
☐ Mikoyan-Gurevich MiG-21				PV

MUSEU DE LA CIENCIA I DE LA TECNICA DE CATALUNYA (SP37)

Address:	Rambla d'Egara 270, Terrassa, 08221 Barcelona
Tel:	093 736 89 66
Fax:	093 736 89 60
Email:	museum.NACTEC@ogiccontrol.ec
Admission:	Tuesday-Friday 1000-1900; Saturday-Sunday 1000-1430.
Location:	In the northern part of the town which is about 25 km north of the city.

This museum is housed in a former textile factory built in 1909. The unusual saw-tooth roof, designed to maximise light for the workers, is a feature of the main building. The courtyard area and some smaller buildings serve as offices and workshops. Restoration and conversion of the complex started in 1986 and the first displays were opened in July 1992. The main themes of the exhibition are energy, textile working, photography and transport. On show are many items of machinery showing the former use of the plant and an excellent collection of vehicles. The small aeronautical section contains five engines and large scale models of a Polikarpov I-15, I-16 and Tupolev SB-2. Three aircraft are currently on display. The German designed SG-38 primary glider is one of several constructed under licence by A.I.S.A. at Cuatro Vientos. The Argus, which was obtained locally, has been restored and is in an all yellow scheme without markings. Two hundred I-115 primary trainers were built in the 1950s and the type was withdrawn from military use in the late 1970s. The Bellanca Viking, which is in store in the building, was imported in to Spain in the late 1960s. The company had a chequered history after World War II and after 1951 produced no aircraft. The designs were taken on and developed by other firms. The Viking first flew in 1966 and the company was again known as Bellanca at this time.

TYPE	REG/SER	CON. NO.	PI/NOTES	STATUS
☐ Aeronáutica Industrial (AISA) I-115	E.9-123	123	E.9-123, EC-DEJ	PV
☐ Aeronáutica Industrial (AISA) P.E.38 [Schneider Grunau SG-38]				PV
☐ Bellanca 17-30 Viking 300	EC-BPL	30140		RA
☐ Fairchild 24R9 Forwarder (UC-61K) (Argus III)				PV

PARQUE DE LAS CIENCIAS (SP38)

Address:	Avenida del Mediterráneo, 18006 Granada.
Tel:	58-131900
Fax:	58-133582
Email:	cpciencas@readysoft.es
Admission:	Tuesday-Saturday 1000-1900;Sunday 1000-1500.
Location:	In the south western suburbs of the town.

This modern museum features many 'hands-on' displays and covers many fields of science. The development of local industry is featured with many interesting machines on view. There is a large botanical section with many plants, an observatory and an excellent planetarium. The Agusta-Bell helicopter, used for search and rescue duties, is parked outside by the main entrance. The type was flown from the nearby military airfield.

TYPE	REG/SER	CON. NO.	PI/NOTES	STATUS
☐ Agusta-Bell 205A	HE.10A-1	4002	EC-AYQ	PV

SWEDEN

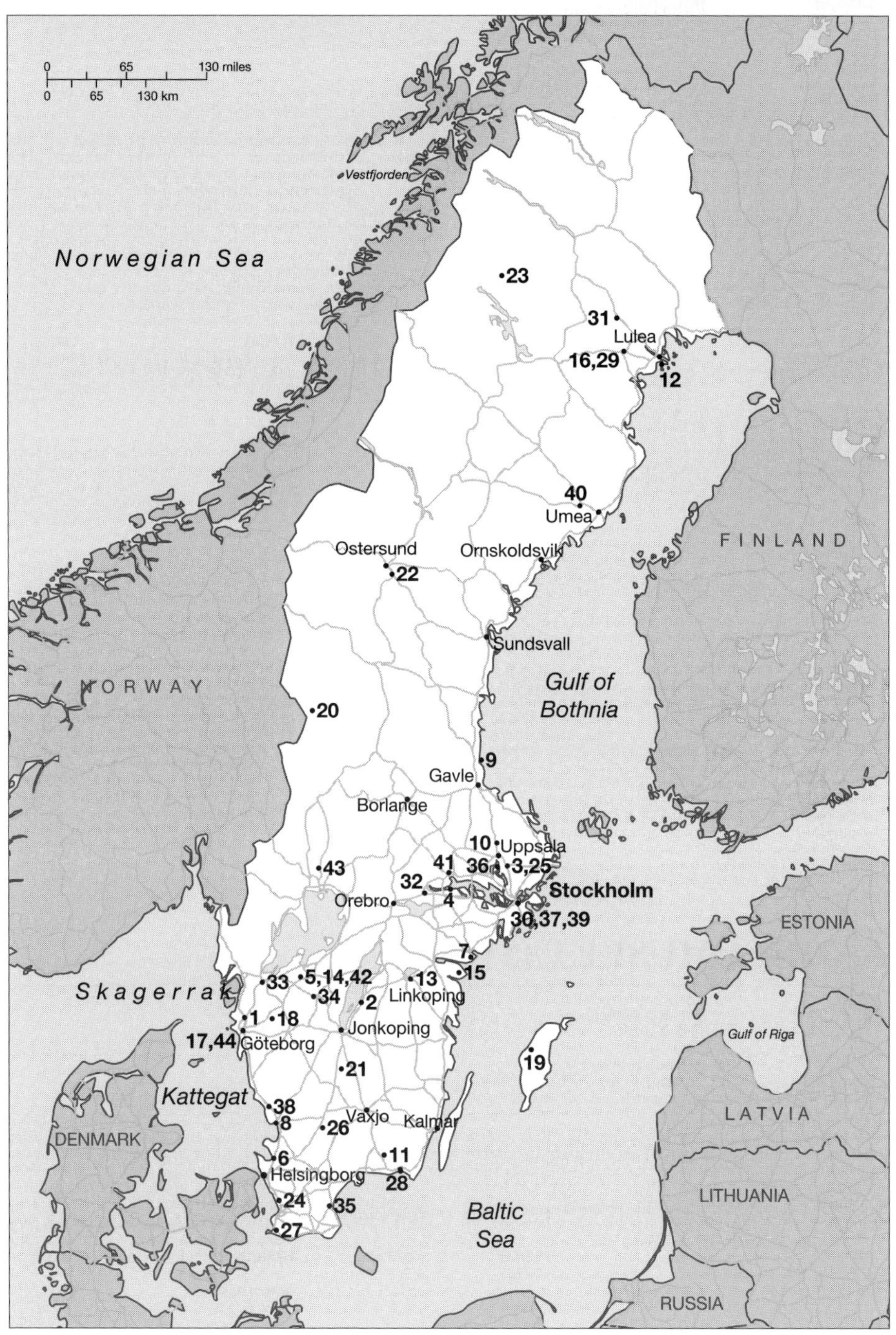

0
65
130 miles
0
65
130 km
Vestfjorden
Norwegian Sea
NORWAY
FINLAND
Gulf of Bothnia
Skagerrak
Kattegat
DENMARK
Baltic Sea
ESTONIA
Gulf of Riga
LATVIA
LITHUANIA
RUSSIA
23
31
Lulea
16,29
12
40
Umea
Ostersund
22
Ornskoldsvik
Sundsvall
20
9
Gavle
Borlange
10
Uppsala
41
36
3,25
43
32
4
Stockholm
Orebro
30,37,39
7
15
33
5,14,42
13
34
2
Linkoping
1
18
Jonkoping
17,44
Göteborg
19
21
38
8
Vaxjo
Kalmar
26
6
11
Helsingborg
28
24
35
27

AEROSEUM (SWE1)

Address:	Box 10117, S 400 70 Göteborg.
Tel:	031-692813
Fax:	031-692898
Email:	info@aeroseum.se
Admission:	By prior permission only.
Location:	About 10 km north of the city off the N.159.

The airfield at Säve was home to F9 wing for many years. In 1942 the first underground hangar complex was completed and a second followed in the early 1950s. These large areas about one hundred feet down were capable of housing all the aircraft and personnel of the unit and had full facilities, The organisation has been trying to preserve the site since 1999. On January 1st 2003 their dream became a reality when the Swedish Defence Ministry handed over the area. The aim is to create an aviation museum and education centre. On top of the bunkers an Aviation Theme Park will be constructed. A restoration centre will be set up and active aircraft will be based in the hangars. The collection is growing steadily and new types are arriving. When the museum is fully operational several private owners will move in with their aircraft. The military authorities are helping and two Viggens have been loaned by the Air Force Museum. A helicopter squadron is still based at Säve and when their Kawasaki-Vertol Hkp 4Bs are withdrawn two will join the exhibition. Some fly-ins have already taken placed and these will become a regular feature.

TYPE	REG/SER	CON. NO.	PI/NOTES	STATUS
☐ Agusta-Bell 204B	226	3032	In Dutch markings.	RA
☐ Beagle A.61 Terrier 2 (Auster Q T.7)	OY-AVV	B.612	WE603, G-ASBT, (D-EKCO), D-EBMU	RA
☐ Cessna F337G Super Skymaster	SE-GMM	F3370077		RA
☐ De Havilland D.H.104 Dove 6A	SE-EUR	04496	HB-LAP, G-ATAP- due soon.	–
☐ Focke-Wulf Fw 44J Stieglitz			Due soon.	–
☐ Gardan GY-80 Horizon 160	SE-EGN	106	(F-WLSE)	RAC
☐ Kawasaki-Vertol KV 107-II-4 (Hkp 4B)			Due soon.	–
☐ Kawasaki-Vertol KV 107-II-4 (Hkp 4B)			Due soon.	–
☐ Klemm Kl 35D (Sk 15)	SE-BHD	1812	Fv5012 – fuselage frame only.	RA
☐ Maule M-4-220C Strata Rocket	SE-FUV	2122C		RA
☐ Scheibe Bergfalke II/55	SE-TAE	316		RA
☐ Scheibe L-Spatz 55	83			RA
☐ Scheibe SF-30A Club Spatz	SE-TVK	6804		RA
☐ Sud-Est SE.3130 Alouette II (Hkp 2)	02034	1137		RA
☐ Sud-Est SE.3130 Alouette II (Hkp 2)	02036	1246		RA
☐ Sud-Est SE.3160 Alouette III	SE-JCR	1208	A-208 (Netherlands)	RA
☐ Sud-Est SE.3160 Alouette III	SE-JCS	1218	A-218 (Netherlands)	RA
☐ Sud-Est SE.3160 Alouette III		1356		RA
☐ Sud-Est SE.3160 Alouette III	SE-JEM	1451	A-451 (Netherlands)	RA
☐ Sud-Est SE.3160 Alouette III	SE-JEI	1471	A-471 (Netherlands)	RA
☐ Sud-Est SE.3160 Alouette III	SE-JEJ	1489	A-489 (Netherlands)	RA
☐ Sud-Est SE.3160 Alouette III	A-495	1495	In Dutch markings.	RA
☐ Sud-Est SE.3160 Alouette III	SE-JEL	1500	A-500 (Netherlands)	RA
☐ Svenska Aeroplan Aktiebolaget (SAAB) 35F-1 Draken (J 35F-1)	Fv35415	35415	Fv35415, (N415J)	RA
☐ Svenska Aeroplan Aktiebolaget (SAAB) 35F-2 Draken (J 35F-2)	Fv35528	35528		RA
☐ Svenska Aeroplan Aktiebolaget (SAAB) 37 Viggen (AJ 37)	Fv37094	37094	On loan from FVM.	RA
☐ Svenska Aeroplan Aktiebolaget (SAAB) 37 Viggen (SH 37) (AJSH 37)	Fv37911	37911	On loan from FVM.	RA
☐ Svenska Aeroplan Aktiebolaget (SAAB) 91A Safir	SE-AUR	91103		RAA

ANDRÉEMUSEET (SWE2)

Address:	Box 82, S 56 300 Gränna.
Tel:	0390-41015
Fax:	0390-10275
Email:	andree@grn.se
Admission:	Summer Daily 1000-1700; Winter Daily 1200-1600.
Location:	In the centre of the town.

Saloman Andrée was born in Gränna in 1854 and in 1897 he attempted to fly with two companions across the North Pole in a balloon. They started at Spitsbergen and never came back. In 1930 their last camp was found on White Island east of their starting point. The equipment, films and diaries found told the story of their three months trek over the ice alter the balloon came down. The Colt 77 is a hot air copy, constructed for a 1981 film, of the hydrogen balloon used by Andrée on his polar flight. The basket is from the first balloon bought by Andrée and dates from 1893. There are also many local history displays in other buildings at the site.

TYPE	REG/SER	CON. NO.	PI/NOTES	STATUS
☐ Colt 77A Hot Air Balloon	SE-ZVD	018		RA
☐ Yon Svea Balloon			Basket only.	PV

ARLANDA FLYGMUSEUM (SWE3)

Address:	Box 38, S 190 45 Stockholm-Arlanda.
Tel:	08-797-6181
Fax:	08-797-6185
Email:	aerospace@am.ifv.sem
Admission:	Saturday-Sunday 1000-1500.
Location:	Arlanda airport is about 40 km north of Stockholm off the E.4.

The Swedish Board of Civil Aviation has been collecting aircraft and material for a proposed museum for almost fifty years. A number of sites in the Arlanda area have been used for storage and workshops. In the early 1980s a display was set up in the former charter terminal but this lasted about two years before the airport reclaimed the building. For the last few years the collection has been housed in a warehouse at the airport and many of the airframes have been restored. Formerly known as the Luftfartsrmuseet a name change took place a few years ago. Many interesting Swedish designs are in the collection. The 1911 Berger was an unsuccessful attempt at a steam-powered machine. The BEDA flying boat fitted with a de Havilland Gipsy engine flew unlicensed for many years in a remote part of the country. The Pou-du-Ciel and the Persson are other examples of aircraft which flew successfully without the knowledge of the authorities. The Persson was obviously inspired by the Fokker D VII and is covered with a form of doped paper. Werner Rieseler and Filip Bendel built the R III in a garage in Stockholm in 1922. There were plans to produce the type in Germany but these came to nothing. The MFH Junior features the rear fuselage of a de Havilland Moth Major, components of an SG-38 glider and a number of new parts. The Moth Major in the collection was flown from the Gothenburg area from 1935 until it was badly damaged in a crash in 1944. The aircraft was rebuilt with a metal tube fuselage modified from a Moth Trainer or Tiger Moth. Flown again until the late 1950s the Moth joined the collection in 1961. Only a few Avro Avians have survived and the example in the collection was converted to a cabin model in 1943. This aircraft was built in 1929 and delivered to a private owner at Mousehold near Norwich. Sold to Sweden in 1933 if often flew on floats. The Avian crashed in 1947 and was stored until donated to the collection in 1972. A rarity is the Junkers W 34 delivered to the Swedish Air Force in 1935 and serving mainly with F4 at Ostersund-Frösön. From 1953 until 1961 it was on the civil register and then given to the group. Two Lockheed twins have been acquired. The Electra Junior arrived in Sweden in 1953 from Holland and the Lodestar made the short journey from Finland the following year. Lightplanes, gliders and airliners have been collected and hopefully a permanent exhibition building will one day be constructed as there is a large amount of material still in store.

TYPE	REG/SER	CON. NO.	PI/NOTES	STATUS
☐ Airspeed AS.10 Oxford I			Wings only.	RAD
☐ Auster J AOP.5	SE-CBT	841	MS977, G-ANIU, LN-BDU	PV
☐ Auster J/5G Cirrus Autocar	SE-CBS	3082	LN-BDA	RAD
☐ Avro 594 Avian IV (modified)	SE-ADT	R3/CN/318	G-AAHD – on show in nearby shopping complex.	PV
☐ Avro 652A Anson I			Major components.	RAD
☐ Beech G50 Twin Bonanza	LN-DBE	GH-98	N186AA	RA
☐ Bell 47D-1	SE-HAD	39	NC185B, LN-ORU – contains parts from others.	PV
☐ Bellanca 8KCAB Decathlon	SE-IGG	605-80		RA
☐ Berger Bo				RA
☐ Blériot XI (R)				PV
☐ Bücker Bü 131B Jungmann	SE-AGU	846	On show at Sundsvall Airport.	PV
☐ Cessna C-34 Airmaster			Fuselage only.	RA
☐ Cessna R172K Hawk XP	SE-KEU	R1722800	N7364N	PV
☐ Convair 440-75	SE-CCX	320	LN-KLB	RA
☐ De Havilland D.H.60GIII Moth Major	SE-AGF	5132	Rebuilt at some time with a steel tube fuselage.	PV
☐ De Havilland D.H.89A Dragon Rapide (D.H.89B Dominie I)	SE-BXZ	6934	RL952, G-AHGH – wings and other parts.	RAD
☐ Douglas Skyraider AEW.1 (AD-4W)	SE-EBB	7962	Bu127947, WT949, G-31-5	PV
☐ Fairchild 24R46A Forwarder (24W41A) (UC-61A) (Argus II)	SE-BXE	W41A-862	43-14898, HB625, LN-MAD	PV
☐ Focke-Wulf Fw 44J Stieglitz (Sk 12)	SE-BWX	2816	Fv5773	PV
☐ Götaverken GV-38 [Rearwin 9000L]	SE-AHD	5		PVC
☐ Hemminger LH-22 Baby-Falk	SE-SGO	5		RA
☐ Jacobs Kranich IIB-1 (D.F.S. 108-30) (SE 103)	Fv8215	076	SE-103	RA
☐ Jacobs Meise (D.F.S. 108-70)	SE-SGF	7		RA
☐ Jacobs Weihe (D.F.S. 108-68) (SE 104)	SE-SND	219	Fv 8304 – on loan to Segelflyg Museum.	–
☐ Junkers Ju 52/3mce	SE-ADR	4017	SE-ADK, SE-ADR, Fv907 – front fuselage only.	PV
☐ Junkers W 34h (Tp 2A)	SE-BYA	2835	Fv6	PV
☐ Klemm Kl 35D (Sk 15)	SE-BGA	1983	Fv5054	PVC
☐ Larsson Flygfisken			Incomplete.	PV
☐ Larsson MFH Junior	'F-AHLE'		Unapproved homebuilt using shortened fuselage of D.H.60GIII Moth c/n 5138 OY-DAK, SE-AEL and SG-38 wings.	PVX
☐ Lockheed 12-26 Electra Junior	SE-BXU	1313	L2-45 (Netherlands), PJ-AKE, CX245, T-3	PVC
☐ Lockheed 18-56-23 Lodestar (C-60A)	SE-BZE	18-2593	43-16433, G-AGIJ, 2593 (Norway), T-AE (Norway), OH-VKP	RA
☐ Malmo Flygindustri MFI-10 Vipan	SE-CFI	10.01		PV
☐ Mignet HM-14 Pou-du-Ciel				PV

Nilsson Beda				PV
Noorduyn Norseman IV (YC-64)	SE-CPB	89	3538 (Canada), 42-5050, RA-Y (Norway), (LN-AEN)	PVC
Nord NC.701 Martinet [Siebel Si 204D-1]	SE-KAL	159	159 (France)	RA
Nordiska Aviatik NAB 9 [Albatros B IIa]			Front fuselage only	PVD
Pelzner P-2				PV
Persson Biplane				PV
Pilatus B4-PC11	SE-TNU	160		PV
Rieseler R.III	S-AAR			PV
Scheibe 138 Specht	D-6680	808	D-4320, D-4680	RA
Scheibe Bergfalke II	SE-SUA	336		RA
Schneider ESG 31 Grunau Baby IIB	SE-SAZ	001	On loan to Segelflyg Museum.	–
Schneider ESG 31 Grunau Baby IIB	SE-SFA	098		PV
Schneider Grunau SG-38 (D.F.S. 108-14)				RA
Schneider Grunau SG-38 (D.F.S. 108-14)	21	210		PV
Stoddard-Hamilton SH-2 Glasair RG	SE-XGF	476R		PV
Sud-Est SE.210 Caravelle III	SE-DAF	112	(HB-ICV)	RA
Taylor J-2 Cub	SE-AGL	989		PVC
Vertol V.44A (Hkp 1)	Fv01007	608	On loan to Marine Museum – front fuselage only.	–

ESKILSTUNA FLYGKLUBB (SWE4)

Address: Ekeby Flygfält.,
S 632 23 Eskilstuna.
Tel: 016-513477
Admission: By prior permission only.
Location: At Ekeby airfield which is about 5 km north west of the town.

The gliding section of the flying club has an active vintage section. The SG-38 is one of a batch of over two hundred constructed by A.B. Flygindustri at Halmstad between 1941 and 1943. The Grunau Baby is also a licence built example and was made by A.B. Flygplan at Malmö in 1944/5. The Anfänger primary glider is one of a batch of seventeen built at Västerås by AB Centrala in 1938/9. Over seventy Sedberghs were ordered for use by the Air Training Corps in Britain. Several of the survivors were sold for civilian use in the mid-1980s and after a short period in England the example in the collection moved to Sweden. The club has just constructed a new hangar and the more modem sailplanes are now housed there. This has released space in the old building where the early types spend most of their time suspended from the ceiling. Vintage days are held during the summer season when some of the fleet are flown and locally based aircraft and cars are invited.

TYPE	REG/SER	CON. NO.	PI/NOTES	STATUS
Jacobs Anfänger II	SE-SMI	1		RAA
Piper PA-25-235 Pawnee	SE-ECC	25-2166	N6613Z	RAA
Piper PA-25-260 Pawnee C	SE-FLA	25-4487	LN-VYM	RAA
Piper PA-25-Volvo Pawnee (PA-25-235B)	SE-EPB	25-3264		RAA
Rolladen-Schneider LS-4	SE-TXD	4182		RAA
Rolladen-Schneider LS-4	SE-TXE	4410		RAA
Scheibe Bergfalke II/55	SE-SXD	263		RAA
Scheibe Bergfalke II/55	SE-THL	5642		RAA
Scheibe Bergfalke III	SE-TEO	5589		RAA
Schneider ESG 31 Grunau Baby II (D.F.S. 108-49)	SE-SFE	113		RAA
Schneider Grunau SG-38 (D.F.S. 108-14)	SE-SMF	162		RAA
Slingsby T.21B Sedbergh TX.1	SE-SME	663	WG496, BGA.3242, BGA.3309	RAA
Slingsby T.61A Falke	SE-TMD	1773	G-AYVJ	RAC

FLYGFLOTTILJ 07 GÅRDS OCH FLOTTILJMUSEUM (SWE5)

Address: Flygflottilj 7,
S 530 32 Såtenäs.
Tel: 0510-87891
Fax: 0510-88778
Email: raymond.andersson@f7.mil.se
Admission: Weekdays by appointment.
Location: Just south of the town which is about 25 km south west of Lidköping.

Såtenäs opened in 1940 and has been an important base ever since. The Caproni Ca.313 bomber was the initial equipment of the wing and these served for almost five years until the arrival of the SAAB B 17. SAAB B 18s, A 21s, A 21Rs A 29s and A 32s were subsequently operated by the unit. F7 was the first wing to fly the Viggen when the type entered service in 1973. The Gripen arrived in 1996 and a transport squadron along with liaison and helicopter flights are in residence. The museum was established in 1981 and ten years later moved to its present building just outside the main gate. The displays trace the history of the Såtenäs estate from the Stone Age as well as that of the base. Rooms have been furnished to show air force life in the 1940s and 1950s. Several of the aircraft in the collection served with F 7. A display showing equipment used by Viggen crews can be seen. The story of the wing and its personnel is portrayed in detail.

TYPE	REG/SER	CON. NO.	PI/NOTES	STATUS
☐ Scottish Aviation Bulldog 100 (Fpl 61C) (Sk 61D)	Fv61074	BH100/192	G-BACU	PV
☐ Sud-Est SE.3130 Alouette II (Hkp 2)	Fv02407	1291		RA
☐ Svenska Aeroplan Aktiebolaget (SAAB) 32A Lansen (A 32A)	Fv32070	32070		RA
☐ Svenska Aeroplan Aktiebolaget (SAAB) 32D Lansen (32B) (J 32B) (J 32D)	Fv32603	32603		RA
☐ Svenska Aeroplan Aktiebolaget (SAAB) 37 Viggen (AJ 37)	Fv37050	37050	At barracks.	RA
☐ Svenska Aeroplan Aktiebolaget (SAAB) 37 Viggen (AJ 37)	Fv37068	37068		RA
☐ Svenska Aeroplan Aktiebolaget (SAAB) 37 Viggen (AJ 37)	Fv37072	37072		PV

FLYGFLOTTILJ 10 FLYGMUSEUM (SWE6)

Address:	Valhall Park, S 262 74 Ängelholm.
Tel:	0431-14810
Email:	info@f10kamratforening.se
Admission:	May-September Saturday-Sunday 1000-1600; June and August Tuesday-Sunday 1200-1600.
Location:	About 5 km north west of the town.

The wing was established in February 1940 and stationed at Bulltofta in Malmö. The first type flown was the Gloster Gladiator which was replaced by the Caproni-Reggiane Re 2000. A move to Barkakra near Ängelholm took place on October 5th 1945. Since then the types operated were the FFVS J 22, the SAAB J 21R, the de Havilland Vampire, the SAAB J 29, the Hawker Hunter, the SAAB Draken and the SAAB Viggen. In 1997 a number of SAAB 105s moved in from Ljungbyhed for pilot training. The museum was set up in 1984 in what was then a restricted area of the base. An excellent display of photographs, models, uniforms, badges, engines and equipment was set up. The history of the wing is portrayed in detail. One of the three J 22s surviving was restored to flying condition for the Heritage Flight. After the outbreak of World War II it became difficult for Sweden to obtain combat aircraft. The J 22 was designed by Bo Lundberg and the prototype flew in September 1942. The fighter entered service in 1943 and the last were withdrawn in 1952. The SAAB J 29 first flew in 1948 and over six hundred and sixty were flown by the Swedish Air Force. The type saw active service in the Congo in 1960. The last combat mission was flown by F 4 at Östersund in May 1967 but a few remained operational at Malmslatt until 1976. The base recently closed and is now a large industrial park.

TYPE	REG/SER	CON. NO.	PI/NOTES	STATUS
☐ Agusta-Bell 204B (Hkp 3B)	Fv03424	3006		PV
☐ Flygforvaltningens Flygverkstad (FFVS) J 22A	Fv22185	185		PV
☐ Svenska Aeroplan Aktiebolaget (SAAB) 35D Draken (J 35D)			Front fuselage only.	PV
☐ Svenska Aeroplan Aktiebolaget (SAAB) 35F-2 Draken (J 35F-2)			Front fuselage only.	PV
☐ Svenska Aeroplan Aktiebolaget (SAAB) 35J Draken (35F-2) (J 35F-2) (J 35J)	Fv35409	35409		PV
☐ Svenska Aeroplan Aktiebolaget (SAAB) 35J Draken (35F-2) (J 35F-2) (J 35J)	Fv35630	35630		PV
☐ Svenska Aeroplan Aktiebolaget (SAAB) 37 Viggen (SF 37) (AJSF 37)	Fv37976	37976		PV

FLYGFLOTTILJ 11 MUSEUM (SWE7)

Address:	Skavsta Flygplats, S 611 92 Nyköping.
Tel:	0155-211898
Email:	f11_museum@hotmail.com
Admission:	Last Sunday in month 1100-1500; July Wednesday 1400-1800.
Location:	About 6 km south west of the town off Road 52.

The wing was formed in 1941 and served in the reconnaissance role until it was disbanded in 1979. The airfield is now used as a civil airport and many budget airlines use it to serve Stockholm even though it is about one hundred kilometres from the city. The museum opened on October 15th 1991 to celebrate the fiftieth anniversary of the unit. Housed in two buildings the displays trace the history of the wing in great detail. Models, photographs, uniforms, documents, equipment and memorabilia present a vivid history of F 11. The first type to be flown was the Caproni Ca 313 which was replaced by the SAAB 18. Spitfires PR.XIXs were operated from 1948 until 1955 and the first jet equipment, the SAAB J 29, arrived in 1954. The Lansen was used from 1958 until 1965 when the Draken took over. Examples of the three SAAB jets can be seen and these have been joined by other types including the unique VLA (Very Light Aircraft) built by Nyge Aero in 1983. A new hall to house the majority of the aircraft was opened for the summer season of 2001.

TYPE	REG/SER	CON. NO.	PI/NOTES	STATUS
☐ Nyge Aero VLA-1 Sparven	SE-ILX			RA
☐ Scheibe Bergfalke II/55	SE-TAT	332		PV
☐ Scottish Aviation Bulldog 101 (Flp 61C) (Sk 61C)	Fv61061	BH100/179	G-AZWH	PV

TYPE	REG/SER	CON. NO.	PI/NOTES	STATUS
☐ Svenska Aeroplan Aktiebolaget (SAAB) 29C (S 29C)	Fv29902	29902		PV
☐ Svenska Aeroplan Aktiebolaget (SAAB) 32C Lansen (S 32C)	Fv32940	32940	Composite.	PV
☐ Svenska Aeroplan Aktiebolaget (SAAB) 35E Draken (S 35E)	Fv35916	35916	On loan from FVM.	PV
☐ Svenska Aeroplan Aktiebolaget (SAAB) 35F-2 Draken (J 35F-2)	Fv35597	35597	Front fuselage only.	PV
☐ Svenska Aeroplan Aktiebolaget (SAAB) 37 Viggen (SF 37)	Fv37961	37961	Front fuselage only.	PV

FLYGFLOTTILJ 14 FÖRSBANDSMUSEUM (SWE8)

Address:	S 305-91 Halmstad.
Tel:	035-266-2037
Admission:	Wednesday 1300-1500
Location:	About 3 km north west of the town.

The display in the museum trace the history of the wing which was formed at the base in 1944. Types flown before the unit disbanded in 1961 were the SAAB B 18B, de Havilland Vampires and SAAB A 32 Lansens. The site is now home to technical training and fire schools. A society was formed to trace the history of Halmstad and its units and in addition to items of memorabilia they have acquired the Lansen.

TYPE	REG/SER	CON. NO.	PI/NOTES	STATUS
☐ Svenska Aeroplan Aktiebolaget (SAAB) 32A Lansen (A 32A)	Fv32094	32094		RA

FLYGFLOTTILJ 15 MUSEUM (SWE9)

Address:	Byggnad 81, S 826 70 Söderhamn.
Tel:	0270-14284
Email:	f15flygmuseum@hotmail.com
Admission:	January-May September-December Sunday 1100-1500; June-August daily 1000-1500
Location:	The airfield is about 10 km west of the town.

F 15 was formed at Söderhamn in 1945 and disbanded on June 1st 1998. Types operated over the years have been mainly SAAB products. The J 21 served until 1952 when the Vampire arrived. Since then J 29s, A 32s and the Viggen, which was taken on strength in the 1980s, have served with the unit. A museum has been set up to trace the history of the wing. Photographs, documents, models, uniforms and components have been collected. A crew of volunteers has restored one of the few surviving J 21 twin boom fighters. The identity of the Vampire is now unknown since the real Fv28391 has been positively identified at Vännäs from its manufacturer's plates.

TYPE	REG/SER	CON. NO.	PI/NOTES	STATUS
☐ Agusta-Bell 204B (Hkp 3B)	Fv03423	3005		PV
☐ De Havilland D.H.100 Vampire FB.50 (J 28B)	'Fv28391'		The real Fv28391 is stored at the Vännäs Motor Museum	PVX
☐ Scottish Aviation Bulldog 101 (Sk 61A)	Fv61015	BH100/117	G-AZEN	PV
☐ Svenska Aeroplan Aktiebolaget (SAAB) 21A-3 (J 21A-3)	Fv21311	21311	On loan from FVM	PV
☐ Svenska Aeroplan Aktiebolaget (SAAB) 29B (J 29B)	Fv29666	29666		PV
☐ Svenska Aeroplan Aktiebolaget (SAAB) 32A Lansen (A 32A)	Fv32085	32085		PV
☐ Svenska Aeroplan Aktiebolaget (SAAB) 32E Lansen (32B) (J 32B) (J 32E)	Fv32530	32530	On loan from FVM.	PV
☐ Svenska Aeroplan Aktiebolaget (SAAB) 37 Viggen (AJ 37)	Fv37031	37031	On pole on Highway E4.	PV
☐ Svenska Aeroplan Aktiebolaget (SAAB) 37 Viggen (AJ 37)	Fv37067	37067		PV
☐ Svenska Aeroplan Aktiebolaget (SAAB) 37 Viggen (AJ 37) (AJS 37)	Fv37009	37009		PV
☐ Svenska Aeroplan Aktiebolaget (SAAB) 37 Viggen (AJ 37) (AJS 37)	Fv37056	37056		PV
☐ Svenska Aeroplan Aktiebolaget (SAAB) 37 Viggen (AJ 37) (AJS 37)	Fv37081	37081		PV
☐ Svenska Aeroplan Aktiebolaget (SAAB) 37 Viggen (Sk 37)	Fv37805	37805	On loan from FVM.	PV
☐ Svenska Aeroplan Aktiebolaget (SAAB) 91B Safir (Sk 50B)	Fv50006	91206		PV
☐ Svenska Aeroplan Aktiebolaget (SAAB) 105 (Sk 60E)	Fv60145	60145		PV

This de Havilland Moth Major has been fitted with a metal fuselage after a crash. The aircraft is in the Arlanda Flygmuseum. (Douglas Rough)

Unfortunately the Gotlands Flymuseum has closed whilst a local dispute is settled. This Vertol 44 is part of the collection. (GF)

The Götaverken GV-38 is a licence built Rearwin 7000. This survivor is in the Jamtlands Museum at Ostersund. (JFM)

FLYGFLOTTILJ 16 MUSEUM (SWE10)

Address:	Flygflottilj 16, Box 645, S 751 27 Uppsala.
Tel:	018-281112
Admission:	By prior permission only.
Location:	The airfield is about 5 km north of the city off the E.4.

This wing was formed in 1943 and has operated mainly fighter and attack aircraft. The first type to be used was the FFVS J 22 which was replaced by the Mustang in 1945. The J 29 arrived in 1945 and served until the Draken took over 1961. The museum opened in 1993 in an old storehouse built in the eighteenth century. Photographs, documents, uniforms and models trace the history of the unit.

TYPE	REG/SER	CON. NO.	PI/NOTES	STATUS
☐ Svenska Aeroplan Aktiebolaget (SAAB) 29A (J 29A)	Fv29171	29171	On loan from FVM.	RA
☐ Svenska Aeroplan Aktiebolaget (SAAB) 35A Draken (J 35A)	Fv35051	35051	On loan from FVM.	RA
☐ Svenska Aeroplan Aktiebolaget (SAAB) 35F-1 Draken (J 35F-1)	Fv35490	35490		RA
☐ Svenska Aeroplan Aktiebolaget (SAAB) 37 Viggen (JA 37)	Fv37410	37410		RA
☐ Svenska Aeroplan Aktiebolaget (SAAB) 37 Viggen (JA 37)	Fv37425	37425		RA
☐ Svenska Aeroplan Aktiebolaget (SAAB) 105 (Sk 60E)	Fv60143	60143		RA

FLYGFLOTTILJ 17 MUSEUM (SWE11)

Address:	Flygflottilj 17, Box 502, S 372 25 Ronneby.
Tel:	0457-471000
Email:	exp.f17@mil.se
Admission:	By prior permission only.
Location:	At Kallinge airfield which is about 8 km north of the town.

Formed in 1944 the unit first flew Junkers Ju 86's from the field. Sweden took delivery of fifty four examples of the Ju 86 between 1937 and 1940. The last were withdrawn in 1958 and the sole survivor of the type is on show in the Flygvapenmuseum. The Ju 86 was replaced by the SAAB 18 in 1947. The Lansen was operated in the attack role from 1956 until 1976. The current equipment is the JA 37 Viggen. Liaison and helicopter flights are also in residence. Members of the unit are setting up a museum in a building on the base. They have collected a large amount of material including documents, models, photographs, components and uniforms.

TYPE	REG/SER	CON. NO.	PI/NOTES	STATUS
☐ Svenska Aeroplan Aktiebolaget (SAAB) 32A Lansen (A 32A)	Fv32151	32151		RA
☐ Svenska Aeroplan Aktiebolaget (SAAB) 37 Viggen (JA 37) (JA 37D) (JA 37DI)	Fv37440	37440		RA

FLYGFLOTTILJ 21 MUSEUM (SWE12)

Address:	Västra Parkgatan 4, S 972 41 Luleå.
Tel:	0920-234135
Admission:	By prior permission only.
Location:	The airfield is about 5 km south of the town.

The wing was initially formed in 1941 as a training unit and did not acquire its first aircraft until eight years later. In 1949 a fleet of North American Mustangs and SAAB B 18s arrived. The Lansen was allocated in 1961 and the SAAB 105 joined the unit in 1973. The current equipment is the Gripen. The Operation Conversion Unit for the Viggen was formerly based at the field and several versions of the type are in the collection. The museum, located in a building on the base, traces the history of the wing and on show are photographs, documents, engines, models, trophies, instruments, components and uniforms. The collection also includes flying clothing and equipment from the days of the Mustang up to the present time.

TYPE	REG/SER	CON. NO.	PI/NOTES	STATUS
☐ Agusta-Bell 204B (Hkp 3B)	Fv03426	3008		RA
☐ Svenska Aeroplan Aktiebolaget (SAAB) 29C (S 29C)	Fv29929	29929	At Military Gate.	PV
☐ Svenska Aeroplan Aktiebolaget (SAAB) 29C (S 29C)	Fv29937	29937	On loan from FVM.	PV

☐ Svenska Aeroplan Aktiebolaget (SAAB) 32E Lansen (32B) (J 32B) (J 32E)	Fv32529	32529	On loan from FVM.	PV
☐ Svenska Aeroplan Aktiebolaget (SAAB) 35E Draken (35D) (J 35D) (S 35E)	Fv35937	35937 (35296)	Fv35296 – front fuselage only.	PV
☐ Svenska Aeroplan Aktiebolaget (SAAB) 35E Draken (35D) (J 35D) (S 35E)	Fv35949	35949 (35295)	Fv35295 – by civil terminal.	PV
☐ Svenska Aeroplan Aktiebolaget (SAAB) 35E Draken (35D) (J 35D) (S 35E)	Fv35952	35952 (35290)	Fv35290	PV
☐ Svenska Aeroplan Aktiebolaget (SAAB) 35F-2 Draken (J 35F-2)	Fv35566	35566		PV
☐ Svenska Aeroplan Aktiebolaget (SAAB) 37 Viggen (JA 37)	Fv37362	37362		PV
☐ Svenska Aeroplan Aktiebolaget (SAAB) 37 Viggen (SF 37)	Fv37977	37977	On loan from FVM.	PV
☐ Svenska Aeroplan Aktiebolaget (SAAB) 37 Viggen (SH 37)	Fv37927	37927		PV
☐ Svenska Aeroplan Aktiebolaget (SAAB) 37 Viggen (SH 37) (AJSH 37)	Fv37905	37905	On base.	RA
☐ Svenska Aeroplan Aktiebolaget (SAAB) 37 Viggen (Sk 37) (Sk 37E)	Fv37817	37817		PV
☐ Svenska Aeroplan Aktiebolaget (SAAB) 91B Safir (Sk 50B)	Fv50059	91268	Fusealge only.	RA
☐ Svenska Aeroplan Aktiebolaget (SAAB) 105 (Sk 60C)	Fv60004	60004		PV

FLYGVAPENMUSEUM MALMEN (SWE13)

Address:	Box 13 300, S 580 13 Linköping.
Tel:	013-283636 or 299270
Fax:	013-299304
Email:	info@sfhm.se
Admission:	May-September Daily 1200-1600; October-April Daily 1200-1500.
Location:	About 6 km west of Linköping off the E.4.

Hugo Beckhammer was the commanding officer of F 3 wing at Malmslatt from 1941 until 1951. He was determined that historic aircraft stored at military bases should not be scrapped and he set up a small museum in a hangar. After be retired he tried to get official support for an Air Force Museum but progress was slow, In 1967 the nearby town of Ryd provided a building. About twenty five aircraft were stored here and the collection was open at weekends in the summer. In 1976 the plans for a new museum were approved and construction began a few years later. The first stage, with about thirty aircraft on show, was opened by the King of Sweden on March 8th 1984. A second hall was ready for the 1989 season and plans for further expansion have been put forward. In addition there is a large outside area where several aircraft are parked. Workshops are located close by and a hangar on the base and the building at Ryd are used for storage. An excellent exhibition tracing the history of the service can be seen with uniforms, badges, photographs, documents and models. The aircraft in the collection show types used by the Air Force from its foundation up to those currently in service. In 1912 four civilians donated a Nieuport IVG to the Army which led to the establishment of an Aviation Corps. The Nieuport survived and in the 1980s a replica of the second aircraft, a Breguet U III, was built near Stockholm by volunteers. An Army Aviation Workshop was set up at Malmslatt and it constructed a number of types under licence including the Austrian Phönix 122, the sole remaining example is a prized exhibit. The display contains many aircraft which cannot be seen anywhere else in the world. These include a Macchi M.7 flying boat which served from 1919 to 1926, a Malmstatt built Albatros 120 flown from 1915-1929, and an ASJA built Raab-Katzenstein RK 26, designed by Gerhard Fieseler, dating from the 1930s. The sole remaining complete Junkers Ju 86 is also on view. Some were imported from Germany and others assembled by SAAB under the supervision of Junkers engineers. Unique Swedish types are the Tummelisa biplane designed at the Army Workshops and the Sparmann S-1A low wing monoplane. The Tummelisa first flew in 1920 and sixteen were built over the next three years. The type was put back into production in 1928 and a further thirteen entered service. Twelve Sparmann S-lAs were constructed between 1934 and 1938 and used as trainers. They were apparently not an easy aircraft to fly. ASJA of Linköping which manufactured railway equipment, took over Svenska Aero of Stockholm and set up a new factory. Types produced under licence included the de Havilland Tiger Moth, Hawker Hart, Raab-Katzenstein Rk 26, and the Focke-Wulf Stieglitz. Some original designs were also built. SAAB set up its aircraft factory at Trollhättan in 1937 and after a period of friction in the industry a new organisation was established with its main facilities at Linköping. Virtually all military types produced by the factory are in the collection. The L-17 attack bomber was first flown in 1940 and was originally an ASJA design. One example of the type has recently been restored to flying condition. The aircraft took to the air again on July 11th 1997, twenty nine years after its last flight. No examples of the B-18 attack bomber were thought to exist but historians located the resting place of one which force landed on the frozen sea off Sundsvall in 1946. The wreck was raised in 1979 and restoration took place at the SAAB factory and at the Air Force Workshops. The aircraft was ready to take its place in the display when the second hall opened. In the post World War II years the company has produced a number of innovative fighter and attack designs. The twin boom J-21 was first powered by a DB 605 piston engine and the design was later modified to take a jet. None of the jet J-21Rs survived but a piston model has been converted to show this variant. Many versions of the famous barrel shaped J 29, the classic Lansen and the double delta Draken are in the collection. Several variants of the Viggen are also present and many have been loaned to museums across Europe. The Gloster Gladiator and Hawker Hart are shown in Finnish colours as they were flown by a wing of Swedish volunteers who helped the country try to stem the Soviet invasion in 1940. A number of complex exchange deals have resulted in several 'missing' types arriving at Malmslatt. The Moth Trainer, exhibited on floats, was traded for a Tiger Moth. The Firefly came from the Malmö Technical Museum and a Moth Major made the journey south. The Spitfire arrived from Canada and as a result several SAAB Lansens, a Dakota and other aircraft went to the U.S.A. There many interesting items still in store and hopefully a new hall can be added to enhance this informative display.

TYPE	REG/SER	CON. NO.	PI/NOTES	STATUS
☐ Agusta-Bell 204B (Hkp 3B)	Fv03422	3004		RA
☐ Agusta-Bell 204B (Hkp 3C)	03306	3040		RA
☐ Agusta-Bell 206A Jet Ranger 2 (Hkp 6A)	06274	8115		RA
☐ Agusta-Bell 206A Jet Ranger 2 (Hkp 6A)	06276	8118		RA
☐ Agusta-Bell 206A Jet Ranger 2 (Hkp 6A)	06281	8125		RA
☐ Beech D18S	N9887A	A-932	N2052D, CN-MAL	RA
☐ Breguet U III			Partial replica	PV
☐ Bücker Bü 181B-1 Bestmann (Sk 25)	Fv25000	1815001	D-EXWB	RA
☐ Bücker Bü 181B-1 Bestmann (Sk 25)	Fv25114	25114	Fv25114, D-EBIH	PV
☐ Caproni Ca.313 (S 16) (FSM)	'2'			PVX
☐ Caproni-Reggiane Re.2000 Falco I (J 20)	Fv2340	405		PV
☐ Centrala Flygverkstader Malmen 01 (Ö 1) Tummelisa	Fv656	147		PV
☐ Consolidated 28-5A Canso A (Tp 47)	Fv47001	CV 244	9810 (Canada)	PV
☐ De Havilland D.H.60T Moth Trainer (Sk 9)	'Fv558'	1720(?)	A composite of c/n 1718 Fv558, Fv5108, SE-BFI and c/n 1720 Fv5110, SE-BFH-the remaining parts with F. Veteranfly.	PVX
☐ De Havilland D.H.82A Tiger Moth (Sk 11)	Fv515	47	Fv515, SE-BYM	PV
☐ De Havilland D.H.98 Mosquito FB.VI	N9909F		PZ474, NZ2384, ZK-BCV – in USA.	RAC
☐ De Havilland D.H.100 Vampire F.1 (J 28A)	Fv28001	EEP42083		PV
☐ De Havilland D.H.100 Vampire FB.50 (J 28B)	Fv28311	V0590		RA
☐ De Havilland D.H.104 Dove 1B	G-ANVU	04082	VR-NAP	RA
☐ De Havilland D.H.112 Venom NF.51 (J 33)	SE-DCA	12364	Fv33015 – on loan to RFN Museum, Vidsel.	–
☐ De Havilland D.H.112 Venom NF.51 (J 33)	Fv33025	12374	Fv33025, SE-DCD	PV
☐ De Havilland D.H.115 Vampire T.55 (Sk 28C-2)	Fv28451	15745		RA
☐ Donnet-Lévêque L11	10		On loan from TM – Stockholm.	RA
☐ Dornier Do 27A-4 (Fpl 53)	53271	2099	On loan to NHS, Boden.	–
☐ Dornier Do 27A-4 (Fpl 53)	53273	2110		PV
☐ Douglas DC-3A-456 Skytrain (C-47A) (Tp 79)	Fv79007	13647	42-93706, LN-IAH, LN-IKH, SE-CFR	PV
☐ Douglas Skyraider AEW.1 (AD-4W)	SE-EBI	7960	Bu127945, WT947, G-31-11 – has parts of c/n 7587 Bu124777, WV185.	RA
☐ English Electric EA.1 Canberra T.11 (B.2) (Tp 52)	Fv52002	SH.1648	WH905	PV
☐ Fairey Firefly TT.1 (F.1)	SE-CAW	F6121	PP392	RA
☐ Fiat CR.42 (J 11)	Fv2543	921		PV
☐ Fieseler Fi 156C-3/trop Storch (S 14)	Fv3815	110203	Composite	PV
☐ Flygforvaltningens Flygverkstad (FFVS) J 22A	Fv22185	185	On loan to F.10 Flygmuseum.	–
☐ Flygforvaltningens Flygverkstad (FFVS) J 22B	Fv22280	280		PV
☐ Flygkompaniets Tygverkstader Malmen Albatros 120 [Albatros B IIa] (Sk 1)	04	464		PV
☐ Focke-Wulf Fw 44J Stieglitz (Sk 12)	Fv670	52	Fv670, SE-EGB	PV
☐ Fokker C.VE (S 6)	Fv386	207		PV
☐ Gloster Gladiator II (J 8A)	Fv278	G5/59066(?)		PV
☐ Gloster Meteor T.7	SE-CAS	G5/1496		RA
☐ Government Aircraft Factories Jindivik 102A (IIA)			On loan to RFN Museum, Vidsel.	–
☐ Grumman G-39 Goose (JRF-5)	'Fv81002'	B-63	Bu37810, N79901	RAX
☐ Hawker Hart (B 4A)	Fv714	52		PV
☐ Hawker Osprey (S 9)	SE-AYR	2403	Fv403	RAD
☐ Hawker P.1067 Hunter F.50 (J 34)	Fv34016	41H/680304		PV
☐ Heinkel HD 35 (Sk 5)	SE-SAM	235	Fv066	RAC
☐ Holmberg Racer			On loan to Collegium Restaurant, Linköping.	–
☐ Hughes 269A (Hkp 5A)	05215	22-0049	On loan to Svedino's Mus.	–
☐ Hughes 269C (Hkp 5B)	Fv05221	100884		RA
☐ Jacobs Anfänger II				RA
☐ Jacobs Kranich IIB-1 (D.F.S. 108-30) (SE 103)	'SE-SAW'	072	SE-SWN	PVX
☐ Jacobs Meise (D.F.S. 108-70)	SE-SDL	2	On loan to Segelflyg Museum.	–
☐ Jacobs Meise (D.F.S. 108-70)	SE-SAE	685	On loan to Segelflyg Museum.	–
☐ Jacobs Weihe (D.F.S. 108-68) (SE 104)	Fv8316	235		RA
☐ Junkers Ju 86K-4 (B 3C2)	Fv155	0860412		PV
☐ Kawasaki-Vertol KV 107-II-4 (Hkp 4B)	Fv04451	401		RA
☐ Klemm Kl 35D (Sk 15)	Fv5075	1596	SE-AIG, Fv5075, SE-AIG, 'Fv5081'	PV
☐ Macchi M.7	Fv945			PV
☐ Malmo Flygindustri MFI-9B Trainer	'801-01'	42	(SE-ENG), 801-42, SE-EUK	PVX
☐ Malmo Flygindustri MFI-10B Vipan (Fpl 54)	54382	10.03	54382, SE-CPI	PV
☐ Max Holste MH.1521M Broussard	SE-BMH	78	78, F-GHUG, LN-WNA	RA
☐ Mignet HM-14 Pou-du-Ciel				RA
☐ Nieuport IVG	M-1	138		PV
☐ Noorduyn Harvard IIB [North American NA-77 (AT-16)] (Sk 16A)	Fv16109	14-366	42-829, FE632	PV
☐ Noorduyn Norseman VI (C-64A) (UC-64A) (Tp 78)	Fv78001	492	43-35418, SE-ASC, Fv78001, SE-CLZ	PV
☐ Nord NC.701 Martinet [Siebel Si 204D-1]	SE-KAE	264	264 (France)	RA
☐ North American NA-16-4M (Sk 14)			Composite of a NA-64 Yale and a Commonwealth CA-7 Wirraway A20-233.	RAC
☐ North American NA-122 Mustang (P-51D) (J 26)	Fv26020	122-31718	44-63992, Fv26020, 54 (Israel)	PV

☐ Percival P.66 Pembroke C.52 (Tp 83)	Fv83008	P.66/52		PV
☐ Phönix 122 (D III) (J 1)	Fv947			PV
☐ Piper PA-18-135 Super Cub (Fpl 51)	51256	18-6803	SE-CKH51256, SE-CGT	PV
☐ Raab-Katzenstein RK 26 Tigerschwalbe (Sk 10)	Fv536	20	Fv536, Fv5536	PV
☐ Schneider ESG 31 Grunau Baby II (D.F.S. 108-49)	'3'	2152	SE-SAP	PVX
☐ Schneider ESG 31 Grunau Baby IIB (SE 102)	SE-STP		8313	RA
☐ Schneider Grunau SG-38 (D.F.S. 108-14) (SE 101)	80			PV
☐ Scottish Aviation Bulldog 100 (Sk 61D)	Fv61030	BH100/137	G-AZJO	RA
☐ Scottish Aviation Bulldog 101 (Sk 61A)	Fv61006	BH100/106	G-AZAK	RA
☐ Scottish Aviation Bulldog 101 (Sk 61C)	Fv61068	BH100/186	G-AZWO	RA
☐ Seversky EP-106 (J 9)	Fv2134	282-19		PV
☐ Sparmann S 1-A (P 1)	Fv814	8		PV
☐ Sud-Est SE.210 Caravelle III (Tp 85)	Fv85172	172	SE-DAG – due soon.	RA
☐ Sud-Est SE.210 Caravelle III (Tp 85)	Fv85210	210	SE-DAI – with Le Caravelle Club.	–
☐ Sud-Est SE.3130 Alouette II (Hkp 2)	Fv02406	1279	Fv02202, SE-HDE	PV
☐ Supermarine 390 Spitfire PR.XIX	'Fv31051'	6S.683524	PM627, HS964 (India)	PVX
☐ Svenska Aeroplan Aktiebolaget (SAAB) L-17B (S 17B)	Fv17005	17005		PV
☐ Svenska Aeroplan Aktiebolaget (SAAB) 18B (B 18B)	Fv18172	18172		PV
☐ Svenska Aeroplan Aktiebolaget (SAAB) 21A-3 (J 21A-3)	Fv21311	21311	On loan to F 15 Museum.	–
☐ Svenska Aeroplan Aktiebolaget (SAAB) 21A-3 (J 21A-3)	Fv21364	21364		PV
☐ Svenska Aeroplan Aktiebolaget (SAAB) 21R (J 21R)	'Fv21463'		Composite incorporating parts of 21A c/n 21286 Fv 21286.	PVX
☐ Svenska Aeroplan Aktiebolaget (SAAB) 29A (J 29A)	Fv29171	29171	On loan to F16 Museum.	–
☐ Svenska Aeroplan Aktiebolaget (SAAB) 29B (J 29B)	Fv29398	29398		PV
☐ Svenska Aeroplan Aktiebolaget (SAAB) 29C (S 29C)	Fv29937	29937	On loan to F 21 Museum.	–
☐ Svenska Aeroplan Aktiebolaget (SAAB) 29C (S 29C)	Fv29970	29970		RA
☐ Svenska Aeroplan Aktiebolaget (SAAB) 29F (29B) (J 29B) (J 29F)	Fv29441	29441	On pole near E.4 road.	PV
☐ Svenska Aeroplan Aktiebolaget (SAAB) 29F (29B) (J 29B) (J 29F)	Fv29507	29507		PV
☐ Svenska Aeroplan Aktiebolaget (SAAB) 29F (29B) (J 29B) (J 29F)	Fv29575	29575		PV
☐ Svenska Aeroplan Aktiebolaget (SAAB) 29F (29B) (J 29B) (J 29F)	Fv29589	29589	On loan to High Chapparal.	–
☐ Svenska Aeroplan Aktiebolaget (SAAB) 32A Lansen (A 32A)	Fv32197	32197		PV
☐ Svenska Aeroplan Aktiebolaget (SAAB) 32B Lansen (J 32B)	Fv32604	32604	May be scrapped.	RA
☐ Svenska Aeroplan Aktiebolaget (SAAB) 32B Lansen (J 32B)	SE-DXL	32605	Fv32605 – May be scrapped.	RA
☐ Svenska Aeroplan Aktiebolaget (SAAB) 32C Lansen (S 32C)	Fv32917	32917		RA
☐ Svenska Aeroplan Aktiebolaget (SAAB) 32D Lansen (32B) (J 32B) (J 32D)	Fv32548	32548	On loan to Gotlands FF.	–
☐ Svenska Aeroplan Aktiebolaget (SAAB) 32E Lansen (32B) (J 32B) (J 32E)				RA
☐ Svenska Aeroplan Aktiebolaget (SAAB) 32E Lansen (32B) (J 32B) (J 32E)	Fv32507	32507	On pole by E4.	PV
☐ Svenska Aeroplan Aktiebolaget (SAAB) 32E Lansen (32B) (J 32B) (J 32E)	Fv32510	32510	On loan to Ost. LM, Austria.	–
☐ Svenska Aeroplan Aktiebolaget (SAAB) 32E Lansen (32B) (J 32B) (J 32E)	Fv32529	32529	On loan to F 21 Museum.	–
☐ Svenska Aeroplan Aktiebolaget (SAAB) 32E Lansen (32B) (J 32B) (J 32E)	Fv32530	32530	On loan to F 15 Museum.	–
☐ Svenska Aeroplan Aktiebolaget (SAAB) 32E Lansen (32B) (J 32B) (J 32E)	Fv32541	32541		PV
☐ Svenska Aeroplan Aktiebolaget (SAAB) 32E Lansen (32B) (J 32B) (J 32E)	Fv32571	32571	May move to new museum at Kalmar.	RA
☐ Svenska Aeroplan Aktiebolaget (SAAB) 32E Lansen (32B) (J 32B) (J 32E)	Fv32601	32601	On loan to Jämtlands Museum.	–
☐ Svenska Aeroplan Aktiebolaget (SAAB) 32E Lansen (32B) (J 32B) (J 32E)	Fv32612	32612	On loan to Hässlögymnasiet, Västerås.	–
☐ Svenska Aeroplan Aktiebolaget (SAAB) 35 Draken	35-5	35-5		RA
☐ Svenska Aeroplan Aktiebolaget (SAAB) 35A Draken (J 35A)	Fv35051	35051	On loan to F16 Museum.	RA
☐ Svenska Aeroplan Aktiebolaget (SAAB) 35A Draken (J 35A)	Fv35090	35090		PV
☐ Svenska Aeroplan Aktiebolaget (SAAB) 35B Draken (J 35B)	Fv35220	35220	On loan to High Chapparal.	–
☐ Svenska Aeroplan Aktiebolaget (SAAB) 35B Draken (J 35B)	Fv35221	35221	On pole at the closed Tullinge Air Base.	–
☐ Svenska Aeroplan Aktiebolaget (SAAB) 35C Draken (35A) (J 35A) (Sk 35C)	Fv35804	35804 (35016)	Fv35016 – on loan to Ost. LM, Austria.	–
☐ Svenska Aeroplan Aktiebolaget (SAAB) 35C Draken (35A) (J 35A) (Sk 35C)	Fv35810	35810 (35019)	Fv35019 – on loan to F 7 Museum.	–

☐ Svenska Aeroplan Aktiebolaget (SAAB) 35C Draken (35A) (J 35A) (Sk 35C)	Fv35811	35811 (35017)	Fv35017	RA
☐ Svenska Aeroplan Aktiebolaget (SAAB) 35C Draken (35A) (J 35A) (Sk 35C)	Fv35824	35824 (35033)	Fv35033 – on loan to Gotlands FM.	–
☐ Svenska Aeroplan Aktiebolaget (SAAB) 35D Draken (J 35D)			Nose only.	PV
☐ Svenska Aeroplan Aktiebolaget (SAAB) 35D Draken (J 35D)	Fv35371	35371	On loan to HTM, Hungary.	–
☐ Svenska Aeroplan Aktiebolaget (SAAB) 35D Draken (J 35D)	Fv35375	35375		RA
☐ Svenska Aeroplan Aktiebolaget (SAAB) 35E Draken (35D) (J 35D) (S 35E)	Fv35959	35959 (35281)		RA
☐ Svenska Aeroplan Aktiebolaget (SAAB) 35E Draken (S 35E)	Fv35902	35902	On display at Stagården about 20 km north west of Söderhamn.	–
☐ Svenska Aeroplan Aktiebolaget (SAAB) 35E Draken (S 35E)	Fv35906	35906		RA
☐ Svenska Aeroplan Aktiebolaget (SAAB) 35E Draken (S 35E)	Fv35916	35916	On loan to F 11 Museum.	–
☐ Svenska Aeroplan Aktiebolaget (SAAB) 35F-1 Draken (J 35F-1)	Fv35410	35410	Front fuselage only.	PV
☐ Svenska Aeroplan Aktiebolaget (SAAB) 35F-1 Draken (J 35F-1)	Fv35432	35432		RA
☐ Svenska Aeroplan Aktiebolaget (SAAB) 35F-1 Draken (J 35F-1)	Fv35477	35477	On pole beside E4.	PV
☐ Svenska Aeroplan Aktiebolaget (SAAB) 35F-2 Draken (J 35F-2)	Fv35550	35550	On pole by SAAB factory – Linköping.	PV
☐ Svenska Aeroplan Aktiebolaget (SAAB) 35J Draken (35F-2) (J 35F-2) (J 35J)	Fv35520	35520	On loan to Muzeum Lotnictwa Polskiego, Pol.	–
☐ Svenska Aeroplan Aktiebolaget (SAAB) 35J Draken (35F-2) (J 35F-2) (J 35J)	Fv35539	35539		RA
☐ Svenska Aeroplan Aktiebolaget (SAAB) 35J Draken (35F-2) (J 35F-2) (J 35J)	Fv35540	35540		PV
☐ Svenska Aeroplan Aktiebolaget (SAAB) 35J Draken (35F-2) (J 35F-2) (J 35J)	Fv35541	35541		PV
☐ Svenska Aeroplan Aktiebolaget (SAAB) 35J Draken (35F-2) (J 35F-2) (J 35J)	Fv35576	35576	On loan to Svedino's Museum.	–
☐ Svenska Aeroplan Aktiebolaget (SAAB) 35J Draken (35F-2) (J 35F-2) (J 35J)	Fv35624	35624	On loan to Gotlands FF.	–
☐ Svenska Aeroplan Aktiebolaget (SAAB) 35XD Draken (TF-35)	AT-160	351160	In Danish markings – on loan from FHS, Denmark.	RA
☐ Svenska Aeroplan Aktiebolaget (SAAB) 37 Viggen	37-1	37-1	Prototype.	RA
☐ Svenska Aeroplan Aktiebolaget (SAAB) 37 Viggen (AJ 37)	Fv37067	37067	On loan to Söderhamns kommun.	–
☐ Svenska Aeroplan Aktiebolaget (SAAB) 37 Viggen (AJ 37) (AJS 37)	Fv37009	37009	On loan to F15 Museum.	–
☐ Svenska Aeroplan Aktiebolaget (SAAB) 37 Viggen (AJ 37) (AJS 37)	Fv37027	37027		PV
☐ Svenska Aeroplan Aktiebolaget (SAAB) 37 Viggen (AJ 37) (AJS 37)	Fv37074	37074	On loan to MA, SP.	–
☐ Svenska Aeroplan Aktiebolaget (SAAB) 37 Viggen (AJ 37)	Fv37094	37094	On loan to Aeroseum.	–
☐ Svenska Aeroplan Aktiebolaget (SAAB) 37 Viggen (AJ 37) (AJS 37)	Fv37097	37097	On loan to Jämtlands FM.	–
☐ Svenska Aeroplan Aktiebolaget (SAAB) 37 Viggen (AJ 37) (AJS 37)	Fv37108	37108		PV
☐ Svenska Aeroplan Aktiebolaget (SAAB) 37 Viggen (JA 37)	Fv37301	37321	On loan to Mus. Europ, FRA.	–
☐ Svenska Aeroplan Aktiebolaget (SAAB) 37 Viggen (JA 37)	Fv37321	37301		PV
☐ Svenska Aeroplan Aktiebolaget (SAAB) 37 Viggen (JA 37)	Fv37364	37364	On pole beside E4 at Söderhamn.	PV
☐ Svenska Aeroplan Aktiebolaget (SAAB) 37 Viggen (JA 37)	Fv37367	37367	On pole beside E4.	PV
☐ Svenska Aeroplan Aktiebolaget (SAAB) 37 Viggen (JA 37) (JA 37D) (JA 37DI)	Fv37347	37347	On loan to MRM, HUN.	–
☐ Svenska Aeroplan Aktiebolaget (SAAB) 37 Viggen (JA 37) (JA 37D) (JA 37DI)	Fv37429	37429	On loan to Lennund. Mus, EST.	–
☐ Svenska Aeroplan Aktiebolaget (SAAB) 37 Viggen (JA 37) (JA 37D) (JA 37DI)	Fv37431	37431	On loan to Osterr LM, AUT.	–
☐ Svenska Aeroplan Aktiebolaget (SAAB) 37 Viggen (SF 37)	Fv37961	37961	Front fuselage only.	RA
☐ Svenska Aeroplan Aktiebolaget (SAAB) 37 Viggen (SF 37)	Fv37972	37972	On loan to Gotlands FM.	–
☐ Svenska Aeroplan Aktiebolaget (SAAB) 37 Viggen (SF 37)	Fv37977	37977	On loan to F 21 Museum.	–
☐ Svenska Aeroplan Aktiebolaget (SAAB) 37 Viggen (SF 37) (AJSF 37)	Fv37951	37951	On loan to STM, SLO.	–
☐ Svenska Aeroplan Aktiebolaget (SAAB) 37 Viggen (SF 37) (AJSF 37)	Fv37954	37954	On loan to MLA, POL.	–
☐ Svenska Aeroplan Aktiebolaget (SAAB) 37 Viggen (SF 37) (AJSF 37)	Fv37957	37957	On loan to HSLM, CZ	–
☐ Svenska Aeroplan Aktiebolaget (SAAB) 37 Viggen (SF 37) (AJSF 37)	Fv37974	37974	On loan to Flugausstellung Junior, GER.	–

☐ Svenska Aeroplan Aktiebolaget (SAAB) 37 Viggen (SH 37) (AJSH 37)	Fv37901	37901	On loan to Aviodrome, NET.	–
☐ Svenska Aeroplan Aktiebolaget (SAAB) 37 Viggen (SH 37) (AJSH 37)	Fv37911	37911	On loan to Aeroseum.	–
☐ Svenska Aeroplan Aktiebolaget (SAAB) 37 Viggen (SH 37) (AJSH 37)	Fv37918	37918	On loan to Newark AM, EN	–
☐ Svenska Aeroplan Aktiebolaget (SAAB) 37 Viggen (Sk 37)	Fv37800	37800		PV
☐ Svenska Aeroplan Aktiebolaget (SAAB) 37 Viggen (Sk 37)	Fv37805	37805	On loan to F 15 Museum.	–
☐ Svenska Aeroplan Aktiebolaget (SAAB) 37 Viggen (Sk 37)	Fv37811	37811	On loan to Mus. Europ, FRA.	–
☐ Svenska Aeroplan Aktiebolaget (SAAB) 37 Viggen (Sk 37) (Sk 37E)	Fv37808	37808	On loan to MA, FRA.	–
☐ Svenska Aeroplan Aktiebolaget (SAAB) 39 Gripen (JAS 39)	39-2	39-2		PV
☐ Svenska Aeroplan Aktiebolaget (SAAB) 91A Safir	'Fv91104'	91104	SE-AYC – on loan to SAAB Mus.	–
☐ Svenska Aeroplan Aktiebolaget (SAAB) 91B Safir (Sk 50B)	Fv50016	91216	On pole by E.4 road.	PV
☐ Svenska Aeroplan Aktiebolaget (SAAB) 91B Safir (Sk 50B)	Fv50046	91258		PV
☐ Svenska Aeroplan Aktiebolaget (SAAB) 91B Safir (Sk 50B)	Fv50051	91260		RA
☐ Svenska Aeroplan Aktiebolaget (SAAB) 91B Safir (Sk 50B)	Fv50068	91278		RA
☐ Svenska Aeroplan Aktiebolaget (SAAB) 91D Safir	SF-18	91364	In Finnish markings – on loan to Svedino's Mus.	–
☐ Svenska Aeroplan Aktiebolaget (SAAB) 105 (Sk 60A)	Fv60113	60113		PV
☐ Svenska Aeroplan Aktiebolaget (SAAB) 105 (Sk 60B)	Fv60080	60080	On pole beside E.4 road.	PV
☐ Svenska Aeroplan Aktiebolaget (SAAB) 105 (Sk 60B)	Fv60091	60091		PV
☐ Svenska Aeroplan Aktiebolaget (SAAB) 105XT	SE-XBZ	105-2	On loan to Svedinos Mus.	–
☐ Svenska Aeroplan Aktiebolaget (SAAB) 210 Lill-Draken				PV
☐ Svenska Aeroplan Aktiebolaget (SAAB) 340	SE-ISF	001	On pole beside E.4 road. – Owned by SAAB.	PV
☐ Svenska Aeroplan Aktiebolaget (SAAB) B3LA			Mock up	RA
☐ Svenska Aeroplan Aktiebolaget – Malmo Flygindustri (SAAB-MFI) 15 Safari	SE-XCB	15001	SE-301	RAA
☐ Thulin G	15	40 (?)		RAC
☐ Vertol V.44A (Hkp 1)	01001	497		PV
☐ Vickers 668 Varsity T.1 (Tp 82)	Fv82001	622	WJ900	PV
☐ Wytwornia Sprzetu Komunikacyjnego (WSK) Lim-2 [MiG-15bis]	215	1B 002-15	In Polish markings.	PV

FLYGVAPNET VETERANFLYGDIVISIONEN (SWE14)

Address:	Stellan Andersson, Veteranflygdivision Flygflottilj 7, S 530 32 Såtenäs.
Admission:	By prior permission only.
Location:	Just south of the town which is about 25 km south west of Lidköping.

The SAAB J 29 owned by the Flygvapenmuseum was kept in an airworthy condition by volunteers at Ängleholm for the last few years. As the last few Lansens and Drakens were withdrawn from service a decision was made to formally set up the flight. Several Lansens and Drakens were then allocated. In 2005 three Viggens joined the group. The flight is run from Såtenäs but some of the aircraft may be at other bases.

TYPE	REG/SER	CON. NO.	PI/NOTES	STATUS
☐ Hughes 269C (Hkp 5B)	SE-JIR	S-1269	Fv05245 – On loan to Patria Helicopters.	–
☐ Hughes 269C (Hkp 5B)	SE-JIS	S-1270	Fv05246 – On loan to Patria Helicopters.	–
☐ Svenska Aeroplan Aktiebolaget (SAAB) L-17A (B 17A)	Fv17239	17239	Fv17239, SE-BYH	RAA
☐ Svenska Aeroplan Aktiebolaget (SAAB) 29F (29B) (J 29B) (J 29F)	SE-DXB	29670	Fv29670	RAA
☐ Svenska Aeroplan Aktiebolaget (SAAB) 32A Lansen (A 32A)	Fv32070	32070		RA
☐ Svenska Aeroplan Aktiebolaget (SAAB) 32B Lansen (J 32B)	Fv32542	32542		RA
☐ Svenska Aeroplan Aktiebolaget (SAAB) 32B Lansen (J 32B)	Fv32620	32620		RA

TYPE	REG/SER	CON. NO.	PI/NOTES	STATUS
☐ Svenska Aeroplan Aktiebolaget (SAAB) 32D Lansen (32B) (J 32B) (J 32D)	Fv32606	32606		RA
☐ Svenska Aeroplan Aktiebolaget (SAAB) 32E Lansen (32B) (J 32B) (J 32E)	Fv32512	32512		RA
☐ Svenska Aeroplan Aktiebolaget (SAAB) 35C Draken (35A) (J 35A) (Sk 35C)	Fv35810	35810 (35019)	Fv35019	RA
☐ Svenska Aeroplan Aktiebolaget (SAAB) 35J Draken (35F-2) (J 35F-2) (J 35J)	Fv35556	35556		RAA
☐ Svenska Aeroplan Aktiebolaget (SAAB) 35J Draken (35F-2) (J 35F-2) (J 35J)	Fv35586	35586		RAA
☐ Svenska Aeroplan Aktiebolaget (SAAB) 37 Viggen (AJ 37) (AJS 37)	Fv37098	37098		RA
☐ Svenska Aeroplan Aktiebolaget (SAAB) 37 Viggen (JA 37) (JA 37D) (JA 37DI)	Fv37415	37415		RA
☐ Svenska Aeroplan Aktiebolaget (SAAB) 37 Viggen (JA 37) (JA 37D) (JA 37DI)	Fv37449	37449		RA

FORENINGEN VETERANFLY (SWE15)

Address:	c/o Hans Bergenfors, Skepparegatan 4, S 602 27 Norrköping.
Tel:	011-159991 or 161430.
Admission:	By prior permission only.
Location:	At Kungsangen Airport which is just north east of the town.

The group was formed in the early 1980s and now has two hangars at the airport along with workshops in the town. The Tiger Moth was obtained from Denmark and underwent a protracted rebuild. The biplane crashed in 1989 soon after it had been completed and it returned to the workshops for repairs. The Hornet Moth was delivered to the Norrköping Flying Club in September 1937 and remained with them until 1946. This aircraft had several owners around the country prior to being withdrawn in 1965. The Hornet returned to Norrköping in the late 1980s and is now in pristine condition. One of the two Moth Trainers known to survive is slowly being rebuilt at workshops in England and Sweden. The Cub normally operates on floats from the local river. The former Swiss Air Force Vampire is a fairly recent addition to the fleet.

TYPE	REG/SER	CON. NO.	PI/NOTES	STATUS
☐ De Havilland D.H.60T Moth Trainer (Sk 9)	SE-BFI	1718	Fv558, Fv5108 – with parts from c/n 1720 Fv5110, SE-BFH	RAC
☐ De Havilland D.H.82A Tiger Moth	SE-AMG	84589	T6122, G-ANTV, D-EKUR, OY-DET	RAA
☐ De Havilland D.H.87B Hornet Moth	SE-AGE	8136		RAA
☐ De Havilland D.H.100 Vampire FB.6	SE-DXS	705	J-1196 (Switzerland)	RAA
☐ De Havilland D.H.C.1 Chipmunk 22 (T.10)	SE-BBS	C1/0205	WB756, G-AOJR, D-EGIM, G-AOJR, D-EGIM, OY-DFB	RAA
☐ Piper J-3C-65 Cub	SE-AHP	2371		RA
☐ Svenska Aeroplan Aktiebolaget (SAAB) 91B-2 Safir	SE-CAB	91334	334 (Norway)	RAA

GARNISONSMUSEET (SWE16)

Address:	Box 9105, Sveavägen, S 961 19 Boden
Tel:	0921-68811
Email:	garnisonsmuseum@i.19.mil.se
Location:	In the south western part of the town.

Boden is an important army town and this museum traces the military history of the region over many years. Uniforms, documents, regimental memorabilia and vehicles can be seen. There is a section devoted to army aviation. The Swedish Army operated sixteen Agusta-Bell 204s and several are still in service.

TYPE	REG/SER	CON. NO.	PI/NOTES	STATUS
☐ Agusta-Bell 204B (Hkp 3C)	03315	3195		PV

GÖTEBORGS STADSMUSEUM (SWE17)

Address:	Norra Hamngatan 12, S 411 14 Göteborg.
Tel:	031-612770
Fax:	031-774-0358
Admission:	May-August daily 1000-1700; September- April Tuesday -Saturday 1000-1700 Sunday 1200-1700.
Location:	In the city centre. Friday 1100-1600 ; Saturday-Sunday 1000- 1700.

The Göteborgs Industrimuseum traced the story of industrial development in the city and the local area. The city has played a prominent part in manufacturing and locally made items featured prominently in the display. The museum moved to new premises in the mid-1980s and has recently combined with other collections to form the City Museum. The Albatros B II dating from 1915, was operated by the Swedish Navy until the early 1930s. Civil registered to a Gothenburg owner in 1931 it was flown for four years and then donated to the museum. After almost forty years on show the aircraft was dismantled and put in store when the museum moved. The Schneider ESG-31 glider is on loan to the Segelflyg Museum.

TYPE	REG/SER	CON. NO.	PI/NOTES	STATUS
☐ Albatros B IIa	SE-ACR		Fv5, SE-94	RA
☐ Schneider ESG 31 Schleisserland	SE-ADP	84	On loan to Segelflygmuseum	–

GÖTEBORGS VETERANFLYGSÄLLSKAP (SWE18)

Address:	Nora Linden 6, S 411-18 Göteborg.
Tel:	031-133660
Admission:	By prior permission only.
Location:	At Alingsås Airfield which is about 40 km north east of Göteborg off the E.3.

The group was formed in 1980 and soon acquired its first aircraft the K.Z.III. Two locally built GV-38s are in the fleet. One has been modified to have a Continental engine and this is in flying condition. The second is being rebuilt and will be fitted with the original Le Blond radial.

TYPE	REG/SER	CON. NO.	PI/NOTES	STATUS
☐ Götaverken GV-38 [Rearwin 9000L]				RAC
☐ Götaverken GV-38 [Rearwin 9000L]	SE-AHG	8		RAA
☐ Piper J-3C-65 Cub (L-4H)	SE-BEL	10951	43-29660, OO-AAO, G-AITP	RAA
☐ Scheibe Bergfalke II/55	SE-TAE	316		RA
☐ Skandinavisk Aero Industri (SAI) KZ III U-2	SE-AMA	81	OY-DVU	RAA

GOTLANDS FLYGMUSEUM (SWE19)

Address:	Hangarvägen 2, S 621 41 Visby.
Tel:	0498-210405
Email:	info@goff.se
Admission:	Currently closed due to a local dispute. Contact the museum for the latest position.
Location:	At Visby Airport which is about 3 km north east of the town off Road 148.

This museum opened on June 27th 1997 in a hangar and the former terminal building at Visby. In the summer of 1996 the aircraft collection of the Käremo Museum was offered for sale. The majority of the airframes were acquired and transported by boat to Gotland. The displays, which are still being developed, aim to trace the history of aviation in the region. The oldest aircraft present is a Caudron Pelican, one of two known to have survived. The prototype of this high wing monoplane first flew in the mid-1930s and about sixty were built. The example in the collection was imported into Sweden in the summer of 1937 and flew until the late 1950s. In recent years the aircraft has moved around the country and is currently under restoration. The well known Swedish designer Björn Andreasson developed the MFI-9 for Malmo Flygindustri. Converted from his BA-7 prototype the Junior first flew in May 1961. Seventy MFI-9s and 9Bs were built in Sweden. Bölkow obtained a licence to produce the type and constructed more than two hundred as the BO 208 Junior. The Aero Brigadyr did not see a great deal of use outside the former Eastern Bloc. The one on show is from a batch of three imported into Switzerland in 1960. The Antonov An-2 was used in an escape bid from the Soviet Union and came down in the sea off an island near the Swedish Coast. One of the Lansens, a Draken and the Viggens have been loaned by the Flygvapenmuseum and all flew into Visby. The engines on the pair of Drakens were run at regular intervals. Two designs originated in Finland. These are the PIK-20 glider and the Tervamaki autogyro. A local dispute threatens the future of this excellent collection.

TYPE	REG/SER	CON. NO.	PI/NOTES	STATUS
☐ Aero L-60 Brigadyr	HB-EZE	150911		RA
☐ Agusta-Bell 204B (Hkp 3B)	Fv03421	3003		RA
☐ Antonov An-2TP	CCCP-70501	1G 144-12	Carries c/n 1G 83-34	RA
☐ Caudron C.510 Pélican	SE-AGA	7338/45	F-AOYC	RAD
☐ Douglas Skyraider AEW.1 (AD-4W)			Nose section only.	RA
☐ Enstrom F-28C	SE-HHT	429	Fuselage only.	RA
☐ Hughes 269B	SE-HCP	38-0358		RA
☐ Malmo Flygindustri MFI-9 Junior	SE-EBP	05	(SE-EBP), OH-MFA	RA
☐ Mignet HM-14 Pou-du-Ciel	SE-464			RA
☐ Mini Cub	SE-SEY			RA
☐ Pitts S-1S Special				RA
☐ Polyteknikkojen Ilmailukerho PIK-20	SE-TNX	20009		RA
☐ Rotorway Scorpion 1				RA

TYPE	REG/SER	CON. NO.	PI/NOTES	STATUS
☐ Svenska Aeroplan Aktiebolaget (SAAB) 29F (29B) (J 29B) (J 29F)	Fv29624	29624		RA
☐ Svenska Aeroplan Aktiebolaget (SAAB) 32B Lansen (J 32B)	Fv32502	32502	Fuselage only.	RA
☐ Svenska Aeroplan Aktiebolaget (SAAB) 32D Lansen (32B) (J 32B) (J 32D)	Fv32548	32548	On loan from FVM.	RA
☐ Svenska Aeroplan Aktiebolaget (SAAB) 35C Draken (35A) (J 35A) (Sk 35C)	Fv35824	35824 (35033)	Fv 35033 – on loan from FVM.	RA
☐ Svenska Aeroplan Aktiebolaget (SAAB) 35F-1 Draken (J 35F-1)	Fv35429	35429	Fuselage only.	RA
☐ Svenska Aeroplan Aktiebolaget (SAAB) 35J Draken (35F-2) (J 35F-2) (J 35J)	Fv35545	35545		RA
☐ Svenska Aeroplan Aktiebolaget (SAAB) 35J) Draken (35F-2) (J 35F-2) (J 35J	Fv35624	35624	On loan from FVM.	RA
☐ Svenska Aeroplan Aktiebolaget (SAAB) 37 Viggen (JA 37)	Fv37432	37432		RA
☐ Svenska Aeroplan Aktiebolaget (SAAB) 37 Viggen (SF 37)	Fv37972	37972	On loan from FVM.	RA
☐ Svenska Aeroplan Aktiebolaget (SAAB) 105 (Sk 60B)	Fv60074	60074		RA
☐ Tervamaki JT-3				RA
☐ Ultralight				RA
☐ Vertol V.44A (Hkp 1)	01009	607		RA

HERMANSSON SAMLINGAR (SWE20)

Address:	Storsätern 334, S 790-91 Idre.
Tel:	0253-23351
Admission:	Currently closed.
Location:	At Grövelsjön which is about 140 km north west of Mora.

This interesting collection of parts recovered from crash sites was on show in several buildings in the town. The promised funding from the locality did not materialise so the items have been put in store. The latest news is that the museum may relocate to Norway. Formerly on show were components from a Heinkel He 111 which crashed nearby on June 1st 1940, parts from a Messerschmitt downed in Norway and pieces of a Spitfire which force landed in 1942. There were many models, photographs, uniforms and weapons tracing the stories of these three aircraft. It can only be hoped that a new site can be found for this fascinating exhibition.

HIGH CHAPARRAL (SWE21)

Address:	Box 56, S 330 33 Hillerstorp
Tel:	0370-82700
Fax:	0370-82485
Email:	bh@highchapparal.se
Admission:	May-September Daily 0800-1800.
Location:	About 7 km south of Hillerstorp off Road 152.

Established in the 1960s the complex features a typical 'wild-west' town and has daily shows of cowboy skills. In the 1970s several museums were added including one featuring transport. A number of interesting aircraft were acquired. A de Havilland Moth Major delivered new to Sweden in 1933 was the highlight. A Fairchild Cornell which served with the Norwegian forces and a Piaggio P.136L were also on view. In 1990 a fire destroyed the museum building and these were lost along with many other historic items.

TYPE	REG/SER	CON. NO.	PI/NOTES	STATUS
☐ Svenska Aeroplan Aktiebolaget (SAAB) 29F (29B) (J 29B) (J 29F)	Fv29589	29589		PV
☐ Svenska Aeroplan Aktiebolaget (SAAB) 35B Draken (J 35B)	Fv35220	35220	On loan from FVM.	PV
☐ Vickers 815 Viscount	SE-IVY	375	AP-AJF, G-AVJB	PV

JÄMTLANDS FLYG & LOTTAMUSEUM (SWE22)

Address:	Rotavägen 14, S 831 73 Östersund.
Tel:	063-35601
Email:	flyg.o.lottamuseum@ostersund.mail.telia.com
Admission:	June-August daily 1000-1700.
Location:	At Optand airfield which is about 10 km south of the town off Road 14.

The museum took over the private collection of the late Hilding Andersson in the early 1990s. The aircraft and other items were moved to Optand airfield which was constructed in 1940. Several hangars, aircraft shelters in the forest, taxiways and runways still survive. The museum opened in 1994 and one section is devoted to the role of women in peace and war. In addition to the aircraft there are engines, components, photographs and documents on show. Flygflottilj 4 was formed at nearby Frösön on July 1st 1926 and the history of the unit is portrayed in the exhibition. The SAAB 29 was operated from 1956 to 1966 when it was replaced by the Lansen. The Draken arrived in 1969 and was succeeded by the Viggen in the mid-1980s. The Harvard was used in the training role for many years and the Norseman served as an ambulance aircraft at Frösön. Three gliders are on show including a Grunau Baby painted in the colours of one flown by the flying club at F 4. The GV 38 is based on the American Rearwin 9000 and fourteen were built in Gothenburg between 1938 and 1943.

TYPE	REG/SER	CON. NO.	PI/NOTES	STATUS
☐ Agusta-Bell 204B (Hkp 3B)	Fv03427	3042		PV
☐ Götaverken GV-38 [Rearwin 9000L]	SE-AHU	12		PV
☐ Janowski J-1B Don Quixote	SE-XFC	085		PV
☐ Noorduyn Norseman VI (C-64A) (UC-64A)	'Fv78002'	649	44-70384, LN-PAD, R-AI (Norwegian), LN-BFN	PVX
☐ North American NA-75 Harvard II (Sk 16A)	Fv16145	75-3497	3223 (Canada)	PV
☐ Polyteknikkojen Ilmailukerho PIK-5b Cumulus	SE-STZ	1		PV
☐ Scheibe Bergfalke II/55	SE-SLL	218		PV
☐ Schneider ESG 31 Grunau Baby IIB	'F4 A'	104	SE-SDE	PVX
☐ Schneider Grunau SG-38 (D.F.S. 108-14)				PV
☐ Scottish Aviation Bulldog 100 (Sk 61B)	Fv61055	BH100/173	G-AZUD	PV
☐ Svenska Aeroplan Aktiebolaget (SAAB) 29F (29B) (J 29B) (J 29F)	Fv29373	29373		PV
☐ Svenska Aeroplan Aktiebolaget (SAAB) 32E Lansen (32B) (J 32B) (J 32E)	Fv32601	32601	On loan from FVM.	PV
☐ Svenska Aeroplan Aktiebolaget (SAAB) 35D Draken (J 35D)	Fv35345	35345	Front fuselage only.	PV
☐ Svenska Aeroplan Aktiebolaget (SAAB) 35D Draken (J 35D)	Fv35392	35392		PV
☐ Svenska Aeroplan Aktiebolaget (SAAB) 35J Draken (35F-2) (J 35F-2) (J 35J)	Fv35502	35502		PV
☐ Svenska Aeroplan Aktiebolaget (SAAB) 35J Draken (35F-2) (J 35F-2) (J 35J)	Fv35604	35604		RA
☐ Svenska Aeroplan Aktiebolaget (SAAB) 37 Viggen (AJ 37) (AJS 37)	Fv37097	37097	On loan from FVM.	PV
☐ Svenska Aeroplan Aktiebolaget (SAAB) 37 Viggen (JA 37)	Fv37392	37392		RA
☐ Svenska Aeroplan Aktiebolaget (SAAB) 37 Viggen (JA 37)	Fv37448	37448		RA
☐ Svenska Aeroplan Aktiebolaget (SAAB) 37 Viggen (JA 37) (JA 37D) (JA 37DI)	Fv37412	37412		PV
☐ Svenska Aeroplan Aktiebolaget (SAAB) 37 Viggen (Sk 37)	Fv37803	37803		RA
☐ Svenska Aeroplan Aktiebolaget (SAAB) 91B Safir (Sk 50B)	Fv50020	91222		PV
☐ Svenska Aeroplan Aktiebolaget (SAAB) 105 (Sk 60B)	Fv60056	60056		PV

KVIKKJOKK FJÄLLSTATION (SWE23)

Address:	962 02 Kvikkjokk.
Tel:	0971-21022
Fax:	0971-21030
Email:	info@kvikkjokk.info
Admission:	When the hostel is open.
Location:	About 100 km west of Jokkmokk.

This tourist hostel houses an exhibition about a Hampden which crashed in the area. Large parts from the site have been salvaged by groups in other countries. The crash location can be visited.

LANDSKRONA MUSEUM (SWE24)

Address:	Slottsgatan, S 261 31 Landskrona.
Tel:	0418-79-532.
Admission:	Daily 1200-1700.
Location:	In the centre of the town which is about 40 km north of Malmö off the E.6.

Exhibitions portraying local history and industry can be seen on four floors in this fascinating museum. There are also sections tracing the cultural life of the region. Enoch Thulin set up a factory in the town in 1915 and over the next four years produced over one hundred aircraft and over seven hundred engines. In all, fourteen different types of aircraft were made. The early models were copies of foreign designs. The A was based on the Blériot XI, the B on the Morane-Saulnier G and the C on the Morane-Saulnier L. His early engines were also developed from successful French motors. His own powerplants included both rotary and radial types.

Aircraft were exported to Denmark, Finland and Holland. A replica of part of his workshop has been constructed and fourteen of his engines are on view. Also on show are many photographs and documents tracing his work. The development of Thulin's designs can be seen in the display which also features models of most types he constructed. The prototype of the two seat NA biplane fighter was built in 1919 but did not enter production. Powered by a 135 hp Thulin G rotary the aircraft did not make its maiden flight until 1921.

TYPE	REG/SER	CON. NO.	PI/NOTES	STATUS
☐ Thulin NA		1/00		PV

LE CARAVELLE CLUB (SWE25)

Address:	Angfartyget Blidösund, Sheppsbron 10, S 111 30 Stockholm.
Email:	andre@grm.se
Admission:	By prior permission only.
Location:	At Arlanda airport which is about 40 km north of Stockholm off the E.4.

Two former S.A.S. Caravelles were transferred to the Air Force in May 1971 and they gave excellent service until September 1988. One aircraft has been acquired by the group who plan to keep it in airworthy condition.

TYPE	REG/SER	CON. NO.	PI/NOTES	STATUS
☐ Sud-Est SE.210 Caravelle III (Tp 85)	SE-DAI	210	SE-DAI, Fv85210 – on loan from FVM.	RAC

LJUNGBYHEDS AERONAUTISKA SÄLLSTAP (SWE26)

Address:	Box 15, S 260 70 Ljungbyhed.
Tel:	0435-45000
Admission:	By prior permission only.
Location:	At Ljungbyhed airfield which is about 25 km north east of Helsingborg south of Road 21.

The area has been in military use for many years and members of the group are working to set up a museum in a restored nineteenth century former officer's mess. A number of other buildings from the same period are located close by. The collection includes many photographs, documents and items of memorabilia and a comprehensive display will be staged. Ljungbyhed was the main pilot training school for the Air Force from 1926 until it closed in the late 1990s. A civilian school and other units remain at the field. The majority of the aircraft represent types which have been flown from the site. The J 29 is parked on the camp awaiting restoration for static display. The two Tiger Moths, the Fokker Dr I and the three Austers are owned by members of the group. One Tiger resides at a private strip near the field and the Austers are currently in local workshops. The Autocrat, which was delivered new to Sweden in 1946, is being converted to the AOP.5 model.

TYPE	REG/SER	CON. NO.	PI/NOTES	STATUS
☐ Auster Alpha 5	SE-CME	3410	G-APNN	RAC
☐ Auster J AOP.5	SE-BZB	1532	TJ513, G-ALCT	RAC
☐ Auster J AOP.5 (J/1 Autocrat)	SE-ARG	1882		RAC
☐ De Havilland D.H.82A Tiger Moth	SE-CWG	3364	G-ADLV, BB750, G-AORA	RAA
☐ De Havilland D.H.82A Tiger Moth	SE-COG	85593	DE639, G-APLI	RAA
☐ De Havilland D.H.115 Vampire T.55	SE-DXV	981	U-1221 (Switzerland)	RAA
☐ Fokker Dr I (R)				RAC
☐ Scottish Aviation Bulldog 100 (Sk 61A)	Fv61033	BH100/141	G-AZJS	RA
☐ Scottish Aviation Bulldog 100 (Sk 61D)	Fv61001	BH100/101	G-AYWN	RA
☐ Svenska Aeroplan Aktiebolaget (SAAB) 91B Safir (Sk 50B)	SE-IIL	91211	Fv50011	RAA
☐ Svenska Aeroplan Aktiebolaget (SAAB) 91B Safir (Sk 50B)	Fv50039	91251		RA
☐ Svenska Aeroplan Aktiebolaget (SAAB) 91B Safir (Sk 50B)	SE-LAR	91270	Fv50061	RAA
☐ Svenska Aeroplan Aktiebolaget (SAAB) 91B Safir (Sk 50B)	Fv50063	91272	Front fuselage only.	RA
☐ Svenska Aeroplan Aktiebolaget (SAAB) 91B Safir (Sk 50B)	SE-LAS	91285	Fv50075	RAA
☐ Svenska Aeroplan Aktiebolaget (SAAB) 91C Safir (Sk 50C)	Fv50083	91398		RA
☐ Svenska Aeroplan Aktiebolaget (SAAB) 91C Safir (Sk 50C)	SE-LAP	91400	Fv50085	RAA
☐ Svenska Aeroplan Aktiebolaget (SAAB) 105 (Sk 60D)	Fv60132	60132		RA
☐ Svenska Aeroplan Aktiebolaget (SAAB) 105 (Sk 60E)	Fv60142	60142		RA

MALMÖ TEKNISKA MUSEUM (SWE27)

Address:	Box 4406, Malmöhusvägen 7 S 201 24 Malmö.
Tel:	040-341000 or 344438 or 344453.
Admission:	Tuesday-Saturday 1200-1600; Sunday 1200-1630. June-August Monday 1200-1600.
Location:	In the city centre near the main parks.

On show at this museum are exhibits tracing the development of industrial engineering and all forms of communication. The aeronautical section contains models, engines, photographs and components. The Thulin A is based on the famous Blériot XI and the B on the Morane-Saulnier G. The Auster was built up in Denmark from spares by members of the K.Z. Club and exchanged for a Rearwin 9000 imported into Sweden by the Götaverken company. The Moth Major was assembled in Finland in 1949 by the Karhumaki company from spares. Originally it featured a raised rear fuselage and enclosed cabin. The biplane was rebuilt to the correct form in the workshops of the Air Force Museum at Malmslatt.

TYPE	REG/SER	CON. NO.	PI/NOTES	STATUS
☐ Auster J/1 Autocrat	OY-DNU	2102		PV
☐ Centrala Flygverkstader Malmen 01 Tummelisa (R)			Front fuselage and wings.	PV
☐ De Havilland D.H.60GIII Moth Major	OH-VKM	4/VK	Finnish built from spares	PV
☐ Hemminger LH-22 Baby-Falk	SE-SHR	18		PV
☐ Klemm Kl 35D (Sk 15)	Fv5010	1806	Fv5010, SE-BHG	PV
☐ Svenska Aeroplan Aktiebolaget (SAAB) 35F-1 Draken (J 35F-1)	Fv35484	35484		PV
☐ Thulin A [Blériot XI]			Front fuselage only.	PV
☐ Thulin B [Morane-Saulnier G]			Fuselage only – on loan from T.M. Stockholm.	PV
☐ Vickers 784D Viscount (745D)	SE-CNK	227	N7465, VH-TVO, (K-AAAA), PI-C772 – front fuselage only.	PV

MARINMUSEET (SWE28)

Address:	Stumholmen, 371 32 Karlskrona.
Tel:	0455-359331
Email:	ann-britt.christensson@maritima.se
Admission:	September-May daily 1100-1700; June-August daily 1000-1800.
Location:	In the southern part of the town.

The maritime history of the nation from Viking times up to the present day is portrayed in this informative museum. On show are documents, photographs, uniforms, boats and models. The Marineflyget, formed in 1947, has used mainly helicopters. The front fuselage of a Vertol Hkp 1, the first type used, can be seen.

TYPE	REG/SER	CON. NO.	PI/NOTES	STATUS
☐ Vertol V.44A (Hkp 1)	Fv01007	608	On loan from Arlanda Flygmuseum – front fuselage only.	PV

NORRLANDS HELIKOPTER SKVADRON SAMLING (SWE29)

Address:	Box 9105, S 961 19 Boden.
Tel:	0921-68655
Email:	info@i19.mil.se
Admission:	By prior permission only.
Location:	In the northern suburbs of the town.

Army flying in Sweden started in 1912 and the service was absorbed in the newly formed Air Force in 1926. The new Arméflyget was set up in 1954 and lasted until 1998 when all helicopter operations were combined under a new wing. The northern headquarters are at Boden where attack and transport units reside.

TYPE	REG/SER	CON. NO.	PI/NOTES	STATUS
☐ Agusta-Bell 204B	4D-BA	3039	In Austrian markings.	RA
☐ Agusta-Bell 204B (Hkp 3C)	03301	3011		RA
☐ Agusta-Bell 204B (Hkp 3C)	03307	3056	With boom from 03156	RA
☐ Agusta-Bell 204B (Hkp 3C)	03312	3080	Cabin only.	RA
☐ Agusta-Bell 204B (Hkp 3C)	03316	3157	4D-BO (Austria)	RA
☐ Agusta-Bell 204B (Hkp 3C)	03314	3194	Boom from 03315.	RA
☐ Dornier Do 27A-4 (Fpl 53)	53271	2099	On loan from FVM.	RA
☐ Sud-Est SE.3130 Alouette II (Hkp 2)	Fv02403	1269		RA

POLISTEKNISKA MUSEET (SWE30)

Address:	Polisshögskolan Sörentorp, Byggnad 29, S 170 82 Solna.
Tel:	08-401 66 92
Email:	polisstekniskamuseet@rps.police.se
Admission:	By prior permission only.
Location:	In the centre of Stockholm.

Two museums are located in this complex. One traces the history of the Swedish Police. Here many documents, photographs and uniforms are on view. The other is concerned with technical advances in the service. Displays featuring cars and motor cycles can be seen. The development of communications devices and forensic work is highlighted. There is also an exhibition of special clothing. The Bell 47 entered service in 1972 and was flown for several years. Helicopters are now an essential part of policing.

TYPE	REG/SER	CON. NO.	PI/NOTES	STATUS
☐ Bell 47G-5A	SE-HPG	25081		PV

ROBOTFÖRSÖKPLATS NORRLAND MUSEUM (SWE31)

Address:	Box 74, S 242 23 Vidsel.
Tel:	0929-37000
Fax:	0929-37105
Admission:	By prior permission only.
Location:	Just south of the town.

The site has been used as a test range for missiles for many years. The museum was proposed by a volunteer group in 1998 and the exhibition was ready on May 11th 1999 to celebrate the fortieth anniversay of the first Jindivik flight. On show are models, equipment, photographs, documents missiles and drones tracing the work that has been carried out. The aircraft represent types which have flown from the airfield. Svensk Flygtjänst used four Venoms from 1958 until the late 1960s on operations from the field. Later a trio of Lansens served with company. Several Jindivik remotely controlled aircraft also carried out missions from Vidsel.

TYPE	REG/SER	CON. NO.	PI/NOTES	STATUS
☐ Agusta-Bell 204B (Hkp 3B)	Fv03156	3156	4D-BN (Austria)	RA
☐ De Havilland D.H.112 Venom NF.51 (J 33)	SE-DCA	12364	Fv33015 – On loan from FVM.	RA
☐ Government Aircraft Factories Jindivik 102A (IIA)			On loan from FVM.	RA
☐ Svenska Aeroplan Aktiebolaget (SAAB) 32B Lansen (J 32B)	Fv32616	32616	Fv32616, SE-DCN	RA
☐ Svenska Aeroplan Aktiebolaget (SAAB) 37 Viggen (JA 37) (JA 37C)	Fv37378	37378		RA

ROBOTMUSEET (SWE32)

Address:	Glasbruksgatan 1, S 732 31 Arboga.
Admission:	Thursday 0900-1200; First Saturday in month 1000-1600.
Location:	In the the centre of thhe town between the railway station and the river.

This private collection contains examples of almost every missile used by the Swedish forces. The Viggen fuselage comes from an aircraft which was recently scrapped at Ängelholm.

TYPE	REG/SER	CON. NO.	PI/NOTES	STATUS
☐ Fieseler Fi 103A-1			On loan from TM Stockholm.	PV
☐ Svenska Aeroplan Aktiebolaget (SAAB) 37 Viggen (SH 37) (AJSH 37)	Fv37910	37910	Fuselage only.	PV

SAABS BILMUSEUM (SWE33)

Address:	Akersjövägen, S 461 80 Trollhätan.
Tel:	0520-84344
Email:	saab.carmuseum@saab.com
Admission:	Monday-Saturday 1100-1600.
Location:	In the north western suburbs of the town.

The group has been producing automobiles since the late 1940s at its Trollhättan plant. Prior to the move to Linköping the factory was used for aircraft production. Over the years their cars have achieved considerable success in rallies. The museum traces the development of the company and has on show versions of all types produced. The only aircraft in the collection is the fifth Safir constructed. First flown in October 1946 the aircraft was active until 1982 when it was acquired by the Flygvapenmuseum.

TYPE	REG/SER	CON. NO.	PI/NOTES	STATUS
☐ Svenska Aeroplan Aktiebolaget (SAAB) 91A Safir	'Fv91104'	91104	SE-AYC – on loan from FVM.	PVX

SEGELFLYG MUSEUM (SWE34)

Address: Segelflygskolan Ålleberg,
Box 750,
S 521 01 Falköping.
Tel: 0515-27155
Admission: Summer daily 1000-1700.
Location: At the gliding site which is at the top of the large hill south east of Falköping just south of Road 47.

Inspired by German gliding progress at the Wasserkuppe the Swedish authorities looked for a suitable site. In 1940 an airfield was opened on the top of the hill at Ålleberg which rises from the plain near Falköping. Operated by the Royal Swedish Aero Club as the national gliding centre the complex includes hangars workshops and residential facilities. The idea of a museum was put forward in the early 1980s and a portion of one of the original wooden hangars was converted for display use. Several vintage gliders are on show with the majority being of German design but built by companies or individuals in Sweden. The rare ESG-31, of which only two were made, was imported into the country in 1933. Piloted by Edmund Sparmann, the aircraft designer, this sailplane flew from Malmö to Copenhagen after being towed to two thousand feet. The ESG-31 was one of the gliders used to test the feasibility of the Ålleberg site. Three primary gliders are in the collection and two are presently on show. The Grunau 9 is in store with the SG-38 and Zögling in the exhibition hall. The Hütter H 17 was the first of the type to be built in Sweden. Constructed by AB Kanoverken at Halmstad it was also used to test the Ålleberg site. Also built at Halmstad was the Fi-1 designed by Tord Lidmalm. The prototype flew in 1943 but only six of the planned batch of fifteen were completed. One was exported to Iceland and this has now returned to Sweden. The Baby Falk was based on the Grunau Baby. Designed by Lennart Hemminger the prototype was completed in 1947. The Kockums company built eighteen over the next few years. Not many American Schweizer designs have come to Europe. The American manufacturer has produced large numbers of sailplanes over the last half century. Two Tiger Moths are in residence at the field and one is normally on show in the museum. One is Norwegian built and the other is the oldest flying example in the world. Formerly used as glider tugs they are now only flown on special occasions. Displays tracing the history of gliding have been set up along with items showing the technical advances made in sailplane construction.

TYPE	REG/SER	CON. NO.	PI/NOTES	STATUS
☐ De Havilland D.H.82 Tiger Moth	SE-ALM	172	163 (Norway)	RAA
☐ De Havilland D.H.82 Tiger Moth (Sk 11)	SE-ADF	3113	SE-ADF, Fv5568, Fv568, SE-ATI	PVA
☐ Fauvel AV.36C-1	D-5030			RAC
☐ Flygindustri Fi-1	SE-SOT		TF-SOR	PVA
☐ Hemminger LH-22 Baby-Falk	SE-SGR			PV
☐ Hütter H 17	SE-SAD	1		PV
☐ Jacobs Kranich IIB-1 (D.F.S. 108-30)				PV
☐ Jacobs Kranich IIB-1 (D.F.S. 108-30) (SE 103)	BGA.964	087	FV8226, SE-STF	PVA
☐ Jacobs Meise (D.F.S. 108-70)	SE-SDL	2	On loan from FVM.	RA
☐ Jacobs Meise (D.F.S. 108-70)	SE-SAE	685	On loan from FVM.	PV
☐ Jacobs Weihe (D.F.S. 108-68) (SE 104)	SE-SND	219	Fv 8304 – on loan from Arlanda FM.	PV
☐ Müller Moswey III	SE-SDX	377		PV
☐ Peltzner P-2 (R)				PV
☐ Rolladen-Schneider LS-1D			Front fuselage only.	PV
☐ Scheibe 138 Specht	SE-SVS			PV
☐ Scheibe Bergfalke II/55	'SE-SUN'		Fuselage only	PVX
☐ Scheibe Bergfalke II/55	SE-SUA			PV
☐ Scheibe L-Spatz 55	SE-SWF	643		PV
☐ Schneider ESG 29 Grunau 9 (D.F.S. 108-10)				RA
☐ Schneider ESG 31 Grunau Baby IIB	SE-SAZ	001	On loan from Arlanda FM.	PV
☐ Schneider ESG 31 Schleisserland	SE-ADP	84	On loan from Göteborgs SM.	PV
☐ Schneider Grunau SG-38 (D.F.S. 108-14)	91			PV
☐ Schweizer SGU.2-22E	SE-SMM	194	N2745Z, CF-WTY, C-FWTY	PV
☐ Slingsby T.21B Sedbergh TX.1	SE-SMK	621	WB960	PVA
☐ Stamer-Lippisch Z-12 Zögling	SE-023			PV

SKJUTFÄLSKEG RINKABY (SWE35)

Address: Box 527,
27 123 Karlskrona.
Tel: 0455 -85000
Email: blekingegrp@mds.mil.se
Admission: By prior permission only.
Location: Just east of Rinkaby which is about 8 km south east of Kristianstad.

Three Drakens have been reported as being preserved at the army training camp which is administered from Karlskrona. One is mounted at the gate and the others are stored inside. There is a range at the site and it is not known whether the pair inside will be put on display or used as targets.

TYPE	REG/SER	CON. NO.	PI/NOTES	STATUS
☐ Svenska Aeroplan Aktiebolaget (SAAB) 35F-1 Draken (J 35F-1)	Fv35498	35498		RA
☐ Svenska Aeroplan Aktiebolaget (SAAB) 35J Draken (35F-2) (J 35F-2) (J 35J)	Fv35582	35582		RA
☐ Svenska Aeroplan Aktiebolaget (SAAB) 35J Draken (35F-2) (J 35F-2) (J 35J)	Fv35608	35608		RA

SKOKLOSTERS MOTORMUSEUM (SWE36)

Address:	Skokloster Castle, S 746 96 Skokloster.
Tel:	018-386106
Email:	skokloster@lsh.se
Admission:	May-September Daily 1100-1700.
Location:	About 50 km north west of Stockholm on a peninsula jutting into the Ekoln Lake.

The adjoining castle is the best example of a Baroque palace in the country. A large collection of furniture, paintings and weapons can be seen in this building. The motor museum, which opened on June 29th 1963, traces the development of the car from 1898-1950 and commercial vehicles and motor-cycles can also be seen along with posters, photographs and models. A number of aero engines are in the building as is the Safir. There are displays tracing the history of military flying in Sweden in this area. The Draken is parked in the courtyard area outside the main building. The C-47 flew into a field next to the museum some years ago. In 1948 it was the second example of the type delivered to the Swedish Air Force. During its U.S.A.A.F. service it participated in the D-Day invasion flying over Omaha Beach. On June 13th 1952 it took part in a clandestine radar trip over the Baltic when its companion Fv79001 was shot down by Soviet fighters. This airframe was recently raised.

TYPE	REG/SER	CON. NO.	PI/NOTES	STATUS
☐ Douglas DC-3A-360 Skytrain (C-47) (Tp 79)	Fv79002	9103	42-32877, SE-APW	PV
☐ Hot Air Balloon			Basket only.	PV
☐ Svenska Aeroplan Aktiebolaget (SAAB) 35E Draken (35D) (J 35D) (S 35E)	Fv35945	35945 (35299)	Fv35299	PV
☐ Svenska Aeroplan Aktiebolaget (SAAB) 91B Safir (Sk 50B)	Fv50023	91225	Fv50023, (SE-IGI)	PV

STIFTELSEN FLYGANDE VETERANER (SWE37)

Address:	Flygplatsinfarten 41, Bromma, S 168 67 Stockholm.
Tel:	08 29 50 33
Fax:	08 2979 05
Email:	flygande.veteraner@telia.com
Admission:	By prior permission only.
Location:	At Bromma Airport which is in the north western suburbs of the city.

The group was formed to keep a C-47, which had seen both military and civilian use in Sweden, in flying condition. After its U.S.A.A.F. service the aircraft joined the Norwegian Airline D.N.L. (later part of S.A.S.) in September 1946 and flew with them for two years before becoming part of the Linjeflyg fleet in Sweden. Bought by the Air Force in 1957 it was sold to the group in 1984 and returned to Bromma where it was once based with Linjeflyg. The aircraft is a regular visitor to meetings around Europe.

TYPE	REG/SER	CON. NO.	PI/NOTES	STATUS
☐ Douglas DC-3A-456 Skytrain (C-47A)	SE-CFP	13883	43-30732, LN-IAF, SE-CFP, Fv79006	RAA

SVEDINOS BIL OCH FLYGMUSEUM (SWE38)

Address:	Ugglarp, S 310 50 Slöinge.
Tel:	0346-43187
Email:	svedinos@algonet.se
Admission:	May-mid June and September Saturday- Sunday 1100-1600 ; mid June-August daily 1100-1800.
Location:	On the coast road from Halmstad to Falkenberg about 25 km north west of Halmstad.

Established in 1961 by the late Lennart Svedfelt, a former circus performer who used the stage name 'Svedino', the museum has an interesting display of cars and aircraft. He started collecting vintage cars in the 1940s and now over one hundred and forty are on show with many rare models. When the first aircraft arrived there was no room inside the building and most were stored under wraps. A planned restoration programme was initiated over thirty five years ago and personnel from the nearby Halmstad Air Force Base and volunteers have worked hard to improve the display. A large new building has recently been completed and now the majority of the aircraft are displayed under cover. One of the Stieglitz and the Klemm 35 have been painted in their former military colours and have, on occasions, been moved to Halmstad for open days. The Cirrus Moth, which is the third oldest surviving Moth, was used by Gösta Andrée on a flight to Cape Town in 1929. The aircraft is now mocked up to represent a Moth Trainer, a type once used at Halmstad. The Tiger Moth, which has been on show in the past, is currently being rebuilt to flying condition at Halmstad. Two Tipsy aircraft constructed in Belgium are comparatively rare exhibits. The single seat S.2 was built in 1936 and arrived in Sweden two years later but saw little use before being withdrawn in 1940. The two seat B was flown from 1937 until 1960. The Miles Messenger has been painted in Royal Air Force colours to represent one used on communications duties during World War II. Co-operation with the Air Force has resulted in many military types joining the exhibition. The Meteor was built by Glosters as the 'Reaper' ground attack version in 1950. No orders were obtained and the front fuselage was replaced by a two seat T.7 unit. Subsequently a T.7 tail and outer wings were fitted before the aircraft was sold to Sweden for target towing duties. Only three examples of the almost two hundred FFVS J 22 fighters produced in the mid-1940s survive and one is on show. The Kamov Ka-26 helicopter was imported from the Soviet Union in 1970, saw little use, and joined the collection three years later. The Spanish built Junkers Ju 52 is in World War II Luftwaffe colours. The GV-38 was flown by 'Svedino' at shows and carries his name on the fuselage.

TYPE	REG/SER	CON. NO.	PI/NOTES	STATUS
☐ Agusta-Bell 204B (Hkp 3C)	Fv03139	3139	4D-BJ (Austria)	PV
☐ Auster J/1 Autocrat	SE-CGR	2230	G-AIZW	PV
☐ Construcciones Aeronáuticas (CASA) 352L [Junkers Ju 52/3m]	'N9+A7'	52	T.2B-142, N9012N	PVX
☐ De Havilland D.H.60 Moth	'Fv5555'	261	G-EBNO, S-AABS, SE-ABS – mocked up as a D.H.60T Moth Trainer.	PVX
☐ De Havilland D.H.82A Tiger Moth	SE-FNA	82003	N6730, D-EMWE, D-EMWT – at Halmstad.	RAC
☐ De Havilland D.H.100 Vampire FB.50 (J 28B)	Fv28307	V0578		PV
☐ De Havilland D.H.115 Vampire T.55 (Sk 28C)	Fv28444	15738		PV
☐ Douglas Skyraider AEW.1 (AD-4W)	SE-EBC	7975	Bu127960, WT962, G-31-6	PV
☐ English Electric EA.1 Canberra T.11 (B.2) (Tp 52)	Fv52001	EEP71174	WH711	PV
☐ Ercoupe 415D	SE-BFY	4409	NC3784H – at Halmstad	RAA
☐ Ercoupe 415D	SE-BNA	4735	OY-FAC	PV
☐ Flygforvaltningens Flygverkstad (FFVS) J 22A	Fv22149	149		PVC
☐ Focke-Wulf Fw 44J Stieglitz (Sk 12)	Fv5787		Fv5787, SE-BWR	PV
☐ Focke-Wulf Fw 44J Stieglitz (Sk 12)	SE-BWZ	29	Fv647	PV
☐ Gloster Meteor T.7	'WS774'	G5/1525	G-AMCJ, G-7-1, G-ANSO, SE-DCC	PVX
☐ Götaverken GV-38 [Rearwin 9000L]	SE-AHY	15		PV
☐ Grankvist Autogyro				PV
☐ Hawker P.1067 Hunter F.50 (J 34)	Fv34070	HABL 003204		PV
☐ Hughes 269C (Hkp 5A)	05215	22-0049	On loan from FVM.	PV
☐ Jacobs Meise (D.F.S. 108-70)	SE-SAI	210		PV
☐ Kamov Ka-26	SE-HDM	7001307		PV
☐ Klemm Kl 35D (Sk 15)	Fv5025	1899	Fv5025, SE-BGF – with parts of c/n 1980 Fv5051, SE-BGN.	PV
☐ Miles M.38 Messenger 2A	SE-BYY	6703	G-AKAO	PV
☐ Noorduyn Harvard IIB [North American NA-77 (AT-16)] (Sk 16A)	Fv16028	14-725	42-12478, FE991 – on loan to Västgöta Veteranfly.	PV
☐ Noorduyn Harvard IIB [North American NA-77 (AT-16)] (Sk 16A)	Fv16033	14-772	42-12525, FH138	PV
☐ Percival P.66 Pembroke C.52 (Tp 83)	Fv83007	P.66/51		PV
☐ Republic F-84G Thunderjet	52-2978		52-2978, MU-B (Norway)	RAD
☐ Schneider ESG 31 Grunau Baby IIB (SE 102)	SE-SNY	033	Fv8118	PV
☐ Schneider Grunau SG-38 (D.F.S. 108-14)	136			PV
☐ Scottish Aviation Bulldog 101 (Sk 61D)	Fv61005	BH100/105	G-AYZM	PV
☐ Svenska Aeroplan Aktiebolaget (SAAB) 29A (J 29A)	Fv29203	29203		PV
☐ Svenska Aeroplan Aktiebolaget (SAAB) 32B Lansen (J 32B)	Fv32599	32599		PV
☐ Svenska Aeroplan Aktiebolaget (SAAB) 32E Lansen (32B) (J 32B) (J 32E)	Fv32569	32569		PV
☐ Svenska Aeroplan Aktiebolaget (SAAB) 35 Draken	35-1	35-1		PV
☐ Svenska Aeroplan Aktiebolaget (SAAB) 35E Draken (35D) (J 35D) (S 35E)	Fv35959	35959 (35281)		RA
☐ Svenska Aeroplan Aktiebolaget (SAAB) 35F-2 Draken (J 35F-2)	Fv35542	35542	Front fuselage only.	PV
☐ Svenska Aeroplan Aktiebolaget (SAAB) 35J Draken (35F-2) (J 35F-2) (J 35J)	Fv35576	35576	On loan from FVM.	PV
☐ Svenska Aeroplan Aktiebolaget (SAAB) 37 Viggen (JA 37) (JA 37D) (JA 37DI)	Fv37386	37386	Front fuselage only.	PV
☐ Svenska Aeroplan Aktiebolaget (SAAB) 91D Safir	SF-18	91364	In Finnish markings – on loan from FVM.	RA
☐ Svenska Aeroplan Aktiebolaget (SAAB) 105XT	SE-XBZ	105-2	On loan from FVM.	RA
☐ Thulin A [Blériot XI]				PV
☐ Tipsy B	SE-AGP	504	OO-DOT	PV
☐ Tipsy S.2	SE-AFT	30	OO-ASC	PV

TEKNISKA MUSEET (SWE39)

Address:	Museivägen 7 N. Djurgården S 115 27 Stockholm.
Tel:	08-450-5681
Email:	info@tekniskamuseet.se
Admission:	Monday-Friday 1000-1600; Saturday 1200-1600.
Location:	About 1 km east of the city centre.

The museum displays cover all aspects of technology with mining equipment industrial machinery, railway engines and rolling stock, cars, commercial vehicles, cycles, motor cycles and ships on view. Space in the main hall is limited but a number of significant aircraft are exhibited. Hjalmar Nyrop and Oscar Ask designed, built and flew the first aircraft in Sweden. Constructed in the Nyrop shipyard at Landskrona the Ask-Nyrop No.1 was based on the Blériot XI. A two cylinder 30 h.p. Fargot motor was fitted but this was unreliable so a 25 h.p. Anzani was installed. Nyrop crashed the No.2 fitted with a 35 h.p. REP. The No.3 was based on the Blériot XXI and powered by a 50 h.p. Gnome motor. Flown in 1911 it was handed over to the Swedish Navy as a gift in December of that year. This was the first Swedish military aircraft but Nyrop received no orders and sold out his aviation assets to the Thulin company. Only one Thulin N biplane was built in 1917. The design was developed into the NA which appeared two years later but was not flown until 1921. The Junkers F 13 was the second aircraft operated by AB Aerotransport and delivered in 1924. Flown on both floats and wheels the F 13 was in use until late 1934 and arrived at the museum the following year. For a long time the aircraft was mounted on a pole outside but fortunately, as befits one of the few survivors of a type which revolutionised air transport in the 1920s, it is now in the main hall. The airframe was totally restored before it moved inside. Rolf von Bahr used a small fleet of Cierva C.30s on rescue work around the coast. During World War II these autogyros were responsible for locating several crash sites and saving many downed aircrew. The example on show was operated from 1935 until 1947 and donated to the museum in 1948. An exhibition tracing developments in aviation has set up on the balcony overlooking the main hall. On show here are engines, models, components and photographs. The history of flying in Sweden is also portrayed in detail.

TYPE	REG/SER	CON. NO.	PI/NOTES	STATUS
☐ Cierva C.30A (Avro 671)	SE-AEA	740		PV
☐ Donnet-Lévêque L11	10		On loan to FVM.	–
☐ Fieseler Fi 103A-1			On loan to Robotmuseet.	–
☐ Junkers F 13 de	SE-AAC	715	D-343, S-AAAC	PV
☐ Lilienthal Normal-Segelapparat (R)				PV
☐ Nyrop 3 [Blériot XXI]				PV
☐ Plym Svenskt Glider				RA
☐ Schneider Grunau SG-38 (D.F.S. 108-14)				RA
☐ Svenska Aeroplan Aktiebolaget (SAAB) 37 Viggen (SF 37) (AJSF 37)	Fv37950	37950	Front fuselage only.	PV
☐ Thulin A [Blériot XI]				RA
☐ Thulin B [Morane-Saulnier G]			Fuselage only – on loan to Malmo T.M.	–
☐ Thulin N		59		PV

VÄNNÄS MOTORMUSEUM (SWE40)

Address:	Lägret, S 911 33 Vännäs
Tel:	070-660-6688
Email:	hangarn@hotmail.com
Admission:	Tuesday-Sunday 1200-1600.
Location:	South west of the town which is about 30 km west of Umeå

This collection, set up by fifteen enthusiasts in 1986, is housed in a 1927 hangar located on Vännäs Läger, an old military camp and airfield. There is an excellent collection of cars, motorcycles, fire engines and memorabilia. The Vampire has now been positively identified so the aircraft carrying these markings in the F 15 museum at Söderhamn is currently a mystery. The replica Pitts Special, built by Per Lundstrom, is painted in the colours of one flown by the 1972 Women's World Aerobatic champion Mary Gaffaney. The wreck of the Mustang has recently been recovered from its crash site. The fighter came down in a swamp and as a result the airframe is in reasonably good condition. The museum estimate it will take about two years to restore it for exhibition. The Pou-du-Ciel was started by a local aviator but sadly he died before he had completed the aircraft. The Bulldog is slightly damaged and the canopy is broken but this should be on show soon. A display tracing the history of aviation in the area and of the airfield is being developed.

TYPE	REG/SER	CON. NO.	PI/NOTES	STATUS
☐ De Havilland D.H.100 Vampire FB.50 (J 28B)	Fv28391	V0768		RA
☐ Evans VP-2M Volksplane	SE-XEL	1308-42		PV
☐ Mignet HM-14 Pou-du-Ciel				PV
☐ North American NA-122 Mustang (P-51D) (J 26)	Fv26084	122-31971	44-72112	RAC
☐ Pitts S-1S Special (R)	'N6W'			PVX
☐ Schleicher K.8B	SE-TCY	8442		PV
☐ Schneider ESG 31 Grunau Baby IIB	SE-STW	LFS-4-58		PV
☐ Schneider Grunau SG-38 (D.F.S. 108-14)				PV
☐ Scottish Aviation Bulldog 101 (Sk 61E)	Fv61044	BH100/156	G-AZPL	RA
☐ Sud-Est SE.3130 Alouette II (Hkp 2)	'02112'	1830	02042 – Composite	PVX

VÄSTERÅS FLYGMUSEUM (SWE41)

Address:	Box 321, S 721 31 Västerås.
Tel:	021-800500
Fax:	021-800502
Email:	info@flygmuseum.com
Admission:	Saturday-Sunday 1300-1600.
Location:	At Hasslo airfield which is about 10 km east of the town off the E.18.

The organisation was formally set up in 1997 when several local groups and private owners pooled their resources. The collection is now housed in a 1930s wooden hangar used for maintenance by the Swedish Air Force before World War II. Flygflottilj 1 was in residence at the field from 1929 until 1983. The Swedish Veteran Wing Museum acquired a former Israeli Mustang in 1986 and this was joined the following year by a Pembroke. They moved into the current hangar in the early 1990s and some static ex-military fighters were put on show. The Västerås Flygande Museum was established in 1997 by owners of vintage and classic machnies. When a technical school moved into another former military hangar they built new structures to house some of their fleet. The collection is constantly changing as types are bought and sold. In addition to the SAAB fighters there are a few Swedish designs owned by members. The BHT-1 Beauty, powered by a 60 h.p. Walter Mikron engine, made its maiden flight in 1944 at Norrtälje. Acquired by SAS pilot Jan Christie the low wing monoplane competed in the 1950 South Coast Air Race in England. The owner stored the Beauty at Bromma in the 1970s and planned to take it to America. He was eventually persuaded to sell it so that it could remain in Sweden.

TYPE	REG/SER	CON. NO.	PI/NOTES	STATUS
☐ Aero L-29 Delfin	ES-YLT	094112	(Soviet), (Estonia)	RAA
☐ Aero L-29 Delfin	ES-YLU	194445	(Soviet), (Estonia)	RAA
☐ Agusta-Bell 204B (Hkp 3C)	03311	3075		PV
☐ Antonov An-2TP	ES-CAK	1G 137-35	CCCP-70161	PVA
☐ Antonov An-2TP	ES-CAJ	1G 137-49	CCCP-70175	PVA
☐ Boeing-Stearman A75N1 Kaydet (PT-17)	SE-AMT	75-5659	42-17496, 4X-AMT, G-BAVN – at Barkaby.	RAA
☐ Brantly B.2B	N2052Y	445		PV
☐ Bratt, Hifling, Tornblom BHT-1 Beauty	SE-ANX	1	SE-ANX, LN-JHC	RAC
☐ Bücker Bü 131B Jungmann				PVA
☐ Bücker T-131P Jungmann	SE-XPL	01	SP-FPF – at Eskilstuna.	RAA
☐ Centralne Studium Samolotow (CSS) 13 [Polikarpov Po-2]	SE-XPP	0430	SP-FZP – at Eskilstuna.	RAA
☐ Construcciones Aeronáuticas (CASA) 1.131E [Bücker Bü 131 Jungmann]	SE-XOB	2075	E.3B-475, EC-332	PVA
☐ Convair 440-75	LN-KLA	397	LN-KLA, SE-FUF – front fuselage only.	PV
☐ De Havilland D.H.82A Tiger Moth (Sk 11)	SE-AMR	47	Fv517	RAA
☐ De Havilland D.H.115 Vampire T.55	SE-DXX	DHP.40303	U-1236 (Switzerland)	PVA
☐ De Havilland D.H.115 Vampire T.55 (T.11)	SE-DXU	15133	WZ513, U-1238 (Switzerland)	RAA
☐ Ercoupe 415C	SE-AYS	3956		PV
☐ Focke-Wulf Fw 44J Stieglitz (Sk 12)	SE-EGT	81	Fv629, SE-EGT, OH-SZS, D-EDYV – at Barkaby.	RAC
☐ Grumman G-164A Ag-Cat	SE-KXR	1120	N5085	PVA
☐ Hawker P.1101 Hunter T.7A (T.7)	SE-DXH	41H/695336	XL616, 9223M	PVC
☐ Humlan Autogyro	SE-HYI	104		PV
☐ Humlan HA-2M Sportster	SE-HXN	121		PV
☐ Humlan HA-2M Sportster	SE-HYP	159		PVA
☐ Jacobs Anfänger II	SE-SMG	20		RAA
☐ Leak Avid Flyer Speedwing	SE-XML	326		PVA
☐ Nord N.3400	SE-XMS	39	39	PVA
☐ Percival P.66 Pembroke C.1	SE-BKH	P.66/82	XK884, G-BNPG	PVA
☐ Pereira G.P.3 Osprey II	SE-XOX	1228		PVA
☐ Piper PA-20-125 Pacer				PVA
☐ Piper PA-23-150 Apache	SE-CBL	23-549		PVA
☐ Pitts S-2B Special	SE-IRX	5039	N53234	PVA
☐ Rand Robinson KR-2	SE-XHN	3405		PVA
☐ Republic RC-3 Seabee	SE-AXY	830	(NC6560K)	PVA
☐ Svenska Aeroplan Aktiebolaget (SAAB) 29C (S 29C)	Fv29969	29969		PV
☐ Svenska Aeroplan Aktiebolaget (SAAB) 29C (S 29C)	Fv29974	29974		PV
☐ Svenska Aeroplan Aktiebolaget (SAAB) 32E Lansen (32B) (J 32B) (J 32E)	Fv32612	32612		PV
☐ Svenska Aeroplan Aktiebolaget (SAAB) 35F-1 Draken (J 35F-1)	Fv35496	35496		PV
☐ Svenska Aeroplan Aktiebolaget (SAAB) 35F-2 Draken (J 35F-2)	Fv35583	35583	At airfield entrance.	PV
☐ Svenska Aeroplan Aktiebolaget (SAAB) 37 Viggen (AJ 37)	'37-61'	37-6		PV
☐ Svenska Aeroplan Aktiebolaget (SAAB) 91B Safir (Sk 50B)	SE-IGM	91256	Fv50044	PVA
☐ Svenska Aeroplan Aktiebolaget (SAAB) 91B Safir (Sk 50B)	SE-KGZ	91259	Fv50047	RAA
☐ Yakovlev Yak-18				PVA
☐ Yakovlev Yak-52	ES-PAB	833113	CCCP-05051	PVA
☐ Zlin Z-526F Trener Master	SE-XLB	1114	At Eskilstuna.	RAA

VÄSTGÖTA VETERANFLYGFÖRENING (SWE42)

Address: Timmervagen 7, S 461 58 Trollhätan.
Email: stellan.aro@swipnet.se
Admission: By prior permission only.
Location: At Såtenäs Airfield which is south of the town which is about 25 km south west of Lidköping.

Two former Swiss Air Force Hunters were bought by the English firm Aeromech in 1995. The pair were painted in Swedish colours and one was exported to Canada. Other aircraft have now joined the group.

TYPE	REG/SER	CON. NO.	PI/NOTES	STATUS
☐ Hawker P.1099 Hunter F.58	SE-DXI	41H/697440	J-4073 (Switzerland), G-RUUD	RAA
☐ Noorduyn Harvard IIB [North American NA-77 (AT-16)] (Sk 16A)	Fv16028	14-725	42-12478, FE991 – on loan from Svedino's Museum.	RA
☐ Noorduyn Harvard IIB [North American NA-77 (AT-16)] (Sk 16A)	Fv16073	14A-1098	43-12799, FS958	RA
☐ Svenska Aeroplan Aktiebolaget (SAAB) 91B Safir	Fv50002	91202		RA
☐ Svenska Aeroplan Aktiebolaget (SAAB) 91B Safir	SE-FVV	91252	Fv50040, 53-040 (Norway), LN-HHW, (SE-LBG), LN-HHW	RA
☐ Svenska Aeroplan Aktiebolaget (SAAB) 91C Safir	SE-EDD	91318	SE-XBE, (EI-AGY), OE-DSA	RA
☐ Svenska Aeroplan Aktiebolaget (SAAB) 105 (Sk 60E)	Fv60140	60140		RA

VETERAN AIRCRAFT ASSOCIATION (SWE43)

Address: c/o Oskar Nillson, Frykmans Vägen 24, S 653 46 Karlstad.
Tel: 0707-371600
Admission: By prior permission only.
Location: At Karlstad Airport which is about 20 km north of the town.

The group has recently moved its base to the new airport at Karlstad from the former site close to the city. Two Stearman PT-13s were acquired and one has now gone to Spain. Mikael Carlsson built a replica of the Tummelisa in the late 1980s and it regularly flies at shows throughout the country. He also found the remains of two Thulin As and rebuilt these to fly. Two Mercedes D III engines were located on a farm in Norway. A replica of a Fokker D VII is well advanced and it will be the only one airworthy with an original engine.

TYPE	REG/SER	CON. NO.	PI/NOTES	STATUS
☐ Boeing-Stearman A75 Kaydet (PT-13B)	SE-BOE	75-0294	40-1737, N56402, N4988G	RAA
☐ Centrala Flygverkstader Malmen 01 Tummelisa (R)	SE-XIL	362		RAA
☐ Fokker D.VII (R)	SE-XVO	10400/18		RAC
☐ Piper J-3C-65 Cub (L-4H)	SE-BEH	12281	44-79985, HB-OWD, D-ELAT	RAA
☐ Piper J-3C-65 Cub (L-4J)	SE-BMC	12847	44-80551, HB-OAB, OE-ABO, LX-ABO, (D-EFPB), OY-ALP, LN-KLT	RAA
☐ Thulin A [Blériot XI]				RAA
☐ Thulin A [Blériot XI]	SE-XMC	82		RAA

VOLVO MUSEUM (SWE44)

Address: Arendal, 405 08 Göteborg.
Tel: 031-664814
Email: museum@volvo.com
Admission: September-May Tuesday-Friday 1200-1700; Saturday-Sunday 1100-1600; June-August Tuesday-Friday 1000-1700; Sunday 1100-1600.
Location: In the western suburbs of the city.

The history of the company is portrayed in the exhibition with many cars and trucks on show. The firm has produced components for aircraft and a Draken and two Viggens can be seen.

TYPE	REG/SER	CON. NO.	PI/NOTES	STATUS
☐ Svenska Aeroplan Aktiebolaget (SAAB) 35J Draken (35F-2) (J 35F-2) (J 35J)	Fv35616	35616		PV
☐ Svenska Aeroplan Aktiebolaget (SAAB) 37 Viggen (AJ 37) (AJS 37)	Fv37058	37058		PV
☐ Svenska Aeroplan Aktiebolaget (SAAB) 37 Viggen (AJ 37) (AJS 37)	Fv37068	37068		PV

This Swiss designed Moswey III is on show in the Segelflygmuseum at Alleberg.

A Tipsy S2 hangs over a Tipsy Trainer in Svedino's Museum at Ugglarp.

The Swedish Air Force operated a small fleet of Percival Pembrokes and one is on show at the Vasteras Flygmuseum. (Douglas Rough)

Many aircraft in the Fliegermuseum at Altenrhein are in flying condition. Shown here is a Pilatus P.3.

The Fahrni family own several vintage and classic gliders including this Rhonsegler.

Alfred Comte built several successful designs. This AC-4 is in the Verkehrshaus in Luzern.

SWITZERLAND

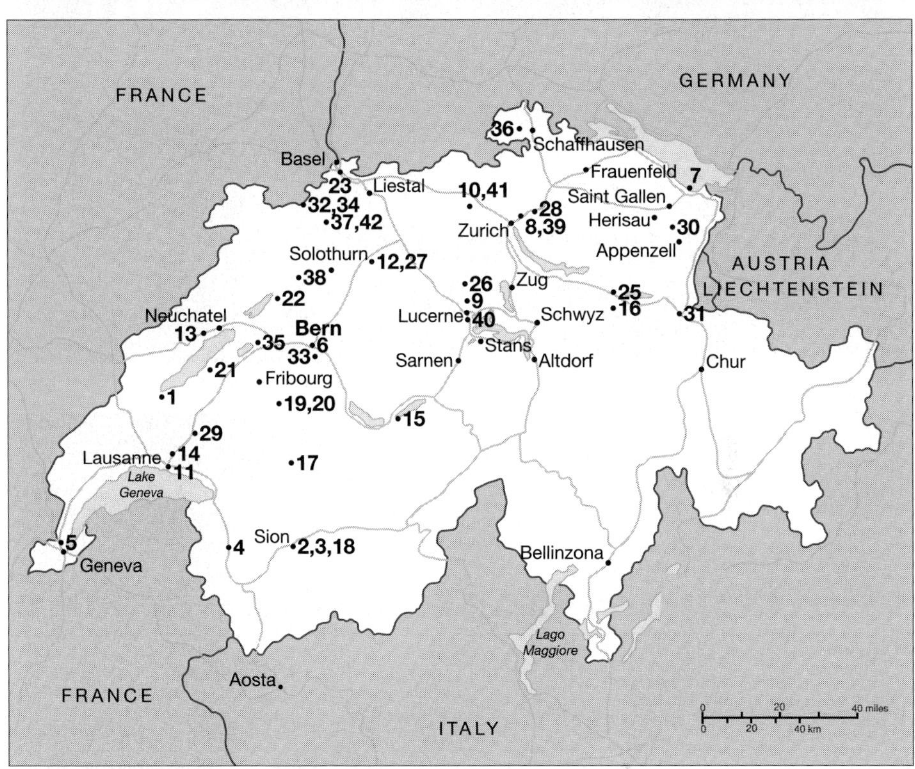

AIR HISTORIQUE (SWI1)

Address:	Route de Prahins 5, CH-1415 Molondin.
Tel:	021-433-1910
Fax:	021-433-1920
Admission:	By prior permission only.
Location:	At Yverdon airfield which is about 4 km south west of the town.

Three aircraft are operated by this group. The French registered Broussard, built in 1958 and used by A.L.A.T. until it became civilianised in 1983, has been based in Switzerland for many years. The prototype Pilatus P.2 made its maiden flight in April 1945 and just over fifty were delivered to the Swiss Air Force. Several were sold to civilian owners in the 1980s. The Czechoslovakian designed Zlin Trener series was a great success and almost fifteen hundred were built in a number of versions between 1947 and the mid 1970s. The example in the collection was used at Government flying schools in France before moving to Switzerland.

TYPE	REG/SER	CON. NO.	PI/NOTES	STATUS
☐ Max Holste MH.1521M Broussard	F-BXCP	149	149	RAA
☐ Pilatus P.2-06	HB-RAW	49	A-103, U-103, U-132	RAA
☐ Zlin Z-326 Trener Master	HB-TCC	925	F-BORV	RAA

AIR VAMPIRES (SWI2)

Address:	Chemin de Sarnets, CH-1951 Sion.
Tel:	027-322-9731
Admission:	By prior permission only.
Location:	About 3 km south west of the town.

Several Vampires, both single and two seat, a Hunter and an Alouette are owned by this group. All the jets enjoyed a long service career in the country. The helicopter was once flown on military duties in France. Another Vampire and a Hunter are preserved on poles by the military gate and are listed here.

TYPE	REG/SER	CON. NO.	PI/NOTES	STATUS
☐ De Havilland D.H.100 Vampire FB.6	HB-RVH	612	J-1103	RAA
☐ De Havilland D.H.100 Vampire FB.6	J-1190	699	By military gate.	PV
☐ De Havilland D.H.100 Vampire FB.6	J-1080	991		RA
☐ De Havilland D.H.115 Vampire T.55	U-1222	982		RA
☐ De Havilland D.H.115 Vampire T.55	HB-RVI	DHP.44352	U-1235	RA
☐ De Havilland D.H.115 Vampire T.55 (T.11)	U-1239	15467	XD544	RA
☐ Hawker P.1099 Hunter F.58	HB-RVU	41H/697453	J-4086	RA
☐ Hawker P.1099 Hunter F.58	J-4100	41H/697467	By military gate.	PV
☐ Sud-Est SE.3130 Alouette II	SE-XQT	1650	(ALAT), F-GNPX	RAA

AMICI DELL'HUNTER (SWI3)

Address: Chemin de Sarnets 2, CH-1295 Tarnay.
Email: info@amicidellhunter.ch
Admission: By prior permission only.
Location: At Sion airfield which is about 3 km south west of the town.

The group was formally established by ex-Swiss Air Force personnel in November 1996. The Hunter, retired at Payerne in late 1994, was then stored at Raron for four years before arriving at Ambri in June 1999. This aircraft moved to Sion in early 2001. The two seater was converted from a Royal Air Force F.4 and is part of the Fondation pour le Mantien du Patrimoine Aéronautique collection.

TYPE	REG/SER	CON. NO.	PI/NOTES	STATUS
☐ Hawker P.1101 Hunter T.68 (P.1067 Hunter F.4)	HB-RVR	41H/670803	WV332, 7673M, G-9-406, J-4201 – On loan from FMPA.	RAA

ASSOCIATION MORANE CHARLY FOX (SWI4)

Address: Mobile Air Service, Aérodrome, CH-1880 Bex.
Tel: 025-62-1033
Admission: By prior permission only.
Location: About 3 km north west of the town off Route 9.

The first licence built Morane 406 (D-3800) was delivered to the Air Force in 1940. The improved D-3801 with a more powerful engine followed in 1941 and two hundred and seven were built. The last was withdrawn in 1959. The group found a derelict airframe and parts of another. The rebuild started in the mid-1990s and the aircraft took to the air again on June 9th 2000. The aircraft is often at the Altenrhein Museum.

TYPE	REG/SER	CON. NO.	PI/NOTES	STATUS
☐ Morane-Saulnier MS.406C-1 (D-3801)	HB-RCF	194	J-143 – with parts from J-276.	RAA

COLLECTION AÉROPORT GENÈVE-COINTRIN (SWI5)

Address: P.O. Box 100, CH-1215 Genève 15.
Tel: 022-717-7111
Fax: 022-798-4377
Email: info@gva.ch
Admission: On permanent view.
Location: About 5 km north west of the city.

The Atlantic fuselage can be seen in the main terminal building. The Hunter is mounted on a pole near the Jet Aviation Hangar. This has now been joined by the recently retired Mirage.

TYPE	REG/SER	CON. NO.	PI/NOTES	STATUS
☐ Breguet 1150 Atlantic	27	27	Fuselage frame with tail from c/n 47 – in French markings.	PV
☐ Dassault Mirage IIIS	J-2314	1004		PV
☐ Hawker P.1099 Hunter F.58	J-4085	41H/697452		PV

COLLECTION GRUNDBACHER (SWI6)

Address:	Place des Tilleuls 53E, CH-2908 Grandfontaine.
Tel:	032-471-2459
Admission:	By prior permission only.
Location:	At Bern Belpmoos which is about 6 km south east of the city and in a private workshop.

This private collection of classic sailplanes contains some interesting machines. The WLM-2 was built in 1954 and is derived from the 1946 WLM-1. The Hütter H-28 made its maiden flight in 1936 and small numbers were built in three versions. The prototype had straight wings and the II gull wings. The III was constructed in Denmark.

TYPE	REG/SER	CON. NO.	PI/NOTES	STATUS
☐ Hütter H 28 II	HB-223			RAC
☐ Neukom Elfe S4A	HB-1199	47		RAA
☐ Schleicher K.8B	HB-701	1059		RAA
☐ Weber, Landolf, Münch WLM-2	HB-562	01		RAA

FLIEGERMUSEUM ALTENRHEIN (SWI7)

Address:	Flugplatz St. Gallen-Altenrhein, CH-9423 Altenrhein.
Tel:	079-430-5151
Fax:	071-737-8260
Email:	sekretariat@fliegermuseum.ch
Admission:	Saturday 1330-1700.
Location:	Just east of the town off Route 7/13.

Altenrhein airfield opened in the 1926 when the Dornier company decided to build a factory on the Swiss side of the Bodensee (Lake Constance) so that a range of military aircraft could be developed thus bypassing the Allied restrictions in Germany. The company continued to trade under the Dornier name when it became Flug und Fahrzeugwerke and is still is business. In 1984 Hanspeter Köstli acquired a former Swiss Air Force Venom and this was later joined by both a single seat and a two seat Vampire. Examples of the Bücker Jungmann and Jungmeister which had been build at Altenrhein by Dornier were added along with a Boeing-Stearman Kaydet which was once used by the Argentinean Navy. The plans for a museum came to fruition when the collection opened to the public on April 8th 1995. The fleet has grown steadily and contains a number of rarities. The only flying Bristol Sycamore, owned by Peter Schmid, is on show along with a static example of this helicopter. The Waco YMF is not common in Europe. The design dates from 1935 but the example on show was built to original specification by Classic Aircraft at Lansing, Michigan in 1993. In addition to the aircraft a number of models, engines, components and items of memorabilia can be seen. The history of Altenrhein is portrayed in detail with many interesting photographs and documents on show.

TYPE	REG/SER	CON. NO.	PI/NOTES	STATUS
☐ Ballonfabrik Stuttgart K-1260/3-STU Balloon	HB-BAO	0281		PV
☐ Boeing-Stearman E75 Kaydet (PT-13D) (N2S-5)	HB-RBG	75-5346	42-17183, Bu61224, LV-GTZ	PVA
☐ Bristol 171 Sycamore HR.52	'XG544'	13475	G-18-148, CA+328, AS+324, SC+206, WE+545, GD+112, 78+17, D-HALD, HB-RXB	PVAX
☐ Bristol 171 Sycamore HR.52	HB-RXA	13483	G-18-156, BD+178, CD+090, LB+102, GD+102, 78+25, D-HELM	PV
☐ Bücker Bü 131APM-150 Jungmann (Bü 131B)	HB-UUY	10	A-3	RAA
☐ Bücker Bü 133C Jungmeister	HB-MKN	36	U-89	PV
☐ Bücker Bü 133C Jungmeister	HB-MKH	40	U-93	RAA
☐ Classic Aircraft Waco F-5	HB-UPZ	F5C-055		PVA
☐ Dassault Mirage IIIS	J-2331	1021		PV
☐ De Havilland D.H.100 Vampire FB.6	HB-RVE	993	J-1082	PVA
☐ De Havilland D.H.112 Venom FB.1R	HB-RVA	840	J-1630	PVA
☐ De Havilland D.H.115 Vampire T.55	HB-RVF	868	U-1208	PVA
☐ De Havilland D.H.115 Vampire T.55	HB-RVJ	988	U-1228	PVA
☐ Flug und Fahrzeugwerke (FFA) AS.202/15 Bravo	HB-HEH	004		PVA
☐ Flug und Fahrzeugwerke (FFA) Diamant 16.5	HB-994	065		PV
☐ Flug und Fahrzeugwerke (FFA) Swiss Delta Hang Glider				PV
☐ Glasflügel H201B Standard Libelle	HB-944	43		PV
☐ Hawker P.1099 Hunter F.58	J-4062	41H/697429	Front fuselage only.	PV
☐ Hawker P.1099 Hunter F.58	HB-RVQ	41H/697431	J-4064	PV
☐ Hawker P.1101 Hunter T.68 (P.1067 Hunter F.50)	HB-RVV	HABL 003207	G-9-48, Fv34072, G-9-413, J-4206	PVA
☐ Hawker P.1101 Hunter T.68 (P.1067 Hunter F.50)	HB-RVP	HABL 003221	Fv34086, G-9-62, G-9-412, J-4205 c/n also given as HABL 003206.	PVA
☐ Morane-Saulnier MS.406C-1 (D-3801)	HB-RCF	194	J-143 – with parts from J-276 – often at Bex.	PVA
☐ Mudry CAP.231	HB-MSR	17	F-GGYX	PVA
☐ Neukom Glider	HB-335			PV
☐ Nord N.1203-II Norécrin	HB-DAI	307		PVA
☐ Piaggio FWP.149D	HB-KIU	175	KB+141, DF+394, 91+53, D-EFCT	RAA

☐ Pilatus P.2-05	HB-RAX	23	A-103, U-103	RA
☐ Pilatus P.2-05	HB-RAY	35	A-115, U-115	PVA
☐ Pilatus P.2-05	HB-RAU	41	A-121, U-121	RA
☐ Pilatus P.3-05	HB-RBX	493-42	A-855	PVA
☐ Piper J-3C-90 Cub (J-3C-65) (L-4H)	HB-ONC	12027	44-79731	PVA
☐ Spalinger S-21H	HB-355			PV
☐ Sud-Est SE.3130 Alouette II	V-68	1924	F-WKQC	RA
☐ Ultralight Flying Machines Easy Rider				PV
☐ Yakovlev Yak-55M	RA-44500			RAA

FLIEGERMUSEUM DUBENDORF (SWI8)

Address: Ueberlandstrasse,
CH-8600 Dübendorf.
Tel: 01-823-2324
Fax: 01-823-2653
Email: angebot@flieger-museum.com
Location: On the south west side of the airfield which is about 8 km east of Zurich on Route 135.
Admission: Tuesday-Friday 1330-1700; Saturday 0900-1700; Sunday 1300-1700.

Military flying started in Switzerland on July 31st 1914 when the Fliegertruppe was established. Bases opened at Bundenfeld near Bern and Dubendorf which was close to Zurich. By the end of the year five monoplanes and five biplanes were in service. Over the years a number of indigenous designs were acquired including Wild biplanes made at Uster and Dubendorf and Häfeli biplanes produced at Thun. Aircraft were procured from many countries and the local industry developed and also built many types under licence. A collection of historic aircraft and material was started at Dubendorf in the early 1960s but this was only accessible on special occasions. In 1978 a museum opened in three small hangars connected by galleries. About twenty aircraft could be seen in the cramped conditions. Plans to enlarge the exhibition space were put forward in 1985 and the new hall with associated offices, a lecture theatre and a gallery overlooking the aircraft was dedicated on July 2nd 1988. In 1996 the Swiss Air Force joined with the Anti Air Artillery service and artefacts relating to this element are slowly being put on show. A fund raising drive for new galleries was started and these opened in April 2002. The museum presents a fascinating history of the Air Force from its formation up to the present day. Imaginative displays cover the development of aircraft used with photographs of all types which have served the military in the country. The history of the bases and their units, are also portrayed. There is a superb collection of over fifty restored engines and nearby is a range of guns and bombs. Replicas of three Häfeli biplanes have been built. Six DH-1s were flown from 1916 to 1919. August Häfeli had been employed in Germany at the Otto works and the design bore a resemblance to the AGO C 1 but was not a success. The DH-5 prototype flew in 1919 and after extensive testing entered service three years later. Two batches comprising fifty nine production aircraft were built and the last were not withdrawn until 1940. All three replicas were built by former Air Force personnel and the DH-5 is fitted with an original LFW-1 engine built in Winterthur. A partial replica of a Fokker D VII has also been constructed. This incorporates an original fuselage and engine plus some small components. Close by is the base of Ju Air which was formed to operate three former Air Force Ju 52s which were in military use from 1939 until 1982. They now fly regularly on pleasure flights to raise funds for the museum and have now been joined by a Spanish built version of the classic tri-motor. On view in the main hall are two prototypes of jet fighters designed in the late 1940s. The delta wing N-20 Aigullon was built at Emmen and made a few short hops in 1952 before the project was abandoned the following year. The F.F.A. works at Altenrhein conceived the conventional low wing P-16. The first prototype made its maiden flight on April 25th 1955 but was lost on its twenty second sortie. A second example was ready the following year and a third joined the development programme in 1957. An order for one hundred machines was placed in March 1958 but the loss of the third prototype which joined its brother at the bottom of Lake Constance caused cancellation of the programme. Two further aircraft were built as private ventures and after a period of storage at Altenrhein one joined the museum. A number of duplicate airframes is in store for possible exchange and as types are withdrawn they will join the collection.

TYPE	REG/SER	CON. NO.	PI/NOTES	STATUS
☐ Beech C18S Expeditor (C-45F) (UC-45F)	HB-GAC	8343	44-87103, NC79848, N79848, SE-BTS, G-8 (Switzerland)	PV
☐ Beech E50 Twin Bonanza	A-713	EH-58	HB-HOW	PV
☐ Blériot XI-2 (R)				PV
☐ Bücker Bü 131B Jungmann	A-32	43	A-32, HB-USP	RA
☐ Bücker Bü 131B Jungmann	A-51	64		PV
☐ Bücker Bü 133C Jungmeister	U-60	7	On loan to VHS Luzern.	–
☐ Bücker Bü 133C Jungmeister	U-61	8		PV
☐ Bücker Bü 133C Jungmeister	U-62	9		RA
☐ Bücker Bü 181B-1 Bestmann (Sk 25)	'A-251'	25027	Fv25027, D-EDOG, D-EDOC	PVX
☐ Comte AC-4 Gentleman	HB-USI	33	CH-249	RA
☐ Construcciones Aeronáuticas (CASA) 352L [Junkers Ju 52/3m]	HB-HOY	96	T.2B-165, D-CIAK	RA
☐ Dassault Mirage IIIC	J-2201			PV
☐ Dassault Mirage IIIDS	J-2011	227F		RA
☐ Dassault Mirage IIIRS	R-2118	1038		RA
☐ Dassault Mirage IIIS	J-2335	1025		PV
☐ De Havilland D.H.100 Vampire F.6	J-1049	960		RA
☐ De Havilland D.H.100 Vampire FB.6	J-1126	635		PV
☐ De Havilland D.H.100 Vampire FB.6	J-1153	662		PV
☐ De Havilland D.H.100 Vampire FB.6	J-1200	709		RA
☐ De Havilland D.H.112 Venom FB.1	J-1580	790	Fuselage only.	PV
☐ De Havilland D.H.112 Venom FB.1R	J-1642	852		RA
☐ De Havilland D.H.112 Venom FB.4	J-1729	899		RA
☐ De Havilland D.H.112 Venom FB.4	J-1734	904		RA

☐ De Havilland D.H.112 Venom FB.4	J-1739	909	Fuselage only.	PV
☐ De Havilland D.H.112 Venom FB.4	J-1751	921	Fuselage only.	PV
☐ De Havilland D.H.112 Venom FB.4	J-1753	923		RA
☐ De Havilland D.H.115 Vampire T.55			Fuselage only.	PV
☐ De Havilland D.H.115 Vampire T.55	U-1203	863		RA
☐ De Havilland D.H.115 Vampire T.55	U-1224	984		PV
☐ Dewoitine D.26	HB-RAG		286	PV
☐ Dewoitine D.27	257			PV
☐ Eidgenössiches Flugzeugwerke Emmen C-3603-1	C-534	314		PV
☐ Eidgenössiches Flugzeugwerke Emmen C-3603-1	C-537	317	On loan to VHS Luzern.	–
☐ Eidgenössiches Flugzeugwerke Emmen C-3605 (C-3603-1)	C-497	277		PV
☐ Eidgenössiches Flugzeugwerke Emmen C-3605 (C-3603-1)	C-498	278		RA
☐ Eidgenössiches Flugzeugwerke Emmen C-3605 (C-3603-1)	C-557	337		RA
☐ Eidgenössiches Flugzeugwerke Emmen N-20 Aiguillon				PV
☐ Eidgenössiches Konstruktions Werkstatte C-35 [Fokker C.X]	180		C-180	PV
☐ Fieseler Fi 156C-3 Storch	A-100	1685	RN+VJ	PV
☐ Fieseler Fi 156C-3/trop Storch	A-97	8063	CN+EL, BA+RI – on loan to VHS Luzern.	–
☐ Flug und Fahrzeugwerke (FFA) P-16	X-HB-VAD	X-05	J-3005	PV
☐ Fokker D VII	'640'		Partial replica	PVX
☐ Fokker C.VE	331	5261	C-331	PV
☐ Häfeli DH-1 (R)	'245'			PVX
☐ Häfeli DH-3 (R)	'DH3'			PVX
☐ Häfeli DH-5 (R)	'459'			PVX
☐ Hanriot HD-1	653			PV
☐ Hawker P.1099 Hunter F.58	J-4020	41H/691768		RA
☐ Hawker P.1099 Hunter F.58 (F.6)	J-4001	41H/679911	XE536	PV
☐ Hawker P.1099 Hunter F.58A (P.1067 Hunter F.4)	J-4118	HABL 003052	XF291, G-9-334 – front fuselage only.	RA
☐ Hawker P.1099 Hunter F.58A (P.1067 Hunter F.4)	J-4152	41H/R/662753	WT716, 7790M, G-9-385	RA
☐ Hawker P.1101 Hunter T.68 (P.1067 Hunter F.4)	J-4204	HABL 003033	XE702, 7794M, G-9-375	PV
☐ Hawker-Siddeley H.S.1182 Hawk 66	U-1251	336/SW001	ZG974	PV
☐ Hiller UH12B	KAB-202	387	KAB-202, V-202 (Switzerland), V-11 (Switzerland), D-HAHU, N94731	PV
☐ Junkers Ju 52/3mg4e	HB-HOS	6580	D-AYWV, A-701, HB-HOS, A-701	RAA
☐ Junkers Ju 52/3mg4e	HB-HOT	6595	A-702, HB-HOT, A-702	RAA
☐ Junkers Ju 52/3mg4e	HB-HOP	6610	A-703, HB-HOP, A-703	RAA
☐ Messerschmitt Bf 108B-2 Taifun	A-209	2083		PV
☐ Messerschmitt Bf 108B-2 Taifun	A-210	2084	On loan to VHS Luzern.	–
☐ Messerschmitt Bf 109E-3	J-355	2242/31647		PV
☐ Morane-Saulnier MS.406C-1 (D-3801)	J-276			PV
☐ Nieuport 28C.1	607	6212		PV
☐ Noorduyn Harvard IIB [North American NA-77 (AT-16)]	U-328	14-545	42-12298, FE811	PV
☐ Nord N.1203 Norécrin	HB-HOI	122		PV
☐ North American NA-122 Mustang (P-51D)	J-2113	122-39808	44-73349	PV
☐ Pilatus P.2-06	U-134	51	U-105	PV
☐ Pilatus P.3-02	A-801	318	HB-HOO	PV
☐ Pilatus P.3-03	A-803	320	A-803, (N321RD)	PV
☐ Pilatus PC.7 (P.3-05)	A-901	509	A-871, HB-HOZ	PV
☐ Sud-Est SE.3130 Alouette II			Fuselage frame only.	PV
☐ Sud-Est SE.3130 Alouette II	V-49	1237	HB-XBM	PV
☐ Sud-Ouest SO-1221S Djinn	'V-23'	FR-56/38		PVX

FLIEGERTRUPPE BASE EMMEN COLLECTION (SWI9)

Address:	P.O. Box 667, CH-6032 Emmen.
Tel:	041-268-3131
Admission:	By prior permission only.
Location:	Just east of the town which is about 5 km north of Luzern.

The airfield is home to training units and the official Air Force aerobatic team 'Patrouille Swiss'. The FFW factory which has built many types under licence as well as original designs is also on the field.

TYPE	REG/SER	CON. NO.	PI/NOTES	STATUS
☐ Dassault Mirage IIIS	J-2302	502		RA
☐ De Havilland D.H.112 Venom FB.4	J-1709	879	J-1709, 'J-1700' – at FFW gate.	RA
☐ Hawker P.1099 Hunter F.58	J-4070	41H/697437		RA

FLUGGRUPE ALBATROS (SWI10)

Address:	Oberburgerstrasse 10, CH-5210 Windisch.
Admission:	By prior permission only.
Location:	At Birrfeld airfield which is about 8 km south west of Baden.

A quartet of immaculate flying aircraft is maintained by this group. The Austrian firm Oberlerchner built many successful glider designs prior to and after World War II. The prototype of a two seat low wing monoplane the JOB 5 flew in 1957. The production version the three seater JOB 15 made its maiden flight four years later. Only twenty three were built with the last leaving the factory in 1966. The Stampe joined the group in the mid-1980s after flying club use in France. Max Brugger designed the MB.1 Kolibri which first flew in 1965. The improved MB.2 followed five years later and several have been built by amateur constructors.

TYPE	REG/SER	CON. NO.	PI/NOTES	STATUS
☐ Brugger MB.2 Kolibri	HB-YAV	41		RAA
☐ Oberlerchner JOB 15-180/2	HB-KEV	064	OE-CAW, D-EHGE, D-EKWK	RAA
☐ Piper J-3C-90 Cub (J-3C-65) (L-4J)	HB-OIA	12619	44-80323	RAA
☐ Stampe & Vertongen S.V.4A	HB-UPR	662	F-BDNG	RAA

FONDATION POUR LE MAINTIEN DU PATRIMOINE AÉRONAUTIQUE (SWI11)

Address:	Case Postale 7, CH-1000 Lausanne 30.
Fax:	021-626-2506
Email:	info@ampa.ch
Admission:	By prior permission only.
Location:	Workshops at Blécherette Airfield which is in the northern suburbs of the town. The aircraft are based at many airfields in the country.

This group was formed in 1981 with the aim of establishing a museum flying vintage and classic aircraft. Plans to build an exhibition hall at Sion have not yet been realised. At the current time workshops have been set up in a former military building at Lausanne airfield. The active machines are based here and at a number of other sites. Many of the fleet are privately owned by members of the organisation. . The Dewoitine D.26 parasol trainer was built under licence by E.K.W. at Thun and eleven were delivered to the Air Force. They served until 1948 when they were donated to sections of the Swiss Aero Club and used for glider towing. Very few now remain in airworthy condition. Fifteen Messerschmitt Bf 108Bs were ordered by the Air Force in 1938. They were purchased to train pilots for the Messerschmitt Bf 109 which entered service in 1939. One further Bf 108 was acquired from a civilian owner and two were interned after they landed in the country during World War II. The Italian designed Meteor is a steel tube fuselage development of the pre-war Avia FL.3. Only thirty seven were built in a number of versions between 1953 and 1959. The C-3605 lies dismantled in the hangars and is awaiting rebuild. The two jets owned by the organisation have been loaned out.

TYPE	REG/SER	CON. NO.	PI/NOTES	STATUS
☐ Bücker Bü 131APM-150 Jungmann (Bü 131B)	HB-UUU	84	A-71	RAA
☐ Bücker Bü 131B Jungmann	HB-AFE	36	HB-AFE, A-88, D-EDMI, G-ATJX	RAA
☐ Bücker Bü 131B Jungmann	A-67	80		RAC
☐ Bücker Bü 133C Jungmeister	HB-MIP	11		RAA
☐ Centre Est Aéronautique DR.221 Dauphin	HB-EUG	99	F-BPCV	RA
☐ Cessna 140A	HB-COR	15351	N9630A	RAA
☐ De Havilland D.H.82A Tiger Moth	HB-UPY	85635	DE694, G-ANOR	RAA
☐ De Havilland D.H.82A Tiger Moth	HB-UPP	DHA.1000	A17-565, VH-FBR, N17565, G-BCRD	RAA
☐ De Havilland D.H.112 Venom FB.1R	HB-RVC	841	J-1631 – with Musée de l'Aviation Militaire.	–
☐ De Havilland D.H.C.1 Chipmunk T.20	HB-TUM	P.62	1372 (Portugal), OO-NPO	RAA
☐ Dewoitine D.26	284	276	284, U-284, HB-RAI	RAA
☐ Eidgenössiches Flugzeugwerke Emmen C-3605 (C-3603-1)	C-555	335		RA
☐ Hawker P.1101 Hunter T.68 (P.1067 Hunter F.4)	HB-RVR	41H/670803	WV332, 7673M, G-9-406, J-4201 – on loan to Amici dell'Hunter.	–
☐ Jodel D.9 Bébé	HB-SAE	AB-11	D-EHAX	RAA
☐ Lilienthal Normal-Segelapparat (R)				RA
☐ Messerschmitt Bf 108B-2 Taifun	HB-HEB	1988	A-201, HB-HEB, A-201	RAC
☐ Meteor FL.55B	HB-EAC	1119	I-FELH	RA
☐ Morane-Saulnier MS.317 (MS.315)	HB-RAO	6583/329	329, F-BCBI	RAA
☐ Morane-Saulnier MS.733 Alcyon	HB-RAN	134	134 (France), F-BNED	RAA
☐ Morane-Saulnier MS.880B Rallye Club	HB-EDE	76		RAA
☐ Pilatus P.2-05	HB-RAS	47	A-127, U-127	RAA
☐ Pilatus P.3-05	HB-RCY	460-9	A-822, HB-RSY	RAC
☐ Piper J-3C-90 Cub (J-3C-65) (L-4H)	HB-OSM	12252	44-79956	RA
☐ Piper PA-12 Super Cruiser	HB-OAP	12-2245	NC2239M, OO-AXZ	RAC
☐ Piper PA-12 Super Cruiser	HB-OOC	12-3206	NC2653M	RA

FUN-FLYERS GAU (SWI12)

Address:	Flugplatz, CH-3368 Bleienbach-Langenthal,
Email:	ffg@fun-flyers.ch
Admission:	By prior permission only.
Location:	About 6 km south west of Langenthal and at a number of other airfields in Aarau Canton.

Members of this group own a variety of types and they regularly appear at air shows and meetings in the country. Under construction is a replica of the Nieuport 23C.1. The Swiss Government purchased five examples of this biplane fighter and they were in service from 1917 until 1921. Original drawings have been acquired and progress is being made on the airframe. Some of the pilots have achieved success at aerobatic competitions flying the Christen Eagle and the Walter Extra. The Gyroflug Speed Canard flew in prototype form in Germany in December 1980 and the type entered production at Baden-Baden four years later.

TYPE	REG/SER	CON. NO.	PI/NOTES	STATUS
☐ Bücker Bü 131APM-150 Jungmann (Bü 131B)	HB-UUD	16	A-9	RAA
☐ Bücker Bü 131APM-150 Jungmann (Bü 131B)	HB-UUO	42	A-31	RAA
☐ Bücker Bü 131B Jungmann	HB-UUT	81	A-68	RAA
☐ Christen Eagle 1	N246RL	L0026		RAA
☐ Construcciones Aeronáuticas (CASA) 1.131E [Bücker Bü 131 Jungmann]	HB-UVN	2142		RAA
☐ Dynaflug SC-01 Speed Canard				RAA
☐ Gardan GY-201 Minicab				RAA
☐ Nieuport 23C.1 (R)				RAC
☐ One Design MSW	HB-YJM	94-0278		RAA
☐ Piper J-3C-85 Cub (J-3C-65) (L-4J)	HB-ODE	12286	44-80570	RAA
☐ Ryan ST-3KR Recruit (PT-22A)	HB-RDD	1799	42-57503, N46382, N2625R, N1799	RAA
☐ Société Pour L'Aviation et ses Dérivés (SPAD) VII (R)				RAA
☐ Walter Extra EA-300/200	HB-MSY	028		RAA

GROUPE DE VOL À VOILE DE NEUCHATEL (SWI13)

Address:	Aérodrome, CH-2013 Colombier.
Tel:	032-841-3156
Fax:	032-841-1391
Email:	gvvn@aero-club-neuchatel.ch
Admission:	By prior permission only.
Location:	About 5 km south west of Neuchatel south of Route 5.

The oldest glider operated by this group is a 1937 Grunau Baby. This successful design was built in vast numbers from the mid-1930s and many pilots were trained on the type. A small group of volunteers maintain this classic sailplane in airworthy condition. The Schleicher K.7 first flew in 1959 and well over four hundred were built over the next five years. The DR.400 prototype appeared in 1972 and the type was produced in five versions.

TYPE	REG/SER	CON. NO.	PI/NOTES	STATUS
☐ Bölkow Phoebus A-1	HB-814	712		RA
☐ Grob G.102 Astir CS-77	HB-1430	1726		RAA
☐ Robin DR.400/180 Regent	HB-EXG	943		RAA
☐ Scheibe SF-25B Falke	HB-2364	4808	(D-KAHP), D-KETT, D-KEBU	RAA
☐ Schleicher K.7	HB-653	777		RAA
☐ Schneider ESG 31 Grunau Baby II (D.F.S. 108-49)	HB-234			RAA

GROUPEMENT DES AVIONS HISTORIQUES (SWI14)

Address:	Case Postale 25, 1018 Lausanne.
Tel:	021-616-37-92
Fax:	021-617-27-18
Admission:	By prior permission only.
Location:	At Blécherette airfield which is in the northern suburbs of Lausanne.

The highlight of the four aircraft flown by this group is the de Havilland Moth Major which was delivered new to Switzerland in 1934. The classic biplane was, during the 1970s and 1980s, the only flying example of its type. The prototype Moth Major flew in 1932 and just over one hundred and fifty were produced. The aircraft has suffered a number of minor crashes during its long and active life.

TYPE	REG/SER	CON. NO.	PI/NOTES	STATUS
☐ Cessna 170	HB-CAO	18720		RAA
☐ De Havilland D.H.60GIII Moth Major	HB-UPE	5078	CH-348	RAA
☐ Piper J-3C-90 Cub (J-3C-65) (L-4J)	HB-ODC	12892	44-80596	RAA
☐ Zlin Z-326 Trener Master	HB-TCB	902	F-BMQX	RAA

HUNTERVEREIN INTERLAKEN (SWI15)

Address: Postfach 662,
CH-3800 Interlaken.
Email: kohler.ueli@bluewin.ch
Admission: By prior permission only.
Location: At the airfield which is about 5 km south east of the town.

The Hunter gave excellent service in Switzerland from 1958 to 1994. One hundred were initially ordered with the first dozen being ex-R.A.F. machines and the others newly built at Kingston and Dunsfold. In the early 1970s fifty two single seat and eight two seat refurbished Hunters were supplied.

TYPE	REG/SER	CON. NO.	PI/NOTES	STATUS
☐ Hawker P.1099 Hunter F.58	J-4018	41H/691766		RA
☐ Hawker P.1099 Hunter F.58	J-4050	41H/697417		RA
☐ Hawker P.1099 Hunter F.58	J-4093	41H/697460		RA
☐ Hawker P.1099 Hunter F.58 (F.6)	J-4007	41H/679920	XE545	RA

HUNTERVEREIN MOLLIS (SWI16)

Address: P.O. Box 235
CH-8753 Mollis.
Email: Peter.Reumer@he.admin.ch
Admission: By prior permission only.
Location: The airfield is about 3 km south of the town on Route 17.

Hunters were regular visitors at this reserve airfield during their long period of service in Switzerland. The group was formed in the mid-1990s with the aim of acquiring an example of the classic jet. They were successful and one is stored in one of the hangars. The fighter is maintained in almost flying condition.

TYPE	REG/SER	CON. NO.	PI/NOTES	STATUS
☐ Hawker P.1099 Hunter F.58	J-4015	41H/691763		RA

HUNTERVEREIN OBERSIMMENTAL (SWI17)

Address: P.O. Box 23,
CH-3772 St. Stephan.
Email: hunterverein@hunterverein.ch
Admission: By prior permission only.
Location: The airfield is about 6 km south of Zweisimmen.

This organisation was formed in 1994 with the aim of acquiring a Hunter which had flown from St. Stephan Air Base. The aircraft was retired in late 1993 and was bought by the group in 1995. It is now painted in an all white scheme with Fliegerstaffel 15 logos and the names of pilots and mechanics adorning the airframe. The classic fighter has appeared at airshows around the country.

TYPE	REG/SER	CON. NO.	PI/NOTES	STATUS
☐ Hawker P.1099 Hunter F.58	HB-RVS	41H/697407	J-4040, 'J-4015'	RAA

JET ALPINE FIGHTERS (SWI18)

Address: Aéroport,
CH-1950 Sion.
Tel: 027-322-0064
Email: contact@jaf.ch
Admission: By prior permission only.
Location: About 3 km south west of the town.

This recently formed group has two aircraft in flying condition. The former United States Navy Trojan is now resplendent in military colours. The aircraft was delivered to the Navy in 1955 and was sold on the civilian market in 1983. The Mitchell spent several years based at Dijon in France and was a regular participant in airshows around Europe. There are plans to acquire more warbirds in the near future.

TYPE	REG/SER	CON. NO.	PI/NOTES	STATUS
☐ North American NA-108 Mitchell (B-25J)	HB-RDE	108-47662	45-8811, N9621C, F-AZID	RAA
☐ North American NA-200 Trojan (T-28B)	HB-RCT	200-337	Bu138266, N391W	RAA

L'AÉROTIQUE GROUPEMENT 'OLDTIMERS' (SWI19)

Address:	Case Postale 38, CH-1701 Fribourg.
Tel:	026-407-1520
Fax:	026-323-1625
Admission:	By prior permission only
Location:	At Ecuvillens airfield which is about 10 km south west of Fribourg off Route 12.

This group of enthusiasts has its own hangar at Ecuvillens. The Pilatus P.3 appeared in late 1953 and eighty were constructed including six for the Brazilian Navy. The type was used for basic training, blind flying instruction, aerobatics and liaison by the Swiss Air Force for forty years. A small number of Norécrins served in Switzerland since the mid-1950s. The group flew one for many years but this crashed in 2004 and has been sold to France for rebuilding. The Storch is probably German built but this has not been confirmed.

TYPE	REG/SER	CON. NO.	PI/NOTES	STATUS
☐ Fieseler Fi 156C-3 Storch			HB-???	RAC
☐ Pilatus P.2-06	HB-RAR	56	U-107, U-136	RAA
☐ Stampe & Vertongen S.V.4A	HB-UPS	243	F-BCKC, OO-EFD	RAA

LES AILES DU PASSÉ (SWI20)

Address:	Les Peuples, CH-1135 Denens.
Email:	vieuxplaneurs@multimedia.com
Admission:	By prior permission only.
Location:	At Ecuvillens airfield which is about 10 km south west of Fribourg off Route 12.

Formed in the late 1980s this group maintains four gliders and a Jodel in flying condition. The tailless Fauvel AV-36 first flew on December 31st 1951 and subsequently fifty were built by the Wassmer company at Issoire. This firm also supplied kits of components and plans were available for amateur constructors. The group rebuilt the aircraft in the early 1990s. The Nord N.1300 dates from 1947 and is a licence built Grunau Baby IIB.

TYPE	REG/SER	CON. NO.	PI/NOTES	STATUS
☐ Fauvel AV.36	HB-568	101		RAA
☐ Jodel DR.1051 Sicile	HB-EBZ	426		RAA
☐ Nord N.1300 [Schneider Grunau Baby IIB]	HB-348	210	F-CAQV, F-CRJP	RAA
☐ Schleicher Ka-6CR Rhönsegler	HB-871	6620		RAA
☐ Schleicher K.7	HB-768	7112		RAA

MUSÉE DE L'AVIATION MILITAIRE (SWI21)

Address:	Aérodrome Militaire CH-1530 Payerne.
Tel:	026-662-2120
Fax:	026-662-2123
Admission:	January-March, October-November Wednesday 1330-1700, Saturday 1330-1630; April-September Tuesday-Friday 1330-1700, Saturday 1300-1700, Sunday 1400-1700.
Location:	Just north of the town, which is 15 km west of Fribourg, and the Autoroute.

When the 5th Escadrille operating Hunters from Payerne was disbanded in 1994 a group was formed to keep alive the traditions of the unit. They soon acquired a Hunter which was stored at Arnex-sur-Orbe along with equipment and items of memorabilia. A Vampire came from the military museum at Morges but this has recently moved to Montpellier in France. Other aircraft were allocated to the organisation. A fund raising drive was started and in April 2002 a purpose built exhibition hall was opened at Payerne. The display has acquired more airframes and the story of the unit and Payerne is told in detail. The history of the Swiss Air Force is also portrayed. There is a section devoted to the Swiss astronaut Claude Nicollier who flew on an Atlantis shuttle mission in July 1992. Also to be seen are models, postcards, components, uniforms, photographs and flight simulators. Three versions of the recently withdrawn Mirage have joined the collection. The Air Force received its first Mirages in 1965 and they gave almost forty years service. Outside is an Air Force Memorial where one Vampire is mounted. Flights can be booked in the two seat Hunter and the Jungmann which also carries out this task at neighbouring airfields. The airfield is currently home to a fighter wing operating the Northrop F-5E Tiger II and the McDonnell F/A-18 Hornet. A helicopter unit with Alouette IIIs and Super Pumas is also in residence. Flying from the base can be observed from the museum. One Mirage is mounted near the main gate to the airfield and a Hunter is preserved at the nearby barracks.

TYPE	REG/SER	CON. NO.	PI/NOTES	STATUS
☐ Bücker Bü 131APM-150 Jungmann (Bü 131B)	HB-UVF	93	A-80	RAA
☐ Dassault Mirage IIIDS	J-2012	228F		RA
☐ Dassault Mirage IIIRS	R-2117	1040		PV
☐ Dassault Mirage IIIS	J-2324	1014		PV
☐ Dassault Mirage IIIS	J-2334	1024	On base.	RA
☐ Dassault Mirage IIIS	J-2312	1046	Front fuselage only.	PV
☐ Dassault Mirage IIIS	J-2301	200		PV
☐ De Havilland D.H.100 Vampire FB.6	J-1156	665		PV
☐ De Havilland D.H.100 Vampire FB.6	J-1157	666		PV
☐ De Havilland D.H.112 Venom FB.1	J-1584	794		PV
☐ De Havilland D.H.112 Venom FB.1R	HB-RVC	841	J-1631 – FMPA aircraft.	RAA
☐ De Havilland D.H.115 Vampire T.55	U-1211	971	U-1211, HB-RVL	PV
☐ Hawker P.1099 Hunter F.58	J-4045	41H/697412	At Kaserne near military base.	RA
☐ Hawker P.1099 Hunter F.58	J-4078	41H/697445		PV
☐ Hawker P.1099 Hunter F.58 (F.6)	J-4003	41H/679916	XE541	RA
☐ Hawker P.1101 Hunter T.68 (P.1067 Hunter F.4)	HB-RVW	41H/670844	WV398, 7667M, G-9-411, J-4203	PVA
☐ Sud-Est SE.3130 Alouette II	HB-XBI	1120	HB-XBI, V-43 – on loan from VHS.	PV

MUSÉE DE SAMY HEUER (SWI22)

Address: Petinesca,
Postfach 110,
CH-2557 Stunden.
Tel: 0373-1323
Admission: By prior permission only.
Location: About 5 km south of Biel off Route 6.

Former Air Force pilot Samy Heuer has three aircraft preserved in a specially built hall at his factory site. The Vampire is one of the hundred built under licence by a consortium of F + W at Emmen, Doflug at Altenrhein and Pilatus at Stans. Final assembly and flight testing was carried out at Emmen.

TYPE	REG/SER	CON. NO.	PI/NOTES	STATUS
☐ Dassault Mirage IIIS	J-2303	993		RA
☐ De Havilland D.H.100 Vampire FB.6	J-1135	644		RA
☐ Hawker P.1099 Hunter F.58	J-4041	41H/697408		RA

MUSEÉ JEAN TINGUELY (SWI23)

Address: P.O. Box 3255,
CH-4002 Basel.
Tel: 051-681-9320
Fax: 051-681-9321
Admission: Tuesday-Sunday 1100-1900.
Location: In the centre of the city.

This Swiss artist and sculptor Jean Tinguely was born in Freiburg in 1925. The museum opened in 1996 and has on show examples of his work. The Spanish built Jungmann was recently put on view.

TYPE	REG/SER	CON. NO.	PI/NOTES	STATUS
☐ Construcciones Aeronáuticas (CASA) 1.131E [Bücker Bü 131 Jungmann]	'E.3B-317'	2053	E.3B-449, G-BSFB (?)	PVX

MUSEUM VON ARX (SWI24)

Address: Rainallée 51,
CH-4125 Riehen.
Admission: By prior permission only.
Location: At Basel Airport which is about 6 km north west of the city.

Werner von Arx has set up the museum in his hangar at Basel Airport. The Hunter is painted in a special scheme. Around the walls are photographs and documents tracing the history of Swissair and the airport.

TYPE	REG/SER	CON. NO.	PI/NOTES	STATUS
☐ Bücker Bü 131B Jungmann	HB-UUC	13	A-6	RAA
☐ Bücker Bü 133C Jungmeister	HB-MIU	29	U-82	RAA
☐ Hawker P.1099 Hunter F.58	J-4026	41H/697392		RA
☐ Piper PA-22-108 Colt	HB-OWB	22-9565	N5726Z	RAA
☐ Piper PA-28-RT-201T Turbo Arrow IV	HB-PKH	28R-8231048	N8205H	RAA
☐ Schneider ESG 31 Grunau Baby IIB	HB-289	AB201		RA

This Dewoitine D.26 is on view at the Verkehrshaus in Luzern.

Two of the four aircraft operated by the Fluggruppe Albatros are shown in a Birrfeld hangar. Behind their Piper Cub is a Stampe SV.4.

The military museum in Istanbul has this Starfighter in its grounds. (Stewart Lanham)

OLDTIMER CLUB SCHÄNIS (SWI25)

Address: c/o Emil Lechner, Drosselstrasse, CH-8038 Zurich.
Tel: 01-480-1932
Fax: 01-480-1395
Admission: By prior permission only.
Location: The airfield is just north of Schänis off Route 17.

The picturesque airfield of Schänis is home to many modern sailplanes. The Oldtimer Club maintains machines from an earlier era. Jacob Spalinger built his S-1 in the World War I period and over the next two decades twenty five designs appeared. The S-18 first flew in 1936 and was developed over the next few years. The Müller brothers built their first glider the Moswey I primary in 1930. They both worked for August Hug for a number of years before Georg designed the Moswey II. The slightly longer span IIA appeared in 1939 and the III followed in 1942. A small number were built in 1945 and a few still exist.

TYPE	REG/SER	CON. NO.	PI/NOTES	STATUS
☐ Karpf Baby	HB-494	1		RAA
☐ Müller Moswey III	HB-374			RAA
☐ Schleicher Ka-2 Rhönschwalbe	HB-724	1064		RAA
☐ Schleicher Ka-4 Rhönlerche II	HB-586	238		RAC
☐ Schleicher Ka-6CR Rhönsegler	HB-703	6006		RAA
☐ Spalinger S-18-III				RA

SAMMLUNG BUHLER (SWI26)

Address: Industriestrasse 5, CH-5712 Beinwil-am-See.
Tel: 062-771-7751
Admission: By prior permission only.
Location: About 25 km north of Luzern on Route 26.

Bernhard Bühler is acquiring a collection of mainly former Swiss Air Force aircraft for possible display in the region. The quintet are currently stored at his premises in the town. In the late 1960s the factory at Emmen converted twenty four C-3603s to C-3605 standard. His plans seem to have changed as the Jungmann and Vampire have recently been put up for sale. They have been moved to another building close by.

TYPE	REG/SER	CON. NO.	PI/NOTES	STATUS
☐ Construcciones Aeronáuticas (CASA) 1.131E [Bücker Bü 131 Jungmann]	E.3B-501	2127		RA
☐ De Havilland D.H.100 Vampire FB.6	J-1193	702		RA
☐ Eidgenössiches Flugzeugwerke Emmen C-3605 (C-3603-1)	C-533	313		RA
☐ Pilatus P.2-05	HB-RAV	48	A-128, U-128	RA
☐ Pilatus P.2-06	U-147	67		RA

SAMMLUNG DÄTWYLER (SWI27)

Address: Flugplatz, CH-3368 Bleienbach-Langenthal
Tel: 062-919-3737
Fax: 062-922-7371
Admission: By prior permission only.
Location: The airfield is about 6 km south west of Langenthal.

The company has an overhaul business at the airfield. A number of Piper Cubs were modified for high altitude work and the Lerche conversion of Bücker Jungmanns was also carried out. The MDC Trailer was a specialised glider tug. This aircraft was constructed in the early 1960s using Piper Super Cub parts. The Trailer is currently operated by the local flying club. An original project the MD-3 Swiss Trainer was conceived in the late 1960s. The project underwent a number of changes before the prototype made its maiden flight in August 1983. The low wing two seater is powered by a 160 h.p. Lycoming engine. The company has a collection of preserved aircraft, the majority of which are stored in a large building near the airfield.

TYPE	REG/SER	CON. NO.	PI/NOTES	STATUS
☐ Dätwyler MDC Trailer	HB-RAL	MDC-1038		RAA
☐ Dätwyler MD-3-160 Swiss Trainer	HB-HOH	001		RAA
☐ Eidgenössiches Flugzeugwerke Emmen C-3605 (C-3603-1)	HB-RBI	327	C-547	RA
☐ Hawker P.1099 Hunter F.58	J-4013	41H/691761		RA
☐ Mooney M.20K	N100EY	25-0802		RA
☐ Pilatus P.2-05	HB-RAZ	46	A-126, U-126	RA
☐ Piper J-3C-65 Cub (L-4J)	HB-OBL	12575	44-80279	RA

SAMMLUNG FAHRNI (SWI28)

Address:	Flugzeugbau, CH-8332 Russikon.
Tel:	01 954 06 45
Fax:	01 954 26 42
Admission:	By prior permission only.
Location:	About 3 km north of Pfaffikon.

Jacob Spalinger built his first glider prior to 1918 and by the mid-1940s he had designed twenty five types. The S-15 first appeared in 1934 and the one in the collection dates from 1940. The S-18 made its maiden flight in 1936 and two took part in the Berlin Olympic Games displays later in the year. The S-18 II featured a longer wing span and this variant was built in some numbers by the Wynau firm. The Kranich is a slightly modified version of the Jacobs design built in Switzerland. Another classic is the Meise which was registered in Switzerland in 1944. The prototype of this Hans Jacobs design flew in 1939 and was selected as the type to be flown by all pilots in the 1940 Olympic Games. More than one thousand were constructed in Germany during World War II and after the war production resumed in England, France, Holland, Switzerland and Germany. The Elfe was designed by Werner Pfenninger and first flew in 1939. In the late 1950s Albert Neukom modified the structure and produced a number of variants over the next few years. The Piper Cub is one of several modified by the Max Datwyler company at Langenthal for use in the thinner mountain air.

TYPE	REG/SER	CON. NO.	PI/NOTES	STATUS
☐ Champion 7GCB Challenger	HB-UAK	48		RA
☐ Jacobs Meise (D.F.S. 108-70)	HB-381			RAA
☐ Karpf Baby	HB-443	443		RAC
☐ Neukom Elfe S2/3P	HB-842	11		RAA
☐ Piper J-3C-90 Cub (J-3C-65) (L-4H)	HB-ODZ	MDC-1049	44-30360 – original c/n 11651.	RAA
☐ Scheibe Bergfalke II/55	HB-690	340		RAA
☐ Scheibe L-Spatz 55	HB-612	646		RAA
☐ Schleicher Ka-6CR Rhönsegler	HB-643	620		RAA
☐ Société Industrielle Pour l'Aéronautique (SIPA) S.903 (S.901)	HB-SPP	48	F-BGAX	RAA
☐ Spalinger Kranich	HB-330			RA
☐ Spalinger S-15K	HB-327			RAC
☐ Spalinger S-18-IIA	HB-286			RA
☐ Szybowcowy Zaklad Doswiadczalny S.Z.D.9bis Bocian 1C	HB-740	F-799		RA
☐ Szybowcowy Zaklad Doswiadczalny S.Z.D.25A Lis	HB-750	F-727	SP-2343	RA

SAMMLUNG POLL (SWI29)

Address:	C.P. 37, CH-1670 Ursy.
Admission:	By prior permission only.
Location:	About 20 km north east of Lausanne.

Dietmar Poll is acquiring an interesting collection of classic gliders. In addition to the Pilatus B-4s built at Stans-Buochs he has a Czech designed Lunak and a Polish Cobra.

TYPE	REG/SER	CON. NO.	PI/NOTES	STATUS
☐ Letov LF-107 Lunak	OK-0975	12	OK-0975, BGA.5015	RAA
☐ Pilatus B4-PC11	HB-1226			RA
☐ Pilatus B4-PC11	BGA.1836	045		RA
☐ Pilatus B4-PC11	OE-05425	071	D-2200, HB-1888	RA
☐ Pilatus B4-PC11AF	HB-3221	111		RA
☐ Pilatus B4-PC11AF	BGA.2352	134	RAFGSA.518, RAFGSA.718	RAA
☐ Pilatus B4-PC11AF	HB-1319	247		RA
☐ Pilatus B4-PC11AF	HB-3268	277		RAA
☐ Szybowcowy Zaklad Doswiadczalny S.Z.D.36A Cobra 15	HB-1213	W-667		RAA

SAMMLUNG ZELLER (SWI30)

Address:	Scheibe 1304, CH-9053 Teufen.
Tel:	071-333-3591
Admission:	By prior permission only.
Location:	About 10 km south of St. Gallen.

The Zeller family who also trade under the name Appair has a fleet of classic types. The Antares is a Jungmeister fitted with a Lycoming engine hidden by a round cowling. Similarly, Lycomings power the APM version of the Jungmann. In the 1930s. small numbers of both types were acquired from Germany before production took place at the Doflug factory at Altenrhein. These biplanes were in military use until the early 1970s before they were sold to civilian owners. The Cubs have all been fitted with more powerful engines.

TYPE	REG/SER	CON. NO.	PI/NOTES	STATUS
☐ Bücker Bü 131APM-150 Jungmann (Bü 131B)	HB-UUN	41	A-30	RAA
☐ Bücker Bü 131APM-150 Jungmann (Bü 131B)	HB-UUP	50	A-39, HB-UTF, A-39, HB-UUP, G-BHGZ	RAA
☐ Bücker Bü 131APM-150 Jungmann (Bü 131B)	HB-UVE	69	A-56	RAA
☐ Bücker Bü 131B Jungmann	HB-UVZ	44	A-33	RAA
☐ Bücker Bü 133C Jungmeister	HB-MKO	1	U-54	RA
☐ Bücker Bü 133C Jungmeister	HB-MKZ	9	U-62	RAA
☐ Bücker Bü 133C Jungmeister	HB-MKN	23	U-76	RAA
☐ Bücker Bü 133C Jungmeister	HB-MKH	40	U-93	RAA
☐ Bücker CBM Antares Bücker (Bü 133C Jungmeister)	HB-MKM	36	U-89	RA
☐ Piper J-3C-90 Cub (J-3C-65) (L-4H)	HB-OFP	12092	44-79796	RAA
☐ Piper J-3C-90 Cub (J-3C-65) (L-4H)	HB-OGZ	12648	44-80352	RAA
☐ Piper J-3C-100 Cub (J-3C-65) (L-4H)	HB-OUN	12316	44-80020	RAA

SEGELFLUGGRUPPE BAD RAGAZ (SWI31)

Address: Mühlebünt,
CH-9479 Oberscham.
Tel: 081-325-1701
Email: andreas.zogg@ntb.ch
Admission: By prior permission only.
Location: The airfield is about 3 km north west of the town off Route 3.

This club flies one of the few remaining Karpf Babies. This design is a close copy of the classic Grunau Baby. Several were constructed in the 1940s when Switzerland was unable to purchase German gliders due to its neutrality. A number of modern types are also in regular use by the club.

TYPE	REG/SER	CON. NO.	PI/NOTES	STATUS
☐ Grob G.102 Astir CS	HB-1376	1490		RAA
☐ Karpf Baby	HB-505			RAA
☐ Pilatus B4-PC11AF	HB-3051	282	D-2230	RAA
☐ Rolladen-Schneider LS-4	HB-1574	4107		RAA
☐ Rolladen-Schneider LS-4	HB-1832	4551		RAA
☐ Schleicher Ka-4 Rhönlerche II	HB-807	3064Br		RAA
☐ Schleicher ASK-21	HB-1959	21368		RAA
☐ Schleicher ASK-23	HB-1786	23012		RAA

SEGELFLUGGRUPPE BEIDER BASEL (SWI32)

Address: Paradiestrasse 10,
CH-5223 Riniken.
Tel: 061-331-6480
Admission: By prior permission only.
Location: At Dittingen airfield which is about 15 km south west of Basel, north of Route 18.

This group operates one of the oldest active gliders in Switzerland. Edmund Schneider designed the famous Grunau Baby which first flew in 1931. The improved Baby II appeared two years later and the IIB fitted with full air brakes was soon to follow. Just over four thousand are known to have been built in Germany prior to World War II. After the conflict was over production resumed in Czechoslovakia, Spain and Sweden. The French Nord N.1300 was a licence built version and the design was the basis for Elliott and Slingsby models in England. A large fleet of modern sailplanes is flown by the club from its picturesque airfield.

TYPE	REG/SER	CON. NO.	PI/NOTES	STATUS
☐ Schleicher Ka-4 Rhönlerche II	HB-595	261		RAA
☐ Schleicher Ka-4 Rhönlerche II	HB-969	3031		RAA
☐ Schleicher Ka-4 Rhönlerche II	HB-786	3054		RAA
☐ Schleicher Ka-4 Rhönlerche II	HB-860	955		RAA
☐ Schleicher Ka-6CR Rhönsegler	HB-651	722		RAA
☐ Schleicher ASK-21	HB-1834	21300		RAA
☐ Schleicher ASK-21	HB-1884	21311		RAA
☐ Schneider ESG 31 Grunau Baby IIB	HB-87	90		RAA

SEGELFLUGGRUPPE BERN (SWI33)

Address: Postfach,
CH-3001 Bern.
Tel: 031-819-3141
Fax: 031-819-4607
Admission: By prior permission only.
Location: At the airport which is about 3 km south east of the city.

This group operate a number of classic gliders. Alexander Schleicher set up a factory at Poppenhhausen near the famous Wasserkuppe hill in 1927. Up to the outbreak of World War II he manufactured several successful Hans Jacobs designs. He resumed sailplane production in 1951 with the Rudolf Kaiser designed Ka-2 Rhönlerche. Several other models followed and the company is still producing high quality designs.

TYPE	REG/SER	CON. NO.	PI/NOTES	STATUS
☐ Pilatus B4-PC11	HB-1103	004		RAA
☐ Pilatus B4-PC11	HB-1125	064		RAA
☐ Scheibe SF-25C Rotax-Falke	HB-2280	44595	D-KTIT	RAA
☐ Schleicher Ka-4 Rhönlerche II	HB-608	379		RAA
☐ Schleicher Ka-4 Rhönlerche II	HB-664	672		RAA
☐ Schleicher K.8B	HB-663	669		RAA
☐ Schleicher ASK-21	HB-1766	21232		RAA
☐ Schleicher ASK-21	HB-1811	21258		RAA

SEGELFLUGGRUPPE DITTINGEN (SWI34)

Address:	Hornelstrass 15 CH-4114 Hofstetten.
Tel:	061-711-0272
Admission:	By prior permission only.
Location:	About 15 km south west of Basel.

Two vintage gliders are in use by the club. The Karpf Zögling primary dates from the 1940s and is based on the famous Stamer-Lippisch design. The Grunau Baby dates from the same period. The club also fly several classics along with a fleet of modern types. The tug is a higher powered Super Cub.

TYPE	REG/SER	CON. NO.	PI/NOTES	STATUS
☐ Karpf Zögling	HB-461			RA
☐ Piper PA-18-180M Super Cub (PA-18-150)	HB-ORL	18-5301	F-OBDM, F-BBOM	RAA
☐ Rolladen-Schneider LS-4	HB-1647	4128		RAA
☐ Rolladen-Schneider LS-4	HB-1643	4168		RAA
☐ Rolladen-Schneider LS-4	HB-1655	4169		RAA
☐ Schleicher ASK-21	HB-1632	21092		RAA
☐ Schleicher ASH-25E	HB-1940	25024		RAA
☐ Schneider ESG 31 Grunau Baby IIB	HB-580			
☐ Szybowcowy Zaklad Doswiadczalny S.Z.D. 51-1 Junior	HB-3013	B-1846		RAA

SEGELFLUGGRUPPE FREIBURG (SWI35)

Address:	Postfach 369, CH-1701 Freiburg.
Tel:	026-673-1933
Fax:	026-673-1933
Email:	c.roux@freesurf.ch
Admission:	By prior permission only.
Location:	At Bellechasse airfield which is about 15 km north of the town and 5 km south of Ins.

In the 1930s the Groupe de Vol à Voile de la Broye was formed using two primary gliders. A Swiss record flight of fifteen hours forty minutes was set in 1948 but was not recognised because the pilot had no licence. Few Karpf Babies survive in airworthy condition and the example at Bellechasse was restored in 1994 after more than twenty years in store. The Pilatus company built more than three hundred PC-11s between 1972 and 1978. The design rights were then sold to the Japanese Nippi-Nihon Kikoki Kabushiki company.

TYPE	REG/SER	CON. NO.	PI/NOTES	STATUS
☐ Jacobs Kranich III	HB-475	1167	LX+WJ	RA
☐ Karpf Baby	HB-442			RAA
☐ Pilatus B4-PC11	HB-1106	007		RAA
☐ Pilatus B4-PC11	HB-1123	57		RAA
☐ Piper PA-18-180M Super Cub (PA-18-150)	HB-ORH	18-7408		RAA
☐ Piper PA-18-180M Super Cub (PA-18-150)	HB-PNU	18-7883	N8019P, D-ENSU	RAA
☐ Rolladen-Schneider LS-4	HB-1595	4112		RAA

SEGELFLUGGRUPPE RANDEN (SWI36)

Address:	Steigstrasse 4, CH-8447 Dachsen.
Tel:	052-659-4884
Admission:	By prior permission only.
Location:	At Schaffhausen airfield which is about 5 km west of the town.

This group has several Swiss designed sailplanes in its fleet. The In the 1960s Bircher and von Voornfeld fitted Glasflügel Libelle wings to a fuselage of their own design. Production rights were acquired by FFA and thirteen Diamant HBVs were constructed. The 16.5 model had a longer span wing to improve performance. There are three versions of the Neukom Elfe in regular use. The S-4 version was produced in his factory near Schaffhausen. The sole Vetterli Sperber single seater was built in 1976.

TYPE	REG/SER	CON. NO.	PI/NOTES	STATUS
☐ Flug und Fahrzeugwerke (FFA) Diamant 16.5	HB-940	060		RAA
☐ Neukom Elfe 17	HB-1165	34		RAA
☐ Neukom Elfe 17	HB-1178	40		RAA
☐ Neukom Elfe 17A	HB-1275	75		RAA
☐ Neukom Elfe S-4A	HB-1219	53		RAA
☐ Rolladen-Schneider LS-4	HB-1705	4332		RAA
☐ Vetterli Sperber	HB-1227	1		RAA

SUPER CONSTELLATION FLYERS ASSOCIATION (SWI37)

Address: P.O. Box 436,
CH-4009 Basel.
Tel: 079-700-1049
Fax: 079-700-1049
Email: InfoE@superconstellation.org
Admission: By prior permission only.
Location: At the airport which is about 6 km north west of the city.

Members of the group bought the former Dominican Super Constellation in the U.S.A. Work has now stopped on this aircraft due to certification problems. In 2004 an agreement was made with the Constellation Historical Society for the long-term lease of their aircraft. This was ferried from Camarillo in California to Basel in April/May 2004. The airliner has since delighted crowds at shows around Europe. Delivered to the U.S.A.F. in 1955 it flew on military duties for eighteen years and later had a spell as a crop sprayer.

TYPE	REG/SER	CON. NO.	PI/NOTES	STATUS
☐ Lockheed 1049-55-96 Super Constellation (C-121C)	N73544	1049F-4175	54-0156 – On loan from Constellation H.S., CA.	RAA
☐ Lockheed 1049B-55-75 Super Constellation (R7V-1) (C-121G)	N105CF	1049B-4137	Bu131636, 54-4062, N2114Z, HI-583CT, N105CF – in U.S.A.	RA

SWISS WARBIRD OWNERS GROUP (SWI38)

Address: CH-2540 Grenchen.
Admission: By prior permission only.
Location: At Grenchen.

The group, which is associated with the Commemorative Air Force in Texas, is aiming to set up a flying museum of warbird aircraft. Their first acquistion is a Stinson Sentinel purchased in the United States.

TYPE	REG/SER	CON. NO.	PI/NOTES	STATUS
☐ Stinson V-76 Sentinel (L-5)	N121MC	76-1684	(USAAF)	RAA

VEREINFREUNDE DER SWISSAIR (SWI39)

Address: Uberlandstrasse 255,
CH-8600 Dubendorf.
Tel: 043-333-8877
Fax: 044-823-2053
Email: info@swissair-dc3.ch
Admission: By prior permission only.
Location: On the south west side of the airfield which is about 8 km east of Zurich on Route 135.

Swissair operated a fleet of DC-3s on its European routes from 1937 until 1969. Classic Air flew two examples of the famous type from Zurich for several years. The group acquired one of these in 2003 and have restored it to the original Swissair scheme. The aircraft made its first flight in April 2004 under its new owners and has since visited a number of shows in Europe. The aircraft will be operated alongside the Ju 52s at Dubendorf.

TYPE	REG/SER	CON. NO.	PI/NOTES	STATUS
☐ Douglas DC-3A-456 Skytrain (C-47A)	HB-ISC	9995	42-24133, NC65266, NC6K, N88Y, N88YA, G-BMCR	RAA

VERKEHRSHAUS DER SCHWEIZ (SWI40)

Address:	Lidostrasse 5, CH-6006 Luzern.
Tel:	041-370-4444
Fax:	041-370-6168
Email:	mail@verkehrshaus.ch
Admission:	March-October daily 0900-1800; November-February Tuesday-Saturday 1100-1600, Sunday 1000-1700.
Location:	On the north side of the Luzernersee about 2 km south of the town centre.

An advisory group was set up in 1940 to look at the possibility of establishing a transport museum. Construction of the building started in 1957 and the collection opened to the public on July 1st 1959. Development of the site has taken place steadily and new attractions have been added over the last four decades. A large Air and Space wing was ready in July 1972. The superb railway section was reorganised at this time, and a second hall opened in 1979 A further improvement occurred in 1997. This large section contains many unique engines and vehicles designed to cope with the steep gradients found in the country. Also featured are road transport, postal and telecommunications, shipping and tourism. A planetarium, an IMAX theatre and other multimedia shows present varied views of the country. The aircraft are displayed at various levels and a system of walkways enables them to be viewed from different angles. There are many associated displays covering different aspects of aviation and space travel. The earliest type is the 1910 Dufaux 4 built in Geneva and demonstrated to the military authorities who found it unsuitable. The Blériot was bought in 1914 from Oskar Bider and used on border patrols. This aircraft was withdrawn in 1919 and used for publicity work in the 1930s. In 1940 the historic machine was flown from Dubendorf to Spreitenbach and used in a film about Bider. Other early Air Force types are the Hanriot built under licence in Italy by the Macchi company and the Nieuport 28 which force landed at Solothurn in 1918 in the hands of an American pilot. Alexander Soldenhoff designed and constructed a number of tailless aircraft in the 1920s and 1930s in both Switzerland and Germany. The S-5, dating from 1935, has survived and is on show. Alfred Comte built a number of types in the same period and on view is an AC-4 high wing monoplane. Only thirteen examples of the type were completed and the one on show is fitted with a Gipsy Major engine. A locally built Pou-du-Ciel which was flown on skis can also be seen. Close co-operation exists with the Air Force Museum and several types have been loaned to the collection. The Arbalete was designed as a small scale test aircraft for the abortive Aigullon project. The latter was on show in the museum grounds for many years but moved to Dubendorf in the mid-1980s to be put on show in the new hall. Willi Farner built his first hang glider in 1931 and two years later set up an overhaul company at Grenchen airfield. The WF-7 sailplane was constructed in the mid-1930s and is his only original design surviving. The collection of transport types shows the development of the airliner over fifty years. The Fokker F VII was delivered in 1927 and used by Swissair and Balair until 1978. Two Lockheed Orions were flown by Swissair between 1932 and 1936. The museum wanted to obtain an example for the exhibition but only one existed. Built as an Altair it was converted to an Orion in 1931 after a few weeks in service and was unique in having a metal fuselage. In the 1950s it was put on show in a museum in California and was purchased by the Verkehrshaus in 1976. This unique aircraft was flown to Zurich in a Boeing 747 and restored to the original red Swissair colours by retired engineers. The Coronado entered Swissair service in 1962 and eight were used until the mid 1970s. The example on show was floated up the lake on a raft and is now parked outside the main buildings.

TYPE	REG/SER	CON. NO.	PI/NOTES	STATUS
☐ Agusta A.109K-2			Fuselage only.	PV
☐ Ailes DeK Hang Glider				PV
☐ Ballonfabrik Stuttgart K-780/2-STU Balloon	HB-BEA	0235	Basket only.	PV
☐ Bell 47G-1	HB-XAE	689		PV
☐ Blériot XI-b	23			PV
☐ Breitling Orbiter 3 Hot Air Balloon				PV
☐ Bucher Canard 2FL	HB-3000			PV
☐ Bücker Bü 131B Jungmann	A-62	75		PV
☐ Bücker Bü 133C Jungmeister	U-60	7	On loan from FM	PV
☐ Chanute Glider (R)				PV
☐ Comte AC-4 Gentleman	HB-KIL	35	CH-264	PV
☐ Convair 30-6 Coronado 990A	HB-ICC	12A (38)		PV
☐ Dewoitine D.26	U-288	320	288, U-288, HB-RAE	PV
☐ Douglas DC-3A-467 Skytrain (C-47B) (Dakota IV)	HB-IRN	16645/33393	44-77061, KN683	PV
☐ Dufaux IV				PV
☐ Eidgenössiches Flugzeugwerke Emmen C-3603-1	C-537	317	On loan from FM	PV
☐ Eidgenössiches Flugzeugwerke Emmen N-20 Arbalete				PV
☐ Farner WF-7	32			PV
☐ Fieseler Fi 156C-3/trop Storch	A-97	8063	CN+EL, BA+RI – on loan from FM	PV
☐ Flug und Fahrzeugwerke (FFA) AS.202/15 Bravo	'HB-FFA'	021	HB-HFB – front fuselage only	PVX
☐ Fokker F.VIIa	HB-LBO	5005	CH-157	PV
☐ Gas Balloon			Basket only.	PV
☐ Grob G.102 Astir CS-77			Cockpit section only	PV
☐ Horlacher Pelaros 3				PV
☐ Hug Spyr IIIB	HB-112			PV
☐ Lockheed 9C Orion (DL-2A Altair)	'CH-167'	180	X12222, NC12222, NR12222, N12222	PVX
☐ Messerschmitt Bf 108B-2 Taifun	A-210	2084	On loan from FM	PV
☐ Michel Ikarus 200 Hang Glider				PV
☐ Mignet/Donat Guignard Pou-du-Ciel	HB-SUR			RA
☐ Mignet/Roland Py Pou-du-Ciel	HBMH-8			PV
☐ Mudry CAP.231EX	HB-MSC	06	F-GKKR, F-WKKR	PV
☐ Neukom AN-20	HB-YBM	01		RA
☐ Neukom Elfe S2/3P	HB-935	21		PV

TYPE	REG/SER	CON. NO.	PI/NOTES	STATUS
☐ Nieuport 28C.1	688			PV
☐ Pilatus B4-PC11			Cockpit section only	PV
☐ Piper PA-18-150 Super Cub	HB-OPR	18-5786		PV
☐ Rech Monoplane				PV
☐ Scottish Aviation Twin Pioneer 3	HB-HOX	570		RA
☐ Soldenhoff S-5				PV
☐ Spalinger S-21H	HB-305			S
☐ Spalinger S-21H	HB-307			PV
☐ Stamer-Lippisch Z-12 Zögling 33	HB-362			PV
☐ Stierlin RS-40 Helicopter	X-HB-XVB	3		PV
☐ Sud-Est SE.210 Caravelle III			Nose only.	PV
☐ Sud-Est SE.3130 Alouette II	V-43	1120	V-43, HB-XBI – on loan to Musée de l'Aviation Militaire.	–
☐ Sud-Est SE.3160 Alouette III	HB-XDF	1216		PV

VETERANO (SWI41)

Address: Wildstrasse 17,,
CH-5600 Lenzberg.
Tel: 062-892-1260
Admission: By prior permission only.
Location: At Birrfeld airfield which is about 8 km south west of Baden.

Birrfeld is home to a number of vintage and classic aircraft. This group has two rarities in its fleet. The Erla 5A low wing monoplane dates from 1934 and was built in small numbers. The example in the collection flew in Germany until the outbreak of World War II when it was hidden near Schwäbisch Gmund in a building disguised as a haystack. The Allied troops failed to discover the aircraft and it rested there until the mid-1950s. The Erla moved to Switzerland in 1962 where it was restored. The original 20 h.p. D.K.W. engine was replaced by a 50 h.p. Volkswagen. This unique machine has been based at Birrfeld since its first post-war flight in 1967. The diminutive Rösgen EPR.301 biplane was registered in 1942 and has been with the group since 1975. The aircraft was built in Geneva by Jean Augsburger between 1936 and 1940 but did not take to the air until 1947. Originally fitted with a 45 h.p. Salmson nine cylinder radial there were engine problems and it was stored from the late 1940s until 1967. Ernst Brugger modified the airframe to take a 65 h.p. Continental and it flew later in the year. The Howard DGA-15P is a rarity in Europe. Benny Howard built a number of racing designs and the 15 was developed from the 1934 Bendix Trophy winner DGA-11 'Mister Mulligan'. First flown in 1940 forty model 15s were sold on the civilian market before the U.S. Navy placed large orders for ambulance and trainer versions. Six hundred and fifty were eventually built and several are active in the U.S.A.

TYPE	REG/SER	CON. NO.	PI/NOTES	STATUS
☐ Beech 35-33 Debonair	HB-EHO	CD-132	OE-DNE	RAA
☐ Bücker Bü 131B Jungmann	HB-UVG	30	A-21	RAA
☐ Bücker Bü 131B Jungmann	HB-UTN	87	A-74	RAA
☐ Centre Est Aéronautique DR.250/160 Capitaine	HB-EMX	25	F-BMZV	RAA
☐ Centre Est Aéronautique DR.250/160 Capitaine	HB-EEZ	48		RAA
☐ Cessna 195B	NC3081B	7966	NC3081B, N3081B	RA
☐ Ercoupe 415C	HB-ERB	4367	OO-EXA	RAA
☐ Erla 5A	HB-SEX	14	D-YBIT, D-ENAL	RAA
☐ Howard DGA-15P	NC42429	528	NC42429, N42429	RAA
☐ Jodel D.112 Club	HB-SVL	459	F-PHFF, TS-ABC	RAA
☐ Jodel DR.1050M1 Sicile Record	HB-EEN	610		RAA
☐ Karpf Baby	HB-444			RAA
☐ Müller Moswey IIa	HB-257			RA
☐ Piper J-3C-65 Cub (L-4J)	HB-OUP	12530	44-80234	RAA
☐ Piper PA-22-150 Tri-Pacer	HB-OPL	22-2865	N2504P	RAA
☐ Rosgen EPR.301	HB-OIX	1		RAA
☐ Spalinger S-21H	HB-280	280		RA
☐ Stamer-Lippisch Z-12 Zögling	HB-190	HS1		RAA

VINTAGE AIRCRAFT CLUB (SWI42)

Address: Postfach 253,
Basel-Flughafen,
CH-4030 Basel.
Admission: By prior permission only.
Location: About 5 km north west of the city.

The former British European Airways Viking was delivered in 1947. The aircraft burst a tyre at Le Bourget in August 1953 and was declared a write off. The airliner arrived at the Schlumpf Museum in Mulhouse shortly after this and some restoration work was carried out. The aircraft was rediscovered in store when the firm went bankrupt and workers took over the site. The National Motor Museum was set up at Mulhouse in 1981 but the Viking did not feature in their plans. The airframe was donated to the group in 2004 and moved to Basel. Restoration work has started and it is hoped to complete the Viking by 2007.

TYPE	REG/SER	CON. NO.	PI/NOTES	STATUS
☐ Vickers 610 Viking 1B	G-AIVG	220		RA

TURKEY

AKINCI HAVA KUVVETLERI UST KOLLEKSION (TU1)

Address:	4 Ana Jet Ust Komutanligu, Akincini.
Admission:	By prior permission only.
Location:	About 10 km north west of Ankara

Formerly known as Mürted this airfield is home to a fighter wing flying F-16s and the factory of Turkish Aircraft Industries. A collection of types used by the unit in the past has been assembled. Turkey acquired more than eighty Canadair Sabre 2s and 4s and these initially equipped a wing containing three squadrons. An aerobatic team called 'The White Swans' flew the type in the early 1960s. The Convair F-102 entered Turkish service in 1969 and these delta wing fighters served for just over ten years.

TYPE	REG/SER	CON. NO.	PI/NOTES	STATUS
☐ Beech C18S Kansan (AT-11)	'46-840'	3377	42-36997, 6840	RAX
☐ Canadair CL-13 Sabre 2 [North American F-86E]	19103	3	19103 (Canada)	RA
☐ Canadair CL-90 Starfighter (CF-104) [Lockheed 683-04-12]	62-713	683A-1013	12713 (Canada), 104713 (Canada)	RA
☐ Convair 8-10 Delta Dagger (F-102A)	53392		55-3392	RA
☐ Lockheed 580 (T-33A)	35062	580-8401	53-5062	RA
☐ Lockheed 580 (T-33A)	35792	580-9131	53-5792	RA
☐ Lockheed 580 (T-33A)	53106	580-9676	55-3106	RA
☐ Lockheed 683-10-19 Starfighter (F-104G)	'260'			RAX
☐ Lockheed 683-10-19 Starfighter (F-104G)	7051	683-7051	KE+351, DC+109, DB+259, 21+82	RA

ANADOLU POLIS HAVACILIK DAIRE BASKANLIGI KOLLEKSION (TU2)

Address:	Anadolu, Eskisehir.
Admission:	By prior permission only.
Location:	In the northern suburbs of the town.

The Turkish Police has its own helicopter service and since 1993 pilots have been trained at Anadolu. A small number of helicopters are detached at major towns throughout the country. The Viscount is also used for instructional duties. Turkish Airlines ordered five examples in the late 1950s and flew them until the early 1970s when the three survivors were transferred to the Air Force. The two Mentors are currently stored in one of the hangars and at least one will be put on display in the near future.

TYPE	REG/SER	CON. NO.	PI/NOTES	STATUS
☐ Beech A45 Mentor (T-34A)	54-5202	CCF34-5	24202 (Canada)	RA
☐ Beech A45 Mentor (T-34A)	54-5208	CCF34-11	24208 (Canada)	RA
☐ Grumman G-121 Tracker (S-2E)	TCB-679	212C	Bu151679	RA
☐ Lockheed 683-10-19 Starfighter (F-104G)	8298	683-8298	KG+398, DB+118, DC+128, 25+23	RA
☐ Vickers 794D Viscount	431	431	TC-SES	RA

ASKERI MÜZESI (TU3)

Address:	Spor ve Sergi Sarayi Carsisi Harbiye, Beyoglu, Istanbul.
Tel:	0212-232-1698
Fax:	0212-233-2720
Admission:	Tuesday-Sunday 1000-1700.
Location:	In the north western part of the city centre.

The military history of the country is portrayed in this museum. The Ottoman period is highlighted with an excellent display of campaign tents, weapons, uniforms and flags. Outside is a gun mounted on a railway wagon and a collection of mortars. There are sections on both World War I and World War II showing the involvement of Turkish forces in these conflicts. The development of the Air Force since its formation is traced with many photographs on view. The two aircraft are displayed in the grounds. The Turkish Air Force obtained over four hundred and fifty Starfighters from other countries and the last were withdrawn in the mid-1990s. The Sioux was the first helicopter flown by the Turkish Army so it is appropriate for one to be on show.

TYPE	REG/SER	CON. NO.	PI/NOTES	STATUS
☐ Bell 47G-3B Sioux (OH-13S)	10397	3959	69-16381	PV
☐ Canadair CL-90 Starfighter (CF-104) [Lockheed 683-04-12]	62-733	683A-1033	12733 (Canada), 104733 (Canada)	PV

BALIKESIR HAVA KUVVETLERI UST KOLLEKSION (TU4)

Address:	9 Ana Jet Ust Komutanligi, Balikesir.
Admission:	By prior permission only.
Location:	In the south eastern suburbs of the town.

This important base, which has been used by fighters for many years, is currently home to two squadrons of F-16s and a detachment of Bell UH-1H Iroquois helicopters. In the late 1950s a number of Beech Kansans were delivered and used mainly as navigational trainers. The type remained in use until 1983 and the majority of the survivors have been preserved. In the early 1950s about three hundred F-84G Thunderjets were supplied and became the first jet operated by the Turkish Air Force. The Thunderjet served with the resident wing and was replaced by the Thunderstreak. Later F-104 Starfighters and F-5 Freedom Fighters flew from the base.

TYPE	REG/SER	CON. NO.	PI/NOTES	STATUS
☐ Beech C18S Kansan (AT-11)	6865	4975	42-37678	RA
☐ Canadair CL-30 Silver Star 3 (CT-133) [Lockheed 580 (T-33AN)]	21536	T33-536		RA
☐ Lockheed 683-04-10 Starfighter (RF-104G)	6622	683-6622	KC+133, EB+102, 21+01	RA
☐ Lockheed 683-10-19 Starfighter (F-104G)	2045	683-2045	KF+21, (DA+249), DA+243, 20+38	RA
☐ Lockheed 683-10-19 Starfighter (F-104G)	8090	683-8090	D-8090 (Netherlands)	RA
☐ Lockheed 683-10-19 Starfighter (F-104G)	9145	683-9145	KH+160, DF+122, 26+11	RA
☐ Northrop N-156A Freedom Fighter (F-5A)	10531	N.6192	65-10531, 1216 (Taiwan), 10531 (Vietnam)	RA
☐ Northrop N-156A Freedom Fighter (F-5A)	'07121'	N.6487	69-7121, 97121 (Taiwan)	RAX
☐ Republic F-84F Thunderstreak	37214		53-7214, DB+369	RA
☐ Republic F-84G Thunderjet	'9-966'		51-10966, 10966	RA

BANDIRMA HAVA KUVVETLERI UST KOLLEKSION (TU5)

Address:	6 Ana Jet Ust Komutanligi, Bandirma.
Admission:	By prior permission only.
Location:	Just south of the town.

Preserved near the gate to the base is a collection of types which have operated from the field in recent years. The Thunderstreak was flown in large numbers for several years from many bases. Bandirma currently has in residence two squadrons of General Dynamics F-16C/Ds along with a small number of Bell UH-1Hs. The Northrop F-5A Freedom Fighter was previously used by the based units.

TYPE	REG/SER	CON. NO.	PI/NOTES	STATUS
☐ Beech C18S Kansan (AT-11)	6833	3297	42-36917	RA
☐ Lockheed 580 (T-33A)	54432	580-9876	55-4432, 54432 (France)	RA
☐ Lockheed 683-04-10 Starfighter (RF-104G)	8164	683-8164	KG+264, EA+122, 24+22	RA
☐ Lockheed 683-10-19 Starfighter (F-104G)	7186	683-7186	KE+486, VB+229, 23+03	RA
☐ Lockheed 683-10-19 Starfighter (F-104G)	22336	683D-6035	62-12336	RA
☐ Northrop N-156A Freedom Fighter (F-5A)	21158	N.6347	67-21158, 1252 (Taiwan)	RA
☐ Republic F-84F Thunderstreak	37040		53-7040, DD+234, DB+370, DB+243, DB+381	RA
☐ Republic F-84G Thunderjet	111001		51-11001	RA

CIGLI AIR HAVA KUVVETLERI UST KOLLEKSION (TU6)

Address: 2 Ana Jet Ust Komutanligi, Cigli.
Admission: By prior permission only
Location: About 15 km north west of Izmir.

Advanced pilot training is carried out by the resident squadrons of the wing. At the current time Cessna T-37s and Northrop T-38s are flown from the field. A number of preserved aircraft are located around the site. The Mentor has now been moved to the nearby reserve airfield of Kalkic. Turkish Air Force Dakotas were a familiar sight at all airfields from the late 1940s. More than one hundred were delivered and gave excellent service. The last were retired in 1998 and a few of the survivors have been preserved. The classic T-33 was used to train many Turkish pilots. Almost one hundred and fifty Lockheed built aircraft were joined by about fifty Canadair examples. The type was first used in 1951 and the last were withdrawn in early 1997.

TYPE	REG/SER	CON. NO.	PI/NOTES	STATUS
☐ Beech A45 Mentor (T-34A)	2-201	CCF34-4	24201 (Canada) – At Kalkiç.	RA
☐ Canadair CL-30 Silver Star 3 (CT-133) [Lockheed 580 (T-33AN)]	'21058'	T33-066	21066	RAX
☐ Canadair CL-30 Silver Star 3 (CT-133) [Lockheed 580 (T-33AN)]	'21121'	T33-436	21436	RAX
☐ Douglas DC-3A-456 Skytrain (C-47A)	6033	12950	42-93078	RA
☐ Lockheed 580 (T-33A)	17519	580-7579	51-17519	RA
☐ Lockheed 683-10-19 Starfighter (F-104G)	8347	683-8347	KG+447, DB+253, DC+129, 25+52	RA

DIYARBAKIR HAVA KUVVETLERI UST KOLLEKSION (TU7)

Address: 8 Ana Jet Ust Komutanligi, Diyarbakir.
Admission: By prior permission only.
Location: In the south western suburbs of the town.

Situated close to the borders with Iraq and Syria this important base houses two squadrons of F-16s and a detachment of UH-1 helicopters. The site is one of three under the control of the 2nd Tactical Air Force. Fighters have been in residence for many years and the preserved aircraft represent types previously flown from the field and those which have visited from other squadrons. Forty four former Canadian Air Force Starfighters were delivered to Turkey from Sollingen in Germany in 1985/6 and these served until the mid-1990s. The country also flew large numbers of both Lockheed and European built examples of the F-104.

TYPE	REG/SER	CON. NO.	PI/NOTES	STATUS
☐ Beech C18S Kansan (AT-11)	6923	4026	42-37433	RA
☐ Canadair CL-90 Starfighter (CF-104) [Lockheed 683-04-12]	63-808	683A-1108	12808 (Canada), 104808 (Canada)	RA
☐ Canadair CL-90 Starfighter (CF-104) [Lockheed 683-04-12]	63-891	683A-1191	12891 (Canada), 104891 (Canada)	RA
☐ Lockheed 580 (T-33A)	35791	580-9130	53-5791	RA
☐ Lockheed 683-04-10 Starfighter (RF-104G)	8128	683-8128	KG+228, EA+116, 23+99	RA
☐ Lockheed 683-10-19 Starfighter (F-104G)	7108	683-7108	KE+408, (VA+126), 22+30	RA
☐ Lockheed 683-10-19 Starfighter (F-104G)	9185	683-9185	KH+184, 26+33	RA
☐ North American NA-224 Super Sabre (F-100D)	52763	224-30	55-2763	RA
☐ Republic F-84F Thunderstreak	37007		53-7007, DC+369	RA
☐ Republic F-84G Thunderjet	111218		51-11218	RA

ERHAC HAVA KUVVETLERI UST KOLLEKSION (TU8)

Address:	7 Ana Jet Ust Komutanligi, Erhac.
Admission:	By prior permission.
Location:	About 20 km north west of Malatya.

The resident wing operates the F-4E Phantom and also serves as the Operation Conversion Unit for the type. Several aircraft have now been upgraded to F-4E-2020 standard. Some were modified by Israeli Aircraft Industries at Lod and the others in the Turkish Air Force maintenance facility at Eskisehir. In addition there is also a detachment of Iroquois helicopters on the field. Until recently RF-4Es were also flown but these have now moved to Eskisehir. For a long period the squadrons flew versions of the North American Super Sabre. The first D model arrived in late 1958 and this variant was in service until 1989. In common with most Turkish bases there is a collection of preserved aircraft representing types previously operated. There are a number of Starfighters in use as instructional airframes and one will eventually be put on show.

TYPE	REG/SER	CON. NO.	PI/NOTES	STATUS
☐ Beech C18S Kansan (AT-11)	6904	3538	42-37158	RA
☐ Lockheed 580 (T-33A)	53092	580-9633	55-3092, 53092 (France)	RA
☐ North American NA-224 Super Sabre (F-100D)	52782	224-49	55-2782, G-782 (Denmark)	RA
☐ Republic F-84F Thunderstreak	28808		52-8808	RA

ESKIŞEHIR HAVA KUVVETLERI UST KOLLEKSION (TU9)

Address:	1 Ana Jet Ust Komuntanligi, Eskisehir.
Admission:	By prior permission only.
Location:	About 5 km north east of the town.

The base is home to a fighter wing which in recent years has seen several types, including the F-100 Super Sabre, F-5 Freedom Fighter, F-4 Phantom and F-16 Fighting Falcon, in use. A collection of preserved aircraft has been assembled. Turkey became a member of NATO in 1952 and this led to modern American equipment being supplied. Many airfields were upgraded and in addition several new bases were constructed. The first of three hundred Thunderjets were delivered and later the Thunderstreak and Thunderflash arrived. Examples of these three types have been saved. Almost eighty new Phantoms were delivered in the mid-1970s and these were followed a few years later by just over one hundred ex-U.S.A.F. machines. Several F-4s have now been upgraded and more are expected to be converted. Eight newly built RF-4Es were delivered from the U.S.A. in 1978 and in the mid-1990s forty seven former Luftwaffe examples were flown to Turkey.

TYPE	REG/SER	CON. NO.	PI/NOTES	STATUS
☐ Beech C18S Kansan (AT-11)	6933	4581	42-37585	RA
☐ Canadair CL-13 Sabre 2 [North American F-86E]				RA
☐ Canadair CL-13 Sabre 2 [North American F-86E]	142	42	19142 (Canada)	PV
☐ Canadair CL-30 Silver Star 3 (CT-133) [Lockheed 580 (T-33AN)]	21410	T33-410		RA
☐ Canadair CL-90 Starfighter (CF-104) [Lockheed 683-04-12]	62-751	683A-1051	12751 (Canada), 104751 (Canada)	RA
☐ Lockheed 580 (T-33A) (RT-33A)	41548	580-9179	54-1548	PV
☐ McDonnell M.98LG Phantom II (RF-4E)	69-7478	4081	69-7478, 35+31	RA
☐ North American NA-224 Super Sabre (F-100D)	52775	224-42	55-2775, G-775 (Denmark)	RA
☐ North American NA-243 Super Sabre (F-100F)	63946	243-222	56-3946	RA
☐ Northrop N-156A Freedom Fighter (F-5A)	10570	N.7018	65-10570, 570 (Norway)	RA
☐ Republic F-84F Thunderstreak	27123		52-7123, DB+127	RA
☐ Republic F-84F Thunderstreak	27142		52-7142, P-110 (Netherlands)	PV
☐ Republic RF-84F Thunderflash	27234		52-7234, 27234 (France)	RA
☐ Republic F-84G Thunderjet	110987		51-10987, 110897 (France)	RA

ESKIŞEHIR HAVACILIK PARKI VE TEYYARE MÜZESI (TU10)

Address:	Yeni Baglar Mahallesi, Bulgar Caddesi, Eskisehir.
Tel:	0222-320-5291
Admission:	Daily 0800-2000 (closes at 2200 in summer)
Location:	Opposite The Yunus Emre campus of Anadolu University.

This museum was set up in the town to portray the history of Turkish aviation with particular reference to the local air base. The display opened in the late 1990s and in addition to the aircraft many photographs, documents, uniforms, equipment and components are on show. A range of aircraft from all branches of services can be seen. The Navy operated a fleet of Trackers from Topel from 1971 to 1993. Fifteen were later converted by Turkish Aerospace Industries into turbo-prop powered water bombers. The Alouette was flown by both the Army and the Police before joining the collection. All the combat types on show have been used by the wing at Eskiseher. The two civilian registered Super Cubs were used by the THK organisation after their military days were over. The museum has made rapid progress since its opening and more aircraft are expected.

TYPE	REG/SER	CON. NO.	PI/NOTES	STATUS
☐ Canadair CL-30 Silver Star 3 (CT-133) [Lockheed 580 (T-33AN)]	21321	T33-321		PV
☐ Douglas DC-3A-456 Skytrain (C-47A)	'052'	18973	42-100510, 6032 – fuselage only	PVX
☐ Grumman G-121 Tracker (S2F-3S) (S-2E)	TCB-849	124C	Bu149849	PV
☐ Lockheed 580 (T-33A)	16772	580-6104	51-6772	PV
☐ Lockheed 580 (T-33A)	29919	580-7890	52-9919	PV
☐ Lockheed 683-10-19 Starfighter (F-104G)	6667	683-6667	D-6667 (Netherlands)	PV
☐ Lockheed 683-10-19 Starfighter (F-104G)	7190	683-7190	KE+490, FB+233, 23+07	PV
☐ McDonnell M.98LG Phantom II (RF-4E)	69-7465	4043	69-7465, 35+18	PV
☐ North American NA-214 Super Sabre (F-100C)	31732	214-24	53-1732	PV
☐ Northrop N-156A Freedom Fighter (F-5A)	13346	N.6115	64-13346 – front fuselage only.	PV
☐ Northrop N-156A Freedom Fighter (F-5A)	69212	N.7035	66-9212, 212 (Norway)	PV
☐ Piper PA-18-95 Super Cub (L-18C)	TC-YSB			PV
☐ Piper PA-18-95 Super Cub (L-18C)	TC-AUA	18-464	50-1808, 10325	PV
☐ Republic RF-84F Thunderflash	28733		52-8733	PV
☐ Sud-Est SE.3130 Alouette II	E-2077	2077	77+45	PV

GÜVERCINLIK MÜZESI (TU11)

Address:	Kara Ordusu Havaciligi, Güverncinlik.
Admission:	By prior permission only.
Location:	About 10 km west of Ankara.

The airfield is the headquarters of army aviation in the country and is home to combat, training, observation and transport squadrons. The aviation branch of the service was established in 1948 at the Artillery School at Polati. The first types used were Piper Cubs and these were followed by Super Cubs, Bird Dogs and Dornier Do 27s. A number of Dornier Skyservants were bought in the 1960s and nineteen ex-Luftwaffe examples arrived in 1996. Helicopters, in the form of the Agusta-Bell 204, arrived in 1966. The museum has been set up to trace the history of the service and many photographs, documents and uniforms can be seen.

TYPE	REG/SER	CON. NO.	PI/NOTES	STATUS
☐ Agusta-Bell 204B	'901'	3176	10459, 11032,	RAX
☐ Agusta-Bell 212ASW	TCB-39			RA
☐ Bell 47G-3B Sioux (OH-13S)	10395	3946	67-15897	RA
☐ Bell 47G-3B-2 Sioux (TH-13T)	10437	3478	65-8045	RA
☐ Bellanca 7GCBC Citabria	10101	1076-79		RA
☐ Bellanca 7GCBC Citabria	10126	1110-79		RA
☐ Cessna 305C Bird Dog (L-19E) (O-1E)	10160			RA
☐ Dornier Do 28D-1 Skyservant	10016	4081	58+06	RA
☐ Piper PA-18-135 Super Cub (L-21B)	'10101'	18-2587	52-6289, TC-EBY	RAX

HAVA HARP OKULU KOLLEKSION (TU12)

Address:	Sahil Yolu, 34150 Yesilkoy.
Email:	webmaster@hho.edu.tr
Admission:	By prior permission only.
Location:	Close to the south eastern corner of Ataturk Airport.

The Turkish Air Force Academy is located close to the airport which serves Istanbul. Displayed in the attractive grounds overlooking the sea are a number of aircraft. These have been put on show to remind personnel of the history and traditions of the service. Two are by the main gate, another pair can be seen on the parade ground and a couple of the Starfighters are located close to the athletic complex across the road.

TYPE	REG/SER	CON. NO.	PI/NOTES	STATUS
☐ Lockheed 583-10-20 Starfighter (TF-104G)	5711	583D-5711	61-3040, KF+210, BB+110, 27+10	RA
☐ Lockheed 683-10-19 Starfighter (F-104G)	8277	683-8277	KG+377, 25+13	RA
☐ Lockheed 683-10-19 Starfighter (F-104G)	8299	683-8299	KG+399, DB+119, 25+24	RA
☐ Lockheed 683-10-19 Starfighter (F-104G)	078	683-9078	FX-38 (Belgium)	RA
☐ Lockheed 683-10-19 Starfighter (F-104G)	083	683-9083	FX-40 (Belgium)	RA
☐ North American NA-217 Super Sabre (F-100C)	42059	217-320	54-2059	RA
☐ Republic F-84F Thunderstreak	28816		52-8816	RA

HAVA KUVVETIERI MÜZESI KOMUTANLIGI (TU13)

Address:	Hava Lojistik Komutanligi, Etimesgut, Ankara.
Tel:	0312-244-8550
Fax:	0312-245-0757
Admission:	Daily 0900-1630.
Location:	About 20 km west of Ankara.

The airfield is home to a transport wing and VIP aircraft for government use are in residence. This new museum opened in the late 1990s to complement the Air Force Museum at Istanbul. It was felt that the capital of the country should have a major collection of military aircraft. Airframes have been moved from bases around the country to give a representative range of types used in recent years. A replica of the P.Z.L.24 has been built and more are planned to show types operated in the past. The Hungarian Air Force donated a MiG-21. This has now been joined by a former Bulgarian MiG-17 and a Chinese built MiG-19 from Pakistan. All the other aircraft on show have been flown by the military in Turkey. The displays are being developed and will trace the history of aviation in the country. The history of the Air Force will also be portrayed.

TYPE	REG/SER	CON. NO.	PI/NOTES	STATUS
☐ Beech C18S Kansan (AT-11)	'3-880'	3225	42-36845, 6830	PVX
☐ Beech A45 Mentor (T-34A)	TC-CCA	CCF34-9	24206 (Canada), 54-5206	PV
☐ Bell 205 Iroquois (UH-1H)	69-16720	12008		PV
☐ Canadair CL-13 Sabre 2 [North American F-86E]	19190	90	19190 (Canada)	PV
☐ Canadair CL-90 Starfighter (CF-104) [Lockheed 683-04-12]	62-711	683A-1011	12711 (Canada), 104711 (Canada)	PV
☐ Canadair CL-90 Starfighter (CF-104) [Lockheed 683-04-12]	62-770	683A-1070	12770 (Canada), 104770 (Canada)	PV
☐ Canadair CL-90 Starfighter (CF-104) [Lockheed 683-04-12]	62-810	683A-1110	12810 (Canada), 104810 (Canada) – at nearby barracks.	PV
☐ Cessna R172F Mescalero (T-41D)	01410	R1720512	72-1410	PV
☐ Convair 8-12 Delta Dagger (TF-102A)	62368		56-2368	RA
☐ Douglas DC-3A-456 Skytrain (C-47A)	073	19529	43-15063, 43-6073	PV
☐ Lockheed 580 (T-33A)	14284	580-5579	51-4284, 14284 (France)	PV
☐ Lockheed 580 (T-33A)	54432	580-9876	55-4432 – front fuselage only.	PV
☐ Lockheed 583-04-15 Starfighter (CF-104D)	62-642	583A-5312	12642 (Canada), 104642 (Canada)	PV
☐ Lockheed 683-04-10 Starfighter (RF-104G)	8205	683-8205	KG+305, EB+108, 24+57	PV
☐ Lockheed 683-10-19 Starfighter (F-104S)	6859	683-6859	At nearby barracks.	RA
☐ McDonnell M.98LG Phantom II (RF-4E)	95703	4133	69-7503, 35+56	PV
☐ Mikoyan-Gurevich MiG-17F	159	591738	In Bulgarian markings.	PV
☐ Mikoyan-Gurevich MiG-21MF	9308	969308	In Hungarian markings.	PV
☐ North American NA-217 Super Sabre (F-100C)	41877	217-138	54-1877	PV
☐ North American NA-217 Super Sabre (F-100C)	41766	217-27	54-1766	PV
☐ Northrop N-156A Freedom Fighter (F-5A)	14465	N.6319	67-14465 – front fuselage only.	PV
☐ Northrop N-156A Freedom Fighter (F-5A)	10575	N.7023	65-10575, 575 (Norway)	PV
☐ Northrop N-156A Freedom Fighter (RF-5A)	21208	N.6395	67-21208	RA
☐ Panstwowe Zaklady Lotnicze (PZL) P.24G (FSM)	'2017'			PVX
☐ Republic F-84F Thunderstreak	7186		53-7186, DB+323	PV
☐ Republic RF-84F Thunderflash	11924		51-1924, P-24 (Netherlands)	PV
☐ Republic F-84G Thunderjet	'62-3011'		52-3011, 23011	PVX
☐ Shenyang J-6 [Mikoyan-Gurevich MiG-19SF]	4123		In Pakistani markings	PV
☐ SIAI-Marchetti SF.260D	2-815	815		PV
☐ Supermarine 361 Spitfire LF.IXe (FSM)	'329'			PVX

HAVACILIK MÜZESI (TU14)

Address:	Hava Harp Okulu, Yesilkoy, 34149 Istanbul.
Tel:	0212-662-8552
Fax:	0212-663-1560
Admission:	Tuesday-Sunday 0900-1130 1300-1630
Location:	At Yesilyurt in the suburbs of Istanbul- on the southern edge of Ataturk Airport.

Foreign pilots flew British, French and German types on behalf of Turkish forces in the 1912/3 Balkan War. During World War I the Flying Corps was manned by mainly German personnel. The Turkish Republic was founded in 1923 and the Turk Hava Kumuru (Turkish Air League) was formed two years later. Its aims were to arouse public interest in aviation and to raise money for the purchase of aircraft. Aircraft factories were set up and an Air Force came into being. In the late 1920s and through the 1930s a variety of American, British, French, German and Polish types were operated along with a few indigenous machines. During World War II Turkey maintained a neutral position. At the end of the conflict Britain and the United States supplied large numbers of surplus aircraft. In 1952 Turkey joined NATO and since then mainly American types have been used. A decision to set up an air museum was made in April 1966 and a hangar at Cumaovasi near Izmir was obtained. Aircraft and memorabilia were collected and the display officially opened in 1971. The location was not on tourist routes and the exhibition closed seven years later. The museum moved to its current site in

1982 and was dedicated on October 16th 1985. Yesilkoy was an airfield during World War I and from this time there were plans for a museum but most of the material collected was destroyed. The displays trace the history of aviation in the country and a varied range of aircraft can be seen. Halls are devoted to Turkish Aviation, Commanders of the Turkish Air Force and World Aviation. A hangar houses engines, components and about ten aircraft. The oldest is a Russian Grigorovich M.5 flying boat dating from 1914. The biplane was forced dawn near Gorele after a flight across the Black Sea. Two more rarities are the Curtiss-Wright Falcon and the P.Z.L. 24. Fifty Falcons were ordered in 1937 and used for training and ground attack duties. The high wing P.Z.L. 24 fighter first flew in 1933 and was improved over the next few years. Forty were ordered from Poland along with parts to construct a further twenty. The first Turkish assembled P.24 flew in May 1937 and production of later versions took place at the factory at Kayseri. About one hundred were eventually made in Turkey. Also built under licence were more than eighty Miles Magisters and the type was developed into the Ugur.

TYPE	REG/SER	CON. NO.	PI/NOTES	STATUS
☐ Altin Kanatlar (R)				PV
☐ Beech C18S Kansan (AT-11)	6930	4561	42-37565	PV
☐ Beech A45 Mentor (T-34A)	2-220	CCF34-24	24220 (Canada), TC-IHK	PV
☐ Bell 205 Iroquois (UH-1H)	69-15724	12012		PV
☐ Bellanca 7GCBC Citabria	10104	1079-79		PV
☐ Canadair CL-13 Sabre 2 [North American F-86E]	19207	107		PV
☐ Canadair CL-13 Sabre 2 [North American F-86E]	19268	168		PV
☐ Canadair CL-226 Freedom Fighter (NF-5A) [Northrop N-156A]	3022	3022	K-3022 (Netherlands)	PV
☐ Canadair CL-226 Freedom Fighter (NF-5A) [Northrop N-156A]	3070	3070	K-3070 (Netherlands)	PV
☐ Cessna 185D Skywagon (U-17A)	11357	185-0846	64-17933, 11061, TC-CDF	PV
☐ Cessna 318C Tweety Bird (T-37C)	39835	40807	63-9835	PV
☐ Convair 8-10 Delta Dagger (F-102A)	53386		55-3386	PV
☐ Curtiss-Wright CW-22B Falcon	TC-TK15		2615(?)	PV
☐ De Havilland D.H.89A Dragon Rapide (D.H.89B Dominie I)	'TC-ERK'		Possibly c/n 6687 HG702, TC-HAD or c/n 6688 HG703, TC-DER	PVX
☐ Dornier Do 27B-1		261	PH+109, PC+110, D-9521, D-EGTY	RA
☐ Dornier Do 27H-2	10294	2114	D-ECPI	RA
☐ Dornier Do 27H-2	10293	2142	D-EFCI	RA
☐ Dornier Do 28B-1	10012	3079	D-IBON	PV
☐ Dornier Do 28B-1	10013	3083	D-IBOT	PV
☐ Dornier Do 28D-2 Skyservant	10020	4021	D-IBBA, 10348	PV
☐ Dornier Do 28D-2 Skyservant	10022	4106	58+31	PV
☐ Douglas DC-3A-456 Skytrain (C-47A)	YSL-52	13877	43-30726, 43-6052	PV
☐ Douglas DC-3A-467 Skytrain (C-47B)	H-008	15011/26456	43-49195, 43-6008	PV
☐ Douglas DC-4 Skymaster (C-54D)	10683	10788	42-72683	PV
☐ Grigorovich M.5				PV
☐ Grumman G-121 Tracker (S2F-3S) (S-2E)	149877	152C	Bu149877	PV
☐ Lockheed 580 (T-33A)	35744	580-9083	53-5744	PV
☐ Lockheed 580 (T-33A) (RT-33A)	1543	580-9174	54-1543, 41543 (France)	PV
☐ Lockheed 583-10-20 Starfighter (TF-104G)	5725	583D-5725	61-3054, KF+224, 27+24	PV
☐ Lockheed 683-10-19 Starfighter (F-104G)	12619	683C-4019	61-2619 – tail from c/n 683-8233 KG+333, EB+231, 24+83	PV
☐ Lockheed 683-10-19 Starfighter (F-104G)	344	683D-6043	62-12344, 22344	PV
☐ Lockheed 683-10-19 Starfighter (F-104S)	6868	683-6868		PV
☐ Makona Ve Kimya Endustri Kumuru (MKEK) 4 Ugur	44	5144/1957	TC-KUJ, 'TC-KUS'	PVX
☐ McDonnell M.98HO Phantom II (F-4E)	67-0360	3234		PV
☐ Miles M.14A Magister	60	60/1946	TC-KAY	RA
☐ Miles M.14A Magister	TC-KAH	77/1948	TC-THK77 – possibly ex 3577	PV
☐ North American NA-182 Texan (T-6G)	7504	182-266	51-14579	PV
☐ North American NA-217 Super Sabre (F-100C)	42089	217-350	54-2089	PV
☐ North American NA-223 Super Sabre (F-100D)	42245	223-125	54-2245	PV
☐ North American NA-243 Super Sabre (F-100F)	63788	243-64	56-3788	PV
☐ Northrop N-156A Freedom Fighter (F-5A)	'14460'	N.6320	66-14466	PV
☐ Northrop N-156A Freedom Fighter (RF-5A)	97147	RF.1027	69-7147	PV
☐ Panstwowe Zaklady Lotnicze (PZL) 104 Wilga 35	TC-ECL	140545	SP-WAA	PV
☐ Panstwowe Zaklady Lotnicze (PZL) P.24G	'2015'			PVX
☐ Piper PA-18-95 Super Cub (L-18C)				RA
☐ Piper PA-18-95 Super Cub (L-18C)	10306		(USAF)	PV
☐ Republic P-47D Thunderbolt	TC-21		44-33712, 7121 (?)	PV
☐ Republic F-84F Thunderstreak	28941		52-8941	PV
☐ Republic RF-84F Thunderflash	11901		51-1901	PV
☐ Republic RF-84F Thunderflash	11917		51-1917	PV
☐ Republic F-84G Thunderjet	110572		51-10572	PV
☐ Republic F-84G Thunderjet	111057		51-11057, MM51-11057	RA
☐ Republic F-84G Thunderjet	19953		51-9953	PV
☐ Robinson R-22 Beta	10370	2061		PV
☐ Sadik AK-2000X				PV
☐ Scheibe Bergfalke IV	5824	5824	TC-PDJ	PV
☐ Siebelwerke ATG (SIAT) 223K-1 Flamingo	TC-EAF	026	D-EABU, 023 (Egypt)	PV
☐ Sikorsky S-55D Chickasaw (H-19B) (UH-19B)	52-7577	55714		PV
☐ Sud-Est SE.210 Caravelle 10B1R	TC-ABA	253	HB-ICN	PV
☐ Transall C-160D	69-022	D22		PV
☐ Turk Havi Kuvvetleri Mavi Isik-G				PV
☐ Vickers 794D Viscount	430	430	TC-SEL	PV

IZMIR HAVA EGITIM KOMUTANLIGI KOLLEKSION (TU15)

Address:	Gaziemir, Izmir.
Admission:	By prior permission only.
Location:	About 5 km south of Izmir.

This airfield houses a large school where technicians are trained for the Air Force. There are several instructional airframes and a collection of preserved types. Some aircraft serve in both roles. The base is responsible for the types displayed at Adnan Menderes International Airport which is nearby.

TYPE	REG/SER	CON. NO.	PI/NOTES	STATUS
☐ Douglas DC-3A-456 Skytrain (C-47A)	6062	20112	43-15646	RA
☐ Lockheed 683-04-10 Starfighter (RF-104G)	12633	683C-4033	61-2633, 633 (Norway)	RA
☐ Lockheed 683-10-19 Starfighter (F-104G)	12620	683C-4020	61-2620 – at Adnan Menderes	RA
☐ North American NA-223 Super Sabre (F-100D)	42172	223-52	54-2172	RA
☐ Northrop N-156A Freedom Fighter (F-5A)	14897	N.7060	67-14897 – Adnan Menderes	PV
☐ Northrop N-156A Freedom Fighter (RF-5A)	97156	RF.1036	69-7156 – at Adnan Mendres	PV
☐ Republic F-84F Thunderstreak	7196		53-7196 , DB+349	RA

KAMAL ATATURK PARK (TU16)

Address:	Balikesir.
Admission:	On permanent view.
Location:	In the centre of the town.

This large public park in the centre of the town is named after the founder of modern Turkey. A collection of military equipment including the two former air force combat aircraft can be seen. The displays have been set up to show the development of the country and its armed forces.

TYPE	REG/SER	CON. NO.	PI/NOTES	STATUS
☐ Lockheed 683-10-19 Starfighter (F-104G)	7122	683-7122	KE+422, DD+114, 22+44	PV
☐ Republic F-84G Thunderjet	110011		51-10011	PV

KONYA HAVA KUVVETLERI UST KOLLEKSION (TU17)

Address:	3 Ana Jet Ust Komutanligi, Konya.
Admission:	By prior permission only.
Location:	About 10 km north of the town.

In 1958 Turkey acquired the first of more than three hundred Super Sabres and the type remained in service for over a quarter of a century. This fighter was used extensively in the support of the 1974 occupation of Northern Cyprus. Konya was home to F-100 units and an example of each variant operated has been preserved along with examples of other fighters flown by the Air Force. At the current time F-4 Phantoms, F-5 Freedom Fighters and UH-1H Iroquois are flown by the resident wing which is part of the Air Training Command.

TYPE	REG/SER	CON. NO.	PI/NOTES	STATUS
☐ Lockheed 580 (T-33A)	29922	580-7893	52-9922, M-27 (Netherlands)	RA
☐ McDonnell M.98HO Phantom II (F-4E)	80313	3335	68-0313	RA
☐ North American NA-217 Super Sabre (F-100C)	42013	217-274	54-2013	RA
☐ North American NA-224 Super Sabre (F-100D)	52910	224-177	55-2910	RA
☐ North American NA-243 Super Sabre (F-100F)	63921	243-197	56-3921	RA
☐ Northrop N-156A Freedom Fighter (F-5A)	13344	N.6113	64-13344	RA
☐ Republic F-84F Thunderstreak	'3-131'		52-7131, P-104 (Netherlands)	RAX
☐ Republic F-84G Thunderjet	'3-133'		51-10133	RA

MÜZE DENIZ (TU18)

Address:	Golcuk, Izmit.
Tel:	0262-414-6601 ext 1651.
Admission:	Wednesday-Sunday 0900-1200 1430-1730 by appointment.
Location:	In the northern part of the town which is about 20 km south west of Izmit.

In 1914 the first naval pilot flew a Nieuport floatplane but it was three years before a decision was made to establish a Turkish Naval Aviation Force. This service lasted only eight years and was reformed in 1971/2 when eight former Dutch Navy Trackers were delivered for observing shipping passing through the Dardanelles. Almost thirty of the S-2E variant were acquired between 1972 and 1987. This museum is located inside the vast Golcuk base. The indoor displays trace the history of the Navy and its airborne element. On show are many photographs, documents, uniforms and badges. There is an excellent collection of model ships to be seen. The Tracker is parked outside along with a number of ships, midget submarines and guns. The Navy currently flies a variety of helicopters along with a few fixed wing types including CN.235s for maritime patrol duties.

TYPE	REG/SER	CON. NO.	PI/NOTES	STATUS
☐ Grumman G-89 Tracker (S2F-1) (S-2A)	TCB-154	715	Bu147644, 154 (Netherlands)	PV

ORTA DOGU TEKNIK ÜNIVERSITESI (TU19)

Address: 06531 Ankara.
Tel: 210 24 71
Fax: 210 11 05
Email: halkilis@metu.edu.tr
Admission: By prior permission only.
Location: In the south western suburbs of the city.

This large institution was founded in the mid-1950s and has many departments. The Aerospace Faculty has a display of aircraft in the grounds surrounding its buildings. These airframes are also used for instruction. Inside are many components and engines used for training. The Cessna Skywagon is one of the batch of over eighty delivered to the Army from 1979. Several of the survivors transferred to the Turkish Air League (THK) in the late 1990s. The Dornier Skyservant is one of a pair used on Elint duties. These were the last examples of the type in military use in Turkey. The example on show also went to the Air League.

TYPE	REG/SER	CON. NO.	PI/NOTES	STATUS
☐ Bellanca 7GCBC Citabria	'TC-THK'			RAX
☐ Cessna 185D Skywagon (U-17A)	TC-CDL	1850860	64-17944, 11164	RA
☐ Dornier Do 28D-2 Skyservant	10070	4132	58+57	RA
☐ Douglas DC-3A-456 Skytrain (C-47A)				RA
☐ Lockheed 580 (T-33A)	14116	580-5410	51-4116, 14116 (France)	RA
☐ Lockheed 683-04-10 Starfighter (RF-104G)	8105	683-8105	D-8105 (Netherlands)	RA

RAHMI M. KOÇ MÜZESI (TU20)

Address: Hashcoy Caddesi 27,
Sutuce,
Istanbul.
Tel: 0212-369-6600
Fax: 0212-369-6606
Email: rmkmuseum@kok.com.tr
Admission: Tuesday-Friday 1000-1700: Saturday-Sunday 1000-1900.
Location: In the northern part of the city.

The industrial development of the country is the main theme of the museum located in historic buildings on the shore of the Golden Horn. There are sections devoted to all forms of transport, engineering and communications. Railway engines, carriages, cars, commercial vehicles can be seen along with bicycles and motor cycles. The maritime section includes ships and a submarine. The aviation display has grown steadily in recent years. The Liberator cockpit section was raised from the sea in 1995. The bomber was built in San Diego and after a ferry flight across the Atlantic it was allocated to the 98th Bomber Group then based near Cairo. On August 1st 1943 it was part of a force raiding the Astro Romano refinery at Ploesti. On its approach to the target it was hit by a shell which exploded in the nose section causing a fatality and serious damage. The bombs were released manually and the B-24 set off for home. Engine problems led to a decision to divert to Cyprus but this was not to be and in a planned landing on the Turkish coast it hit the water. There are long term plans to recover more of the airframe which is still in a reasonable condition. This aircraft was named ' Hadley's Harem' and the story of its flight and recovery is portrayed. The DC-3 has served in large numbers in Turkey both with the Air Force and airlines and an example of the classic type joined the display in 2001. The aircraft is mounted on pylons outside the main building. The Turkish Army flew forty Bellanca Citabrias from 1979 until the late 1990s. The survivors were then transferred to the Turkish Air League for civilian pilot and aerobatic training. The Pitts Special was built by two late stalwarts of the Shuttleworth Collection, Wally Berry and Bert Etheridge in the late 1960s. Withdrawn from use in 1991 it was stored in Bedfordshire before going on display.

TYPE	REG/SER	CON. NO.	PI/NOTES	STATUS
☐ Bellanca 7GCBC Citabria	10133	1117-79		PV
☐ Canadair CL-226 Freedom Fighter (NF-5A) [Northrop N-156A]	'70-00341'		Front fuselage only.	PV
☐ Consolidated 32 Liberator (B-24D)	41-24311	1106	Front fuselage only.	PV
☐ Douglas DC-3A-456 Skytrain (C-47A)	TC-ALI	12830	42-92970, NC57779, N5108, N51080, N622NU, N62DN	PV
☐ Lockheed 683-10-19 Starfighter (F-104S)	6895	683-6895		PV
☐ Pitts S-1C Special	G-AXNZ	EB.1		PV

The display at the Middle East Technical University in Ankara contains this Dornier Do-28 Skyservant which was used on Elint duties. (MDeniz Ayvaz)

This Antonov An-2 is outside the offices of the design bureau in Kiev (Bob Ruffle)

The National Museum of the Great Patriotic War in Kiev exhibits this replica Yakovlev Yak-9D. (Bob Ruffle)

TURK HAVA KURUMU MÜZESI (TU21)

Address:	Hippodrom Caddesi 2, Ankara.
Tel:	0312-311-3013
Email:	thk@thk.org.tr
Admission:	Daily 1000-1600.
Location:	In the centre of the city.

The Turkish Air League was formed on February 16th 1925 with the aim of creating interest in aviation with particular emphasis on encouraging young people to take up flying. The headquarters was set up in Ankara and almost five hundred branches were established around the country. Money was raised for the purchase of aircraft for the armed forces and flying, gliding and parachute clubs were formed. In 1942 they set up at factory at Etimesgut where eighty Miles Magisters were built. In addition original designs were constructed. A museum has been established at the headquarters to trace the history of the league. The collection opened on May 19th 2002. On show are many documents, photographs and models. Three replica aircraft are on show. Just over twenty THK-4 gliders were built in the late 1940s and several were in use until the mid-1960s. The MKEK company took over the THK factory in 1952 and sixty Ugurs were supplied to the Air Force.

TYPE	REG/SER	CON. NO.	PI/NOTES	STATUS
☐ Makona Ve Kimya Endustri Kurumu (MKEK) 4 Ugur (FSM)				PV
☐ Panstwowe Zaklady Lotnicze (PZL) P.24G (FSM)				PV
☐ Turk Hava Kurumu THK-4 (FSM)				PV

UKRAINE

ANTONOV OKB MUSEUM (UKR1)

Address:	Tupoleva Street 1, 25062 Kiev.
Tel:	044-454-3149
Fax:	044-442-4144
Email:	info@antonov.com
Admission:	By prior permission only.
Location:	In the suburbs of the city. Svyastoshino is about 12 km north west of Kiev.

Oleg Antonov was born in Moscow on February 7th 1906 and died on April 4th 1984. He built his first aircraft in 1924 and two years later became a student in Leningrad. He was appointed chief engineer at the Moscow Glider Factory in 1930 and was later promoted to chief designer. After a period at Yakovlev he set up his own design bureau at Novosibirsk in 1946 and moved to Kiev the following year. The An-2 biplane appeared in 1947 and over eighteen thousand have been built since. The museum in town traces the history of the bureau with models of all designs on show. A collection is being set up at the factory airfield at Svyastoshino and others may arrive from the test centre at Gostomel. Some aircraft may move to the State Aviation Museum.

TYPE	REG/SER	CON. NO.	PI/NOTES	STATUS
☐ Antonov An-2	'CCCP-1947'		At museum in the city.	RAX
☐ Antonov An-2T	UR-28860	1G 05-14 (?)	CCCP-28860	RA
☐ Antonov An-12				RA
☐ Antonov An-22PS (An-22)	UR-64459	5340101	CCCP-46191, 40, 01, 10, CCCP-180151, CCCP-64459	RA
☐ Antonov An-24				RA
☐ Antonov An-28				RA
☐ Antonov An-28R				RA
☐ Antonov An-71	CCCP-780361	02		RA
☐ Antonov An-72P	06	76096906		RA
☐ Antonov An-74	CCCP-72003	003		RA
☐ Antonov An-124	CCCP-680125	1930501001	CCCP-680125, CCCP-48094	RA

ARMED FORCES ACADEMY OF THE UKRAINE COLLECTION (UKR2)

Address:	28/30 Povitryanoflotsky Avenue, 0349 Kiev.
Tel:	044-276-3111
Admission:	By prior permission only.
Location:	In the suburbs of the city.

The academy trains officers for a variety of tasks. Many academic courses are also run for the students. A small collection of recently withdrawn aircraft has been placed in the grounds.

TYPE	REG/SER	CON. NO.	PI/NOTES	STATUS
☐ Mikoyan-Gurevich MiG-23	47			PV
☐ Mikoyan-Gurevich MiG-27	57			PV
☐ Mikoyan-Gurevich MiG-29	77			PV
☐ Mil Mi-24	24			PV

CHORTKOV COLLECTION (UKR3)

Address:	Chortkov
Admission:	By prior permission only.
Location:	In a park in the town.

A number of preserved aircraft have been reported in the town. The Ukraine inherited several Tu-16 jet bombers from the former Soviet Air Force. It is not know whether the aircraft listed are still there.

TYPE	REG/SER	CON. NO.	PI/NOTES	STATUS
☐ Tupolev Tu-16	83	4200805		RA
☐ Tupolev Tu-16	17	7204003		RA
☐ Yakovlev Yak-28I	119	4940303		RA
☐ Yakovlev Yak-28R		8961210		RA
☐ Yakovlev Yak-28U		3931402		RA

DISTRICT MUSEUM (UKR4)

Address:	Chapayevka Village, Perialov.
Admission:	On permanent view.
Location:	About 150 km south of Kiev.

A semi-derelict Antonov An-2 has been photographed at this local history museum. The Polish built aircraft was delivered in 1968 and withdrawn in 1984. I have no other details of any exhibits.

TYPE	REG/SER	CON. NO.	PI/NOTES	STATUS
☐ Antonov An-2R	CCCP-32114	1G 93-20		PVD

KHARKOV AIRCRAFT FACTORY MUSEUM (UKR5)

Address:	134 Sumskaya Atreet, 61023 Kharkov.
Tel:	057-700-3429
Fax:	057-707-0834
Email:	prdirector@ksamc.com
Admission:	By prior permission only.
Location:	In the north eastern suburbs of the town.

The factory was built during 1923/4 and initially produced Kalinn designs. Later Sukhoi and Yakovlev types were manufactured. After World War II a batch of MiG-15UTIs left the lines and Tupolev aircraft were made. The first Tu-104 first flew on June 17th 1955 and entered Aeroflot service on the Moscow-Irkutsk route in September 1956. A visit to Heathrow by the prototype on March 22nd 1956 took the West by surprise, as it was not known that a jet airliner had been flown in the Soviet Union. The Tu-104 went into production at Kharkov and about two hundred were built. A military version is on show at the factory. The small museum traces the history of the plant and the types produced. In recent years the Antonov An-72 and An-140 were built.

TYPE	REG/SER	CON. NO.	PI/NOTES	STATUS
☐ Mikoyan-Gurevich MiG-15UTI	01			RA
☐ Tupolev Tu-104AK (Tu-104A)	47	8350704	CCCP-42389	RA
☐ Tupolev Tu-124	CCCP-45092	5351807 (?)		RA
☐ Tupolev Tu-134A	CCCP-65655	0351101		RA
☐ Yakovlev Yak-18	75			RA

LUGANSK AIRCRAFT REPAIR PLANT MUSEUM (UKR6)

Address:	Lugansk 4, 91004 Lugansk.
Tel:	0642-345321
Fax:	0642-428817
Admission:	By prior permission only.
Location:	About 5 km south east of the town.

The works was set up in August 1931 and now specialises in major aircraft engine repairs. Helicopter reduction gears are also overhauled. Until 1997 there was also an Air Force school on the airfield. Almost thirty aircraft are now preserved at the factory along with a similar number of engines. There is a display of photographs and components in a building on the site. The Ilyushin Il-38 and the Tupolev Tu-142 were in use as instructional airframes before being passed on to the locality. The Ilyushin Il-38 is a patrol version of the Il-18 airliner. The prototype flew in September 1961 and about one hundred were produced between 1965 and 1968 with five exported to India. The Tu-142 is a derivative of the Tu-95 and was primarily designed for ASW work. The Tu-124Sh navigational trainer was built in small numbers at Kharkov and served with many bomber regiments. The example on show has been at the field for at least seven years. A rarity is one of the few Ilyushin Il-12s which have survived for preservation. The first example of the twin engined transport, designed as a Li-2 replacement, took off from the historic Khodynka airfield in Moscow in August 1945. The type was the first Soviet airliner to operated scheduled services to the west when it flew Aeroflot services from Moscow to Stockholm and Paris. Just over six hundred and sixty were built. The former Soviet Air Force used the twin engined transport for many years. One was at a technical school at Slavyansk in the late 1990s and this may be the aircraft on show here. The prototype Beriev Be-12 made its first flight in October 1960. Subsequently one hundred and forty left the Taskent lines. After the break up of the Soviet Union the Ukrainian Navy operated fourteen examples of the amphibian on coastal patrol work. The unidentified microlight is a locally built design. More aircraft are expected and according to company literature there are at least three additional types in the collection.

TYPE	REG/SER	CON. NO.	PI/NOTES	STATUS
☐ Aero L-39C Albatros				RA
☐ Antonov An-14A				RA
☐ Antonov An-26				RA
☐ Beriev Be-12				RA
☐ Ilyushin Il-12		2602		RA
☐ Ilyushin Il-38	10	870010106		RA
☐ Ilyushin Il-76PS	CCCP-76621	0043456695		RA
☐ Kamov Ka-25				RA
☐ Microlight				RA
☐ Mikoyan-Gurevich MiG-17	21			RA
☐ Mikoyan-Gurevich MiG-21MF	01			RA
☐ Mikoyan-Gurevich MiG-23				RA
☐ Mikoyan-Gurevich MiG-27				RA
☐ Mikoyan-Gurevich MiG-29				RA
☐ Mil Mi-24A	05			RA
☐ Sukhoi Su-7B				RA
☐ Sukhoi Su-17M2				RA
☐ Sukhoi Su-24				RA

TYPE	REG/SER	CON. NO	PI/NOTES	STATUS
☐ Sukhoi Su-25				RA
☐ Sukhoi T-10				RA
☐ Tupolev Tu-124Sh	50	3350603		RA
☐ Tupolev Tu-141				RA
☐ Tupolev Tu-142				RA
☐ Yakovlev Yak-28				RA
☐ Yakovlev Yak-38U				RA

LYUBOTIN COLLECTION (UKR7)

Address: Lyubotin,
Kharkov.
Admission: On permanent view.
Location: At an airfield about 16 km west of Kharkov.

A report of this collection was received in 1991. A friend on holiday drove past the aircraft which were parked on this then DOSAAF airfield. The display consisted of military types which were parked outside the hangars. A sport field still exists here so perhaps the collection is still here. There is also an abandoned grass military airfield in the area so is this the site? I would welcome further details.

TYPE	REG/SER	CON. NO	PI/NOTES	STATUS
☐ Aero L-29 Delfin				PV
☐ Kamov Ka-26				PV
☐ Mikoyan-Gurevich MiG-21F-13				PV
☐ Mikoyan-Gurevich MiG-23				PV
☐ Mikoyan-Gurevich MiG-29				PV
☐ Mil Mi-4	04	0193		PV
☐ Mil Mi-8T	'20'	0406		PV
☐ Mil Mi-24V				PV
☐ Sukhoi Su-25				PV

MUSEUM OF PARTISAN GLORY (UKR8)

Address: Nerubayske,
Odessa
Admission: Daily 1000-1600
Location: About 8 km north west of the town.

In the nineteenth century over 1000 kilometres of tunnels were dug in the area to quarry sandstone. This complex has since been used by smugglers, revolutionaries and World War II partisans. The museum has been set up in part of the catacombs to honour the work carried out against the Germans in World War II. A reconstruction of their quarters has been built along with documents and photographs and items of memorabilia to show their hazardous work. The area saw many conflicts during the Great Patriotic War and the German advance was hindered by the work of the resistance. With their knowledge of system of underground passages they were able to mount surprise attacks. The Polikarpov may be a replica or one recovered from a crash site.

TYPE	REG/SER	CON. NO.	PI/NOTES	STATUS
☐ Polikarpov I-16	100			PV
☐ Sukhoi Su-15	10			PV

NATIONAL AVIATION UNIVERSITY COLLECTION (UKR9)

Address: Kosmonatava Komarove 1,
03058 Kiev.
Tel: 044-406-7013
Fax: 044-497-3161
Email: post@nau.edu.ua
Admission: By prior permission only.
Location: In the western suburbs of the city.

Founded in 1933 this organisation has trained thousands of aircraft engineers. The history of the college is portrayed in a series of photographs and documents. A collection of aircraft is used both for display and instructional duties. A number have left for the State Aviation Museum at Zhuliany and more may follow. The University combined with the Civil Aviation College and some aircraft may still be at the old site. Nearby, mounted on poles, is small biplane which is believed to have been built as a student project. This is painted in the national colours of blue and yellow. The An-26 is outside the main entrance. The Tu-134 in the collection was operated by the Tupolev design bureau and used for trials. It was later fitted with the engines which powered the Tu-134A model. It retained the shorter fuselage of the Tu-134 during these tests. The Czech designed Let L-410 was one of the most successful feeder liners ever produced. The prototype made its maiden flight in April 1969 and about eleven hundred emerged from the Kunovice factory.

TYPE	REG/SER	CON. NO.	PI/NOTES	STATUS
☐ Antonov An-2	CCCP-01880	115347320	CCCP-47580	RA
☐ Antonov An-2	10	1G 52-06		RA
☐ Antonov An-24	UR-46713	27300101	CCCP-46713	RA
☐ Antonov An-24B	CCCP-46245	773003203		RA
☐ Antonov An-26	UR-26194	0202	CCCP-26184	RA
☐ Biplane				PV
☐ Ilyushin Il-18V	CCCP-75661	184007705	Rear fuselage only.	RA
☐ Kamov Ka-26	CCCP-24056	6800204		RA
☐ Let L-410MU Turbolet	CCCP-67250	780901		RA
☐ Mikoyan-Gurevich MiG-21PFM	49	940AK14		RA
☐ Mil Mi-2	CCCP-23853	521303119		RA
☐ Mil Mi-2	CCCP-15792	522846033		RA
☐ Mil Mi-4A	CCCP-02299	03172		RA
☐ Mil Mi-8T	CCCP-25269	0208	CCCP-11069	RA
☐ Sukhoi Su-22	06	5703		RA
☐ Tupolev Tu-134	CCCP-65601	6350003		RA
☐ Tupolev Tu-154	UR-85009	70M009	CCCP-85009	RA
☐ Yakovlev Yak-42D	CCCP-42403	2116588		RA

NATIONAL MUSEUM OF THE GREAT PATRIOTIC WAR (UKR10)

Address:	Sichnevoho Povstannia 44, Kiev.
Tel:	044-285-9452
Email:	nmhpw@ln.ua
Admission:	Tuesday-Sunday 1000-1700.
Location:	In the centre of the city.

On show at the museum are many military vehicles and guns. The displays trace the development of warfare with particular emphasis on local campaigns. There are dioramas depicting battles in the area and a comprehensive range of weapons can be seen. The aircraft are all displayed outside. The Yak-9 replica was built at the Yakovlev OKB in Moscow. This famous design served in large numbers in the Great Patriotic War and by 1944 outnumbered all other fighter types in the Soviet Air Force. In the late 1930s Boris Lisunov was sent to the Douglas factory at Santa Monica in California to prepare for the production of a licence built DC-3. Many modifications were made and the PS-84, later Lisunov Li-2, was first built at Khimki and later at Tashkent. Almost five thousand were completed by 1954 and the type served with distinction in both military and civil roles for many years. Versions of famous MiG jet fighters can be seen along with a Mil-24 helicopter.

TYPE	REG/SER	CON. NO.	PI/NOTES	STATUS
☐ Lisunov Li-2 [Douglas DC-3 modified]				PV
☐ Mikoyan-Gurevich MiG-17	02	1407100	71	PV
☐ Mikoyan-Gurevich MiG-21PFM	01	3313 or 3314		PV
☐ Mikoyan-Gurevich MiG-23M	01	642300		PV
☐ Mil Mi-24V	03			PV
☐ Yakovlev Yak-9D (FSM)				PV

POLTAVA AVIATION MUSEUM (UKR11)

Address:	Pervomayski Prospect 16, 36000 Poltava.
Tel:	035222-72582
Admission:	By prior permission only
Location:	About 5 km north west of the town.

This museum is being set up at Poltava Air Force Base which once housed bomber squadrons of the Soviet Air Force. After independence it was operational for a short time. A range of Tupolev bombers is on display to represent this period. More types have been acquired and these include a Tupolev Tu-134UBL. This type was fitted with an extended nose similar to that on the Tu-160 and used for converting pilots to the type. The Tu-160 first flew in 1981 and was one of the most powerful combat aircraft ever produced. Several of the aircraft in the collection never served operationally with the Ukrainian Air Force but are now painted in their colours. Associated displays tracing the history of the Air Force and the base are being prepared.

TYPE	REG/SER	CON. NO.	PI/NOTES	STATUS
☐ Aero L-29 Delfin				RA
☐ Antonov An-2				RA
☐ Antonov An-2				RA
☐ Antonov An-26	61			RA
☐ Let L-410UVP Turbolet	HA-LAG		Either c/n 800425 or 820902.	RA
☐ Sukhoi Su-15UM	56			RA
☐ Tupolev Tu-22KD	63			RA
☐ Tupolev Tu-22M3	80			RA

TYPE	REG/SER	CON. NO.	PI/NOTES	STATUS
☐ Tupolev Tu-95MS	01			RA
☐ Tupolev Tu-134UBL	43			RA
☐ Tupolev Tu-160	26			RA

RIVNE MUSEUM OF LOCAL HISTORY (UKR12)

Address:	33005 Rivne.
Admission:	Aircraft on permanent view.
Location:	In the town which is about 150 km west of Kiev.

A photo of the Yak-50 outside a museum in the town has appeared on the interenet. The area has several museums but the one listed seems the most likely. In the background several tractors and pieces of agricultural machinery can be seen. The type was first flown in the early 1970s but was not announced to the public until 1975. In the 1976 World Aerobatic Championships the Soviet team was equipped with Yak-50s and was first in both the men's and women's sections. The one on show presumably flew from the local airfield.

TYPE	REG/SER	CON. NO.	PI/NOTES	STATUS
☐ Yakovlev Yak-50				PV

STATE AVIATION MUSEUM (UKR13)

Address:	vul Medova 1, 03048 Kiev.
Tel:	044-404-9944
Fax:	044-241-2649
Email:	oberst@nau.edu.org
Admission:	Wednesday-Sunday 1000-1900.
Location:	Near Zhuliany Airport which is about 6 km south west of the city.

The National Aviation University had over the years acquired aircraft for instructional purposes and still has a collection of airframes. Several leading figures in Ukrainian aviation including the Rector of the University put forward a plan to save some of these aircraft along with others which were being scrapped around the country. The Government authorised the founding of the museum in 2001 and land owned by the university close to Zhuliany Airport was allocated. The display was officially opened in September 30th 2003 with about thirty five aircraft on show. The size of the grounds has now doubled, further acquisitions have occurred and more airframes are scheduled to arrive. There are plans to erect exhibition halls tracing the history of aviation in the country. Factories and colleges around the Ukraine have assisted in restoring types for the display. Among the highlights are the three versions of the Tupolev Tu-22 supersonic bomber, a range of MiG and Sukhoi fighters and several Mil helicopters. The local manufacturer Antonov is at the present time sparsely represented. However the company does have a collection of its products at its Gostomel and Svyastoshino airfields, the University still has several Antonov types for training and there are others around the country so this should soon be resolved. About eight more products of the bureau are expected. A rarity is the two seat Yakovlev Yak-28. Very few of the just over one hundred and eighty built at Irkutsk have survived. Constructed for use in a film the Yak-3 is in the colours in wore during the story about pilots during The Great Patriotic War. The Tupolev ANT-7 dating from the 1930s has rebuilt at an aircraft repair plant in the city. Recovered from a crash site the aircraft will be put on show in the not too distant future. The Tu-104 displayed was the fourth to leave the Kharkov factory. It flew the first Moscow-Vnukovo to Tblisi service on September 22nd 1956. The airliner was withdrawn in 1959 to serve as an instructional airframe at the then Kiev Technical School. The museum has made significant progress in a short time and could well develop into one of the major collections in Europe.

TYPE	REG/SER	CON. NO.	PI/NOTES	STATUS
☐ Aero L-29 Delfin	07	390722		PV
☐ Aero L-39C Albatros	18	831144 (?)		PV
☐ Antonov An-2R	UR-54812	1G 184-19	CCCP-54812	PV
☐ Antonov An-2T	14	1G 52-06		RA
☐ Antonov An-2TD	40	16047306		RAD
☐ Antonov An-24B	CCCP-46801	57302010		PV
☐ Antonov An-24B	UR-46459	87304710	CCCP-46459	PV
☐ Ilyushin Il-14P	CCCP-52036			PV
☐ Ilyushin Il-18V	CCCP-75634	187000101		PV
☐ Ilyushin Il-62	CCCP-86696	21205		PV
☐ Ilyushin Il-76T	'UR-UCI'	083414444	CCCP-76511	PVX
☐ Ilyushin Il-86	CCCP-86000	0101		PV
☐ Mikoyan-Gurevich MiG-15UTI	31	612341	64	PV
☐ Mikoyan-Gurevich MiG-17	77	6101		PV
☐ Mikoyan-Gurevich MiG-21PFMA	'21'		40	PVX
☐ Mikoyan-Gurevich MiG-23ML	54	0390310389		PV
☐ Mikoyan-Gurevich MiG-25RB	06			PV
☐ Mikoyan-Gurevich MiG-27	05			PV
☐ Mikoyan-Gurevich MiG-27K	57	76802662515		PV
☐ Mikoyan-Gurevich MiG-29	06	2960505534		PV
☐ Mil Mi-1M	CCCP-02299			PV
☐ Mil Mi-2U	UR-23943	531925061	CCCP-23943	PV
☐ Mil Mi-4	CCCP-48983	01164		PVD
☐ Mil Mi-6	28			PV

TYPE	REG/SER	CON. NO.	PI/NOTES	STATUS
☐ Mil Mi-6T	04			PV
☐ Mil Mi-8T	CCCP-22186	2108		PV
☐ Mil Mi-8TB	04			PV
☐ Mil Mi-14BT	53			PV
☐ Mil Mi-24V	07	3532464506098		PV
☐ Mil Mi-26	64 UN			PV
☐ Sukhoi Su-7B				PVD
☐ Sukhoi Su-15TM	16	0946		PV
☐ Sukhoi Su-17M	06			PV
☐ Sukhoi Su-17UM3	80	17532351902		PV
☐ Sukhoi Su-24	56			PV
☐ Sukhoi Su-25	105	25508101024 ?		PV
☐ Tupolev ANT-7 (R-6)				RA
☐ Tupolev Tu-22M0	156			RA
☐ Tupolev Tu-22M2	20			PV
☐ Tupolev Tu-22M3				PV
☐ Tupolev Tu-104	CCCP-L5415	6350102	Reported as c/n 5350101	PV
☐ Tupolev Tu-134A	CCCP-65743	2351605		PV
☐ Tupolev Tu-142MZ				PV
☐ Tupolev Tu-154	CCCP-85020	71A-020		PV
☐ Wright Flyer (R)				PV
☐ Yakovlev Yak-3 (FSM)	'09'			PVX
☐ Yakovlev Yak-28U	03	8931906		PV
☐ Yakovlev Yak-38	46	7977664503511		PV
☐ Yakovlev Yak-40	UR-87685	9840502	CCCP-87685	PV

STATE MUSEUM OF HANG GLIDING AND PARAGLIDING (UKR14)

Address:	12/1 Kuybisheva Uk, 98100 Krym Feodosia.
Tel:	0380-52
Admission:	Unknown
Location:	About 5 km south west of the town.

The local hills provide an ideal site for soaring with hang-gliders. The museum has displays tracing the development of the sport with many photographs and documents to be seen. I do not know if there are any full size machines in the collection. Another reference mentions a museum of gliding in the area. Many pioneers of the Soviet aircraft industry such as Antonov, Ilyushin and Tupolev flew from here. Another person who started his career here was the pioneer of the Soviet space programme Korolev. In the 1920s and 1930s several competitions were held and many original designs were constructed. An article in a German gliding book inferred that several sailplanes were on show and more were in store in the locality. However there was no specific mention of any types. There was also a suggestion that replicas of early designs had been built and that some withdrawn modern types could be seen. The history of soaring flight was portrayed in some detail. Other articles have mentioned that this collection is temporarily closed while the main exhibition hall is being rebuilt. Are these the referring to the same museum or are there two in the area? Further details would be appreciated.

TEMRUYK MILITARY MUSEUM (UKR15)

Address:	Temruyk
Admission:	Unknown.
Location:	About 10 km east of Kerch.

Recent reports in magazines have mentioned a military museum in this town. Military vehicles and tanks are said to be on show. Russia once had access to the port and the collection may be on one of their former bases. The Antonov An-24 was delivered to Aeroflot in 1965 and served with their Ukraine and Siberia divisions. It was withdrawn from use in 1987. Whether it served with the military or has been painted in false colours is not known. Large numbers of Mil Mi-4s flew from bases in the region.

TYPE	REG/SER	CON. NO.	PI/NOTES	STATUS
☐ Antonov An-24	'30'	57301804	CCCP-46791	PVX
☐ Mil Mi-4	40			PV

UKRAINIAN AIR STAFF COLLECTION (UKR16)

Address:	Chervonoarmiyska Street 105, Vinnitsa.
Tel:	0432-219269
Admission:	By prior permission only.
Location:	About 5 km east of the town.

The site houses the Staff College where serving officers are trained. A small display of aircraft has been set up in the grounds to show the students the history and traditions of the force. There is also a traditions room in the buildings which traces the military history of the country with specific reference to the Air Force.

TYPE	REG/SER	CON. NO.	PI/NOTES	STATUS
☐ Mikoyan-Gurevich MiG-21	98			RA
☐ Mikoyan-Gurevich MiG-29				RA
☐ Mil Mi-8T				RA
☐ Sukhoi Su-15				RA
☐ Yakovlev Yak-28				RA

UKRAINIAN STATE FLIGHT ACADEMY MUSEUM (UKR17)

Address:	1 Dobrovolskeho Str, 25005 Kirovograd.
Tel:	0522-294528
Fax:	0522-270572
Email:	asup@glau.frk.kr.ua
Admission:	By prior permission only.
Location:	About 5 km north of the town.

The school trained crews for the Soviet Air Force until 1960. For the next eighteen years it was run by Aeroflot. It now concentrates on pilots, aircrew and technicians for the civilian market. A display tracing the history of the site is located in the buildings. The Let L-410 is mounted at the main gate.

TYPE	REG/SER	CON. NO.	PI/NOTES	STATUS
☐ Let L-410UVP Turbolet	UR-67417	831108		RA

VASILKOV AVIATION TECHNICAL COLLEGE COLLECTION (UKR18)

Address:	08603 Vasilkov.
Tel:	0271-51616
Admission:	By prior permission only.
Location:	About 7 km north of the town.

This college trains Air Force technicians in many trades. The MiG-21 is mounted by the main gate and at least six more aircraft are known to be inside. They may also serve as instructional airframes.

TYPE	REG/SER	CON. NO.	PI/NOTES	STATUS
☐ Ilyushin Il-76M	CCCP-86854	0003425728		RA
☐ Mikoyan-Gurevich MiG-21PFM	24			PV
☐ Mil Mi-2				RA
☐ Sukhoi Su-17				RA
☐ Sukhoi Su-24M	22			RA
☐ Sukhoi Su-25				RA
☐ Sukhoi Su-27				RA

ZAPOROZHYE-SHIROKE AIRFIELD COLLECTION (UKR19)

Address:	Shiroke.
Admission:	By prior permission only.
Location:	About 13 km north west of Zaporozhye.

A number of training aircraft were once preserved at this former military field now used for general aviation. There have been no reports from the site for many years and it is not known if the collection still exists.

TYPE	REG/SER	CON. NO.	PI/NOTES	STATUS
☐ Aero L-29 Delfin	07	37062 (?)		RA
☐ Aero L-29 Delfin	38	390416	In the town.	RA
☐ Antonov An-2M	CCCP-35176	1G 113-15		RA
☐ Yakovlev Yak-18T	44476	22202044531		RA
☐ Yakovlev Yak-52		811515		RA

INDEX

All aircraft are listed alphabetically by manufacturers or designer (in the case of some gliders and homebuilt aircraft) followed by the type. Each country is denoted by a two or three letter code and each museum by a number e.g. GER 77 – the seventy seventh museum/collection in alphabetical order in Germany. For France the museums/collections are arranged by Department and alphabetically within each. See map at start of the section for this country. I have included accents and umlauts but these are not taken into account in the alphabetical listing.

Country codes are as follows.
ALB Albania; **ARM** Armenia; **BEL** Belarus; **BLG** Belgium; **BOS** Bosnia and Herzegovenia; **BUL** Bulgaria; **CRO** Croatia; **CY** Cyprus, **CZ** Czech Republic; **DEN** Denmark; **EST** Estonia: **FIN** Finland; **FRA** France; **GER** Germany; **GRE** Greece; **HUN** Hungary; **ICE** Iceland; **ITA** Italy; **LAT** Latvia; **LIT** Lithuania; **LUX** Luxembourg; **MAL** Malta; **NET** Netherlands; **NOR** Norway; **POL** Poland; **POR** Portugal; **ROM** Romania; **RS** Republica Srpska; **RU** Russia; **SER** Serbia; **SLO** Slovak Republic; **SLV** Slovenia; **SP** Spain; **SWE** Sweden; **SWI** Switzerland: **TU** Turkey: **UKR** Ukraine.